SHEPPARD'S BRITISH ISLES

SHEPPARD'S
BRITISH ISLES

THIRTY-FIRST EDITION

**A DIRECTORY OF
ANTIQUARIAN AND SECONDHAND
BOOK DEALERS IN THE
UNITED KINGDOM, THE CHANNEL ISLANDS,
THE ISLE OF MAN AND THE
REPUBLIC OF IRELAND**

RICHARD
JOSEPH
PUBLISHERS

First Edition published 1951
Thirty-first published 2010

RICHARD JOSEPH PUBLISHERS LIMITED
P.O. BOX 15, TORRINGTON
DEVON EX38 8ZJ
ENGLAND
TEL: 01805 625750 FAX: 01805 625376

E-MAIL:

For book sales:
office@sheppardsworld.co.uk

For enquiries and subscription to
Sheppard's World
info@sheppardsworld.co.uk

I.S.S.N. 0950-0715
ISBN 978-1-872699-86-8

CONTENTS

SPECIALITY INDEX SUMMARY 8

MISCELLANEOUS INFORMATION
    Abbreviations 14
    Sizes of Books 15
    Metric Conversions.. 16
    The British Book Trade.. 17

ANTIQUARIAN BOOKSELLERS' ASSOCIATIONS.. 20

PERIODICALS 24

CURRENT REFERENCE BOOKS 26

SUPPLIES AND SERVICES
    Appraisals and Valuations 30
    Book Auctioneers.. 30
    Book Display and Storage Equipment 33
    Book Fair Organisers.. 33
    Catalogue Printers 34
    Craft Bookbinders 34
    Packaging Materials Suppliers 37
    Wholesalers and Distributors (New Book Trade).................................... 39
    Remainder Merchants 39
    Suppliers of Materials & Tools for Binding and Restoring..................... 40
    Useful Websites.. 41

INDEX OF CITIES AND TOWNS 45

USE OF THE DIRECTORY 51

INTRODUCTION.. 52

GEOGRAPHICAL DIRECTORY OF DEALERS

    ENGLAND (see following pages)... 53
    THE CHANNEL ISLANDS 258
    ISLE OF MAN.. 259
    NORTHERN IRELAND.. 260
    REPUBLIC OF IRELAND 262
    SCOTLAND 267
    WALES.. 281

ALPHABETICAL INDEXES
    List of dealers by name of Business.. 293
    List of dealers by name of Proprietor 309
    Speciality Index (See following pages)... 317
    Booksearch Service 554
    Large Print Books 557

ENGLAND (by Counties)

BEDFORDSHIRE 53
BERKSHIRE 55
BRISTOL (incl. Unitary Authority of Bristol).. 58
BUCKINGHAMSHIRE 61
CAMBRIDGESHIRE 63
CHESHIRE 68
CORNWALL 72
CUMBRIA 76
DERBYSHIRE.. 82
DEVON 84
DORSET 91
DURHAM (incl. Unitary Authorities of Darlington, Hartlepool & Stockton-on-Tees) 97
EAST SUSSEX.. 99
EAST YORKSHIRE (incl. Unitary Authorities of East Riding & Kingston-upon-Hull)............ 106
ESSEX 108
GLOUCESTERSHIRE (incl. Unitary Authority of South Gloucestershire)......................... 113
GREATER MANCHESTER (incl. the Unitary Authorities of Bolton, Bury,
  Manchester, Oldham, Rochdale, Salford, Stockport, Tameside, Trafford & Wigan)................... 118
HAMPSHIRE 121
HEREFORDSHIRE.. 127
HERTFORDSHIRE.. 129
ISLE OF WIGHT 133
KENT 135
LANCASHIRE... 142
LEICESTERSHIRE 145
LINCOLNSHIRE (incl. the Unitary Authorities of North East Lincolnshire)
  & North Lincolnshire) 148
LONDON (EAST POSTAL DISTRICTS)... 154
LONDON (EAST CENTRAL POSTAL DISTRICTS)... 155
LONDON (NORTH POSTAL DISTRICTS).. 156
LONDON (NORTH WEST POSTAL DISTRICTS).. 160
LONDON (SOUTH EAST POSTAL DISTRICTS) 163
LONDON (SOUTH WEST POSTAL DISTRICTS).. 166
LONDON (WEST POSTAL DISTRICTS) 171
LONDON (WEST CENTRAL POSTAL DISTRICTS) 176
LONDON (GREATER LONDON, OUTER)... 180
MERSEYSIDE (incl. the Unitary Authorities of Knowsley, Liverpool,
  St. Helens, Sefton & Wirral) 184
NORFOLK.. 186
NORTH YORKSHIRE (incl. the Unitary Authorities of Cleveland,
  Middlesbrough, Redcar & York) 192
NORTHAMPTONSHIRE.. 199
NORTHUMBERLAND 201
NOTTINGHAMSHIRE... 203
OXFORDSHIRE.. 205
RUTLAND.. 211
SHROPSHIRE 212
SOMERSET (incl. the Unitary Authorities of Bath & North East Somerset
  & North Somerset) 215
SOUTH YORKSHIRE (incl. the Unitary Authorities of Barnsley, Doncaster, Rotherham
  & Sheffield) 221
STAFFORDSHIRE 223
SUFFOLK... 225
SURREY... 230

TYNE AND WEAR (incl. the Unitary Authorities of Gateshead,
Newcastle upon Tyne, North Tyneside, South Tyneside & Sunderland) 235
WARWICKSHIRE 236
WEST MIDLANDS (incl. the Unitary Authorities of Birmingham, Coventry,
Dudley, Sandwell, Solihull, Walsall & Wolverhampton) 238
WEST SUSSEX 241
WEST YORKSHIRE (incl. the Unitary Authorities of Bradford, Calderdale,
Kirklees, Leeds & Wakefield) 245
WILTSHIRE 251
WORCESTERSHIRE 255

ENGLAND (by Unitary Authorities)

To locate a dealer within a Unitary Authority, use the page references shown below in conjuction with the County Index shown above.

Barnsley 221
Bath 215
Birmingham 238
Bolton 118
Bradford 245
Bristol 58
Bury 118
Calderdale 245
Cleveland 192
Coventry 238
Darlington 97
Doncaster 221
Dudley 238
East Riding 106
Gateshead 235
Hartlepool 97
Kingston-upon-Hull 106
Kirklees 245
Knowsley 184
Leeds 245
Liverpool 184
Manchester 118
Middlesbrough 192
Newcastle upon Tyne 235
North East Lincolnshire 148
North East Somerset 215

North Lincolnshire 148
North Tyneside 235
North Somerset 215
Oldham 118
Redcar 192
Rochdale 118
Rotherham 221
St. Helens 184
Salford 118
Sandwell 238
Sefton 184
Sheffield 221
Solihull 238
South Gloucestershire 113
South Tyneside 235
Stockport 118
Stockton-on-Tees 97
Sunderland 235
Tameside 118
Trafford 118
Wakefield 245
Walsall 238
Wigan 118
Wirral 184
Wolverhampton 238
York 192

SPECIALITY INDEX

The following list has been created from the subjects
provided by dealers' entry forms

Aboriginal 317
Academic/Scholarly 317
Accountancy 318
Acupuncture................... 318
Adirondack Mountains,
  The 318
Adult 318
Adventure...................... 319
Advertising 319
Aeronautics................... 319
Aesthetic Movement 319
Aesthetics 319
Africana 319
African-American Studies. 320
Agriculture.................... 320
Aids Crisis, The 320
Aircraft 320
Alchemy........................ 321
Alcoholics Anonymous.... 321
Almanacs....................... 321
Alpinism/Mountaineering. 321
Alternative Medicine....... 322
Amatuer Radio.............. 322
American Indians 322
American Northwet 322
American Revolution 322
Americana 322
Americana Southwest...... 322
Amish........................... 322
Amusements................... 322
Anatomy 323
Animals and Birds.......... 323
Annuals......................... 323
Anthologies................... 324
Anthropology 324
Anthroposophy.............. 324
Antiquarian................... 324
Antique Paper 327
Antique Stoves.............. 327
Antiques........................ 327
Antiquitities 328
Anti-semitism 328
Apiculture..................... 328
Applied Art................... 328
Appraisals &
  Valuations 328
Aquatics........................ 329
Arabica 329
Arachnology.................. 329
Archaeology................... 329
Archaeology
– Industrial 330

Architecture.................. 330
– Theatre 331
Archives....................... 331
Artic
  - Antarctica 332
Armed Forces - Australia
– Air Force 332
– Army......................... 332
– Australian Navy 332
Armenian...................... 332
Arms and Armour 332
Army, The 332
Art - General................ 332
– Afro-American 335
– British....................... 335
– Encaustic................... 335
– Technique................... 335
– Theory...................... 335
Art Deco 336
Art History 336
Art Nouveau 337
Art Reference 337
Arthurian (King Arthur) . 338
Artists 338
Artists - Chicago 339
Arts & Crafts Era.......... 339
Arts, The 339
Asian Studies 339
Asian-American Studies .. 339
Assassinations 339
Associations
- Gaelic Athletic 339
Astrology..................... 339
Astronautics 340
Astronomy 340
Atlases........................ 340
Atomic 340
Auction Catalogues........ 340
Audio/Sound/Acoustics... 340
Australiana................... 340
Author
– General 341
– Specific (A–Z) 341
Authors
– Australian.................. 368
– British....................... 368
– Local......................... 369
– National..................... 369
– Women 369
Autism 369
Autobiography 369
Autographs 370

Autolithography 370
Automata..................... 370
Automobilia/Automotive . 370
Avant-Garde................. 370
Aviation...................... 370
Award Winners 371
Ayurveda 371

Bacteriology................. 372
Bamboo 372
Banking and Insurance.... 372
Beat Writers................. 372
Beer 372
Bees & Beekeeping 372
Belle-Lettres 372
Bell-ringing
  (Campanology)............. 372
Bibles 372

Biblical Studies 373
Bibliography 373
Bibliophily 373
Bicycles and Cyling 373
Bindings...................... 373
Biochemistry 374
Biography..................... 374
Biology 376
– Marine 376
Black Studies................ 376
Bohemianism 376
Book Arts 376
Book Auctions 376
Book of Hours 376
Bookbinding 376
Booker Prize 376
Books about Books 376
Books in Greek 377
Botany......................... 377
Brewing........................ 378
Braziliana 378
Brewing........................ 378
Bridge......................... 378
British Art & Design....... 378
British Books 378
Broadcasting 378
Broadsides 378
Building and Construction 378
Bull Fighting................ 379
Buses/Trams 379
Bushmen 379
Business Studies............. 379
Byzantium 379

Calligraphy 379
Canadiana 379
Canals/Inland Waterways.. 379
Capitalism 380
Caricature...................... 380
Carpets 380
– Oriental 380
Carriages and Driving 380
Cartography................... 380
Cartoons 380
Catalogues Raisonné........ 380
Catering & Hotel
   Management 381
Cats............................. 381
Cattlemen 381
Celtica 381
Cemeteries 381
Censorship..................... 381
Ceramics 381
Charity......................... 381
Chemistry 381
Chess........................... 382
Children's – General 382
– Early Titles................. 384
– Illustrated................... 384
Christmas 385
Churchilliana.................. 386
Cinema/Film 386
Circus 387
Cities 387
– City of London 387
– New York & Brooklyn .. 387
Civil Engineering............. 387
Civil Rights.................... 387
Classical Studies............. 387
Classics, The 387
Climatology................... 388
Coastal Defence.............. 388
Cockfighting................... 388
Coffee 388
Collectables................... 388
Collecting 388
Colonial 389
Colour-Plate.................. 389
Comedy 389
Comic Books and
   Annuals 389
Comics......................... 390
Commerce - General........ 390
Commercial Vehicles........ 390
Communication 390
Communism................... 390
Company History............ 390
Computing..................... 391
Conchology.................... 391
Conservation 391
Conspiracy..................... 391
Cookery - Professional 391
Cookery/Gastronomy....... 391

Cornish 392
Cornish History 392
Cosmology...................... 392
Counselling 392
Counterculture................ 392
Counties in England 392
Countries and Regions
– General....................... 393
– Specific (A–Z) 393
Country Houses 405
County - Local 405
Courtesy........................ 405
Cowboys 405
Crafts 405
Crime (True) 406
Criminal Law 406
Criminology 406
Critical Theory 406
Crochet 406
Crustacea....................... 407
Cryptography 407
Cryptozoology 407
Cults............................. 407
Cultural Studies 407
Culture
– Foreign 407
– National 407
– Popular....................... 407
Cuneiform Studies 407
Curiosa 407
Curiosities 407
Current Affairs 407
Customs & Excise 407
Cybernetics 407

D.I.Y (Do It Yourself) 407
Dadaism........................ 407
Dance 408
Darwinism...................... 408
Death & Funerals............. 408
Decorative Art................ 408
Deep Sea Diving 408
Demography 408
Dentistry 408
Design........................... 408
Diaries 409
Dictionaries.................... 409
Dinosaurs 409
Directories - General........ 409
– British 409
Disneyana 409
Divining 409
Documents - General 409
Dogs............................. 409
Dolls and Dolls' Houses ... 410
Domesticity.................... 410
Drama 410
Drawing 410
Drugs 410

Dyes............................. 411

Early Imprints 411
Earth Mysteries............... 411
Earth Sciences................. 411
Easter 411
Eastern Philosophy 411
Ecclesiastical History and
   Architecture................. 411
Ecclesiology.................... 412
Ecology 412
Economics 412
Education and School 412
Egyptology...................... 413
Elections........................ 413
Electricty & Gas.............. 413
Electronics 413
Emblemata...................... 413
Embroidery 413
Enamel.......................... 413
Encyclopaedias................ 413
Energy - General............. 413
– Alternative................... 413
– Fuels 414
– Power......................... 414
Engineering - General....... 414
– Electrical 414
English 414
Engraving 414
Entertainment................. 414
Entomology 414
Environment, The............ 415
Erotica 415
Eskimos......................... 415
Esoteric 415
Espionage 415
Ethics........................... 415
Ethnobotany 416
Ethnography 416
Ethnology 416
Etiquette........................ 416
European Books............... 416
European Studies 416
Evolution........................ 416
Examination Papers 416
Exhibitions..................... 416
Exlibris.......................... 416
Exotic Books................... 416
Ex-Pat Literature............. 416
Expeditions..................... 417
Exploration - General....... 417
–Polar........................... 417
Explosives 417
Expressionism.................. 417

Fables........................... 417
Fairgrounds..................... 417
Fairy/Folk Tales 417
Family 418

Famous People (A-Z).......418
Farming & Livestock 418
Farriers 419
Fashion and Costume 419
Feminism.......................419
Fiction
– General.....................419
– 18th Century...............421
– Adventure 421
– Crime, Detective, Spy,
   Thrillers....................421
– Fantasy, Horror 422
– Gay Fiction 423
– Historical 423
– Pony Novels 423
– Romantic...................423
– Science Fiction 423
– Supernatural 424
– Westerns 424
– Women.......................424
– Young Adult Mystery&
   Adventure...................424
Fictional Chracters 425
Finance 425
Fine and Rare 425
Fine Art 426
Fine Leather Bindings 426
Fine Printing..................426
Fire and Firefighters 426
Firearms/Guns.................427
First Editions 427
Fisheries 428
Fishes 428
Flags 428
Flora & Fauna 428
Flower Arranging.............429
Folio Society, The 429
Folklore 429
Food and Drink 430
Fore-Edge Paintings.........430
Foreign Texts 430
Forestry 430
Fossils...........................430
Fourth Way 431
Free Thought 431
Freemasonry and
   Anti-Masonry..............431
French Foreign Legion.....431
French Revolution Period
   Publications 431
Freudiana 431
Fruitarianism...................431
Fungi............................431
Fur Trade.......................431
Furniture........................431

Gambling 431
Games 432
Gandhiana......................432

Gardening - General 432
– Organic......................433
Gemmology....................433
Gender Studies...............433
Genealogy......................433
Genetics.........................433
Geography 433
Geology.........................433
Geophysics 434
Ghosts...........................434
Glamour 434
Glass.............................434
Gnostics 434
Gold Rush 434
Goldsmiths.....................434
Gothic Revival...............434
Grand Canyon &
   Colorado River, The 434
Graphic Novels 435
Graphics 435
Graphology 435
Graveyards.....................435
Guide Books 435
Gynaecology...................435
Gypsies..........................435

Hairdressing 435
Halloween......................435
Hand Bookbinding 435
Handwriting 435
Handwritten Books.........435
Health...........................435

Hebraica 436
Heraldry 436
Herbalism 436
Heredity 436
Heritage.........................436
Hermeticism 436
Herpetology....................436
Himalayan Kingdoms......436
Hispanica.......................436
History
– General.....................437
– Specific (A–Z) 439
History of Civilisation 446
History of Ideas 446
Hobbies 447
Holocaust 447
Holy Land 447
Home Improvements.......447
Homeopathy...................447
Homosexuality and
   Lesbianism 447
Horizon Writers 447
Horology 447
Horses...........................447
Horticulture...................448
Hospitals 448

Housekeeping.................448
Hudson Bay Company.....448
Humanism.......................448
Humanities 448
Humour.........................448
Hydrography 449
Hymnology.....................449
Hypnotism......................449
I-Ching 449
Ichthyology....................449
Iconography....................449
Illuminated Manuscripts...449
Illustrated - General 449
– 19th & 20th Century 450
Illustrators.....................451
Imaginary Voyages..........451
Imigration 451
Immunology....................451
Imprints.........................451
Incunabula 451
Indology 451
Industrial Design 451
Industry 451
Institutions 451
Interior Design 452
International Affairs 452
Inventors &
   Inventions...................452
Investments....................452
Iridology 452
Irish Interest
   & Literature 452
Irish Interest 452
Islands 453

Japanology 453
Jewellery 453
Journalism 453
Journals - General...........453
– Maritime 453
Judaica 453
Jungiana 453
Juvenile.........................453
Kabbala/Cabbala/Cabala..454
Knitting 454
Ku Klux Klan 454

Lace.............................454
Landscape 454
Languages
– African......................454
– Ancient 454
– Foreign 454
– National 455
– Pidgin and Creole........455
Law - General.................455
– Constitutional..............455
Legal Paperwork.............455
Leninism 455

Lepidoptera....................455
Lepidopterology.............455
Lettering......................455
Letterpress Broadsides.....455
Letters 455
Libertarianism 456
Libraries - Everyman's 456
Library Science 456
Limited Editions
– General......................456
– Club Books 456
Linguistics....................456
Literacy........................456
Literary Criticism 456
Literary Travel...............457
Literature
– General......................457
– 17th Century...............460
– 19th Century...............460
– African 460
– African-American 460
– Canadian 460
– Dispensational Christian461
– French......................461
– German 461
– Irish 461
– New Zealand 461
– Proletariat 461
– Scottish.....................461
– South African 461
– Spanish.....................461
– Victorian...................461
– Western American 462
Literature in Translation..462
Liturgies 462
Local History 462
Local Studies
– Lincolnshire................462
– Sussex 462
Locks and Locksmiths.....462
Logging/Lumbering 462
Logic 462
London 462
Lost civilizations 462

Mafia...........................462
Magazines & Periodicals
– General......................463
– Women's....................463
Magic & Conjuring.........463
Magic Lanterns..............463
Magick.........................463
Magnetism....................463
Malacology 463
Mammals 463
Management 463
Manuals
– General......................464
– Seamanship 464

Manufacturing 464
Manuscripts.................. 464
Maori.......................... 464
Maps &
    Mapmaking................ 464
Marine Biology 465
Marine Sciences............. 465
Maritime/Nautical
– General 465
– History 466
– Log Books................. 466
Marque Histories
    (see also motoring)...... 466
Marxism 466
Mathematics 466
Mayflower, Voyage
    of 1620 467
Mechanical Engneering... 467
Media 467
Medicine...................... 467
Medicine - History of 468
Medieval...................... 468
Memoirs 468
Memorabilia 448
Memory/Mnemonics 468
Metaphysics.................. 468
Meteorology 469
Mexicana 469
Microbiology 469
Microscopy 469
Military - General.......... 469
– History 470
– Modelling................... 472
– Uniforms................... 472
Mind, Body and Spirit.... 472
Mineralogy................... 472
Miniature Books 472
Mining 472
Minority Studies............ 473
Missionaries & Missions.. 473
Missouriana 473
Model Engineering......... 473
Model Railways 473
Model Theatre 473
Modern 473
Modern Art.................. 473
Modern First Editions 473
Monographs.................. 475
Motorbikes................... 475
Motoring 475
Mountain Men.............. 475
Mountains 475
Moveable &
    3D......................... 476
Movie & Television
    Scripts...................... 476
Music
– General...................... 476
– Specific (A–Z) 477

Musical Instruments
– General 480
– Guitars...................... 481
Musicians 481
Mycology 481
Mysteries..................... 481
Mysticism..................... 481
Mythology..................... 481
National Geographic 481
National Parks 482
Native American............ 482
Native Canadian............ 482
Natural Health 482
Natural History 482
Natural Sciences 484
Nature......................... 484
Naturism...................... 484
Naval 484
Navigation.................... 485
Navy, The - General....... 485
– Royal Navy Patrol
    Service...................... 485
Needlework 485
Neurology 486
New Age...................... 486
New Naturalist.............. 486
New World................... 487
Newbery & Caldecott
    Award Winners 487
Newspapers 487
Non-Fiction.................. 487
Nostalgia...................... 487
Novelty........................ 487
Nuclear Issues 487
Numerology................... 487
Numismatics 497
Nursery Rhymes............ 487

Nurses / Doctors 488

Occult......................... 488
Ocean Liners................. 488
Oceanography 488
Odd & Unusual............. 488
Oil Industry 488
Oil Lamps 488
Old West...................... 488
On-line Author 488
Ophthalmology.............. 489
Optical........................ 489
Orders, Decorations &
    Medals 489
Organs......................... 489
Oriental 489
Ornithology 489
Osteopathy 489
Ottoman Empire............ 489
Out of Print.................. 489
Outdoors...................... 490

Outlaws..........................490
Oxford Movement...........490
Pacifism.........................490
Packaging.......................490
Paddleboats....................490
Paganism........................490
Painting..........................490
Palaeography..................491
Palaeontology.................491
Palmistry & Fortune
    Telling 491
Pantomime.....................491
Paper Collectables 491
Paperbacks 1940-1972 491
Papermaking 491
Parapsychology...............491
Parasitology 491
Parish Registers 491
Parks & Gardens.............491
Passenger Liners.............492
Patents..........................492
Pathology 492
Patristics........................492
Performing Arts 492
Periodicals & Magazines
– see Magazines and
    Periodicals
Petroleum Geology 492
Petroluem Technology......492
Pharmacy/Pharmacology...492
Phenomena 492
Philately 492
Philology 493
Philology - German 493
Philosophy.....................493
Phonology 494
Photography 494
Phrenology.....................494
Physical Culture 494
Physics 494
Physiology 494
Picture Research 494
Pigs 495
Pilgrims.........................495
Pioneers 495
Pirates...........................495
Planning - City 495
Plant Hunting..................495
Plato..............................495
Plays.............................495
Poetry 495
Police............................497
Police Force Histories 497
Political History 497
Politics 497
Pomolgy........................497
Pop-Up, 3D, Cut Out
    and Movable................498
Pornography 498

Pottery & Glass.............. 498
Poultry 498
Prayer Books 498
Precious Metals - Silver.... 498
Prehistory 498
Pre-Raphaelites 498
Presidential.................... 498
Printed Textiles 498
Printing
– General...................... 499
– Nth of England
    Provincial 499
– Printing and
    Mind of Man 499
Private Press.................. 499
Proof Copies.................. 499
Prostitution 500
Provinces of Canada 500
Psychic 500
Physic Surgery 500
Psychoanalysis 500
Psychokiness.................. 500
Psychology/Psychiatry...... 500
Psychotherapy................ 501
Public Administration...... 501
Public Health................. 501
Public Houses................ 501
Public Schools................ 501
Public Transport............. 501
Publishers
– General...................... 501
– Specific (A–Z) 501
Publishing 504
Pulps............................ 504
Punk Fazines 504
Puppets and Marionettes.. 505
Puzzles 505

Quakers, The 505

Radar............................ 505
Radical Issues 505
Radio/Wireless 505
Radiology 505
Railways & Railroads...... 505
Rationalism 506
Recycling and Waste
    Management................ 506
Reference 506
Registers 506
Religion
– General...................... 506
– Specific (A–Z) 507
Religious Texts............... 510
Remainders 510
Revolutions 510
Rhetoric 511
Rhodesia....................... 511
River Boats & River Men 511

River Thames................. 511
Rock Art 511
Role Playing 511
Romance........................ 511
Romanticism.................. 511
Ropemaking & Knots...... 511
Rosicrucianism 511
Royalty
– General 511
– European..................... 511
Roycroft 511
Rubaiyat of Omar
    Khayyam 511
Rugs 511
Rupert Bear................... 512
Rural Life 512

Sales &Marketing 512
Salvation Army 512
Satire............................ 512
School Registers/Rolls
    of Honour 512
Schools - General............ 512
Science
– General 513
– Food 513
– Forensic 513
– History of 513
– Pure and Applied 514
Scientific Instruments 514
Scientists 514
Scottish Enlightenment..... 514
Scottish Interest 514
Scouts and Guides 515
Scrimshaw 515
Sculpture....................... 515
Sea-Faring & Shipping..... 515
Seamanship.................... 515
Secret Societies 516
Seeds............................ 516
Self-Help 516
Self-Improvement............ 516
Self-Sufficiency 516
Series............................ 516
Sets of Books 516
Sette of Odd Volumes...... 516
Sexology 516
Sheep/Shepherding 516
Sherlockiana 516
Ship Modelling................ 517
Shipbuilding & Shipping... 517
Shipwrecks 517
Shorthand 517
Show Business
    Memorabelia................ 517
Sigillography 517
Signed Editions............... 517
Silversmiths................... 518
Sixties, The.................... 518

Slavery 518
Small Press Published
  Books 518
Social Economics 518
Social History 518
Social Sciences 519
Socialism 519
Sociology 519
South Australiana 519
South Seas 519
Southern Americana 519
Space 519
Spanish Literature 519
Special Collections 519
Spiritism 520
Spiritual 520
Spiritualism 520
Sport
– General 520
– Specific (A–Z) 521
Sport in Art 527
Stage 527
Stained Glass 527
States of America 528
States of Australia 528
Statistics 528
Steam Engines 528
Stone Masonry 528
Student Activism 528
Suffolk 528
Suffragettes 528
Suffism 528
Sundials 528
Supernatural 528
Surgery 529
Surrealism 529
Surveying 529
Survival 529
Symbolism 529

Talking Books 529
Tapistry 529
Taxation 529
Taxidermy 529
Tea 529
Teaching 529
Technical 529
Technology 529
Teddy Bears 530
Telegraph 530
Television 530
Terrorism/Guerilla
  Warfare 530
Teutonic History &
  Culture 530
Texana 530
Textbooks 530
Textiles 530
Theatre 530

Theology 531
Theosophy 532
Therapy – Marital &
  Family 532
Tiles 532
Timber Technology 532
Tobacco 532
Topography
– General 532
– Local 534
Topology 536
Town Planning 536
Town Plans 536
Toys 536
Traction Engines 536
Trade Catalogues 537
Trade Unions 537
Trades & Professions 537
Traditional Chinese
  Medicine 537
Traditions 537
Transport 537
Travel
– General 538
– Specific (A–Z) 540
Trials 543
Tribal 543
Tropical Fish 543
Trotskyism 543
Typography 544

U.F.O.s 544
U.S. Presidents 544
Umbrellas/Parasols 544
Unexplained, The 544
University Histories 544
University Press 544
University Texts 544
Urban History 544
Utopias 544

Vatican and Papal
  History, The 545
Vegetariasm 545
Ventriloquism 545
Veterinary 545
Victorian Multi-Deckers .. 545
Victoriana 545
Vintage Cars 545
Vintage Paperbacks 545
Virology 545
Visual 545
Viticulture 545
Voyages and Discovery ... 546

Wall Street & Stock
  Exchange 546
War
– General 546

– Specific (A–Z) 547
Wargames 550
Washing 550
Watches 550
Watercolours 550
Wayside and Woodland .. 550
Weapons 550
Weird and Wonderful 550
Welsh Interest 550
West Yorkshire
– Local History 551
Western Americana 551
Whaling 551
Whisky 551
Windmills and Watermills 551
Wine 551
– Burgundy 551
Witchcraft 551
Women 552
Woodcut Novels 552
Woodland Crafts 552
Woodwork 552
World Fairs &
  Exhibitions 552
Wristwatches 552
Writing & Writing
  Equipment 552

X-ray 552

Year Books 552
Yoga 552
Yorkshire 553
Youth Movements 553

Zoology 553
Zoos 553

ABBREVIATIONS
USED IN DESCRIBING BOOKS

Some booksellers and buyers use highly individualistic systems of abbreviations and others have adapted traditional terms for the Internet. The following are sufficiently well known to be generally used, but all other words should be written in full, and the whole typed if possible. Condition is described by the following scale:– Mint – Fine – Very good – Good – Fair – Poor.

A.D.	Autograph document	Lea.	Leather
A.D.s.	Autograph document, signed	Ll.	Levant Morocco
A.D.*	Autograph document with seal	Ll.	Leaves
A.e.g.	All edges gilt	L.P.	Large paper
A.L.s.	Autograph letter, signed	M.	Mint
a.v.	Authorized version	Mco., mor	Morocco
B.A.R.	Book Auction Records	M.e.	Marbled edges
Bd.	Bound	M.S.(S.)	Manuscripts
Bdg.	Binding	N.d.	No date
Bds.	Boards	n.ed.	new edition
B.L.	Black letter	n.p.	no place (of publication)
C., ca.	Circa (approximately)	Ob., obl.	Oblong
C. & p.	Collated and perfect	Oct.	Octavo
Cat.	Catalogue	O.p.	Out of print
Cent.	Century	P.	Page
Cf.	Calf	P.f.	Post free
C.I.F.	Cost, insurance and freight	Pict.	Pictorial
Cl.	Cloth	Pl(s).	Plate(s)
Col(d).	Colour(ed)	Port.	Portrait
C.O.D.	Cash on delivery	P.P.	Printed privately
Cont.	Contemporary	Pp.	Pages
C.O.R.	Cash on receipt	Prelims.	Preliminary pages
Cr. 8vo.	Crown octavo	Pseud.	Pseudonym(ous)
d.e.	Deckle edges	Ptd.	Printed
Dec.	Decorated	q.v.	Quod Vide (which see)
D-j., d-w.	Dust jacket, dust wrapper	Qto.	Quarto
E.D.L.	Edition de luxe	Rev.	Revised
Edn.	Edition	Rom.	Roman letter
Endp., e.p.	Endpaper(s)	S.L.	Sine loco (without place of
Eng., engr.	Engraved, engraving		publication)
Ex-lib.	Ex-library	Sgd.	Signed
Facs.	Facsimile	Sig.	Signature
Fcp.	Foolscap	S.N.	Sine nomine (without name
F.	Fine		of printer)
F.,ff.	Folio, folios	Spr.	Sprinkled
Fo., fol.	Folio (book size)	T.e.g.	Top edge gilt
F.O.B.	Free on board	Thk.	Thick
Fp., front.	Frontispiece	T.L.s.	Typed letter, signed
Free	Post Free	T.p.	Title page
G.	Good	T.S.	Typescript
G., gt.	Gilt edges	Unbd.	Unbound
G.L.	Gothic letter	Uncut	Uncut (pages not trimmed)
Hf. bd.	Half bound	Und.	Undated
Illum.	Illuminated	V.d.	Various dates
Ill(s).	Illustrated, illustrations	V.g..	Very good
Imp.	Imperial	Vol,	Volume
Impft.	Imperfect	W.a.f.	With all faults
Inscr.	Inscribed, inscription	Wraps.	Wrappers
Ital.	Italic letter		

SIZES OF BOOKS

These are only approximate, as trimming varies and all sizes ignore the overlap of a book case.

	Octavo (8vo)		Quarto (4to)	
	Inches	*Centimetres*	*Inches*	*Centimetres*
FOOLSCAP	$6^3/_4$ x $4^1/_4$	17.1 x 10.8	$8^1/_2$ x $6^3/_4$	21.5 x 17.1
CROWN	$7^1/_2$ x 5	19.0 x 12.7	10 x $7^1/_2$	25.4 x 19.0
LARGE POST	$8^1/_4$ x $5^1/_4$	20.9 x 13.3	$10^1/_2$ x $8^1/_4$	26.6 x 20.9
DEMY	$8^3/_8$ x $5^5/_8$	22.3 x 14.2	$11^1/_4$ x $8^3/_4$	28.5 x 22.2
MEDIUM	9 x $5^3/_4$	22.8 x 14.6	$11^1/_2$ x 9	29.2 x 22.8
ROYAL	10 x $6^1/_4$	25.4 x 15.8	$12^1/_2$ x 10	31.7 x 25.4
SUPER ROYAL	$10^1/_4$ x $6^3/_4$	26.0 x 17.5	$13^3/_4$ x $10^1/_4$	34.9 x 26.0
IMPERIAL	11 x $7^1/_2$	27.9 x 19.0	15 x 11	38.0 x 27.9
FOOLSCAP FOLIO			$13^1/_2$ x $8^1/_2$	34.2 x 21.5
METRIC A5	$8^1/_4$ x $5^7/_8$	21.0 x 14.8		
A4	$11^3/_4$ x $8^1/_4$	29.7 x 21.0		
'A' FORMAT PAPERBACK		17.8 X 11.1		
'B' FORMAT PAPERBACK		19.8 X 12.9		

BRITISH PAPER SIZES (untrimmed)

Sizes of Printing Papers

	Inches	*Centimetres*
Foolscap	17 x $13^1/_2$	43.2 x 34.3
Double Foolscap	27 x 17	68.6 x 43.2
Crown	20 x 15	50.8 x 38.1
Double Crown	30 x 20	76.2 x 50.8
Quad Crown	40 x 30	101.6 x 76.2
Double Quad Crown	60 x 40	152.4 x 101.6
Post	$19^1/_4$ x $15^1/_2$	48.9 x 39.4
Double Post	$31^1/_2$ x $19^1/_2$	80.0 x 49.5
Double Large Post	33 x 21	83.8 x 53.3
Sheet and $^1/_2$ Post	$23^1/_2$ x $19^1/_2$	59.7 x 49.5
Demy	$22^1/_2$ x $17^1/_2$	57.2 x 44.5
Double Demy	35 x $22^1/_2$	88.9 x 57.2È
Quad Demy	45 x 35	114.3 x 88.9
Music Demy	20 x $15^1/_2$	50.8 x 39.4
Medium	23 x 18	58.4 x 45.7
Royal	25 x 20	63.5 x 50.8
Super Royal	$27^1/_2$ x $20^1/_2$	69.9 x 52.1
Elephant	28 x 23	71.1 x 58.4
Imperial	30 x 22	76.2 x 55.9

METRIC CONVERSIONS

	SIZES				WEIGHTS	
inches	m.m.	inches	m.m.		lbs.	kgs.
$1/4$	6	$7^3/_4$	197		1	0.45
$1/2$	13	8	203		2	0.91
$3/4$	19	$8^1/_4$	210		3	1.36
1	25	$8^1/_2$	216		4	1.81
$1^1/_4$	32	$8^3/_4$	222		5	2.27
$1^1/_2$	38	9	229		6	2.72
$1^3/_4$	44	$9^1/_4$	235		7	3.18
2	51	$9^1/_2$	241		8	3.63
$2^1/_4$	57	$9^3/_4$	248		9	4.08
$2^1/_2$	64	10	254		10	4.54
$2^3/_4$	70	$10^1/_4$	260		11	4.99
3	76	$10^1/_2$	267		12	5.44
$3^1/_4$	83	$10^3/_4$	273		13	5.90
$3^1/_2$	89	11	279		14	6.35
$3^3/_4$	95	$11^1/_4$	286		15	6.80
4	102	$11^1/_2$	292		16	7.26
$4^1/_4$	108	$11^3/_4$	298		17	7.71
$4^1/_2$	114	12	305		18	8.16
$4^3/_4$	121	$12^1/_4$	311		19	8.62
5	127	$12^1/_2$	318		20	9.07
$5^1/_4$	133	$12^3/_4$	324		21	9.53
$5^1/_2$	140	13	330		22	9.98
$5^3/_4$	146	$13^1/_4$	337		23	10.43
6	152	$13^1/_2$	343		24	10.89
$6^1/_4$	159	$13^3/_4$	349		25	11.34
$6^1/_2$	165	14	356		26	11.79
$6^3/_4$	171	$14^1/_4$	362		27	12.25
7	178	$14^1/_2$	368		28	12.70
$7^1/_4$	184	$14^3/_4$	375		56	25.40
$7^1/_2$	191	15	381		112	50.80

To convert inches to millimetres multiply by 25.4. Millimetres to inches may be found by multiplying by .0394.

To convert pounds to kilogrammes multiply by .4536. Kilogrammes to pounds may be found by multiplying by 2.205.

Use the 'Find a Dealer' service on www.sheppardsconfidential.com

THE BRITISH BOOK TRADE

NEW BOOKS

In the United Kingdom, marketing of new books is well organised and controlled by individual publishers. However, the British Book Trade has two highly organised trade associations, The Publishers Association and The Booksellers Association which represent a vast majority of their respective parts of the trade.

The Booksellers Association publishes an annual directory of members, which lists retail outlets. This is an essential reference source used by all publishers. In addition, the Booksellers Association publishes an annual directory of book publishers, distributors and wholesalers.

The directory of B.A. Members includes not only general booksellers, but businesses that concentrate on specific subjects. Although, in fact, it confers no right to buy books at trade terms, entry in this directory confirms to publishers that they are eligible for trade terms.

Bibliographic information is supplied to the book trade through Nielsen BookData Ltd. Publishers supply information on the titles they have published and this is disseminated by this company to booksellers.

THE BOOKSELLERS ASSOCIATION OF THE UNITED KINGDOM AND IRELAND LIMITED, 272 Vauxhall Bridge Road, London SW1V 1BA. Tel: (020) 7802-0802. Fax: (020) 7802-0803. E-Mail: mail@booksellers.org.uk. Web Site: www.booksellers.org.uk. Est: 1895 as the Associated Booksellers of Great Britain and Ireland and changed to its present name in 1999. Chief Executive: Tim Godfray. The Association's aims are: to provide services to help members increase book sales and develop the market for new books; to assist members to reduce costs; to improve distribution between publishers, booksellers and consumers; to represent booksellers' interests; and to provide a forum for members to discuss matters of common interest. It is not concerned with the secondhand or antiquarian trade: membership is open to all those engaged in the sale of new books, some of whom also sell secondhand and antiquarian books. The Association is governed by an Annual General MeetingConference and a Council which meets four times a year, delegating much work to specialist committees and encouraging members to join groups concerned with academic bookselling, Christian bookselling, children's bookselling etc. National Book Tokens, and batch.co.uk - an electronic clearing house for the payment of accounts – are some of the services provided for members. The Association is linked with similar bodies overseas.

THE PUBLISHERS ASSOCIATION, 29B Montague Street, London WC1B 5BW. Tel: (020) 7691-9191. Fax: 7691-9199. E-Mail: mail@publishers.org.uk. Web: www.publishers.org.uk. Est: 1896. President: Stephen Page. Chief Executive: Ronnie Williams. Including the Trade Publishers Council, International Division, the Educational Publishers Council (School Books division), the Academic and Professional Publishers Division the Electronic Publishers Forum. The Association represents the interests of UK publishers of books, electronic publications and journals to governments, other bodies in the trade and the public at large. It seeks to promote the sales of British books by all suitable means, and provides members with a wide range of services and help on publishing problems and opportunities.

SECONDHAND AND ANTIQUARIAN BOOKS

Anyone who is so minded can enter this branch of the trade without any formality at all and, indeed, book lovers and collectors, buying items for their own libraries and selling duplicate or unwanted copies, have sometimes, almost unwittingly, drifted into a habit of rather casual regular dealing. This sounds easy and pleasant but, to enter seriously into business and make a profit in any way commensurate with the work involved, a great deal of expert knowledge is required.

Some dealers have large and impressive premises, but retail shops are still relatively few as most dealers now work from warehouses, storerooms, and private premises, and using the Internet as their sales platform. In addition to these outlets, there are numerous book fairs of varying size around the country from which

dealers trade. Recently, there has been a resurgence of conventional selling methods as more dealers are also issuing catalogues again.

While most dealers in second-hand and antiquarian books will try to obtain for a customer any required item which they do not have in stock, sometimes asking specialist dealers in that subject.

The Internet has become a very useful tool to search for titles. In some respects, websites devoted to the second-hand and antiquarian book trade are better organised than those for the new book trade. Many dealers, like collectors, use the major book websites to acquire titles but in recent times, these sites are making it more difficult for the buyer to have direct contact with the seller. *Sheppard'sWorld* offers buyers a database which includes contact information - and the ability to send e-mails to the seller (assuming they have registered). Both our websites, *Sheppard's World* (www.sheppardsworld.co.uk) and Sheppard's Confidential (www.sheppardsconfidential.com), include useful information. There are others and most of the major ones are listed in these pages.

The current weekly newsletter, *Sheppard's Confidential* now provides the trade with news, calendars of auctions, book fairs, trade events, profiles, letters, and reviews of books and catalogues. The newsletter is supplied free to all dealers listed on Sheppard's World, and to serious collectors and members of the trade.

A distinctive feature of the second-hand book trade, however, is its high degree of specialisation. Almost every dealer has a particular interest, and some will be found who deal only in books on one subject, or indeed in the works of one author or group of authors. If one requires a second-hand or antiquarian book he should go or write directly to the specialist. This directory is intended to provide a handy guide that will enable the booklover to do this with the minimum of trouble, to fill its place as an essential reference book for the trade.

There are two national trade associations for antiquarian book dealers:

THE ANTIQUARIAN BOOKSELLERS' ASSOCIATION, Sackville House, 40 Piccadilly, London W1J 0DR. Tel: (020) 7439-3118. Fax: 7439-3119. E-Mail: admin@aba.org.uk. Web Site: www.aba.org.uk Est: 1906. President: Julian Rota. Vice President: Laurence Worms. Honorary Treasurer: Jonathan Potter. Administrators: John Critchley, Marianne Harwood and Clare Pedder. The Antiquarian Booksellers' Association includes the leading dealers in antiquarian, fine and scarce secondhand books throughout Great Britain as well as in some other countries. It is the founding member of the twenty two similar associations, scattered throughout Europe, the Americas, and the Far East which together form the International League of Antiquarian Booksellers.

The Association seeks to provide a comprehensive service to its members. It organises the prestigious and renowned Antiquarian Book Fair each June at Olympia, London and a more broadly-based Book Fair at Chelsea Town Hall every autumn. A combined fair is are also held with the PBFA in Edinburgh. All members receive an informative newsletter each month and there is a fine reference library ready to answer their bibliographical queries. Their interests are further looked after by representatives sitting on various government bodies and dealing with such subjects as the export of manuscripts, the National Book Committee, the monitoring of V.A.T. and customs regulations both here and in the Common Market. The Association organises, through the year, a series of events – sporting, social, and educational – aimed at promoting friendship and understanding among colleagues at both national and international levels. There is a Benevolent Fund upon which members may call in times of financial difficulty. Members may also benefit from advantageous rates on credit card processing, and insurance negotiated on their behalf by the Association.

There are various ways in which the Association looks after the interest of the general public. By requiring of all its members a good experience of the trade, and high professional standards and ethics, it ensures that the public may approach with confidence any dealer displaying the A.B.A. badge. In rare cases of difficulty or dispute, the Association stands ready to arbitrate between dealer and client.

The public, especially institutions and public libraries, are further served by a sophisticated security system founded and developed by the Association and now copied throughout the world. It has already accounted for the apprehension of an impressive list of book-thieves and for the recovery and restoration to their rightful owners of many hundreds of stolen books.

From within its ranks, the Antiquarian Booksellers' Association can produce experts on most aspects of bibliography and book-collecting, and their collective expertise is available to the general public through the Association's office. A list of Members is published every two years and is available on request from the Administrators, or through the website.

PROVINCIAL BOOKSELLERS' FAIRS ASSOCIATION, The Old Coach House, 16 Melbourn Street , Royston, Hertfordshire SG8 7BZ. Tel: (01763) 248400. Fax: 248921. Fairs Information line: 249212. E-Mail: info@pbfa.org. Web: www.pbfa.org. Est: 1974. Chairman: Peter Moore. Honorary Secretary: Clare Brightman. Administrator: Becky Wears. With over 560 members, the PBFA is the largest association of antiquarian and secondhand booksellers in Great Britain and, indeed, the world. It is non-profit making, co-operative association managed by its members. The full-time administrative headquarters are in Royston.

The Association organizes around 100 book fairs each year. The core programme comprises Premier Fairs, including York in September; regular London fairs in Bloomsbury; and two 'Summer International' fairs, one each in Bloomsbury and Hammersmith. These are supplemented by a very lively schedule from other two day events to smaller one day fairs throughout the UK from Cornwall to Scotland , and Dublin . A series of specialist, thematic fairs runs as part of the main programme and includes Travel & Exploration, Performing Arts, Natural History & Rural Life, and Illustrated, Children's' & Detective Fiction. The full calendar for the current year can be viewed at www.pbfa.org or a printed copy can be sent on request.

As the largest membership association of it's type, the PBFA offers a range of member-only benefits which include very attractive rates on parcel services, insurance, and merchant services. In addition it has its own charity and a Credit Union.

Enquiries from members of the public wishing to sell or buy books are directed to PBFA members, whose details are widely publicized via the Directory of Members and the new, full colour Directory of Antiquarian and Secondhand Bookshops. The website - www.pbfa.org also lists details of all members, and their specialist areas, as well as providing details of all PBFA fairs including venues and exhibitors.

Applications for membership are welcomed; enquiries should be sent to info@pbfa.org

PRIVATE LIBRARIES ASSOCIATION, Ravelston, South View Road, Pinner, Middlesex HA5 3YD. Est: 1956. Web: www.plabooks.org. The Private Libraries Association is an international society of book collectors with about 500 private members (about one quarter of them in America) and about 100 institutional members. The Association publishes a quarterly journal (*The Private Library*, which contains articles, notes and other items), an annual checklist of Private Press Books, a quarterly *Newsletter and Exchange List*, a *Members' List*, and other books about various aspects of book collecting. Annual subscription £30.

SOCIETY OF BOOKBINDERS, 2 Lower Faircox, Henfield, West Sussex BBN5 9UT. For all contacts, please use the web site: www.societyofbookbinders.com. E-mail: info@societyofbookbinders.com. Membership is open to anyone intersted in books, whether a binder or not, although most members are either binders already, or aspiring to learn the craft. Current President: David Laming.

The website includes a gallery of pictures showing the work of a number of members.

BOOK PLATE SOCIETY, 11 Nella Road, London W6 9PB. Web: www.bookplatesociety.org. President: James Wilson.

ANTIQUARIAN BOOKSELLERS' ASSOCIATIONS

Australia and New Zealand

AUSTRALIAN AND NEW ZEALAND ASSOCIATION OF ANTIQUARIAN BOOKSELLERS, (ANZAAB) PO Box 7127, McMahons Point, NSW 2060 Tel: (612) 9966 9925. Fax: (612) 9966-9926. E-mail: admin@anzaab.com. Web: www.anzaab.com. Est 1977. President: Peter Tinslay. (peter@ antiquebookshop.com) Vice-President: Sally Burdon. Secretary: Sam Haymes. Treasurer: Michael Sprod.

Austria

VERBAND DER ANTIQUARE ÖSTERREICHS, Grünangergasse 4, A-1010 Wien, Austria. Tel: (01) 512 15 35. Fax: (01) 512 84 82. E-mail: sekretariat@ hvb.at. Web: www.antiquare.at. Chairman: Mr Norbert Donhofer (norbert.donhofer@antiquariat-donhofer.at)

Belgium

CHAMBRE PROFESSIONNELLE BELGE DE LA LIBRAIRIE ANCIENNE ET MODERNE / BELGISCHE BEROEPSKAMER VAN ANTIQUAREN (B.B.A.). Secretary: Henri Godts, Avenue Louise, Henri Godts 230 (6), B-1050 Brussels. Fax: (+32) (0) 2 640 73 32. E-Mail: henri.godts@godts.com. Web: www.clam-bba.be. Est: 1946. President: Eric Speeckaert. Vice President: Jan Ceuleers. Treasurer: Alain Ferraton.

Brazil

ASSOCIAÇÃO BRASILEIRA DE LIVERIROS ANTIQUÁRIOS, Rua Xavier da Silveira 105 apt 501, 22061-010 Copacabana Rio de Janeiro. Tel: 55-21 22558987. Fax: 55-21 22558987. Est: 1945 President: Ana Maria Bocayuva de Miranda Jordão. E-mail: sebofino@uol.com.br.

Canada

ANTIQUARIAN BOOKSELLERS' ASSOCIATION OF CANADA, (A.B.A.C). 329-6540 East Hastings Street, Burnaby, British Columbia V5B 4Z5 Canada. President: Eric P. Waschke. Secretary: Alexandre Arjomand (Tel: 604 320- 0375). E-mail: info@abac.org.

Czech Republic

SVAZ ANTIKVÁRU CR, c/o Tomas Madera, Antikvariat Arco Diazdena 4 110 00 Praha 1. Czech Republic. Tel: & Fax: (420) 224 213 259. Est: 1922. E-mail: svaz-forward@ilab.org

Denmark

DEN DANSKE ANTIKVARBOGHANDLERFORENING, Herman H.J. Lynge & Son A/S, Silkegade 11, DK-1113 Kobenhavn K, Denmark. E-mail: abf@antikvar.dk. Web: www.antikvar.dk. Est: 1920. President: Maria Girsel.

Finland

SUOMEN ANTIKVARIAATTIYHDISTYS. (Finnish Antiquarian Booksellers Association), c/o Antikvaria atti Kauppamakaslini Vuorimiehenkatu, 10 FIN-00140 Helsinki. Tel: 358-9-628-004. Est: 1941. E-mail: timo.surojegin@ welho.com. Web: www.antikvariaatit.net. Pres: Timo Surojegin. Secretary: Berndt Wikgren.

France

SYNDICAT NATIONAL DE LA LIBRAIRIE ANCIENNE ET MODERNE, 4 rue Gît-le-Cœur, F-75006 Paris, France. Tel: (01) 43 29 46 38. Fax: (01) 43 25 41 63. E-mail: slam-livre@wanadoo.fr. Web: www.slam-livre.fr. Est: 1914. President: Mr Alain Nicolas.

Germany

VERBAND DEUTSCHER ANTIQUARE e.V., Geschaftstelle, Norbert Munsch Seeblick 1, D-56459 Elbingen. Tel: (0 64 35) 90 91 47. Fax: (0 64 35) 90 91 48. E-mail: buch@antiquare.de. Web: www.antiquare.de. Est: 1949. President: Eberhard Köstler.

Italy

ASSOCIAZIONE LIBRAI ANTIQUARI D'ITALIA, via Cassia 1020, 1-00189 Rome, Italy. Tel: (039) 347 64-69-147. Fax: (039) 06 233-28-979. E-mail: alai@alai.it. Web: www.alai.it. Est: 1947. President: Umberto Pregliasco.

Japan

THE ANTIQUARIAN BOOKSELLERS' ASSOCIATION OF JAPAN (ABAJ), 29 San-ei-cho, Shinjuku-ku, Tokyo 160-0008, Japan. Tel: (03) 3357-1411. Fax: (03) 3351-5855. Est: 1963. President: Mr Takehiko Sakai. E-mail: abaj@abaj.gr.jp.

Korea

ANTIQUARIAN BOOKSELLERS' ASSOCIATION OF KOREA (A.B.A.K.), 1F, Eunsung Bldg, 218-9 Bongsan-dong, Jung-Gu, 700-400 Daegu. Tel: (053) 428-70 05. E-mail: koreas-forward@ilab.org. Web: www.koreasa.co.kr. President: Mr Sun-Kyun Kim.

Netherlands

NEDERLANDSCHE VEREENIGING VAN ANTIQUAREN, Singel 319, 1012 WJ Amsterdam. Tel: 070-3649840. Fax: 070 3643340. Web: www.nvva.nl. President: Mr. Ton Kok. Est: 1935. E-mail: info@antiquariaatbrinkman.nl.

Norway

NORSK ANTIKVARBOKHANDLERFORENING, Postboks 1420, Vika N-0115 Oslo, Norway. Tel: (47) 73 52 44. Fax: (47) 73 52 44 58. Web: www. antikvariat.no. President: Vidar Wangsmo. E-mail: wangsmo@wangsmo.com.

Spain

ASOCIACION IBERIA DE LIBRERIAS ANTICUARIAS, Rambla de Cataunya, 15, 2o, 2a, E-08007 Barcelona. Tel: + 34 66 029 98 10. Fax: + 34 93 342 65 18. President: Mr Gonzalo Fernandez Pontes. E-mail: info@ pontesmaps.com

Sweden

SVENSKA ANTIKVARIATFÖRENINGEN, Box 22 549, SE-104 22 Stockholm, Sweden. Tel: (08) 654 80 86. Fax: (08) 654 80 06. E-Mail: main@svaf.se. Web: www.svaf.se. President: Sigbjörn Ryö. E-mail: ryo@ryo.se.

Switzerland

VEREINIGUNG DER BUCHANTIQUARE UND KUPFER-STICHHÄNDLER IN DER SCHWEIZ (V.E.B.U.K.U.) / LIBRARIE ANCIENNE ET DU COMMERCE DE L'ESTAMPE EN SUISSE (S.L.A.C.E.S.). Secretay: Frau Sabine Koitka, Im Haus sur Zwischenzeit Spalenvorstadt 33CH-4051 Basel. Tel: +41-61-261-52 03. E-mail: buch-forward@ilab.org. Web: www.vebuku.ch. President: Alain Moirandat.

United Kingdom

THE ANTIQUARIAN BOOKSELLERS' ASSOCIATION, Sackville House, 40 Piccadilly, London W1J 0DR. Tel: (020) 7439-3118. Fax: 7439-3119. E-Mail: admin@aba.org.uk. Web: www.aba.org. Est: 1906. President: Julian Rota. Secretary: John Critchley.

PRIVATE LIBRARIES ASSOCIATION, Ravelston, South View Road, Pinner, Middlesex HA5 3YD. Est: 1956. The Private Libraries Association is an international society of book collectors with about 600 private members (about one third of them in America) and about 150 library members.

PROVINCIAL BOOKSELLERS FAIRS ASSOCIATION, The Old Coach House, 16 Melbourn Street, Royston, Hertfordshire SG8 7BZ. Tel: (01763) 248400. Fax: (01763) 248921. Fairs information line: (01763) 249212. E-Mail: info@pbfa.org. Web Site: www.pbfa.org. Est: 1974. Chairman: Peter Moore. Honorary Secretary: Claire Brightman. Administrator: Becky Wears. Over 560 members.

United States of America

ANTIQUARIAN BOOKSELLERS' ASSOCIATION OF AMERICA (A.B.A.A.), 20 West 44th Street, Fourth Floor, New York, N.Y. 10036-6604, U.S.A. Tel: (212) 944-8291. Fax: 944-8293. E-Mail: hq@abaa.org. Web: www.abaa.org. Est: 1949. President: Stuart Bennett.

INTERNATIONAL LEAGUE OF ANTIQUARIAN BOOKSELLERS (I.L.A.B.) to which most national associations belong. President: Adrian Harrington, 64a Kensington Church Street, Kensington, London W8 4DB. E-mail: rare@harringtonrarebooks.co.uk. General Secretary: Paul Feain, 112 Glebe Point Road, Glebe, Sydney, NSW 2037. E-mail: books@cornstalkbooks.com.au.

PERIODICALS

Literary Magazines and Book Trade Papers

Please note that magazine prices and subscriptions are given as a guide only, and are liable to change.

THE AFRICAN BOOK PUBLISHING RECORD (ABPR). Covers new and forthcoming African publications, as well as publishing articles & news. Est: 1975. Quarterly. Subscription: EURO 377.00. Editor: Cécile Lomer. Published by: K.G. Saur Verlag GmbH, Mies-van-der-Rohe-Strasse 180807 Müchen, Germany. Tel: +49-89-76902-0; Fax: +49-89-76902-150; E-mail: info@degruyter.com. Web: www.saur.de.

ANTIQUES TRADE GAZETTE. 115 Shaftesbury Avenue, London WC2H 8AF. Tel: (020) 7420-6600. Fax: (020 7420 6605. Contains comprehensive weekly reports on antiquarian book sales world-wide plus auction calendar. Est: 1971. Weekly. Subscription: £50.00 E-mail: info@antiquestradegazette.com

AUS DEM ANTIQUARIAT. German journal on Antiquarian booktrade by subscription. Published six times a year by MVB Marketing- und Verlagservice des Buchhandels GmbH, Grosser Hirschgraben 17-21, 60311 Frankfurt am Main, Germany. Tel: +49 (69) 1306 469. Fax: 1306 394. Subscription 450 Euros. E-mail: b.beister@mvb-online.de. Web:: www.boersenblatt.net/antiquariat

BOOK AND MAGAZINE COLLECTOR. Biographies and bibliographies of collectable 19th and 20th Century authors and illustrators, plus lists of books for sale and wanted. Est: 1984. Monthly. Subscription: £40.00 a year (13 issues, U.K.). Warners Group Publications PLC, The Maltings, West Street, Bourne, Lincs. PE10 9PH. Tel: (01778) 391000. Editor: Chris Peachment. Web: www.warners.co.uk.

THE BOOK COLLECTOR. Est: 1952. Quarterly. Subscription: £50.00 (Europe £60, by airmail, Rest of the World £65). Editor: Nicolas Barker. Published by: The Collector Ltd., 32 Swift Way, Thurlby, Nr Bourne, Lincolnshire PE10 0QA. Tel: 01778 338095. Fax: 01778 338096. E-mail: info@thebookcollector.co.uk.

BOOKS FROM FINLAND English-language journal presenting Finnish literature and writers. Est. 1967. Editor-in-chief: Soila Lehtonen. Subscription: 28 euros a year (Finland and Scandinavia), 27 euros (all other countries). Published by: Finnish Literature Society, P.O. Box 259, FI-00171 Helsinki, Finland. Tel: +358 (0) 201 131345. E-mail: info@booksfromfinland.fi. Website: www.finlit.fi/booksfromfinland.

BOOKDEALER. P.O. Box 543, Tonbridge, Kent. TN9 9JR. Tel: (01732) 353183. E-mail: admin@ bookdealer.org.uk Web: www.bookdealer.org.uk. Annual Subscription £29.00.

THE BOOKSELLER. Journal of the book trade in Great Britain. Weekly. Subscription: (magazine plus online) £186.00 a year (U.K.), EU £192.00, £264 Rest of the World. Editor-in-chief: Neill Denny. Published by: Nielsen Business Media, Inc., 189 Shaftesbury Avenue, London WC2H 8TJ. Tel: (020) 7420-6006.

BOOK SOURCE MAGAZINE. Published since 1985, contains articles, news, reviews and information for the secondhand/antiquarian book trade in the USA. Published bi-monthly. Subscription (Voluntary) $15 for US addresses (by standard mail); $24.00 (library rate, Canada and Mexico); $40/£28.00 (overseas airmail). Editor: John C. Huckans. Published at: 2007 Syosett Drive, Cazenovia, NY 13035-9753. Tel / Fax: (315) 655-8499. E-Mail: sales@booksourcemagazine.com. Website: www.booksourcemagazine.com.

CONTEMPORARY REVIEW. On international Affairs, Politics, Literature and The Arts. Quarterly publication. Web: www.contemporaryreview.co.uk. Subscription: £49.00 a year (U.K. surface mail), $195.00 (U.S.A. and Canada, airfreight), others on application. Editor: Dr. Richard Mullen. Published by: The Contemporary Review Co. Ltd., P.O. Box 1242, Oxford, OX1 4FJ, England. Tel: & Fax: (01865) 201529. E-mail: subscriptions@comtemporaryreview.co.uk. Editorial office: editorial@comtemporaryreview.co.uk.

FINE BOOKS AND COLLECTIONS. Published by OP Media, LLC, 4905 Pine Cone Drive #2, Durham NC 27707. Published quarterly. Subscripion £25. Editor: Rebecca Barry. E-mail: rebecca@finebooksandcollections.com. Web www.finebooksand collections.com.

THE LITERARY REVIEW. Covers books, arts and poetry. Est: 1978. Eleven issues a year. Subscription: £35.00 a year (U.K.), £45.00 (Europe), $77.00 (U.S.A. & Canada Airspeed), $106.00 (rest of the world Air Mail). Web: www.literaryreview.co.uk. Editor: Nancy Sladek. Published by: The Literary Review, 44 Lexington Street, London W1F 0LW. Tel: (020) 7437-9392. Fax: (020) 7734-1844.

MINIATURE BOOK NEWS. Est: 1965. Three times a year. (Now incorporated in the Miniature Book Society Newsletter – Subscription to both: $40.00 per year USA residents, $45 (Canada), $55 Rest of the World. (Business rates differ). Treasurer / Membership: Karen Nyman, 702 Rosecrans Street, San Diego , CA92106-3013, USA. Web: www.mbs.org. E-mail: member@mbs.org.

THE PRIVATE LIBRARY. Established 1957. Quarterly. Distributed free to members of the Private Libraries Association, annual subscription £30.00 ($55.00). Membership Secretary: Jim Maslen. Published by: The Private Libraries Association, Ravelston, South View Road, Pinner, Middlesex HA5 3YD. Web: www.plabooks.org.

PRIVATE PRESS BOOKS. An annual bibliography of books printed by private presses in the English speaking world. Editor: Paul W. Nash. Published by: The Private Libraries Association, Ravelston, South View Road, Pinner, Middlesex HA5 3YD.

QUILL AND QUIRE. Keeps its readers up-to-date on Canada's exciting book publishing scene and provides the earliest and most complete look at new Canadian books. In addition, the Canadian Publishers Directory, which puts the book industry at your fingertips, is delivered free bi-annually. 12 issues a year for CAN$ 59.95; USA and Overseas CAN $99.95 (includes postage). Est: 1935. Editor: Derek Weiler. Published at: PO Box 819 Markham, Toronto, ON L3P8A2 Canada. Subscriptions tel: (905) 946-0406. Fax: 905 946-0410. Email: subscriptions@quillandquire.com. Web: www.quillandquire.com.

TRIBUNE. Books Editor: Chris McLaughlin. Published by: Tribune Publications Ltd., PO Box 2068, Bushey, Hertfordshire WD23 3ZF. Subscriotion 49 issues (1 year) £75.00. Tel: (020) 7433-6410. E-mail: mail@tribunemagazine.co.uk. Web: www.tribunemagazine.co.uk.

INTERNET BASED NEWSLETTERS AND TRADE MAGAZINES

AMERICANA EXCHANGE. A free trade newsletter for the antiquarian and used book trade. See www.americanaexchange.com.

BOOKBRUNCH. A free newsletter for the new book trade. Trade news and information. See www.bookbrunch.co.uk.

BOOK THINK. A free newsletter based in the USA. A more comprehensive version, Gold Edition, is available by subscription. See at www.bookthink.com

BOOKSELLER.COM. An e-mail newsletter where the latest trade news about the new book trade can be read. Register on www.bookseller.com

FINE BOOKS & COLLECTIONS. Available as an e-newsletter. Published by OP Media LLC 4905 Pine Cone Drive, Suite 2, Durham NC 27707. E-mail: subscriptions@finebooksmagazine.com. Website: www.finebokksmagazine.com.

SHEPPARD'S CONFIDENTIAL. A free e-mail newsletter published weekly for the antiquarian and second-hand book trade: news, calendars for book fairs and auctions. Events and book reviews as well as extensive coverage of views and opinions from members of the trade. Register on www.sheppardsworld.co.uk.

CURRENT REFERENCE BOOKS

A & C BLACK COLOUR BOOKS. A collector's guide and bibliography 1900–1930. Author: Colin Inman. £30.00. Published by Werner Shaw Ltd and distributed by Veronica Daniels, Flat 1, 33 Atlantic Road, Weston-Super-Mere BS23 2DQ. Tel: 01934 641317. E-mail: vron.daniels@ukonline.co.uk. A bibliography covering 800 books in 50 series, with full historical account of this great publishing venture.

ABC OF BOOKBINDING. By Jane Greenfield. $49.95. Published by: Oak Knoll Press, 310 Delaware Street, New Castle, DE 19720, U.S.A. Tel: (302) 328-7232. Fax: 328-7274. E-Mail: oakknoll@oakknoll.com.

ABC OF LEATHER BOOKBINDING: A MANUAL FOR TRADITIONAL CRAFTSMANSHIP. Edward R. Lhotka. Illustrated manual shows the science of fine leather bindings. $19.95. Published by: Oak Knoll Press, 310 Delaware Street, New Castle, DE 19720, U.S.A. Tel: (302) 328-7232. Fax: 328-7274. E-Mail: oakknoll@oakknoll.com.

ABPC on CD-ROM. The auction season September 1975 to today. Available on line and flash drive. Published by: Bancroft Parkman Inc., P.O. Box 1236, Washington, CT 06793, U.S.A. Tel: (860) 868-7408. Fax: (860) 868-0080. E-Mail: abpc@snet.net. Website: www.bookpricescurrent.com.

AMERICAN BOOK TRADE DIRECTORY. Profiles retail and antiquarian book dealers plus book and magazine wholesalers, distributors and jobbers in the United States. 2009/2010: $309 plus $25 postage. Published by Information Today, Inc., 143 Old Marlton Pike, Medford, NJ 08055-8750. E-mail: custserv@infotoday.com. Website: www.infotoday.com.

TICKETED BOOK BINDINGS from 19th Century Britain. Willman Spawn and Thomas E. Kinsella. $65.00. First edn. Published by: Oak Knoll Press, 310 Delaware Street, New Castle, DE 19720, U.S.A. Tel: (302) 328-7232. Fax: 328-7274. E-Mail: oakknoll@oakknoll.com.

ANTIQUARIAN BOOKS: A Companion for Booksellers, Librarians and Collectors. Edited by Philippa Bernard, Leo Bernard and Angus O'Neill. £80 (£75 on line) . Published by: Ashgate Publishing Ltd., Gower House, Croft Road, Aldershot, Hampshire GU11 3HR. Website: www.ashgate.com. E-mail: info@ashgatepublishing.com.

BOOKBINDING & CONSERVATION BY HAND: A working guide. By Laura S. Young. Hardback $65.00. Paperback $24.95. Published by: Oak Knoll Press, 310 Delaware Street, New Castle, DE 19720, U.S.A. Tel: (302) 328-7232. Fax: 328-7274. E-Mail: oakknoll@oakknoll.com.

BOOKDEALING FOR PROFIT. By Paul Minet. The philosophy behind the business as well as a look into the future and how the Internet is having a major effect on the trade. Hardback £10.00. Published by Richard Joseph Publishers Ltd, P.O. Box 15, Torrington, Devon EX38 8ZJ. UK. Tel: (01805) 625750. Fax: (01805) 625376. E-mail: office@sheppardsworld.co.uk. Website: www.sheppardsdirectories.co.uk.

BOOKWORMS. The Insect Pests of Books. Norman Hickin. Hardback £24.00. Published by Richard Joseph Publishers Ltd, P.O. Box 15, Torrington, Devon EX38 8ZJ. UK. Tel: (01805) 625750. Fax: (01805) 625376. E-mail: office@sheppardsworld.co.uk. Website: www.sheppardsdirectories.co.uk.

CHILDREN'S FICTION 1900 – 1950. John Cooper and Jonathan Cooper. £65. Published by: Ashgate Publishing Ltd., Gower House, Croft Road, Aldershot, Hampshire GU11 3HR. Website: www.ashgate.com. E-mail: info@ashgatepublishing.com.

EDWARD SEYMOUR AND THE FANCY PAPER COMPANY: The Story of a British Marbled Paper Manufacturer.. Sidney E. Berger. $150. Published by: Oak Knoll Press, 310 Delaware Street, New Castle, DE 19720, U.S.A. Tel: (302) 328-7232. Fax: 328-7274. E-Mail: oakknoll@oakknoll.com.

ENCYCLOPEDIA OF THE BOOK. By: Geoffrey Ashall Glaister. Hardcover $75.00, Paperback $49.95. Published by Oak Knoll Press, 310 Delaware Street, New Castle, DE 19720, U.S.A. Tel: (302) 328-7232. Fax: 328-7274. E-Mail: oakknoll@oakknoll.com.

T.N. FOULIS: The History and Bibliography of an Edinburgh Publishing House. By Ian Elfick & Paul Harris. £30.00. Published by Werner Shaw Ltd and distributed by Veronica Daniels, Flat 1, 33 Atlantic Road, Weston-Super-Mere BS23 2DQ. Tel: 01934 641317. E-mail: vron.daniels@ukonline.co.uk.

GREATER LONDON HISTORY AND HERITAGE HANDBOOK. Next edition 2007. c. 150pp. Illus. £25 + £2p&p. Borough by borough directory and bibliographic listings with substantial London wide chapter. Editor: Peter Marcan. Published by: Peter Marcan Publications, P.O. Box 3158, London SE1 4RA. Tel: (020) 7357-0368.

HEADBANDS, HOW TO WORK THEM. Jane Greenfield and Jenny Hille. $14.95. Published by: Oak Knoll Press, 310 Delaware Street, New Castle, DE 19720, U.S.A. Tel: (302) 328-7232. Fax: 328-7274. E-Mail: oakknoll@oakknoll.com.

HISTORY OF ENGLISH CRAFT BOOKBINDING TECHNIQUE. By Bernard C. Middleton. $55.00. Published by: Oak Knoll Press, 310 Delaware Street, New Castle, DE 19720, U.S.A. Tel: (302) 328-7232. Fax: 328-7274. E-Mail: oakknoll@oakknoll.com. Sales rights: Worldwide outside of UK. Available in the UK from The British Library.

THE ILLUSTRATIONS OF W. HEATH ROBINSON: A COMMENTARY AND BIBLIOGRAPHY. By Geoffrey Beare. The bibliography which follows the long introduction to Heath Robinson's work as an illustrator, was compiled from primary sources. £18.95. Published by Werner Shaw Ltd and distributed by Veronica Daniels, Flat 1, 33 Atlantic Road, Weston-Super-Mere BS23 2DQ. Tel: 01934 628645. E-mail: vron.daniels@ukonline.co.uk.

INTERNATIONAL DIRECTORY OF ANTIQUARIAN BOOKSELLERS. A world list of members of organisations belonging to the International League of Antiquarian Booksellers (I.L.A.B.). Published every 2 years: 2005-6 edition £15.00 plus £2.00 p&p. 2007-2008 edition available summer 2007. Published by: I.L.A.B. Distributed in the UK by: The Antiquarian Booksellers' Association, Sackville House, 40 Piccadilly, London W1J 0DR. Tel: (020 7439-3118. Fax: (020) 7439-3119. E-mail: admin@aba.org.uk.

JOHN UPDIKE: A BIBLIOGRAPHY OF PRIMARY AND SECONDARY MATERIALS, 1948-2007. De Bellis and Jack & Michael Broomfield. $195.00. Published by: Oak Knoll Press, 310 Delaware Street, New Castle, DE 19720, U.S.A. Tel: (302) 328-7232. Fax: 328-7274. E-Mail: oakknoll@oakknoll.com.

LIBRARIES AND INFORMATION SERVICES IN THE UNITED KINGDOM AND REPUBLIC OF IRELAND, 2009-2010. £49.95. Published by: Facet Publishing, 7 Ridgmount Street, London WC1E 7AE. Tel: (020) 7255-0590. Fax: 7255-0591. E-mail: info@facetpublishing.co.uk. Website: www.facetpublishing.co.uk.

MINIATURE BOOKS. Louis Bondy. The history of miniature books up to 1981. Published by Richard Joseph Publishers Ltd, PO 15, Torrington, Devon EX38 8ZJ. E-mail: office@sheppardsworld.co.uk. Website: www.sheppardsworld.co.uk. Hardback 220 pages £24.

THE MARCAN VISUAL ARTS HANDBOOK: where to go for British contacts, expertise and speciality in the fine and applied arts. vi 150pp Illus. £25 + £2.50 p&p. Almost 200 descriptive centres with many bibliogrphic listings; keywords and subject index. Published by: Peter Marcan Publications, P.O. Box 3158, London SE1 4RA. Tel: (020) 7357-0368.

NEW SCIENCE OUT OF OLD BOOKS. Studies in manuscripts and early printed books in honour of A.I. Doyle. £80.00. Edited by: Richard Beadle and A.J. Piper. Published by: Ashgate Publishing Ltd., Gower House, Croft Road, Aldershot, Hampshire GU11 3HR.

A POCKET GUIDE TO THE IDENTIFICATION OF FIRST EDITIONS. An essential guide to identifying first editions for collectors, dealers, librarians, cataloguers and auctioneers. 6th Edition $15.95 per copy plus $1 shipping 40% discount on 5 or more copies; shipping for 5 copies is $5 by Priority Mail. International orders: single copies shipping $2.50; five copies $8 by Air/Printed Matter. Published by: The Jumping Frog, McBride/Publisher, 56 Arbor Street, Hartford, CT 06106, U.S.A. Tel: (860) 523–1622. Website: www.firsteditionguide.com. E-mail: bill@firsteditionguide.com.

THE TARTARUS PRESS GUIDE TO FIRST EDITION PRICES 2008/9. Edited by: R.B. Russell. £25.00 inc. p&p. Published by: Tartarus Press, Coverley House, Carlton-in-Coverdale, Leyburn, North Yorks DL8 4AY. Tel: & Fax: (01969) 640399. E-Mail: tartarus@pavilion.co.uk.

TRUE TO TYPE. By Ruari McLean. A Typographical Autobiography. £25.00. Published by Werner Shaw Ltd and distributed by Veronica Daniels, Flat 1, 33 Atlantic Road, Weston-Super-Mere BS23 2DQ. Tel: 01934 628645. E-mail: vron.daniels@ukonline.co.uk.

SUPPLIES AND SERVICES

APPRAISALS AND VALUATIONS

THE BOOK BUSINESS, 90 Greenford Avenue, London W7 3QS. Tel: (020) 8840 1185. E-mail: bookbusiness@homechoice.co.uk. Contact: Giles Levete.

CHURCH STREET BOOKS, 6 Church Street, Diss, Norfolk IP22 4DD. Tel: (01379) 652020. E-mail: atvidion@yahoo.co.uk. Contact: Andy Vidion.

FINE ART, 38 Tooting, London SW17 9QS. Tel: and Fax: (0208) 6961 1921. E-mail: sheppards@fineart.tm. Web: www.fineart.tm. Contact: Robert Walker.

STEVE LIDDLE, 8 Morley Square, Bishopston, Bristol BS7 9DW. Tel: (0117) 924 4846. E-mail: mail@steveliddle.co.uk. Contact: Steve Liddle.

SAX BOOKS, 4a High Street, Saxmundham, Suffolk IP17 1DF. Tel: (01728) 605775. E-mail: richard@saxbooks.co.uk. Contact: Richard W.L. Smith, MVO.

BOOK AUCTIONEERS

ARMCHAIR AUCTIONS, 98 Junction Road, Andover, Hampshire SP10 3JA. Tel: and Fax: 01264 362048. Postal auction specialising in military, naval and aviation books, relics and ephemera. Monthy sales. Contact George Murdock.

ANDERSON AND GARLAND, Anderson House, Crispin Court, Westerhope, Newcastle upon Tyne NE5 1BF. Tel: 0292 430 3000. Fax: 0191 430 3001. E-mail: info@andersonandgarland.com. Website: www.andersonandgarland.com.

BELLMAN'S, Newpound, Wisborough Green, Billinghurst, West Sussex RH14 0AZ. Tel: 01403 700858. E-mail: enquiries@bellmans.co.uk. *Regular sales of books, maps, autographs, ephemera and photographs.*

BLOOMSBURY AUCTIONS, Bloomsbury House, 24 Maddox Street, London W1S 1PP. Tel: (020) 7495-9494. Fax: 7495-9499. E-Mail: info@bloomsburyauctions.com. Web site: www.bloomsburyauctions.com.

BONHAMS, 101 New Bond Street, London W1S 1SR Tel: (020) 7447 7447. Fax: (020) 7447 7400. E-Mail: books@bonhams.com. View our catalogues on-line at www.bonhams.com. *At least 10 sales each season on books, maps, photographs, autographs and historical manuscripts.*

CAPES DUNN & CO., 38 Charles Street, Manchester M1 7DB. Tel: (0161) 273-1911. Fax: 273-3474. *Catalogues can be accessed on* – www.ukauctioneers.com.

DOMINIC WINTER BOOK AUCTIONS, Mallard House, Broadway Lane, South Cerney, Nr Cirencester, Gloucestershire GL7 5UQ. Tel: (01285) 860006. Fax: 862461. E-Mail: info@dominicwinter.co.uk. Web: www.dominicwinter.co.uk.

FINAN & CO., The Square, Mere, Wiltshire BA12 6DJ. Tel: (01747) 861411. Fax: 861944. E-Mail: post@finanandco.co.uk. Website: www.finanandco.co.uk. 3 auctions annually, including specialist books, manuscripts, photographs and ephemera. Enquiries to Julia Finan

GEORGE KIDNER, The Saleroom, Emsworth Road, Lymington, Hampshire SO41 8GM. Tel: (01590) 670070. Fax: 675167. E-Mail: info@georgekidner.co.uk. Website: www.georgekidner.co.uk. Enquiries to: Andrew Reeves.

GOLDING YOUNG & CO, Old Wharf Road, Grantham, Lincolnshire NG31 7AA. Tel: (01476) 565118. Fax: (01476) 561475. E-mail: enquiries@goldingyoung.com. Website: www.goldingyoung.com.

HAMPTON & LITTLEWOOD AUCTIONEERS, The Auction Rooms, Alphin Brook Road, Alphington, Exeter, Devon EX2 8TH. Tel: (01392) 413100. Fax: (01392) 413110. E-Mail: info@bhandl.co.uk. Website: www.hamptonandlittlewood.co.uk.

KEYS AUCTIONEERS, 8 Market Place, Aylsham, Norwich, Norfolk NR11 6EH. Tel: (01263) 733195. Fax: (01263) 732140. E-mail: mail@aylshamsalerooms.co.uk. Website: www.aylshamsalerooms.co.uk.

DAVID LAY, F.R.I.C.S., The Penzance Auction House, Alverton, Penzance, Cornwall TR18 4RE. Tel: (01736) 361414. Fax: 360035. E-Mail: david.lays@btopenworld.com. Website: www.davidlay.co.uk.

LYON AND TURNNBULL, 33 Broughton Place, Edinburgh, EH1 3RR. Tel: (0131) 557 8844. Fax: (0131) 557 8668. Email: info@lyonandturnbull.com. Catalogues viewable at: www.lyonandturnbull.com.

MEALY'S LTD, Chatsworth Street, Castlecomer, County Kilkenny, Ireland. Tel: (056) 444-1229. Fax: (056) 444-1627. E-mail: info@mealys.com. Website: www.mealys.com.

OUTHWAITE & LITHERLAND, Kingsway Galleries, Fontenoy Street, Liverpool L3 2BE. Tel: (0151) 236-6561. Fax: 236-1070. E-mail: auction@lots.uk.com. Website: www.lots.uk.com.

SCARBOROUGH PERRY FINE ARTS, Unit 2, Grange Industrial Estate, Southwick, West Sussex BN42 4EN. Tel: (01273) 870371. Fax: 595706. E-Mail: info@scarboroughfinearts.co.uk. Website: www.scarboroughfinearts.co.uk

STRIDE & SON AUCTIONEERS, Southdown House, St. John's Street, Chichester, West Sussex PO19 1XQ. Tel: (01243) 780207. Fax: 786713. E-Mail: enquiries@stridesauctions.co.uk. Website: www.stridesauctions.co.uk. Appointment necessary for consultations. Book department open Wednesdays 9am – 12.30pm for appointments. Buyers premium 15% + VAT.

LAWRENCES AUCTIONEERS, The Linen Yard, South Street, Crewkerne, Somerset TA18 8AB. Tel: 01460 73041. Fax: (01460) 270799. E-Mail: enquiries@lawrences.co.uk. Specialist book sales in January and July.

SWORDERS INCORPORATING OLIVERS, The Salesroom, Burkitts Lane, Sudbury, Suffolk CO10 1HB. Tel: 01787 880305. E-mail: olivers@sworder.co.uk. Website: www.sworder.co.uk/olivers

TENNANTS, The Auction Centre, Leyburn, North Yorkshire DL8 5SG. Tel: 01969 623780. E-mail: enquiry@tennants-ltd.co.uk. Website: www.tennants.co.uk.

THOMAS MAWER & SON LTD., Dunston House, Portland Street, Lincoln, Lincolnshire LN5 7NN. Tel: 01522 524984. Fax: 01522 535600. E-mail: auctions@thosmawer.com. Web: www.thosmawer.com

THOMSON, RODDICK & MEDCALF, Coleridge House, Shaddongate, Carlisle CA2 5TU. Tel: (01228) 528939. Fax: 592128. E-mail: auctions@thomsonroddick.com. Web: www.thomsonroddick.com.

P.F. WINDIBANK, The Dorking Halls, Reigate Road, Dorking, Surrey RH4 1SG. Tel: (01306) 884556/876280. Fax: 884669. E-Mail: sjw@windibank.co.uk. Website: www.windibank.co.uk.

BOOK DISPLAY AND STORAGE EQUIPMENT, ETC

D AND M PACKAGING, 5a Knowl Road, Mirfield, West Yorkshire WF14 8DG. Tel: (01924) 495768. Fax: (01924) 491267. E-mail: packaging@dandmbooks.com. Website: www.bookcovers.co.uk. *Suppliers of all types of covers for hardbacks, paperbacks and dust jackets. Also comprehensive range of packaging and book-care materials, adhesives, book cleaners, tapes, etc. Free catalogue on request. We supply both trade and private customers and have no minimum order.*

P.B.F.A., The Old Coach House, 16 Melbourn Street, Royston, Hertfordshire SG8 7BZ. Tel: (01763) 248400. Fax: 248921. E-mail: info@pbfa.org. *Website: www.pbfa.org. Folding bookshelves in natural beech and new books on book collecting.*

POINT EIGHT LTD., Unit 14, Narrowboat Way, Blackbrook Valley Industrial Estate, Dudley, West Midlands DY2 0EZ. Tel: (01384) 238282. Free Phone 0800 731 4887. Fax: 455746. E-mail: info@point8.co.uk. Website: www.pointeight.co.uk. *Bookshop and P.O.S. display equipment designer and manufacturer in wood, metal, plastic etc..*

RAPID RACKING, Kemble Enterprise Park, Kemble, Cirencester, Gloucestershire GL7 6BQ. Tel: (01285) 686868. Fax: (01285) 686968. E-mail: customerservice@rapidracking.com. Web: www.rapidracking.com.

SEALINE BUSINESS PRODUCTS LIMITED, Media House, 27 Postwood Green, Hertford Heath, Herts., SG13 7QJ. Tel: (01992) 558001. Fax: (01992) 304569. E-mail: sales@sealinemediastorage.com. Website: www.sealinemediastorage.com. *An attractive range of multi purpose cabinets designed to house a variety, or mix, of media types including CD, DVD, Video, Microfilm, DAT Tapes, Cassettes, Index Cards and much more. Complete with lock and anti-tilt in a choice of colour finishes. Shelving, mobile solutions and fire resistant storage compliment the range. Please visit our web site for full details.*

BOOK FAIR ORGANISERS

ANTIQUARIAN BOOKSELLERS ASSOCIATION. Sackville House, 40 Piccadilly, London W1J 0DR. Tel: (020) 7439-3118. Fax: 7439-3119. E-Mail: admin@aba.org.uk. Website: www.aba.org.uk. Est: 1906. International Book Fair held annually in London, in June, also in Chelsea (UK dealers only) in Autumn and, occasional book fairs elsewhere. *For complimentary tickets or handbook of members, please contact:* Antiquarian Booksellers' Association.

BUXTON BOOK FAIRS, Tel: (01782) 542258. Stoke on Trent, Staffordshire. Tel: (01782) 542258. E-mail: jane.millimgton@yahoo.co.uk. *Enquiriesto:* Mrs Jane Millington. 9 fairs a year, held at Pavilion Gardens.

CHURCHGATE BOOKS, 47 Churchgate Street, Bury St Edmunds, Suffolk IP33 1RG. Tel: 01284 704604. E-mail: thebookman@btinternet.com. (See also under Long Melford Book Fair.)

CIANA LTD., 24 Langroyd Road, London SW17 7PL. Tel: (020) 8682 1969. Fax: 8682 1997. E-mail: enquiries@ciana.co.uk. Organisers of remainder and promotional book fairs, held in London in September and in Brighton in January.

HD FAIRS LTD., 38 Fleetside, West Molesey, Surrey KT8 2NF. Tel: (020) 8224-3609. Fax: (020) 8224 3576. E-mail: admin@hdbookfairs.co.uk. Web: www.hdfairs.co.uk/books. Independent organisers for over 20 years, running the largest UK monthly Book Fairs in London – 100 plus exhibitors. Fairs in Farnham, Surrey and Kempton Park Racecourse – widest choice of books both Antiquarian and modern, as well as printed collectables. Free diary of events available on request; new exhibitors always welcome. Phone, fax, write, or e-mail HD Fairs Ltd: Wendy Collyer or Peter Sheridan.

FOREST BOOKS, 7 High Street West, Uppingham, Rutland LE15 9QB. Tel: (01572) 821173. Fax: (0870) 1326314. E-Mail: forestbooks@rutlanduk.fsnet.co.uk. *3 Book Fairs organised annually: 2 at Farndon Memorial Hall, near Newark, Nottinghamshire and 1 at Uppingham School, Rutland.* Please phone or e-mail for booking details. Maps & photos on our website.

GERRARDS CROSS BOOK FAIR. Est: 1974. Fairs held at the Memorial Centre, East Common, Gerrards Cross, Bucks. Enquiries to: David Ford. (07884) 425450. E-mail: info@davodfordbooks.co.uk.

LEEDS BOOK FAIR, at St Margaret's Hall, Church Road, Horsforth, Leeds, LS18 5LQ. Fair organiser: Pauline Walker, 13 Harecroft Road, Otley, West Yorkshire LS21 2BG. Tel: 01943 467204. E-mail: paulinemary.d@ukonline.co.uk.

LONG MELFORD BOOKFAIRS. Fair Manager: Stephen Cook. Tel: (01284) 723512. E-mail: thebookman@btinternet.com. Web: www.longmelfordbookfair.co.uk.

MISSING BOOK FAIRS. Est: 1994. Book fairs: Peterborough (4 a year), Great Dunmow (2 a year), and Dedham (1 a year), Long Melford (7 a year). *Enquiries to:* Chris Missing, 'Coppers', Main Road, Great Leighs, Essex CM3 1NR. Tel: (01245) 361609. E-mail: missingbooks@ madasafish.com

NOTTINGHAMSHIRE BOOK FAIRS. Contact: J and J Books, Tel: (01522) 869597.

PROVINCIAL BOOKSELLERS' FAIRS ASSOCIATION. Est: 1974. Fairs held in Central London (monthly) and in more than 80 other towns in Great Britain. *Enquiries to:* Becky Wears, Provincial Booksellers' Fairs Association, The Old Coach House, 16 Melbourn Street, Royston, Herts, SG8 7BZ. Tel: (01763) 248400. Fax: 248921. Fairs Information Service: (24 hrs) (01763) 249212. E-Mail: info@pbfa.org. Website: www.pbfa.org. (See display advertisement).

SOUTHAMPTON BOOK FAIRS. Organiser: Steve Tanti Tel: 01489 783041. E-mail: sjtbooks@ yahoo.co.uk. Venue: St Anne's School, Carlton Road, SO15 2WZ.

TITLE PAGE BOOK FAIRS, 176 Elmbridge Avenue, Surbiton, Surrey KT5 9HF. Tel: & Fax: (020) 8399 8168. Mobile (07966) 162758. *Fairs in Surrey: Dorking 6 a year, Cobham 4 a year, Banstead 4 a year. Fairs in Kent: Dorking open 10.00–15.30, Banstead and Cobbam open 09.15–15.30.* Contact: Keith Alexander.

WAVERLEY FAIRS, 9 Hayley Park Road, Halesowen B63 1EJ. Tel: (0121) 550-4123. Kinver Book Fair established 1981. 3rd Sunday of every month. Also at Powick, Malvern, Worcestershire. (2nd Sunday)

WINCHESTER BOOK FAIR. Jeremy LeLean. Tel: 01264) 362620. E-mail: info@winchesterbookfair.com. Web: www.winchesterbookfair.co.m. Venue: Saxon Suite of Winchester Guildhall, The Broadway, Winchester SO23 9LJ.

WING BOOK FAIR. Richard Frost, Sunhaven, Northchurch Common, Berkhamstead HP4 1LR. Tel: (01442) 862011. E-mail: richardfrost4@btinternet.com. Fairs run first Sunday every month at Village Hall, Wing, Buckinghamshire LU7 0NN.

WORLD WAR BOOKFAIRS, Oaklands, Camden Park, Tunbridge Wells, Kent TN2 5AE. Tel: & Fax: (01892) 538465. E-Mail: wwarbooks@btinternet.com. Contact: Tim Harper. *Specialist military, aviation and naval bookfairs.*

CATALOGUE PRINTERS

BERFORTS GROUP LTD, 23-25 Gunnels Wood Park, Gunnels Wood Road, Stevengae, Hertfordshire SG1 2BH. Tel: (01438) 312777. Fax: (01438) 365521. Catlogues, booklets, book.

THE DOLPHIN PRESS, 96 Whitehill Road, Whitehill Industrial Estate, Glenrothes, Fife KY6 2RP. Tel: (01592) 771652. Fax: 630913. E-Mail: liz@dolphinpress.co.uk. Web: www.dolphinpress.co.uk *Catalogues and booklets printed.*

JOSHUA HORGAN PRINT PARTNERSHIP, 246 Marston Road, Oxford OX3 0EL. Tel: (01865) 246762. Fax: (01865) 250555. E-mail: print@joshuahorgan.co.uk. Website: www.joshuahorgan.co.uk

PARCHMENT PRINTERS, Printworks, Crescent Road, Cowley, Oxford OX4 2PB. Tel: (01865) 747547. Fax: 747551. E-mail: print@ParchmentUK.com. Website: www.PrintUK.com. Specialist in short run production. Contact Ian Kinch.

CRAFT BOOKBINDERS

ATKINSON BOOK BINDERS, 19 Glenmore Business Park, Telford Road, Salisbury, Wiltshire SP2 7GL. Tel (01722) 329846. E-mail: atkinsonbinders@ukonline.co.uk. Web: www.atkinsonbinders.co.uk

JOSEPHINE BACON, 197 Kings Cross Road, London WC1X 9BD. Tel: (020) 7278 9490. Fax: 7278 2447. E-mail: bacon@langservice.com. *Specialist in foreign language material, judaica and cookery and funghi.*

GEORGE BAYNTUN, incorporating Robert Riviere, Manvers Street, Bath BA1 1JW. Tel: (01225) 466000. Fax: 482122. E-mail: ebc@georgebayntun.com. Website: www.georgebayntun.com. *Fine binding in leather, restoration and case-making since 1894 (and Robert Riviere since 1829).*

CLIVE BOVILL, "Greenburn" River Lane, East Bilney, Dereham NR20 4HS. Tel: (01362) 860174. *Letterpress fine bindings, gold tooling and design. Special interest in conservation of 17th to 19th Century books.*

BRADY BOOKBINDERS, Library Building, Library Avenue, Lancaster University LA1 4YH. Tel: (01524) 592512. E-mail: gerard.brady@yahoo.co.uk. Contact: Gerard Brady. *Craft binding, thesis and book restoration.*

BRISTOL BOUND BOOKBINDING, 300 North Street, Ashton Gate, Bristol BS3 1JU. Tel: (0117) 966 3300. E-mail: information@bristolbound.co.uk. Website: www.bristolbound.co.uk. Rachel and Richard James. *We are a husband and wife team first established in 1986 when Rachel gained distinctions in bookbinding from Brunel Technical College, Bristol. We aim to offer a professional, yet friendly service to our customers, whilst maintaining a high standard of workmanship. We undertake new and restoration binding, thesis and dissertation binding, limited editions, corporate presentation binding, binding of newspapers, journals, magazines, personal memoirs, visitors books, photograph albums, wedding albums and much more.*

PHILIP N. BROOK (BOOKBINDER AND BOOK RESTORER), Bell Hill Farm, Lindale in Cartmel, Grange over Sands, Cumbria LA11 6LD. Tel: (01539) 534241. *Bookbinding, book restoration and conservation. To include single volume restorations, fine binding, short run (up to 1,000) publishers. Case work. All aspects of bookbinding work considered. Serving collectors, libraries and dealers for over twenty-one years.*

FRANCIS BROWN CRAFT BOOKBINDER, 24 Camden Way, Dorchester, Dorset DT1 2RA. Tel: (01305) 266039. *Francis Brown is a journeyman bookbinder who undertakes all kinds of binding work, ranging from simple repairs to the restoration of antiquarian volumes, fine limited editions or designed bindings. He has restored books for Balliol College, Wimborne Minster chained library and the Thomas Hardy Memorial Collection in the County Museum in Dorchester.*

CHIVERS BOOKBINDERS, Aintree Avenue, White Horse Business Park, Trowbridge, Wiltshire BA14 0XB. Tel: (01225) 752888. Fax: (01225) 752666. E-mail: ivor@chivers-period.com. Website: www.cromwellpressgroup.co.uk. Contact: Ivor Stone. *Binding, rebinding and repairing books since 1878. Conserving paper for a quarter of a century.*

FORMBYS LTD, 19-21 Market Place, Ramsbottom, Lancashire BL0 9AJ. Tel: and Fax: (01706) 825771. E-mail: formbys@tiscali.co.uk. Website: www.artisanbooks.co.uk. *Craft Bookbinding and book restoration.*

CHRIS HICKS BOOKBINDER, Tor View, Cary Hill, Castle Cary, Somerset BA7 7HL. Tel: (01963) 359019. E-Mail: chrishicksbookbinder@btinternet.com. Website: www.book-binder.co.uk. *Binding, rebinding, repairs, theses, slipcases, solander cases, fine bindings, short-run edition binding, blank books etc.*

FELICITY HUTTON, Fielden, Underhayes Lane, Launceston, Cornwall PL15 8HA. Tel: (01566) 773831. E-Mail: fachutton@btinternet.com. *Bookbinding and restoration.*

KEW BOOKBINDING, 61a North Street, Thame, Oxfordshire OX9 3BH. Tel: and Fax: (01844) 212035. E-mail: malcolmkew@mac.com. Web: www.kewbookbinding.co.uk. *Quality binding, short run, restoration, journals.*

KINGSWOOD BOOKS, 17 Wick Road, Milborne Port, Sherborne, Dorset DT9 5BT. Tel: & Fax: (01963) 250280. E-mail: kingswoodbooks@btinternet.com. Website: www.kingswoodbooks.btinternet.co.uk. *Bookbinding & conservation.* Enquiries to A.J. Dollery.

NEWCASTLE BOOKSHOP AT HALTWHISTLE, Market Square, Haltwhistle, Northumberland NE49 0BG. Tel: 01434 320103. Mobile: 07837 982809. E-mail: newcstlbk@aol.com. Website: www.newcastlebookshop.com. *Repair and restore books; make wedding albums, blank journals, visitors books, and custom made drop-back bozes. Also, mount artwork using archival board.*

D SANDERSON, Primrose Mill, London Road, Preston, Lancashire. PR1 4BX. Tel: (01772) 253594. Fax: (01772) 253592. E-mail: sandersons94@hotmail.com. Contact: Mr J. Doherty. *Book restoration and print finishers.*

CHARLES SYMINGTON, 145 Bishopthorpe Road, York YO23 1NZ. Tel: (01904) 633995. *Bookbinding and restoration.*

JAYNE TANDY (CRAFT BOOKBINDING AND RESTORATION), Bowhayes Cross, Williton, Somerset TA4 4NL. Tel: (01984) 632293. *Bookbinding, book restoration, conservation and repair.*

COLIN TATMAN, Corner House, 121A Lairgate, Beverley, E. Yorskire HU17 8JG. Tel: (01482) 880611 (day) & 882153 (evening). *Traditional craft bookbinding; paper repair; slipcases & book boxes; restoration & conservation.*

TEASDALE BOOKBINDERS, Caxton House, Corwen, Denbighshire LL21 0AA. Tel: (01490) 412 713. 7316. E-Mail: info@teasdalebookbinders.co.uk. *Hand bookbinding and restoration. Prop: Catherine Hore.*

TEMPLE BOOKBINDERS, 10 Quarry Road, Headington, Oxford OX3 8NU. Tel: (01865) 451940. E-Mail: enquiries@templebookbinders.co.uk. Website: www.templebookbinders.co.uk. Mr. Ian Barnes. *Hand bookbinder in fine leathers, vellum, linens, cloth & buckrams. Quality restorer of antiquarian books.*

JOHN TEMPLE BOOK BINDER, 5 Celia Heights, Bodmin, Cornwall PL31 1EH. Tel: 01208 76252. Mobile: 07963 199145. E-mail: johntemple1@virgin.net. *Hand book binding in leather, full, half and quarter; slipcases, boxes; and traditional casebinding. French marble to plain ends. Wide choice of materials, goat, calfskin and skivers, as well as cloth. Also binds PPC and paperbacks.*

TRADITIONAL BOOKCRAFTS, 28 Drayton Mill Court, Cheshire Street, Market Drayton, Shropshire TF9 1EF. Tel: (01630) 654410. *Craft bookbinder, antique and modern book repair and restoration, boxes, slipcases, gold tooling, handmade and scribed books. Established: 1983. Limited edition bindings. Prices on request. Prop: Monica Thornton.*

TUDOR BOOKBINDING LTD., 3 Lyon Close, Wigston, Leicestershire LE18 2BJ Tel: (0116) 288 3988. Fax: (0116) 288 4878. E-mail: sales@tudor-bookbinding.co.uk. Antique and modern book restoration, repair and rebinding; gold tooling; single copy restorations work undertaken.

PERIOD FINE BINDINGS, Yew Tree Farm, Stratford Road, Wootton Wawen, Warwickshire B95 6BY. Telephone: (01564) 793800. E-mail: periodfinebindings@googlemail.com. Website: http://periodfinebindings.typepad.com/royal_bindings. *Restorer of antiquarian books using ancient formulae and hand-made materials. Fox marks, inkstains etc removed. Rare books bought, sold and valued.*

RILEY DUNN & WILSON LTD., Glasgow Road, Falkirk, Scotland FK1 4HP. Tel: 01324 621591 Fax: 01324 611508. E-mail: enquiry@rdw.co.uk. Website: www.rdw.co.uk. *Restoration of antiquarian books, fine bindings, presentation bindings and expert paper conservation.*

PACKING MATERIALS SUPPLIERS

BOOK PROTECTORS & CO., Protector House, 76 South Grove, Walthamstow, London, E17 7NU. Tel: 0181 520 0012. *Unique protective covers for paperbacks and hardbacks, adjustable sleeving and other materials.*

D AND M PACKAGING, 5a Knowl Road, Mirfield, West Yorkshire WF14 8DG. Tel: (01924) 495768. Fax: (01924) 491267. E-mail: packaging@dandmbooks.com. Website: www.bookcovers.co.uk. Contact: Daniel Hanson. *Suppliers of all types of covers for hardbacks, paperbacks and dust jackets. Also comprehensive range of packaging and book-care materials, adhesives, book cleaners, tapes, etc. Free catalogue on request. We supply both trade and private customers and have no minimum order.*

MACFARLANE GROUP PLC., **Group Head Office:** 21 Newton Place, Glasgow, Scotland G3 7PY. Tel: (0141) 333 9666. Fax: (0141) 333 1988. Website: www.macfarlanegroup.net

PACKING CASE MANUFACTURERS: **Grantham Branch:** PO Box 16, Alma Park Industrial Estate, Grantham, Lincolnshire NG31 9SF. Tel: (0870) 150 4506. Fax: (0870) 150 4507. **Westbury Branch:** Quartermaster Road, West Wilts Trading Estate, Westbury, Wiltshire BA13 4JT. Tel: (01373) 858555. Fax: (01373) 858999.

PACKAGING DISTRIBUTION: **Bristol Branch:** Unit 2 Concorde Road, Patchway Industrial estate, Bristol BS34 5TB Tel: 0844 770 1401. Fax: 0844 770 1402. **Coventry Branch:** Siskin Parkway East, Middlemarch Business Park, Coventry, West Midlands CV3 4PE. Tel: 0844 770 1407. Fax: 0844 770 1408. **Enfield Branch:** Unit 5, Delta Park, Millmarsh Lane, Enfield, EN3 7QJ. Tel: 0844 770 1409. Fax: 0844 770 1410. **Exeter Branch:** Windsor Court, Manaton Close, Matford Business Park, Exeter, Devon EX2 8PF, Tel: 0844 770 1411. Fax: 0844 770 1412. **Fareham Branch:** Unit 1, Stephenson Road, Midpoint 27, Segensworth, Fareham, Hampshire PO15 5RZ. Tel: 0844 770 1413. Fax: 0844 770 1414. **Glasgow Branch:** Unit 1 Linwood Industrial Estate, Burnbrae Road, Linwood, Paisley PA3 3BD. Tel: 0844 770 1421. Fax: 0844 770 1422. **Grantham Branch:** Alma Park Industrial Estate, Grantham, Lincolnshire NG31 9SE. Tel: 0844 770 1415. Fax: 0844 770 1416. **Horsham Branch:** Oakhurst Business Park, Wilberforce Way, Southwater, Horsham, West Sussex RH13 9RT Tel: 0844 770 1419. Fax: 0844 770 1420. **Manchester Branch:** Empire Court, Fifth Avenue, Trafford Park, Manchester M17 1TN. Tel: 0844 770 1423. Fax: 0844 770 1424. **Milton Keynes Branch:** Kingston Gateway, Whitehall Avenue, Milton Keynes, Buckinghamshire MK10 0BU. Tel: 0844 770 1425. Fax: 0844 770 1426. **Newcastle:** The

Waterfront, Kingfisher Boulevard, Newburn Riverside, Tyne & Wear NE15 8NZ. Tel: 0844 770 1427. Fax: 0844 770 1428. **Sudbury Branch:** Windham Road, Chilton Industrial Estate, Sudbury, Suffolk CO10 2XD. Tel: 0844 770 1429. Fax: 0844 770 1430. **Telford Branch:** Unit D2, Horton Park Industrial Estate, Hortonwood 7, Telford, Shropshire TF7 7GX. Tel: 0844 770 1431. Fax: 0844 770 1432. **Wakefield Branch:** Unit H, Brunel Road, Wakefield 41 Industrial Estate, Wakefield WF2 0XG. Tel: 0844 770 1433. Fax: 0844 770 1434. **Wigan Branch:** Northgate Distribution Centre, Caxton Close, Wheatlea Park Industrial Estate, Wigan WN3 6XU. Tel: 0844 770 1437. Fax: 0844 770 1438.

Macfarlane Packaging provides a complete range of packaging materials, including New Book Pack and Super Book Pack, Postal bags and Easywrap.

PLASPAK, Piperell Way, Haverhill, Suffolk CB9 8QW (A Division of Marchant Manufacturing). Tel: (01440) 765300. Fax: 765302. E-mail: sales@marchant.co.uk. Website: www.plaspak.co.uk *Polythene manufacturer and specialist packaging.*

DISTRIBUTORS AND WHOLESALERS (NEW BOOK TRADE)

GARDNERS BOOKS LTD., 1 Whittle Drive, Willington Drove, Eastbourne, BN23 6QH. Tel: (01323) 521555. Fax: (01323) 521666. Web: www.gardners.com. Wholesalers.

GAZELLE BOOK SEVICES Ltd., White Cross Mills, High Town, Lancaster LA1 4XS. Tel: (01524) 68765. Fax: (01524) 63232. E-mail: sales@gazellebooks.co.uk. Web: www.gazellebooks.co.uk. Distributors.

REMAINDER MERCHANTS

AWARD PUBLICATIONS LTD., The Old Riding School, Welbeck Estate, Worksop, Nottinghamshire S80 3LR. Tel: (01909) 478170. Fax: (01909) 484632. E-mail: info@awardpublications.co.uk Web: www.awardpublications.co.uk. *Genuine remainders for adults and children.*

BOOKMARK REMAINDERS LTD., Rivendell, Illand, Launceston, Cornwall PL15 7LS. Tel: (01566) 782728. Fax: (01566) 782 059. E-mail: info@book-bargains.co.uk. WebSite: www.book-bargains.co.uk. *Range of genuine remainders and bargain books. Trade sales only.*

BLAKETON HALL LTD., Unit 1, 26 Marsh Green Road, Marsh Barton, Exeter EX2 8PN. Tel: (01392) 210602. Fax: 421165. E-Mail: sales@blaketonhall.co.uk. *Remainders and overstocks, including scientific, technical, academic, gardening, crafts & children's.* Enquiries to: Martin Shillingford.

CONSOLIDATED BOOKS LTD., Units 2, 3 Tyler Way, Sheffield, Yorkshire S9 1DT. Tel: (01142) 436323. Fax: (01142) 436085. E-mail: consobooks@btconnect.com. Publishers end-of lines and a cash and carry warehouse.

FANSHAW BOOKS, Unit 7, Lysnader Mews, Lysander Grove, London N19 3QP. Tel: (0207) 281 9387. Fax: (0207) 561 3502. E-Mail: info@roybloom.com. www.roybloom.com. *General remainders. Exhibits at all major book fairs.*

GRANGE BOOKS PLC., Head Office & Showroom - 35 Riverside, Sir Thomas Longley Road, Medway City Estate, Rochester, Kent ME2 4DP. Tel: (01634) 739173. Fax: 295921. E-Mail: sales@grangebooks.co.uk. Website: www.grangebooks.co.uk. *Distributors of remainders, and publisher of promotional books and reprints to the adult illustrated non-fiction and children's market.*

HCB Wholesale, Unit 2, Forest Road Enterprise Park, Hay-on-Wye HR3 5DS. Tel: (01497) 820 333. Fax: (01497) 821 192. E-mail: sales@hcbwholesale.co.uk. Approx. 100,000 books on view in warehouse.

JIM OLDROYD BOOKS, 14/18 London Road, Sevenoaks, Kent TN13 1AJ. Tel: (01732) 463356. Fax: 464486. E-Mail: paula@oldroyd.co.uk. Web site: www.oldroyd.co.uk. *Adult and children's remainders.*

PUMKIN WHOLESALE. Grove Farms, Milton Hill Road, Abingdon, Oxfordshire OX14 4DP. Tel: (01235) 833450. Fax: (01235) 833490. E-Mail: info@pumpkinwholesale.com. Web: www .pumpkinwholesale.com

SANDERSON BOOKS LTD, Front Street, Klondyke, Cramlington, Northumberland NE23 6RF. Tel: (01670) 735855. Fax: (01670) 730974. E-mail: sales@sandersonbooks.co.uk. Website: www. sandersonbooks.co.uk.

SANDPIPER BOOKS LTD., Offices and Showroom, 24 Langroyd Road, London SW17 7PL. Tel: (020) 8767-7421. Fax: 8682-0280. E-Mail: enquiries@sandpiper.co.uk. Website: www.sandpiper.co.uk. *Scholarly and literary remainders, academic reprints and mail order.*

SUPPLIERS OF MATERIALS AND TOOLS FOR BINDING AND RESTORING BOOKS, ETC.

CHARNWOOD BOOKS, Charnwood View, Broad Lane, Markfield, Leicestershire LE67 9TB. Tel: 01530 245996. Fax: 0207 1173315. E-mail: sales@charnwoodbooks.co.uk. Website: www.charnwoodbooks.co.uk. Tools, materials and equipment for repairing and restoring books.

SHEPHERDS BOOKBINDERS, 76 Southampton Row, London WC1B 4AR. Tel: (020) 7831-1151. E-mail: info@falkiners.com. Web: www.falkiners.com. *PAPERS. Wide selection of papers for repairs, marbled papers and coloured end papers. LEATHERS AND BOOKCLOTHS for repairs and bindings. BOOKS in print on bookbinding, calligraphy, typography, papermaking and printing history. All items can be supplied by post. Price lists available.*

FINE CUT GRAPHIC IMAGING LTD., Marlborough Road, Lancing Business Park, Lancing, West Sussex BN15 8UF. Tel: (01903) 751666. Fax: 750462. E-Mail: info@finecut.co.uk. Website: www.finecut.co.uk. *Manufacturers of bookbinders' finishing tools and accessories. Catalogue available (also available on-line) showing brass type, handle letters, hand tools and brass rolls. Special designs to order.*

HARMATAN LEATHER LTD, Westfield Avenue, Higham Ferrers, Northamptonshire NN10 8AX. Tel: (01933) 412151. Fax: (01933) 412242. E-mail: contact@harmatan.co.uk. Website: www.harmatan.co.uk.

HANDMADE PAPER COMPANY LTD., 16 Daleham Gardens, London NW3 5DA. Tel: (0207) 435 8008. *Fax: 020 7435 8400. Papercrafts, and paper making, handmade paper, artists paper.*

J. HEWIT AND SONS LIMITED, Kinauld Leather Works, Currie, Edinburgh, Scotland EH14 5RS. Tel: (0131) 449-2206. Fax: (0131) 451-5081. E-Mail: sales@hewit.com. Website: www.hewit.com. *BOOKBINDERS' TOOLS AND SUPPLIES, adhesive (paste, glue, P.V.A.), bone folders, brass type and type holders, brushes, knives, papers (marbled, etc.), presses, tapes, threads. BINDING LEATHERS, in a wide range of colours. BOOKCLOTHS, buckram, linen, cloth, mull, etc. BOOKBINDERS STARTER PACKS, basic tools to get you started.*

ANN MUIR MARBLING, 18 Ravensmead Road, Bromley, Kent BR2 0BT. Tel: & Fax: (0208) 249 8439. E-mail: annmuir@marbling.com. Website: www.annmuirmarbling.co.uk. *Marbled paper in both modern and traditional patterns and colourways. Matching service for old papers in restoration work. New papers designed for individual projects. Send for catalogue of samples and price list.*

PAPERSAFE, 2 Green Bank, Adderley, Market Drayton TF9 3TH. Tel: (01630) 652217. E-Mail: philip@papersafe.demon.co.uk. Website: www.papersafe.demon.co.uk. *Suppliers of archival quality repair materials for book and paper collectors.*

PICREATOR ENTERPRISES LIMITED, 44 Park View Gardens, Hendon, London NW4 2PN. Tel: (020) 8202-8972. Fax: (020) 8202-3435. E-mail: info@picreator.co.uk. Website: www.picreator.co.uk. *Fine–art conservation and restoration materials. Manufacturers of Renaissance wax polish, Vulpex liquid soap and Groom/stick non–abrasive document dry cleaner. Bookdealers are increasingly undertaking basic cleaning and restorative treatment of books and paper. Picreator Enterprises supply professional products which are simple to use and advice is given on their application. The Company has held a Royal warrant of appointment to H.M. The Queen since 1984 as suppliers of products for (fine–art) restoration and conservation.*

RUSSELL BOOKCRAFTS, Unit 1, Bluntswood Hall, Throcking, Buntingford, Hertfordshire SG9 9RN. Tel: (01763) 281430. Fax: (01763) 281431. E-Mail: office@russels.com. Website: www.russels.com. *Major supplier of very fine leathers. Range includes the world renowned, and only genuine "OASIS" goatskin, calf and sheepskin skivers – handmade bookbinders' equipment includes, specially designed work benches, nipping presses, lying presses, ploughs, sewing frames and Digby Stuart presses. We offer a fine colour range of Buckrams and bookcloths, mulls, Jaconette, tapes, threads and headbands; a large selection of specialised papers, marbled end papers, & millboards. Tools include: paring knives, bridled glue brushes, decorative hand tools and brass letters. Backing hammers, bone folders, burnishing agates and all types of bookbinders adhesives.*

USEFUL WEBSITES

Please note that in this selection the details are correct when going to press but changes and new ones may appear during the year. **Those in bold are multi-search sites.** *Some trade associations also offer book searching facilities, see pages 20–23.*

FOR SEARCHING TITLES

ABooksearch	www.abooksearch.com
Addall	**www.addall.com**
Advanced Book Exchange	www.abebooks.com
Abebooks Europe GmbH	www.abebooks.co.uk
Alibris	www.alibris.com
Alibris (UK)	www.alibris.co.uk
Amazon	www.amazon.com
Antiqbook (The Netherlands)	www.antiqbook.com
Antiquarian Booksellers Association of America (ABAA)	www.abaa.org
Barnes & Noble	www.bn.com
ANZAAB (Australia & New Zealand)	www.anzaab.com.au
Biblio.com	www.biblio.com
Biblion	www.biblion.co.uk
Bibliophile	www.bibliophile.net
Bibliopoly (England)	www.bibliopoly.com
BiblioQuest International (Australia)	www.biblioz.com
Books and Collectibles	www.booksandcollectibles.com.au
Bookfinder.com	**www.bookfinder.com**
Bookfinder4U.com (for new and used)	www/bookfinder4u.com
Independent Booksellers Network (England)	www.ibooknet.co.uk
Independent OnLine Booksellers Association	www.iobabooks.com
International League of Booksellers (ILAB)	www.ilab.org
The Internet Bookshop UK Ltd	www.ibuk.com
Maremagnum (Italy)	www.maremagnum.com
Powell's Books	www.powells.com
Provincial Book Fairs Association (PBFA)	www.booksatpbfa.com
Rare Books International	www.rarebooksinternational.com
Strand Books (USA)	www.strandbooks.com
Tom Folio	www.tomfolio.com
UKBookWorld	www.ukbookworld.com
Used Books Central (USA)	www.usedbookcentral.com
Zentrales Verzeichnis Antiquarischer Bücher (ZVAB, Germany)	www.zvab.com

FOR SEARCHING DEALERS

Advanced Book Exchange	www.abebooks.com
Sheppard's World	www.sheppardsworld.co.uk

GENERAL SEARCH SITES

Ask Jeeves	www.askjeeves.com
EBay	www.ebay.co.uk
Google	www.google.co.uk
Dog Pile	**www.dogpile.com**
Mamma	**www.mamma.com**

INDEX OF CITIES AND TOWNS

Dealer locations listed alphabetically by country, city, town and village, as shown in the Geographical section.

ABERDEEN.................... 271
ABERFELDY 279
ABERGAVENNY............ 286
ABERYSTWYTH 282
ABINGDON.................. 205
ADARE 266
ADDINGHAM 245
ADDLESTONE............... 230
AIRDRIE 277
ALCESTER................... 236
ALFRETON................... 82
ALFRISTON 99
ALNWICK.................... 201
ALRESFORD 121
ALTON....................... 121
ALTRINCHAM 68
ALTRINCHAM (GR MAN)118
ALVERSTOKE 121
AMERSHAM 61
AMMANFORD 281
ANDOVER 121
ANSTRUTHER 270
APPLEBY–IN–
   WESTMORLAND 76
ARBROATH 279
ARMAGH 260
ARUNDEL 241
ASCOT 55
ASHBURTON 84
ASHFORD.................... 135
ASHPERTON, LEDBURY 127
ASHTEAD.................... 230
ASHTON-UNDER-LYNE . 142
ATHERSTONE............... 236
ATHERTON 118
AUSTWICK 192
AYLESBURY................. 61
AYLSHAM 186
AYR.......................... 278
AYSGARTH 192
BAKEWELL 82
BALDERTON, NEWARK. 203
BALLATER 272
BALLINTEER 263
BALLYDEHOB............... 262
BALLYGOWAN 261
BALLYNAHINCH 261
BANBURY 205
BANCHORY,
   KINCARDINESHIRE 272
BANGOR (N. I.) 261

BANGOR 285
BANTRY...................... 263
BARNARD CASTLE 97
BARNSTAPLE................ 84
BARRINGTON 215
BARROW–IN–FURNESS.. 76
BARTON–ON–HUMBER.. 148
BASINGSTOKE 122
BATH 215
BATHEASTON 216
BATLEY 245
BATTLE...................... 99
BEACONSFIELD 61
BEADNELL 201
BEAMINSTER............... 91
BECCLES 225
BECKENHAM 135
BEDDINGTON............... 230
BEDFORD.................... 53
BEDWORTH................. 236
BELFAST 260
BERE ALSTON 84
BERKELEY 113
BERKHAMSTED............ 129
BESFORD 255
BETHESDA 285
BEULAH..................... 287
BEVERLEY 106
BEWDLEY 255
BEXHILL 99
BEXLEY 135
BIDDENDEN................. 135
BIDEFORD 84
BILLERICAY 108
BILLINGBOROUGH 148
BILLINGHAM 192
BILLINGHAY, LINCOLN 148
BILLINGSHURST........... 241
BILSTON 238
BINHAM..................... 186
BIRCH....................... 108
BIRCHWOOD 68
BIRKENHEAD.............. 184
BIRMINGHAM 238
BISHOP AUCKLAND...... 97
BISHOP'S CASTLE.......... 212
BISHOPS CLEEVE 113
BISHOP'S STORTFORD... 129
BISHOPSTON................. 58
BLACKBURN 142
BLACKPOOL................. 142

BLACKROCK 263
BLAENAU FFESTINIOG . 285
BLAENAVON 292
BLAIRGOWRIE 279
BLANDFORD FORUM ... 91
BLUNTISHAM 63
BOGNOR REGIS 241
BOLTON 118
BOOTLE 184
BOTESDALE.................. 225
BOTLEY 125
BOTTESFORD 203
BOURNEMOUTH........... 91
BOXFORD 225
BRACKLEY................... 199
BRACKNELL................. 55
BRADFORD.................. 245
BRADFORD ON AVON... 251
BRECON 287
BRENCHLEY................. 135
BRENTWOOD 108
BRIDGATER 216
BRIDGEWATER 216
BRIDGNORTH 212
BRIDLINGTON.............. 106
BRIDPORT................... 92
BRIGHOUSE 245
BRIGHTON 99
BRINSCALL 142
BRISTOL...................... 58
BRIXHAM.................... 84
BROADSTAIRS 135
BROCKENHURST 122
BROOM...................... 53
BROUGH 76
BUCKINGHAM 61
BUDE........................ 72
BUILTH WELLS............. 287
BULLWELL................... 203
BUNCLODY 266
BUNGAY 225
BURES 225
BURFORD 205
BURNHAM-ON-SEA 216
BURTON UPON TRENT . 223
BURY........................ 142
BURY ST. EDMUNDS..... 225
BUSHEY 130
BUXTON 82
BUXTON, NORWICH...... 186
BY DUNBLANE............. 268

BYFLEET...................... 230
CAISTER–ON–SEA 186
CALLANDER 268
CALLINGTON 72
CALNE...................... 251
CAMBORNE.................. 72
CAMBRIDGE 63
CAMBRIDGE (GLOS)...... 113
CAMPBELTOWN 278
CANNOCK 223
CANTERBURY 136
CARDIFF..................... 281
CARDIGAN................... 282
CARLISLE.................... 76
CARLTON.................... 53
CARMARTHEN 282
CARNDONAGH............. 263
CARNFORTH 142
CARRICK–ON
   –SHANNON................. 266
CARSHALTON 180
CASTLE CARY 216
CASTLE DOUGLAS 268
CASTLETHORPE............ 61
CASTLETON 82
CATTERICK VILLAGE ... 192
CAVERSHAM 55
CHAGFORD.................. 85
CHALFORD STROUD..... 113
CHARD 216
CHARMOUTH 92
CHATHAM 136
CHATTERIS 65
CHEADLE.................... 68
CHEADLE HULME 68
CHELMSFORD 108
CHELTENHAM.............. 113
CHEPSTOW................... 285
CHESHAM 61
CHESHUNT................... 130
CHESTER..................... 68
CHESTERFIELD 82
CHICHESTER 241
CHILBOLTON............... 122
CHIPPENHAM............... 251
CHIPPING CAMPDEN 114
CHIPPING NORTON 206
CHORLEY.................... 143
CIRENCESTER 114
CLAPTON–IN–
   GORDANO 216
CLARE 226
CLECKHEATON 245
CLEETHORPES.............. 148
CLEVEDON 217
CLIFTON 60
CLIFTONWOOD 60
CLITHEROE.................. 143

CLONTARF................... 264
CLUN........................ 212
COBHAM.................... 230
COCKERMOUTH.......... 76
COLCHESTER 108
COLEFORD.................. 114
COLERNE.................... 252
COLWYN BAY 283
COLYTON.................... 85
COMBE MARTIN.......... 85
COOKHAM 55
COOTEHILL................. 262
CORBY GLEN 149
CORSHAM 252
COUNTESS WEAR 85
COVENTRY 238
COWES...................... 133
CREWE...................... 69
CREWKERNE............... 217
CRICCIETH 285
CROCKENHILL............ 136
CROFTON.................... 76
CROMER.................... 186
CROMFORD 82
CROWBOROUGH 100
CROWTHORNE............. 55
CROYDON, SURREY...... 180
CULBOKIE................... 273
DACRE...................... 192
DAGENHAM................. 109
DALBEATTIE 269
DARLINGTON 97
DARTMOUTH.............. 85
DAWLISH 86
DEAL 137
DEBENHAM.................. 226
DERBY...................... 83
DEREHAM................... 186
DEVIZES.................... 252
DIDCOT 206
DIDSBURY 118
DINNET, NR ABOYNE ... 273
DISS........................ 186
DITCHLING 100
DOLGELLAU 286
DOLLAR..................... 268
DONAGHADEE 261
DONCASTER................. 221
DOOLIN 262
DORCHESTER...............92
DORCHESTER ON
   THAMES.................... 206
DORKING 230
DOUGLAS 259
DOWNHAM MARKET.... 187
DRIFFIELD.................. 106
DROITWICH 255
DUBLIN 264

DUCKLINGTON 206
DULVERTON 217
DUMFRIES 269
DUN LAOGHAIRE........ 265
DUNDEE 279
DUNFERMLINE 271
DUNKELD................... 279
DUNMANWAY.............. 263
DUNSTABLE................. 53
DUNSTER................... 217
DURNESS 273
EAGLE 149
EARLSDON.................. 145
EAST EWELL 230
EAST GRINSTEAD 242
EAST HAGBOURNE....... 206
EAST HOATHLY........... 101
EAST HORSLEY 231
EAST LOOE................. 72
EAST MOLESEY 231
EAST RUDHAM 187
EASTBOURNE.............. 101
EASTCOTE.................. 180
ECKINGTON 221
EDINBURGH 275
EGGINGTON 54
EGHAM...................... 231
EGREMONT.................. 77
ELLESMERE 212
ELLON 273
ELSTEAD.................... 231
ELSTREE 130
ELY 65
EMSWORTH.................. 122
ENFIELD.................... 180
ENGLEFIELD GREEN 231
ENNIS 262
ENNISKILLEN.............. 261
EPSOM 231
EWELL 232
EXETER 86
EYE 226
EYE GREEN.................. 66
FAIRFORD 114
FAKENHAM 187
FALMOUTH................. 72
FAREHAM................... 122
FARINGDON 206
FARNBOROUGH 122
FARNHAM 232
FARNINGHAM 137
FAVERSHAM 137
FELIXSTOWE................. 226
FENCE 143
FERNDALE.................. 285
FINNINGHAM 227
FLAMBOROUGH........... 106
FLEET....................... 122

FOCHABERS 273
FOLKESTONE 137
FORDINGBRIDGE 123
FOREST ROW 102
FORFAR 280
FORRES 273
FORT WILLIAM 274
FOWEY 72
FRAMLINGHAM 227
FRESHWATER 133
FRESHWATER BAY 133
FRISTON 102
FRODSHAM 69
FROGGATT 83
FROME 217
FYFIELD 207
GAINSBOROUGH 149
GALWAY 265
GIGGLESWICK 192
GILDERSOME 245
GILLINGHAM 93
GLASBURY 127
GLASGOW 278
GLOSSOP 83
GODALMING 232
GORING–BY–SEA 242
GORING–ON–THAMES ... 207
GORLESTON-ON-SEA 187
GOSPORT 123
GRANGE OVER SANDS.. 77
GRANTHAM 149
GRASMERE 78
GREAT DRIFFIELD 106
GREAT DUNMOW 109
GREAT ELLINGHAM 187
GREAT LEIGHS 109
GREAT MALVERN 255
GREAT WALFORD 236
GREAT YARMOUTH 187
GREENFORD 180
GRIMSBY 106
GUILDFORD 232
GUISBOROUGH 192
GUNTHORPE 203
HADDINGTON 277
HALESOWEN 239
HALESWORTH 227
HALIFAX 245
HALTON 143
HAMBROOK 60
HAMPTON HILL 180
HAMPTON 181
HARLESTON 187
HARLOW 109
HARPENDEN 130
HARROGATE 193
HARWICH 109
HASLEMERE 232

HASSOCKS 242
HASTINGS 102
HATLWHISTLE 201
HAVANT 123
HAWORTH 246
HAYLING ISLAND 123
HAY–ON–WYE 127
HAY–ON–WYE, POWYS.. 287
HEATHFIELD 103
HEBDEN BRIDGE 246
HELENSBURGH 279
HELMSLEY 193
HELSTON 73
HENLEY ON THAMES ... 207
HENLEY–IN–ARDEN 236
HENSTRIDGE 217
HEREFORD 127
HERNE BAY 138
HERTFORD 130
HERTFORD HEATH 130
HESWALL 184
HEXHAM 201
HINCKLEY 145
HINDLEY 143
HINDRINGHAM 188
HITCHIN 130
HOLBEACH 149
HOLMFIRTH 246
HOLT 188
HOLYWOOD 261
HONITON 86
HOOK NORTON 207
HORAM 103
HORBURY 246
HORLEY 232
HORNCASTLE 149
HORNDEAN 123
HORSHAM 242
HOVE 103
HOYLAKE 69
HUDDERSFIELD 246
HULL 107
HUNGERFORD 55
HUNSTANTON 188
HUNTINGDON 66
HUNTLY 273
HYDE 69
IBSTOCK 145
ILFORD 181
ILKLEY 247
ILMINSTER 217
INGLETON 193
INNERLEITHEN 267
INVERNESS 274
IPSWICH 227
IRCHESTER 199
IRVINE 279
ISLE OF ARRAN 274

ISLE OF COLONSAY 274
ISLE OF IONA 275
ISLEWORTH 181
IVER 62
JACKFIELD 212
JEDBURGH 267
KEMPSFORD 115
KENDAL 78
KENILWORTH 236
KENLEY 181
KESWICK 78
KEW 181
KIBWORTH HARCOURT 145
KIDDERMINSTER 255
KILLIECRANKIE 280
KILMARNOCK 279
KINETON 236
KING'S LYNN 188
KINGSBRIDGE 86
KINGSCLERE 55
KINGSTON 181
KINGSWINFORD 239
KINGTON 128
KIRKBY FLEETHAM 193
KIRKBY STEPHEN 78
KIRKBY–IN–ASHFIELD.. 203
KIRKCALDY 271
KIRKCUDBRIGHT 269
KIRKELLA 107
KIRKSTALL 248
KIRKWALL 275
KIRTON 149
KNARESBOROUGH 193
KNUTSFORD 69
LACK 261
LAMPETER 282
LANCASTER 143
LANCING 243
LANGPORT 218
LARBERT 268
LAUNCESTON 73
LEALHOLM 193
LEAMINGTON SPA 237
LEATHERHEAD 233
LEDBURY 128
LEEDS 248
LEICESTER 145
LEIGH–ON–SEA 109
LEOMINSTER 128
LETCHWORTH GARDEN
    CITY 131
LEWES 103
LEYLAND 143
LICHFIELD 223
LIMERICK 266
LINCOLN 150
LIPHOOK 123
LISBURN 260

LISKEARD	73	
LISS	124	
LITTLEBOROUGH	118	
LITTLEHAMPTON	243	
LITTLEOVER	83	
LIVERPOOL	184	
LIVERSEDGE	249	
LLANDRINDOD WELLS	289	
LLANDUDNO	284	
LLANGOLLEN	284	
LLANIDLOES	289	
LLANRWST	283	
LLANVAPLEY	286	
LLANWRTYD WELLS	289	
LOCHCARRON	274	
LONDON (E)	154	
LONDON (EC)	155	
LONDON (N)	156	
LONDON (NW)	160	
LONDON (SE)	163	
LONDON (SW)	166	
LONDON (W)	171	
LONDON (WC)	176	
LONDON (O)	180	
LONDONDERRY	260	
LONG BURTON	93	
LONG MELFORD	228	
LONG PRESTON	193	
LONGHOPE	275	
LOOE	73	
LOUGHBOROUGH	146	
LOUTH	150	
LOWER EARLEY	55	
LOWESTOFT	228	
LUDLOW	212	
LYDD	138	
LYME REGIS	93	
LYMINGE	138	
LYMINGTON	124	
LYMM	70	
LYMPSTONE	87	
LYNG	188	
LYTHAM ST. ANNES	144	
MACCLESFIELD	70	
MACHYNLLETH	290	
MADELAY	213	
MAIDENHEAD	56	
MAIDSTONE	138	
MALDON	110	
MALMESBURY	252	
MALVERN	256	
MALVERN WELLS	256	
MANCHESTER	118	
MANNINGTREE	110	
MANSFIELD	203	
MARKET DEEPING	151	
MARKET HARBOROUGH	147	
MARLBOROUGH	252	
MARPLE BRIDGE	70	
MATLOCK	83	
MEDSTEAD	124	
MEGAVISSY	73	
MELROSE	267	
MELTON MOWBRAY	147	
MERE GREEN	223	
MIDHURST	243	
MIDSOMER NORTON	218	
MILBORNE PORT	94	
MILLINGTON	107	
MILTON KEYNES	62	
MILVERTON	218	
MINEHEAD	218	
MIRFIELD	249	
MITCHAM	233	
MODBURY	87	
MOFFAT	269	
MOLD	284	
MONKLEIGH	87	
MONTGOMERY	290	
MONTPELIER	115	
MORDEN	182	
MORETONHAMPSTEAD	87	
MORETON–IN–MARSH	115	
MORPETH	201	
MOTTRAM IN LONGDENDALE	119	
MOULTON SEAS END	151	
MOYARD	265	
MUCH HADHAM	131	
MUCH WENLOCK	213	
MUIR OF ORD	274	
NAILSEA	60	
NAILSWORTH	115	
NANTWICH	70	
NEATH	285	
NEW BARNET	131	
NEW BUCKENHAM	189	
NEW MALDEN	233	
NEW MILLS	290	
NEW MILTON	124	
NEW ROSS	266	
NEW TREDEGAR	281	
NEWARK–ON–TRENT	203	
NEWBURY	56	
NEWCASTLE UPON TYNE	235	
NEWCASTLE, CO DUBLIN	265	
NEWCASTLE-UNDER -LYME	224	
NEWENT	115	
NEWHAVEN	104	
NEWMARKET	228	
NEWNHAM ON SEVERN	115	
NEWPORT (I.O.W)	133	
NEWPORT	213	
NEWPORT (WALES)	286	
NEWPORT ON TAY	271	
NEWPORT PAGNELL	62	
NEWQUAY	74	
NEWTON ABBOT	87	
NEWTOWN	290	
NORMANTON	249	
NORTH BERWICK	277	
NORTH CHERITON	218	
NORTH COTES	151	
NORTH SHIELDS	235	
NORTH WALSHAM	189	
NORTHAMPTON	199	
NORTHWICH	70	
NORWICH	189	
NOTTINGHAM	204	
OAKHAMPTON	87	
OAKLEY	124	
OLD COLWYN	284	
OLD COSTESSEY	190	
OLDBURY	239	
OLDHAM	119	
ORPINGTON	138	
OSGODBY	151	
OSTERLEY	182	
OSWESTRY	213	
OTLEY	249	
OVER LANE	115	
OVERTON	124	
OXFORD	207	
OXTED	233	
PADDOCK WOOD	138	
PAIGNTON	87	
PAULTON	59	
PEASEDOWN ST. JOHN	218	
PEN SELWOOD	218	
PENN	62	
PENRITH	78	
PENZANCE	74	
PERSHORE	256	
PERTH	280	
PETERBOROUGH	66, 151	
PETERSFIELD	124	
PETWORTH	243	
PICKERING	194	
PITLOCHRY	280	
PLYMOUTH	88	
PONTARDAWE	291	
POOLE	94	
PORT ERIN	259	
PORTSLADE	104	
PORTSMOUTH	124	
POTTERNE	253	
PRENTON	184	
PRESCOT	184	
PRESTEIGNE	291	
PRESTON	144	

PRESTWICH.................. 120
PUDDLETOWN 94
PURBROOK 125
QUEEN CAMEL............. 218
RADCLIFFE 120
RADLETT 131
RAINHAM 138
RAINTON 194
RAMSBURY 253
RAMSGATE 139
RAYLEIGH 110
READING.................... 56
REDCAR 98
REDHILL...................... 233
REDMILE 204
RHYL.............................. 284
RICHMOND.................. 194
RICHMOND (SURREY)... 233
RICKMANSWORTH 131
RINGWOOD.................. 125
RIPON............................. 194
ROBERTSBRIDGE.......... 104
ROCHDALE 120
ROCHE.......................... 74
ROCHESTER 139
ROMFORD 110
ROMSEY 125
ROSCREA..................... 266
ROSSCARBERY 263
ROSS–ON–WYE 128, 241
ROTHERFIELD 104
ROTHERHAM 221
ROTHLEY...................... 147
RUISLIP MANOR........... 182
RUNCORN......................71
RUSHDEN 199
RYDE.............................. 133
RYE................................ 104
SAFFRON WALDEN 110
SALISBURY 253
SALTDEAN................... 105
SANDIACRE 204
SANDY......................... 54
SAXMUNDHAM 228
SCARBOROUGH............ 194
SEATON 88
SEDBERGH 79
SELBY......................... 195
SELKIRK 267
SETTLE 195
SEVENOAKS 139
SHAFTESBURY 94
SHARNBROOK.............. 54
SHEFFIELD................... 221
SHENFIELD 110
SHENTON...................... 147
SHERBORNE................. 94
SHERINGHAM 190

SHINFIELD 57
SHOREHAM–BY–SEA 244
SHREWSBURY 213
SIBLE HEDINGHAM 110
SIDCUP 139
SILVERSTONE.............. 199
SIMONSBATH 219
SITTINGBOURNE 139
SKIPTON 195
SLEAFORD 151
SMARDEN.................... 140
SOLIHULL 239
SOMERTON 219
SOUTH BRENT...............88
SOUTH BURLINGHAM .. 191
SOUTH KELSEY 152
SOUTH WOODHAM
   FERRERS................... 111
SOUTHAMPTON............ 125
SOUTHEND–ON–SEA 111
SOUTHPORT 185
SOUTHSEA 125
SOUTHWOLD................ 229
SPALDING.................... 152
ST. MARGARETS........... 182
ST. PETER PORT........... 258
ST. AGNES 74
ST. ALBANS 131
ST. ANDREWS 271
ST. HELENS 133
ST. HELENS 144
ST. HELIER 258
ST. IVES...................... 74
ST. JUST 75
ST. LEONARD'S–ON–SEA 105
STAFFORD 224
STAITHES 196
STAMFORD 152
STANSTED.................... 111
STEYNING.................... 244
STILLORGAN................ 265
STOCKPORT 120
STOCKSFIELD.............. 202
STOCKTON-ON-TEES 98
STOCKTON-ON-THE-
   FOREST.................... 196
STOKE-ON-TRENT......... 224
STONESFIELD.............. 209
STOURPORT 256
STOW–ON–THE–WOLD... 115
STRATFORD-UPON-
   AVON......................... 237
STRATHTAY 280
STROUD 115
STUDLEY 237
STURMINSTER NEWTON 95
SUDBURY 229
SURBITON.................... 233

SUTTON 234
SUTTON IN ASHFIELD .. 204
SUTTON 182
SWANAGE.................... 95
SWANLAND.................. 107
SWANSEA 291
SWANTON ABBOT........ 191
SWINDON.................... 253
TALGARTH 291
TAMWORTH 224
TATTENHALL................ 71
TAUNTON 219
TAVISTOCK 89
TEDDINGTON............... 182
TEIGNMOUTH 89
TELFORD 214
TENBY 286
TETBURY 117
TEWKESBURY 117
THIRSK 196
THORNHILL 269
THORNTON CLEVELEYS 144
THURCASTON 147
THURSO 274
TICEHURST 105
TICKENHAM 219
TIMPERLEY.................. 71
TINTERN 286
TITCHFIELD 126
TIVERTON.................... 89
TODMORDEN 249
TONBRIDGE 140
TORQUAY 89
TORRINGTON............... 90
TOTNES....................... 90
TOWCESTER 199
TREFRIW 284
TREGARON 283
TRURO 75
TUNBRIDGE WELLS...... 140
TWICKENHAM 182
ULVERSTON 80
UPPINGHAM 211
UTTOXETER................. 224
VALE 258
VENTNOR 134
VICARSTOWN 265
WADEBRIDGE 75
WAKEFIELD 250
WALDERTON 244
WALLASEY................... 185
WALLINGFORD 209
WALLINGTON 234
WALSALL..................... 239
WALTHAMSTOW........... 154
WALTON–ON–THAMES.. 234
WANTAGE.................... 209
WARBOROUGH 209

WAREHAM 95
WARFIELD 57
WARMINSTER 254
WARRINGTON.............. 71
WARSASH 126
WARWICK 237
WATERINGBURY 141
WATFORD.................... 132
WATTON 191
WEETON 144
WEIR 144
WELLING 183
WELLINGBOROUGH 200
WELLINGTON.............. 219
WELLS-NEXT-THE-SEA .. 191
WELSHPOOL................. 291
WELTON 80
WELWYN GARDEN
  CITY 132
WEM.......................... 214
WEOBLEY.................... 128
WEST BROMWICH......... 240
WEST CROSS................ 291
WEST KIRBY 185
WEST LINTON 267
WEST PENNARD 220
WESTBURY 254

WESTBURY-ON-SEVERN 117
WESTCLIFF-ON-SEA......111
WESTERHAM 141
WESTLETON 229
WESTON-SUPER-MARE .220
WETHERBY 250
WEYBRIDGE 234
WEYMOUTH 96
WHITBY 196
WHITCHURCH 214
WHITEHAVEN.............. 80
WHITHORN 269
WHITLEY BAY 235
WHITSTABLE 141
WICKFORD..................111
WICKHAM BISHOPS.......111
WIGAN.......................120
WIGSTON 147
WIGTON 80
WIGTOWN 269
WILLAND 90
WILLINGTON.............. 98
WILLITON 220
WIMBORNE 96
WINCHESTER...............126
WINDERMERE............. 81
WINDLESHAM 234

WINDSOR 57
WINESTEAD 107
WINSFORD.................. 71
WINTERTON 153
WIRKSWORTH 83
WISBECH 67
WITNEY...................... 210
WOKING..................... 234
WOKINGHAM 57
WOLVERHAMPTON 240
WOMBOURN 224
WOODBRIDGE.............. 229
WOODFORD GREEN 112
WOOLER...................... 202
WOOTTON BASSETT 254
WORCESTER 257
WORTHING.................. 244
WREXHAM 292
WYMONDHAM............. 191
WYMONHAM 191
YARKHILL................... 128
YARM........................ 196
YARMOUTH................. 134
YORK 196
YOXALL 224
YSTRAD MEURIG......... 291

USE OF THE DIRECTORY

This directory is divided into four sections. The first is the *Geographical Directory of Dealers*, in which full details, where supplied, are given for each business or private dealer. These are listed alphabetically by town in which the shop or business premises are located. The details, as supplied by dealers, are presented in the following manner:

Name of business.	As provided. ■ Indicates that the type of premises is a Shop.
Postal address.	(∗) Indicates the dealer's preference for indexing or where we have imposed current county boundaries.
Prop:	Name of proprietor(s).
Website:	Website address. Users should ignore the full point at the end of the entry.
Tel:	Telephone number(s), together with the new codes followed by fax and/or mobile number. NOTE: If the code for the fax number is the same as for the telephone, it has sometimes been omitted.
E-Mail:	No longer appear - e-mails can be sent direct to dealers via our website www.sheppardsworld.co.uk.
Est:	Date at which business was established.
Type of premises occupied:	Shop, private, mail order/internet, market stall or storeroom.
Opening times:	Of shop, or if premises are private, whether appointments to view stock may be made, or if for contacting if postal business only.
Normal level of total stock:	Very small (less than 2,000), small (2,000–5,000), medium (5,000–10,000), large (10,000–20,000) or very large (more than 20,000).
Spec:	Subjects of books in which the dealer specialises. NB: only the first eight are shown in the Geographical Section. All dealers' subjects are shown in the Speciality Index
PR:	Price range of stock. This is intended as a guideline only.
CC:	Selection of Credit & Debit Cards eg. AE – American Express, DC – Diners Club, DI – Discovery, EC – Eurocard, JCB – Japanese Credit Bureau, MC – Mastercard, SO – Solo, SW – Switch, V – VISA.
Important lines of business:	Other than secondhand antiquarian books.
Cata:	Approximate frequency and subject of catalogues, if issued.
Corresp:	Languages, other than English, in which correspondence may be conducted.
Mem:	Membership of book trade organisations, eg. A.B.A. – Antiquarian Booksellers' Association B.A. – Booksellers Association of Great Britain & Ireland P.A. – Publishers Association P.B.F.A. – Provincial Booksellers' Fairs Association
Notes	These appear exactly as entered by the dealer in their Free Entry Form on Sheppard's World.

The next section is an alphabetical *Index of Businesses*, giving full name and county with the page on which their full entry is to be found.

This is followed by an alphabetical *Index of Proprietors*, giving their name and trading name followed by their page reference.

The fourth section is the *Speciality Index*. This is presented in alphabetical order by subject heading, giving the dealer's name, county and page on which their details may be found. Certain headings have extended listings - eg., Authors, History, Religion and Sport.

INTRODUCTION

Sheppard's British Isles, like printed directories in other fields, has been affected by the Internet and most databases are now only available on line. If viable, it is our intention to continue to print directories and investigations are currently taking place that will allow printed directories to be produced but in a modified format. The construction and indexing will differ from the existing format but we will only proceed after lengthy testing. The objective - to automate every step and significantly reduce the time it takes to produce typeset pages ready to send to a book printer. We will post progress reports to our website, as and when, we have something to report.

The trade is currently facing more threats to its traditional existence - perhaps more than other industries. Yet dealers are quick to adapt and many have not only survived but prospered. The Internet continues to both aid and abet the trade, but dealers' presence in the high street has diminished. While traditional book dealers have quit the high street premises, it is galling to many in the trade that vacant premises are then taken over by national charities. These charities, which we accept have an important place in society and carry out good work, often open specialist book shops adjacent, or near, to existing dealers' premises. As they do not pay for their stock and their staff are unpaid volunteers, many of whom have little or scant, knowledge of books, it would be a disservice to genuine collectors to list them in this directory. Anyone wishing to buy from them can easily find them in other reference sources.

This edition is significant for several reasons. There are more than fifty extra speciality classifications which suggests that dealers are marking their book shelves according to buyer's current interests which are for ever changing.

E-mail addresses, which have been shown in previous editions, are now omitted. Most buyers of this directory, who have contacted our offices, have specifically stated that they do not use the Internet. It is also known that whether e-mail addresses are published on websites or in print, they are open to copying (or 'harvesting' as it is called from websites). 'Spam' (unwanted e-mails) are the result and receiving numerous unsolicited e-mails is one reason why dealers change their e-mail addresses. As subscribers to Sheppard's World know, they can use the website to e-mail other dealers via the website, but the sender never knows the recipient's e-mail address until they reply. Dealer's e-mail addresses cannot be seen on our website – thus we offer dealers some safeguards against abuse. But, we appreciate there are some dealers who can make use of a printed directory also use the Internet. For a limited period we are therefore offering every registered book dealer or collector at the time of publication, who buys a copy direct from our offices, or who can supply a copy receipt of the purchase, a free on-line subscription to Sheppard's World for twelve months. These subscriptions must be requested in witing within the first year of publication.

Collectors and users of this directory should always remember that dealers are often slow to amend their entry and if embarking on a lengthy buying trip around the country, our best advice is to visit our website Sheppard's World to see the up-to-date information provided by the dealer. One of the conditions of being listed is that they visit their entry at least once a year.

Richard Joseph, May 2010

BEDFORDSHIRE

BEDFORD

Books With Care, 7 Barford Road, Willington, Bedford, MK44 3QP. Prop: Gerald Ford. Tel: (01234) 8312T14088. Fax: (01234) 831288. Web: www.bookswithcare.net. Est: 1996. Private premises. Internet and Postal. Appointment necessary. Small stock. PR: £1–200. CC: MC; V; Paypal.

Bunyan Books, 57 Purbeck Close, Goldington, Bedford, MK41 9LX. Prop: R.G. Sancto. Tel: (01234) 345518. Est: 2002. Private premises. Internet and Postal. Appointment necessary. Large stock. Spec: Antiquarian; Apiculture; Arctic - Antarctica; Author - Bunyan, John; Biblical Studies; Bindings; Bookbinding; Children's - Illustrated. PR: £10–500. Corresp: French, German. Notes: *Advertises occasionally in Book & Magazine Collector. Also, restoration, repair and binding. Rare and unusual items.*

The Eagle Bookshop, ■ 101 - 103 Castle Road, Bedford, MK40 3QP. Prop: Peter Budek. Tel: (01234) 269295. Fax: (01234) 290920. Web: www.eaglebookshop.co.uk. Est: 1991. Shop; Internet and Postal. Open: **M:** 10:00–17:30; **T:** 10:00–17:30; **W:** 10:00–17:30; **Th:** 10:00–17:30; **F:** 10:00–17:30; **S:** 09:30–17:00. Very large stock. Spec: Academic/Scholarly; Antiquarian; County - Local; History - General; History of Ideas; Mathematics; Physics; Science - General. PR: £1–2,000. CC: MC; V; Debit Cards. Cata: Science, Mathematics, Bedfordshire. Mem: PBFA. VAT No: GB 563 7690 08. Notes: *The shop expanded in 2004, and now has six large display rooms, covering most subjects. Emphasis is on scholarly, antiquarian and collectable books.*

Kingsmere Books, 41 Haylands Way, Bedford, MK41 9BY. Prop: Brian Webb. Tel: 01234.302132. Est: 1985. Private premises. Internet and Postal. Appointment necessary. Spec: Biography; Music - Classical; Music - Composers; Natural History; Poetry; Religion - Christian; Topography - General. Corresp. French, Spanish.

BROOM

Bolland Books, 14 The Woodlands, Broom, SG18 9NH. Prop: Les & Anne Bolland. Tel: 01767 310481. Web: www.Bollandbooks.com. Est: 1997. Mail Order; Internet and Postal. Open: **M:** 0900–1700; **T:** 0900–1700; **W:** 09:00–1700; **Th:** 09:00–1700; **F:** 09:00–1700; **S:** 09:00–1700. Closed for lunch: 13:00–14:00. Spec: Crime (True); Criminology; Espionage; Famous People - Kennedy, John F; Mafia; Police; Police Force Histories; Science - Forensic. CC: MC; V; Maestro. Cata: True Crime, Kennedy. VAT No: GB 806 1492 42.

CARLTON

Twiggers Booksearch, 28 High Street, Carlton, MK43 7LA. Prop: Ruth Rothschild. Tel: 01234 720378. Web: www.twiggers.com. Est: 1980. Private premises. Postal only. Contactable. M: 09:00–17:30; **T:** 09:00–17:30; **W:** 09:00–17:30; **Th:** 09:00–17:30; **F:** 09:00–17:30.Very small stock. Spec: Booksearch. CC: AE; D; E; JCB; MC; V. VAT No: GB 726 1475 36. Notes: *Booksearch company.*

DUNSTABLE

Adrian Walker, 107 Great Northern Road, Dunstable, LU5 4BW. Prop: Adrian Walker. Tel: 01582 605824. Est: 1965. Private premises. Postal only. Open in Summer. Cata: Falconry worldwide.

The Book Castle, ■ 12 Church St., Dunstable, LU5 4RU. Prop: Paul Bowes. Tel: (01582) 605670. Fax: (01582)662431. Web: www.book-castle.co.uk. Est: 1981. Shop open: **M:** 09:00–17:00; **T:** 09:00–17:00; **W:** 09:00–17:00; **Th:** 08:00–17:00; **F:** 09:00–17:00; **S:** 09:00–17:00. CC: AE; MC; V; Solo. Mem: PBFA.

Dealers – visit your entry at least once a year.
Check your details are correct. Go to:

www.sheppardsworld.co.uk

EGGINGTON

Robert Kirkman Ltd., Kings Cottage, Eggington, LU7 9PG. Prop: Robert Kirkman. Tel: (01525) 210647. Fax: (01525) 211184. Web: www.robertkirkman.co.uk. Est: 1987. Private premises. Internet and Postal. Appointment necessary. Small stock. Spec: Antiquarian; Author - Bunyan, John; Author - Churchill, Sir Winston; Bibles; Bindings; Cinema/Film; Famous People - Churchill, Sir Winston; Fine & Rare. PR: £20–100. CC: MC; V. Cata: 24 different subjects. Mem: ABA; PBFA; ILAB. VAT No: GB 491 0095 56. Notes: *prints and engravings, bookbinding restoration, literary memorabilia.*

SANDY

H.J. Morgan, 47 Bedford Road, Sandy, SG19 1ES. Tel: (01767) 691383. Est: 1980. Private premises. Book fairs only. Appointment necessary. Small stock. Spec: Academic/Scholarly; History - General; Literature; Travel - General. Mem: PBFA. VAT No: GB 467 3823 19.

SHARNBROOK

Ouse Valley Books, 16 Home Close, Sharnbrook, Bedford, MK44 1PQ. Prop: Barrie Farnsworth. Tel: (01234) 782411. Est: 1990. Private premises. Book fairs only. Contactable. Very small stock. General Stock; History - Local; Topography - General; Topography - Local. PR: £5–500. Mem: PBFA. Notes: *Payment accepted via Paypal.*

BERKSHIRE

ASCOT

Ian Cross, 83 Gainsborough Drive, Ascot, SL5 8TA. Tel: (01344) 872100. Fax: (01344) 872544. Est: 1972. Private premises. Postal only. Appointment necessary. Small stock. Spec: Art. PR: £25–1,500. Corresp: Italian. Notes: *Books, ephemera and original art relating to Silhouettes and occassionaly Portrait Minatures*

BRACKNELL

BookzoneBracknell, 5 Flintgrove, Bracknell, RG12 2JN. Prop: John Bacon. Tel: (01344) 421770. Est: 1990. Private premises. Internet and Postal. Appointment necessary. Small stock. Spec: Sport - General; Sport - Athletics; Sport - Boxing; Sport - Cricket; Sport - Football (Soccer); Sport - Golf; Sport - Horse Racing (inc. Riding/Breeding/Equestrian); Sport - Racing. PR: £5–50. CC: MC; V; PayPal. Notes: *Exhibits at bookfairs. Alternative Tel. No. (01344) 488825.*

CAVERSHAM

Douglas Saville Numismatic Books, Chiltern Thameside, 37c St Peters Avenue, Cavasham, Reading RG4 7DH. Prop: Douglas Saville. Tel: (0118) 946 1067. Web: www.douglassaville.com. Est: 2006. Office and/or bookroom. Appointment necessary. Medium stock. Spec: PR: all ranges. CC: AE; MC; V. Cata: online - numismatics. Mem: International Association of Professional Numismatists. Notes: *One of the largest stocks of out of print and rare books relating to numismatics, in all laguages, of all periods, and all price ranges.*

COOKHAM

Jean Hedger, Poultons, Cookham, SL6 9HW. Prop: Jean Hedger. Tel: 01628 523911. Fax: 01628 528217. Web: www.booksatpbfa.com. Est: 1977. Private premises. Internet and Postal. Contactable. Spec: Amusements; Art; Art - British; Artists; Author - Aesop; Author - Ahlberg, Janet & Allan; Author - Alcotts, The; Author - Aldin, Cecil. CC: D; JCB; MC; V. Cata: Illustrated; Artwork; Children's; Stanley Spencer. Corresp: French; Spanish; German; Chinese (Mandarin). Mem: ABA; PBFA; ILAB. Also at: PBFA and ABA Book Fairs in UK. VAT No: GB 492 0257 50. Notes: *I specialise in Illustrated Books and Original Artwork; Children's Books of the last three centuries; Reference Books related to these areas; Stanley Spencer. In addition I stock a small selection of quality books outside these subject areas.*

CROWTHORNE

Malcolm Applin, 21 Larkswood Drive, Crowthorne, RG45 6RH. Prop: Malcolm Applin. Tel: (01344) 776881. Est: 1993. Private premises. Postal only. Small stock. Spec: Biography; Fiction - General; Fiction - Women; Literary Criticism; Poetry. PR: £5–250.

HUNGERFORD

Hungerford Antiques Centre, High Street, Hungerford. Tel: 01488 683701. Shop and/or gallery. Open: **M:** 09:15–17:30; **T:** 09:15–17:30; **W:** 09:15–17:30; **Th:** 09:15–17:30; **F:** 09:15–17:30; **S:** 09:15–18:00; **Su:** 11:00–17:00. Notes: *Includes stock from Countryside Books, Andover.*

KINGSCLERE

Wyseby House Books, ■ Kingsclere Old Bookshop, 2a George Street, Kingsclere, Nr. Newbury, RG20 5NQ. Prop: Dr. T. Oldham. Tel: (01635) 297995. Fax: (01635) 297677. Web: www.wyseby.co.uk. Est: 1978. Shop; Internet and Postal. Open: **M:** 09:00–17:00; **T:** 09:00–17:00; **W:** 09:00–17:00; **Th:** 09:00–17:00; **F:** 09:00–17:00; **S:** 09:00–17:00. Very large stock. Spec: Applied Art; Architecture; Art; Art History; Art Reference; Artists; Arts, The; Biology - General. PR: £1–1,000. CC: AE; JCB; MC; V. Mem: PBFA. VAT No: GB 295 3261 54.

LOWER EARLEY

K C Brown, 11 Easington Drive, Lower Earley, Reading, RG6 3XN. Prop: K C Brown. Tel: 01189 667013. Fax: 01189 667013. Est: 1991. Private premises. Internet and Postal. Appointment necessary.

MAIDENHEAD

Cymric Books, Regency Cottage, The Pound, Cookham, Maidenhead, SL6 9QD. Prop: Pablo Dubois. Tel: 01628 521002. Web: www.cymricbooks.co.uk. Est: 2008. Mail Order Only. Internet and Postal. Open: **M:** 09:00–18:30; **T:** 09:00–18:30; **W:** 09:00–12:30; **Th:** 09:00–18:30; **F:** 09:00–15:30; **S:** 10:00–12:30. Spec: Celtica; Countries - Wales; Religion - Druidism; Welsh Interest. CC: Paypal, UK cheques. Cata: Wales, Welsh language and literature, Patagonia. Corresp: Welsh, Spanish, French, Portuguese. Mem: Will be applying to PBFA. Notes: *We specialise in antiquarian and rare books about Wales and Welsh culture, including the druids, mainly written in English or Welsh. Our emphasis is on the intrinsic interest of the content and on high-quality bindings.*

Valerie Peel, t/a Kiandra Associates, 40 Culley Way, Cox Green, Maidenhead, SL6 3PX. Tel: (01628) 822439. Fax: (01628) 826118. Web: www.http://ukbookworld.com/members/valeriepeel. Est: 1985. Private premises. Internet and Postal. Appointment necessary. Small stock. Spec: Dogs; Booksearch. PR: £4–750. CC: Paypal. Cata: Dog Books. Notes: *Free Booksearch.*

NEWBURY

Eastleach Books, 3 Preston Place, Newbury, RG14 2SE. Prop: Daniel Unwin. Tel: +44 (0)1635 48444. Fax: +44 (0)1635 48444. Web: www.eastleach-book.co.uk. Est: 1997. Private premises. Internet and Postal. Telephone First. Open: **M:** 09:00–18:00; **T:** 09:00–18:00; **W:** 09:00–18:00; **Th:** 09:00–18:00; **F:** 09:00–18:00; **S:** 09:00–18:00. Very large stock. Spec: Academic/Scholarly; Alpinism/Mountaineering; Antiquarian; Applied Art; Art; Biography; History - General. PR: £2–4,500. CC: E; JCB; MC; V. Corresp: Little French. Mem: PBFA. Notes: *Good stocks of Academic History, and good general non fiction.*

Invicta Bookshop, ■ 8 Cromwell Place, Northbrook Street, Newbury, RG14 1AF. Prop: Simon & Tina Hall. Tel: (01635) 31176. Est: 1969. Shop open: **M:** 10:30–17:30; **T:** 10:30–17:30; **Th:** 10:30–17:30; **F:** 10:30–17:30; **S:** 10:30–17:30. Large stock. Spec: Aviation; Cookery/Gastronomy; Military; Naval; Topography - Local. PR: £1–200. CC: MC; V. Mem: PBFA. Notes: *Hungerford Arcade Antiques Centre.*

Railway Book and Magazine Search, The Warren, Curridge, Newbury, RG18 9DN. Prop: N.J. Bridger. Tel: (01635) 200507. Web: www.nevis-railway-bookshops.co.uk. Est: 1981. Private premises. Postal only. Very small stock. Spec: Railways and Railroads; Ephemera. PR: £1–200. Notes: *Nevis Railway Bookshop, Goring-on-Thames, Oxon (q.v.) Nevis Railway Bookshop, Marlborough, Wiltshire (q.v.).*

READING

Books for Amnesty, Reading Shop, ■ 71 Wokingham Road, Reading, RG6 1LH. Prop: Amnesty International UK. Tel: 01189661646. Est: 2003. Shop open: **M:** 10:00–17:00; **T:** 10:00–17:00; **W:** 10:00–17:00; **Th:** 10:00–17:00; **F:** 10:00–17:00; **S:** 10:00–17:00.

Mary Butts Books, 219 Church Road, Earley, Reading, RG6 1HW. Prop: Mary Butts. Tel: (0118) 926-1793. Est: 1985. Private premises. Internet and Postal. Appointment necessary. Open: **M:** 09:00–17:00; **T:** 09:00–17:00; **W:** 09:00–17:00; **Th:** 09:00–17:00; **F:** 09:00–17:00; **S:** 09:00–17:00. Medium stock. Spec: Applied Art; Architecture; Art; Art - British; Art History; Art Reference; Artists; British Art & Design. PR: £2–50. Corresp: French. Notes: *I specialise in children's books & modern art books.*

Footballana, 275 Overdown Road, Tilehurst, Reading, RG31 6NX. Prop: Bryan Horsnell. Tel: (0118) 942 4448. Fax: (0118) 942 4448. Private premises. Postal only. Very small stock. Spec: Sport - Football (Soccer); Collectables; Ephemera. PR: £5–100. Notes: *Also, pre-1950 football programmes, postcards and ephemera wanted. 'Wants' lists welcome.*

Forbury Fine Books, 46 Tredegar Road, Reading, RG4 8QF. Prop: Stephen Gardner. Tel: (0870) 063 8680. Fax: (0870) 286 6874. Web: www.forburyfinebooks.co.uk. Est: 2004. Private premises. Internet and Postal. Appointment necessary. Open: **M:** 09:00–18:00; **T:** 09:00–18:00; **W:** 09:00–18:00; **Th:** 09:00–18:00; **F:** 09:00–18:00. Small stock. PR: £2–1,000. Notes: *Booksearch.*

J.B. Books, 3 Wenlock Edge, Charvil, Reading, RG10 9QG. Prop: John A. Baker. Tel: (0118) 934-0679. Web: www.balloonbooks.co.uk. Est: 1978. Private premises. Postal only. Telephone First. Small stock. Spec: Aircraft; Aviation; Sport - Ballooning; Transport. PR: £1–250. Corresp: French.

Keegan's Bookshop, ■ Merchant's Place (off Friar Street), Reading, RG1 1DT. Prop: John & Judith Keegan. Tel: (0118) 958-7253. Web: www.keegansbookshop.com. Est: 1979. Shop and Postal. Open: **M:** 09:00–17:30; **T:** 09:00–17:30; **W:** 09:00–17:30; **Th:** 09:00–17:30; **F:** 09:00–17:30; **S:** 09:00–17:30. Medium stock. Spec: Aviation; Maritime/Nautical; Military; Military History; Naval; Railways and Railroads; Topography - General; Topography - Local. PR: £1–100. CC: MC; V; Switch. Corresp: Italian.

Veronica Mayhew, Trewena, Behoes Lane Woodcote, Reading, RG8 0PP. Tel: (01491) 680743. Est: 1972. Private premises. Appointment necessary. Small stock. Spec: Animals and Birds; Apiculture; Cats; Farming & Livestock; Ornithology; Prints and Maps. PR: £1–500. VAT No: GB 537 6954 02.

SHINFIELD

Books & Bygones, 40 Hollow Lane, Shinfield, RG2 9BT. Prop: Pamela Pither and John Lilly. Tel: 0118 988 4346. Web: www.booksbygones.com. Est: 1990. Mail Order Only. Internet and Postal. Telephone First. Spec: Cookery - Professional; Cookery/Gastronomy; Food & Drink. CC: MC; V; Maestro. Mem: Ibooknet. Notes: *Speciality - cookery and food related.*

WARFIELD

Moss End Bookshop, ■ Moss End Garden Centre, Moss End, Warfield, Nr. Bracknell, RG42 6EJ. Prop: K. & M.A. Precious. Tel: (01344) 422110. Est: 1981. Shop open: **T:** 10:00–17:00; **W:** 10:00–17:00; **Th:** 10:00–17:00; **F:** 10:00–17:00; **S:** 10:00–17:00; **Su:** 10:00–17:00. Spec: Antiques; Rural Life; Sport - Field Sports; Prints and Maps. PR: £2–250. CC: MC; V. Notes: *Also, prints: see under Prints & Map Sellers for more details.*

WINDSOR

Eton Antique Bookshop, ■ 88 High Street, Eton, Windsor, SL4 6AF. Prop: Maurice Bastians. Tel: (01753) 855534. Est: 1975. Shop open: **M:** 11:00–18:00; **T:** 11:00–18:00; **W:** 11:00–18:00; **Th:** 11:00–18:00; **F:** 11:00–18:00; **S:** 11:00–18:00; **Su:** 12:00–17:00. Medium stock. Spec: Antiquarian; Antiques; Bindings; History - General; Literature; Military; Poetry; Sets of Books. PR: £3–2,000. CC: E; MC; V. Corresp: Spanish. Mem: Eton Traders Assoc. VAT No: GB 787 1877 65. Notes: *Old prints and maps, bookbinding and repairs. Often open early and late - call first.*

WOKINGHAM

John Townsend, 33 Bishop's Drive, Wokingham, RG40 1WA. Tel: (0118) 978-5463. Web: www. johntownsend.demon.co.uk. Est: 1991. Private premises. Internet and Postal. Contactable. Medium stock. Spec: Genealogy; Heraldry; History - General; Manuscripts; Parish Registers; School Registers/Rolls of Honour; Topography - General; Topography - Local. PR: £10–200. Cata: Genealogy, Heraldry, Local History, Manuscripts. Corresp: French, German. VAT No: GB 591 8061 25.

BRISTOL

BISHOPSTON

Steve Liddle, 8 Morley Square, Bishopston, BS7 9DW. Tel: (0117) 924 4846. Est: 1983. Private premises. Appointment necessary. Spec: Antiquarian; Archaeology - Industrial; Architecture; Art; Art - British; Author - Austen, Jane; Author - Rolt, L.T.C.; Bindings. Cata: Railways, Canals, Industrial Revolution etc. Mem: ABA; PBFA; ILAB. VAT No: GB 869 4504 83. Notes: *Fine books in many subject areas. We exhibit at the major UK bookfairs and would be pleased to meet customers who remember our old bookshops (Patterson Liddle) in Bristol and Bath. Books and libraries purchased, valuations undertaken.*

BRISTOL

Lesley Aitchison, 22 West Shrubbery, Redland, Bristol, BS6 6TA. Prop: Lesley Aitchison. Tel: (0117) 907-6899. Fax: (0117) 974-1962. Web: www.localhistory.co.uk/la. Est: 1993. Private premises. Postal only. Appointment necessary. Spec: Auction Catalogues; Broadsides - Letterpress; Canals/Inland Waterways; Cornish; Cornish history; Counties in England; Genealogy; History - 19th Century. PR: £10–1,000. CC: MC; V; Switch. Cata: Maps, ephemera, manuscripts. Notes: *Also at these premises: Ambra Books. (q.v.) Also, sales particulars, prints & photographs.*

Ambra Books, 22 West Shrubbery, Redland, Bristol, BS6 6TA. Prop: Ivor Cornish. Tel: (0117) 907-6899. Fax: (0117) 974-1962. Web: www.localhistory.co.uk/ambra. Est: 1972. Private premises. Internet and Postal. Appointment necessary. Small stock. Spec: Counties in England; County - Local; Genealogy; History - Local; Topography - Local. PR: £10–3,000. CC: MC; V; SW. Corresp: French, Italian. Notes: *I mainly deal in books on the West Country (Bristol, Cornwall, Devon, Dorset, Gloucestershire, Somerset, Wiltshire)*

Arthur Hook, 54 Egerton Road, Bristol, BS7 8HL. Tel: (0117) 9144673. Web: www.hooksbooks.co.uk. Est: 1997. Private premises. Internet and Postal. Appointment necessary. Spec: Atlases; London; Maps & Mapmaking; Railways and Railroads; War - World War I; War - World War II. CC: Paypal. Cata: London, Railway maps & guides, World War I & II. Corresp: French. Mem: PBFA. Notes: *booksatpbfa.com has a selection of my stock on line. Many maps are not listed.*

Avon Books, ■ 4 Waterloo Street, Clifton, Bristol, BS8 4 BT. Prop: John Ray. Tel: 0117 973 9848. Est: 1991. Shop open: **M:** 10:00–16:00; **T:** 10:00–16:00; **W:** 10:00–16:00; **Th:** 10:00–16:00; **F:** 10:00–16:00; **S:** 10:00–16:00. CC: MC; V.

Beware of the Leopard, Stalls 77 and 66 - 69 the Covered Market, Saint Nicholas Markets, Saint Nicholas Street, Bristol, BS1 1LJ. Prop: David Jackson. Tel: 01179 257277. Est: 1991. Market stand/stall; Market Stall. Open: **M:** 10:00–17:00; **T:** 10:00–17:00; **W:** 10:00–17:00; **Th:** 10:00–17:00; **F:** 10:00–17:00; **S:** 10:00–17:00 Spec: Aircraft; Art Reference; Arts, The; Autobiography; Aviation; Cinema/Film; Classics, The; Computing. CC: MC; V.

Bishopston Books, ■ 259 Gloucester Road, Bristol, BS7 8NY. Prop: Bill Singleton. Tel: 0117 9445303. Web: www.ibooknet.co.uk. Est: 1993. Shop open: **T:** 10:00–17:00; **W:** 10:00–17:30; **Th:** 10:00–17:30; **F:** 10:00–17:30; **S:** 09:30–16:30. CC: MC; V; Maestro. Mem: Ibooknet.

Books for Amnesty, ■ 103 Gloucester Road, Bishopston, Bristol, BS7 8AT. Prop: Amnesty International U.K. Tel: (0117) 942-2969. Est: 1998. Shop open: **M:** 10:00–16:30; **T:** 10:00–16:30; **W:** 10:00–16:30; **Th:** 10:00–16:30; **F:** 10:00–16:30; **S:** 11:00–17:00. Medium stock. PR: £1–10. Notes: *Bristol Book Fairs at BAWA.*

James Burmester, Pipley Old Farm, Upton Cheyney, Bristol, BS30 6NG. Prop: James & Rosamund Burmester. Tel: (0117) 932-7265. Fax: (0117) 932-7667. Est: 1985. Private premises. Appointment necessary. Small stock. Spec: Agriculture; Author - Austen, Jane; British Books; Broadsides - Letterpress; Cookery/Gastronomy; Courtesy; Economics; Education & School. PR: £50–10,000. CC: MC; V. Cata: Rare and unusual English books, 1600-1900. Mem: PBFA. VAT No: GB 404 6808 60.

Deverell Books, 86a Memorial Road, Hanham, Bristol, BS15 3LA. Prop: Paul Deverell Hughes. Tel: (0117) 961-6234. Est: 2001. Private premises. Appointment necessary. Small stock. Spec: Author - Dahl, Roald; Author - Watkins-Pitchford, Denys ('B.B.'); Books about Books; Children's; Children's - Illustrated; Illustrated - General; Illustrated - 19th & 20th Century; Illustrators. PR: £10–2,000. Cata: children's & illustrated. Mem: PBFA.

Double-B-Books Ltd, 12 Gregorys Tyning, Paulton, Bristol BS39 7PH. Prop: Bruce Bell. Tel: 0176) 1419463. (*) Private premises. Internet only. Small stock. Spec: Books about Books; History - eneral; History - British. PR: £10-100.

Harlequin Books, ■122 High Street, Staple Hill, Bristol, BS16 5HH. Prop: Brian W. Ball. Tel: (0117) 970-1801. Fax: (0117) 970-1801. Web: www.harlequinbooks.co.uk. Est: 1994. Internet and Postal. Shop open: **M:** 09:30–16:30; **T:** 09:30–16:30; **W:** 09:30–13;00; **Th:** 09:30–16:30; **F:** 09:30–16:30; **S:** 09:30–16:30. Medium stock. Spec: Aviation; Maritime/Nautical; Military; Military History; Motoring; Railways and Railroads; Topography - Local; War - General. PR: £1–250. CC: AE; JCB; MC; V. VAT No: GB 639 7296 86.

A. R. Heath, 62 Pembroke Road, Clifton, Bristol, BS8 3DX. Tel: (0117) 974-1183. Fax: (0117) 973-2901. Web: www.heathrarebooks.co.uk. Est: 1964. Private premises. Internet and Postal. Spec: Fine & Rare; Manuscripts. PR: £50–10,000. CC: AE; D; E; JCB; MC; V. Mem: ABA.

Higher Octave Books, ■ 58 Cotham Hill, Redland, Bristol, BS6 6JX. Prop: Kevin Fortey-Jones F.E.A.A. Tel: 0117 946 7772. Fax: 0117 973 0522. Web: www.higher-octave-books.co.uk. Shop open: **M:** 10:00–18:00; **T:** 10:00–18:00; **W:** 10:00–18:00; **Th:** 10:00–18:00; **F:** 10:00–18:00; **S:** 10:00–18:00. CC: E; MC; V. VAT No: GB 713 5195 47. Notes: *General stock bordering on the academic. Specialist subjects are Mind, Body & Spirit, Humanities, Literary Criticism, Military History and American History.*

A.J. Kitley, 31 Perrys Lea Bradley Stoke, Bristol, BS32 0EE. Tel: (01454) 615261. Est: 1986. Private premises. Postal only. Small stock. Spec: Musical Instruments. PR: £1–150.

Rachel Lee Rare Books, The Old Bakery, 30 Poplar Road, Warmley, Bristol, BS30 5JU. Prop: Rachel Lee. Tel: (0117) 960-6891. Fax: (0117) 960-6935. Web: www.rleerarebooks.co.uk. Est: 1979. Private premises. Internet and Postal. Appointment necessary. Small stock. Spec: Academic/Scholarly; Economics; History of Ideas; Humanities; Philosophy; Booksearch. PR: £30–20,000. CC: MC; V. Cata: philosophy, economics. Mem: ABA; ILAB. VAT No: GB 783 5078 02. Notes: *Also, a booksearch service for philosophy only.*

M. G. Manwaring, 9 Glentworth Road, Bristol, BS6 7EG. Tel: 0117 942 2934. Est: 1975. Private premises. Internet and Postal. Telephone First. Open: **M:** 09:00–18:00; **T:** 09:00–18:00; **W:** 09:00–18:00; **Th:** 09:00–18:00; **F:** 09:00–18:00. Spec: Applied Art; Archaeology; Architecture; Art; Art Reference; Author - 20th Century; Book Arts; Botany. CC: MC; V. Cata: All. Corresp: French.

Paperbacks Plus, ■ Regent Street Shopping Arcade, 98 Regent Street, Kingswood, Bristol, BS15 8HP. Prop: Mr. T. Nicholls. Tel: (0117) 9566232. Web: www.pbplus.freeserve.co.uk. Est: 1994. Internet and Postal. Shop open: **M:** 09:00–17:00; **T:** 09:00–17:00; **W:** 09:00–17:00; **Th:** 09:00–17:00; **F:** 09:00–17:00; **S:** 09:00–17:00. Spec: Biography; Children's; Fiction - General; Fiction - Crime, Detective, Spy, Thrillers; Fiction - Fantasy, Horror; Fiction - Science Fiction; Fiction - Women; Military History. PR: £1–20.

John Roberts Wine Books, 3 Weston Close, Sea Mills, Bristol, BS9 2JG. Prop: John Roberts. Tel: 0117 373 7904. Est: 1977. Private premises. Internet and Postal. Spec: Viticulture; Wine. Mem: ABA; ILAB. VAT No: GB 561 9002 57.

S.P.C.K., ■ 79 Park Street, Bristol, BS1 5PF. Tel: (0117) 9273461. Fax: (0117) 9293525. Web: www.spck.org.uk. Est: 1698. Shop open: **M:** 09:00–17:30; **T:** 09:00–17:30; **W:** 09:30–17:30; **Th:** 09:00–17:30; **F:** 09:00–17:30; **S:** 09:00–17:30. Small stock. Spec: Bibles; Biblical Studies; Ecclesiastical History & Architecture; Gnostics / Gnosticism; Oxford Movement; Prayer Books; Religion - Catholic; Religion - Christian. PR: £1–250. CC: MC; V. Mem: BA. VAT No: GB 232 8071 82. Notes: *Theological Booksellers, specialising in secondhand and new Christian Theology. Also secondhand vestments and communion ware.*

Morris & Juliet Venables, 270 Henbury Road, Bristol, BS10 7QR. Prop: Morris & Juliet Venables. Tel: (0117) 950-7362. Est: 1970. Private premises. Appointment necessary. Medium stock. Spec: Academic/Scholarly; Antiquarian; Art; Fine & Rare; Literary Criticism; Literature; Music - General; Music - Classical. PR: £5–1,000. CC: MC; V. Cata: Stained glass. Mem: PBFA. VAT No: GB 397 3454 11.

CLIFTON

Gerald Baker, 28 Beaconsfield Road, Clifton, BS8 2TS. Prop: Gerald Baker. Tel: (0117) 974-4319. Est: 1991. Private premises. Postal only. Small stock. Spec: Author - Watkins-Pitchford, Denys ('B.B.'); Natural History; Railways and Railroads; Shell County Guides (UK only); Sport - General; Topography - General; Topography - Local; Transport. PR: £5–200. CC: Paypal. Cata: Official publicity of British railway companies.

CLIFTONWOOD

Byass Rare Books, 22 Bellevue Crescent, Cliftonwood, BS8 4TE. Prop: Dean Byass. Tel: (0117) 9299400. Est: 1994. Private premises. Internet and Postal. Telephone First. Spec: Antiquarian; Chemistry; Earth Sciences; Fine & Rare; History - Science; History of Ideas; Law - General; Literature. PR: £50–10,000. CC: AE; MC; V. VAT No: GB 799 9334 44.

HAMBROOK

Bristol Books, Champion House, Moorend Farm Road, Hambrook, Bristol, BS16 1SP. Prop: Garth O'Donnell. Tel: (0117) 910 9829. Web: www.abebooks.com/home/bs6books. Est: 1985. Private premises. Internet and Postal. Appointment necessary. Medium stock. Spec: Art; Humanities; Literature; Pulps. PR: £1–50. CC: PayPal.

NAILSEA

The Old Music Master, 16 Scotch Horn Way, Nailsea, BS48 1TE. Prop: Joseph Tooley. Tel: 01275 856320. Est: 1992. Private premises. Postal only. Appointment necessary. Spec: Music - Illustrated Sheet Music; Music - Printed, Sheet Music & Scores. CC: Paypal. Notes: *Main stock is music sheets with illustrated covers. The music is secondary to the cover illustrations. From 'mid 19th century to 1960's. Have American, British and French.*

BUCKINGHAMSHIRE

AMERSHAM

Gill Bilski, 4 Sheepfold Lane, Amersham, HP7 9EL. Prop: Gill Bilski. Tel: (01494) 433895. Web: www.gillbilski.com. Est: 1983. Private premises. Internet and Postal. Appointment necessary. Small stock. Spec: Author - Alcotts, The; Author - Brent-Dyer, Elinor M.; Author - Bruce, Mary Grant; Author - Crompton, Richmal; Author - Fairlie–Bruce, D.; Author - Forest, A.; Author - Goudge, Elizabeth; Author - Hill, Lorna. PR: £2–200. CC: via Paypal for overseas customers. Cata: Children's books with a few adult & non-fiction. Corresp: French. Notes: *Also a booksearch service.*

AYLESBURY

Great Hall Bookshop, ■ The King's Head, Market Square, Aylesbury, HP20 2RW. Prop: The National Trust. Tel: 01296 381501. Fax: 10296 381502. Web: www.nationaltrust.org.uk. Est: 2004. Shop open: **M:** 10:30–16:00; **T:** 10:30–16:00; **W:** 10:30–16:00; **Th:** 10:30–16:00; **F:** 10:30–16:00; **S:** 10:30–16:00. Spec: Biography; Fiction - General; History - General; Travel - General; Collectables.

David Wilson, 95 Worlds End Lane, Weston Turville, Aylesbury, HP22 5RX. Tel: (01296) 612247. Est: 1969. Private premises. Postal only. Appointment necessary. Spec: Countries - Scotland; Natural History; Topography - Local. Notes: *Stocks major on Highlands and Islands and natural hstory (ornithology).*

BEACONSFIELD

Barn Books, Old Hay Barn, Holtspur Top Lane, Beaconsfield, HP9 1BS. Prop: Elisabeth & Wolfgang Ansorge. Tel: (01494) 671122. Fax: (01494) 671122. Est: 1991. Private premises. Internet and Postal. Appointment necessary. Small stock. Spec: Africana; Archaeology; Art; Churchilliana; Cinema/Film; Collecting; Countries - General; Countries - Africa. PR: £5–3,000. CC: PayPal. Corresp: German. VAT No: GB 578 4204 21. Notes: *We now offer a large selection from our stock to customers in South Africa at BAOBAB BOOKS, 210 Long Street, Cape Town 8001 and also offer a search service though this shop.*

BUCKINGHAM

Corvus Books, 11 Parsons Close, Winslow, Buckingham, MK18 3BX. Prop: Chris Corbett. Tel: (01296) 713393. Fax: (01296) 713393. Est: 1990. Private premises. Internet and Postal. Appointment necessary. Small stock. Spec: Atlases; Colour-Plate; Natural History; Travel - General. PR: £50–5,000. CC: Pay Pal. Mem: PBFA. Notes: *Also attends 11 P.B.F.A. fairs a year at the Holiday Inn near Rusell Square.*

E. & J. Shelley, Quakers Orchard, 12 Moreton Road, Buckingham, MK18 1LA. Prop: Jennifer Shelley. Tel: (01280) 812307. Est: 1996. Private premises. Postal only. Telephone First. Large stock. Spec: Children's; First Editions; Illustrated - General; Illustrators; Literature; Poetry. PR: £10–2,000.

CASTLETHORPE

Butler Rare Books, Castlethorpe Lodge, Hanslope Road, Castlethorpe, MK19 7HD. Prop: Stephen & Sara Butler. Tel: +44 1908 511625. Fax: 44 1908 483925. Web: www.butlerrarebooks.co.uk. Est: 1984. Private premises. Internet and Postal. Appointment necessary. Open: **M:** 09:00–17:30; **T:** 09:00–17:30; **W:** 09:00–17:30; **Th:** 09:00–17:30; **F:** 09:00–17:30; **S:** 09:00–17:30; Closed for lunch: 13:00–14:00. Spec: Antiquarian; Bibles; Biblical Studies; Bibliography; Book of Hours; Books about Books; Books in Greek; Children's. CC: MC; V. Cata: Theology, Antiquarian, Children's, Early Printing. Mem: PBFA.

CHESHAM

David Mundy at Nooks and Crannies, ■ 9a Market Square, Chesham, HP5 1HG. Prop: Dave Mundy. Tel: (020) 7482 7087. Est: 2000. Shop open: **M:** 09:30–17:30; **T:** 09:30–17:30; **W:** 09:30–17:30; **Th:** 09:30–17:30; **F:** 09:30–17:30; **S:** 09:30–17:30; **Su:** 11:00–16:30. Small stock. PR: £1–50. CC: JCB; MC; V; Maestro, Solo.

IVER

Pemberley Books, ■ 18 Bathurst Walk, Richings Park, Iver, SL0 9AZ. Prop: Ian A. Johnson. Tel: (01753) 631114. Fax: (01753) 631115. Web: www.pemberleybooks.com. Est: 1985. Internet and Postal. Shop open: **M:** 10:00–17:00; **T:** 10:00–17:00; **W:** 10:00–17:00; **Th:** 10:00–17:00; **F:** 10:00–17:00; **S:** 11:00–16:00. Medium stock. Spec: Antiquarian; Botany; Entomology; Herpetology; Lepidopterology; Mammals; Medicine; Medicine - History of. PR: £1–20,000. CC: AE; E; JCB; MC; V. Cata: Bi-annually, Natural History, Entomology. Corresp: German, French. Mem: PBFA; BA. VAT No: GB 646 2266 34. Notes: *Also, new books on specialities.*

MILTON KEYNES

Daeron's Books, ■ 3 Timor Court, Stony Stratford, Milton Keynes, MK11 1EJ. Prop: Angela Gardner. Tel: (01908) 568989. Fax: (01908) 266199. Web: www.daerons.co.uk. Est: 1992. Internet and Postal. Shop open: **M:** 11:00–16:00; **T:** 11:00–16:00; **W:** 11:00–16:00; **F:** 11:00–16:00; **S:** 09:15–17:15. Medium stock. Spec: Antiquarian; Arthurian; Author - Chesterton, G.K.; Author - Inklings, The; Author - Kipling, Rudyard; Author - Lewis, C.S.; Author - MacDonald, George; Author - Pratchett, Terry. PR: £1–500. CC: AE; D; E; JCB; MC; V. Mem: FSB, SSBA. VAT No: GB 776 7066 85. Notes: *We have now expanded our range of both books and ephemera. Dragons, Daleks, fairies with a hint of Wicca are now part of our range. Still the largest collection of Tolkien and Lewis.*

Periplus Books, 160 Waterside, Peartree Bridge, Milton Keynes, MK6 3DQ. Prop: John Phillips. Tel: (01908) 663579. Fax: (01908) 663579. Web: www.periplusbooks.co.uk. Est: 1997. Private premises. Postal only. Appointment necessary. Small stock. Spec: Biology - Marine; Earth Sciences; Geology; Marine Sciences; Meteorology; Oceanography. PR: £5–200. Mem: PBFA.

NEWPORT PAGNELL

Ken's Paper Collectables, ■ 29 High Street, Newport Pagnell, MK16 8AR. Prop: Ken Graham. Tel: (01908) 610003. Fax: (01908) 610003. Web: www.kens.co.uk. Est: 1983. Shop open: **M:** 09:30–17:00; **T:** 09:30–17:00; **W:** 09:30–17:00; **F:** 09:30–17:00; **S:** 09:30–16:00. Large stock. Spec: Autographs; Comics; Magazines & Periodicals - General; Manuscripts; Newspapers; Paper Collectables; Collectables; Ephemera. PR: £1–400. CC: MC; V. Mem: Ephemera Society. Notes: *We sell Autographs vintage magazines, newspapers, British comics, posters, ephemera, show business memorabilia and all manner of paper collectables. No books, stamps or currency.*

PENN

The Cottage Bookshop, ■ Elm Road, Penn, HP10 8LB. Prop: Mrs E S Tebbutt. Tel: 01494 812632. Est: 1951. Shop open: **T:** 10:00–17:00; **W:** 10:00–17:00; **Th:** 10:00–17:00; **F:** 10:00–17:00; **S:** 10:00–17:00. Mem: BA.

CAMBRIDGESHIRE

BLUNTISHAM

Bluntisham Books, Oak House, 4 East Street, Bluntisham, Huntingdon, PE28 3LS. Prop: D.W.H. & S.A. Walton. Tel: 01487 840449. Fax: 01487 840894. Web: www.bluntishambooks.co.uk. Est: 1976. Private premises. Internet and Postal. Spec: Arctic - Antarctica; Countries - Antarctic, The; Countries - Arctic, The; Countries - Falklands, The; Countries - Greenland; Countries - Iceland; Countries - Polar; Exploration - Polar Regions. CC: MC; V. Cata: 3 a year. VAT No: GB 344 2959 39. Notes: *Also, publishers of Antarctic books, including reprints of classics and translations.*

CAMBRIDGE

Alister & Garon Books, Cambridge, CB4 3AQ. Prop: Paul Neeve. Tel: (07967) 227882. Est: 1980. Market stand/stall open at: Market Square, Cambridge. Open: **M:** 09:00–17:00; **W:** 09:00–17:00; **F:** 09:00–17:00; **S:** 09:00–17:00; **Su:** 09:00–17:00. Medium stock. Spec: Art; Fiction - General; History - General; Literature; Mind, Body & Spirit; Music - General. PR: £1–25. VAT No: GB 215 8289 51.

Bookbarrow, 93 Cam Causeway, Cambridge, CB4 1TL. Prop: Frank Edwards. Tel: 01223 424 429. Fax: n/a. Web: www.bookbarrow.co.uk. Est: 1988. Private premises. Internet and Postal. Appointment necessary. Spec: Africana; American Indians; Art; Astrology; Children's; Comics; Eastern Philosophy; Esoteric. Mem: PBFA. Notes: *General stock on market stall, Cambridge City Centre Market, Thursdays only 9a.m. until 4p.m. Some P.B.F.A. bookfairs attended in East Anglia. Also the monthly Long Melford Bookfair in Suffolk.*

Books & Collectables Ltd., ■ Unit 7/8 Railway Arches, Coldhams Road, Cambridge, CB1 3EW. Prop: A. Doyle, J. Cross, D.B. & M. Doyle & P. Brown. Tel: (01223) 412845. Web: www.booksandcollectables .com. Est: 1993. Internet and Postal. Shop open: **M:** 10:00–17:00; **T:** 10:00–17:00; **W:** 10:00–17:00; **Th:** 10:00–17:00; **F:** 10:00–17:00; **S:** 10:00–17:00; **Su:** 10:00–16:00. Very large stock. Spec: Antiques; Art; Children's; Cinema/Film; Comic Books & Annuals; Comics; Cookery/Gastronomy; Fiction - General. PR: £1–300.

Bracton Books, 25 Lode Road Lode, Cambridge, CB25 9ER. Prop: Mrs S.J. Harrison. Tel: (01223) 811976. Web: www.bractonbooks.co.uk. Est: 1981. Private premises. Postal only. Appointment necessary. Large stock. Spec: Academic/Scholarly; Anthropology; Archaeology; Biology - General; Books about Books; Countries - Africa; Countries - Americas, The; Countries - Asia. PR: £2–100. CC: Paypal.

G. David, ■ Bookshop, 16 St. Edward's Passage, Cambridge, CB2 3PJ. Prop: D.C. Asplin, N.T. Adams & B.L. Collings. Tel: (01223) 354619. Web: www.n/a. Est: 1896. Shop open: **M:** 09:00–17:00; **T:** 09:00–17:00; **W:** 09:00–17:00; **Th:** 09:00–17:00; **F:** 09:00–17:00; **S:** 09:00–17:00. Medium stock. Spec: Academic/Scholarly; Antiquarian; Art; Bindings; Children's; Early Imprints; Fine & Rare; Illustrated - General. PR: £1–1,000. CC: JCB; MC; V. Corresp: Japanese, Swedish. Mem: ABA; PBFA; BA. VAT No: GB 599 5999 44. Notes: *Please contact us regarding books for sale, wanted etc., via N. Adams or D.Asplin by telephone 01223 354619. Exhibits at PBFA fair (June), York (September), ABA Chelsea (November).*

de Visser Books, 309 Milton Road, Cambridge, CB4 1XQ. Prop: Erik de Visser. Tel: (01223) 500909. Fax: (01223) 500909. Est: 1988. Private premises. Internet and Postal. Appointment necessary. Small stock. Spec: Academic/Scholarly; Countries - Albania; Countries - Austria; Countries - Balkans, The; Countries - Baltic States; Countries - Bulgaria; Countries - Central East Europe; Countries - Czech Republic. PR: £10–750. CC: JCB; MC; V; Delta, Maestro, Solo. Cata: 4/5 a year on Central & East Europe only. Corresp: French, Dutch, German. VAT No: GB 493 3891 05.

Galloway & Porter Limited, ■ 30 Sidney Street, Cambridge, CB2 3HS. Prop: Mr Paul Ogdan. Tel: (01223) 367876. Fax: (01223) 360705. Est: 1900. Shop open: **M:** 08:45–17:00; **T:** 08:45–17:00; **W:** 08:45–17:00; **Th:** 08:45–17:00; **F:** 08:45–17:00; **S:** 09:00–17:15; **Su:** 11:00–17:00. Spec: Academic/ Scholarly; Mythology. PR: £1–2,000. Mem: ABA; PBFA; BA; BT. VAT No: GB 213 4374 92. Notes: *Also, remainders and bargain books.* [In adminstration April 2010]

The Haunted Bookshop, ■ 9 St. Edward's Passage, Cambridge, CB2 3PJ. Prop: Sarah Key & Phil Salin. Tel: 01223 312913. Web: www.sarahkeybooks.co.uk. Shop open: **M:** 10:00–17:00; **T:** 10:00–17:00; **W:** 10:00–17:00; **Th:** 10:00–17:00; **F:** 10:00–17:00; **S:** 10:00–17:00. CC: JCB; MC; V. Cata: Children's & Illustrated. Corresp: French. Mem: PBFA. VAT No: GB 572 9580 04. Notes: *Specialising in children's and illustrated books 19th and 20th century, but also stocking some poetry, literature, fine bindings, East Anglian interest and some general stock. We are happy to post books, our site has secure CC facility.*

J & J Burgess Booksellers, 2 St Thomas's Road, Cambridge, CB1 3TF. Prop: John Burgess, Janet Burgess. Tel: 01223 249037. Est: 1997. Private premises. Postal only. Appointment necessary. Spec: Africana; Aircraft; American Revolution, The; Anatomy; Animals and Birds; Archaeology; Arms & Armour; Author - General.

Sarah Key, ■The Haunted Bookshop, 9 St. Edward's Passage, Cambridge, CB2 3PJ. Prop: Sarah Key & Phil Salin. Tel: (01223) 312913. Web: www.sarahkeybooks.co.uk. Est: 1985. Shop open: **M:** 10:00– 17:00; **T:** 10:00–17:00; **W:** 10:00–17:00; **Th:** 10:00–17:00; **F:** 10:00–17:00; **S:** 10:00–17:00. Medium stock. Spec: Annuals; Author - Ardizzone, Edward; Author - Barker, Cecily M.; Author - Blyton, Enid; Author - Brent-Dyer, Elinor M.; Author - Buckeridge, A.; Author - Carroll, Lewis; Author - Crompton, Richmal. PR: £1–2,000. CC: JCB; MC; V. Cata: Childrens's & Illustrated. Corresp: French. Mem: PBFA. VAT No: GB 572 9680 04. Notes: *Local interest items & a booksearch service within our specialist field.*

Paul Kunkler Books, 6 Hardwick Street, Cambridge, CB3 9JA. Tel: (01223) 321419. Fax: (01223) 321419. Private premises. Appointment necessary. Small stock. Spec: Art History; Manuscripts.

Adam Mills Rare Books, 328 High Street, Cottenham, Cambridge, CB24 8TX. Prop: Adam Mills. Tel: (01954) 250106. Fax: (01954) 250106. Web: www.adammillsbooks.com. Est: 1981. Private premises. Internet and Postal. Appointment necessary. Small stock. Spec: Bibliography; Books about Books; Fine Printing; Illustrated - General; Limited Editions - General; Literature; Private Press; Typography. CC: MC; V. Cata: English Literature, Private Press & Illustrated. Corresp: French, Italian. Mem: PBFA.

Peter Moore Bookseller, Unit 12, The Old Maltings, 135 Ditton Walk, Cambridge, CB5 8PY. Prop: Peter Moore. Tel: (01223) 411177. Web: www.aus-pacbooks.co.uk. Est: 1970. Office and/or bookroom; Internet and Postal. Appointment necessary. Small stock. Spec: Countries - Australia; Countries - New Zealand; Countries - Pacific, The; Countries - Papua New Guinea; Travel - Australasia/ Australia. PR: £1–500. CC: JCB; MC; V. Cata: Australia and the Pacific. Mem: PBFA; BCSA. VAT No: GB 215 3610 02. Notes: *Some stock may be viewed on: www.booksatpbfa.com www.booksandcollectibles.com.au, www.abebooks.com.*

Mike Parker Books, 2 Mill Lane, Duxford, Cambridge, CB22 4PT. Tel: (01223) 835935. Est: 1995. Private premises. Internet and Postal. Appointment necessary. Small stock. Spec: Adventure; Annuals; Antiquarian; Autobiography; Fiction - General; History - General; Literature; Military. PR: £5–500.

Plurabelle Books, The Grey Barn (Bldg 3), The Michael Young Centre, Purbeck Road, Cambridge, CB2 8HN. Prop: Dr. Michael Cahn. Tel: (01223) 415671. Fax: (01223) 413241. Web: www. plurabelle.co.uk. Est: 1993. Warehouse. Postal only. Telephone First. Open: **M:** 09:00–16:00; **T:** 09:00–16:00; **W:** 09:00–16:00; **Th:** 09:00–16:00; **F:** 09:00–16:00. Very large stock. Spec: Academic/ Scholarly; Computing; Humanities; Linguistics; Literature; Philosophy; Science - General; Science - History of. PR: £8–500. CC: E; MC; V; Switch, Maestro. Corresp: French, German, Italian. Mem: Tom Folio, IBookNnet. VAT No: GB 636 8493 00. Notes: *We buy academic libraries and surplus library stock in all subjects, visitors welcome by appointment.*

Quest Booksearch, 24 Hawthorne Road, Stapleford, Cambridge, CB22 5DU. Prop: Dr. Rosemary Scott. Tel: (01223) 844080. Fax: (01223) 844080. Est: 1997. Private premises. Postal only. Very small stock. Spec: Literature; Literature - Victorian; Poetry. PR: £3 – 1,000.

Frances Wetherell, 8 Highworth Avenue, Cambridge, CB4 2BG. Tel: (01223) 363537. Est: 1988. Private premises. Postal only. Appointment necessary. Small stock. Spec: Art; Art History; Art Reference; Economics; Literature; Social History. PR: £10–100. Notes: *Also, a booksearch service*

David White, The Old Guildhall, 4 Church Lane, Linton, Cambridge, CB1 6JX. Prop: David White. Tel: (01223) 894447. Web: www.davidwhitebooks.co.uk. Est: 1987. Private premises. Internet and Postal. Appointment necessary. Small stock. Spec: Medicine; Medicine - History of; Pharmacy/ Pharmacology. PR: £10–2,000. CC: MC; V. Cata: medicine, history of medicine, pharmacy.

Peter Wood, 51 Telegraph Street, Cottenham, Cambridge, CB24 8QU. Tel: (01954) 251056. Web: www.booksatpbfa.com. Est: 1973. Private premises. Appointment necessary. Small stock. Spec: Art; Broadcasting; Cinema/Film; Entertainment - General; Music - General; Performing Arts; Theatre; Ephemera. PR: £20–500. CC: MC; V. Mem: PBFA. VAT No: GB 214 4339 88. Notes: *Contactable Monday to Friday 08:30 – 18:00. Attends Perfoming Arts fairs at National Theatre Apr-Oct.*

.Joan Stevens, Books, ■ 3 High Street, Chatteris, PE16 6BE. Prop: Joan Stevens. Tel: (01354) 696874. Fax: (01354) 696874. Est: 2000. Shop. Appointment necessary. Small stock. Spec: Academic/Scholarly; Art - Afro-American; Art - Theory; Art Reference; Artists; Author - 19th Century; Authors - Women; Autographs. PR: £1–200. CC: cash/cheque. Cata: author lists. Corresp: French. Notes: *Ring the door bell between 10:00 and 17:00, other times by appointment. Stock includes 19thC Women's Lives.*

ELY

P.G. Bright, 11 Ravens Court, Ely, CB6 3ED. Tel: (01353) 661727. Est: 1982. Private premises. Appointment necessary. Medium stock. Spec: Children's; Illustrated - General; Literature; Sport - Cricket. PR: £1–500. Mem: PBFA.

Charles Bossom, Book House, 34 Cambridge Road, Ely, Cambridgeshire, CB7 4HL. Prop: Charles Bossom. Tel: 01353 610285. Web: www.ukbookworld.com/members/bossomc. Est: 2000. Private premises. Internet and postal. Appointment necessary. Open: **M:** 11:00–17:30; **T:** 11:00–17:30; **W:** 11:00–17:30; **Th:** 11:00–17:30; **F:** 11:00–17:30. Large stock. Spec: Academic/Scholarly; Author - Dickens - Charles; Author - Henty, G.A.; Author - Rackham, Arthur; Biography; Children's; Children's - Early Titles; Children's - Illustrated. PR: £1–1,000. CC: AE, JCB; MC; V; Delta; Solo; Switch; Maestro; Pin Train; Electron; Fortoak. VAT: GB 881 0233 45. Notes: *Charles Bossom has worked in the book trade since 1963, commencing at W H Smith Oxford and retiring in 1999 as Regional Manager. We offer a changing selection of books in a wide range of subjects.*

Ely Books, 24 Downham Road, Ely, CB6 1AF. Prop: Michael G. Kousah. Tel: (01353) 661824. Web: www.elybooks.com. Est: 1986. Private premises. Internet only. Appointment necessary. Small stock. Spec: Americana - General; Antiquarian; Art; Australiana; Author - General; Author - Baring-Gould, S.; Bindings; Biography. PR: £5–2,000. Mem: PBFA. VAT No: GB 572 9042 32.

Dealers who need to update their entry
should visit their page on
Sheppard's World

Hereward Books, ■ 17 High Street, Haddenham, Ely, CB6 3XA. Prop: Roger J. Pratt. Tel: (01353) 740821. Fax: (01353) 741721. Web: www.herewardbooks.co.uk. Est: 1985. Internet and Postal. Telephone First. Open: **S:** 10:00–13:00. Medium stock. Spec: Bindings; Illustrated - General; Natural History; Sport - Angling/Fishing; Sport - Falconry; Sport - Field Sports; Travel - General. PR: £15–1,000. CC: JCB; MC; V; Debit. Cata: Field Sports & Angling. Mem: PBFA. VAT No: GB 382 3886 03.

Octagon Books, ■ 14 Pilgrims Way, Ely, CB6 3DL. Prop: John Williams. Tel: (01353) 610244. Est: 1982. Shop at: Cloisters Antiques, 1-1b Lynn Rd, Ely CB7 4EG. Open: **M:** 10:00–16:30; **W:** 10:00–16:30; **Th:** 10:00–16:30; **F:** 10:00–16:30; **S:** 10:00–16:30; **Su:** 12:30–16:30. Small stock. Spec: Architecture; Art. PR: £5–50. CC: MC; V. Mem: PBFA. VAT No: GB 393 2186 39. Notes: *We also sell on the internet at www.abebooks.com and at Book Fairs. Interesting and scarce books on many subjects with some emphasis on art and architecture.*

EYE GREEN

authorshome, ■ 22 Northam Close, Eye Green, Peterborough, PE6 7TS. Prop: Mr Jeremy Seaton. Tel: 07972 253109. Web: www.authors home ebay. Est: 2007. Shop. Appointment necessary. Open: **M:** 09:00–17:30; **T:** 09:00–17:30; **W:** 09:00–17:30; **Th:** 09:00–17:30; **F:** 09:00–17:30; **S:** 09:00–17:30; **Su:** 09:00–17:30; Closed for lunch: 13:00–14:00. Mem: Market Traders Federation, Small Business Assn & EBay power sellers assn. Notes: *I am a general book seller,covering all subjects and ages, I sell some online, I also have 2 shop units, aim to roll out a further 12 over the next 12 months. I welcome all enquiries, the postal address is not shop address so all enquiries by phone.*

HUNTINGDON

Roger Gaskell Rare Books, 17 Ramsey Road, Warboys, Huntingdon, PE28 2RW. Tel: (01487) 823059. Fax: (01487) 823070. Web: www.rogergaskell.com. Est: 1989. Private premises. Postal only. Appointment necessary. Small stock. Spec: Engineering; Medicine; Science - General; Technology. PR: £100–10,000. CC: AE; MC; V. Mem: ABA; ILAB. VAT No: GB 550 6050 74.

MK Book Services, 7 East Street, Huntingdon, PE29 1WZ. Prop: Melvyn R King. Tel: (01480) 353710. Fax: (01480) 431703. Est: 1983. Private premises. Postal only. Appointment necessary. Small stock. Spec: Africana; Australiana; Authors - Local; Bibliography; Countries - Ascension Islands; Countries - Baltic States; Countries - Burma; Countries - South Atlantic Islands. PR: £1–50. CC: E; MC; V; UKMaestro. Mem: BA. VAT No: GB 958 0474 91.

John Robertshaw, 5 Fellowes Drive, Ramsey, Huntingdon, PE26 1BE. Tel: (01487) 813330. Fax: (01487) 711901. Est: 1983. Office and/or bookroom. Appointment necessary. Small stock. Spec: Antiquarian; Foreign Texts; Languages - Foreign. Cata: English and continental antiquarian books. Corresp: French, German. Mem: ABA; PBFA; ILAB. VAT No: GB 360 1311 09.

Ken Trotman, P.O. Box 505, Huntingdon, PE29 2XW. Prop: Richard & Roz Brown. Tel: (01480 454292. Fax: (01480 384651. Web: www.kentrotman.com. Est: 1949. Storeroom. Postal only. Appointment necessary. Spec: History - Napoleonic; Military; Military - Modelling; Military History; Military Uniforms. PR: £5–1,500. CC: MC; V. Cata: military history & antique weapons. Corresp: French. Mem: PBFA. VAT No: GB 386 4614 23.

PETERBOROUGH (SEE ALSO UNDER LINCOLNSHIRE)

A. & H. Peasgood, 144 Broadway, Peterborough, PE1 4DG. Prop: Alan & Marion Peasgood. Tel: (01733) 565055. Est: 1997. Private premises. Book fairs only. Small stock. Spec: Architecture; Art; History - General; Literature; Topography - General; Travel - General. PR: £1–25. Corresp: Spanish. Notes: *attends Cambridge Book Fair 2nd Tues each month.*

Francis Bowers Chess Suppliers, 62 Pennine Way, Gunthorpe, Peterborough, PE4 7TE. Prop: Mr Francis Bowers. Tel: (01733) 579569. Fax: 01733 579569. Web: www.home.aol.com/chessbower. Est: 1991. Private premises. Appointment necessary. Open: **M:** 17:00–22:00; **T:** 17:00–22:00; **W:** 17:00–22:00; **Th:** 17:00–22:00; **F:** 17:00–22:00; **S:** 08:00–22:00; **Su:** 08:00–22:00; Closed for lunch: 07:00–08:00. Spec: Chess; Games. PR: £1–1,000. CC: AE; D; E; JCB; MC; V; all. Cata: Chess, Bridge, Frank Richards, General. Corresp: German, Russian, French, Italian, Turkish, Greek, spanish. Notes: *We buy and sell Chess Books and Chess Magazines.*

Brian Cocks, 18 Woodgate, Helpston, Peterborough, PE6 7ED. Prop: Brian Cocks. Tel: 01733-252791. Fax: 01733-252791. Web: www.aviationbookhouse.co.uk. Est: 1983. Private premises. Internet and Postal. Appointment necessary. Open: **M:** 09:00–17:30; **T:** 09:00–17:30; **W:** 09:00–17:30; **Th:** 09:00–17:30; **F:** 09:00–17:30; **S:** 09:00–17:30; **Su:** 09:00–17:30; Closed for lunch: 13:00–14:00. Spec: Aeronautics; Aircraft; Aviation; War - World War I; War - World War II. CC: PayPal. Cata: Aviation (all aspects). Corresp: French, Spanish, German. Mem: PBFA.

Paul Green, 83b London Road, Peterborough, PE2 9BS. Tel: Withheld. Est: 1998. Private premises. Postal only. Small stock. Spec: Naturism; Poetry. PR: £2–50. Notes: *Also booksearch.*

Peakirk Books, ■ Peakirk Book Shop, 15 St Pegas Road, Peakirk, Peterborough, PE6 7NF. Prop: Heather & Jeff Lawrence. Tel: 01733 253182. Web: www.peakirkbooks.com. Est: 1997. Shop open: **Th:** 09:00–17:00; **F:** 09:00–17:00; **S:** 09:00–17:00. Very large stock. Spec: Author - Clare, John; Children's; Children's - Illustrated; Children's - Early Titles; Fiction - Crime, Detective, Spry, Thrillers; Fiction - Young Adult Mystery & Adventure Series. General Stock; Juvenile. PR: £1–1,000. CC: AE; MC; V. Mem: PBFA. VAT No: GB 694 8457 71. Notes: *Internet hours are more extensive than shop hours. Phone not attended on Tuesdays & Sundays.*

Frank T. Popeley, 27 Westbrook Park Road, Woodston, Peterborough, PE2 9JG. Tel: (01733) 562386. Private premises. Postal only. Small stock. Spec: Animals and Birds; Countries - Africa; Countries - Kenya; Countries - Tanzania; Countries - Uganda; Sport - Big Game Hunting; Tribal. PR: £1–3,000. Notes: *Books on early administration in East Africa.*

T V Coles Books, ■ 981 Lincoln Road, Peterborough, PE4 6AH. Tel: 01733 577268. Est: 1980. Shop open: **M:** 09:00–15:00; **T:** 09:00–15:00; **W:** 09:00–15:00; **Th:** 09:00–15:00; **F:** 09:00–15:00; **S:** 09:00–15:00. Spec: Aeronautics; Military; Military History; Naval; War - General.

Wizard Books, 106 Church Street, Deeping St. James, Peterborough, PE6 8HB. Prop: Steve Blessett. Tel: (01778) 343175. Fax: (01778) 380538. Private premises. Internet and Postal. Small stock. Spec: Academic/Scholarly; Arms & Armour; Arthurian; Arts, The; Classical Studies; Cryptozoology; Divining; Ghosts. PR: £5–100. CC: JCB; MC; V.

WISBECH

Oasis Booksearch, ■ 88 Norfolk Street, Wisbech, PE13 2LF. Prop: R.G.M. & M.E. Welford. Tel: (01945) 420438. Fax: (01945) 465187. Web: www.oasisbookswisbech.co.uk. Est: 1998. Internet and Postal. Shop open: **T:** 09:00–17:00; **W:** 09:00–17:00; **Th:** 09:00–17:00; **F:** 09:00–17:00; **S:** 09:00–17:00. Small stock. Spec: Author - Ballantyne, Robert M.; Author - Blyton, Enid; Author - Bunyan, John; Author - Crompton, Richmal; Author - Goudge, Elizabeth; Author - Lewis, C.S.; Author - Morton, H.V.; Author - Newman, Cardinal. PR: £1–25. CC: AE; JCB; MC; V; Paypal. Cata: Christian, Theology. Mem: BA.

CHESHIRE

ALTRINCHAM (SEE ALSO UNDER GREATER MANCHESTER)

Christopher Baron, 15 Crossfield Road, Hale, Altrincham, WA15 8DU. Tel: (0161) 980-1014. Fax: (0161) 980-1415. Web: www.ukbookworld.com/members/chrisbaron. Est: 1979. Private premises. Internet and Postal. Medium stock. Spec: Games; Horology; Locks & Locksmiths; Microscopy; Natural History; Science - General; Science - History of; Scientific Instruments. CC: JCB; MC; V; Maestro. Mem: PBFA. VAT No: GB 678 5926 67. Notes: *Payment may also be made via Paypal.*

BIRCHWOOD

Sensawunda Books, 59 Dunnock Grove, Birchwood, Warrington, WA3 6NW. Prop: Grant Flexman-Smith. Tel: 01925 838501. Est: 1994. Private premises. Postal only. Spec: Fiction - Fantasy, Horror; Fiction - Science Fiction; First Editions; Signed Editions. Cata: Science Fiction, Fantasy, Horror.

CHEADLE

Geoff Booth Booksearch, 2 Hastings Close, Cheadle Hulme, Cheadle, SK8 7BE. Prop: Geoff Booth. Tel: (0161) 485-4246. Est: 1980. Private premises. Internet and Postal. Appointment necessary. Open: **M:** 09:00–16:00; **T:** 09:00–16:00; **W:** 09:00–16:00; **Th:** 09:00–16:00; **F:** 09:00–16:00; **S:** 09:00–12:00. Small stock. Spec: Adventure; Aircraft; Alpinism/Mountaineering; Annuals; Antiquarian; Architecture; Art; Art History. PR: £5–400. CC: Paypal. Corresp: French, Spanish. Notes: *Out-of-Print Booksearch Service in operation - no search fee & no obligation to buy.*

Mainly Fiction, 21 Tennyson Road, Cheadle, SK8 2AR. Prop: Christopher J. Peers. Tel: (0161) 428-6836. Est: 1986. Private premises. Book fairs only. Spec: Author - Fleming, Ian; Children's; Fiction - Crime, Detective, Spy, Thrillers; First Editions; Modern First Editions. PR: £5–200. CC: V. Mem: PBFA.

Tennis Collectables, 31 Syddall Avenue, Cheadle, SK8 3AA. Prop: Fiona & John Partington. Tel: (0161) 718-5378. Private premises. Postal only. Small stock. Spec: Magazines & Periodicals - General; Sport - Tennis. PR: £2–200. CC: AE; MC; V. Cata: Tennis. VAT No: GB 748 5252 10.

CHEADLE HULME

Clifford Elmer Books Ltd., 8, Balmoral Avenue, Cheadle Hulme, Cheadle, SK8 5EQ. Prop: Clifford & Marie Elmer. Tel: 0161 485 7064. Web: www.cliffordelmerbooks.com. Est: 1978. Private premises. Internet and Postal. Appointment necessary. Open: **M:** 09:00–17:30; **T:** 09:00–17:30; **W:** 09:00–17:30; **Th:** 09:00–17:30; **F:** 09:00–17:30; **S:** 09:00–17:30. Closed for lunch: 13:00–14:00. Spec: American Indians; Americana - General; Antiquarian; Assassinations; Biography; Crime (True); Criminology; Famous People - Kennedy, John F. CC: MC; V. Cata: Non-fiction crime and criminology. Mem: PBFA. Notes: *We specialise in rare and unusual true crime and criminology.*

CHESTER

Gildas Books, ■ 2, City Walls, Chester, CH1 2JG. Prop: Mike Bowden. Tel: 01244 311910. Web: www.gildasbooks.co.uk. Est: 2005. Shop open: **M:** 10:00–16:00; **T:** 10:00–16:00; **W:** 10:00–16:00; **Th:** 10:00–16:00; **F:** 10:00–16:00; **S:** 10:00–16:00; **Su:** 10:00–16:00. Spec: Academic/Scholarly; Alpinism/Mountaineering; Archaeology; Author - White, T.H.; Author - Wilson, Colin; British Books; Celtica; Countries - Wales. CC: AE; MC; V. Notes: *Specialists in History, Archaeology, Sci-Fi, Esoterica, Modern First editions, Topography, Folklore, Literary Criticism, General Fiction. We also stock Jazz, Blues and Classical cds*

Richard Nicholson of Chester, Stoneydale, Pepper Street Christleton, Chester, CH3 7AG. Tel: (01244) 336004. Fax: (01244) 336138. Web: www.antiquemaps.com. Est: 1961. Private premises. Postal only. Small stock. Spec: Atlases; Voyages & Discovery; Prints and Maps. PR: £10–3,000. CC: MC; V. Cata: Maps, prints, atlases. VAT No: GB 159 3368 36. Notes: *See web site for stocks.*

Stothert Old Books, ■ 4 Nicholas Street, Chester, CH1 2NX. Prop: Alan Checkley. Tel: (01244) 340756. Est: 1970. Shop open: **M:** 10:00–17:00; **T:** 10:00–17:00; **W:** 10:00–17:00; **Th:** 10:00–17:00; **F:** 10:00–17:00; **S:** 10:00–17:00. Medium stock. Spec: Antiquarian; Antiques; Art; Children's; History - General; Illustrated - General; Sport - General; Topography - General. PR: £1–1,000. CC: E; MC; V. Corresp: French. Mem: PBFA. VAT No: GB 691 9276 88. Notes: *York and Haydock Park and other local fairs.*

CREWE

Copnal Books, ■ 18 Meredith Street, Crewe, CW1 2PW. Prop: Ruth Ollerhead. Tel: (01270) 580470. Web: www.copnalbooks.co.uk. Est: 1980. Shop open: **M:** 09:30–16:30; **T:** 09:30–16:30; **W:** 09:30–16:30; **Th:** 09:30–16:30; **F:** 09:30–16:30; **S:** 09:30–16:30; Closed for lunch: 12:00–13:00. Large stock. Spec: Bibles; Religion - Brethren; Religion - Christian; Theology; Topography - Local. PR: £1–50. Corresp: French. Notes: *Open other times by appointment.*

FRODSHAM

Cheshire Book Centre, ■ Lady Hayes Kingsley Road, Frodsham, WA6 6SU. Prop: J. R. S. Hall. Tel: 01928 788743. Web: www.cheshirebookcentre.com. Est: 1950. Shop open: **M:** 10:00–17:00; **T:** 10:00–17:00; **W:** 10:00–17:00; **Th:** 10:00–17:00; **F:** 10:00–17:00; **S:** 10:00–17:00; **Su:** 11:00–17:00. Spec: Aeronautics; Agriculture; Alpinism/Mountaineering; Animals and Birds; Annuals; Antiquarian; Antiques; Applied Art. CC: E; MC; V. Corresp: French and German.

HOYLAKE

Marine and Cannon Books, Naval & Maritime Dept. 'Nilcoptra', 3 Marine Road, Hoylake, Wirral, CH47 2AS. Prop: Michael & Vivienne Nash and Diane Churchill-Evans. Tel: (0151) 632-5365. Fax: (0151) 632-6472. Est: 1983. Private premises. Internet and Postal. Appointment necessary. Open: **M:** 09:00–18:00; **T:** 09:00–18:00; **W:** 09:00–18:00; **Th:** 09:00–18:00; **F:** 09:00–18:00; **S:** 09:00–17:00; Closed for lunch: 13:00–13:30. Medium stock. Spec: Academic/Scholarly; Aircraft; Antiquarian; Armed Forces - Australian Air Force; Armed Forces - Australian Army; Armed Forces - Australian Navy; Army, The; Autobiography. PR: £10–20,000. CC: JCB; MC; V; UK Maestro Visa Delta. Cata: Naval & Maritime, Military & Aviation. Mem: ABA; ILAB. VAT No: GB 539 4137 32. Notes: *Military & Aviation Dept., (see separate entry) Outlets: RN Museum Portsmouth; Merseyside Maritime Museum, Albert Dock Liverpool.*

HYDE

Andrew's Books & Collectables, 38 Dowson Road, Hyde, SK14 1JS. Prop: Andrew R. Mays. Tel: 0161 351 1851. Fax: 0161 351 1851. Est: 1997. Private premises. Internet and Postal. Contactable. Spec: Theology; Topography - General; Topography - Local. CC: PayPal. Notes: No viewing facilities. Internet and mail order only: Abe, Biblio. Telephone inquiries welcome.

J.A. Heacock, ■ 155 Market Street, Hyde, SK14 1HG. Prop: Joseph A. Heacock. Tel: 0161 3665098. Est: 2000. Shop. Telephone First. Notes: *Traditional secondhand and antiquarian bookshop, interesting stock, reasonable prices, trade and public welcome, open a lot but prior phone call or e-mail is very strongly advised.*

KNUTSFORD

The Arts & Antiques Centre, ■ 113 King Street, Knutsford. Shop open: **T:** 10:00–17:00; **W:** 10:00–17:00; **Th:** 10:00–17:00; **F:** 10:00–17:00; **S:** 10:00–17:00. Spec: Topography - General. Notes: *Cavern Books stock: general stock and topography. See Cavern Books, Nantwhich, Cheshire (q.v.)*

BC Books, 12 Mallard Close, Knutsford, WA16 8ES. Prop: Brian Corrigan. Tel: (01565) 654014. Est: 1993. Private premises. Postal only. Contactable. Small stock. Spec: Collectables; Dolls & Dolls' Houses; First Editions; History - Ancient; History - British; Humour; Literature; Modern First Editions. PR: £1–250. Corresp: French. Notes: *Pre Conquest history and literature, dolls and collectables, modern firsts.*

Fiction First, The Old Chapel, Knolls Green Village, Knutsford, WA16 7BW. Tel: (01565) 872634. Fax: (01565) 873226. Web: www.abebooks.com. Est: 1992. Private premises. Internet and Postal. Appointment necessary. Medium stock. Spec: Author - Pratchett, Terry; Author - Rankin, Ian; Author - Rice, Anne; Fiction - General; Fiction - Crime, Detective, Spy, Thrillers; Fiction - Fantasy, Horror; Fiction - Science Fiction; First Editions. PR: £10–2,000. CC: AE; MC; V.

Available from Richard Joseph Publishers Ltd

CLEANING, REPAIRING AND CARING FOR BOOKS

by Robert L. Shep

Revised Edition

148pp £12.00

LYMM

Jef Kay, 60 Mardale Crescent, Lymm, WA13 9PJ. Prop: Jef & Janet Kay. Tel: (01925) 755736. Web: www.ukbookworld.com/members/kbooks. Est: 1994. Private premises. Appointment necessary. Small stock. Spec: Annuals; Astronautics; Author - Blyton, Enid; Author - Charteris, Leslie; Author - Kent, Alexander; Children's; Comic Books & Annuals; Famous People - Kennedy, John F. PR: £1–100. Corresp: German. Notes: *We exhibit at bookfairs in Buxton and in Northwest England.*

MACCLESFIELD

George Longden, 71 Grimshaw Lane, Bollington, Macclesfield, SK10 5LY. Prop: George Longden. Tel: (01625) 572584. Est: 1998. Private premises. Postal only. Small stock. Spec: Cartoons; Comic Books & Annuals; Comics. PR: £2–200. Notes: *Exhibits at book fairs in the North and Midlands.*

Mereside Books, ■ 75 Chestergate, Macclesfield, SK11 6DG. Prop: Venita Pettit. Tel: Shop (01625) 425352. Est: 1996. Shop open: **T:** 10:00–17:00; **W:** 10:00–17:00; **Th:** 10:00–17:00; **F:** 10:00–17:00; **S:** 10:00–17:00. Small stock. Spec: Illustrated - General. PR: £3–500. CC: E; JCB; MC; V.

Roger J. Treglown, Sunderland House, Sunderland Street, Macclesfield, SK11 6JF. Prop: Roger Treglown. Tel: 01625 618978. Est: 1980. Office and/or bookroom. Open: **M:** 09:30–17:30; **T:** 09:30–17:30; **W:** 09:30–17:30; **Th:** 09:30–17:30; **F:** 09:30–17:30; **S:** 09:30–13:00. Spec: Antiquarian; Chess; Early Imprints; Esoteric; Odd & Unusual. CC: E; MC; V. Cata: Chess. Mem: ABA; PBFA; ILAB; Macclesfield Booksellers Association. Notes: *Also, valuations for probate etc.*

MARPLE BRIDGE

Talisman Books, ■ 42 Town Street, Marple Bridge, Stockport, SK65AA. Prop: Frank Leonard and Jean Cessford. Tel: 01614499271. Est: 1989. Shop open: **M:** 12:00–17:00; **T:** 12:00–17:00; **Th:** 11:00–17:00; **F:** 11:00–17:00; **S:** 11:00–17:00. Spec: Author - Blyton, Enid; Author - David, Elizabeth; Author - King, Stephen; Author - Koontz, Dean; Author - Pratchett, Terry; Children's - Early Titles; Cookery/Gastronomy; General Stock. CC: MC; V; Debit cards accepted. Notes: *Good general stock including children's collectables and literature. Specialists in Cookery and Modern 1sts especially Terry Pratchett and Stephen King.*

NANTWICH

Cavern Books, ■ Units 2-4 & 16 Dagfields Antique Centre, Audlem Rd, Walgherton, Nantwich, CW5 7LG. Prop: Harry Madden. Tel: (01270) 841594. Est: 1997. Shop open: **M:** 11:00–17:00; **T:** 11:00–17:00; **W:** 11:00–17:00; **Th:** 11:00–17:00; **F:** 11:00–17:00; **S:** 10:00–17:00; **Su:** 10:00–17:00. Very large stock. Spec: Americana - General; Annuals; Art; Buses/Trams; Canals/Inland Waterways; Crafts; Crime (True); Egyptology. PR: £1–1,500. CC: AE; E; MC; V; SO, Mae. VAT No: GB 823 5392 30. Notes: *Internet Bookshop, Gloucestershire (q.v.), & The Arts & Antiques Centre, Knutsford (qv). Also, CDs, Records (50s & 60s)& maps, postcards & stamps.*

Guildmaster Books, 81 Welsh Row, Nantwich, CW5 5ET. Prop: Guildmaster. Tel: (01270) 629982. Fax: (01270) 629982. Est: 1986. Office and/or bookroom; Internet and Postal. Appointment necessary. Small stock. Spec: Agriculture; Antiquarian; Churchilliana; Culture - National; Firearms/Guns; Herbalism; History - British; Maritime/Nautical. PR: £10–500. CC: Most major.

NORTHWICH

Forest Books of Cheshire, Northwich, CW8 2AT. Prop: E.M. Mann. Tel: 01606 882388. Est: 1986. Private premises. Book fairs only. Appointment necessary. Spec: Architecture; Art History; Collecting; Drama; Fashion & Costume; Gynaecology; History - Local; Humanities. PR: £1–600. Corresp: French, German. Notes: *The books are currently in cramped storage so the longer the time before viewing the better, plus we need to know what you particularly wish to see: many are in boxes in front of the shelves. We hope to return to a better outlet soonish.*

KSC Books, 48 Chapel Street, Castle, Northwich, CW8 1HD. Prop: Stuart Crook. Tel: 01606 79975. Fax: On request. VOIPpro: BT. VOIPnum: 05602512144. Est: 1995. Private premises. Internet and Postal. Telephone First. Spec: Academic/Scholarly; Author - Laithwaite, Eric; Canals/Inland Waterways; Engineering; Geology; History - British; Music - Folk & Irish Folk; Musical Instruments. VAT No: GB 798 2130 04.

RUNCORN

Kirk Ruebotham, 16 Beaconsfield Road, Runcorn, WA7 4BX. Tel: (01928) 560540. Web: www.abebooks.com/home/kirk61. Est: 1993. Private premises. Postal only. Contactable. Small stock. Spec: Crime (True); Fiction - Crime, Detective, Spy, Thrillers; Fiction - Fantasy, Horror; Fiction - Science Fiction; Fiction - Supernatural; First Editions; Vintage Paperbacks. PR: £2–150. CC: Paypal. Cata: Fantasy, Horror, SF, Crime Fiction.

TATTENHALL

Marine & Cannon Books, Square House Farm, Tattenhall Lane, Tattenhall, CH3 9NH. Prop: Mrs Diane Churchill-Evans (Military & Aviation Dept). Tel: (01829) 771109. Fax: (01829) 771991. Est: 1983. Private premises. Internet and Postal. Open in Summer. Open: **M:** 09:00–18:00; **T:** 09:00–18:00; **W:** 09:00–18:00; **Th:** 09:00–18:00; **F:** 09:00–18:00; **S:** 09:00–17:00. Medium stock. Spec: Academic/ Scholarly; Aircraft; Antiquarian; Armed Forces - Australian Army; Armed Forces - Australian Navy; Army, The; Autographs; Aviation. PR: £10–20,000. CC: JCB; MC; V; UK Maestro. Cata: Naval & Maritime, Military & Aviation. Mem: ABA; ILAB. VAT No: GB 539 4137 32. Notes: *We offer a free booksearch. We also stock manuscripts, engravings, photographs, postcards, and other items of ephemera in our fields of interest. We are always interested in purchasing naval, military and aviation books.*

TIMPERLEY

Oopalba Books, 136 Moss Lane, Timperley Altrincham, WA15 6JQ. Prop: Ann J Ferguson. Tel: 0161 973 2065. Web: www.oopalbabooks.moonfruit.com. Est: 1999. Mail Order and Internet only. Appointment necessary. Spec: Academic/Scholarly; Alternative Medicine; Applied Art; Architecture; Art; Art - Technique; Autobiography; Biography. CC: Paypal /Cheque/Postal Order. Cata: Children's, Maths, Science, Textbooks, Literature. Coresp: French German. Notes: *Books listed on Abebooks and Amazon. Current 5 star rating on Abebooks and 99% positive feedback on Amazon.*

WARRINGTON

Halson Books, The Oaks Farnworth Road, Penketh, Warrington, WA5 2TT. Prop: Les Wilson. Tel: (01925) 726699. Web: www.users.zetnet.co.uk/halsongallery. Private premises. Internet and Postal. Appointment necessary. Large stock. Spec: Colour-Plate; Dogs; Natural History; Ephemera. CC: PayPal. Coresp: via Google language.

Dr. B.L. Shakeshaft, Springfield, 15 Marlborough Crescent, Grappenhall, Warrington, WA4 2EE. Prop: Dr. B.L. Shakeshaft. Tel: (01925) 264790. Est: 1999. Private premises. Postal only. Small stock. Spec: Americana - General; Animals and Birds; Annuals; Author - Watkins-Pitchford, Denys ('B.B.'); Authors - British; Biography; Children's; Children's - Illustrated. PR: £1–500. Cata: Ladybird books, Rupert annuals, New Naturalists.

Naomi Symes Books, 2 Pineways, Appleton Park, Warrington, WA4 5EJ. Prop: Naomi Symes. Tel: 44 (0)1925 602898. Fax: 44 (0)1925 602898. Web: www.naomisymes.com. Est: 1994. Private premises. Postal only. Contactable. Open: **M:** 10:00–18:00; **T:** 10:00–18:00; **W:** 10:00–18:00; **Th:** 10:00–18:00; **F:** 10:00–18:00; **S:** 10:00–18:00; **Su:** 10:00–18:00. Medium stock. Spec: Academic/Scholarly; Authors - Women; Feminism; Fiction - Women; History - General; History - 19th Century; History - 20th Century; History - British. PR: £5–1,000. CC: AE; E; JCB; MC; V; Maestro, Solo. Cata: Women's History, Social History. Coresp: French. Mem: PBFA. Notes: *History A Level tuition; booksearch service; proof reading; copy-editing and history resource centre on-line.*

The Warrington Book Loft, Quadrant House, Church Street, Warrington, WA1 2ST. Prop: Mrs Pat Devlin. Tel: (01925) 633907. Web: www.warringtonbookloft.com. Est: 1994. Storeroom. Very large stock. Spec: Academic/Scholarly; Fiction - General; University Texts. PR: £4–250. CC: JCB; MC; V; Maestro. VAT No: GB 811 6681 37.

WINSFORD

Blackman Books, 46 The Loont, Winsford, CW7 1EU. Prop: Margaret & Roger Blackman. Tel: (01606) 558527. Web: www.abebooks.com/home/rtmb. Est: 1997. Private premises. Internet and Postal. Appointment necessary. Small stock. PR: £10–1,000. Coresp: French.

CORNWALL

BUDE

David Eastwood, Ardoch Poundstock, Bude, EX23 0DF. Tel: (01288) 361847. Est: 1970. Private premises. Internet and Postal. Appointment necessary. Small stock. Spec: Antiquarian; Children's - Illustrated; Fine & Rare; Fine leather bindings (see also Fine & Rare); First Editions; Illustrated - General; Limited Editions - General; Literature. PR: £10–1,000. Mem: PBFA. Notes: *Always interested in buying illustrated books and fine bindings. Also PBFA bookfairs.*

CALLINGTON

Music By The Score, South Coombe, Downgate, Callington, PL17 8JZ. Prop: Eileen Hooper–Bargery. Tel: (01579) 370053. Fax: (01579) 370053. Web: www.musicbythescore.co.uk. Est: 1993. Private premises. Internet and Postal. Appointment necessary. Large stock. Spec: Music - General; Music - Classical; Music - Composers; Music - Folk & Irish Folk; Music - Illustrated Sheet Music; Music - Music Hall; Music - Opera; Music - Orchestral. PR: £4–40. CC: AE; MC; V; PayPal. Notes: *Stock also available through Biblio.com. All credit cards accepted plus Paypal.*

CAMBORNE

Humanist Services, 15 Basset Street, Camborne, TR14 8SW. Prop: Linnea Timson. Tel: (01209) 716470. Fax: 0870 139774. Web: www.cornwallhumanists.org.uk. Est: 1964. Private premises. Internet and Postal. Appointment necessary. Spec: Evolution; Free Thought; Humanism; Philosophy; Rationalism. PR: £1–15. Mem: Rationalist Press Association. Notes: *Will issue catalogue on request. Customers invited to phone anytime*

EAST LOOE

Bosco Books, ■ The Old Hall Bookshop, Chapel Court, Shutta Road, East Looe, PL13 1BJ. Prop: Mr. & Mrs. S. Hawes. Tel: (01503) 263700. Fax: (01503) 263700. Est: 1971. Internet and Postal. Shop open: **T:** 10:30–17:00; **W:** 10:30–17:00; **Th:** 10:30–17:00; **F:** 10:30–17:00; **S:** 10:30–17:00. Very large stock. Spec: Alpinism/Mountaineering; Archaeology; Architecture; Art; Art History; Art Reference; Author - Tangye, D.; Biography. PR: £1–750. CC: MC; V; Switch. Corresp: French, Italian. Notes: *We're also happy to accept Paypal. In winter please ring to confirm opening hours.*

FALMOUTH

Browsers Bookshop, ■ 13/15 St George's Arcade, Church Street, Falmouth, TR11 3DH. Prop: Crispin Crofts. Tel: 01326 313464. Est: 1980. Shop open: **M:** 10:00–17:30; **T:** 10:00–17:30; **W:** 10:00–17:30; **Th:** 10:00–17:30; **F:** 10:00–17:30; **S:** 10:00–17:30. Spec: Archaeology - Industrial; Art; Art History; History - General; History - 19th Century; History - Local; Maritime/Nautical; Maritime/Nautical - History. CC: MC; V; Maestro. Notes: *Stock includes books on Cornish history.*

Falmouth Bookshop, ■ 13/15 St George's Arcade, Market Street, Falmouth, TR11 3DH. Prop: Crispin Crofts. Tel: 01326 313464. Est: 1980. Shop open: **M:** 10:00–17:00; **T:** 10:00–17:00; **W:** 10:00–17:00; **Th:** 10:00–17:00; **F:** 10:00–17:00; **S:** 10:00–17:00; **Su:** 09:00–17:30. CC: MC; V.

FOWEY

Bookends of Fowey, ■ 4 South Street, Fowey, PL23 1AR. Tel: (01726) 833361. Web: www.bookendsoffowey.com. Est: 1985. Shop open: **M:** 10:00–17:30; **T:** 10:00–17:30; **W:** 10:00–17:30; **Th:** 10:00–17:30; **F:** 10:00–17:30; **S:** 10:00–17:30; **Su:** 11:00–17:00. Large stock. Spec: Author - du Maurier, Daphne; Author - Quiller-Couch, Sir A.T.; Naval; Sport - Yachting (& Boating); Topography - Local. CC: MC; V. VAT No: GB 813 0114 90.

Ronald C. Hicks, Ardwyn, 22 Park Road, Fowey, PL23 1ED. Tel: (01726) 832739. Est: 1964. Private premises. Postal only. Small stock. Spec: Architecture; Art; History - Local; Maritime/Nautical - Log Books; Booksearch. PR: £1–500. Notes: *Books on Cornish history.*

Sue Moore, 37 Passage Street, Fowey, PL23 1DE. Prop: Susan M. Moore. Tel: (01726) 832397. Est: 1986. Private premises. Appointment necessary. Small stock. Spec: Modern First Editions; Booksearch. PR: £2–50.

HELSTON

J.T. & P. Lewis, 'Leaway', Tresowes Green, Ashton, Helston, TR13 9SY. Prop: John T. & Pearl Lewis. Tel: (01736) 762406. Web: www.http://ukbookworld.com/members/JTLANDPL. Est: 1990. Private premises. Internet and Postal. Small stock. Spec: Fiction - General; History - General; Modern First Editions; Odd & Unusual; Religion - General; Science - General; Theology; Topography - General. PR: £5–1,000. CC: Paypal. VAT No: GB 803 4711 59. Notes: *We always reply to emails promptly, so if you do not receive a reply within 24 hours please check your spam filters. Credit Card payments are welcomed via Paypal, please email for a Paypal Invoice, which makes payment quick and simple.*

Peter Clay, Heatherbank, North Corner, Coverack, Helston, TR12 6TH. Prop: Peter Clay. Tel: 01326 280475. Est: 1984. Private premises. Internet and Postal. Appointment necessary.

LAUNCESTON

Abbey Books, ■ White Hart Arcade, Launceston, PL15 8AA. Prop: Spencer Magill. Tel: 01566 779113. Web: www.abbeybookshop.co.uk. Est: 2003. Shop open: **M:** 09:00–17:00; **T:** 09:00–17:00; **W:** 09:00–17:00; **Th:** 09:00–17:00; **F:** 09:00–17:00; **S:** 09:00–16:00. Spec: Art Reference; Cinema/Film; Countries - Ireland; Fiction - General; Fiction - Crime, Detective, Spy, Thrillers; Fiction - Science Fiction; History - General; History - Irish.

Charles Cox Rare Books, River House, Treglasta, Launceston, PL15 8PY. Tel: (01840) 261085. Fax: (01840) 261464. Web: www.abebooks.com. Est: 1974. Private premises. Internet and Postal. Appointment necessary. Small stock. Spec: Aesthetic Movement; Antiquarian; Author - Browning, Robert; Author - Byron, Lord; Author - Hardy, Thomas; Author - Housman, A.E.; Author - Newman, Cardinal; Author - Rossetti, C. PR: £10–2,500. CC: JCB; MC; V; Paypal. Cata: Literature 1780-1920, Literary Autographs. Mem: ABA; ILAB. VAT No: GB 797 4887 40.

R & B Graham Trading, ■ The Bookshop, Church Street, Launceston, PL15 8AP. Prop: Richard & Beryl Graham. Tel: 01566 774107. Fax: 01566 777299. Web: www.cookery-books-online.com. Est: 1999. Shop and/or gallery; Shop open: **M:** 09:00–17:30; **T:** 09:00–17:30; **W:** 09:00–17:30; **Th:** 09:00–17:30; **F:** 09:00–17:30; **S:** 09:00–17:30. Spec: Author - Quiller-Couch, Sir A.T.; Cookery - Professional; Cookery/Gastronomy; County - Local; Poetry. CC: AE; E; JCB; MC; V. Mem: BA. VAT No: GB 750 5071 55.

LISKEARD

Ian Marr Rare Books, 23 Pound Street, Liskeard, PL14 3JR. Prop: Ian Marr. Tel: 01579 345 310. Est: 2005. Private premises. Appointment necessary. Spec: Advertising; Antiquarian; Archaeology; British Books; Cornish history; Manuscripts; Outlaws. Cata: Antiquarian, Ephemeral. Corresp: German. Mem: ABA.

LOOE

A. & R. Booksearch, High Close, Lanreath, Looe, PL13 2PF. Prop: Avis & Robert Ronald. Tel: (01503) 220246. Web: www.musicbooksrus.com. Est: 1984. Private premises. Postal only. Appointment necessary. Open: **M:** 10:00–16:00; **T:** 10:00–16:00; **W:** 10:00–16:00; **Th:** 10:00–16:00; **F:** 10:00–16:00. Medium stock. Spec: Children's; Children's - Illustrated; Cookery/Gastronomy; Fiction - General; General Stock; Music - Country & Western; Music - Jazz & Blues; Music - Popular. PR: £1–500. CC: MC; V; Maestro, Electron, Delta, PayPal. Cata: Popular music. VAT No: GB 187 4977 94. Notes: *Also sell new books.*

MEGAVISSY

Loft Bookshop, ■ Church Street, Megavissy, PL16 6SP. Prop: Mr David S Pain. Tel: 01726 843757. Fax: 01726 843757. Est: 1988. Shop open: **M:** 10:30–17:00; **T:** 10:30–17:00; **W:** 10:30–17:00; **Th:** 10:30–17:00; **F:** 10:30–17:00; **S:** 10:30–17:00; **Su:** 10:30–17:00. CC: E; JCB; MC; V; Maestro, Solo, Electron. Mem: BA. Notes: *Only open 6 days a week in winter.*

NEWQUAY

Recollectionsbookshop.co.uk, Old Kiddlywink Cottage, Tresean, Newquay, TR8 5HN. Prop: Ray Frith, Valerie Frith. Tel: 01637 830539. Web: www.recollectionsbookshop.co.uk. Est: 1996. Private premises. Contactable. Open: **M:** 09:00–17:30; **T:** 09:00–17:30; **W:** 09:00–17:30; **Th:** 09:00–17:30; **F:** 09:00–17:30; **S:** 09:00–17:30; **Su:** 09:00–17:30; Closed for lunch: 13:00–14:00. CC: MC; V. VAT No: GB 760 4240 56. Notes: *We specialise in Railway Books and Cornish Books.*

PENZANCE

Green Meadow Books, 2 Bellair House, Bellair Road, Madron, Penzance, TR20 8SP. Prop: Sue Bell. Tel: (01736) 351708. Web: www.greenmeadowbooks.co.uk. Est: 1982. Private premises. Internet and Postal. Telephone First. Medium stock. Spec: Annuals; Author - Barrie, J.M.; Author - Blyton, Enid; Author - Brent-Dyer, Elinor M.; Author - Crompton, Richmal; Author - Dahl, Roald; Author - Durrell, Gerald; Author - Fairlie–Bruce, D. PR: £2–2,500. CC: MC; V; Switch. Cata: Children's & Illustrated books. Notes: *Also, a variety of toys, games, and ephemera in stock. Booksearch service if required. Always pleased to welcome visitors to the bookroom, where a warm welcome & a friendly cat await! Coffee and discount available!*

Mount's Bay Books, Sea Glimpses, Garth Road, Newlyn, Penzance, TR18 5QJ. Prop: Tim Scott. Tel: 07792 797902. Web: www.seaglimpses.com. Est: 1994. Private premises. Internet and Postal. Appointment necessary. Open: **M:** 10:00–17:00; **T:** 10:00–17:00; **W:** 10:00–17:00; **Th:** 10:00–17:00; **F:** 10:00–17:00; **S:** 10:00–16:00. Small stock. Spec: Author - Baker, Denys V.; Author - Seymour, John; Non-Fiction; Rural Life; Self-Sufficiency; Topography - Local. PR: £2–150.

Newlyn Books, ■ 9 The Old Posthouse, Chapel Street, Penzance, TR18 4AJ. Prop: Kelvin Hearn. Tel: (01736) 332266. Est: 1992. Shop open: **M:** 10:00–17:00; **T:** 10:00–17:00; **W:** 10:00–17:00; **Th:** 10:00–17:00; **F:** 10:00–17:00; **S:** 10:00–17:00. Medium stock. Spec: Art; Art History; Art Reference; Arts, The; Topography - General; Topography - Local. PR: £1–350. CC: MC; V. Cata: art Cornwall. Notes: *Try to be selective and have an interesting range of any subject that sells but always lots of art & local books.*

ROCHE

Roger Collicott Books, Beacon Cottage, Belowda, Roche, St. Austell, PL26 8NQ. Prop: Roger Collicott. Tel: 01726 891885. Fax: 01726 891885. Web: www.rogercollicottbooks.com. Est: 1978. Private premises. Appointment necessary. Spec: Antiquarian; Bindings; County - Local; Directories - General; Dogs; Earth Sciences; Flora & Fauna; Fossils. CC: MC; V. Cata: Antiquarian. Topography. History of Sciences. Mem: PBFA. Notes: *Specialising in topographical books, maps, and prints with an emphasis on the counties of Cornwall and Devon. Always a good selection of antiquarian books, with an emphasis on the history of science, and early printed books.*

ST. AGNES

Paul Hoare, Trevaunance Point House, Trevaunance Cove, St. Agnes, TR5 0RZ. Prop: Paul Hoare. Tel: 01872 553235. Est: 1990. Private premises. Internet and Postal. Appointment necessary. Open: **M:** 09:00–17:30; **T:** 09:00–17:30; **W:** 09:00–17:30; **Th:** 09:00–17:30; **F:** 09:00–17:30; **S:** 09:00–17:30; **Su:** 09:00–17:30; Closed for lunch: 13:00–14:00. Spec: Antiquarian; Art; Collectables; Colour-Plate; Comic Books & Annuals; Countries - Channel Islands, The; Countries - East Mediterranean, The; Countries - England. Cata: A&C Black, Illustrated & Topographic. Notes: *Specialist in A&C Black publications. General Illustrated items.*

ST. IVES

The Book Gallery, 2B Bedford Road, St. Ives, TR26 1SP. Prop: David Wilkinson. Tel: (01736) 795616. Web: www.abebooks.com/home/tinyworld. Est: 1991. Private premises. Internet and Postal. Telephone First. Small stock. Spec: Archives; Art; Art - British; Art History; Art Reference; First Editions; Topography - Local; Ephemera. PR: £5–2,500. Cata: Art from Cornwall.

Tregenna Place Second Hand Books, ■ Tregenna Place, St. Ives, TR26 1AA. Prop: Linda Donaldson and Steven Macleod. Tel: 01736 799933. Est: 2004. Shop open: **M:** 10:00–17:00; **T:** 10:00–17:00; **W:** 10:00–17:00; **Th:** 10:00–17:00; **F:** 10:00–17:00; **S:** 10:00–17:00. CC: MC; V. Notes: *General stock.*

ST. JUST

Bosorne Books, ■ The Cook Book, 4 Cape Cornwall Street, St. Just, TR19 7JZ. Prop: David James. Tel: 01736 787266. Web: www.bosornebooks.co.uk. Est: 2003. Shop open: **M:** 10:00–17:00; **T:** 10:00–17:00; **W:** 10:00–17:00; **Th:** 10:00–17:00; **F:** 10:00–17:00; **S:** 10:00–17:00; **Su:** 10:00–17:00. Spec: Archaeology; Art; Biography; Cookery/Gastronomy; Cornish; Cornish history; County - Local; General Stock. CC: AE; MC; V; Maestro. Mem: FSB. Notes: *Café and second-hand bookshop. Books repaired, restored & rebound.*

TRURO

Bonython Bookshop, ■ 16 Kenwyn Street, Truro, TR1 3BU. Prop: R.D. Carpenter. Tel: (01872) 262886. Web: www.bonythonbookshop.co.uk. Est: 1996. Shop open: **M:** 10:30–16:30; **T:** 10:30–16:30; **W:** 10:30–16:30; **Th:** 10:30–16:30; **F:** 10:30–16:30; **S:** 10:30–16:30. Medium stock. Spec: Archaeology; Author - du Maurier, Daphne; Author - Tangye, D.; Countries - England; Countries - India; County - Local; Folio Society; History - Local. PR: £1–1,000. CC: D; E; JCB; MC; V. Corresp: French. Notes: *booksearch undertaken, specialist area – out of print books on Cornwall, ie mining, Cornish History, Cornish Language, Art etc.*

Just Books, ■ 9 Pydar Mews, Truro, TR1 2UX. Prop: Jennifer Wicks. Tel: (01872) 242532. Web: www.www.pydarmewsbooks.com. Est: 1987. Shop open: **M:** 10:00–17:00; **T:** 10:00–17:00; **W:** 10:00–17:00; **Th:** 10:00–17:00; **F:** 10:00–17:00; **S:** 10:00–17:00. Medium stock. Spec: Antiquarian; Archaeology; Art; Art - British; Art - Technique; Art - Theory; Art History; Art Reference. PR: £1–1,000. CC: AE; E; JCB; MC; V. VAT No: GB 789 3503 84. Notes: *Small friendly bookshop, covering all subjects, and specializing in Cornwall and Extraordinary Art Books.*

Reg & Philip Remington, Belvedere Newbridge, Truro, TR3 6BN. Tel: 01872-279820. Fax: 01727 893531. Web: www.remingtonbooks.com. Est: 1979. Private premises. Appointment necessary. Spec: Travel - General, Africa, Americas, Asia, Asia (South East), Australasia/Australia, Burma, Caribbean, China. PR: £5–5,000. CC: MC; V. VAT No: GB 330 7013 08. Cata: bi-annual, Voyage & Travel. Mem: ABA; BA; ILAB.

WADEBRIDGE

Polmorla Books, Hostyn Mill Burlawn, Wadebridge, PL27 7LD. Tel: (01208) 813345. Est: 2002. Private premises. Postal only. Medium stock. Spec: History - General; History - Local; Literary Criticism; Literature; New Naturalist; Painting; Poetry; Women.

CUMBRIA

APPLEBY–IN–WESTMORLAND

Barry McKay Rare Books, Kingstone House Battlebarrow, Appleby–in–Westmorland, CA16 6XY. Prop: Barry McKay. Tel: 017683 52282. Web: www.barrymckayrarebooks.org. Est: 1986. Shop and/ or showroom; Appointment necessary. M: 10:00–17:00; **T:** 10:00–17:00; **W:** 10:00–17:00; **Th:** 10:00–17:00; **F:** 10:00–17:00; **S:** 10:00–13:00. Medium stock. Spec: Advertising; Bibliography; Bindings; Book Arts; Bookbinding; Calligraphy; Early Imprints; Fine & Rare. CC: MC; V. Cata: Bibliography; rare and interesting books. Corresp: French. Mem: PBFA. VAT No: GB 448 5469 09.

BARROW–IN–FURNESS

Americanabooksuk, 72 Park Drive, Barrow–in–Furness, LA13 9BB. Prop: Alan R. Beattie. Tel: (01229) 829722. Web: www.www.ukbookworld.com/members/AMERICANABKS. Est: 1980. Private premises. Appointment necessary. Very small stock. Spec: American Indians; American Northwest; Americana - General; Americana - Southwest; Art; Cattlemen; Countries - Americas, The; Countries - U.S.A. PR: £3–250. CC: Paypal. Cata: Often - Western Americana.

BROUGH

The Book House, ■ Grand Prix Buildings, Main Street, Brough, nr. Kirkby Stephen, CA17 4AY. Prop: Chris, Mary & Brigid Irwin. Tel: 017683 42748. Web: www.thebookhouse.co.uk. Est: 1963. Shop. open: **T:** 10:30–16:30; **W:** 10:00–16:30; **Th:** 10:00–16:30; **F:** 10:00–16:30; **S:** 10:00–16:30. Large stock. Spec: Children's; Engineering; Fiction - General; Gardening - General; History - Industrial; Industry; Languages - Foreign; Languages - National. PR: £1–750. CC: AE; E; MC; V. Cata: Industrial History & Transport, Railways, Gardeni. Corresp: French, Italian. Mem: PBFA. VAT No: GB 113 8746 69. Notes: *Ample parking. If you are making a special journey please check we are open before setting out as occasionally I am away at book fairs or exhibitions. For further details please visit our website.*

CARLISLE

Bookcase, ■ 17 - 19 Castle Street, Carlisle, CA3 8SY. Prop: S. & G. Matthews. Tel: 01228 544560. Est: 1979. Shop open: **M:** 10:00–17:00; **T:** 10:00–17:00; **W:** 10:00–17:00; **Th:** 10:00–17:00; **F:** 10:00–17:00; **S:** 10:00–17:00. Spec: Antiquarian; Antiques; Art; Bibliography; Fiction - General; Languages - Foreign; Literary Criticism; Modern First Editions. CC: AE; MC; V. Corresp: French, German. Notes: *Classical and jazz CDs(new). Also booksearch.*

Anne Fitzsimons, 3 Croft Park Wetheral, Carlisle, CA4 8JH. Tel: (01228) 562184. Fax: (01228) 562184. Est: 1978. Private premises. Postal only. Small stock. Spec: Cinema/Film; Circus; Dance; Magic & Conjuring; Music - General; Music - Music Hall; Music - Opera; Performing Arts.

Pages of Ages, West View, Shaw Wood Road, Crofton, Nr. Carlise CA7 6QG. Prop: Ray Riodan. Tel: 019673 44616. Est: 1992. Warehouse. Internet Only. Medium Stock. Spec: General stock. PR: £1–300. CC: PayPal. Notes: *Printed collectables. Books of all ages and genre; maps, postcards, cigarette card etc. Let us have your list of wants amd we will prepare a catalogue for you. Discounts for dealers.*

COCKERMOUTH

Alauda Books, ■ Market Place Books, 30 Market Place, Cockermouth, CA13 9NG. Prop: Michael Green. Tel: 01900 821300. Est: 1986. Shop open: **M:** 10:00–17:00; **T:** 10:00–17:00; **W:** 10:00–17:00; **Th:** 10:00–17:00; **F:** 10:00–17:00; **S:** 10:00–17:00. Spec: Animals and Birds; Archaeology; Book Arts; Bookbinding; Botany; Cartography; Fishes; Flora & Fauna. Cata: Natural History; Angling. Mem: PBFA.

Ian Dodsworth, 1 Banks Court, Market Place, Cockermouth, CA13 9NG. Prop: Ian Dodsworth. Tel: (01900) 823599. Est: 1986. Storeroom. Appointment necessary. Small stock. PR: £1–150. Notes: *Attends day fairs in Northern England.*

Market Place Books, ■ 30 Market Place, Cockermouth, CA13 9NG. Prop: Michael Green. Tel: 01900 821300. Est: 2006. Shop open: **M:** 10:00–17:00; **T:** 10:00–17:00; **W:** 10:00–17:00; **Th:** 10:00–17:00; **F:** 10:00–17:00; **S:** 10:00–17:00. Small stock. Spec: General. PR: £1-500. Mem: PBFA. Notes: *A small shop with a constantly changing stock of quality secondhand books.*

EGREMONT

Esoteric Dreams Bookshop, ■ 1 St Bridgets Lane, Egremont, CA22 2BB. Prop: Mrs Sue Wright. Web: www.amazon.co.uk/shops/esotericdreams. Est: 2004. Shop open: **T:** 10:00–16:00; **W:** 10:00–14.00; **Th:** 10:00–16:00; **F:** 10:00–16:00; **S:** 10:00–16:00. Spec: Alternative Medicine; Animals and Birds; Annuals; Art History; Author - Asimov, Isaac; Author - Dinesen, Isak; Authors - Local; Authors - Women. Notes: *We sell old and new books both in the shop and on the internet. We also sell cards, postcards, local maps and unusual gifts.*

GRANGE–OVER–SANDS

Daisyroots Book Centre (Daisyroots Books Ltd), Holker School, Cark in Cartmel, Grange over Sands, LA11 7PQ. Prop: Chris and Elaine Ware. Tel: 015395 59328. Web: www.daisyroots.net. Est: 1996. Internet and postal. Shop; open **M:** 10.00–16:30; **T:** 10.00–16:30; **Th:** 10.00–16:30; **F:** 10.00–16:30; **S:** 10.00–16:30; **Su:** 11:00–16:00. Very large stock. Spec: Alpinism/Mountaineering; Sport - Climbing and Trekking; Sport - Horseracing (inc Riding/Breeding/Equestrian; Topography - General; Topography - Local. PR: £1–£1,000. CC: JCB, Mastercard, Visa, Maestro. Cata: online only. Notes: *Internet warehouse open to the public from Easter 2010. Seasonal opening Easter to 31 October. Extensive general stock of a very high standard. Largest collection of fiction in the North West of England.*

Rosemary Dooley, Crag House Witherslack, Grange–over–Sands, LA11 6RW. Prop: R.M.S. Dooley. Tel: (01539) 552286. Fax: (01539) 552013. Web: www.booksonmusic.co.uk. Est: 1992. Private premises. Postal only. Appointment necessary. Medium stock. Spec: Academic/Scholarly; Dance; Music - General; Music - Classical; Music - Composers; Music - Folk & Irish Folk; Music - Gregorian Chants; Music - Musicians. PR: £3–500. CC: AE; E; MC; V. Cata: books about music. Mem: PBFA. VAT No: GB 393 1979 09. Notes: *European distributor for Pendragon Press (USA)- scholarly books on music. Worldwide distributor for Royal Musical Association Research Chronicle and back issues of British Journal of ethnomusicology.*

Norman Kerr Booksellers, Priory Barn, Cartmel, Grange–over–Sands, LA11 6PX. Prop: Hilda & John Kerr. Tel: (015395) 36247 / 32508. Est: 1933. Shop and/or showroom; Internet and Postal. Telephone First. Open: **T:** 13.30–16:30; **W:** 13.30–16:30; **F:** 13.30–16:30; **S:** 13:30–16:30. Medium stock. Spec: Antiquarian; Aviation; Canals/Inland Waterways; Engineering; Fine & Rare; Illustrated - General; Maritime/Nautical; Motoring. PR: £5–1,500. Cata: General Catalogue Fine & Rare. Mem: PBFA. VAT No: GB 312 3475 89. Notes: *Reserve stock is available for viewing by appointment. A wide selection of our stock is now listed online at Abebooks.com.*

Over-Sands Books, ■ The Old Waiting Room, The Station, Grange-Over-Sands, LA11 6EH. Prop: Mr. S.R. Tyson. Tel: (01539) 534387. Web: www.oversandsbooks.co.uk. Est: 1995. Shop open: **M:** 11:00–17:00; **T:** 11:00–17:00; **W:** 11:00–17:00; **F:** 11:00–17:00; **S:** 11:00–17:00; **Su:** 13:00–17:00. Small stock. Spec: Literature; Railways and Railroads; Topography - General; Topography - Local; Transport; Booksearch; Collectables; Ephemera. PR: £3–250. CC: PayPal. Cata: Various subjects. Notes: *Opening times vary between November and March, call first. Also, a booksearch service.*

Looking for ephemera? Then search Sheppard's on-line directories at:

www.sheppardsconfidential.com

For all dealers selling ephemera

GRASMERE

Yewtree Books, ■ The Lakes Crafts & Antiques Gallery, 3 Oakbank Broadgate, Grasmere, LA22 9TA. Prop: Joe and Sandra Arthy. Tel: (015394) 35037. Fax: (015394) 44234. Est: 1990. Shop open: **M:** 10:00–17:00; **T:** 10:00–17:00; **W:** 10:00–17:00; **Th:** 10:00–17:00; **F:** 10:00–17:00; **S:** 10:00–17:00; **Su:** 10:00–17:00. Small stock. Spec: Alpinism/Mountaineering; History - General; Railways and Railroads; Sport - General; Topography - General; Topography - Local; Travel - General. PR: £1–300. CC: JCB; MC; V.

KENDAL

Kirkland Books, ■ 11 Colin Croft, Kendal, LA9 4TH. Prop: Linden Burke. Tel: 0800 0112368. Fax: 0800 0112568. Web: www.kirklandbooks.biz. Est: 1980. Shop open: **Th:** 10:00–17:00; **F:** 10:00–17:00; **S:** 10:00–17:00. Small stock. Spec: Alpinism/Mountaineering; Author - Ransome, Arthur; Author - Ruskin, John; Author - Wainwright, Alfred; Author - Wainwright, Arthur; Author - Wordsworth, William; Exploration; Railways and Railroads. PR: £20-5,000. CC: D; E; JCB; MC; V. Cata: occasionally on Alfred Wainwright, Arthur Ramsome, Beartrix Potter. VAT No: GB 893 3880 75. Notes: *Specialists in modern first edition, antiquarian, signed and collectable books, especially Arthur Ransome, Alfred Wainwright, Beatrix Potter, William Wordsworth, John Ruskin, The Lakes Poets, The English Lake District and Mountaineering.*

Left on The Shelf, Yard 91, Highgate, Kendal, LA9 4ED. Prop: Dave Cope. Tel: (01539) 729599. Web: www.leftontheshelfbooks.co.uk. Est: 1992. Storeroom; Internet and Postal. Telephone First. Very large stock. Spec: Civil Rights; Communism; Countries - Russia; Cultural Studies; Economics; Free Thought; History - Labour/ Radical Movements; History - Spanish Civil War. PR: £2–150. CC: MC; V. Cata: Socialism. Corresp: French. Mem: PBFA.

KESWICK

Jean Altshuler, 54 St. John Street, Keswick, CA12 5AB. Tel: (01768) 775745. Est: 1996. Private premises. Internet and Postal. Appointment necessary. Small stock. Spec: Children's; Fiction - Science Fiction. PR: £5–200.

Jane & John Kinnaird, ■ Keswick Bookshop, 4 Station Street, Keswick, CA12 5HT. Tel: 017687 75535 or 01228 528567. Shop open: **M:** 10:30–17:00; **T:** 10:30–17:00; **Th:** 10:30–17:00; **F:** 10:30–17:00; **S:** 10:30–17:00. Spec: Alpinism/Mountaineering; Antiques; Applied Art; Architecture; Art; Art History; Art Reference; Artists. CC: MC; V. Mem: PBFA. Notes: *From Easter to the end of October our shop is open most days, but a telephone call is advised. From the end of October until Easter we are open Saturdays only and the Christmas holiday period. Stock includes books on the Lake District.*

- **Keswick Bookshop,** ■ 4 Station Street, Keswick, CA12 5HT. Prop: Jane & John Kinnaird. Tel: (017687) 75535. Est: 1994. Shop. Telephone First. Open: **M:** 10:30–17:00; **T:** 10:30–17:00; **W:** 10:30–17:00; **Th:** 10:30–17:00; **F:** 10:30–17:00; **S:** 10:30–17:00. Medium stock. Spec: Antiques; Applied Art; Architecture; Art; Children's; Decorative Art; First Editions; Illustrated - General. PR: £1–300. CC: JCB; MC; V. VAT No: GB 531 4987 33. Notes: *Winter opening: Saturday only (Nov-March) and Christmas holiday and New Year's day. Telephone first. And mail only to: Winterbourne, 18 Houghton Road, Carlisle CA3 OLA*

KIRKBY STEPHEN

2 Ravens, ■ 2 Market Street, Kirkby Stephen, CA17 4QS. Prop: Val and Peter Harrison. Tel: 017683 71519. Est: 1997. Shop open: **W:** 10:00–16:00; **Th:** 10:00–16:00; **F:** 10:00–16:00; **S:** 10:00–16:00. Spec: Gypsies; New Age; Paganism; Rural Life; Topography - Local. Notes: *Please telephone if making a special journey; openings can be a little erratic!*

PENRITH

Beckside Books, 31 St Andrews View, Penrith, CA8 9DH. Prop: Didi Evason. Tel: 01768 895951. Est: 2007. Shop, open M: 10:00–17:00; **T:** 10:00–17:00; **W:** 10:00–16:00; **Th:** 10:00–17:00; **F:** 10:00–17:00; **S:** 10:00–17:00. Medium stock. PR: £1 – 500.

David A.H. Grayling, Verdun House Main Street, Shap, Penrith, CA10 3NG. Prop: David A H Grayling. Tel: (01931) 716746. Fax: (01931) 716746. Web: www.davidgraylingbooks.com. Est: 1970. Private premises. Internet and Postal. Appointment necessary. Medium stock. Spec: Africana; Animals and Birds; Colour-Plate; Countries - Africa; Countries - Asia; Countries - Central Asia; Countries - Ethiopia; Countries - Himalayas, The. PR: £20–5,000. CC: MC; V; All cards except Amex. Cata: Angling. Hunting. Shooting. Natural History. Corresp: French, German. Mem: PBFA; FSB. VAT No: GB 154 6592 46. Notes: *Binding & restoration undertaken. Valuations for insurance, probate etc. Detailed cataloguing of collections and libraries. Comprehensive advice on the purchase, storage and care of books. Booksearch.*

G.K. Hadfield, Old Post Office, Great Salkeld, Penrith, CA11 9LW. Prop: G.K. & J.V. Hadfield & N.R. Hadfield–Tilly. Tel: (01768) 870111. Web: www.gkhadfield-tilly.co.uk. Est: 1974. Office and/or bookroom; Internet and Postal. Appointment necessary. Large stock. Spec: Antiques; Astronomy; Bell-Ringing (Campanology); Furniture; Gemmology; Horology; Mathematics; Microscopy. CC: AE; JCB; MC; V; SO, ELEC. Cata: horology, lathes, turning, music boxes sundial,. Corresp: French. Mem: B.H.I. A.H.S. British Watch & Clockmakers Guild. VAT No: GB 114 809 578. Notes: *Also, a booksearch service, quality bookbinding and restoration. Buy, sell and restore antique clocks. Mobile: 07738 546488*

Phenotype Books, 39 Arthur Street, Penrith, CA11 7TT. Prop: J.E. Mattley. Tel: (01768) 863049. Fax: (01768) 890493. Web: www.phenotypebooks.co.uk. Est: 1985. Private premises. Internet and Postal. Telephone First. Small stock. Spec: Agriculture; Animals and Birds; Carriages & Driving; Cattlemen; Cockfighting; Cowboys; Farming & Livestock; Farriers. PR: £5–1,800. Cata: Agriculture Livestock Vet Farriery & related. Mem: PBFA. VAT No: GB 442 8614 47. Notes: *Private premises. Visitors welcome by appointment.*

Summerfield Books 2007 Ltd, ■ 3 Phoenix Park, Skelton, Penrith, CA11 9SD. Prop: Paul & Chris O'Hara. Tel: 017684 84909. Fax: 017684 84910. Web: www.summerfieldbooks.com. Est: 1986. Shop. Telephone First. Open: **M:** 09:00–17:00; **T:** 09:00–17:00; **W:** 09:00–17:00; **Th:** 09:00–17:00; **F:** 09:00–17:00. Spec: Botany; Flora & Fauna; Forestry; Fungi; Gardening - General; Horticulture; Natural Sciences; Nature. CC: AE; E; JCB; MC; V. Cata: Botany, Forestry, Gardening, Horticulture. Corresp: French. Mem: PBFA; BA. VAT No: GB 911 0787 43. Notes: *We are specialist booksellers, selling from shop premises, by mail order & via the internet. Our stock is almost exclusively in the plant sciences, although we keep a small range of other natural history and local Cumbrian topography.*

SEDBERGH

The Bookseller, ■ 77 Main Street, Sedbergh, LA10 5AB. Prop: C. J. Chambers. Tel: 015396 20991. Fax: 015396 20589. Est: 1994. Shop open: **M:** 10:00–17:00; **T:** 10:00–17:00; **W:** 10:00–17:00; **Th:** 10:00–12:00; **F:** 10:00–17:00; **S:** 10:00–17:00. Spec: Children's; Children's - Illustrated. CC: AE; E; JCB; MC; V. Corresp: French. Notes: *Book repairs undertaken.*

Dales & Lakes Book Centre, ■ 72 Main Street, Sedbergh, LA10 5AD. Tel: 015396 20125. Est: 2005. Shop open: **M:** 10:00–17:00; **T:** 10:00–17:00; **W:** 10:00–17:00; **Th:** 10:00–17:00; **F:** 10:00–17:00; **S:** 10:00–17:00; **Su:** 10:00–17:00. Spec: Academic/Scholarly; Agriculture; Alpinism/Mountaineering; Alternative Medicine; Animals and Birds; Annuals; Anthologies; Antiquarian. CC: MC; V. VAT No: GB 859 4936 61. Notes: *Sedbergh - England's Booktown.*

Henry Wilson Books, Dales & Lakes Book Centre, Main Street, Sedbergh, LA10 5AB. Prop: Harry Wilson. Tel: (015396) 21111. Fax: 012702 19059. Web: www.henrywilsonbooks.co.uk. Est: 2005. Shop and/or gallery. Shop open: **M:** 10:00–17:00; **T:** 10:00–17:00; **W:** 10:00–17:00; **Th:** 10:00–17:00; **F:** 10:00–17:00; **S:** 10:00–17:00; **Su:** 10:00–17:00. Small stock. Spec: Archaeology - Industrial; Author - Rolt, L.T.C.; Buses/Trams; Canals/Inland Waterways; History - Industrial; Maritime/Nautical - History; Model Engineering; Model Railways. PR: £2–500. CC: MC; V; Maestro. Cata: on railways, transport and industrial history. Corresp: French, German. Mem: PBFA; FSB. VAT No: GB 439 7672 03. Cata: annually on railways, transport and industrial history. Notes: *New and secondhand books & back issues of railway journals.*

R.F.G. Hollett and Son, 6 Finkle Street, Sedbergh, LA10 5BZ. Prop: C.G. & R.F.G. Hollett. Tel: (01539) 620298. Fax: (01539) 621396. Web: www.holletts-rarebooks.co.uk. Est: 1950. Shop and/or showroom; Internet and Postal. Appointment necessary. Open: **F:** 01:00–00:00. Very large stock. Spec: Alpinism/Mountaineering; Antiquarian; Antiques; Biography; Children's; Collecting; Colour-Plate; Fine Art. PR: £30–50,000. CC: AE; E; JCB; MC; V; Maestro. Mem: ABA; ILAB. VAT No: GB 343 4391 63. Notes: *Valuations.*

Dealers need to update their entry at least once a year. Visit your page on *Sheppard's World*

Orange Skies Books, ■ 46 Main Street, Sedbergh, LA10 5BL. Prop: David Johnston-Smith. Tel: 0161 408 1182. Web: www.orangeskies.co.uk. Est: 2005. Shop open: **M:** 09:00–17:30; **T:** 09:00–17:30; **W:** 09:00–17:30; **Th:** 09:00–17:30; **F:** 09:00–17:30; **S:** 09:00–17:30; **Su:** 09:00–17:30.

Sleepy Elephant Books & Artefacts, ■ 41 Main Street, Sedbergh, LA10 5BL. Prop: Avril Whittle and Partners. Tel: 015396 21770. Fax: 015396 21770. Est: 2003. Shop open: **M:** 10:00–17:00; **T:** 10:00–17:00; **W:** 10:00–17:00; **Th:** 10:00–17:00; **F:** 10:00–17:00; **S:** 10:00–17:00; **Su:** 12:00–17:00. Spec: Applied Art; Art - Technique; Art History; Children's; Cinema/Film; Cookery/Gastronomy; Crafts; Crochet. CC: MC; V. Cata: Art Craft & Design. VAT No: GB 875015816. Notes: *We specialise in the Arts, Crafts and Design subjects, especially textile arts. Other strong sections iclude Theatre & Drama, Food & Drink, Folio Society publications & good paperback literature. New to us - small Boer War collection!*

Westwood Books Ltd, ■ Long Lane, Sedbergh, LA10 5AH. Tel: 015396 21233. Est: 1987. Shop open: **M:** 10:30–17:30; **T:** 10:30–17:30; **W:** 10:30–17:30; **Th:** 10:30–17:30; **F:** 10:30–17:30; **S:** 10:30–17:30; **Su:** 10:30–17:30. Very large stock. Spec: Academic/Scholarly; Alternative Medicine; Antiquarian; Archaeology; Architecture; Art; Art History; Art Reference. PR: £2–1,000. CC: Euro; JCB; MC; V. Corresp: French. Mem: ABA; PBFA.

Avril Whittle Bookseller, ■ Whittle's Warehouse, 7-9 (rear) Bainbridge Road, Sedbergh, LA10 5AU. Prop: Avril Whittle & Partners. Tel: (015396) 21770. Fax: (015396) 21770. Est: 1980. Shop open. At: Sleepy Elephant Books & Artefacts, 41 Main Street, SEDBERGH, Cumbria LA10 5BL. Open: **M:** 10:00–17:00; **T:** 10:00–17:00; **W:** 10:00–17:00; **Th:** 10:00–17:00; **F:** 10:00–17:00; **S:** 10:00–17:00; **Su:** 12:00–17:00. Medium stock. Spec: Antiques; Art - Technique; Art - Theory; Art History; Calligraphy; Cinema/Film; Cookery/Gastronomy; Crafts. PR: £1–600. CC: MC; V. Cata: Arts & Crafts, Theatre & Cinema Food & Drink,. Corresp: French. VAT No: GB 875 0158 16. Notes: *We also sell rugs, jewellery, tassels & artefacts from Morocco; ladies' & gents' knitwear; cards & interesting gifts; textiles, yarns (inc local alpaca), needles & patterns.*

ULVERSTON

Bookfare, Lowick Hall, Ulverston, LA12 8ED. Prop: Dr. A.C.I. Naylor. Tel: (01229) 885240. Fax: (01229) 885240. Web: www.bookfare.co.uk. Est: 1977. Private premises. Postal only. Appointment necessary. Small stock. Spec: History - General. PR: £6–300. CC: PayPal. Corresp: French.

WELTON

The Little Bookshop, Sebergham Castle House, Welton, Near Carlisle, CA5 7HG. Prop: Frank Grant. Fax: (016974) 76079. Est: 1994. Private premises. Postal only. Appointment necessary. Small stock. Spec: Alpinism/Mountaineering; Biography; Countries - Nepal; Geology; Palaeontology; Sport - Climbing & Trekking; Topography - Local. PR: £2–500. Cata: Lake District Literature/ Mountaineering/Climbing/. Notes: *Also, a booksearch service.*

WHITEHAVEN

Michael Moon's Bookshop, ■ 19 Lowther Street, Whitehaven, CA28 7AL. Prop: Michael Moon. Tel: (01946) 599010. Est: 1970. Shop open: **M:** 09:30–17:00; **T:** 09:30–17:00; **W:** 09:30–17:00; **Th:** 09:30–17:00; **F:** 09:30–17:00; **S:** 09:30–17:00. Very large stock. Spec: Cinema/Film; History - Local; Topography - Local; Booksearch; Prints and Maps. PR: £1–1,000. CC: JCB; MC; V. Mem: PBFA; SBA. VAT No: GB 288 1073 42. Notes: *Closed Wed - from October to April. Publisher on Cumbrian history.*

WIGTON

Chelifer Books, Todd Close Curthwaite, Wigton, CA7 8BE. Prop: Mike Smith & Deryn Walker. Tel: (01228) 711388. Web: www.military-books.biz. Est: 1985. Private premises. Internet and Postal. Appointment necessary. Small stock. Spec: American Indians; Antiquarian; Arms & Armour; Aviation; Military; Military - Modelling; Military History; Military Uniforms. PR: £5–1,500. CC: MC; V; Maestro. Cata: on general military.

Fine Art Catalogues, The Hollies, Port Carlisle, Wigton CA7 5BU. Prop: Michael Bennett. Tel: (01697) 51398. Est: 1977. PR: £3–500.

Rosley Books, Rosley Farmhouse, Rosley, Wigton, CA7 8BZ. Prop: Ian Blakemore. Tel: (016973) 49924. Fax: (016973) 45149. Web: www.rosleybooks.co.uk. Est: 2000. Private premises. Appointment necessary. Medium stock. Spec: Academic/Scholarly; Antiquarian; Author - Belloc, Hilaire; Author - Browning, Robert; Author - Bunyan, John; Author - Chesterton, G.K.; Author - Eliot, T.S.; Author - Inklings, The. PR: £5–5,000. CC: AE; MC; V; PayPal. Cata: Inklings, Keswick, Commentaries. Notes: *Specialist in; C.S. Lewis, George MacDonald, Inklings, D.L. Saters, G.K. Chesterton, Antiquarian Theology, Literature, Bibles.*

WINDERMERE

Bridge Books, 2 Sunnybrae, Brook Road, Windermere. Prop: John Taylor. Tel: (01539) 445015. Est: 1993. Postal only. Spec: Poetry; Topography - Local. PR: £3–750.

Fireside Bookshop, ■ 21 Victoria Street, Windermere, LA23 1AB. Prop: Mr R.D. Sheppard. Tel: (015394) 45855. Web: www.firesidebookshop.co.uk. Est: 1977. Shop open: **M:** 11:00–17:00; **T:** 11:00–17:00; **W:** 11:00–17:00; **Th:** 11:00–17:00; **F:** 11:00–17:00; **S:** 11:00–17:00; **Su:** 11:00–17:00. Large stock. Spec: Academic/Scholarly; Aeronautics; Alpinism/Mountaineering; American Indians; Americana - General; Anthropology; Antiquarian; Art. PR: £1–1,000. CC: AE; JCB; MC; V; Maestro. Mem: PBFA. Notes: *An ever increasing selection of our stock of antiquarian, academic and secondhand books is listed on our online store at www.thehumanitiesbookstore.com with full search facilities and secure online purchasing.*

DERBYSHIRE

ALFRETON

John Titford, Yew Tree Farm Hallfieldgate, Higham, Alfreton, DE55 6AG. Tel: (01773) 520389. Fax: (01773) 833373. Est: 1987. Private premises. Postal only. Appointment necessary. Small stock. Spec: Genealogy; Heraldry; History - General; Topography - General; Booksearch. PR: £2–1,000. Cata: Genealogy & heraldry. Corresp: French. Mem: PBFA.

BAKEWELL

Country Books, Courtyard Cottage, Little Longstone, Bakewell, DE45 1NN. Prop: Richard J.T. Richardson. Tel: 01629 640670. Est: 1992. Private premises. Postal only. Appointment necessary. Spec: Academic/Scholarly; Agriculture; Architecture; Author - Baring-Gould, S.; Author - Barnes, William; Author - Bates, H.E.; Author - Bell, Adrian; Author - Belloc, Hilaire. CC: MC; V. Cata: country writers, Gypsies, rural life, village his. Notes: *Publisher of local history books Derbyshire and Sussex.*

BUXTON

Birdnet Optics Ltd., ■ 5 London Road, Buxton, SK17 9PA. Prop: Paul and Sandi Flint. Tel: (01298) 71844. Fax: (01298) 27727. Web: www.birdnet.co.uk. Est: 1998. Shop open: **M:** 09:30–17:30; **T:** 09:30–17:30; **W:** 09:30–17:30; **Th:** 09:30–17:30; **F:** 09:30–17:30; **S:** 09:30–17:30. Small stock. Spec: Natural History; New Books; New Naturalist; Ornithology; Publishers - Poysers. PR: £1–2,000. CC: MC; V.

Scrivener's Books & Bookbinding, ■ 42 High Street, Buxton, SK17 6HB. Prop: Alastar Scrivener. Tel: 01298 73100. Est: 1994. Shop open: **M:** 09:00–17:00; **T:** 09:00–17:00; **W:** 09:00–17:00; **Th:** 09:00–17:00; **F:** 09:00–17:00; **S:** 09:00–17:00; **Su:** 12:00–16:00; Closed for lunch: 13:00–14:00. Spec: Annuals; Antiquarian; Applied Art; Archaeology; Architecture; Art; Art - Technique; Art - Theory. CC: AE; D; E; JCB; MC; V. Notes: *Bookbinding, tuition, day courses, lectures.*

CASTLETON

Hawkridge Books, The Cruck Barn, Cross Street, Castleton, Hope Valley, S33 8WH. (up to March 2010, then at 119 Manchester Road, Sheffield S10 5DN. See website for other details.) Prop: Dr. J. & Mrs. I. Tierney. Web: www.hawkridge.co.uk. Est: 1995. Bookroom. Appointment necessary. Large stock. Spec: Natural History; Ornithology. PR: £5–2,000. CC: AE; JCB; MC; V.

CHESTERFIELD

Ian Broddon, Meynell Close, Chesterfield, S40 3BL. Prop: Ian Briddon. Tel: 01246 208411. Est: 2004. Private premises. Internet and Postal. Contactable. Open: **M:** 09:00–17:30; **T:** 09:00–17:30; **W:** 09:00–17:30; **Th:** 09:00–17:30; **F:** 09:00–17:30; **S:** 09:00–17:30; **Su:** 09:00–17:30; Closed for lunch: 13:00–14:00. Spec: Annuals; Antiquarian; Children's - Illustrated; Fine & Rare; First Editions; Food & Drink; Homosexuality & Lesbianism; Humour.

Tilleys Vintage Magazines, ■ 21 Derby Road, Chesterfield, S40 2EF. Prop: Albert Tilley. Tel: (01246) 563868. Web: www.tilleysvintagemagazines.com. Est: 1978. Shop. Telephone First. Open: **M:** 10:00–16:30; **T:** 10:00–16:30; **W:** 10:00–16:30; **Th:** 10:00–16:30; **F:** 10:00–16:30; **S:** 10:00–16:30. Very large stock. Spec: Comic Books & Annuals; Glamour; Magazines & Periodicals - General; Magazines - Women's; Newspapers; Collectables; Ephemera. PR: £1–100. CC: MC; V; PayPal. Notes: *Warehouse at Barrow Hill Roundhouse Railway Centre, Chesterfield - open for major events. Mail order, Ebay listings - 1 million + items in stock 1890s-present.*

CROMFORD

Scarthin Books, ■ The Promenade, Scarthin, Cromford, DE4 3QF. Prop: Dr. D.J. Mitchell. Tel: (01629) 823272. Fax: (01629) 825094. Web: www.scarthinbooks.com. Est: 1974. Shop open: **M:** 09:30–18:00; **T:** 09:30–18:00; **W:** 09:30–18:00; **Th:** 09:30–18:00; **F:** 09:30–18:00; **S:** 09:30–18:00; **Su:** 12:00–18:00. Very large stock. Spec: Academic/Scholarly; Alpinism/Mountaineering; American Indians; Animals and Birds; Antiquarian; Architecture; Author - Uttley, Alison; History - Industrial. PR: £1–5,000. CC: MC; V. Corresp: French, German. Mem: BA; IPG. VAT No: GB 127 6427 64. Notes: *Also, new books, publishers of local history and walking books.*

DERBY

Saracen Books, 24 Kirkleys Avenue, North, Spondon, Derby, DE21 7FX. Prop: Graham & Sandra Mansey. Tel: 01332 678084. Web: www.saracenbooks.com. Est: 2002. Private premises. Internet and Postal. Open in Summer. Open: **M:** 09:00–17:30; **T:** 09:00–17:30; **W:** 09:00–17:30; **Th:** 09:00–17:30; **F:** 09:00–17:30; **S:** 09:00–17:30; **Su:** 09:00–17:30; Closed for lunch: 13:00–14:00. Spec: Gardening - Organic; General Stock; History - British; History - British Empire, The; Military; Natural History; Politics. CC: PayPal. Corresp: None. Notes: *We have a broad stock base with an emphasis on Military, History, Natural History and Politics.*

FROGGATT

Jarvis Books, Valleyside, Malthouse Lane, Froggatt, Hope Valley, S32 3ZA. Prop: Grant & Valerie Jarvis. Tel: (01433) 631 951. Fax: (01433) 631 951. Web: www.mountainbooks.co.uk. Est: 1979. Private premises. Internet and Postal. Telephone First. Small stock. Spec: Alpinism/Mountaineering; Expeditions; Exploration; Exploration - Polar Regions; Guide Books; Himalayan Kingdoms; Mountain Men; Mountains. CC: AE; MC; V. Cata: Mountaineering. Mem: PBFA. Notes: *Catalogues issued in mountaineering.*

GLOSSOP

George St. Books, ■ 14 - 16 George Street, Glossop, SK13 8AY. Prop: David & Emma Jones. Tel: 01457 853413. Web: www.georgestreetbooks.co.uk. Est: 1986. Shop open: **M:** 09:00–17:00; **T:** 09:00–17:00; **W:** 09:00–17:00; **Th:** 09:00–17:00; **F:** 09:00–17:00; **S:** 09:00–17:00; **Su:** 11:00–15:00. Spec: Alpinism/ Mountaineering; Architecture; Art; Autobiography; Biography; Children's; Crafts; Fiction - General. CC: MC; V; Maestro. Mem: BA. Notes: *Weekly Childrens Story session, Reading Group, Quarterly Storytelling Presentations/events, Reading Room with free refreshments,Book searches, new books.*

LITTLEOVER

Bob Mallory (Books), 14 Dean Close, Littleover, Derby, DE23 4EF. Tel: 01332 511663. Telephone First. Open: **M:** 09:00–17:30; **T:** 09:00–17:30; **W:** 09:00–17:30; **Th:** 09:00–17:30; **F:** 09:00–17:30; **S:** 09:00–17:30; **Su:** 09:00–17:30; Closed for lunch: 13:00–14:00. Spec: Autobiography; Automobilia/ Automotive; Biography; Cinema/Film; Horses; Humour; Journalism; Management. CC: paypal. Notes: *Horse Racing, Gambling, Entertainment, Autobiography, Biography, Sport: Football, Cricket, Television, Cinema.*

MATLOCK

Hunter and Krageloh, Honeybee Cottage, In the Dale, Wensley, Matlock, DE4 2LL. Prop: J.A. Hunter. Tel: (01629) 732845. Est: 1993. Telephone First. Spec: Alpinism/Mountaineering; Countries - Central Asia; Countries - Himalayas, The; Countries - Ladakh; Countries - Nepal; Countries - Switzerland; Countries - Tibet; Mountains. PR: £1–12,000. Cata: Mountaineering, Central Asia, Mountain Travel. Mem: PBFA. VAT No: GB 598 6024 96. Notes: *We have an unusually fine stock that includes some of the rarest books in our subjects. Many items are signed by the authors or are association copies. The discerning collector will not be disappointed by contact with us.*

John O'Reilly - Mountain Books, Netherlea Barn, Bracken Lane, Holloway, Matlock, DE4 5AS. Prop: John O'Reilly. Tel: (01629) 534559. Est: 1972. Private premises. Postal only. Small stock. Spec: Alpinism/Mountaineering; Exploration; Exploration - Polar Regions; Mountains; Sport - Caving (Spelaeology); Sport - Climbing & Trekking; Travel - Asia; Travel - Polar. PR: £5–500. CC: MC; V. Cata: Mountaineering.

WIRKSWORTH

Pastmasters, ■ 15 The Causeway, Wirksworth, DE4 4DL. Prop: Brian Jones. Tel: (01629) 823775. Est: 1998. Shop open: **T:** 10:00–17:00; **F:** 10:00–17:00; **S:** 10:00–17:00. Small stock. Spec: Journalism; Music - General; Plays; Theatre. PR: £1–40. Notes: *Also, classical cds.*

DEVON

ASHBURTON

The Dartmoor Bookshop, ■ 2 Kingsbridge Lane, Ashburton, TQ13 7DX. Prop: Brenda Greysmith & Andy Collins. Tel: (01364) 653356. Web: www.thedartmoorbookshop.co.uk. Est: 1981. Shop open: **W:** 10:00–17:30; **Th:** 10:00–17:30; **F:** 10:00–17:30; **S:** 10:00–17:30. Very large stock. Spec: Alpinism/Mountaineering; Antiquarian; Architecture; Art; Art History; Art Reference; Artists; Fiction - General. PR: £1–250. CC: JCB; MC; V. VAT No: GB 803 1119 82. Notes: *Having bought the business from Paul and Barbara Heatley on their retirement in Oct 2006, we have closed Pedlars Pack Books in Totnes and are now happily continuing the Dartmoor Bookshop tradition.*

Pedlar's Pack Books, ■ 2 Kingsbridge Lane, Ashburton, TQ13 7DX. Prop: Brenda Greysmith & Andy Collins. Tel: 01364 653356. Est: 2003. Internet and Postal. Shop open: **W:** 10:00–17:30; **Th:** 10:00–17:30; **F:** 10:00–17:30; **S:** 10:00–17:30. Very large stock. Spec: Military; Booksearch. PR: £1–500. CC: JCB; MC; V; Switch. VAT No: GB 803 1119 82.

BARNSTAPLE

Sol Books, ■ 2 Bridge Chambers, The Strand, Barnstaple, EX31 1HB. Tel: 01271 327319. Fax: 01271321640. Web: www.sol.org.uk. Shop open: **M:** 10:00–16:00; **T:** 10:00–16:00; **W:** 10:00–16:00; **Th:** 10:00–16:00; **F:** 10:00–16:00; **S:** 10:00–13.00. Spec: Fiction - General; out-of-print. Notes: *Sol Books is a charity bookshop. We sell books in our shop and on the Internet to raise funds for SOL - our internaional language school.*

Tarka Books, ■ 5 Bear Street, Barnstaple, EX32 7BU. Prop: Fiona Broster. Tel: (01271) 374997. Web: www.tarkabooks.co.uk. Est: 1988. Shop open: **M:** 09:45–17:00; **T:** 09:45–17:00; **W:** 09:45–17:00; **Th:** 09:45–17:00; **F:** 09:45–17:00; **S:** 09:45–17:00. Very large stock. Spec: Aircraft; Animals and Birds; Annuals; Antiques; Art; Author - Williamson, Henry; Autobiography; Aviation. PR: £1–100. CC: MC; V; So. Mem: BA; FSB. Notes: *New books to order, booksearch available, book tokens. A small range of stationary gifts. Handmade cards.*

Woodland Books, Woodland Books, 8 St Peter's Close, West Buckland, Barnstaple, EX32 0TX. Tel: 01271 828242. Fax: 01271 828072. VOIPpro: Skype. VOIPnum: kevgrim. Est: 2004. Private premises. Internet and Postal. Contactable. Spec: Adult; Aircraft; Amateur Radio [Ham Radio]; Computing. CC: PayPal. Mem: BA. Notes: *Mainly used computer books but all with a high technical content.*

BERE ALSTON

The Victoria Bookshop, ■ 9 Fore Street, Bere Alston, PL20 7AA. Prop: Peter Churcher. Tel: (01822) 841638. Est: 2000. Shop open: **M:** 10:00–16:30; **T:** 10:00–16:30; **Th:** 10:00–16:30; **F:** 10:00–16:30; **S:** 10:00–16:30. Very large stock. Spec: Academic/Scholarly; Alchemy; Occult; Psychology/Psychiatry; Religion - Christian; Topography - Local. PR: £3–600. CC: AE; MC; V; SW. Notes: *Over 80,000 books in stock. In an area of outstanding natural beauty. Near Plymouth and Tavistock*

BIDEFORD

Allhalland Books, ■ 7 Allhalland St., Bideford, EX39 2JD. Prop: J.P. Simpson O'Gara and S. Sutherland. Tel: (01237) 479301. Est: 1997. Shop open: **M:** 09:00–17:00; **T:** 09:00–17:00; **W:** 09:00–17:00; **Th:** 09:00–17:00; **F:** 09:00–17:00; **S:** 09:00–17:00. Small stock. Spec: Natural History; Topography - General. PR: £2–500. Notes: *Also, bookbinding.*

Peter Hames, Devon Cottage, Churchill Way, Northam, Bideford, EX39 1NS. Prop: Peter Hames. Tel: (01237) 421065. Fax: (01237) 421065. Est: 1980. Market stand/stall; Book fairs only. Appointment necessary. Open: **M:** 09:30–17.30; **T:** 09:30–17:30; **W:** 09:30–17:30; **Th:** 09:30–17:30; **F:** 09:30–17:30; **S:** 09:30–17:30. Small stock. Spec: Motoring; Music - Jazz & Blues; Topography - Local; Ephemera. PR: £1–100. Mem: PBFA. Notes: *Barnstaple Market: Tues, Fri, Sat and South Molton Market: Thursday and book fairs in South West. Local topography includes Exmoor, and Lundy Island.*

BRIXHAM

Kate Armitage (Booksearch), 5 Park Court, Heath Road, Brixham, TQ5 9AX. Tel: (01803) 850277. Est: 1998. Private premises. Internet and Postal. Spec: Children's; Military History; Modern First Editions. PR: £1–20. CC: PayPal.

Katesbooks, 5 Park Court, Heath Road, Brixham, TQ5 9AX. Prop: Kate Armitage. Tel: 01803 850277. Est: 1998. Private premises. Internet only. Spec: Children's; Children's - Illustrated. CC: PayPal. Notes: *Specialising in Children's.*

CHAGFORD

Dave Jelfs (Bookseller), 11 Bretteville Close, Chagford, TQ13 8DW. Prop: Dave Jelfs. Tel: (01647) 432659. Web: www.moretonbooks.co.uk. Est: 1994. Private premises. Appointment necessary. Open: **M:** 10:00–17:00; **T:** 10:00–17:00; **W:** 10:00–17:00; **Th:** 10:00–17:00; **F:** 10:00–17:00; **S:** 10:00–17:00. Medium stock. Spec: Antiquarian; Art History; Art Reference; Autobiography; Literature; Modern First Editions; Natural History; Poetry. PR: £1–500. CC: E; MC; V; SO, SW. Mem: PBFA. Notes: *Stock include Dartmoor and West Country topography.*

COLYTON

Chandos Books, ■ London House, Market Place, Colyton, EX24 6JS. Prop: George Janssen. Tel: 01297 553344. Est: 1997. Shop open: **M:** 10:00–16:00; **T:** 10:00–16:00; **W:** 10:00–16:00; **Th:** 10:00–16:00; **F:** 10:00–16:00; **S:** 10:00–13:00. Spec: Animals and Birds; Antiquarian; Architecture; Art; Bibles; Bindings; Bookbinding; Books about Books. Corresp: Dutch, German. Notes: *Bookbinding and book repairs on premises.*

Island Books, Shutes Farm, Northleigh, Colyton, EX24 6BL. Tel: (01843) 866999. Fax: (01843) 866999. Web: www.ukbookworld.com/members/islandbooks. Est: 1974. Private premises. Internet and Postal. Appointment necessary. Medium stock. Spec: Academic/Scholarly; Aeronautics; Agriculture; Aircraft; Animals and Birds; Antiquarian; Applied Art; Archaeology. PR: £10–10,000. CC: JCB; MC; V.

COMBE MARTIN

Golden Books Group, Blurridge Ridge Hill, Combe Martin, EX34 0NR. Prop: Ivan and Ann Golden. Tel: (01271) 883204. Fax: (01271) 889389. Web: www.goldenbooksgroup.co.uk. Est: 1991. Private premises. Internet only. Appointment necessary. Large stock. Spec: Antiquarian; Author - Dickens, Charles; Bindings; Early Imprints; Fine & Rare; History - General; Sets of Books; Travel - General. PR: £5–10,000. CC: MC; V; Switch, Maestro. Mem: PBFA; LAPADA, CINOA, IOBA. VAT No: GB 822 1619 54. Notes: *Specialist antiquarain leather book library builders and installers.*

COUNTESS WEAR

Richard Connole, 12 Seabrook Avenue, Countess Wear, EX2 7DW. Prop: Richard Connole. Tel: O1392 2O1735. Web: www.yesteryearvision.co.uk. Mail order only; Internet and Postal. Telephone First. Open: **M:** 09:00–17:30; **T:** 09:00–17:30; **W:** 09:00–17:30; **Th:** 09:00–17:30; **F:** 09:00–17:30; **S:** 09:00–17:30; **Su:** 09:00–17:30. Closed for lunch: 13:00–14:00. Cata: Film, T.V, Childrens, General.

DARTMOUTH

Compass Books, ■ 24 Lower Street, Dartmouth, TQ6 9AN. Prop: Emilie and Lucy Wright. Tel: 01803 835915. Fax: 01803 835915. Est: 2000. Shop open: **M:** 10:00–16:00; **T:** 10:00–16:00; **W:** 10:00–16:00; **Th:** 10:00–16:00; **F:** 10:00–16:00; **S:** 10:00–16:00. Spec: History - Local; Maritime/Nautical; Topography - Local. CC: MC; V; Maestro, Solo. VAT No: GB 777 3192 94.

DAWLISH

Dawlish Books, ■ White Court, Beach Street, Dawlish, EX7 9PN. Prop: S. French. Tel: (01626) 866882 / 01626 779500. Est: 2000. Shop open: **M:** 11:00–16:30; **T:** 11:00–16:30; **Th:** 11:00–16:30; **F:** 11:00–16:30; **S:** 11:00–16:30. Medium stock. Spec: Annuals; Comic Books & Annuals; Esoteric; New Age; Occult; Psychic; Spiritualism; U.F.O.s. PR: £1–100. Notes: *Open Friday & Saturday only in winter, 11:00– 15:00. 6 days a week in summer (closed Weds) Trade most welcome all year round but best telephone before calling in winter.*

EXETER

Lisa Cox Music, The Coach House, Colleton Crescent, Exeter, EX 2 4DG. Prop: Ms. L. Cox. Tel: (01392) 490290. Fax: (01392) 277336. Web: www.lisacoxmusic.co.uk. Est: 1984. Private premises. Internet and Postal. Appointment necessary. Open: **M:** 10:00–17:00; **T:** 10:00–17:00; **W:** 10:00–17:00; **Th:** 10:00–17:00; **F:** 10:00–17:00. Medium stock. Spec: Aids Crisis, The; Autographs; Manuscripts; Music - Printed, Sheet Music & Scores. PR: £100–50,000. CC: MC; V. Corresp: French. Mem: ABA; BA. VAT No: GB 631 4239 64.

Exeter Rare Books, ■ 13a Guildhall Shopping Centre, Exeter, EX8 5AX. Prop: R.C. Parry M.A. Tel: (01392) 436021. Web: www.exeterrarebooks.co.uk. Est: 1977. Shop open: **M:** 10:00–17:00; **T:** 10:00– 17:00; **W:** 11:00–17:00; **Th:** 10:00–17:00; **F:** 10:00–17:00; **S:** 10:00–17:00; Closed for lunch: 13:00– 14:00. Medium stock. Spec: Topography - Local. PR: £2–500. CC: MC; V. Corresp: German. Mem: ABA; PBFA. VAT No: GB 142 3267 91.

Exeter's Antiques Centre on the Quay, ■ The Antiques Centre, The Quay, Exeter, EX2 4AP. Prop: P. Bliss, M. Desforges, and T. Hughes. Tel: 01392 493501. Web: www.exeterquayantiques.co.uk. Est: 1986. Shop open: **M:** 10:00–18:00; **T:** 10:00–18:00; **W:** 10:00–18:00; **Th:** 10:00–18:00; **F:** 10:00–18:00; **S:** 10:00–18:00; **Su:** 10:00–18:00. Spec: Antiques; Collectables; Ephemera; Music - Popular; Music - Printed, Sheet Music & Scores; Publishers - Ladybird Books; Collectables; Ephemera. Corresp: French, Spanish. Notes: *NB: Winter opening times 10:00 – 17:00.*

John S. Hill, 78 Pinhoe Road, Exeter, EX4 7HL. Tel: (01392) 439753. Fax: (01392) 439753. Est: 1988. Private premises. Internet and Postal. Appointment necessary. Small stock. Spec: Fiction - Crime, Detective, Spy, Thrillers; Fiction - Science Fiction; First Editions; Military; Booksearch. PR: £5– 1,500.

Joel Segal Books, 27 Fore Street, Topsham, Exeter, EX3 0HD. Tel: 01392877895. Web: www.segalbooks.com. Open: **M:** 10:30–17:00; **T:** 10:30–17:00; **W:** 10:30–17:00; **Th:** 10:30–17:00; **F:** 10:30–17:00; **S:** 10:30–17:00; Closed for lunch: 13:00–14:00. Spec: Academic/Scholarly; Acupuncture; Adventure; Advertising; Aesthetics; Africana; Agriculture; Aircraft. CC: MC; V; Maestro/Switch. Corresp: French. Mem: Federation of Small Businesses.

HONITON

Ænigma Designs (Books), Whites Plot, Luppitt, Honiton, EX14 4RZ. Prop: James Dalgety. Tel: (01404) 891560. Web: www.puzzlemuseum.com. Est: 1973. Private premises. Internet and Postal. Appointment necessary. Spec: Puzzles. CC: PayPal. Cata: puzzles, recreational math,.

High Street Books, ■ 150 High Street, Honiton, EX14 8JX. Prop: Geoff Tyson. Tel: (01404) 45570. Est: 1992. Shop open: **T:** 10:00–17:00; **W:** 10:00–17:00; **Th:** 10:00–17:00; **F:** 10:00–17:00; **S:** 10:00–17:00. Spec: Applied Art; Art; Aviation; Erotica; Esoteric; General Stock; History - British; Maritime/ Nautical. CC: MC; V. Mem: ABA; PBFA; ILAB. VAT No: GB 800 492558. Notes: *We also stock a fair selection of prints and maps.On street parking is also possible, and unloading for anyone wishing to bring books to sell is possible directly outside the shop.*

Graham York Rare Books, ■ 225 High Street, Honiton, EX14 1LB. Prop: Graham York. Tel: (01404) 41727. Fax: (01404) 44993. Web: www.gyork.co.uk. Est: 1982. Internet and Postal. Shop open: **M:** 09:30–17:00; **T:** 09:30–17:00; **W:** 09:30–17:00; **Th:** 09:30–17:00; **F:** 09:30–17:00; **S:** 09:30–17:00. Large stock. Spec: Africana; Antiquarian; Art Reference; Author - Borrow, George; Countries - Europe; Countries - Portugal; Countries - Spain; County - Local. PR: £0–5,000. CC: AE; MC; V. Cata: Gypsies, George Borrow, Spain. Corresp: Spanish, French. Mem: ABA; PBFA; ILAB. VAT No: GB 429 2623 48. Notes: *Stock includes books on Devon, Dorset, Somerset, Cornwall; British and Foreign Topography; Art; History; Literature; Natural History; Maps and Prints.*

KINGSBRIDGE

Booktrace International, The Hald Kernborough, Kingsbridge, TQ7 2LL. Prop: Richard Newbold. Tel: (01548) 511366. Est: 1995. Private premises. Postal only. Spec: Booksearch.

LYMPSTONE

Reaveley Books, 1 Church Road, Lympstone, Nr Exmouth, EX8 5JU. Prop: Jane Johnson. Tel: (01395) 225462. Web: www.reaveleybooks.co.uk. Est: 1998. Private premises. Internet and Postal. Telephone First. Small stock. Spec: Author - Murdoch, I.; Fiction - General; Fiction - Crime, Detective, Spy, Thrillers; Fiction - Historical; Fiction - Young Adult Mystery & Adventure Series; Limited Editions - General; Literature; Modern First Editions. PR: £5–500. CC: PayPal, cheque. Cata: modern literary first editions. Mem: FSB. Notes: *Monthly newsletter e-mailed on request - see www.reaveleybooks.co.uk for list of stock.*

MODBURY

Lamb's Tales Books, 63 Brownston Street, Modbury, Ivybridge, PL21 0RQ. Prop: James & Elizabeth Lamb. Tel: (01548) 830317. Web: www.lambstales.co.uk. Est: 1988. Private premises. Internet and Postal. Contactable. Small stock. Spec: Cookery/Gastronomy; Maritime/Nautical; Military. PR: £5–150. VAT No: GB 768 6509 77.

MONKLEIGH

Catalyst Booksearch Services, Catsborough Cottage, Catsborough Cross, Monkleigh, Nr Bideford, EX39 5LE. Prop: Patrick Blosse. Tel: 01805 624056. Web: www.catalystbooksearch.co.uk. Est: 1997. Private premises. Internet and Postal. Appointment necessary. **M:** 09:00–17:30; **T:** 09:00–17:30; **W:** 09:00–17:30; **Th:** 09:00–17:30; **F:** 09:00–17:30; **S:** 09:00–17:30; **Su:** 09:00–13:00; Closed for lunch: 12:00–14:00. Medium stock. Spec: Annuals; Art; Autobiography; Biography; Children's; Cinema/ Film; Countries - Great Britain; Countries - India; Countries - Pakistan; Crime (True). PR: £2–400. CC: AE, MC, V, PayPal. Notes: *We specialise in childrens & adult fiction, biography, performing arts & travel, with a sprinkling of history & politics. Visitors by appointment. We also provide a comprehensive, free booksearch service. Please send wants with a large sae.*

MORETONHAMPSTEAD

Dartmoor Book Gallery, ■ 3 A The Square, Moretonhampstead, TQ13 8NF. Prop: Roger Collicott. Tel: 01647 440649. Web: www.rogercollicottbooks.com. Est: 2007. Shop open: **T:** 10:00–17:00; **W:** 10:00–17:00; **Th:** 10:00–17:00; **F:** 10:00–17:00; **S:** 13:00–17:00; Closed for lunch: 13:00–14:00. Spec: Antiquarian; Art; Cornish history; Geology; History - Mining; Literature; Maps & Mapmaking; Natural History. CC: AE; MC; V. Mem: PBFA. Notes: *A small but select stock of antiquarian books, inc. good sections of Travel, Natural History, Literature, Antiquarian, with an emphasis on Devon books, including a large selection of Antique maps. West Country arts and crafts also stocked.*

NEWTON ABBOT

DPE Books, PO Box 5 Chudleigh, Newton Abbot, TQ130YZ. Prop: David Porteous. Tel: 01626 853310. Web: www.davidporteous.com. Mail and postal Only. Spec: Art - Technique; Art History; Crafts; Embroidery; Folklore; Hobbies; Housekeeping; Illustrated - General. VAT No: GB 441 2746 66.

OAKHAMPTON

J C Books, ■ 9 The Arcade Fore Street, Oakhampton, EX20 1EX. Tel: 01837 659339. Est: 1998. Shop open: **M:** 09:00–17:00; **T:** 09:00–17:00; **W:** 09:00–17:00; **Th:** 09:00–17:00; **F:** 09:00–17:00; **S:** 09:00–17:00. Spec: History - Local; New Books; Railways and Railroads; Science - General; Topography - Local; Transport. Notes: *Sadly closing in 2009.*

PAIGNTON

The Old Celtic Bookshop, ■ 43 Hyde Road, Paignton, TQ4 5BP. Prop: Michael Sutton. Tel: (01803) 558709. Est: 1989. Shop open: **M:** 09:00–18:00; **T:** 09:00–18:00; **W:** 09:00–18:00; **Th:** 09:00–18:00; **F:** 09:00–18:00; **S:** 09:00–18:00; **Su:** 12:00–18:00. Medium stock. Spec: Alternative Medicine; Annuals; Author - Blyton, Enid; Author - Herbert, James; Author - King, Stephen; Author - Koontz, Dean; Author - Rice, Anne; Celtica. PR: £1–50. Notes: *Extended opening until 21:30 July to September.*

The Pocket Bookshop, ■ 159 Winner Street, Paignton, TQ3 3BP. Prop: Leon Corrall. Tel: (01803) 529804. Est: 1985. Shop open: **T:** 10:30–17:30; **W:** 10:30–17:30; **Th:** 10:30–17:30; **F:** 10:30–17:30; **S:** 10:30–17:30. PR: £1–50. Notes: *Open Mondays in from July to September.*

The Sheet Music Warehouse, Primley Mount, 17 Primley Park, Paignton, TQ3 3JP. Web: www.sheetmusicwarehouse.co.uk. Est: 1991. Warehouse. Internet and Postal. Appointment necessary. Open: **M:** 09:00–17:30; **T:** 09:00–17:30; **W:** 09:00–17:30; **Th:** 09:00–17:30; **F:** 09:00–17:30; **S:** 09:00–17:30; **Su:** 09:00–17:30; Closed for lunch: 13:00–14:00. Spec: Music - General; Music - Chart Histories & Research; Music - Classical; Music - Composers; Music - Country & Western; Music - Folk & Irish Folk; Music - Gregorian Chants; Music - Illustrated Sheet Music. CC: PayPal.

PLYMOUTH

Anne Harris Books & Bags Books, 38 Burleigh Park Road, Peverell, Plymouth, PL3 4QH. Tel: (01752) 775853. Est: 2000. Private premises. Postal only. Appointment necessary. Small stock. Spec: Architecture; Art; Plant Hunting; Travel - General. PR: £1–500.

Bookcupboard, ■ Old Customs House, 18 The Parade, Barbican, Plymouth, PL1 2JW. Prop: A. Donoghue. Tel: (01752) 226311. Est: 1995. Shop open: **M:** 10:30–16:30; **T:** 10:30–16:30; **W:** 10:30–16:30; **Th:** 10:30–16:30; **F:** 10:30–15:30; **S:** 10:30–16:30; **Su:** 10:30–16:30. Very large stock. CC: AE; D; E; JCB; MC; V. Mem: FSB.

books2books, 64 Glendower Road, Peverell, Plymouth, PL3 4LD. Prop: R.J.A. Paxton-Denny. Tel: 01752 510234. Web: www.abebooks/home/BOOKS2BOOKS. Est: 1984. Private premises. Internet and Postal. Contactable. Open: **M:** 07:30–23:30; **T:** 07:30–23:30; **W:** 07:30–23:30; **Th:** 07:30–23:30; **F:** 07:30–23:30; **S:** 07:30–23:30; **Su:** 07:30–23:30. Spec: Annuals; Art History; Art Reference; Author - General; Author - 20th Century; Author - Johns, W.E.; Autobiography; Aviation. CC: MC; V; Debit cards. Cata: Modern 1sts, Childrens, Illustrated, Biogs, Milit. Corresp: French, German. Notes: *Good quality general stock. View by arrangement, tel/email/mail. Ship worldwide. Insurance extra.*

Cornerstone Books, ■ New Street Antiques Centre, 27 New Street, The Barbican, Plymouth, PL3 4LE. Prop: Mark Treece. Tel: (01752) 661165. Web: www.abe.books.com. Est: 1985. Shop open: **M:** 10:00–17:00; **T:** 10:00–17:00; **W:** 10:00–17:00; **Th:** 10:00–17:00; **F:** 10:00–17:00; **S:** 10:00–17:00. Large stock. PR: £1–100. Mem: ABA. Notes: *General stock.*

Rods Books, ■ 20–21 Southside Street, Barbican, Plymouth, PL1 2LD. Prop: R.P. Murphy. Tel: (01752) 253546. Est: 1996. Internet and Postal. Shop open: **M:** 10:00–16:00; **T:** 10:00–16:00; **W:** 10:00–16:00; **Th:** 10:00–16:00; **F:** 10:00–16:00; **S:** 10:00–15.45; **Su:** 10:00–15.00. Spec: Adventure; Alpinism/ Mountaineering; Arms & Armour; Army, The; Deep Sea Diving; Fiction - Science Fiction; Fiction - Westerns; French Foreign Legion, The. PR: £2–40. CC: AE; E; JCB; MC; V; Paypal.

The Sea Chest Nautical Bookshop, ■ Queen Anne's Battery, Marina Coxside, Plymouth, PL4 0LP. Prop: Roger & Gill Boyns. Tel: (01752) 222012. Fax: (01752) 252679. Web: www.seachest.co.uk. Est: 1987. Shop open: **M:** 09:00–17:30; **T:** 09:00–17:30; **W:** 09:00–17:30; **Th:** 09:00–17.30; **F:** 09:00–17:30; **S:** 09:00–17:00. Small stock. Spec: Manuals - Seamanship (see also under Seamanship); Maps & Mapmaking; Marine Biology; Marine Sciences; Maritime/Nautical; Maritime/Nautical - History; Maritime/Nautical - Log Books; Military. PR: £2–750. CC: AE; MC; V. Mem: BA. VAT No: GB 777 4131 12. Notes: *Also, new nautical books, pilots & charts, a booksearch service & British Admiralty chart agent.*

SEATON

Hill House Books, Hill House, Highcliffe Crescent, Seaton, EX12 2PS. Prop: Phil Beard. Tel: (01297) 20377. Est: 1982. Private premises. Internet and Postal. Appointment necessary. Small stock. Spec: Advertising; Art; Art History; Photography. PR: £1–500.

The End Bookshop, ■ 54 Queen Street, Seaton, EX12 2RB. Prop: Mark Elbro. Tel: 01297 20808. Est: 1993. Shop open: **M:** 09:30–16:00; **T:** 09:30–16:00; **W:** 09:30–16:00; **F:** 09:30–16:00; **S:** 09:30–13:00. Spec: Children's.

SOUTH BRENT

Patrick Pollak Rare Books, Moorview, Plymouth Road, South Brent, TQ10 9HT. Prop: Prop Patrick & Jeanne Pollak. Tel: (01364) 73457. Fax: (01364) 649126. Web: www.rarevols.co.uk. Est: 1973. Private premises. Internet and Postal. Telephone First. Small stock. Spec: Academic/Scholarly; Aeronautics; Alchemy; Anatomy; Anthropology; Author - Darwin, Charles; Biology - General; Earth Sciences. PR: £50–5,000. CC: AE; JCB; MC; V. Cata: History, Medicine & Science. Corresp: German, French. Mem: ABA; ILAB; Linnean Society. VAT No: GB 267 5364 31.

Rosemary Stansbury, 25 Church Street, South Brent, TQ10 9AB. Tel: (01364) 72465. Est: 1985. Private premises. Appointment necessary. Small stock. Spec: Children's. PR: £1–100. Notes: *Children's titles only.*

TAVISTOCK

Bookworm Alley, 36 Brook Street, Tavistock, PL19 0HE. Prop: Joan Williams. Tel: (01822) 617740. Web: www.bookwormalley.org.uk. Est: 2000. Private premises. Appointment necessary. Small stock. Spec: Religion - Christian; Religion - Salvation Army. PR: £1–50.

Lee Furneaux Books, 6 Lopes Road, Dousland, Yelverton, Tavistock, PL20 6NX. Prop: Lee Furneaux. Tel: (01822) 853243. Est: 1991. Market stand/stall; Internet and Postal. Telephone First. Shop at: Trade at Tavistock Market (Permanent shop within indoor market). Open: **T:** 08:30–16:00; **W:** 08:30–16:00; **Th:** 08:30–16:00; **F:** 08:30–16:00; **S:** 08:30–16:00. Small stock. Spec: Art; Children's; Crafts; Gardening - General; History - General; Literature; Local History; Maritime/Nautical. PR: £1–100. CC: PayPal. VAT No: GB 802 9873 14. Notes: *Open occasional Sundays - see local press.*

TEIGNMOUTH

IKON, Magnolia New Road, Teignmouth, TQ14 8UD. Prop: Dr. Nicholas & Clare Goodrick–Clarke. Tel: (01626) 776528. Fax: (01626) 776528. Est: 1982. Private premises. Postal only. Appointment necessary. Spec: Academic/Scholarly; Alchemy; Alternative Medicine; Esoteric; Gnostics / Gnosticism; Health; Herbalism; Hermeticism. PR: £10–75. Cata: History; Health; Esoteric;. Corresp: German.

Milestone Books, ■ 43 Northumberland Place, Teignmouth, TQ14 8DE. Prop: V. K. Marston. Tel: 01626 775436. Fax: 01626 777023. Web: www.milestonebooks.co.uk. Est: 1996. Internet and Postal. Telephone First. Open: **M:** 09:30–17:30; **T:** 09:30–17:30; **W:** 09:30–17:30; **Th:** 09:30–13:30; **F:** 09:30–13:30; **S:** 09:30–17:30; Closed for lunch: 13:30–14:00. Spec: Aeronautics; Aviation; Buses/Trams; Manuals - Seamanship (see also under Seamanship); Maritime/Nautical; Model Railways; Naval; Navigation. CC: AE; MC; V. VAT No: GB 585 7083 03. Notes: *We operate from within the Quayside Bookshop, which sells new books.*

TIVERTON

Heartland Old Books, ■ 12–14 Newport Street, Tiverton, EX16 6NL. Prop: Jeremy Whitehorn. Tel: (01884) 254488. Est: 2001. Shop open: **M:** 10:00–17:00; **T:** 10:00–17:00; **W:** 10:00–17:00; **Th:** 10:00–17:00; **F:** 10:00–17:00; **S:** 10:00–17:00. Medium stock. Spec: Military; Sport - Field Sports; Travel - General. PR: £1–500. Corresp: French. Notes: *Easy parking in Pannier Market opposite. Strong emphasis on uncommon military, field sports, local and railway titles. Good, broad coverage in most other subject areas.*

Kelly Books Limited, 6 Redlands, Tiverton, EX16 4DH. Prop: Props: Len & Lynda Kelly. Tel: (01884) 256170. Fax: (0871) 661 8229. Web: www.kellybooks.net. Est: 1972. Private premises. Internet and Postal. Appointment necessary. Open: **M:** 09:00–18:00; **T:** 09:00–18:00; **W:** 09:00–18:00; **Th:** 09:00–18:00; **F:** 09:00–18:00; **S:** 09:00–18:00. Medium stock. Spec: Advertising; Broadcasting; Cinema/Film; Journalism; Media; Radio/Wireless; Television; Ephemera. PR: £5–600. CC: AE; MC; V; PayPal. Cata: Broadcasting and Mass Communications. VAT No: GB 799 7192 48. Notes: *We stock thousands books and periodicals on broadcasting history, including back numbers of Radio Times, The Listener, TV Times, and many other radio and television magazines.*

Kelly Books Ltd, 6 Redlands, Tiverton, EX16 4DH. Prop: Len & Lynda Kelly. Tel: 01884 256170. Fax: 0871 661 8229. Web: www.kellybooks.net. Est: 1972. Private premises. Postal only. Appointment necessary. Open: **M:** 09:00–17:30; **T:** 09:00–17:30; **W:** 09:00–17:30; **Th:** 09:00–17:30; **F:** 09:00–17:30; **S:** 09:00–17:30; **Su:** 09:00–17:30; Closed for lunch: 13:00–14:00. Spec: Audio/Sound/Acoustics; Broadcasting; Journalism; Media; Newspapers; Radar; Radio/Wireless; Technical. CC: AE; MC; V; PayPal. Cata: Broadcasting and mass communications. VAT No: GB 799 7192 48. Notes: *Our specialist subjects include the history of radio and television, including early wireless telegraphy and telephony, audio & high-fi, journalism, and some cinema.*

TORQUAY

Colin Baker - Books for the Collector, 66 Marldon Road, Shiphay, Torquay, TQ2 7EH. Prop: Colin and Sally Baker. Tel: (01803) 613356. Est: 1994. Private premises. Internet and Postal. Appointment necessary. Open: **M:** 10:00–17:00. Small stock. Spec: Author - Betjeman, Sir John; Author - Buckeridge, A.; Author - Cook, Beryl; Author - du Maurier, Daphne; Author - Goudge, Elizabeth; Author - Heyer, Georgette; Author - Pargeter, Edith; Author - Peters, Ellis. PR: £5–500. Notes: *We organise Torquay & Sherborne Book Fairs (3rd Saturday of each Month) and are regular attendees at Wells Bristol Cardiff & all Cornish Fairs. Also Lit. Fests - Ways With Words, Dartington & Port Eliot St Germans each July & Appledore Sept.*

The Good Book Shop, ■ 176 Union Street, Torquay, TQ2 5NQ. Prop: Jim Goodchild. Tel: 01807 294081. Est: 2006. Shop open: **M:** 10:00–17:00; **T:** 10:00–17:00; **W:** 10:00–17:00; **Th:** 10:00–17:00; **F:** 10:00–17:00; **S:** 10:00–17:00; **Su:** 10:00–17:00. Spec: Music - Sheet Music; Ephemera. Notes: *Memorabilia, postcards, sheet music.*

Westcountry Oldbooks, Lilburn House, 215 Babbacombe Road, Torquay, TX1 3SX. Prop: David Neil. Tel: (01803) 322712. Web: www.davidneilrarebooks.co.uk. Est: 1988. Private premises. Appointment necessary. Open: **M:** 09:00–17:30; **T:** 09:00–17:30; **W:** 09:00–17:30; **Th:** 09:00–17:30; **F:** 09:00–17:30; **S:** 09:00–17:30. Small stock. Spec: Antiquarian; Literature; Topography - General. Mem: PBFA.

TORRINGTON

The Archivist, Priory Cottage, Frithelstock, Torrington, EX38 8JH. Tel: (01805) 625750. Fax: (01805) 625376. Web: www.thebookarchivist.co.uk. Est: 1990. Private premises. Internet and Postal. Appointment necessary. Small stock. Spec: Cats; Journalism; Literature; Publishers - Joseph Ltd., Michael; Reference. PR: £1–1,000. CC: PayPal.

Books Antiques & Collectables, ■ 3 Well Street, Torrington, EX38 8EP. Tel: (01805) 625624. Web: www.antiquesbooks.co.uk. Shop open: **T:** 10:30–16:00; **W:** 10:30–16:00; **Th:** 10:00–16:00; **F:** 10:00–16:00; Closed for lunch: 13:00–14:00. Small stock. Spec: Art; Biography; Children's; Fiction - General; History - General; Philosophy; Plays; Poetry. PR: £1–25.

Brown and Rivans Ltd, Heywood House, South Street, Torrington, EX38 8HE. Prop: David Brown. Steven Rivans. Tel: 01805 623771. Est: 2002. Office and/or bookroom; Internet and Postal. Appointment necessary. CC: PayPal.

Jack and Molly's Trading Company, ■ 4 Well Street, Torrington, Devon EX38 8EP. Prop: Adrian Shearing. Tel: (01805) 622259. Web: www.jackandmolly'stradingco.co.uk. Shop; open **M:** 09:00–17:00; **T:** 09:00–17:00; **W:** 09:00–17:00; **Th:** 09:00–17:00; **F:** 09:00–17:00; **S:** 09:00–17:00. Very small stock. Spec: Animals and birds; Annuals; Artists; Author - 19th Century; Author - 20th Century. Autobiography; Childrens; Countries - General. PR: £1–200. CC: MC; V. Notes: *Jack and Molly's Trading Company is a new and friendly bookshop in Torrington, having traded on the Interenet for 4 years. Happy to help, appy to booksearch. Offers a quick efficient service.*

River Reads Bookshop, ■ 21 South Street, Torrington, EX38 8AA. Prop: Sandy Armishaw. Tel: (01805) 625888. Fax: (01805) 625888. Web: www.riverreads.co.uk. Est: 2002. Shop open: **M:** 10:00–16:00; **T:** 10:00–16:00; **W:** 10:00–13:00; **Th:** 10:00–16:00; **F:** 10:00–16:00; **S:** 10:00–16:00. Large stock. Spec: Art; Author - Watkins-Pitchford, Denys ('B.B.'); Author - Williamson, Henry; Children's; Cookery/Gastronomy; Firearms/Guns; Fishes; Gardening - General. PR: £2–200. CC: MC; V. Notes: *Also, vintage fishing tackle, fishing prints and publishers of collector's limited editions of 'BB' titles.*

TOTNES

Collards Bookshop, ■ 4 Castle Street, Totnes, TQ9 5NU. Prop: Belle Collard. Tel: (01548) 550246. Est: 1970. Shop open: **M:** 10:30–17:00; **T:** 10:30–17:00; **W:** 10:30–17:00; **Th:** 10:30–17:00; **F:** 10:30–17:00; **S:** 10:30–17:00. Medium stock. PR: £1–300. Notes: *Opening varies according to season but open every weekday in summer. Closed Wednesdays in winter.*

Geoff Cox, Lower West Wing, Tristford House, Harberton, Totnes, TQ9 7RZ. Tel: (01803) 866181. Est: 1978. Private premises. Book fairs only. Appointment necessary. Open: **M:** 10:00–19:00; **T:** 10:00–19:00; **Th:** 10:00–19:00; **F:** 10:00–12:00; **S:** 10:00–12:00. Closed for lunch: 12:00–13.00. Medium stock. Spec: Adventure; Aeronautics; Aircraft; Archaeology - Industrial; Aviation; Buses/Trams; Canals/Inland Waterways; Civil Engineering. PR: £1–500. Cata: Transport & Indusrial Archaeology. Corresp: French, German, Dutch. Mem: PBFA. Notes: *Other interests - West Country topography, travel & exploration, history incl. military & maritime, ephemera, maps & postcards.*

Harlequin, ■ 41 High Street, Totnes, TQ9 5NP. Prop: Paul Wesley. Tel: (01803) 865794. Est: 1983. Shop open: **M:** 10:00–17:30; **T:** 09:00–17:30; **W:** 10:00–17:30; **Th:** 10:00–17:30; **F:** 10:00–17:30; **S:** 10:00–17:30. Medium stock. PR: £1–50.

WILLAND

ULoveBooks, 12 Celandine Lawns, Willand, Devon, EX15 2TN. Prop: Andreas Bush. Tel: 01884 820189. Web: wwwulovebooks.com. Est: 2003. Private Premises. Internet only. Very small stock. Spec: Antiquarian; History - General; Topography - General. PR: £2 – 500. Notes: *UloveBooks.com is a growing internet-based business offering a great range of books at very competirive prices. Fast international service from our own stock.*

DORSET

BEAMINSTER

John E. Spooner, 18 Glebe Court, Barnes Lane, Beaminster, DT8 3EZ. Tel: (01308) 862713. Est: 1975. Private premises. Postal only. Small stock. Spec: Aviation; Military; Naval. PR: £5–100.

BLANDFORD FORUM

The Dorset Bookshop, ■ 69 East Street, Blandford Forum, DT11 7DX. Prop: Kevin and Denny Cook. Tel: (01258) 452266. Est: 1950. Shop open: **M:** 10:00–17:00; **T:** 10:00–17:00; **W:** 10:00–17:00; **Th:** 10:00–17:00; **F:** 10:00–17:00; **S:** 10:00–17:00. Small stock. PR: £1–100. Notes: *Huge variety of new and secondhand books on three floors in interesting Georgian building.*

BOURNEMOUTH

African Studies, 67A Muscliffe Road, Winton, Bournemouth, BH9 1GA. Prop: Alan Painter. Tel: 01202 528678. Fax: 01202 528678. Est: 1998. Private premises. Appointment necessary. Open: **M:** 14:00–17:00; **T:** 08:00–17:00; **W:** 20:00–22:00; **Th:** 20:00–22:00; **F:** 20:00–22:00. Spec: Africana. Mem: Private Libraries Association. Notes: *Deals in Africana only, in indigenous peoples, anthropology, history, ethnology and ethnographic.*

Dunstan Books, 13 Lascelles Road, Bournemouth, BH7 6NF. Prop: Steven Powrie. Tel: (01202) 246160. Fax: (01202) 246160. Web: www.abebooks.com. Est: 1992. Private premises. Internet and Postal. Contactable. Open: **M:** 09:00–18:00; **T:** 09:00–18:00; **W:** 09:00–18:00; **Th:** 09:00–18:00; **F:** 09:00–18:00; **S:** 09:00–17:00. Small stock. Spec: Bridge; Crime (True); Fiction - Crime, Detective, Spy, Thrillers; Medicine; Politics; Psychotherapy; Sport - Golf. PR: £5–200. CC: via abebooks or cheques. VAT No: GB 797 8711 57.

Facet Books, 18 Dolphin Avenue, Bournemouth, BH10 6DU. Prop: Mr James Allinson and Mrs Margit Allinson. Tel: (01202) 269269. Web: www.jallinson.freeserve.co.uk. Est: 1982. Private premises. Internet and Postal. Telephone First. Large stock. Spec: Academic/Scholarly; Advertising; Aeronautics; Author - Blyton, Enid; Author - Cook, Beryl; Author - Crompton, Richmal; Author - Henty, G.A.; Author - Johns, W.E. PR: £1–2,500. Corresp: German. Notes: *Specialist in Giles Cartoon Annuals/Other Items, Plus other Cartoon Books, Childrens Annuals (Beano, Dandy, Rupert etc) and British Comics (Beano, Dandy, Cowboy Picture Library, Super Detective Library etc).*

Holdenhurst Books, ■ 275 Holdenhurst Road, Bournemouth, BH8 8BZ. Prop: R.W. Reese. Tel: (01202) 397718. Est: 1985. Shop open: **M:** 10:00–17:00; **T:** 09:00–17:00; **Th:** 10:00–17:00; **F:** 10:00–17:00; **S:** 10:00–17:00. Medium stock. Spec: Aeronautics; Maritime/Nautical; Military; Motorbikes / motorcycles; Motoring. PR: £5–150.

P.F. & J.R. McInnes, 59 Richmond Park Road, Bournemouth, BH8 8TU. Prop: Mrs Jane McInnes. Tel: (01202) 394609. Est: 1981. Private premises. Postal only. Telephone First. Small stock. Spec: Dogs; Sport - Boxing; Sport - Prizefighting. PR: £1–3,000. Cata: boxing and prizefighting. Notes: *Due to death of P F. JR has sold most of the books but still has record books for sale many rare early ones. Also memorabilia photos magazines bound vol. catalogue will be ready shortly or send wants list or phone for appointment to view.*

H. & S.J. Rowan, ■ 459 Christchurch Road, Boscombe, Bournemouth, BH1 4AD. Prop: H. Rowan. Tel: (01202) 398820. Est: 1969. Shop open: **M:** 09:00–17:30; **T:** 09:00–17:30; **W:** 09:00–17:30; **Th:** 09:00–17:30; **F:** 09:00–17:30; **S:** 09:00–18:00. Large stock. Spec: Antiquarian; Antiques; Art; Aviation; Topography - Local; Collectables; Prints and Maps. PR: £1–1,000. VAT No: GB 185 3287 39. Notes: *Also, booksearch*

Sue Sims, 21 Warwick Road, Pokesdown, Bournemouth, BH7 6JW. Tel: (01202) 432562. Est: 1978. Private premises. Postal only. Contactable. Small stock. Spec: Author - Brent-Dyer, Elinor M.; Author - Fairlie–Bruce, D.; Author - Forest, A.; Author - Oxenham, Elsie; Children's; Religion - Catholic; Booksearch. PR: £1–500. Corresp: French, German. Notes: *Major stock of girl's books and school stories.*

Yesterday Tackle & Books, 59a Southbourne Grove, Southbourne, Bournemouth, BH6 3QU. Prop: David Dobbyn. Tel: (01202) 476586. Est: 1983. Private premises. Appointment necessary. Small stock. Spec: Author - Watkins-Pitchford, Denys ('B.B.'); Sport - Angling/Fishing; Ephemera. PR: £1–100. CC: AE; PayPal. Notes: *Also, fishing tackle and related items.*

Yesterday's Books, 6 Cecil Avenue, Bournemouth, BH8 9EH. Prop: David & Jessica L. Weir. Tel: (01202) 522442. Est: 1974. Office and/or bookroom; Internet and Postal. Telephone First. Open: **M:** 09:00–17:00; **T:** 09:00–17:00; **W:** 09:00–17:00; **Th:** 09:00–17:00; **F:** 09:00–17:00; **S:** 09:00–13:00. Medium stock. Spec: African-American Studies; Africana; Anthropology; Antiquarian; Black Studies; Countries - Africa; Countries - East Africa; Countries - Egypt. PR: £5–500. CC: JCB; MC; V. Cata: Africa. Corresp: French, German. Mem: PBFA. Notes: *Dealers & collectors most welcome. Please telephone first. Large general stock as well as our AFRICA books.*

ECR Books, 58 Strouden Avenue, Bournemouth, BH8 9HX. Prop: John Aris. Tel: (01202) 537365. Fax: 01202 523399. Est: 1987. Private premises. Appointment necessary. Medium stock. Spec: Bibles; Children's; Hymnology; Natural History; Printing. PR: £10–100. Notes: *Have been inactive for last 10 years.*

BRIDPORT

Bridport Old Bookshop, ■ 11 South Street, Bridport, DT6 3NR. Prop: Caroline Mactaggart & Rosie Young. Tel: (01308) 425689. Est: 1981. Shop open: **M:** 10:00–17:00; **T:** 10:00–17:00; **W:** 10:00–17:00; **Th:** 10:00–17:00; **F:** 10:00–17:00; **S:** 10:00–17:00. Small stock. Spec: Children's; Children's - Illustrated. PR: £2–500. CC: MC; V. Mem: PBFA.

Caroline Mactaggart, Manor Farmhouse Swyre, Bridport, Dorchester, DT2 9DN. Tel: (01308) 898174. Est: 1984. Private premises. Shop at: Bridport Old Bookshop, 11 South Street, Bridport. Open: **M:** 10:00–17:00; **T:** 10:00–17:00; **W:** 10:00–17:00; **Th:** 10:00–17:00; **F:** 10:00–17:00; **S:** 10:00–17:00. Medium stock. Spec: Scottish Interest. PR: £5–500. CC: MC; V. Mem: PBFA.

CHARMOUTH

The Lighthouse Books, ■ Langley House, The Street, Charmouth, DT6 6PE. Prop: Mr Jean Vaupres. Tel: (01297) 560634. Est: 2004. Shop open: **M:** 10:00–17:00; **T:** 10:00–17:00; **Th:** 10:00–17:00; **F:** 10:00–17:00; **S:** 10:00–17:00; **Su:** 10:00–17:00. Medium stock. Spec: Architecture; Country Houses; Fashion & Costume; Folio Society, The; Irish Interest; Odd & Unusual; Sculpture; Travel - General. PR: £1–300. Corresp: French, Italian. Notes: *From May to October Mon to Sat 10:00 to 17:00 and other times telephone before calling.*

DORCHESTER

John Clifford, Lilliput House, 35 Glyde Path Road, Dorchester DT1 1XE. Prop: John Clifford. Tel: 01305 263151. Est: 1978. Private premises. Internet and postal. Small stock. Spec: Author: Hardy, Thomas; County - Local; Gneral stock; History - General. PR: £10-2,000. CC: MC; V. Mem: PBFA.

The Dorchester Bookshop, ■ 3 Nappers Court, Charles Street, Dorchester, DT1 1EE. Prop: Michael J. Edmonds. Tel: (01305) 269919. Est: 1993. Shop open: **T:** 10:00–17:00; **W:** 10:00–17:00; **Th:** 10:00–17:00; **F:** 10:00–17:00; **S:** 10:00–17:00. Medium stock. PR: £1–500.

Marco Polo Travel & Adventure, Marco Polo House, West Bexington, Dorchester, DT2 9DE. Prop: Mark A. Culme-Seymour. Tel: (01308) 898420. Fax: (01308) 898416. Web: www.marcopolobooks.co.uk. Est: 1977. Private premises. Internet and Postal. Appointment necessary. Small stock. Spec: Travel - General. PR: £15–300. CC: MC; V. VAT No: GB 717 8378 00. Notes: *Booksearches.*

Judith Stinton, 21 Cattistock Road, Maiden Newton, Dorchester, DT2 OAG. Tel: (01300) 320778. Web: www.abebooks.com. Est: 1989. Private premises. Internet and Postal. Appointment necessary. Small stock. Spec: Author - Hardy, Thomas; Author - Townsend Warner, Sylvia; Authors - British; Authors - Local; Children's; History - Local; Literature; Topography - Local. PR: £1–100.

Steve Walker Fine Books, Willow Tree House, 1 Sydenham Way, Dorchester, DT1 1DN. Tel: 01350 260690. Est: 1985. Private premises. Postal only. Appointment necessary. Small stock. Spec: Author - Hardy, Thomas; Author - Johnson, Samuel; Bibles; Biblical Studies; Bookbinding; Books about Books; Dictionaries; Folklore. PR: £5–500. Mem: Society of Bookbinders. Notes: *Bookbinding and Restoration.*

Woolcott Books, Kingston House, Higher Kingston, Dorchester, DT2 8QE. Prop: H.M. & J.R. St. Aubyn. Tel: (01305) 267773. Fax: (01305) 751899. Est: 1978. Private premises. Appointment necessary. Small stock. Spec: Colonial; Countries - Africa; Countries - India; History - National; Military; Travel - Africa; Travel - Asia; Travel - Middle East. PR: £5–500. Notes: *Also, booksearch.*

Words Etcetera Bookshop, ■ 2 Cornhill, Dorchester, DT1 1BA. Prop: Simon Rushbrook. Tel: 01305 251919. Fax: 01305 251919. Web: www.wordsetcetera.co.uk. Est: 1974. Shop open: **M:** 10:00–17:00; **T:** 10:00–17:00; **W:** 10:00–17:00; **Th:** 10:00–17:00; **F:** 10:00–17:00; **S:** 9:30–17:00. Spec: Antiquarian; Art; Art History; Author - Hardy, Thomas; Author - Heaney, Seamus; Author - Lawrence, T.E.; Author - Powys Family, The; Author - Woolf, Virginia. CC: MC; V. Cata: Illustrated, Poetry, Mod 1sts, T. Hardy. Corresp: French. Mem: BA. Notes: *We have a few shelves rented out to other booksellers, specialising in antiquarian maps, collectible childrens, military history and Dorset topography.*

GILLINGHAM

DaSilva Puppet Books, 58 Shreen Way, Gillingham, SP8 4HT. Prop: Ray DaSilva. Tel: (01747) 835558. Web: www.puppetbooks.co.uk. Est: 1986. Private premises. Internet and Postal. Appointment necessary. Open: **M:** 09:00–17:30; **T:** 09:00–17:30; **W:** 09:00–17:30; **Th:** 09:00–17:30; **F:** 09:00–17:30; Closed for lunch: 12:30–02:00. Small stock. Spec: Entertainment - General; Performing Arts; Puppets & Marionettes; Theatre; Ventriloquism; Ephemera. PR: £1–200. CC: MC; V; SW. Cata: Puppets, Toy Theatre. Corresp: French.

Lilian Modlock, Southcote Langham Lane, Wyke, Gillingham, SP8 5NT. Tel: (01747) 821875. Fax: (01747) 821875. Est: 1995. Private premises. Internet and Postal. Appointment necessary. Medium stock. Spec: Biography; Children's; Cinema/Film; Cookery/Gastronomy; Illustrated - General; Landscape; Poetry; Topography - General. PR: £3–600. Notes: *Also, a booksearch service. PayPal payments accepted.*

LONG BURTON

Grahame Thornton, Bookseller, Monghyr House, Spring Lane, Long Burton, Sherborne, DT9 5NZ. Prop: Grahame Thornton. Tel: 01963 210443. Fax: 01963 210443. Web: www.grahamethornton.f9.co.uk. Est: 1995. Private premises. Internet and Postal. Contactable. Open: **M:** 09:00–17:30; **T:** 09:00–17:30; **W:** 09:00–17:30; **Th:** 09:00–17:30; **F:** 09:00–17:30; **S:** 09:00–17:30; **Su:** 09:00–17:30; Closed for lunch: 13:00–14:00. Spec: Animals and Birds; Antiquarian; Author - Williamson, Henry; Autobiography; Belle-Lettres; Biography; Children's; Churchilliana. CC: E; MC; V; Maestro. Cata: Early Penguin, Antiquarian, Non Fiction, Medical. Corresp: French. VAT No: GB 608 6389 14. Notes: *Catalogues are not routinely issued, but lists can be produced on demand. Visit my website to see the subjects covered. Regular stall at the monthly Sherborne Book Market (every third Saturday).*

LYME REGIS

Lymelight Books & Prints, 15 Haye Close, Lyme Regis, DT7 3NJ. Prop: Nigel Cozens. Tel: (01297) 443464. Fax: (01297) 443464. Web: www.lymelight-books.demon.co.uk. Est: 1994. Private premises. Appointment necessary. Medium stock. Spec: Antiquarian; Arachnology; Architecture; Art; Art Deco; Art Nouveau; Atlases; Author - Darwin, Charles. PR: £5–10,000. CC: AE; E; MC; V; Cirrus. Cata: Natural History / Science, Art & Illustrated. Corresp: French. Mem: PBFA. VAT No: GB 684 4800 14. Notes: *Bookbinding and Booksearch. Print & Map Search and Restoration.*

The Bookshop, ■ The Old Bonded Store Marine Parade, The Cobb, Lyme Regis, DT7 3JF. Tel: (01297) 444820. Est: 2003. Shop open: **M:** 11:00–16:30; **T:** 11:00–16:30; **W:** 11:00–16:30; **Th:** 11:00–16:30; **F:** 11:00–16:30; **S:** 11:00–16:30. Medium stock. Spec: Fiction - General; Maritime/Nautical; Poetry; Psychology/Psychiatry. PR: £1–100. Notes: *Open 7 days per week in school holidays, less in term time.*

The Sanctuary Bookshop, ■ 65 Broad Street, Lyme Regis, DT7 3QF. Prop: Bob & Mariko Speer. Tel: 01297-445815. Web: www.lyme-regis.com. Est: 1982. Shop and/or showroom; Shop open: **M:** 10:30–17:30; **T:** 10:30–17:30; **W:** 10:30–17:30; **Th:** 10:30–17:30; **F:** 10:30–17:30; **S:** 10:30–17:30; **Su:** 11:00–17:30. Spec: Academic/Scholarly; Art History; Art Reference; Author - Fowles, John; Author - Shute, Neville; Authors - Local; Bibliography; Biography. CC: AE; E; JCB; MC; V. Corresp: Japanese, French. Notes: *General Bookshop, 2 floors + 2 floors above, each with B & B book stocked accommodation. Two doubles, with private bath. Antiques and curiosa. John Fowles, Beryl Cook, Hundertwasser & Ollie Lett stockists. Free booksearch. Japanese spoken.*

MILBORNE PORT

Kingswood Books, 17 Wick Road, Milborne Port, Sherborne, DT9 5BT. Prop: Anne Rockall & Allan Dollery. Tel: (01963) 250280. Fax: (01963) 250280. Web: www.kingswoodbooks.btinternet.co.uk. Est: 1985. Private premises. Internet and Postal. Appointment necessary. Medium stock. Spec: Academic/Scholarly; Anthropology; Antiquarian; Archaeology; Archaeology - Industrial; Architecture; Art History; Countries - Far East, The. PR: £1–2,000. CC: PayPal. Mem: PBFA. Notes: *We also trade at various book fairs in the South West. These are listed on our web site. Contact us should you wish to have an invitation giving free admission to any of these fairs. Also Bookbinders & restorers. See our website.*

POOLE

Bookstand, 53 Kings Ave., Poole, BH14 9QQ. Prop: Eleanor Smith & Wendy Marten. Tel: (01202) 716229. Fax: (01202) 734663. Web: www.abebooks.com/home/bookstand. Est: 1997. Private premises. Internet only. Appointment necessary. Small stock. Spec: Antiquarian; Author - Milne, A.A.; Author - Potter, Beatrix; Author - Thelwell, N; Author - Wheatley, Dennis; Autographs; Children's - Illustrated; Fine Printing. PR: £15–5,000. CC: MC; V.

R.H. & P. Haskell, 64 Winston Avenue, Branksome, Poole, BH12 1PG. Prop: Reg Haskell. Tel: (01202) 243608. Est: 1973. Private premises. Postal only. Appointment necessary. Small stock. Spec: Architecture; Ecclesiastical History & Architecture; Gothic Revival; Interior Design; Landscape; Planning - City; Town Planning. PR: £5–1,000. CC: Paypal.

PUDDLETOWN

The Antique Map and Bookshop, ■ 32 High Street, Puddletown, DT2 8RU. Prop: C.D. & T.A. Proctor. Tel: (01305) 848633. Fax: (01305) 848992. Web: www.puddletownbookshop.co.uk. Est: 1976. Internet and Postal. Shop open: **M:** 09:00–17:00; **T:** 09:00–17:00; **W:** 09:00–17:00; **Th:** 09:00–17:00; **F:** 09:00–17:00; **S:** 09:00–17:00. Medium stock. Spec: Antiquarian; Arachnology; Architecture; Arctic - Antarctica; Author - Barnes, William; Author - Conan Doyle, Sir Arthur; Author - Hardy, Thomas; Author - Henty, G.A. PR: £5–3,000. CC: AE; JCB; MC; V; SW. Corresp: German. Mem: ABA; PBFA; ILAB. VAT No: GB 291 7495 21.

SHAFTESBURY

Dorset Rare Books, Ethelgiva, St John's Hill, Shaftesbury, SP7 8LA. Prop: Peter Shouler. Tel: 01747 852532. Web: www.dorsetrarebooks.co.uk. Private premises. Internet and Postal. Contactable. Mem: PBFA. VAT No: GB 723 3951 38.

Paul Goldman, Meadow View, East Orchard, Shaftesbury, SP7 0LG. Tel: (01747) 811380. Fax: (01747) 811380. Web: www.abebooks.com. Est: 1997. Private premises. Postal only. Appointment necessary. Small stock. Spec: Academic/Scholarly; Art; Art History; Art Reference; Cartoons; Comedy; Humour; Illustrated - General. PR: £10–500. Cata: Illustrated books. Corresp: French, Italian, Greek. Mem: ABA; PBFA; ILAB. Notes: *Contactable at any reasonable time.*

Not Just Books, ■ 7a, High Street, Shaftesbury, SP7 8QZ. Prop: F. W. Barrett-Selbie. Tel: 01747 850003. Est: 1996. Shop open: **W:** 10:00–16:00; **Th:** 10:00–16:00; **F:** 10:00–16:00; **S:** 10:00–16:00; Closed for lunch: 12:00–14:00. Spec: Aircraft; Archaeology; Architecture - Theatre; Army, The; Artists; Auction Catalogues; Author - Wodehouse, P.G.; Military History. Notes: *Also militaria, china, silver and coins, including hammered.*

SHERBORNE

Chapter House Books, ■ Trendle Street, Sherborne, DT9 3NT. Prop: Claire Porter, Tudor Books Ltd. Tel: (01935) 816262. Web: www.chapterhouse-books.co.uk. Est: 1988. Shop open: **M:** 10:00–17:00; **T:** 10:00–17:00; **W:** 10:00–17:00; **Th:** 10:00–17:00; **F:** 10:00–17:00; **S:** 10:00–17:00. Large stock. Spec: Booksearch. PR: £1–500. CC: AE; MC; V. Mem: PBFA. VAT No: GB 799 9885 07. Notes: *Also, booksearch, 2nd hand CDs, videos, DVDs and sheet music.*

Verandah Books, Stonegarth, The Avenue, Sherborne, DT9 3AH. Prop: Michael Hougham. Tel: (01935) 815900. Fax: (01935) 815900. Web: www.verandahbooks.co.uk. Est: 1992. Private premises. Postal only. Appointment necessary. Medium stock. Spec: Author - Kipling, Rudyard; Countries - Afghanistan; Countries - Burma; Countries - Himalayas, The; Countries - India; Countries - Nepal; Countries - North West Frontier Province; Countries - Pakistan. PR: £10–500. CC: Paypal. Cata: India and South Asia, Pakistan, Burma, Himalayas. Notes: *All our stock can be searched online by author, title, place or topic.*

STURMINSTER NEWTON

Stour Bookshop, ■ Bridge Street, Sturminster Newton, DT10 1AP. Prop: Tony Butler. Tel: (01258) 473561. Est: 1982. Shop open: **M:** 10:00–18:00; **T:** 10:00–18:00; **W:** 10:00–13:00; **Th:** 10:00–18:00; **F:** 10:00–18:00; **S:** 10:00–13:00. Small stock. Spec: Aviation; Illustrated - General; Juvenile; Motoring. PR: £5–200. CC: MC; V. Notes: *Also bookbinding and restoration.*

SWANAGE

Reference Works Ltd., 9 Commercial Road, Swanage, BH19 1DF. Prop: Barry Lamb. Tel: (01929) 424423. Fax: (01929) 422597. Web: www.referenceworks.co.uk. Est: 1984. Office and/or bookroom; Telephone First. Open: **M:** 10:00–4:00; **T:** 10:00–4:00; **W:** 10:00–4:00; **Th:** 10:00–4:00; **F:** 10:00–4:00; **S:** 10:30–1:00. Small stock. Spec: Antiques; Ceramics; Decorative Art. PR: £5–800. CC: MC; V. Cata: Ceramics, Pottery & Porcelain. Notes: *Specialists in all areas of collecting and researching British, European and Oriental ceramics.*

Trigon Books, Treetops Durnford Drove, Langton Matravers, Swanage, BH19 3HG. Prop: Roger Sheppard. Tel: 01929 425135. Storeroom. Shop open: **M:** 09:00–17:30; **T:** 09:00–17:30; **W:** 09:00–17:30; **Th:** 09:00–17:30; **F:** 09:00–17:30; **S:** 09:00–17:30; **Su:** 09:00–17:30; Closed for lunch: 13:00–14:00. Spec: Art Reference; Author - Powys Family, The; Crafts; Horticulture; Modern First Editions; Signed Editions.

Norman Wright, 18 Lighthouse Road, Swanage, BH19 2JJ. Tel: (01929) 426241. Est: 1989. Private premises. Postal only. Small stock. Spec: Author - Blake, Sexton; Author - Blyton, Enid; Author - Johns, W.E.; Author - Richards, Frank; Cartoons; Children's; Cinema/Film; Comic Books & Annuals. PR: £5–500. Cata: Children's books, British comics.

WAREHAM

Calluna Books, Moor Edge, 2 Bere Road, Wareham, BH20 4DD. Prop: Neil Gartshore. Tel: 01929 552560. Web: www.callunabooks.co.uk. Est: 1997. Private premises. Internet and Postal. Appointment necessary. Spec: Animals and Birds; Botany; Conservation; Ecology; Entomology; Flora & Fauna; Fungi; Herpetology. Cata: Natural History, Birds, Flora, New Naturalists. PR: £1–1,000. Cata: occasionally, Natural History, Birds, Flora, New Naturalists. Notes: *We specialise in buying/selling out of print natural history titles. Birds, mammals, flora, invertebrates in the UK and worldwide, inc the Poyser and New Naturalist series, and general natural history, conservation and countryside titles.*

Reads, Beehive Cottage, East Stoke, Wareham, BH20 4JW. Prop: Reg Read & Anthony Hessey. Tel: (01929) 554971, or 5. Est: 1998. Private premises. Postal only. Small stock. Spec: Anthroposophy; Applied Art; Archaeology; Architecture; Art; Autobiography; Biography; Cinema/Film. PR: £5–3,000. CC: JCB; MC; V. Cata: on specialities. Corresp: French. Mem: PBFA. Notes: *Exhibits at major PBFA fairs. Stock listed on abe.com.*

WEYMOUTH

Books Afloat, ■ 66 Park Street, Weymouth, DT4 7DE. Prop: John Ritchie. Tel: (01305) 779774. Est: 1983. Shop open: **M:** 09:30–17:30; **T:** 09:30–17:30; **W:** 09:30–17:30; **Th:** 09:30–17:30; **F:** 09:30–17:30; **S:** 09:30–17:30. Large stock. Spec: Author - Hardy, Thomas; Author - Powys Family, The; Aviation; Canals/Inland Waterways; Fiction - General; Maritime/Nautical; Military History; Navigation. PR: £1–140. Notes: *Also, maritime collectables (ship models), marine paintings, ephemera and postcards. Open 10:00 – 17:00 in winter (November - March). Shop near railway station.*

The Nautical Antique Centre, ■ 3 Cove Passage, Hope Square, opposite Brewers Quay, Weymouth, DT4 8TR. Prop: Mr D.C. Warwick. Tel: (01305) 777838. Web: www.nauticalantiques.org. Est: 1989. Internet and Postal. Telephone First. Open: **T:** 14:00–17:00; **W:** 10:00–17:00; **Th:** 10:00–17:00; **F:** 10:00–17:00; Closed for lunch: 13:00–14:00. Small stock. Spec: Judaica; Manuals - Seamanship (see also under Seamanship); Maritime/Nautical; Maritime/Nautical - Log Books; Naval; Navigation; Shipbuilding and Shipping; Steam Engines. PR: £5–300. Notes: *Ships Registers, Directories, and Manuals of Seamanship plus other shipping books in stock to compliment exclusively genuine Nautical items. Please see website: www.nauticalantiques.org.*

WIMBORNE

John Graham, 52 Blandford Road Corfe Mullen, Wimborne, BH21 3HQ. Prop: John Graham. Tel: (01202) 692397. Fax: (01202) 692397. Est: 1987. Private premises. Postal only. Small stock. Spec: Biography; History - General; History - Industrial; History - Local; History - National; Social History; Booksearch; Ephemera. PR: £1–100.

DURHAM

BARNARD CASTLE

ALLTHINGSBOOKS, ■ 3 The Bank, Barnard Castle, DL12 8PH. Prop: Janet Rogers and Phil Webb. Tel: 01833 695123. Web: www.allthingsbooks.co.uk. Est: 2005. Shop open: **M:** 09:00–17:00; **W:** 09:00–17:00; **Th:** 09:00–17:00; **F:** 09:00–17:00; **S:** 09:00–17:00; **Su:** 12:00–17:00. CC: AE; MC; V.

Book Aid, ■ 5 Galgate, Barnard Castle, DL12 8EQ. Prop: M J Abrahams. Tel: 01833 630209. Est: 1990. Shop open: **M:** 10:00–16:00; **T:** 10:00–16:00; **W:** 10:00–16:00; **Th:** 10:00–16:00; **F:** 10:00–16:00; **S:** 10:00–17:00. Spec: Theology.

Curlews, ■ 11 Market Place, Barnard Castle, DL12 8NF. Prop: M. J. Abrahams. Tel: 01833 630455. Est: 1984. Shop open: **M:** 09:00–17:00; **T:** 09:00–17:00; **W:** 09:00–17:00; **Th:** 09:00–17:00; **F:** 09:00–17:00; **S:** 09:00–17:00; **Su:** 12:00–16:00. Notes: *Books on theology are at Book Aid, 5 Galgate, Barnard Castle.*

Greta Books, Lodge Farm, Scargill, Barnard Castle, DL12 9SY. Prop: Gordon Thomson. Tel: (01833) 621000. Fax: (01833) 621000. Private premises. Postal only. Spec: Agriculture; Animals and Birds; Antiquarian; Architecture; Author - Baden-Powell, Lord Robert; Author - Barrie, J.M.; Author - Buchan, John; Author - Chesterton, G.K. PR: £5–50. VAT No: GB 502 3822 85.

The Village Bookshop, ■ 36 Market Place, Middleton-in-Teesdale, Barnard Castle, DL12 0RJ. Prop: Susan and David Fielden. Tel: 01833 640373. Fax: 01833 640373. Web: www.villagebookshop.co.uk. Est: 2000. Shop open: **T:** 10:00–17:00; **Th:** 10:00–17:00; **F:** 10:00–17:00; **S:** 10:00–17:00; **Su:** 14:00–16:00. Small general stock. PR: £1 – 50. CC: AE; DC; EC: JCB; MC; V. VAT No: GB 604 5606 61. Notes: *We are now pleased to be able to offer a selction of books for sale online with UKBookworld. Please note that our online stock only represents a small proportion of the booksthat we have in our shop.*

BISHOP AUCKLAND

Vinovium Books, PO Box 236, Bishop Auckland, DL14 6AL. Prop: Paul Hughes. Tel: 07806 572838. Web: www.vinoviumbooks.co.uk. Est: 1996. Private premises. Internet and Postal. Appointment necessary. Spec: Academic/Scholarly; Antiquarian; Firearms/Guns; Mining; Natural History; Sport - Angling/Fishing; Sport - Field Sports; Sport - Hunting. CC: JCB; MC; V; Debit. Mem: PBFA. VAT No: GB 746 9734 81.

DARLINGTON

Combat Arts Archive, 12 Berkeley Road, Darlington, DL1 5ED. Prop: Mr. J. Sparkes. Tel: (01325) 465286. Web: www.combatbooks.co.uk. Est: 1995. Private premises. Postal only. Appointment necessary. Small stock. Spec: Physical Culture; Sport - Boxing; Sport - Duelling; Sport - Fencing; Sport - Martial Arts; Sport - Sumo; Sport - Weightlifting/Bodybuilding; Sport - Wrestling. PR: £1–150. CC: MC; V; Maestro Delta. Cata: Martial Arts, Boxing, Wrestling, Fencing. Notes: *Books and magazines for sale on Eastern and Western Martial Arts. Also Physical Culture.*

Tony and Gill Tiffin, 144 Coniscliffe Road, Darlington, DL3 7RW. Prop: G.A. & M.G. Tiffin. Tel: (01325) 487274. Est: 1990. Private premises. Book fairs only. Appointment necessary. Very large stock. Spec: Academic/Scholarly; Autobiography; Biography; Children's; Children's - Early Titles; Children's - Illustrated; Education & School; First Editions. PR: £1–1,000. Corresp: French. Mem: PBFA. Notes: *PBFA and local book fairs.*

Jeremiah Vokes, ■ 61 Coniscliffe Road, Darlington, DL3 7EH. Prop: Jeremiah Vokes. Tel: (01325) 469449. Est: 1979. Shop open: **M:** 09:30–17:00; **T:** 09:30–17:00; **W:** 09:30–17:00; **Th:** 09:30–17:00; **F:** 09:30–17:00; **S:** 09:30–17:00; Closed for lunch: 12:00–13:00. Medium stock. Spec: Fiction - Crime, Detective, Spy, Thrillers; Sherlockiana; Booksearch. PR: £1–1,000. Mem: PBFA. Notes: *Stocks mainly fiction (crime and detective) and Sherlockiana.*

REDCAR

Xanadu Books, 16 Kirkleatham Lane., Redcar, TS10 5BZ. Prop: Sylvia Wallace and John Wallace. Tel: 01642 485516. Web: www.xanadubooks.co.uk. Est: 1987. Private premises. Internet only. Appointment necessary. Spec: Annuals; Art; Children's; Children's - Illustrated; Illustrated - General; Military. CC: PayPal.

STOCKTON-ON-TEES

P.R. Brown (Books), 39 Sussex Walk Norton–on–Tees, Stockton-on-Tees, Cleveland, TS20 2RG. Prop: (*) P. Robinson–Brown. Tel: (01642) 871704. Est: 1975. Private premises. Appointment necessary. Small stock. Spec: Botany; History - Local; Ornithology; Prints and Maps. PR: £5–500.

WILLINGTON

John Turton, ■ 83 High Street, Willington. Prop: John Turton. Tel: (01388) 747600. Fax: (01388) 746741. Est: 1978. Shop at: 1/2 Cochrane Terrace, Willington, Crook, DL15 0HN. Shop open: **F:** 12:00–17:00; **S:** 10:00–17:00. Large stock. Spec: Antiquarian; Bindings; Ecclesiastical History & Architecture; Free Thought; Genealogy; Heraldry; Journals; Military History. PR: £5–500. CC: JCB; MC; V. Cata: Topography. Mem: PBFA. Also at: 1/2 Cochrane Terrace, Willington, Crook, DL15 0HN. Notes: *1-2 Cochrane Terrace, Willington (q.v.)*

John Turton, ■ 1–2 Cochrane Terrace, Willington, Crook, DL15 0HN. Prop: John Turton. Tel: (01388) 745770. Fax: (01388) 746741. Est: 1978. Shop open: **F:** 12:00–17:00; **S:** 10:00–17:00. Large stock. Spec: Antiquarian; Bindings; Ecclesiastical History & Architecture; Free Thought; Genealogy; Heraldry; History - Family; History - Local. PR: £50–2,000. CC: JCB; MC; V. Mem: PBFA. Notes: *83 High Street, Willington (q.v.) credit payments only by postal sales.*

EAST SUSSEX

ALFRISTON

David Summerfield Books, 4 Wingrove, The Tye, Alfriston, BN26 5TL. Tel: (01323) 870003. Est: 1987. Private premises. Appointment necessary. Small stock. Spec: Sport - Cricket. PR: £5–500.

Much Ado Books, ■ 1 Steamer Cottage, High Street, Alfriston, BN26 5TY. Prop: Nash Robbins and Cate Olson. Tel: 01323 871222. Fax: 01323 871333. Web: www.muchadobooks.com. Est: 2003. Shop open: **M:** 10:00–17:00; **T:** 10:00–17:00; **W:** 10:00–17:00; **Th:** 10:00–17:00; **F:** 10:00–17:00; **S:** 10:00–17:00; **Su:** 11:00–17:00. Spec: Author - Bloomsbury Group, The; Children's; Cookery/Gastronomy; Fiction - General; Food & Drink. CC: MC; V. Mem: PBFA; BA. Notes: *British Book Industry Awards Independent Bookshop of the Year 2007. Literary lunches and events run throughout the year. Stock also includes extensive collection of specially selected new books and some fine press books.*

BATTLE

R.A. Whistler, The Dodo House, Caldbec Hill, Battle, TN33 0JR. Prop: Mr Ralfe Whistler. Tel: (01424) 774152. Fax: (01424) 774152. Est: 1992. Private premises. Internet and Postal. Spec: Canadiana; Natural History. PR: £1–100. Notes: *Accepts US and Canadian dollars.*

BEXHILL

Raymond Elgar, 6 Blackfields Avenue, Bexhill, TN39 4JL. Prop: Raymond Elgar. Tel: (01424) 843539. Private premises. Postal only. Small stock. Spec: Bindings; Bookbinding; Magic & Conjuring; Music - General; Musical Instruments.

BRIGHTON

Arslan Books Etc., Flat 1, Surrenden Lodge, Brighton, BN1 6QB. Prop: Mustafa Mersinoglu. Tel: 01273559702. Est: 2005. Private premises. Internet and Postal. Telephone First. Open: **M:** 09:00–17:30; **T:** 09:00–17:30; **W:** 09:00–17:30; **Th:** 09:00–17:30; **F:** 09:00–17:30; **S:** 09:00–17:30; **Su:** 09:00–17:30; Closed for lunch: 13:00–14:00. Spec: Countries - Turkey; Ottoman Empire; Travel - General; Travel - Islamic World; Travel - Middle East. CC: Cheques, Postal Orders, Paypal. Cata: Ottoman, Turkey, Travel, Mediterrenean, Black Sea. Corresp: Turkish. Notes: *We have an extensive database on books, journals and rare reports on Turkey and will provide searches and copies of articles etc that is not copyrighted. We also deal with maps and ephemera.*

Brighton Books, ■ 18 Kensington Gardens, Brighton, BN1 4AL. Prop: Paul Carmody & Catherine Clement. Tel: (01273) 693845. Fax: (01273) 693845. Est: 1996. Shop open: **M:** 10:00–18:00; **T:** 10:00–18:00; **W:** 10:00–18:00; **Th:** 10:00–18:00; **F:** 10:00–18:00; **S:** 10:00–18:00. Large stock. Spec: Academic/Scholarly; Architecture; Art; Biography; Children's; Cinema/Film; Drama; Fiction - General. PR: £1–500. CC: AE; JCB; MC; V; SW.

Colin Page Books, ■ 36 Duke Street, Brighton. Prop: John Loska. Tel: 01273 325954. Est: 1969. Shop open: **M:** 09:30–17:30; **T:** 09:30–17:30; **W:** 09:30–17:30; **Th:** 09:30–17:30; **F:** 09:30–17:30; **S:** 09:30–17:30. CC: AE; D; MC; V. Mem: ABA; BA. VAT No: GB 550 5008 78. Notes: *Attends ABA Olympia and Chelsea Fairs.*

Cooks Books, 34 Marine Drive, Rottingdean, Brighton, BN2 7HQ. Prop: Tessa McKirdy. Tel: (01273) 302707. Fax: (01273) 301651. Est: 1975. Private premises. Appointment necessary. Medium stock. Spec: Cookery/Gastronomy; Food & Drink; Ephemera. PR: £1–500. CC: MC; V. Corresp: French. Mem: E.S. VAT No: GB 509 0878 31.

Turner Donovan Military Books, 12 Southdown Avenue, Brighton, BN1 6EG. Tel: (01273) 566230. Web: www.turnerdonovan.com. Est: 1985. Private premises. Postal only. Medium stock. Spec: Countries - India; Military; Military History; War - Napoleonic; War - World War II; Ephemera; Prints and Maps. PR: £15–2,500. CC: MC; V. Notes: *Also, soldier's diaries, trench maps, memories and regimental histories.*

Fisher Nautical, Huntswood House, St. Helena Lane Streat, Hassocks, Brighton, BN6 8SD. Prop: (*) S. & J. Fisher. Tel: (01273) 890273. Fax: (01273) 891439. Web: www.fishernauticalbooks.co.uk. Est: 1969. Private premises. Postal only. Telephone First. Open: **M:** 09:00–16:16; **T:** 09:00–16:15; **W:** 09:00–16:16; **Th:** 09:00–16:16; **F:** 09:00–15:15; **S:** 09:00–12:00. Very large stock. Spec: Maritime/Nautical; Booksearch. PR: £10–3,000. CC: MC; V. Mem: PBFA.

Invisible Books, Unit 8, 15-26 Lincoln Cottage Works, Lincoln Cottages, Brighton, BN2 9UJ. Prop: Paul Holman & Bridget Penney. Tel: (01273) 694574. Web: www.invisiblebooks.co.uk. Est: 1994. Storeroom. Internet and Postal. Appointment necessary. Medium stock. Spec: Academic/Scholarly; Counterculture; Esoteric; New Age; Occult. PR: £1–1,000. VAT No: GB 825 8052 27.

Kenya Books, 31 Southdown Ave., Brighton, BN1 6EH. Prop: J. McGivney. Tel: (01273) 556029. Web: www.abebooks.com/home/kenyabooks. Private premises. Internet and Postal. Contactable. Open: **M:** 09:00–19:00; **W:** 09:00–19:00; **Th:** 09:00–19:00; **F:** 09:00–19:00; **S:** 09:00–19:00. Medium stock. Spec: Academic/Scholarly; Africana; Anthropology; Coffee; Countries - Africa; Countries - East Africa; Countries - France; Countries - Indian Ocean, The. PR: £1–500. Corresp: French; Swahili. Mem: PBFA. Notes: *East & Southern Africa and all sub-Saharan countries. Travel & exploration, trans-Africa travel, history, social studies, politics, memoirs, African ethnography, linguistics, archaeology, art & literature, natural history, agriculture.*

Rainbow Books, ■ 28 Trafalgar Street, Brighton, BN1 4ED. Prop: Kevin Daly. Tel: (01273) 605101. Est: 1998. Shop open: **M:** 10:30–18:00; **T:** 10:30–18:00; **W:** 10:30–18:00; **Th:** 10:30–18:00; **F:** 10:30–18:00; **S:** 10:30–18:00. Very large stock. PR: £1–20.

Savery Books, ■ 257 Ditchling Road, Brighton, BN1 6JH. Prop: Marianne, James, Sarah & Anne Savery. Tel: 01273 564 899. Est: 1992. Shop open: **W:** 10:00–16:00; **Th:** 10:00–16:00; **F:** 10:00–16:00; **S:** 10:00–16:00. Spec: Art - Theory; Art History; Art Reference; Fiction - General; Fiction - Crime, Detective, Spy, Thrillers; Military; Philosophy; Psychoanalysis.

Studio Bookshop, ■ 68 St. James's Street, Brighton, BN2 1PJ. Prop: Paul Brown. Tel: 01273 691253. Web: www.studiobookshop.co.uk. Est: 1995. Shop open: **M:** 11:00–17:00; **T:** 11:00–17:00; **W:** 11:00–17:00; **Th:** 11:00–17:00; **F:** 11:00–17:00; **S:** 11:00–17:00. Spec: Academic/Scholarly; Antiques; Art; Art Reference; Artists; Auction Catalogues; Catalogues Raisonnes; Countries - Spain. CC: JCB; MC; V; Maestro, Visa Electron. Cata: Glass, Exhibition Catalogues. Corresp: French, Spanish. Notes: *Major specialities are books on Glass and Exhibition Catalogues, books on Spain, Academic and Scholarly books in the humanities.*

Waxfactor, ■ 24 Trafalgar Street, Brighton, BN1 4EQ. Prop: M. Driver. Tel: (01273) 673744. Est: 1985. Shop open: **M:** 10:00–17:30; **T:** 10:00–17:30; **W:** 10:00–17:30; **Th:** 10:00–17:30; **F:** 10:00–17:30; **S:** 10:00–17:30. Medium stock. Spec: Art; Astrology; Cinema/Film; Esoteric; Fiction - Science Fiction; History - General; Literature; Occult. PR: £1–25. CC: JCB; MC; V; Mae, So. Notes: *Also, records & CDs, DVDs and tapes.*

CROWBOROUGH

Dennys Sanders & Greene Ltd., Heaslands, Steep Road, Crowborough, TN6 3RX. Prop: Nicholas Dennys. Tel: (07973) 178922. Est: 1983. Private premises. Internet and postal. Appointment necessary. Medium stock. Spec: Antropology; Antiquarian; Arts, The; Author - Greene, Graham; Children's; Espionage; Ethography; Fiction - General. CC: MC; V. GB VAT: 394 5021 50. Cata: occasionally.

Ray Hennessey Bookseller, Panfield House, Crowborough Hill, Crowborough, TN6 2HJ. Prop: Ray & Deanna Hennessey. Tel: (01892) 653704. Fax: (0870) 0548776. Web: www.rayhennesseybookseller .co.uk. Est: 1954. Private premises. Internet and Postal. Appointment necessary. Open: **M:** 10:00–17:00; **T:** 10:00–17:00; **W:** 10:00–17:00; **Th:** 10:00–17:00; **F:** 10:00–17:00; **S:** 10:00–17:00. Medium stock. Spec: Africana; Antiquarian; Antiques; Applied Art; Art; Art - British; Art - Technique; Art Deco. PR: £6–1,000. CC: AE; E; JCB; MC; V. Mem: PBFA. Notes: *Showroom at Olinda House, Rotherfield, East Sussex. Open to Public 10:30 to 5:00 Tuesday to Saturday.*

Simply Read Books, Badgers, Wood Fielden Road, Crowborough, TN6 1TP. Prop: W.L. & W.P. Banks. Tel: 01892 664584. Web: www.abenooks.com. Est: 1998. Private premises. Internet and Postal. Contactable. Open: **M:** 08:00–24:00; **T:** 08:00–24:00; **W:** 08:00–24:00; **Th:** 08:00–24:00; **F:** 08:00–24:00; **S:** 09:00–24:00; **Su:** 09:00–24:0. Spec: Crime (True); Famous People - Monroe, Marilyn; Modern First Editions; Travel - General; Booksearch. CC: MC; V; PayPal. Corresp: French. Notes: *Booksearch carried out.*

DITCHLING

Kenneth Ball, 7 Mulberry Lane, Ditchling, BN6 8UH. Prop: Kenneth Ball. Tel: 01273 845000. Fax: 01273 844444. Est: 1947. Storeroom; Appointment necessary. Spec: Commercial Vehicles; Journals; Marque Histories (see also motoring); Motorbikes / motorcycles; Motoring; Steam Engines; Vintage Cars; Ephemera. PR: £5–1,000. Corresp: French.

EAST HOATHLY

Claras Books, 20 High Street, East Hoathly, Nr Lewes, BN8 6EB. Prop: Jane Seabrook. Tel: 01825 840263. Est: 2000. Private premises. Internet and Postal. CC: MC; V; Maestro. Notes: *Large general stock.*

EASTBOURNE

Camilla's Bookshop, ■ 57 Grove Road, Eastbourne, BN21 4TX. Prop: Camilla Francombe & Stuart Broad. Tel: (01323) 736001. Est: 1976. Shop open: **M:** 10:00–17:30; **T:** 10:00–17:30; **W:** 10:00–17:30; **Th:** 10:00–17:30; **F:** 10:00–17:30; **S:** 10:00–17:30. Very large stock. Spec: Aeronautics; Animals and Birds; Annuals; Arts, The; Aviation; Bindings; Botany; Children's. PR: £1–300. CC: E; MC; V; Mae, SO. VAT No: GB 583 7350 18. Notes: *Closed on Bank Holidays.*

Roderick Dew, 10 Furness Road, Eastbourne, BN21 4EZ. Tel: (01323) 720239. Est: 1975. Private premises. Appointment necessary. Small stock. Spec: Applied Art; Architecture; Bibliography; Fine Art. PR: £5–500. Corresp: French, German.

Alan Gibbard Books, ■ 1 and 2 Calverley Walk, Eastbourne, BN21 4UP. Prop: Alan Gibbard. Tel: (01323) 734128. Fax: (01323) 734128. Est: 1993. Shop open: **T:** 10:00–17:00; **W:** 10:00–17:00; **Th:** 10:00–17:00; **F:** 10:00–17:00; **S:** 10:00–17:00. Medium stock. Spec: Natural History; Topography - Local; Travel - General. PR: £1–1,000. CC: AE; MC; V. Corresp: Italian, Spanish. Mem: PBFA. VAT No: GB 621 5744 53.

Green Man Books, 14 Bath Road, Eastbourne, BN21 4UA. Prop: Jerry Bird. Tel: (01323) 735364. Web: www.greenman-books.co.uk. Est: 1999. Private premises. Market Stall. Appointment necessary. Spec: Antiquarian; Archaeology; Arthurian; Astrology; Author - Powys Family, The; Celtica; Earth Mysteries; Esoteric. PR: £2–200. CC: MC; V. Cata: Folklore, Mythology, Paganism, Occult. Mem: NMTA. Notes: *Also, new books on the above subjects, selling at Pagan conferences and folk festivals in the UK. Also medieval history books and early music books & cds, mostly at medieval re-enactment fairs. Also trading in books by the Powys brothers.*

London & Sussex Antiquarian Books & Print Services, Southwood, 15 Dittons Road, Eastbourne, BN21 1DR. Prop: Dr. G.B. Carruthers. Tel: (01323) 730857. Fax: (01323) 737550. Est: 1970. Mail Order Only. Postal only. Appointment necessary. Spec: Alternative Medicine; Dogs; Medicine - History of; Memoirs; Nurses/Doctors; out-of-print; Prints and Maps. PR: £10–100. Cata: Hospital History, Medicine, London, Collecting, Misc.

The Meads Book Service, 1 Meadhurst, 31 Meads Road, Eastbourne BN20 7ET. Prop: Clive Ogden. Tel: (01323) 646776. Est: 1988. Mail order. Postal only. Small stock. Spec: Author - Benson, E.F. PR: £1–1,500. CC: cheque only. Cata: occasionally. Notes: My mobile telephone number: 077471 03697.

Mellon's Books, ■ The Enterprise Centre, 1 Station Parade, Eastbourne, BN21 1BD. Tel: 01323749254. Web: www.mellonsbooks.co.uk. Est: 2005. Shop open: **M:** 09:30–17:00; **T:** 10:00–16:00; **W:** 09:30–17:00; **Th:** 09:30–17:00; **F:** 09:30–17:00; **S:** 09:30–17:00; Closed for lunch: 13:00–14:00. Spec: Academic/Scholarly; Author - 20th Century; Children's; Churchilliana; Cinema/Film; Cookery/Gastronomy; Drama; Famous People - Churchill, Sir Winston. CC: AE; MC; V; Maestro/Switch. Corresp: Basic French.

R. & A. Books, 4 Milton Grange, 6 Arundel Road, Eastbourne, BN21 2EL. Prop: Robert Manning and Alan Millard. Tel: (01323) 647690. Web: www.raenterprises.co.uk/. Est: 2000. Private premises. Internet and Postal. Large stock. Spec: Aboriginal; Academic/Scholarly; Adult; Adventure; Advertising; Aeronautics; Aesthetic Movement; Aesthetics. PR: £1–500. CC: PayPal. Cata: All General Subjects. Notes: *Worldwide orders accepted. Payment in sterling through PayPal. UK cheques accepted.*

Dealers need to update their entry at least once a year.

Visit your page on

Sheppard's World

FOREST ROW

Simon Crosby, Hindleap Corner, Forest Row, RH18 5JF. Tel: (01342) 824545. Fax: (01342) 824545. Web: www.rarerugbooks.co.uk. Private premises. Appointment necessary. Small stock. Spec: Carpets - General; Oriental. PR: £5–2,000.

FRISTON

Liz Seeber, 16 The Brow, Friston, BN20 0ES. Tel: (01323) 423 777. Web: www.lizseeberbooks.co.uk. Est: 1994. Private premises. Postal only. Appointment necessary. Small stock. Spec: Author - David, Elizabeth; Cookery/Gastronomy; Food & Drink; Gardening - General; Booksearch. PR: £5–3,000. CC: MC; V. Cata: cookery, food and wine. Corresp: French. VAT No: GB 629 3954 04.

HASTINGS

Anthony Sillem, 9 Tackleway, Old Town, Hastings, TN34 3DE. Prop: Anthony Sillem. Tel: 01424 446602. Est: 1994. Private premises. Appointment necessary. Open: **M:** 09:00–17:30; **T:** 09:00–17:30; **W:** 09:00–17:30; **Th:** 09:00–17:30; **F:** 09:00–17:30; **S:** 09:00–17:30; **Su:** 09:00–17:30; Closed for lunch: 13:00–14:00. Spec: Art - British; First Editions; Literary Travel; Literature; Literature - French. CC: MC; V; Switch. Cata: Literature, Art & Illustrated. Mem: PBFA.

Boulevard Books, ■ Boulevard Book Shop, 32 George Street, Hastings, TN34 3EA. Prop: Graham Frost. Tel: 01424436521. Web: www.thehastingstrawler.co.uk. Est: 2004. Shop open: **M:** 10:30–17:30; **T:** 10:30–17:30; **W:** 10:30–17:30; **Th:** 10:30–17:30; **F:** 10:30–17:30; **S:** 10:30–17:30; **Su:** 10:30–17:30; Closed for lunch: 13:00–14:00. CC: Cash or Cheque only. Corresp: French, German, Swedish, Dutch. Notes: *Open seven days a week and we only accept cash or cheques.*

Chthonios Books, 7 Tamarisk Steps, Off Rock-a-Nore Road, Hastings, TN34 3DN. Prop: Stephen Ronan. Tel: (01424) 433302. Web: www.esotericism.co.uk/index.htm. Est: 1985. Private premises. Internet and Postal. Telephone First. Small stock. Spec: Acupuncture; Alchemy; Author - Crowley, Aleister; Classical Studies; Earth Mysteries; Eastern Philosophy; Egyptology; Esoteric. PR: £3–300. CC: MC; V; PayPal. Cata: esotericism, ancient philosophy, ancient religion. Corresp: French. Notes: *Specialists in esotericism, ancient philosophy, ancient religion, occult.*

High Street Book Shop, ■ High Street Book Shop, 78 High Street, Hastings, TN34 3EA. Prop: Graham Frost. Tel: 01424200833. Est: 1997. Shop open: **M:** 10:30–17:30; **T:** 10:30–17:30; **W:** 10:30–17:30; **Th:** 10:30–17:30; **F:** 10:30–17:30; **S:** 10:30–17:30; **Su:** 10:30–17:30; Closed for lunch: 13:00–14:00. CC: cash or cheque only. Corresp: French, German, Italian, Spanish. Notes: *We are open seven days a week and only accept cash or cheques.*

Hoovey's Books, P.O. Box 27, St. Leonards–on–Sea, Hastings, TN37 6TZ. Prop: (*). Tel: (01424) 753407. Fax: (01424) 753407. Web: www.hooveys.co.uk. Est: 1968. Office and/or bookroom; Appointment necessary. Small stock. Spec: Booksearch. VAT No: GB 397 8504 94. Notes: *Catalogue printing, cleaning materials, jacket coverings.*

Howes Bookshop, ■ Trinity Hall, Braybrooke Terrace, Hastings, TN34 1HQ. Prop: Miles Bartley. Tel: (01424) 423437. Fax: (01424) 460620. Web: www.howes.co.uk. Est: 1921. Shop open: **M:** 09:30–17:00; **T:** 09:30–17:00; **W:** 09:30–17:00; **Th:** 09:30–17:00; **F:** 09:30–17:00; Closed for lunch: 13:00–14:00. Large stock. Spec: Antiquarian; Bibliography; Bindings; Classical Studies; History - General; Literature; Theology; Topography - Local. PR: £1–5,000. CC: E; JCB; MC; V. Mem: ABA; PBFA. Notes: *Storeroom, also attends book fairs.*

Jill Howell, Badgers Mount, Farley Way, Fairlight, Hastings, TN35 4AS. Prop: Jill Howell. Tel: 01424 815256. Fax: 01424 814381. Est: 1993. Private premises. Postal only. Appointment necessary. Spec: History - Photography; Photography. Cata: Photography. Corresp: French.

Nakota Curios, ■ 12 Courthouse Street, Hastings, TN34 3AU. Prop: Robert M. Mucci. Tel: (01424) 445340. Est: 1978. Shop open: **S:** 11:00–17:00; **Su:** 11:00–17:00. Spec: Ethnography; Travel - General.

Robert's Shop, ■ 68 High Street, Old Town, Hastings, TN34 3EW. Prop: Robert M. Mucci. Tel: (01424) 445340. Est: 1989. Shop open: **M:** 11:00–18:00; **T:** 11:00–18:00; **W:** 11:00–18:00; **Th:** 11:00–18:00; **F:** 11:00–18:00; **S:** 11:00–18:00; **Su:** 11:00–18:00. Small stock. Spec: Collectables; Ephemera; Prints and Maps. PR: £1–10.

Underwater Books, 104d High Street, Hastings, TN24 3ES. Prop: J.A. Barak. Tel: (01424) 435905. Web: www.underwater-books.co.uk. Est: 1980. Office and/or bookroom; Internet and Postal. Appointment necessary. Small stock. Spec: Sport - Diving/Sub-Aqua. PR: £10–150. CC: Paypal. Notes: *Books cover all aspects of diving.*

HEATHFIELD

Botting & Berry, ■ 41 High Street, Heathfield, TN21 8HU. Prop: John Botting and Dave Berry. Tel: (01435) 868555. Est: 2001. Shop open: **M:** 10:00–17:00; **T:** 10:00–17:00; **W:** 10:00–17:00; **Th:** 10:00–17:00; **F:** 10:00–17:00; **S:** 10:00–17:00. Small stock. PR: £1–500. CC: MC; V. Notes: *Fairs: Royal National, Bloomsbury, London.*

HORAM

Period & Classical Collections, Lyndhurst House, High Street, Horam, TN21 0EZ. Prop: Fiona Voice-Joyce. Tel: 01435 810337. Fax: 01435 810337. Est: 2005. Private premises. Internet and Postal. Telephone First. Open: **T:** 10:00–17:00; **W:** 10:00–17:00; **Th:** 10;00–17:00; **F:** 10;00–17:00; **S:** 10:00–17:00; Closed for lunch: 13:00–14:00. Spec: Academic/Scholarly; Antiquarian; Antique Paper; Architecture; Art; Art History; Auction Catalogues; Author - Brontes, The. CC: PayPal. Mem: Law Society. Notes: *Antique and rare books including literature, art/architecture, gardening, illustrated and children's books.*

HOVE

Dinnages Transport/Picture Publishing, Unit 11, Lion Mews, Hove, BN3 5RA. Prop: Mr. G. & Mrs. C. Dinnage. Fax: (0871) 433 8096. Web: www.TransportPostcards.co.uk/shop/. Est: 1989. Storeroom; Internet and Postal. Appointment necessary. Shop at: Stall/event & Internet sales. Visitors by prior arrangement. Open: **S:** 10:00–14:00. Small stock. Spec: Buses/Trams; Commercial Vehicles; Publishers - General; Publishers - Harding, Peter A; Publishers - Southdown Club; Railways and Railroads; Transport; Collectables. PR: £1–25. CC: Cards via internet. Cata: Some books/DVD & photo lists. Notes: *Regular stall Maidstone Collectors Fair 5x pa + others. Publisher of nostalgic transport & local photographs/postcards, book distributor of Southdown 'Works Driver'.*

S.L. Francis, 27 Shanklin Court, Hangleton Road, Hove BN3 7SB. Tel: 10273 418244. Private premises. Very small stock. Spec: Art; Biography, Music - General; Poetry. PR: £3 up. Corresp: French. Notes: *Exhibits at Lewes Book fair.*

Simon Hunter Antique Maps, 21 St Johns Road, Hove, BN3 2FB. Prop: Simon Hunter. Tel: (01273) 746983. Web: www.antiquemaps.org.uk. Internet and Postal. Medium stock. PR: £5–1,000. CC: AE; E; JCB; MC; V. Corresp: French. Mem: IMCoS. VAT No: GB 587 4541 02. Notes: *Antique Maps only.*

Whitehall Books, 3 Leighton Road, Hove, BN3 7AD. Prop: Peter Batten. Tel: (01273) 735252. Web: www.whitehallbooks.co.uk. Est: 1991. Private premises. Internet and Postal. Appointment necessary. Small stock. Spec: Art; Crime (True); Criminology; Illustrated - General; Literary Criticism; Literature. PR: £1–100. Corresp: French, Russian. Notes: *Translation. Literary detective work and general literary information.*

LEWES

Richard Beaton, 24 Highdown Road, Lewes, BN7 1QD. Prop: Dr. Richard Beaton. Tel: (01273) 474147. Web: www.victorian-novels.co.uk. Est: 1996. Private premises. Internet and Postal. Appointment necessary. Small stock. Spec: Antiquarian; Author - 19th Century; Author - 20th Century; Author - Ballantyne, Robert M.; Author - Baring-Gould, S.; Author - Benson, E.F.; Author - Benson, R.H.; Author - Braddon, Mary Elizabeth. PR: £5–1,000. CC: MC; V; Maestro, also PayPal. Cata: C19th & early C20th fiction. Corresp: French. Notes: *Visits by appointment only.*

John Beck, 29 Mill Road, Lewes, BN7 2RU. Tel: (01273) 477555. Fax: (01273) 480339. Est: 1982. Private premises. Postal only. Appointment necessary. Open: **M:** 10:00–16:00; **T:** 10:00–16:00; **W:** 10:00–16:00; **Th:** 10:00–16:00; **F:** 10:00–16:00; **S:** 10:00–16:00; **Su:** 10:00–16:00. Small stock. Spec: Author - Blyton, Enid; Author - Buckeridge, A.; Author - Crompton, Richmal; Author - Saville, M.; Author - Tourtel, M; Children's; Children's - Early Titles; Children's - Illustrated. PR: £1–1,000. Notes: *Some books are displayed in "The Boxroom" at "The Needlemakers", West Street, Lewes. I currently have the largest stock of Rupert books (copies of all from 1920 to date)in the country. Most other children's authors available.*

Bow Windows Book Shop, ■ 175 High Street, Lewes, BN7 1YE. Prop: Alan & Jennifer Shelley. Tel: (01273) 480780. Fax: (01273) 486686. Web: www.bowwindows.com. Est: 1964. Shop open: **M:** 09:30–17:00; **T:** 09:30–17:00; **W:** 09:30–17:00; **Th:** 09:30–17:00; **F:** 09:30–17:00; **S:** 09:30–17:00. Medium stock. Spec: Antiquarian; Artists; Author - Bloomsbury Group, The; Author - Rackham, Arthur; Author - Sackville-West, Vita; Author - Woolf, Virginia; Children's - Illustrated; Countries - China. PR: £1–5,000. CC: AE; MC; V. Cata: General. Corresp: German. Mem: ABA; PBFA; ILAB. VAT No: GB 370 1163 88.

Brimstones, 7f The Holdings, Uckfield Road, Ringmer, Lewes, BN8 5RY. Prop: Geoff Kinderman. Tel: (01273) 814361. Web: www.brimstones.co.uk. Est: 1990. Storeroom; Postal only. Appointment necessary. Open: **M:** 09:00–16:00; **T:** 09:00–16:00; **W:** 09:00–16:00; **Th:** 09:00–16:00; **F:** 09:00–16:00. Very large stock. Spec: Biography; History - General; International Affairs; Memoirs; Philosophy; Political History; Politics; Psychology/Psychiatry. PR: £1–500. CC: AE; MC; V; Mae. VAT No: GB 550 1571 71.

A. & Y. Cumming Limited, ■ 84 High Street, Lewes, BN7 1XN. Prop: A.J. Cumming. Tel: (01273) 472319. Fax: (01273) 486364. Est: 1976. Shop open: **M:** 10:00–17:00; **T:** 10:00–17:00; **W:** 10:00–17:00; **Th:** 10:00–17:00; **F:** 10:00–17:00; **S:** 10:00–17:30. Very large stock. Spec: Art; Atlases; Bindings; Illustrated - General; Literature; Natural History; Topography - General; Travel - General. CC: AE; MC; V. Cata: Library sets, leather bindings, atlases. Mem: ABA; PBFA. VAT No: GB 412 4098 80. Notes: *Books bought, libraries, small collections or individual volumes. Buyer will call anywhere in the UK.*

The Fifteenth Century Bookshop, ■ The Fifteenth Century House, 99/100 High Street, Lewes, BN7 1XH. Prop: Mrs S.J. Mirabaud. Tel: 01273 474160. Web: www.oldenyoungbooks.co.uk. Est: 1936. Shop open: **M:** 10:00–17:30; **T:** 10:00–17:30; **W:** 10:00–17:30; **Th:** 10:00–17:30; **F:** 10:00–17:30; **S:** 10:00–17:30. Spec: Annuals; Arthurian; Author - 19th Century; Author - 20th Century; Author - Aesop; Author - Ahlberg, Janet & Allan; Author - Aldin, Cecil; Author - Ardizzone, Edward. CC: AE; MC; V. Corresp: French. Mem: PBFA. Notes: *Postal and Internet enquiries and sales welcome.*

Derek Wise, Berewood House, Barcombe, Lewes, BN8 5TW. Tel: (01273) 400559. Fax: (01273) 400559. Est: 1986. Private premises. Internet and Postal. Appointment necessary. Small stock. Spec: Author - Byron, Lord; Education & School; Literature; Maritime/Nautical; Military; Natural History; Naval; Public Schools. PR: £1–1,500. Corresp: French. Mem: PBFA.

NEWHAVEN

32 Seconds, ■ 32 High Street, Newhaven, BN9 9PD. Prop: G.G.J. Haynes. Tel: 01273 611350. Est: 2000. Shop open: **T:** 10:00–16:00; **W:** 10:00–16:00; **Th:** 10:00–16:00; **F:** 10:00–16:00; **S:** 10:00–16:00. Spec: Philately; Ephemera; Prints and Maps.

PORTSLADE

Peter Scott, 14 Vale Road, Portslade, BN41 1GF. Prop: Peter Scott. Tel: (01273) 410576. Web: www.scottbooks.freeuk.com. Est: 1986. Private premises. Internet and Postal. Appointment necessary. Small stock. Spec: Academic/Scholarly; Archaeology; Art; Books about Books; General Stock; History - General; Literature; Religion - General. PR: £1–200.

ROBERTSBRIDGE

Spearman Books, ■The Old Saddlery Bookshop, 56 High Street, Robertsbridge, TN32 5AP. Prop: John & Janet Brooman. Tel: (01580) 880631. Est: 1970. Shop open: **M:** 10:00–17:00; **T:** 10:00–17:00; **Th:** 10:00–17:00; **F:** 10:00–17:00; **S:** 10:00–17:00; Closed for lunch: 13:00–14:15. Medium stock. Spec: Travel - General. PR: £1–1,000. Corresp: French.

ROTHERFIELD

Kennedy & Farley, 2 Brook Cottages, New Road, Rotherfield, TN6 3JT. Prop: Helen Kennedy & Fran Farley. Tel: (01892) 853141. Est: 1987. Private premises. Internet and Postal. Telephone First. Small stock. Spec: Africana; Anthologies; Art; Author - Francis, Dick; Author - Huxley, Aldous; Horses; Modern First Editions; Music - Classical. PR: £4–1,000. CC: Paypal. Corresp: French. Mem: PBFA. Notes: *Current catalogue on UKBookWorld.com. Only a portion of our stock is catalogued so far, so please don't hesitate to contact us with your enquiries. 01892 853141 or kennedyandfarley@ care4free.net.*

RYE

Rye Old Books, ■ Rye Old Books, 7 Lion Street, Rye, TN31 7LB. Prop: Ms Aoife Coleman. Tel: 01797 225410. Web: www.ukbookworld.com/members/ryeoldbooks. Est: 1993. Shop open: **M:** 10:30–18:00; **T:** 10:30–18:00; **W:** 10:30–18:00; **Th:** 10:30–18:00; **F:** 10:30–18:00; **S:** 10:30–18:00; **Su:** 14:00–17:00. Spec: Antiquarian; Author - Austen, Jane; Author - Clare, John; Author - Dulac, Edmund; Author - Eliot, G.; Author - Rackham, Arthur; Author - Robinson, Heath W.; Children's. CC: AE; E; MC; V. Cata: Childrens, Illustrated, Dulac, Pogany, Rackham. Notes: *For Sunday opening in winter. If calling in January, phone to confirm. Usually open only by appointment in January.*

SALTDEAN

N1 Books, 29 Tumulus Road, Saltdean, BN2 8FR. Prop: Michael Sassen. Tel: 01273 230532. Est: 2001. Private premises. Internet and Postal. Telephone First. Open: **M:** 11:00–23:30; **T:** 11:00–23:30; **W:** 11:00–23:30; **Th:** 11:00–23:30; **F:** 11:00–23:30; **S:** 11:00–23:30. Spec: Adult; Aeronautics; Antiquarian; Antiquities; Applied Art; Archaeology; Arms & Armour; Army, The. Cata: History, Illustrated, Bindings, Arts, Oddities.

ST. LEONARD'S–ON–SEA

The Book Jungle, ■ 24 North Street, St. Leonard's–on–Sea, TN38 0EX. Prop: Michael Gowen. Tel: (01424) 421187. Web: www.thebookjungle.co.uk. Est: 1991. Internet and Postal. Shop open: **T:** 10:00–16:00; **Th:** 10:00–16:00; **F:** 10:00–16:00; **S:** 10:00–16:00. Large stock. PR: £1–20.

Raymond Kilgarriff, 15 Maze Hill, St. Leonard's–on–Sea, TN38 0HN. Tel: (01424) 426146. Web: www.ilab.org. Est: 1947. Private premises. Internet and Postal. Appointment necessary. Small stock. Spec: Antiquarian; Fine & Rare; History - General; Literature. PR: £100–2,000. Mem: ABA; ILAB. VAT No: GB 794 2047 15.

Bruce Holdsworth Books, Vale House, 9 Eversley Road, St. Leonard's-on-Sea, TN37 6QD. Prop: Bruce Holdsworth. Tel: 01424 446400. Web: www.bruceholdsworthbooks.com. Est: 1994. Private premises. Internet and Postal. Appointment necessary. Open: **M:** 09:00–14:30; **T:** 09:00–14:30; **W:** 09:00–14:30; **Th:** 09:00–14:30; **F:** 09:00–14:30. Spec: Applied Art; Art; Art - Technique; Art - Theory; Art History; Art Reference; Artists; Arts & Crafts Era. CC: AE; E; JCB; MC; V. Cata: Art and Design and related subjects. Mem: PBFA. VAT No: GB 686 9604 74. Notes: *Stock emphasis is on on British art new, used, second hand, scarce and collectible including most art subjects and related and exhibition catalogues. Informative books with good illustrations are a speciality.*

Gerald Lee Maritime Books, PO Box 7 , St. Leonard's-on-Sea, TN38 8WX. Prop: Gerald Lee. Tel: 02424 853006. Web: www.leemaritimebooks.com. Est: 1990. Private premises. Postal only. Contactable. Open: **M:** 09:00–17:30; **T:** 09:00–17:30; **W:** 09:00–17:30; **Th:** 09:00–17:30; **F:** 09:00–17:30; **S:** 09:00–17:30; **Su:** 09:00–17:30; Closed for lunch: 13:00–14:00. Spec: Maritime/Nautical; Maritime/Nautical - History; Maritime/Nautical - Log Books; Naval; Navy, The; Navy, The - Royal Naval Patrol Service; Ocean Liners; Paddle Boats. CC: JCB; MC; V. Cata: naval history -maritime; yachting and boating. VAT No: GB 690.748987.

John Gorton Booksearch, 22 Charles Road, St. Leonard's-on-Sea, TN38 0QH. Prop: John Gorton. Tel: (0779) 1549 745. Est: 1983. Private premises. Appointment necessary. Small stock. Spec: Art Reference; Fiction - Crime, Detective, Spy, Thrillers; Mathematics; Philosophy. PR: £1–200. Cata: on specialities.

TICEHURST

Piccadilly Rare Books, Church Street, Ticehurst, TN5 7AA. Prop: Paul P.B. Minet. Tel: 01580 201221. Fax: 01580 200957. Web: www.picrare.com. Est: 1972. Shop and/or showroom; Shop open: **M:** 9:00–17:00; **T:** 9:00–17:00; **W:** 9:00–17:00; **Th:** 9:00–17:00; **F:** 9:00–17:00; **S:** 10:00–17:00. Large stock. Spec: Diaries; Folio Society, The; Maritime/Nautical; Royalty - General; Royalty - European. PR: £5–2,000. CC: AE; MC; V. Cata: Royalty. Corresp: French, Greek, Spanish. Mem: ABA; PBFA. VAT No: GB 583 9618 89. Notes: *Combined coffee shop and large general bookshop. Also owns Baggins Book Bazaar in Rochester (q.v.)*

EAST YORKSHIRE

BEVERLEY

Beverley Old Bookshop, ■ 2 Dyer Lane, Beverley, HU17 8AE. Prop: Colin Tatman. Tel: (01482) 880611. Est: 1993. Shop open: **M:** 10:00–17:00; **T:** 10:00–17:00; **W:** 10:00–17:00; **Th:** 10:00–17:00; **F:** 10:00–17:00; **S:** 10:00–17:00. Medium stock. Spec: Bookbinding; Children's; History - Local; Illustrated - General. PR: £1–200. Notes: *Also, book restoration.*

Eastgate Bookshop, ■ 11 Eastgate, Beverley, HU17 0DR. Prop: Barry Roper. Tel: (01482) 868579. Web: www.eastgatebooks.karoo.net. Est: 1983. Shop open: **W:** 10:00–17:00; **Th:** 10:00–17:00; **F:** 10:00–17:00; **S:** 10:00–16:30. Large stock. Spec: Aircraft; Antiques; Archaeology; Army, The; Art; Aviation; Books about Books; Countries - British North Borneo. PR: £1–500. CC: JCB; MC; V; Switch. Notes: *Open Monday and Tuesday by appointment only.*

BRIDLINGTON

Family-Favourites, 51 First Ave, Bridlington, YO15 2JR. Prop: Shirley Jackson. Tel: 01262 6606061. Web: www.http://ukbookworld.com/members/famfav. Est: 1989. Private premises. Postal only. Contactable. Spec: Autobiography; Aviation; Biography; Bookbinding; Books about Books; First Editions; Large Print Books. CC: Paypal.

J.L. Book Exchange, ■ 72 Hilderthorpe Road, Bridlington, YO15 3BQ. Prop: John Ledraw. Tel: (01262) 601285. Est: 1971. Shop open in summer: **M:** 08:30–18:00; **T:** 08:30–18:00; **W:** 08:30–18:00; **Th:** 08:30–18:00; **F:** 08:30–18:00; **S:** 08:30–18:00; **Su:** 08:30–18:00. Medium stock. PR: £1–80. Notes: *Winter opening: Mon-Sat 09:30–17:30.*

DRIFFIELD

Peter Riddell, 3 Hudson Terrace, Bainton, Driffield, YO25 9NH. Tel: (01377) 217219. Est: 1989. Private premises. Internet and Postal. Appointment necessary. Small stock. Spec: Alpinism/Mountaineering; Countries - Central Asia; Countries - Polar; Mountains. PR: £1–250.

Solaris Books, Flat 4, 13 Lockwood St., Driffield, YO25 6RU. Prop: Jim Goddard. Tel: (01377) 272022. Web: www.solaris-books.co.uk/store. Private premises. Internet and Postal. Telephone First. Medium stock. Spec: Fiction - Fantasy, Horror; Fiction - Science Fiction; History - Napoleonic; Military History; Modern First Editions; Photography; Booksearch. PR: £2–1,200. CC: PayPal. Cata: sf, modern firsts.

FLAMBOROUGH

Resurgam Books, ■ The Manor House, Flamborough, Bridlington, York, YO15 1PD. Prop: Geoffrey Miller. Tel: (01262) 850943. Fax: (01262) 850943. Web: www.resurgambooks.co.uk. Est: 1998. Internet and Postal. Shop open: **M:** 09:00–17:00; **T:** 09:00–17:00; **W:** 09:00–17:00; **Th:** 09:00–17:00; **F:** 09:00–17:00; **S:** 09:00–17:00; **Su:** 10:00–16:00. Small stock. PR: £1–400. CC: E; JCB; MC; V.

GREAT DRIFFIELD

The Driffield Bookshop, ■ 21 Middle Street North, Great Driffield, YO25 6SW. Prop: G.R. Stevens. Tel: (01377) 254210. Est: 1981. Shop open: **M:** 10:00–17:30; **T:** 10:00–17:30; **W:** 10:00–17:30; **Th:** 10:00–17:30; **F:** 10:00–17:30; **S:** 10:00–17:30. Medium stock. Spec: Fiction - Science Fiction; History - General; Literature; Military History; Modern First Editions; Travel - General. PR: £1–150.

GRIMSBY

Hullbooks Ltd, Unit 20, Grimsby Business Centre, King Edward Street, Grimsby, DN31 3JH. Prop: Ian & Karren Barfield. Web: www.hullbooks.com. Est: 1991. Office and/or bookroom; Shop open: **M:** 10:00–17:00; **T:** 10:00–17:00; **W:** 10:00–17:00; **Th:** 10:00–17:00; **F:** 10:00–17:00; **S:** 10:00–17:00. Large stock. Spec: Academic/Scholarly; Authors - Local; Criminology; Education & School; Fisheries; History - General; History - 19th Century; History - 20th Century. PR: £2–200. CC: E; JCB; MC; V. Notes: *We have a large general stock with unusually high turnover. We are always looking for large collections of academic and specialist books.*

HULL

Bowie Books & Collectables, 19 Northolt Close, Hull, HU8 0PP. Prop: James Bowie. Tel: (01482) 374609. Web: www.bowiebooks.com. Est: 2003. Private premises. Internet and Postal. Appointment necessary. Open: **M:** 09:00–18:00; **T:** 09:00–18:00; **W:** 09:00–18:00; **Th:** 09:00–18:00; **F:** 09:00–18:00; **S:** 09:00–15:00. Small stock. Spec: Antiquarian; Fiction - General; First Editions; Literature; Modern First Editions; Religion - General; Collectables. PR: £2–150.

Harry Holmes Books, 85 Park Avenue, Hull, HU5 3EP. Prop: H.H. & P.A. Purkis. Tel: (01482) 443220. Est: 1989. Private premises. Appointment necessary. Small stock. Spec: Alpinism/Mountaineering; Biography; Countries - Scotland; Literature; Religion - Christian; Spiritualism; Topography - Local; Travel - Polar. PR: £1–100. Corresp: French and German. Notes: *Books on literary biography are also stocked.*

Colin Martin - Bookseller, 3 Village Road, Garden Village, Hull, HU8 8QP. Prop: Colin and Jane Martin, L.L.B., B.A. Tel: (01482) 585836. Web: www.colinmartinbooks.com. Est: 1991. Mail order only; Internet and Postal. Appointment necessary. Open: **M:** 10:00–16:00; **T:** 10:00–16:00; **W:** 10:00–16:00; **Th:** 10:00–16:00; **F:** 10:00–16:00. Very large stock. Spec: Applied Art; Architecture; Art; Art History; Art Reference; Artists; Arts, The; Design. PR: £3–4,000. CC: AE; D; JCB; MC; V; SW, SO. Corresp: French, German, Italian. VAT No: GB 780 4607 24. Notes: *Very large stock of Art reference books.*

KIRKELLA

East Riding Books, 13 Westland Road, Kirkella, HU10 7PH. Prop: Gill Carlile. Tel: (01482) 650674. Web: www.eastridingbooks.co.uk. Est: 1996. Private premises. Internet and Postal. Small stock. Spec: Music - General; Music - Classical; Music - Composers; Music - Gregorian Chants; Music - Jazz & Blues; Music - Musicians; Music - Opera; Music - Orchestral. PR: £1–500. CC: JCB; MC; V. Mem: PBFA; Ibooknet. VAT No: GB 747 0534 31. Notes: *Books on all aspects of Classical Music, a very small stock of scores.*

MILLINGTON

Quest Books, Harmer Hill, Millington, York, YO42 1TX. Prop: Dr. Peter Burridge. Tel: (01759) 304735. Fax: (01759) 306820. Est: 1984. Private premises. Postal only. Appointment necessary. Very small stock. Spec: Academic/Scholarly; Archaeology; Byzantium; Classical Studies; Countries - Arabia; Countries - Asia Minor; Countries - Balkans, The; Countries - Cyprus. PR: £5–1,000. CC: JCB; MC; V. Cata: Byzantines, Near & Middle East, Early Travellers. Mem: PBFA. Notes: *Greece, Turkey.*

SWANLAND

Cygnet Books, 86 Main Street, Swanland, HU14 3QR. Prop: Jackie Kitchen. Tel: 01482 633282. Web: www.swanlandbooks.co.uk. Est: 1995. Private premises. Internet and Postal. Appointment necessary. Open: **M:** 09:00–17:30; **T:** 09:00–17:30; **W:** 09:00–17:30; **Th:** 09:00–17:30; **F:** 09:00–17:30; **S:** 09:00–13:00; Closed for lunch: 13:00–14:00. Spec: Author - Blyton, Enid; Author - Ransome, Arthur; Author - Read, Miss; Children's; Children's - Early Titles; Children's - Illustrated; Christmas; Comic Books & Annuals. CC: PayPal and cheques. Cata: Children's out of Print Books. Notes: *Booksearch for hard to find titles.*

WINESTEAD

Alex Alec–Smith Books, The Old Rectory, Winestead, Hull, HU12 0NN. Prop: Alex Alec-Smith. Tel: (01964) 630548. Fax: (01964) 631160. Web: www.alexalec-smithbooks.co.uk. Est: 1985. Private premises. Appointment necessary. Small stock. Spec: Academic/Scholarly; Agriculture; Antiquarian; Author - Byron, Lord; Author - Coleridge, Samuel T.; Author - Keats, John; Author - Marvell, Andrew; Author - Shelley, Percy B. PR: £5–3,000. CC: MC; V. Cata: Byron & The Romantics, Slavery, Reference, E York. Mem: ABA; PBFA; ILAB. VAT No: GB 433 6879 22.

ESSEX

BILLERICAY

Engaging Gear Ltd., Lark Rise, 14 Linkdale, Billericay, CM12 9QW. Prop: D.E. Twitchett. Tel: (01277) 624913. Est: 1965. Private premises. Postal only. Appointment necessary. Small stock. Spec: Author - Moore, John; Horology; Sport - Cycling. PR: £5–500. Notes: *Stock includes titles on cycling history and travel.*

BIRCH

John Cowley, Auto–in–Print, Mill Lodge, Mill Lane, Birch, Colchester, CO2 0NG. Tel: (01206) 331052. Web: www.autoinprint.com. Est: 1975. Private premises. Internet and Postal. Appointment necessary. Very large stock. Spec: Automobilia/Automotive; Motoring; Booksearch; Ephemera.

BRENTWOOD

Book End, ■ 36–38 Kings Road, Brentwood, CM14 4DW. Prop: G.E. & M.K. Smith. Tel: withheld. Est: 1980. Shop open: **M:** 10:00–17:30; **T:** 10:00–17:30; **W:** 10:00–17:30; **Th:** 10:00–13:00; **F:** 10:00–17:30; **S:** 10:00–17:00. Medium stock. PR: £1–100.

CHELMSFORD

Christopher Heppa, 48 Pentland Avenue, Chelmsford, CM1 4AZ. Prop: Christopher Heppa. Tel: (01245) 267679. Est: 1982. Private premises. Internet and Postal. Appointment necessary. Medium stock. Spec: Author - Bates, H.E.; Author - Blyton, Enid; Author - Buchan, John; Author - Cornwell, Bernard; Author - Crofts, Freeman Wills; Author - Farnol, Jeffery; Author - Forester, C.S.; Author - Orwell, George. PR: £1–3,000. Cata: crime fiction; H.E. Bates; Modern firsts; Childrens. Corresp: Spanish. Mem: PBFA. Notes: *Exhibits at some PBFA Fairs and Long Melford Bookfair, Suffolk.*

COLCHESTER

Barcombe Services, 43 Church Lane, Colchester, CO3 4AE. Prop: Dr. Stephen M. Williams. Tel: (01206) 510461. Fax: (01206) 574420. Web: www.homepage.ntlworld.com/steve.williams7/book_menu. Est: 2004. Private premises. Internet and Postal. Appointment necessary. Small stock. Spec: Academic/Scholarly; Biography; Biology - General; Business Studies; Chemistry; Chess; Communication; Computing. PR: £1–20. Corresp: French, German. Notes: *The stock is relatively strong on academic titles. We offer discounts for multiple purchases and may be ready also to negotiate a lower price for any particular book.*

Castle Bookshop, ■ 40 Osborne St., Colchester, CO2 7DB. Prop: J.R. Green. Tel: (01206) 577520. Fax: (01206) 577520. Est: 1947. Shop open: **M:** 09:00–17:00; **T:** 09:00–17:00; **W:** 09:00–17:00; **Th:** 09:00–17:00; **F:** 09:00–17:00; **S:** 09:00–17:00. Very large stock. Spec: Archaeology; Aviation; First Editions; History - Local; Military History; Modern First Editions; Topography - General; Topography - Local. PR: £1–1,500. CC: MC; V; ask for others. Mem: PBFA; others - please ask. VAT No: GB 360 3502 89. Notes: *Over 40,000 books in stock.*

GfB: the Colchester Bookshop, ■ 92 East Hill, Colchester, CO1 2QN. Prop: Pauline & Simon Taylor. Tel: (01206) 563138. Web: www.gfb.uk.net. Est: 1983. Shop open: **M:** 10:00–17:30; **T:** 10:00–17:30; **W:** 10:00–17:30; **Th:** 10:00–17:30; **F:** 10:00–17:30; **S:** 10:00–17:30. Very large stock. Spec: Academic/Scholarly; Archaeology; Architecture; Art; Art Reference; Gardening - General; History - Ancient; History - British. PR: £2–200. Corresp: French. VAT No: GB 759 8699 37.

Quentin Books Ltd, 38 High Street, Wivenhoe, Colchester, CO7 9BE. Prop: Mr Paterson. Tel: (01206) 825433. Fax: (01206) 822990. Est: 1990. Storeroom; Internet and Postal. Appointment necessary. Medium stock. Spec: Author - Shaw, George Bernard; Author - Trollope, Anthony; Bibliography; Bindings; Biography; Books about Books; History - General; History - American. PR: £1–1,000. Corresp: French, German. Notes: *Local topography majors on Essex.*

DAGENHAM

John Thorne, 19 Downing Road, Dagenham, RM9 6NR. Tel: (020) 8592-0259. Web: www. liquidliterature.co.uk. Est: 1985. Private premises. Internet and Postal. Small stock. Spec: Beer; Brewing; Public Houses; Viticulture; Whisky; Wine; Wine - Burgundy. PR: £1–300. CC: PayPal. Cata: Wines, Beers, Spirits and related subjects. Notes: *Books on whisky sold via separate website at www.whiskywords.co.uk.*

GREAT DUNMOW

Clive Smith, Brick House North Street, Great Dunmow, CM6 1BA. Tel: (01371) 873171. Fax: (01371) 873171. Est: 1975. Private premises. Appointment necessary. Small stock. Spec: Antiquarian; Cookery/Gastronomy; Medicine; Military; Natural History; Topography - General; Topography - Local; Travel - General. PR: £10–1,000. Corresp: French, Indonesian. VAT No: GB 571 6001 67.

GREAT LEIGHS

Missing Books, 'Coppers', Main Road, Great Leighs, CM3 1NR. Prop: Chris Missing. Tel: (01245) 361609. Est: 1994. Private premises. Book fairs only. Appointment necessary. Small stock. Spec: Architecture; Biography; Cities - City of London; Countries - England; History - Local; Publishers - Black, A. & C.; Rural Life; Topography - General. PR: £2–500. CC: JCB; MC; V. Mem: PBFA. Notes: *Some stock displayed at Finchingfield antiques centre, Finchingfield, Essex.*

HARLOW

The First Edition, PO Box 2146, Harlow, Essex CM19 5AB. Prop: Pauras Kolah. Tel: (01279) 43 00 45. Web: www.the-first-edition.com. Internet and Mail order only. Small stock. Spec: Author - Barker, Cecily M.; Author - Barrie, J.M.; Author - Caldicott, R.; Author - Carroll, Lewis,; Author - Christie, Agatha; Author - Churchill, Sir Winston; Author - Conan Doyle, Sir Arthur; Author - Coward, Noel. CC: PayPal. Notes: *The First Edition is an international book dealer specialising in children's, modern first, and antiquarian books with (probably) the highest average number of images per book anywhere on the Net. You are guaranteed low prices and high service.*

HARWICH

The Book Annex, 18 Church Street, Harwich, CO12 3DS. Prop: Martin Ellingham and Peter J. Hadley. Tel: 01255 551667. Web: www.thebookannex.co.uk. Est: 2004. Shop and/or showroom; Telephone First. Spec: Art; Art - Technique; Art - Theory; Art History; Arts, The; Science - General; Science - Pure & Applied; University Press. CC: MC; V. Notes: *Wide ranging stock of Academic Titles including many remainders / overstocks as well as strong sections in History, Science, Arts subjects, Literature and Media. Visitors welcome by chance or ideally by appointment.*

Harwich Old Books (Peter J Hadley Bookseller Ltd.), ■ 21 Market Street, Harwich, CO12 3DX. Prop: Peter J. Hadley. Tel: (01255) 551667. Web: www.hadley.co.uk. Est: 1982. Telephone First. Shop open: **F:** 10:00–17:00; **S:** 10:00–17:00; **Su:** 13:00–17:00. Medium stock. Spec: Academic/Scholarly; Architecture; Art Reference; Artists; Arts, The; Illustrated - General; Limited Editions - General; Literature. PR: £1–5,000. CC: MC; V; Switch. Corresp: French, Italian. Mem: ABA; ILAB. VAT No: GB 489 0588 89. Notes: *Open by chance or by Appointment.*

HOLLAND-ON-SEA

Bookworm, ■ 100 Kings Avenue, Holland-on-Sea, CO15 5EP. Tel: 01255 815984. Prop: Miss H.P. Addison. Est: 1995. Shop open: **M:** 09:00–16:00; **T:** 09:00–13:00; **W:** 09:00–14:30; **Th:** 09:00–13:00; **F:** 09:00–14:30; **S:** 09:00–16:00. Large stock. Spec: Alpininsm/ Mountaineering; American Revolution, The; Annuals; Antiquarian; Artic/Antartica; Art; Art History. PR: £1.50-100 plus. Notes: *Find my E-bay shop at: http://stores/.ebay.co.uk/bookwormhos.*

LEIGH–ON–SEA

Caliver Books, ■ 816-818 London Road, Leigh–on–Sea, SS9 3NH. Prop: Dave Ryan. Tel: 01702 473986. Fax: 01702 473986. Web: www.caliverbooks.com. Est: 1983. Shop open: **M:** 09:00–18:00; **T:** 09:00–18:00; **W:** 09:00–18:00; **Th:** 09:00–18:00; **F:** 09:00–18:00; **S:** 09:00–18:00. Spec: Arms & Armour; Byzantium; Colonial; Fashion & Costume; Firearms/Guns; History - General; History - British Empire, The; History - Colonial. CC: E; MC; V; Paypal. Cata: 3 a year on specialities. Notes: *Mainly Military: History: Costume: Living History: Wargaming.*

Leigh Gallery Books, ■ 135–137 Leigh Road, Leigh–on–Sea, SS9 1JQ. Prop: Barrie Gretton. Tel: (01702) 715477. Fax: (01702) 715477. Web: www.abebooks.com/home/BOO/. Est: 1983. Shop open: **Th:** 10:00–17:00; **F:** 10:00–17:00; **S:** 10:00–17:00. Large stock. Spec: Art; Illustrated - General; Literature; Topography - Local; Ephemera; Prints and Maps. PR: £1–200. CC: AE; MC; V. Notes: *Large, reasonably priced, general stock plus ephemera, prints, records & CDs. Open 3 days, other times by appointment. Leigh is worth a visit... more bookshops, lots of charity shops, cafes, bars, pleasant walks and views. A nice day out.*

Othello's Bookshop, ■ 1376 London Road, Leigh–on–Sea, SS9 2UH. Prop: F.G. Bush & M.A. Layzell. Tel: (01702) 473334. Web: www.Othellos.org.uk. Est: 1999. Shop open: **T:** 09:30–17:00; **W:** 09:30–17:00; **Th:** 09:30–17:00; **F:** 09:30–17:00; **S:** 09:30–17:00. Medium stock. PR: £6–200.

MALDON

Philip Hopper, 29 Keeble Park, Maldon, CM9 6YG. Tel: 01621 850709. Est: 1985. Private premises. Internet and Postal. Small stock. Spec: Angling/Fishing; Occult; Folklore; Country Traditions. PR: £2–500. Cata: quarterley on Occult, Country Life and Angling.

MANNINGTREE

John Drury Rare Books, Strandlands, Wrabness, Manningtree, CO11 2TX. Prop: David Edmunds. Tel: (01255) 886260. Fax: (01255) 880303. Web: www.johndruryrarebooks.com. Est: 1971. Private premises. Appointment necessary. Small stock. Spec: Agriculture; Antiquarian; Banking & Insurance; Economics; Education & School; Fine & Rare; History - Dutch East India Company; History - Economic Thought. PR: £30–3,000. CC: JCB; MC; V; PayPal. Cata: Economics, Education, Law, Philosophy, Social History. Corresp: French. Mem: ABA; PBFA; ILAB. VAT No: GB 325 6594 41. Notes: *We specialise in fine & rare 17th, 18th & 19th century books, pamphlets & manuscripts, on a wide range of subjects, but broadly in the social & human sciences.*

RAYLEIGH

Fantastic Literature Limited, 35 The Ramparts, Rayleigh, SS6 8PY. Prop: Simon & Laraine Gosden. Tel: (01268) 747564. Fax: (01268) 747564. Web: www.fantasticliterature.com. Est: 1984. Private premises. Internet and Postal. Large stock. Spec: Author - Blackwood, A.; Author - Conan Doyle, Sir Arthur; Author - Crichton, Michael; Author - King, Stephen; Author - Pratchett, Terry; Author - Wells, H.G.; Fiction - Crime, Detective, Spy, Thrillers; Fiction - Fantasy, Horror. PR: £1–900. CC: E; MC; V; Switch, Paypal. Corresp: French. Notes: *Also, booksearch and scans available of any title.*

ROMFORD

Ken Whitfield, 5 Eugene Close, Romford, RM2 6DJ. Tel: (01708) 474763. Est: 1984. Private premises. Internet and Postal. Contactable. Open: **M:** 09:00–21:00; **T:** 09:00–21:00; **W:** 09:00–21:00; **Th:** 09:00–21:00; **F:** 09:00–21:00; **S:** 09:00–17:00; **Su:** 09:00–17:00. Small stock. Spec: Art; Biography; Entertainment - General; Fiction - General; History - General; Topography - General; Transport; Travel - General. PR: £2–80. CC: Paypal.

SAFFRON WALDEN

Lankester Antiques and Books, ■The Old Sun Inn, Church Street and Market Hill, Saffron Walden, CB10 1JW. Prop: Paul Lankester. Tel: (01799) 522685. Est: 1964. Shop open: **T:** 10:00–17:00; **W:** 10:00–17:00; **Th:** 10:00–17:00; **F:** 10:00–17:00; **S:** 10:00–17:00. Very large stock. Spec: Collectables; Ephemera; Prints and Maps. PR: £1–50. CC: MC; V.

SHENFIELD

Booknotes, 6 York Road, Shenfield, CM15 8JT. Prop: Tony Connolly. Tel: (01277) 226130. Web: www.ascon.demon.co.uk. Est: 1985. Private premises. Internet and Postal. Medium stock. Notes: *Moving in January 2008.*

SIBLE HEDINGHAM

Brad Books, The Downeys, Lamb Lane, Sible Hedingham, CO9 3RT. Prop: Arnold Bradbury. Tel: (01787) 460405. Est: 1995. Private premises. Internet and Postal. Telephone First. Spec: Aircraft; Americana - General; Antiquarian; Archaeology; Architecture; Army, The; Art; Autobiography. PR: £1–250.

SOUTH WOODHAM FERRERS

All Books, 83 Gandalfs Ride, South Woodham Ferrers, CM3 5WX. Prop: Mr. Kevin Peggs. Tel: (01245) 325628. Web: www.allbooks.demon.co.uk. Est: 1969. Private premises. Internet and Postal. Telephone First. Very large stock. Spec: Academic/Scholarly; Advertising; Aeronautics; Africana; Arts, The; Aviation; History - General; History - Renaissance, The. PR: £1–500.

SOUTHEND–ON–SEA

Gage Postal Books, P.O. Box 105, Westcliff–on–Sea, Southend–on–Sea, SS0 8EQ. Prop: (*) Simon A. Routh. Tel: (01702) 715133. Fax: (01702) 715133. Web: www.gagebooks.com. Est: 1971. Storeroom; Internet and Postal. Appointment necessary. Very large stock. Spec: Bibles; Biblical Studies; Ecclesiastical History & Architecture; Religion - General; Religion - Brethren; Religion - Catholic; Religion - Christian; Religion - Church of England. PR: £3–1,000. CC: MC; V. Cata: Theology Church History Religion. Corresp: German. Mem: PBFA. Notes: *Visitors welcome by appointment.*

Tony Peterson, 11 Westbury Road, Southend–on–Sea, SS2 4DW. Prop: Tony Peterson. Tel: (01702) 462757. Web: www.chessbooks.co.uk. Est: 1993. Private premises. Internet and Postal. Appointment necessary. Small stock. Spec: Chess. PR: £4–200. CC: PayPal. Cata: Chess.

STANSTED

Paul Embleton, 12 Greenfields, Stansted, CM24 8AH. Prop: Paul Embleton & Mrs. Gill Lebrun. Tel: (01279) 812627. Fax: (01279) 817576. Web: www.abebooks.com/home/embleton. Est: 1994. Private premises. Internet and Postal. Appointment necessary. Small stock. Spec: Advertising; Antique Paper; Artists; Children's - Illustrated; Collecting; Illustrated - General; Illustrators; Maritime/Nautical. PR: £5–1,000. CC: Paypal. Cata: Picture Postcards, Illustrated, Childrens. Notes: *Booksearch service. Books & ephemera for the picture postcard collector. Victorian & Edwardian Illustrated books & ephemera including greetings cards & chromolithographic scraps. Vintage jigsaws, board games etc.*

WESTCLIFF–ON–SEA

Clifton Books, 34 Hamlet Court Road, Westcliff–on–Sea, SS0 7LX. Prop: John R. Hodgkins. Tel: (01702) 430101. Est: 1970. Private premises. Internet and Postal. Appointment necessary. Large stock. Spec: Academic/Scholarly; Agriculture; Economics; History - British; Social History; Trade Unions; Transport. CC: AE; D; E; JCB; MC; V. Mem: PBFA. Notes: *All related to West Ham.*

Marjon Books, 16 Mannering Gardens, Westcliff–on–Sea, SS0 0BQ. Prop: R.J. Cooper. Tel: (01702) 347119. Est: 1975. Private premises. Appointment necessary. Small stock. PR: £2–120.

WICKFORD

Hugh MacFarlane Books, 40 Chaucer Walk, Wickford, SS12 9DZ. Prop: Mr H. MacFarlane. Tel: (01268) 570892. Web: www.tudorblackpress.co.uk. Est: 1997. Private premises. Internet and Postal. Appointment necessary. Small stock. Spec: Astronomy; Fine Printing; Printing; Private Press; Science - General; Typography. PR: £2–150. Cata: Scientific, Letterpress & Fine press. Notes: *Books on letterpress printing.*

WICKHAM BISHOPS

Baldwin's Scientific Books, Fossilis, 18 School Road, Wickham Bishops, Witham, CM8 3NU. Prop: Stuart A. Baldwin, PhC, BSc (Open), FGS, FLS, FRI. Tel: 01621 891526. Fax: 01621 891522. Web: www.secondhandsciencebooks.com. Est: 1962. Private premises. Internet and Postal. Appointment necessary. Open: **M:** 10:00–17:30; **T:** 10:00–17:30; **W:** 10:00–17:30; **Th:** 10:00–17:30; **F:** 10:00–17:30; **S:** 10:00–17:30; **Su:** 10:00–17:30. Spec: Antiquarian; Archaeology; Astronomy; Biography; Botany; Dinosaurs; Earth Sciences; Evolution. CC: MC; V. Cata: Geology, palaeontology, science, natural history. Mem: PBFA. VAT No: GB 219 1793 51. Notes: *We have 33 catalogues on www.booksatpbfa.com that are updated frequently. Our stock is accessible on ukbookworld.com/members/fossil. Our total stock comprises some 7,000 books, many journal runs & some 200,000 offprints/reprints.*

WOODFORD GREEN

Handsworth Books, 8 Warners Close, Woodford Green, IG8 0TF. Prop: Stephen Glover. Tel: (07976) 329042. Web: www.handsworthbooks.co.uk. Est: 1987. Private premises. Postal only. Medium stock. Spec: Academic/Scholarly; Applied Art; Company History; Fine Art; History - General; History - 19th Century; History - 20th Century; History - Ancient. PR: £2–650. CC: Paypal. Mem: PBFA.

Salway Books, 47 Forest Approach, Woodford Green, IG8 9BP. Prop: Barry Higgs. Tel: 020 8491 7766. Web: www.salwaybooks.co.uk. Est: 1995. Private premises. Contactable. Spec: Aeronautics; Aircraft; Archaeology - Industrial; Buses/Trams; Canals/Inland Waterways; Company History; Engineering; History - Industrial. CC: MC; V. Cata: Industrial & Transport History. Mem: PBFA.

GLOUCESTERSHIRE

BERKELEY

Volumes of Motoring, Hertsgrove, Wanswell, Berkeley, GL13 9RR. Prop: Terry Wills. Tel: (01453) 811819. Fax: (01453) 811819. Est: 1979. Private premises. Internet and Postal. Appointment necessary. Open: **M:** 08:00–22:00; **T:** 08:00–22:00; **W:** 08:00–22:00; **Th:** 08:00–22:00; **F:** 08:00–22:00; **S:** 08:00–21:00; **Su:** 09:00–22:00. Small stock. Spec: Motoring; Sport - Motor Racing. PR: £2–60. CC: MC; V. Notes: *Wide range of motoring remainders available to the trade.*

BISHOPS CLEEVE

Courtyard Books, ■Tarlings Yard, Church Road, Bishops Cleeve, Cheltenham, GL52 8RN. Tel: 01242 674335. Fax: 01242 674335. Web: www.courtyardbooks.co.uk. Est: 2000. Shop open: **M:** 09:00–17:00; **T:** 09:00–17:00; **W:** 09:00–17:00; **Th:** 09:00–17:00; **F:** 09:00–17:00; **S:** 09:00–17:00. Spec: Music - Jazz & Blues. CC: AE; MC; V. Cata: Jazz Books. Mem: BA. Notes: *Comprehensive range of books on jazz.*

CAMBRIDGE

Internet Bookshop UK Ltd., ■Unit 2, Wisloe Road, Cambridge, GL2 7AF. Prop: Mr. G. Cook. Tel: (01453) 890278. Fax: (0870) 442 5292. Web: www.ibuk.com. Est: 1996. Internet and Postal. Telephone First. Open: **M:** 09:00–17:00; **T:** 09:00–17:00; **W:** 09:00–17:00; **Th:** 09:00–17:00; **F:** 09:00–17:00. Very large stock. Spec: Academic/Scholarly; Alpinism/Mountaineering; Art; Aviation; Children's; Cookery/Gastronomy; Gardening - General; Military. PR: £8–1,000. CC: AE; MC; V; Switch.

CHALFORD STROUD

Surprise Books, 14 Padin Close, Chalford Stroud, GL6 8FB. Prop: John Norman. Tel: 01453 887403. Est: 1995. Private premises. Internet and Postal. Appointment necessary. Open: **M:** 09:00–17:30; **T:** 09:00–17:30; **W:** 09:00–17:30; **Th:** 09:00–17:30; **F:** 09:00–17:30; **S:** 09:00–17:30; **Su:** 09:00–17:30; Closed for lunch: 13:00–14:00. Spec: Annuals; Author - Bainbridge, Beryl; Author - Blyton, Enid; Author - Charteris, Leslie; Author - Cook, Beryl; Author - Cornwell, Bernard; Author - Crompton, Richmal; Author - Dahl, Roald. CC: MC; V. Mem: PBFA. VAT No: GB 811 2130 94.

CHELTENHAM

Cotswold Internet Books, Unit 2, Maida Vale Business Centre Maida Vale Road, Cheltenham, GL53 7ER. Prop: John & Caro Newland. Tel: 01242-261170 or 01242-261428. Web: www. cotswoldinternetbooks.com. Est: 1989. Warehouse; Internet and Postal. Shop open: **M:** 08:30–17:50; **T:** 08:30–17:50; **W:** 08:30–17:50; **Th:** 08:30–17:50; **F:** 08:30–17:50. Very large stock. Spec: Author - Johns, W.E.; Aviation; Children's; Classical Studies; Cookery/Gastronomy; Countries - General; Fiction - Crime, Detective, Spy, Thrillers; Military. PR: £5–300. CC: AE; E; JCB; MC; V; Maestro. Mem: ibooknet. VAT No: GB 535 5039 51. Notes: *Stock of over 60,000 out-of-print books on all subjects. Particularly strong in detective fiction and children's books.*

Bruce Marshall Rare Books, Foyers, 20 Gretton Road, Gotherington, Cheltenham, GL52 9QU. Tel: (01242) 672997. Fax: (01242) 675238. Web: www.marshallrarebooks.com. Est: 1972. Private premises. Appointment necessary. Small stock. Spec: Atlases; Colour-Plate; Natural History; Travel - General. Cata: Atlases; Voyages & Exploration; Natural History. Mem: ABA; ILAB. Notes: *Other specialities: Colour Plate; Early Illustrated; Kelmscott Press.*

Moss Books, ■ 8–9 Henrietta Street, Cheltenham, GL50 4AA. Prop: Christopher Moss. Tel: (01242) 222947. Est: 1992. Shop open: **M:** 10:00–18:00; **T:** 10:00–18:00; **W:** 10:00–18:00; **Th:** 10:00–18:00; **F:** 10:00–18:00; **S:** 09:00–18:00. Large stock. PR: £1–100. CC: JCB; MC; V. Corresp: Japanese. VAT No: GB 618 3105 62.

Peter Lyons Books, ■ 11 Imperial Square, Cheltenham, GL50 1QB. Prop: Peter Lyons. Tel: (01242) 260345. Est: 2000. Shop open: **W:** 10:00–17:00; **Th:** 10:00–17:00; **F:** 10:00–17:00; **S:** 10:00–17:00. Medium stock. Spec: Art; Art - Technique; Art - Theory; Art History; Art Reference; Artists; Arts, The; Children's. PR: £2–500. Notes: *Open at other times by appointment.*

Pittville Books, ■ 78A Marle Hill Parade, Cheltenham, GL50 4LH. Prop: Brecken McPhee. Tel: 001242245100. Est: 2007. Shop open: **M:** 10:30–17:00; **T:** 10:30–17:00; **F:** 10:30–17:00; **S:** 10:30–17:00. Spec: Academic/Scholarly; Aesthetics; Biblical Studies; Biology - General; Children's - Illustrated; Classical Studies; Criminal Law; Cultural Studies. CC: AE; D; E; JCB; MC; V. Notes: *It's always best to telephone ahead in winter.*

John Wilson Manuscripts Ltd, Painswick Lawn, 7 Painswick Road, Cheltenham, GL50 2EZ. Prop: John & Gina Wilson. Tel: (01242) 580344. Fax: (01242) 580355. Web: www.manuscripts.co.uk. Est: 1967. Private premises. Internet and Postal. Appointment necessary. Very large stock. Spec: Autographs; Documents - General; Manuscripts; Collectables; Ephemera. PR: £20–50,000. CC: AE; MC; V. Cata: Manuscripts. Corresp: French, Italian. Mem: ABA; ILAB; PADA. VAT No: GB 194 9050 39.

CHIPPING CAMPDEN

Draycott Books, ■ 2 Sheep Street, Chipping Campden, GL55 6DX. Prop: Robert & Jane McClement. Tel: Business (01386) 841392. Est: 1981. Shop open: **T:** 10:00–17:00; **W:** 10:00–17:00; **Th:** 10:00–17:00; **F:** 10:00–17:00; **S:** 10:00–17:30. Medium stock. PR: £1–1,000.

CIRENCESTER

Aviabooks, ■8 Swan Yard, West Market Place, Cirencester, GL7 2NH. Prop: Paul Gentil. Tel: (01285) 641700. Web: www.abebooks.com. Est: 1997. Shop open: **M:** 09:30–17:00; **T:** 09:30–17:00; **W:** 09:00–12:30; **Th:** 09:30–17:00; **F:** 09:30–17:00; **S:** 09:30–18:00. Small stock. Spec: Aeronautics; Antiques; Applied Art; Architecture; Art; Art - Technique; Art History; Art Reference. PR: £1–1,000. CC: AE; MC; V; Maestro. Mem: PBFA. Notes: *Also, some book fairs & specialist events, bookbinding & repair service available.*

Cirencester Arcade, ■ 25 Market Place, Cirencester, GL7 2NX. Prop: Paul Bird and Brian Ward. Tel: 01285 644214. Web: www.cirencesterarcade.co.uk. Est: 1995. Shop open: **M:** 09:30–17:00; **T:** 09:30–17:00; **W:** 09:30–17:00; **Th:** 09:30–17:00; **F:** 09:30–17:00; **S:** 09:30–17:00; **Su:** 11:00–17:00. CC: AE; MC; V.

COLEFORD

Past & Present Books, ■ 19a Gloucester Road, Coleford, GL16 8BH. Prop: Mr and Mrs J Saunders. Tel: 01594 833347. Shop open: **Th:** 16:00–17:30; **F:** 14:00–17:30; **S:** 10:00–17:30. Spec: Brewing; Industry; Mining; Topography - General; Topography - Local. Notes: *Major stockist of books on Gloucestershire and Forest of Dean - over 2,500.*

Simon Lewis Transport Books, PO Box 9, Coleford, GL16 8YF. Prop: Simon Lewis. Tel: 01594 839369. Web: www.simonlewis.com. Est: 1985. Mail order only; Internet and Postal. Appointment necessary. Open: **M:** 09:00–16:30; **T:** 09:00–16:30; **W:** 09:00–16:30; **Th:** 09:00–16:30; **F:** 09:00–16:30; Closed for lunch: 13:00–14:00. Spec: Buses/Trams; Motorbikes / motorcycles; Motoring; Railways and Railroads; Sport - Motor Racing; Traction Engines; Transport; Vintage Cars. CC: MC; V; Solo, Electron, Maestro. Cata: Car, Motorcycle, Truck & Bus, Rail. VAT No: GB 575 9030 21. Notes: *Anything Motoring, Motorcycles, Trucks, Buses, Trains, Planes & Boats related. Motor sport is our particular field. Regular bookstall run at Shelsley & Prescott speed hillclimb events & many other motor sport events during the season.*

FAIRFORD

Jacques Gander, 14 Keble Lawns, Fairford, GL7 4BQ. Tel: (01285) 712988. Est: 1996. Private premises. Internet and Postal. Spec: Children's; Modern First Editions. CC: MC; V; Debit.

KEMPSFORD

Ximenes Rare Books Inc., Kempsford House, Kempsford, GL7 4ET. Prop: Stephen Weissman. Tel: (01285) 810640. Fax: (01285) 810650. Est: 1965. Private premises. Appointment necessary. Small stock. Spec: Antiquarian. PR: £50–10,000. CC: MC; V. Corresp: French. Mem: ABA; PBFA; ILAB; ABAA. VAT No: GB 672 4533 30.

MINCHINHAMPTON

Christopher Holtom, 12 Butt Street, Minchinhampton, GL6 9JS. Tel: (01453) 884407. Est: 1972. Private premises. Postal only. Small stock. Spec: Antiquarian; Children's; Education & School; Fables; Folklore; Juvenile; Mathematics. PR: £3–150. Corresp: French.

MONTPELIER

Cooking = The Books, ■ 2 The Courtyard, Montpelier, Cheltenham, GL50 1SR. Prop: Dr Keith R. Aris. Tel: 01242 577908. Est: 1995. Shop open: **M:** 09:00–17:00; **T:** 09:00–17:00; **W:** 09:00–17:00; **Th:** 09:00–17:00; **F:** 09:00–17:00; **S:** 09:00–17:00. Spec: Cookery - Professional; Cookery/Gastronomy; Food & Drink; New Books. CC: JCB; MC; V; Mae, De. VAT No: GB 666 5230 26. Notes: *Greetings cards - many handmade. New, out of print and used cookery books only.*

MORETON–IN–MARSH

Jeffrey Formby Antiques, ■ Orchard Cottage, East Street, Moreton–in–Marsh, GL56 0LQ. Tel: (01608) 650558. Fax: (01608) 650558. Web: www.formby-clocks.co.uk. Est: 1993. Shop and/or gallery; Internet and Postal. Telephone First. Open: **S:** 10:00–17:00. Small stock. Spec: Horology; Scientific Instruments. PR: £5–500. CC: E; JCB; MC; V. Cata: Horology. Mem: British Antique Dealers Association. Notes: *Specialists in books on horology and related subjects.*

NAILSWORTH

Keogh's Books, ■Old Clothier's Arms,Market St, Nailsworth, GL6 0BX. Prop: J. Keogh. Tel: (01453) 833922. Web: www.keoghsbooks.com. Est: 1985. Internet and Postal. Shop open: **M:** 09:30–17:00; **T:** 09:30–17:00; **W:** 09:30–17:00; **Th:** 09:30–17:00; **F:** 09:30–17:00; **S:** 09:30–17:30. Small stock. Spec: Art; Art History; Art Reference; Artists; Countries - Ireland; Gloucestershire; History - Irish; Irish History & Literature. PR: £2–200. CC: AE; MC; V; SW.

NEWENT

Oakwood Books, 37 Church Street, Newent, GL18 1AA. Prop: Jim Haslem, A.L.A. Tel: (01531) 821040. Web: www.abebooks.com/home/oakwoodbooks. Est: 1987. Private premises. Internet and Postal. Appointment necessary. Small stock. Spec: Countries - England; Countries - Scotland; Countries - Wales; County - Local; History - Local; Local History; Topography - Local. PR: £2–450.

NEWNHAM ON SEVERN

Christopher Saunders (Orchard Books), Kingston House, High Street, Newnham on Severn, GL14 1BB. Prop: Chris Saunders. Tel: 01594 516030. Fax: 01594 517273. Web: www.cricket-books.com. Est: 1981. Office and/or bookroom; Appointment necessary. Open: **M:** 09:00–17:00; **T:** 09:00–17:00; **W:** 09:00–17:00; **Th:** 09:00–17:00; **F:** 09:00–17:00. Spec: Sport - Cricket. CC: MC; V; Maestro. Cata: on cricket. Mem: ABA; PBFA; ILAB.

OVER LANE

Michael Garbett Antiquarian Books, 1 Over Court Mews, Over Lane, Almondsbury, BS32 4DG. Prop: Michael & Jeanne Garbett. Tel: (01454) 617376. Fax: (01454) 617376. Web: www.michaelgarbett .theanswer.co.uk. Est: 1965. Private premises. Appointment necessary. Small stock. Spec: Bindings; Miniature Books. Mem: ABA. VAT No: GB 358 1080 58.

STOW–ON–THE–WOLD

Bookbox, ■Chantry House, Sheep Street, Stow–on–the–Wold, GL54 1AA. Prop: Pat Brown & Connie Fisher. Tel: (01451) 831214. Est: 1987. Shop open: **M:** 11:00–16:30; **T:** 11:00–16:30; **Th:** 11:00–16:30; **F:** 11:00–16:30; **S:** 11:00–17:00. Closed for lunch: 13:00–14:15. Medium stock. Spec: Arts, The; Author - Woolf, Virginia; Cookery/Gastronomy; Drama; Folio Society, The; Gardening - General; History - General; Sport - Field Sports. PR: £2–1,000. CC: MC; V. Mem: PBFA. Notes: *In winter, telephone first.*

Evergreen Livres, ■ 2 Talbot Court, The Square, Stow-on-the-Wold, GL54 1BQ. Prop: Nick & Stella O'Keeffe. Tel: (01451) 832253. Fax: (01367) 244773. Est: 1984. Shop open: **M:** 10:30–17:00; **T:** 10:30– 17:00; **Th:** 10:30–17:00; **F:** 10:30–17:00; **S:** 10:00–13:00. Small stock. Spec: First editions, General stoc; Horticulture; Natural History; Paperbacks 1940-1972; Publishers - Batsford PR: £2–500. Corresp: French. Notes: *Large stock of Batsford titles, Cotswolds, all categories stocked, many fiction titles deeply unfashionable but a darned good read. Sheet music from last century to date. Posta service. Good quality books bought esp. Batsford titles.*

Paper Moon Books, ■ 6 Durham House, Antiques Centre Sheep Street, Stow–on–the–Wold, GL54 1AA. Prop: Elaine Fletcher. Tel: 01451 870404. Fax: Shop (01451) 870404. Est: 1977. Shop and/or gallery; Shop open: **M:** 10:00–17:00; **T:** 10:00–17:00; **W:** 10:00–17:00; **Th:** 10:00–17:00; **F:** 10:00–17:00; **S:** 10:00–17:00; **Su:** 11:00–17:00. Spec: Bibles; Bindings; Gardening - General; Literature; Poetry; Prayer Books; Topography - General. PR: £5–300. CC: D; E; JCB; MC; V; Solo, Switch.

Wychwood Books, ■ Sheep Street, Stow–on–the–Wold, GL54 1AA. Prop: Miss. Lucy Baggott & Mr. Henry Baggott. Tel: 01451 831880. Fax: 01451 870631. Web: www.wychwoodbooks.com. Est: 2001. Shop open: **M:** 09:30–17:30; **T:** 09:30–17:30; **W:** 09:30–17:30; **Th:** 09:30–17:30; **F:** 09:30–17:30; **S:** 09:30–17:30. Medium stock. Spec: Antiques; Antiquities; Architecture; Art; Children's; Cookery/ Gastronomy; Literature; Modern First Editions. PR: £3–4,000. CC: MC; V. Mem: PBFA.

STROUD

Anthroposophical Books, Fromehall Mill - Blk 2 Rm 9 2nd Flr Lodgemore Lane, Stroud, GL5 3EH. Prop: H. & A. Tandree. Tel: (01453) 764932. Fax: (01453) 764 932. Est: 1988. Office and/or bookroom; Internet and Postal. Appointment necessary. Open: **M:** 09:00–18:00; **T:** 09:00–18:00; **W:** 09:00–18:00; **Th:** 09:00–18:00; **F:** 09:00–18:00. Small stock. Spec: Anthroposophy; Author - Steiner, Rudolf; Occult; Philosophy. PR: £8–50. CC: MC; V. Cata: Anthroposophy, Rudolf Steiner. Corresp: French, German. Notes: *Please call in advance for an appointment.*

Herb Tandree Philosophy Books, Fromehall Mill - Blk 2/Rm 9 Lodgemore Lane, Stroud, GL5 3EH. Prop: Herb Tandree. Tel: (01453) 764 932. Fax: (01453) 764 932. Web: www.philosophy-books.co.uk. Est: 2000. Office and/or bookroom; Internet and Postal. Appointment necessary. Open: **M:** 09:00– 18:00; **T:** 09:00–18:00; **W:** 09:00–18:00; **Th:** 09:00–18:00; **F:** 09:00–18:00. Medium stock. Spec: Academic/Scholarly; Economics; History of Ideas; Philosophy; Religion - General. CC: AE; JCB; MC; . Cata: Philosophy. Corresp: French, German. VAT No: GB 783 4154 17. Notes: *Please call in advance for an appointment.*

Ian Hodgkins and Company Limited, Upper Vatch Mill, The Vatch, Slad, Stroud, GL6 7JY. Prop: G.A. Yablon, I. Hoy, Simon Weager. Tel: (01453) 764270. Fax: (01453) 755233. Web: www .ianhodgkins.com. Est: 1974. Private premises. Internet and Postal. Appointment necessary. Medium stock. Spec: Applied Art; Art; Art Reference; Artists; Author - Austen, Jane; Author - Brontes, The; Author - Crane, Walter; Author - Gaskell, E. PR: £5–5,000. CC: MC; V. Mem: ABA; PBFA; BA.

Inprint, ■ 31 High Street, Stroud, GL5 1AJ. Prop: Joy & Mike Goodenough. Tel: (01453) 759731. Fax: (01453) 759731. Web: www.inprint.co.uk. Est: 1978. Internet and Postal. Shop open: **M:** 10:00–17:00; **T:** 10:00–17:00; **W:** 10:00–17:00; **Th:** 10:00–17:00; **F:** 10:00–17:00; **S:** 10:00–17:00. Medium stock. Spec: Applied Art; Architecture; Art; Art Reference; Cinema/Film; Fine Art; Gardening - General; Music - Popular. PR: £5–500. CC: AE; D; E; JCB; MC; V.

R & R Books, ■ Nelson Street, Stroud, GL5 2HL. Prop: Ruth Pyecroft & Ron Cree. Tel: (01453) 755788. Web: www.randrbooks.co.uk. Est: 1994. Shop open: **M:** 10:00–17:30; **T:** 10:00–17:30; **W:** 10:00–17:30; **Th:** 10:00–17:30; **F:** 10:00–17:30; **S:** 10:00–17:30. Medium stock. Spec: Advertising; Children's; Comic Books & Annuals; Comics; Culture - Popular; Earth Mysteries; Entertainment - General; Esoteric. PR: £1–20. CC: D; E; JCB; MC; V.

Alan & Joan Tucker, The Bookshop, Epworth Lodge Field Road, Stroud, GL5 2HZ. Prop: Alan and Joan Tucker. Tel: (01453) 764738. Fax: (01453) 766899. Web: www.abebooks.com/home/ SANDITON. Est: 1963. Mail order only; Internet and Postal. Appointment necessary. Small stock. Spec: Arts, The; Authors - Women; Children's; Fine Printing; Limited Editions - General; Literary Criticism; Literary Travel; Literature. PR: £1–100. CC: MC; V. Cata: Humanities, children's. VAT No: GB 275 0258 60. Notes: *Shop closed in 2006, now retired selling only part-time on internet, ABE and UKBookWorld. Over 40 years members of BA we have left as we no longer have a new book turnover.*

TETBURY

The Bookroom at Brown & White, ■ 3 Tetbury Upton, Tetbury, GL8 8AA. Prop: Brian & Margaret Jarvis. Tel: 078 3789 6270. Est: 2006. Office and/or bookroom; Shop open: **M:** 10:00–17:00; **T:** 10:00–17:00; **W:** 10:00–17:00; **Th:** 10:00–17:00; **F:** 10:00–17:00; **S:** 10:00–17:00; **Su:** 11:00–16:00. CC: MC; V. Notes: *Bookroom within an antiques centre.*

Tetbury Old Books, ■ 21 Long Street, Tetbury, GL8 8AA. Prop: Tetbury Old Books Ltd. Tel: (01666) 504330. Est: 1994. Shop open: **M:** 09:30–18:00; **T:** 09:30–18:00; **W:** 09:30–18:00; **Th:** 09:30–18:00; **F:** 09:30–18:00; **S:** 09:30–18:00; **Su:** 12:00–17:00. Small stock. Spec: General Stock; Publishers - Black, A. & C.; Prints and Maps. PR: £1–5,000. CC: AE; E; JCB; MC; V; Paypal.com. Mem: TADA. Notes: *Retail antiquarian, rare, collectable and second-hand book and print sellers prominently located in the centre of Tetbury. We have a carefully-selected general stock which varies from time to time. Some titles on abebooks.com.*

TEWKESBURY

Cornell Books, ■The Wheatsheaf, 132 High Street, Tewkesbury, GL20 5JR. Prop: Graham Cornell. Tel: (01684) 293337. Est: 1996. Internet and Postal. Shop open: **M:** 10:30–17:00; **T:** 10:30–17:00; **W:** 10:30–17:00; **Th:** 10:30–17:00; **F:** 10:30–17:00; **S:** 10:30–17:00. Large stock. Spec: Author - Moore, John; Children's; Countries - England; Countries - Scotland; Countries - Wales; Maps & Mapmaking; Prints and Maps. PR: £1–500. CC: AE; MC; V. Mem: PBFA. VAT No: GB 754 2601 43. Notes: *Stocks a range of Ordnance Survey Maps.*

WESTBURY-ON-SEVERN

Dive In Books, ■Dive In, Lecture Hall, The Village, Westbury-on-Severn, GL14 1PA. Prop: Patricia Larkham. Tel: (01452) 760124. Fax: (01452) 760590. Web: www.diveinbooks.co.uk. Est: 1975. Internet and Postal. Shop open: **M:** 09:00–14:00; **T:** 09:00–14:00; **W:** 09:00–14:00; **Th:** 09:00–14:00; **F:** 09:00–14:00. Small stock. Spec: Archaeology; Calligraphy; D.I.Y. (Do It Yourself); Deep Sea Diving; Maritime/Nautical; Natural History; Pacifism; Sport - Cycling. PR: £1–150.

GREATER MANCHESTER

ALTRINCHAM (SEE ALSO UNDER CHESHIRE)

Abacus Books, ■ 24 Regent Road, Altrincham, WA14 1RP. Prop: C.D. Lawton. Tel: 0161 928 2220. Est: 1979. Shop open: **T:** 10:00–17:00; **W:** 10:00–16:00; **Th:** 10:00–17:00; **F:** 10:00–17:00; **S:** 10:00–17:00; Spec: Antiques; Architecture; Art; County - Local; Natural History; Plant Hunting; Pottery & Glass; Watercolours.

Edward Yarwood Rare Books, 61 Fairywell Road, Timperley, Altrincham, WA15 6XB. Tel: (withheld). Est: 1994. Private premises. Postal only. Medium stock. Spec: Author - Gurdjieff, W.I.; Author - Wilson, Colin; Biography; Philosophy. PR: £5–250. Notes: *Also; book plates, manuscripts, booksearch and attends fairs.*

ATHERTON

Michael S Kemp Bookseller, 52 Oxford Road, Atherton, M42 9GB. Prop: Mike Kemp. Tel: 01942 870536 or 07711 856075. Web: www.kempbooksellers.co.uk. Est: 1979. Private premises. Appointment necessary. Spec: Antiquarian; Author - Peake, Mervyn; Bindings; Counties in England; Directories - British; History - General; Local Studies - Lincolnshire; Topography - General. CC: MC; V; Maestro. Cata: British Topography. Corresp: French. Mem: PBFA. Notes: *Stock includes books on Cheshire.*

BOLTON

Martin Bott (Bookdealers) Ltd., ■ 6 St.Leonards Avenue, Bolton, BL6 4JE. Prop: M.L.R. & M.H. Bott. Tel: (01204) 691489. Fax: (01204) 698729. Web: www.bottbooks.com. Est: 1997. Internet and Postal. Telephone First. Shop at: 28-30 Lee Lane, Horwich, Bolton, BL6 7BY. Open: **M:** 10:15–15:30; **T:** 10:15–15:00; **Th:** 10:15–15:00; **F:** 10:15–15:00; **S:** 10:30–16:00. Large stock. Spec: Archaeology - Industrial; Author - Rolt, L.T.C.; Aviation; Buses/Trams; Canals/Inland Waterways; Commercial Vehicles; Company History; Engineering. PR: £1–1,000. CC: AE; JCB; MC; V; Maestro, Solo. Cata: Transport & Industrial History. Also at: 28-30 Lee Lane, Horwich, Bolton, BL6 7BY. Notes: *Shop is usually closed during school holidays and some Saturdays - please telephone before travelling.*

Red Rose Cricket Books, 2 Kimberley Road, Bolton, BL1 7HZ. Prop: K.M. Tebay. Tel: 01204 308080. Web: www.redrosebooks.co.uk. Est: 1993. Office and/or bookroom; Internet and Postal. Appointment necessary. Small stock. Spec: Sport - Cricket. PR: £1–1,000. CC: MC; V; PayPal. Cata: cricket. VAT No: GB 693 2135 32. Notes: *Specialist cricket booksellers and publishers.*

DIDSBURY

Barlow Moor Books, 29 Churchwood Road, Didsbury, M20 6TZ. Prop: Dr. Roger & Dr. L.A. Finlay. Tel: (0161) 434 5073. Fax: (0161) 448 2491. VOIPpro: Skype. VOIPnum: drrogerfinlay. Est: 1990. Private premises. Postal only. Contactable. Small stock. Corresp: French. VAT No: GB 560 9236 38.

LITTLEBOROUGH

George Kelsall Booksellers, ■The Bookshop, 22 Church Street, Littleborough, OL15 9AA. Prop: George Kelsall and Ben Kelsall. Tel: (01706) 370244. Est: 1979. Shop open: **M:** 10:00–17:00; **T:** 13:00–17:00; **W:** 10:00–17:00; **Th:** 10:00–17:00; **F:** 10:00–17:00; **S:** 10:00–17:00. Large stock. Spec: Architecture; Art History; Art Reference; History - General; History - Industrial; Politics; Social History; Topography - Local. PR: £1–500. CC: AE; MC; V; Switch. Mem: PBFA. VAT No: GB 306 0657 81.

MANCHESTER

Camedia Ltd, Unit 1, Roundthorn House, Floats Road, Manchester, M23 9LJ. Prop: Paul Johnson. Web: www.bookacademy.co.uk. Est: 1996. Mail order only; Internet and Postal. Appointment necessary. Large stock. Spec: Academic/Scholarly; Black Studies; Culture - Popular; History - General; Holocaust; Homosexuality & Lesbianism; Irish Interest; Philosophy. PR: £1–50.

Browzers, Prestwich, Manchester, M25 9NE. Prop: Alan Seddon. Tel: 01617732327. Web: www.browzers.co.uk. Est: 1980. Mail order only; Internet and Postal. Contactable. Shop at: 2 Buckingham Road, Prestwich. Open: **M:** 09:00–17:30; **T:** 09:00–17:30; **W:** 09:00–17:30; **Th:** 09:00–17:30; **F:** 09:00–17:30; **S:** 09:00–17:30; **Su:** 09:00–17:30; Closed for lunch: 13:00–14:00. Spec: Antiques; Collecting; Horses; Sport - Horse Racing (inc. Riding/Breeding/Equestrian); Sport - Racing. CC: MC; V. Mem: ABA.

Classic Crime Collections, 95a Boarshaw Road, Middleton, Manchester, M24 6AP. Prop: Rob Wilson. Tel: (0161) 653-4145. Est: 1989. Private premises. Postal only. Small stock. Spec: Author - Christie, Agatha; Author - Creasey, John; Author - Fleming, Ian; Buses/Trams; Canals/Inland Waterways; Crime (True); Fiction - Crime, Detective, Spy, Thrillers; Railways and Railroads. PR: £2–400. Notes: *Also, a booksearch service.*

Franks Booksellers, Suite 33, 4th Floor, St Margaret's Chambers, 5 Newton Street, Piccadilly, Manchester, M1 1HL. Prop: H. Franks. Tel: (0161) 237-3747. Fax: (0161) 237-3747. Est: 1960. Office and/or bookroom; Appointment necessary. Open: **M:** 10:00–14:00; **T:** 10:00–14:00; **W:** 10:00–14:00; **Th:** 10:00–14:00; **F:** 10:00–14:00. Small stock. Spec: Advertising; Autographs; Children's; Cinema/Film; Comic Books & Annuals; Magazines & Periodicals - General; Magic & Conjuring; Performing Arts. PR: £1–1,000. Notes: *Also, postcards.*

Gibbs Bookshop Ltd., ■13 Howard Road, Northenden, Manchester, M22 4EG. Tel: (0161) 998-2794. Fax: (0161) 998-2794. Web: www.gibbsbookshop.co.uk. Est: 1922. Internet and Postal. Shop open: **M:** 10:00–17:00; **T:** 10:00–17:00; **W:** 10:00–17:00; **Th:** 10:00–17:00; **F:** 10:00–17:00; **S:** 10:00–17:00. Very large stock. PR: £5–50. CC: JCB; MC; V. Mem: ABA. VAT No: GB 145 4624 68.

Tim Kendall-Carpenter, 633 Wilmslow Road, Manchester, M20 6DF. Tel: (0161) 445-6172. Web: www.timkcbooks.com. Est: 1996. Private premises. Internet and Postal. Appointment necessary. Medium stock. Spec: First Editions; Modern First Editions; Poetry; Proof Copies; Signed Editions. PR: £5–1,000. CC: AE; MC; V; Maestro. VAT No: GB 781 2657 13.

The Little Bookshop, PO Box 134, Manchester, M8 4DJ. Prop: Valerie Clark. Tel: (0161) 740 1335. Web: www.littlebookshop.net. Est: 1989. Private premises. Internet and Postal. Medium stock. Spec: Arts, The; Autobiography; Biography; Fiction - General; History - General; Poetry; Religion - General; Travel - General. PR: £1–100. CC: PayPal. Notes: *Also sells new books under Thanatos Books.*

E.J. Morten (Booksellers), ■ 6 Warburton Street, Didsbury, Manchester, M20 6WA. Prop: John A. Morten. Tel: (0161) 445-7629. Fax: (0161) 448-1323. Est: 1959. Shop open: **M:** 09:30–17:30; **T:** 09:30–17:30; **W:** 09:30–17:00; **Th:** 09:30–17:30; **F:** 09:30–17:30; **S:** 09:30–17:30. Large stock. Spec: Military History; Sport - General; Travel - General. CC: MC; V; So, De. Cata: Military History. Corresp: French, German. Mem: PBFA; BA; BT, NBL.

Philip Nevitsky, P.O. Box 364, Manchester, M60 1AL. Tel: (0161) 228-2947. Fax: (0161) 236-0390. Est: 1974. Storeroom; Postal only. Small stock. Spec: Cinema/Film; Entertainment - General; Music - Popular; Collectables. Mem: Postcard Traders Assoc.

Star Lord Books, 72 Chester Avenue, Dukinfield, Cheshire, Manchester, SK16 5BW. Prop: Steve Starlord. Tel: (0161) 338-8465. Est: 1990. Private premises. Internet and Postal. Contactable. Small stock. Spec: Anthroposophy; Astrology; Author - General; Author - Wilson, Colin; Biography; Crime (True); Earth Mysteries; Eastern Philosophy. PR: £1–100. Notes: *Esoteric, Astrology, Theosophy, Occult, Kabbalah, QBL, Crowley, OTO, New Age, History, Socialism, Biography, general.*

Thanatos Books, PO Box 134, Manchester, M8 4DJ. Prop: Valerie Clark. Tel: 0161 740 1335. Est: 2000. Private premises. Internet and Postal. CC: PayPal. Notes: *For other details see under entry for The Little Bookshop, Manchester.*

The Treasure Island, 4 Evesham Road, Blackley, Manchester, M9 7EH. Prop: Ray Cauwood. Tel: (0161) 795 7750. Web: www.abebooks.com/home/RAYJC2000. Est: 2003. Private premises. Postal only. Appointment necessary. Small stock. Spec: Animals and Birds; Antiques; Art; Art - British; Autobiography; Autographs; Aviation; British Art & Design. PR: £1–50. CC: V.

MOTTRAM IN LONGDENDALE

Rose Books, 26 Roe Cross Green, Mottram in Longdendale, Hyde, SK14 6LP. Prop: (*) E. Alan Rose. Tel: (01457) 763485. Fax: (01457) 763485. Est: 1990. Private premises. Appointment necessary. Small stock. Spec: History - Local; Religion - Christian; Theology. PR: £2–150.

OLDHAM

Towpath Bookshop, ■ 27 High Street Uppermill, Oldham, OL3 6HS. Prop: (*) Janet and Martin Byrom. Tel: (01457) 877078. Est: 1992. Shop open: **T:** 11:00–17:00; **W:** 10:30–17:00; **Th:** 10:30–17:00; **F:** 10:30–17:00; **S:** 10:30–17:00; **Su:** 11:00–17:00. Small stock.

PRESTWICH

Ctesiphon Books, 14 Breeze Mount, Prestwich, M25 0AH. Prop: Ali Wahab. Tel: 01617731542. Web: www.ctesiphon.com. Est: 2003. Private premises. Internet and Postal. Open: **M:** 09:00–17:30; **T:** 09:00–17:30; **W:** 09:00–17:30; **Th:** 09:00–17:30; **F:** 09:00–17:30; **S:** 09:00–17:30; **Su:** 09:00–17:30; Closed for lunch: 13:00–14:00. Spec: Countries - Afghanistan; Countries - Algeria; Countries - Arabia; Countries - Arabian Peninsula; Countries - Asia; Countries - Asia Minor; Countries - China; Countries - Egypt. CC: PayPal.

RADCLIFFE

Delph Books, 437 Bury and Bolton Road, Radcliffe, M26 4LJ. Prop: Frank Lamb. Tel: 0161 764 4488. Web: www.delphbooks.co.uk. Est: 1979. Private premises. Internet and Postal. Telephone First. Open: **M:** 09:00–21:00; **T:** 09:00–21:00; **W:** 09:00–21:00; **Th:** 09:00–21:00; **F:** 09:00–21:00; **S:** 09:00–21:00; **Su:** 09:00–21:00. Spec: Antiquarian; Company History; County - Local; Directories - British; Education & School; Genealogy; History - Family; History - Industrial. CC: MC; V; Maestro. Corresp: French. Mem: PBFA. Notes: *I also stand at book fairs in the North of England. I have a good stock of Lancs & Yorks Parish Registers, Co-op histories, Golf club histories, Clocks & Watches, Rolls of Honour, Lancs & Yorks Topography, Local History and Dialect.*

ROCHDALE

Mrs. C. Crabtree, 35 Bankfield Lane, Norden, Rochdale, OL11 5RS. Tel: (01706) 655187. Web: www.http://ukbookworld.com/members/membooks. Est: 1995. Mail order only; Internet and Postal. Spec: Antiques; Art; Art - Technique; Autobiography; Biography; Cats; Collecting; Computing. PR: £2–100. CC: Cheque. Paypal, Postal Order.

Rochdale Book Company, 59 Bagslate Moor Road, Rochdale, OL11 5YH. Prop: J.S. & S.M. Worthy. Tel: (01706) 658300. Fax: (01706) 713294. Est: 1971. Warehouse; Appointment necessary. Large stock. Spec: Antiquarian; Architecture; Canals/Inland Waterways; Children's; Company History; Fine & Rare; History - Industrial; Illustrated - General. CC: MC; V. Mem: PBFA. Notes: *We have interesting books on most subjects plus a large stock of Lancashire material.*

STOCKPORT

Richard Coulthurst, 97 Green Pastures, Stockport, SK4 3RB. Tel: (0161) 431-3864. Est: 1995. Private premises. Postal only. Small stock. Spec: Aviation; Buses/Trams; Canals/Inland Waterways; Energy - Alternative; Energy - Fuels; Energy - General; Energy - Power; History - Industrial. PR: £5–100.

WIGAN

R.D.M. & I.M. Price (Books), 25 Coniston Avenue, Whitley, Wigan, WN1 2EY. Prop: Robert and Irene Price. Tel: (01942) 242607. Est: 1997. Private premises. Postal only. Small stock. Spec: Autobiography; Biography; Colonial; Countries - South Africa; Fiction - General; Booksearch. PR: £1–65.

Rolling Stock Books, ■16 Upper Dicconson Street, Wigan, WN1 2AD. Prop: Nick Howell. Tel: (01942) 493949. Est: 1996. Shop open: **T:** 10:00–17:00; **W:** 10:00–17:00; **Th:** 10:00–17:00; **F:** 10:00–17:00; **S:** 10:00–17:00. Medium stock. Spec: Buses/Trams; Canals/Inland Waterways; History - Industrial; Railways and Railroads; Transport; Booksearch. PR: £5–500. Cata: on transport. Mem: PBFA. VAT No: GB 692 8123 15. Notes: *Valuations, booksearch, some new books on transport.*

HAMPSHIRE

ALRESFORD

Bolton Books, 60 The Dean, Alresford, SO24 9BD. Prop: David Bolton. Tel: (01962) 734435. Fax: (01962) 734435. Web: www.boltonbooks.com. Est: 1997. Private premises. Internet and Postal. Appointment necessary. Small stock. Spec: Colour-Plate; Illustrated - General; Publishers - Black, A. & C.; Publishers - Foulis, T.N.; Topography - General. PR: £5–1,250. Mem: PBFA. Notes: *Also exhibits at bookfairs.*

Laurence Oxley Ltd, ■The Studio Bookshop 17 Broad Street, Alresford, Nr. Winchester, SO24 9AW. Prop: Anthony Oxley. Tel: (01962) 732188. Web: www.LAURENCEOXLEY.CO.UK. Est: 1950. Shop open: **M:** 09:00–17:00; **T:** 09:00–17:00; **W:** 09:00–17:00; **Th:** 09:00–17:00; **F:** 09:00–17:00; **S:** 09:00–17:00. Large stock. Spec: Countries - Far East, The; Countries - India; Topography - General; Topography - Local. PR: £1–25,000. CC: AE; D; MC; V. Mem: ABA; BA; FATG. VAT No: GB 188 5081 31. Notes: *Also, picture dealers, picture frame makers and restoration work.*

ALTON

Alton Secondhand Books, ■ 43 Normandy Street, Alton, GU34 1DQ. Prop: Mrs. J. Andrews. Tel: (01420) 89352. Est: 1989. Shop open: **M:** 09:30–17:30; **T:** 09:30–17:30; **W:** 09:30–17:00; **Th:** 09:30–17:30; **F:** 09:30–17:30; **S:** 09:30–17:00. Medium stock. Spec: Booksearch. PR: £1–100. VAT No: GB 631 9874 13.

Dance Books Ltd, The Old Bakery, 4 Lenten Street, Alton, GU34 1HG. Prop: David Leonard & John O'Brien. Tel: 01420 86138. Fax: 01420 86142. Web: www.dancebooks.co.uk. Est: 1960. Office and/or bookroom; Internet and Postal. Shop open: **M:** 10:00–16:00; **T:** 10:00–17:00; **W:** 10:00–17:00; **Th:** 10:00–17:00; **F:** 10:00–17:00. Spec: Dance. CC: E; MC; V. Mem: BA. VAT No: GB 238 6405 53.

Peter White Books, Westbrooke House, 76 High Street, Alton, GU34 1EN. Prop: Peter White. Tel: (01420) 86745. Fax: (01420) 86745. Est: 1995. Office and/or bookroom; Internet and Postal. Telephone First. Small stock. Spec: History - Local; Modern First Editions; Railways and Railroads; Sport - Football (Soccer); Topography - General; Transport. PR: £4–60. CC: MC; V. Corresp: French. Notes: *Also, stocks titles on local history in most counties.*

ALVERSTOKE

R.W. Forder, 12 St Mark's Road, Alverstoke, Gosport, PO12 2DA. Prop: R.W. Forder. Tel: (023) 9252-7965. Est: 1985. Private premises. Internet and Postal. Telephone First. Spec: Free Thought; Humanism; Radical Issues; Rationalism. PR: £1–200. Corresp: German. Notes: *Also, a booksearch service.*

ANDOVER

Any Old Books, Unit 17 Focus 303 Business Centre, Focus way, Andover SP10 5NY. Prop: Jeremy Lelean. Tel: (01264) 362620. VOIP: Skype. VOIP Adderess: anyoldbooks. Web: www.anyoldbooks.com. Est: 2003. Office and/or bookroom. Internet and Postal. Telephone first. Medium stock. Spec: Autobiography; Classics, The; Fiction - General; Fiction - Crime, Detective, Spy, Thrillers; Fiction - Historical; History - General; Military History; Modern First Editions. PR: £1–200 CC: AE; D; Euro; JCB; MC; V. VAT: GB 910 0466 69.

Armchair Auctions, 98 Junction Road, Andover, SP10 3JA. Prop: George Murdoch. Tel: (01264) 362048. Fax: (01264) 362048. Est: 1989. Private premises. Postal only. Small stock. Spec: Aviation; Military; Naval; War - World War I; War - World War II; Booksearch; Prints and Maps. PR: £5–500. CC: AE; MC; V. Notes: *Main activity: postal auctions.*

Countryside Books, Fouracres Penton Mewsey, Andover, SP11 ORA. Prop: Martin Smith. Tel: (01264) 773943. Est: 1978. Private premises. Postal only. Spec: Animals and Birds; Ornithology; Sport - Falconry. PR: £1–500. Mem: PBFA. Notes: *Mainly general stock.*

Sheppard's Confidential

- for calendars of book fairs and auctions

BASINGSTOKE

Byblos Antiquarian & Rare Books Ltd., Broadmead, 5 Worting Road, Basingstoke, RG21 8TL. Tel: 01256417092. Web: www.byblos.uk.com. VOIPpro: Skype. VOIPnum: henrystanton. Est: 2005. Private premises. Internet and Postal. Appointment necessary. Small stock. Spec: Antiquarian; Fine & Rare; Booksearch; Collectables. PR: £5–1,500. CC: AE; MC; V. Corresp: French, Italian.

Squirrel Antiques, 9a New Street Joices Yard, Basingstoke, RG21 DQ. Prop: Alan Stone. Tel: (01256) 464885. Est: 1981. Office and/or bookroom; Shop open: **M:** 10:00–17:30; **T:** 10:00–17:30; **W:** 10:00–17:30; **Th:** 10:00–17:30; **F:** 10:00–17:30; **S:** 10:00–17:30. Small stock. PR: £1–75. Notes: *Small general stock. Also antiques, curios and jewellery.*

BROCKENHURST

Hugh Pagan Limited, P.O. Box 354, Brockenhurst, SO42 7PS. Tel: (0) 1590 624455. Fax: (0) 1590 624455. Web: www.hughpagan.com. Est: 1987. Private premises. Internet and Postal. Appointment necessary. Spec: Antiquarian; Applied Art; Architecture; Architecture - Theatre; Art History; Art Reference; Arts & Crafts Era; British Art & Design. CC: MC; V. Cata: Architecture and the Allied Arts 16th to 20th cen. Mem: ABA; ILAB. VAT No: GB 468 6672 90.

CHILBOLTON

Nigel Phillips, The Cart House, Paddock Field, Chilbolton, SO20 6AU. Prop: Nigel Phillips. Tel: 01264 861186. Fax: 01264 860269. Web: www.nigelphillips.com. Est: 1981. Private premises. Appointment necessary. Medium stock. Spec: Antiquarian; History of Ideas; Medicine; Science - General; Science - History of; Technology. PR: £15–50,000. CC: MC; V. Cata: Medicine, science. Mem: ABA; ILAB. VAT No: GB 451 0394 74.

EMSWORTH

Bookends, ■ Gibson House, 7 High St., Emsworth, PO10 7AQ. Prop: Carol Waldron. Tel: (01243) 372154. Web: www.bookends.me.uk. Est: 1982. Shop open: **M:** 09:00–17:00; **T:** 09:00–17:00; **W:** 09:00–17:00; **Th:** 09:00–17:00; **F:** 09:00–17:00; **S:** 09:00–17:00; **Su:** 10:00–15:00. Large stock. Spec: Booksearch. PR: £1–300. Corresp: French. Notes: *Booksearches undertaken.*

Peter Hill, 3 Westbourne Avenue, Emsworth, PO10 7QT. Tel: (01243) 379956. Fax: (01243) 379956. Est: 1986. Private premises. Book fairs only. Appointment necessary. Open: **M:** 09:00–17:00; **T:** 09:00–17:00; **W:** 09:00–17:00; **Th:** 09:00–17:00; **F:** 09:00–17:00. Small stock. Spec: Alpinism/Mountaineering; Classical Studies; Countries - Antarctic, The; Countries - Arctic, The; Topography - Local; Travel - General. PR: £10–2,000. Corresp: French. Mem: PBFA.

FAREHAM

Portus Books, 9 Union Street, Fareham, PO16 9EB. Prop: Philip Elston. Tel: 01329 220419. Web: www.portusbooks.co.uk. Private premises. Postal only. Telephone First. Spec: Academic/Scholarly; Alpinism/Mountaineering; Author - Baker, Denys V.; Author - Churchill, Sir Winston; Author - Shute, Neville; Author - Thurber, James; Autobiography; British Art & Design. Corresp: German. Notes: *All books are accurately described, professionally packaged and promptly dispatched by an experienced book collector and dealer.*

FARNBOROUGH

Farnborough Gallery, 26 Guildford Road West, Farnborough, GU14 6PU. Prop: P.H. Taylor. Tel: (01252) 518033. Fax: (01252) 511503. Web: www.farnboroughgallery.co.uk. Est: 1978. Storeroom; Internet and Postal. Appointment necessary. Open: **M:** 08:00–18:00; **T:** 08:00–18;00; **W:** 08:00–18:00; **Th:** 08:00–18;00; **F:** 08:00–18:00; **S:** 08:00–17:00. Spec: Academic/Scholarly; Aircraft; Army, The; Art; Art - British; Art - Technique; Art - Theory; Art Reference. PR: £5–1,000. CC: AE; MC; V. Cata: military history, literature, travel, history. Mem: Fine Art Trade Guild. VAT No: GB 296 4807 13. Notes: *picture framing, mount cutting, framed artwork for sale.*

FLEET

War & Peace Books, 32 Wellington Ave., Fleet, GU51 3BF. Prop: Dr G.M. Bayliss. Tel: (01252) 677902. Fax: (01252) 677902. Web: www.abebooks.com. Est: 1998. Private premises. Postal only. Contactable. Small stock. Spec: Army, The; Aviation; Biography; History - 20th Century; Literary Travel; Literature; Maritime/Nautical; Military. PR: £5–100.

FORDINGBRIDGE

Bristow & Garland, 45–47 Salisbury Street, Fordingbridge, SP6 1AB. Prop: David Bristow & Victoria Garland. Tel: (01425) 657337. Fax: (01425) 657337. Web: www.bristowandgarland.co.uk. Est: 1970. Office and/or bookroom; Internet and Postal. Appointment necessary. Small stock. Spec: Autographs; Fine & Rare; Manuscripts. PR: £5–5,000. CC: MC; V. Cata: Manuscripts.

GOSPORT

Richard Martin Bookshop & Gallery, ■ 16 Cooperage Green, Royal Clarence Yard., Gosport, PO12 1AX. Prop: Directors - Richard and Elaine Martin. Tel: (023) 9252-0642. Web: www. richardmartingallery.co.uk. Est: 1976. Shop and/or gallery open: **Th:** 10:30–16:00; **F:** 10:30–16:00; **S:** 10:30–13:00. Medium stock. Spec: Antiquarian; Illustrated - General; Maritime/Nautical; Maritime/Nautical - History; Maritime/Nautical - Log Books; Naval; Navy, The; Topography - General. PR: £10–3,000. CC: MC; V. Cata: maritime, naval, voyaging, yachting, etc. Mem: PBFA. VAT No: GB 430 6603 81. Notes: *High quality restoration of watercolours and prints. Valuations for probate, insurance, family division, etc. Antiquarian book restoration. We would advise clients to phone ahead if travelling a long distance.*

Sub Aqua Prints and Books, 3, Crescent Road, Gosport, PO12 2DH. Prop: Kevin F. Casey. Tel: (023) 9252 0426. Fax: (023) 9250 2428. Web: www.buyhistoryprints.com. Est: 1991. Private premises. Internet and Postal. Appointment necessary. Small stock. Spec: Aviation; Conchology (see also Malacology); Deep Sea Diving; Fishes; Ichthyology; Marine Biology; Marine Sciences; Maritime/Nautical. PR: £5–1,000. CC: JCB; MC; V.

HAVANT

Coopercollectablebooks, 75 Farringdon Road, Havant, PO9 2LP. Prop: Mr B Cooper. Tel: 07850 596594. Web: www.http://stores.ebay.co.uk/coopercollectables. Mail Order only; Internet and Postal. Telephone First. Open: **M:** 09:00–19:00; **T:** 09:00–19:00; **W:** 09:00–19:00; **Th:** 09:00–19:00; **F:** 09:00–19:00; **S:** 09:00–19:00; **Su:** 09:00–19:00. Spec: Fiction - General; First Editions.

HAYLING ISLAND

DBS Childrens Collectable Books, 43 Sea Front, Hayling Island, PO11 0AN. Prop: Dennis Cowan. Tel: 02392 637456. Fax: 02392 637456. Web: www.dbschildrenscollectablebooks.com. Est: 1998. Private premises. Shop open: **M:** 10:30–17:30; **T:** 10:30–17:30; **W:** 10:30–17:30; **Th:** 10:30–17:30; **F:** 10:30–17:30.

HORNDEAN

Milestone Publications, Goss & Crested China Club, ■ 62 Murray Road, Horndean, PO8 9JL. Prop: Mrs. Lynda Pine. Tel: (023) 9259-7440. Fax: (023) 9259-1975. Web: www.gosschinaclub.co.uk. Est: 1970. Shop and/or showroom; Shop open: **M:** 09:00–16:00; **T:** 09:00–16:00; **W:** 09:00–16:00; **Th:** 09:00–16:00. Small stock. Spec: Antiques; Author - Goss, W.H.; Author - Hall S.C.; Author - Jewett, S.O.; Ceramics; Collectables; Collecting; Decorative Art. PR: £1–40. CC: E; JCB; MC; V; all others. Cata: Goss & Crested China. Mem: F.R.S.A. VAT No: GB 193 7217 45. Notes: *Open at other times by appointment Also, dealers in souvenir ware china, Goss & Crested china c.1850-1940, heraldic porcelain & new books of the same topics.*

LIPHOOK

Pauline Harries Books, 4, Willow Close, Liphook, GU30 7HX. Prop: Pauline Harries. Tel: 01428 723764. Fax: 01428 722367. Est: 1980. Private premises. Internet and Postal. Appointment necessary. Open: **M:** 09:00–17:30; **T:** 09:00–17:30; **W:** 09:00–17:30; **Th:** 09:00–17:30; **F:** 09:00–17:30; **S:** 09:00–17:30; **Su:** 09:00–17:30; Closed for lunch: 13:00–14:00. Spec: Antiques; Architecture; Art; Biography; Folio Society, The; General Stock; History - General; Literature. CC: JCB; MC; V; Switch, Maestro, Solo. Mem: PBFA.

LISS

William Duck, Highfield Farm, Hatch Lane, Liss, GU33 7NH. Prop: William Duck. Tel: (01730) 895594. Fax: (01730) 894548. Est: 1963. Private premises. Appointment necessary. Small stock. Spec: Architecture; Arms & Armour; Astronautics; Aviation; Canals/Inland Waterways; Cities - General; Civil Engineering; Decorative Art. PR: £10–5,000. Mem: ABA; PBFA.

LYMINGTON

Alastor Rare Books, 12 Wisbech Way, Hordle, Lymington, SO41 0YQ. Prop: J.A. Eaton. Tel: 01425 629756. Private premises. Appointment necessary. Spec: Antiquarian; Illustrated - General. Cata: Early English & Continental books. Corresp: Italian, French. Mem: PBFA.

M. & B. Clapham, ■ 4 Priestmands Place, Lymington, SO41 9GA. Prop: Peter Clapham. Tel: (01590) 677019. Est: 1978. Shop open: **M:** 10:00–17:00; **T:** 10:00–17:00; **W:** 10:00–17:00; **Th:** 10:00–17:00; **F:** 10:00–17:00; **S:** 09:00–17:00. Medium stock. Spec: Music - General; Sport - Yachting (& Boating). CC: MC; V.

MEDSTEAD

Soldridge Books Ltd, Soldridge House, Medstead, GU34 5JF. Prop: John & Jan Lewis. Tel: 01420 562 811. Fax: 01420 562811. Web: www.SoldridgeBooks.co.uk. Est: 1991. Private premises. Internet and Postal. Appointment necessary. Open: **M:** 09:00–17:30; **T:** 09:00–17:30; **W:** 09:00–17:30; **Th:** 09:00–17:30; **F:** 09:00–17:30; **S:** 09:00–17:30; **Su:** 09:00–17:30; Closed for lunch: 13:00–14:00. Spec: Aviation; Photography. CC: JCB; MC; V. Cata: Aviation, Photography. Corresp: French. Mem: PBFA. VAT No: GB 799 6939 25.

NEW MILTON

J.H. Day, 33 Ashley Common Road, New Milton, BH25 5AL. Tel: 01425 619406. Est: 1988. Private premises. Internet and Postal. Open: **M:** 09:00–17:30; **T:** 09:00–17:30; **W:** 09:00–17:30; **Th:** 09:00–17:30; **F:** 09:00–17:30; **S:** 09:00–17:30; **Su:** 09:00–17:30. Spec: General; General Stock; Sport - Horse Racing (inc. Riding/Breeding/Equestrian). CC: PayPal. Cata: General.

OAKLEY

David Flint, 30 Barn Lane, Oakley, Basingstoke, RG23 7HT. Prop: David Flint. Tel: 01256 781413. Est: 1985. Private premises. Postal only. Contactable. Spec: Art; Artists; Children's; Children's - Early Titles; Design; Ephemera. Cata: Children's & Illustrated.

OVERTON

David Esplin, 30 High Street, Overton, RG25 3HA. Tel: (01256) 771108. Est: 1978. Private premises. Postal only. Small stock. Spec: Astronomy; Mathematics; Medicine - History of; Natural Sciences; Physics; Science - History of; Technology. PR: £5–1,000. CC: MC; V; SW, So. Cata: History of Science, Medicine and Technology. Corresp: French.

PETERSFIELD

The Petersfield Bookshop, ■ 16a Chapel Street, Petersfield, GU32 3DS. Prop: Frank, Ann, John & David Westwood. Tel: (01730) 263438. Fax: (01730) 269426. Web: www.petersfieldbookshop.com. Est: 1918. Shop open: **M:** 09:00–17:30; **T:** 09:00–17:30; **W:** 09:00–17:30; **Th:** 09:00–17:30; **F:** 09:00–17:30; **S:** 09:00–17:30. Spec: Sport - Angling/Fishing; Travel - General; Booksearch; Prints and Maps. PR: £1–2,000. CC: AE; D; MC; V. Mem: ABA; PBFA; BA; ILAB. VAT No: GB 192 6013 72. Notes: *Also, maps, prints, new books, art materials, picture framing & a booksearch service.*

David Schutte, 'Waterside', 119 Sussex Road, Petersfield, GU31 4LB. Tel: (01730) 269115. Fax: (01730) 231177. Web: www.http://davidschutte.co.uk. Est: 1980. Private premises. Internet and Postal. Appointment necessary. Spec: Author - Blyton, Enid; Author - Buckeridge, A.; Author - Crompton, Richmal; Author - Johns, W.E.; Author - Ransome, Arthur; Author - Richards, Frank; Author - Saville, M.; Children's. PR: £3–1,500. CC: MC; V. Cata: Children's and original artwork. Mem: PBFA.

PORTSMOUTH

Art Reference Books, 3 Portswood Road, Portsmouth, PO2 9QX. Prop: Andy Ralph. Tel: (023) 92790861. Fax: (023 92650761. Web: www.artreferencebooks.com. Est: 1999. Private premises. Internet and Postal. Appointment necessary. Medium stock. Spec: Antiquarian; Antiques; Applied Art; Architecture; Art; Art History; Art Reference; Artists. PR: £2–1,000. CC: E; MC; V.

PURBROOK

Hobgoblin Books, 66 Privett Road, Purbrook, PO7 5JW. Prop: Jacqueline & Philip Barrett. Tel: (023) 9271-3129. Est: 1988. Private premises. Appointment necessary. Medium stock. Spec: Authors - Women; Countries - China; Countries - Japan; Folklore; Medieval; Women. PR: £5–500. CC: PayPal.

RINGWOOD

E. Chalmers Hallam, Trees, 9 Post Office Lane, St. Ives, Ringwood, BH24 2PG. Prop: Laura Hiscock. Tel: (01425) 470060. Fax: (01425) 470060. Web: www.hallam-books.co.uk. Est: 1946. Private premises. Internet and Postal. Appointment necessary. Large stock. Spec: Africana; Anthropology; Arms & Armour; Author - Baden-Powell, Lord Robert; Author - Chapman, Abel; Author - Dinesen, Isak; Author - Jefferies, R.; Author - Niall, Ian. PR: £5–5,000. CC: MC; V; Debit card. Cata: Angling. Africa. Travel. Field Sports. BB. Guns. Mem: PBFA.

ROMSEY

Bufo Books, 32 Tadfield Road, Romsey, SO51 5AJ. Prop: Ruth Allen & Peter Hubbard. Tel: (01794) 517149. Fax: (08700) 516786. Web: www.bufobooks.demon.co.uk. Est: 1979. Private premises. Internet and Postal. Appointment necessary. Medium stock. Spec: Military; War - General. PR: £1–200. CC: JCB; MC; V; Maestro/Switch. Cata: Military. Corresp: basic French. Mem: PBFA; Cardsave. VAT No: GB 522 4988 32. Notes: *Mainly internet & postal but we also still exhibit at a few bookfairs each year.*

SOUTHAMPTON

Vincent G. Barlow, 24 Howerts Close, Warsash, Southampton, SO31 9JR. Tel: (01489) 582431. Est: 1981. Storeroom; Book fairs only. Appointment necessary. Small stock. Spec: Art Reference; Catalogues Raisonnes; Children's - Illustrated; Decorative Art; Fine Printing; Graphics; Illustrated - General; Illustrated - 19th & 20th Century. PR: £3–2,000. CC: none. Mem: PLA; IBIS. Notes: *Attends monthly fairs at Royal National. Also prints.*

Broadwater Books, 62 Britannia Gardens, Hedge End, Southampton, SO30 2RP. Prop: J.E. Dancy. Tel: (01489) 786035. Est: 1988. Private premises. Postal only. Large stock. Spec: Author - General; Author - Wheatley, Dennis; Countries - England; Countries - Great Britain; Countries - Melanesia; Countries - Scotland; History - General; History - European. PR: £1–400. Notes: *Also, wants lists welcomed.*

Fair Hair Books, ■ Botley Mills, Mill Hill, Botley SO30 2GB. Prop: Nancy Hamilton. Tel: (01489) 795917. Shop open: **M:** 10:00–16:00; **T:** 10:00–16:00; **W:** 10:00–16:00; **Th:** 10:00–16:00; **F:** 10:00–16:00; **S:** 10:00–16:00. Small stock. PR: £1-150. Notes: *New, small village shop with good general stock across the board, intending to build up natural sciences, oceanography and exploration.*

W.E. Jackson, 6 Shepherds Close, Bartley, Southampton, SO40 2LJ. Prop: Bill Jackson. Tel: (023) 80812640. Est: 1988. Private premises. Postal only. Telephone First. Small stock. PR: £1–100. Notes: *Also organiser of Southampton and Winchester Book Fairs - and attends other fairs.*

Morley Case, 24 Wildburn Close, Calmore, Southampton, SO40 2SG. Prop: David Case. Tel: (023) 8086-4264. Web: www.abebooks.com/home/case. Est: 1973. Private premises. Internet and Postal. Appointment necessary. Small stock. Spec: Art; Aviation; Military; Sport - Golf. PR: £5–200. CC: Pay Pal.

Peter Rhodes, Bookseller, ■ 21 Portswood Road, Southampton, SO17 2ES. Tel: (02380) 399003. Est: 1996. Shop open: **T:** 10:00–17:00; **W:** 10:00–17:00; **Th:** 10:00–17:00; **F:** 10:00–17:00; **S:** 10:00–17:00. Large stock. Spec: Anthropology; Author - 20th Century; Children's - Illustrated; Countries - India; Photography; Theatre. Notes: *Insurance and probate valuation. Also coffee shop.*

SOUTHSEA

Palladour Books, 23 Eldon Street, Southsea, PO5 4BS. Prop: Jeremy & Anne Powell. Tel: (02392) 826935. Fax: (02392) 826935. Est: 1985. Private premises. Internet and Postal. Appointment necessary. Small stock. Spec: First Editions; Literature; Magazines & Periodicals - General; Military; Poetry; School Registers/Rolls of Honour; War - General; War - World War I. PR: £1–500. Cata: World War One poetry and literature.

Jade Mountain Bookshop, ■ 17-19 Highland Road, Southsea, Portsmouth, PO4. 9AD. Prop: Mr. Ian Stemp. Tel: 023 9273 2951. Web: www.jademountain.co.uk. Est: 1990. Shop open: **M:** 09:30–17:30; **W:** 09:30–17:30; **F:** 09:30–17:30; **S:** 09:30–17:30. Spec: Accountancy; Agriculture; Aircraft; Animals and Birds; Antiquarian; Antiques; Archaeology; Architecture.

TITCHFIELD

Ardis Books, 3, Mill Street, Titchfield, Fareham, PO14 4AB. Prop: Robert Newbury. Tel: 01329 517724. Web: www.ardis.co.uk. Est: 1989. Mail order only; Internet only. Telephone First. Open: **M:** 09:00–17:30; **T:** 09:00–17:30; **W:** 09:00–17:30; **Th:** 09:00–17:30; **F:** 09:00–17:30; **S:** 09:00–17:30; **Su:** 09:00–17:30; Closed for lunch: 13:00–14:00. Spec: Antiquarian; Author - Johns, W.E.; Author - Saville, M.; Bibles; Business Studies; Comics; Commerce - General; Computing. VAT No: GB 522 2143 96.

WARSASH

Warsash Nautical Bookshop, ■ 6 Dibles Road, Warsash, Southampton, SO31 9HZ. Prop: Mr. Andrew Marshall. Tel: (01489) 572384. Fax: (01489) 885756. Web: www.nauticalbooks.co.uk. Est: 1973. Internet and Postal. Shop open: **M:** 09:00–17:30; **T:** 09:00–17:30; **W:** 09:00–17:30; **Th:** 09:00–17:30; **F:** 09:00–17:30; **S:** 09:30–17:00. Small stock. Spec: Academic/Scholarly; Maritime/Nautical; Maritime/Nautical - Log Books; Navigation; Booksearch; Prints and Maps. PR: £5–500. CC: AE; D; E; JCB; MC; V. Mem: BA. VAT No: GB 108 3293 82.

WINCHESTER

H.M. Gilbert & Son, 5 Rooks Down, Winchester, SO22 4QN. Prop: Richard Gilbert. Tel: (023) 8022-6420. Est: 1859. Private premises. Appointment necessary. Small stock. Spec: Antiquarian; Literature; Topography - General; Topography - Local. PR: £1–500. CC: MC; V. Mem: PBFA.

John Barton, 84 Old Kennels Lane, Winchester, SO22 4JT. Tel: 01962 866543. Est: 1966. Private premises. Postal only. Appointment necessary. Spec: Archaeology; History - Local; Topography - Local.

Kingsgate Books & Prints, ■ Kingsgate Arch, Winchester, SO23 9PD. Prop: Michael Fowkes. Tel: (01962) 864710. Fax: (01962) 864710. Est: 1992. Shop open: **T:** 12:30–17:00; **W:** 12:30–17:00; **Th:** 12:30–17:00; **F:** 12:30–17:00; **S:** 10:30–17:00. Small stock. Spec: Art History; Art Reference; History - Local; Literary Criticism; Literature; Natural History; Poetry; Prints and Maps. PR: £1–150. CC: AE; MC; V; Any.

Peter M Daly, Ronald Bowker Court, Greenhill Road, Winchester, SO22 5EA. Prop: Peter Daly. Tel: 01962 867732. Fax: 01962 867732. Est: 1978. Office and/or bookroom; Internet and Postal. Appointment necessary. Open: **M:** 10:30–17:00; **T:** 10:30–17:00; **W:** 10:30–17:00; **Th:** 10:30–17:00; **F:** 10:30–17:00; **S:** 10:30–16:30; Closed for lunch: 13:00–14:00. Small stock. Spec: Africana; Agriculture; Alpinism/Mountaineering; Animals and Birds; Anthropology; Antiquarian; Antiques; Applied Art. PR: 2.50–2,000. CC: JCB; MC; V; Solo, Maestro, Switch. Mem: PBFA. VAT No: GB 411 8630 76. Notes: *Books are listed online at ABE, Biblio, Antiqbook & PBFA.*

S.P.C.K., ■ 24 The Square, Winchester, SO23 9EX. Tel: (01962) 866617. Fax: (01962) 890312. Est: 1698. Shop open: **M:** 09:00–16:30; **T:** 08:00–17:30; **W:** 09:00–17:30; **Th:** 09:00–17:30; **F:** 09:00–17:30; **S:** 08:00–17:30. Large stock. Spec: Religion - Christian; Theology; Booksearch. PR: £1–300. CC: MC; V. Mem: BA. VAT No: GB 232 8071 82. Notes: *Also, wide Christian booksearch service.*

Sen Books, 3 Long Barrow Close, South Wonston, Winchester, SO21 3ED. Prop: Andrew Duckworth. Tel: (01962) 884405. Fax: (01962) 884405. Est: 1975. Private premises. Appointment necessary. Small stock. Spec: Author - Trollope, Anthony; Author - White, Gilbert; Booksearch; Collectables; Ephemera; Prints and Maps. PR: £1–200.

The Winchester Bookshop, ■ (next to Ladbroke's) 10a St George's Street, Winchester, SO23 8BG. Prop: Messrs Barnes & Brown. Tel: 01962855630. Est: 1991. Shop open: **M:** 10:00–17:00; **T:** 10:00–17:00; **W:** 10:00–17:00; **Th:** 10:00–17:00; **F:** 10:00–17:00; **S:** 10:00–17:00. Spec: Academic/Scholarly; Antiquarian; Archaeology; Architecture; Army, The; Art; Canals/Inland Waterways; Civil Engineering. CC: MC; V; Most debit cards. Corresp: German. Notes: *A general bookshop, with particular strengths in Winchester local history, fishing and literature. Some good antiquarian and modern firsts are stocked.*

HEREFORDSHIRE

ASHPERTON

Books for Content, Spring Grove Farm, Woodend, Ashperton, Ledbury, HR8 2RS. Prop: H.M. Jones. Tel: (01432) 890279. Est: 1989. Private premises. Postal only. Small stock. Spec: Agriculture; Author - Street, A.G.; Cookery/Gastronomy; Crafts; Farming & Livestock; Gardening - General; Horticulture; Rural Life. PR: £3–100. Notes: *Booksearch service incorporates the Hilary Rittner Booksearch which is now closed.*

GLASBURY

babelog books, Victoria House, Glasbury, Hereford, HR3 5NR. Prop: Simon Cartwright. Tel: (01497) 847190. Web: www.ukbookworld.com/members/mason. Est: 2000. Private premises. Postal only. Appointment necessary. Small stock. Spec: Drama; English; Fiction - General; Literature; Literature - 19th C; Literature in Translation; Modern First Editions; Plays. PR: £5–1,000.

HAY–ON–WYE

Backfold Books, ■ Oxford Road, Hay–on–Wye, HR3 5DG. Prop: Ms A. Harrison. Tel: 01497 820171. Est: 1999. Shop open: **M:** 10:00–16:30; **T:** 10:00–16:30; **W:** 10:00–16:30; **Th:** 10:00–16:30; **F:** 10:00–16:30; **S:** 10:00–16:30; **Su:** 10:00–16:00. Medium stock. Spec: Animals and Birds; Authors - Women; Autobiography; Canals/Inland Waterways; Cats; Children's; Children's - Illustrated; Cookery/Gastronomy. PR: £1–200. CC: E; MC; V.

Richard Booth's Bookshop, ■ 44 Lion Street, Hay–on–Wye, HR3 5AA. Prop: Elizabeth Haycox and Paul Greatbatch. Tel: (01497) 820322. Fax: (01497) 821150. Web: www.richardbooth.demon.co.uk. Est: 1961. Shop open: **M:** 09:00–17:30; **T:** 09:00–17:30; **W:** 09:00–17:30; **Th:** 09:00–17:30; **F:** 09:00–17:30; **S:** 09:00–17:30; **Su:** 11:00–17:00. Very large stock. PR: £1–1,000. CC: JCB; MC; V. Mem: WBA. VAT No: GB 915 9365 00. Notes: *We buy books from all over the U.K. Over 400,000 titles in an extensive range of subjects. Late opening during Hay Festival.*

The Children's Bookshop, ■ Toll Cottage, Pontvaen, Hay–on–Wye, HR3 5EW. Prop: Judith M Gardner. Tel: (01497) 821083. Web: www.childrensbookshop.com. Est: 1980. Internet and Postal. Shop open: **M:** 09:30–17:30; **T:** 09:30–13:00; **W:** 09:30–17:30; **Th:** 09:30–17:30; **F:** 09:31–17:30; **S:** 09:30–17:30. Medium stock. Spec: Author - Aldin, Cecil; Author - Ardizzone, Edward; Author - Brent-Dyer, Elinor M.; Author - Buckeridge, A.; Author - Caldicott, R.; Author - Crompton, Richmal; Author - Dahl, Roald; Author - Dr. Zeuss. PR: £5–500. CC: JCB; MC; V. Corresp: French, German. Notes: *Hay-on-Wye (q.v.) Also, a booksearch service.*

David Lees, The Kimberley's, Saint Mary's Road, Hay–on–Wye, HR3 5EA. Prop: David Lees. Web: www.davidleesbooks.com. Est: 1985. Mail order only; Internet and Postal. Medium stock. Spec: Antiquarian. PR: £1–1,000. CC: MC; V; Debit Card. VAT No: GB 488 7008 07. Notes: *Selected fairs also Attended.*

Outcast Books, ■ 15a Broad St., Hay–on–Wye, HR3 5DB. Prop: David Howard. Tel: (01497) 821292. Web: www.ukbookworld.com/members/outcastbooks. Est: 1993. Shop open: **M:** 10:30–17:00; **T:** 10:30–17:00; **W:** 10:30–17:00; **Th:** 10:30–17:00; **F:** 10:30–17:00; **S:** 11:30–17:00; **Su:** 12:00–14:00. Small stock. Spec: Academic/Scholarly; Alternative Medicine; Counselling; Medicine; Psychoanalysis; Psychology/Psychiatry; Psychotherapy; Self-Help. PR: £1–150. CC: AE; E; JCB; MC; V. Cata: Applied social studies, psychology, medicine. Mem: Welsh Booksellers Association. Notes: *Specialising in material of a therapeutic nature, for people working in the caring professions, or anyone interested in self-improvement*

HEREFORD

D. & D.H.W. Morgan (est 1977), The Pippens, Allensmore, Hereford HR2 9HB. Prop: D. & D.H.W. Morgan. Tel: (01432) 276054. Private premises. Postal only. Medium stock. PR: 50p upwards. Cata: occssionally on Gardening and Botany, Bird & Natural History and Periodicals. Notes: *Gardening and Botany £1-50; Bird and Natural History Periodicals 50p up.*

The New Strand, ■ Eardisley, Hereford, HR3 6PW. Prop: Mr & Mrs R. Cardwell. Tel: 01544 327285. Fax: 01544 327285. Web: www.thenewstrand.co.uk. Est: 1986. Shop open: **M:** 09:30–19:00; **W:** 09:30–19:00; **Th:** 09:30–19:00; **F:** 09:30–19:00; **S:** 09:30–19:00; **Su:** 09:30–19:00. Spec: Agriculture; Animals and Birds; Antiques; Art; Children's; Fiction - General; Folio Society, The; Food & Drink. CC: MC; V. Notes: *Closed in January.*

B.A. & C.W.M. Pratt, Huntington House, Huntington Lane, Hereford, HR4 7RA. Tel: (01432) 350927. Fax: (01432) 350927. Est: 1967. Private premises. Postal only. Spec: Medicine.

KINGTON

Castle Hill Books, ■ 12 Church Street, Kington, HR5 3AZ. Prop: Peter Newman. Tel: (01544) 231195/ 231161. Fax: (01544) 231161. Web: www.castlehillbooks.co.uk. Est: 1987. Shop open: **M:** 10:30– 13:00; **T:** 10:30–13:00; **W:** 10:30–13:00; **Th:** 10:30–13:00; **F:** 10:30–13:00; **S:** 10:30–16:00. Very large stock. Spec: Agriculture; Antiquarian; Archaeology; History - General; History - Local; Natural History; Topography - General; Topography - Local. PR: £3–15,000. CC: MC; V. Cata: Catalogues issued on request. Mem: BA. VAT No: GB 489 2054 19. Notes: *Also, new books and maps in stock.*

LEDBURY

Keith Smith Books, ■ 78b The Homend, Ledbury, HR8 1BX. Prop: Keith Smith. Tel: Day (01531) 635336. Est: 1986. Shop open: **T:** 10:00–17:00; **W:** 10:00–17:00; **Th:** 10:00–17:00; **F:** 10:00–17:00; **S:** 10:00–17:00. Medium stock. Spec: Author - Brooke, Rupert; Author - Dymock Poets, The; Author - Frost, Robert; Author - Masefield, John; Author - Thomas, Edward; Crafts; Embroidery; History - General. PR: £1–250. CC: E; JCB; MC; V; Switch, Delta. Cata: Needlecrafts, Textiles and Rugmaking. Notes: *General secondhand booksellers specialising in The Dymock Poets, First World War Poetry. Ivor Gurney, F.W. Harvey, Needlecrafts and Local Interest Books.*

LEOMINSTER

Hummingbird Books, ■ 16 South Street, Leominster, HR6 8JB. Prop: Jill Gibbs. Tel: (01568) 616471. Est: 2001. Shop open: **T:** 10:00–17:00; **W:** 10:00–17:00; **Th:** 10:00–17:00; **F:** 10:00–17:00; **S:** 09:00– 16:00. Medium stock. Spec: Illustrated - General; Maritime/Nautical; Military History; Sport - General; Topography - General. CC: AE; MC; V. Notes: *Concession at 6 Broad Street, Hay-on-Wye specialising in maritime, military and sport.*

ROSS-ON-WYE

Ross Old Books, ■ 51 & 52 High Street, Ross–on–Wye, HR9 5HH. Prop: Phil Thredder. Tel: +44 (0)1989 567458. Web: www.rossoldbooks.co.uk. Est: 1986. Internet and Postal. Shop open: **W:** 10:00– 17:00; **Th:** 10:00–17:00; **F:** 10:00–17:00; **S:** 10:00–17:00. Medium stock. Spec: Folio Society, The; History - Local; Local History; Topography - General; Topography - Local; Prints and Maps. PR: £1–1,000. CC: AE; MC; V; SW, SO. Mem: PBFA. VAT No: GB 435 3892 33. Notes: *From June 2008 we will be dealing from home specialising in U.K. Topography, Books, Maps, Guides, Prints and Ephemera on www.springwellbooks.co.uk 01594 860187.*

WEOBLEY

Hereford Booksearch (John Trevitt), Rose Cottage, Church Road, Weobley, HR4 8SD. Tel: 01544 318388. Est: 2004. Private premises. Postal only. Appointment necessary. Small stock. Notes: *I plan to specialise in books about books, private presses and illustrated books, but at present my stock includes other subjects as well.*

Weobley Bookshop, ■ Broad Street, Weobley, HR4 8SA. Prop: Nick Hooper. Tel: 01544 319292. Web: www.weobleybooks.co.uk. Est: 1999. Shop open: **M:** 10:0–16:00; **T:** 10:00–16:00; **W:** 10:00–16:00; **Th:** 10:00–16:00; **F:** 10:00–16:00; **S:** 09:00–17:00. Closed for lunch: 13:15–14:00. Spec: New Books; Ephemera. CC: MC; V; Maestro, Solo. Mem: BA. Notes: *New and secondhand books, CDs and greetings cards.*

YARKHILL

David Warnes Books, One Pound Cottage, Yarkhill, HR1 3TA. Tel: 01432 890275. Private premises. Book fairs only. Telephone first. Open: **M:** 09:00–17:30; **T:** 09:00–17:30; **W:** 09:00–17:30; **Th:** 09:00– 17:30; **F:** 09:00–17:30; **S:** 09:00–17:30; **Su:** 09:00–17:30; Closed for lunch: 13:00–14:00. Spec: Alpinism/ Mountaineering; Anthropology; Countries - Afghanistan; Countries - Alaska; Countries - Arabia; Countries - Armenia; Countries - Asia; Countries - Balkans, The. Mem: PBFA.

HERTFORDSHIRE

BERKHAMSTED

Bookroom at Heritage Antiques Centre, ■ 24 Castle Street, Berkhamsted, HP4 2DW. Prop: David Mundy. Tel: 020 7482 7087. Est: 1994. Shop open: **M:** 10:00–17:30; **T:** 10:00–17:30; **W:** 10:00–17:30; **Th:** 10:00–17:30; **F:** 10:00–17:30; **S:** 10:00–17:30; **Su:** 10:00–17:30; Closed for lunch: 13:00–14:00. CC: MC; V; Maestro. Notes: *Attends Bloomsbury book fairs.*

Richard Frost, ■ 'Sunhaven', Northchurch Common, Berkhamsted, HP4 1LR. Prop: Richard Frost. Tel: (01442) 862011. Est: 1989. Telephone First. Shop at: Jordans Antiques Centre, 63 Old High Street, Hemel Hempstead, Hertfordshire HP1 3AF. Shop open: **M:** 10:00–17:00; **T:** 10:00–17:00; **W:** 10:00–17:00; **Th:** 10:00–17:00; **F:** 10:00–17:00; **S:** 10:00–17:00; **Su:** 10:00–16:00. Medium stock. Spec: Author - Greene, Graham; Biography; Botany; Ecclesiastical History & Architecture; First Editions; History - General; Literary Criticism; Philately. PR: £1–200. Notes: *Organiser of Wing Book Fair Buckinghamshire (first Sunday each month) and Berkhamsted Book Fair (first Saturday alternate months). Also at Riverside Antiques Centre, Sawbridgeworth Maltings, Essex, and Wendover Antiques, High St, Wendover, Bucks.*

David Mundy at Heritage Antiques, ■ 24 Castle Street, Berkhamsted, HP4 2DD. Prop: David Mundy. Tel: (020) 7482 7087. Est: 1994. Shop open: **M:** 10:00–17:30; **T:** 10:00–17:30; **W:** 10:00–17:30; **Th:** 10:00–17:30; **F:** 10:00–17:30; **S:** 10:00–17:30; **Su:** 10:00–17:30. Small stock. Spec: Art; Fiction - General; History - General; Military; Sport - General; Topography - General; Topography - Local. PR: £1–50. CC: MC; V. Notes: *Nooks & Crannies, Chesham, Bucks HP5 1HG (q.v.)*

Red Star Books, 4 Hamilton Road, Berkhamsted, HP4 3EF. Prop: Conor Pattenden. Tel: (01442) 870775. Web: www.http://ukbookworld.com/members/redstarbooks. Est: 2001. Private premises. Internet and Postal. Appointment necessary. Medium stock. Spec: Academic/Scholarly; Antiquarian; Bindings; Communism; Countries - Ireland; Feminism; Fine leather bindings (see also Fine & Rare); History - Anarchism. PR: £2–1,000.

James Wilson, 22 Castle Street, Berkhamsted, HP4 2DW. Tel: (01442) 873396. Est: 1975. Private premises. Appointment necessary. Spec: Books about Books; Colour-Plate. PR: £2–500. Mem: Pres: Book Plate Society. Notes: *Mainly book plates in stock.*

BISHOP'S STORTFORD

Sheila Rainford, White Pine Cottage, High St., Henham, Bishop's Stortford, CM22 6AS. Tel: (01279) 851129. Fax: (01279) 851129. Est: 1983. Private premises. Internet and Postal. Small stock. Spec: Banking & Insurance; Cookery/Gastronomy; Economics; History - Industrial; Industry; Literature. PR: £5–1,000. CC: V. Corresp: French and German. Mem: PBFA. VAT No: GB 632 2122 89.

Ray Smith, 'Lynwood', 111 Parsonage Lane, Bishop's Stortford, CM23 5BA. Tel: (01279) 324780. Fax: (01279) 324780. Est: 1994. Private premises. Postal only. Small stock. Spec: Africana; Countries - South Africa; Rhodesiana; Travel - Africa. PR: £5–250. Notes: *Also, Cecil Rhodes, Rhodesiana and Southern Africa.*

Edwin Trevorrow, 5 Pryors Close, Bishop's Stortford, CM23 5JX. Tel: (01279) 652902. Est: 1994. Private premises. Appointment necessary. Small stock. Spec: Biography; Fiction - General; Fiction - Historical; Fiction - Science Fiction; First Editions; Literature; Modern First Editions; Vintage Paperbacks. PR: £1–200.

www.AntiqueWatchStore.com, Grooms Cottage, Elsenham Hall, Bishop's Stortford, CM22 6DP. Tel: 01279-814946. Web: www.antiquewatchstore.com. Est: 1994. Private premises. Internet and Postal. Appointment necessary. Small stock. Spec: Antiques; Watches. PR: £1–20,000. CC: AE; MC; V. Mem: FBHI. VAT No: GB 354 3041 82.

BUSHEY

G. & R. Leapman Ltd., 37 Hogarth Court, Steeplands, Bushey, WD23 1BT. Prop: Gillian Leapman. Tel: (020) 8950-2995. Est: 1970. Private premises. Internet only. Appointment necessary. Small stock. Spec: Countries - Bermuda; Countries - Caribbean, The; Countries - West Indies, The; Travel - Americas; Booksearch; Prints and Maps. PR: £10–1,000. CC: Cheques. Corresp: French. VAT No: GB 197 6103 41. Notes: *West Indies material.*

CHESHUNT

Denis W. Amos, 10 Mill Lane, Cheshunt, Waltham Cross, EN8 0JH. Tel: (01992) 630486. Est: 1948. Private premises. Postal only. Large stock. Spec: Gambling; Sport - General; Sport - Football (Soccer); Sport - Horse Racing (inc. Riding/Breeding/Equestrian); Sport - Tennis. Notes: *Majors on horse racing only.*

ELSTREE

Elstree Books, 12 West View Gardens, Elstree, WD6 3DD. Prop: Shirley Herbert. Tel: 0208 953 2999. Est: 1991. Private premises. Postal only. Appointment necessary. Open: **M:** 09:00–17:30; **T:** 09:00–17:30; **W:** 09:00–17:30; **Th:** 09:00–17:30; **F:** 09:00–17:30; **S:** 09:00–17:30; Closed for lunch: 13:00–14:00. Spec: Classics, The; Illustrated - General; Private Press; Publishers - Oxford World's Classics; Topography - General; Topography - Local; Woodcut novels; Booksearch. CC: through ABE only. Notes: *Worlds Classics specialist and Booksearch. Also illustrated, especially wood engravings.*

HARPENDEN

Mavis Eggle, 34 Cowper Road, Harpenden, AL5 5NG. Prop: Mavis Eggle. Tel: (01582) 762603. Fax: (01582) 762603. Est: 1979. Private premises. Book fairs only. Appointment necessary. Small stock. Spec: Antiquarian; Social History; Sport - Angling/Fishing; Technology; Ephemera. PR: £1–500. Mem: PBFA.

HERTFORD

David Ford Books, ■ The Gillmark Gallery, 25 Parliament Square, Hertford, SG14 1EX. Tel: (01263) 741690. Est: 1985. Shop and/or gallery open: **T:** 10:00–17:00; **W:** 10:00–17:00; **Th:** 10:00–13.00; **F:** 10:00–17:00; **S:** 10:00–17:00. Large stock. Spec: Animals and Birds; Archaeology; Art; Art History; Biography; Children's; Cinema/Film; Cookery/Gastronomy. PR: £1–500. CC: JCB; MC; V. Mem: PBFA. Notes: *Postal and Internet Sales, and Book Fairs.*

Gillmark Gallery, 25 Parliament Square, Hertford, SG14 1EX. Prop: Mark Pretlove & Gill Woodhouse. Tel: (01992) 534444. Web: www.gillmark.com. Est: 1997. Shop and/or gallery open: **T:** 10:00–17:00; **W:** 10:00–17:00; **Th:** 10:00–12:00; **F:** 10:00–17:00; **S:** 10:00–17:00. Medium stock. Spec: Antiquarian; Atlases; Natural History; Topography - General; Topography - Local; Booksearch; Prints and Maps. PR: £1–3,000. CC: AE; JCB; MC; V. VAT No: GB 740 8541 36. Notes: *Special interest: English county maps.*

HERTFORD HEATH

G Collins Bookdealers, 18 Postwood Green, Hertford Heath, SG13 7QJ. Tel: 01992 509928. Fax: 01992 584190. Mail order only; Postal only. Spec: Sport - Yachting (& Boating); Topography - Local. Cata: Hertfordshire topography sailing history. Notes: *Specialist in Hertfordshire books.*

HITCHIN

Adrem Books, 7 Bury End, Pirton, Hitchin, SG5 3QB. Prop: David Braybrooke. Tel: 01462712668. Fax: 01462712668. Est: 1992. Private premises. Internet and Postal. Appointment necessary. Open: **M:** 06:00–24:00; **T:** 06:00–24:00; **W:** 06:00–24:00; **Th:** 06:00–24:00; **F:** 06:00–24:00; **S:** 06:00–24:00; **Su:** 06:00–24:00; Closed for lunch: 06:00–24:00. Spec: Academic/Scholarly; Adult; Aeronautics; Aircraft; American Revolution, The; Animals and Birds; Antiquarian; Arctic - Antarctica. CC: AE; E; MC; V.

Eric T. Moore Books, ■ 24 Bridge Street, Hitchin, SG5 2DF. Prop: John Leeson. Tel: (01462) 450497. Web: www.erictmoore.co.uk. Est: 1965. Internet and Postal. Shop open: **M:** 09:30–17:30; **T:** 09:30–17:30; **W:** 09:30–17:30; **Th:** 09:30–17:30; **F:** 09:30–17:30; **S:** 09:30–17:30; **Su:** 11:00–16:00. Very large stock. CC: MC; V; Most Major Debit Cards. VAT No: GB 759 7801 77. Notes: *Eric T. Moore Books was established in 1965 and sells secondhand, rare and antiquarian books, maps and prints. Housed in two converted cottages, the shop contains approximately 35,000 books.*

Phillips of Hitchin (Antiques), ■The Manor House, 26 Baycroft, Hitchin, SG5 1JW. Prop: Jerome Phillips. Tel: (01462) 432067. Fax: (01462) 441368. Est: 1884. Shop open: **M:** 09:00–17:30; **T:** 09:00–17:30; **W:** 09:00–17:30; **Th:** 09:00–17:30; **F:** 09:00–17:30. Medium stock. Spec: Antiques; Applied Art; Architecture; Furniture; Interior Design; Woodwork; Booksearch. PR: £5–3,000. CC: AE; E; MC; V. Corresp: French, German, Italian, Spanish, Russian, Portuguese. Mem: PBFA; British Antique Dealers Association. VAT No: GB 197 1842 28. Notes: *Open Saturdays by appointment. Also, antique furniture.*

LETCHWORTH (GARDEN CITY)

David's Bookshop, ■ (Wallace Books Ltd., trading as), 14 Eastcheap, Letchworth, SG6 3DE. Prop: Paul Wallace. Tel: 01462 684631. Fax: 01462 485118. Web: www.davids-bookshops.co.uk. Est: 1963. Shop open: **M:** 08:00–19:00; **T:** 08:00–19:00; **W:** 08:00–19:00; **Th:** 08:00–19:00; **F:** 08:00–19:00; **S:** 08:00–19:00; **Su:** 11:00–17:00. PR: £1–200. CC: AE; MC; V. Mem: BA. VAT No: 973 1336 17. Notes: *Large independent book and music shop on 2 floors. Also, new books, remainders, new and collectable vinyl, cds, dvds and sheet music. Trade welcome, very keen prices. Regular discount days/weekends.*

Gallimaufry Books, ■ 50 Leys Avenue, Letchworth Garden City, SG6 3EQ. Prop: Barry Meaden. Tel: 01462 686129. Web: www.ukbookworld.com/members/spitfire. Est: 2005. Shop open: **M:** 10:00–17:00; **T:** 10:00–17:00; **Th:** 10:00–17:00; **F:** 10:00–17:00; **S:** 10:00–17:00. Spec: Aircraft; Army, The; Aviation; Knitting; Military; Military - Modelling; Military History; Military Uniforms. Cata: Aviation. Notes: *Attends Wing Book Fair.*

MUCH HADHAM

H.M. Fletcher, Wynches Barn, Much Hadham, SG10 6BA. Prop: Marina & Keith R. Fletcher. Tel: (01279) 843883. Fax: (01279) 842830. Web: www.hmfletcher.co.uk. Est: 1902. Private premises. Appointment necessary. Spec: Antiquarian; Bindings; Fine & Rare; Illustrated - General; Incunabula. PR: £50–20,000. CC: MC; V. Cata: General antiquarian. Corresp: French. Mem: ABA; PBFA; ILAB. VAT No: GB 626 2128 60.

NEW BARNET

ForensicSearch, 17 Greenacres, Glyn Avenue, New Barnet, EN4 9PJ. Prop: Nick Danks and Samantha Sproates. Tel: (020) 8440-8896. Est: 1999. Private premises. Postal only. Small stock. Spec: Crime (True); Science - Forensic; Booksearch. PR: £2–200.

RADLETT

G.L. Green Ltd., 18 Aldenham Avenue, Radlett, WD7 8HX. Prop: G. L. Green. Tel: (01923) 857077. Fax: (01923) 857077. Web: www.glgreen.co.uk. Est: 1972. Storeroom; Internet and Postal. Appointment necessary. Small stock. Spec: Deep Sea Diving; History - Napoleonic; Maritime/ Nautical; Naval; Navigation; Navy, The; Navy, The - Royal Naval Patrol Service; Passenger Liners. PR: £1–1,000. CC: AE; JCB; MC; V; PayPal. Cata: Naval and Maritime. Mem: PBFA. Notes: *Booksearch service.*

RICKMANSWORTH

Clive A. Burden Ltd., Elmcote House, The Green Croxley Green, Rickmansworth, WD3 3HN. Tel: (01923) 778097. Fax: (01923) 896520. Web: www.caburden.com. Est: 1966. Private premises. Appointment necessary. Very large stock. Spec: Atlases; Botany; Cartography; Illustrated - General; Natural History; Topography - General; Topography - Local; Town Plans. PR: £5–10,000. Mem: ABA; ILAB; IMCoS; IAMA. VAT No: GB196 7570 11. Notes: *Also, decorative books.*

ST. ALBANS

Hindsight Books Limited, Suite 3, St. Albans House, St. Albans Lane, St. Albans, NW11 7QE. Tel: (020) 8458 5613. Fax: (020) 8458 6712. Web: www.hindsightbooks.com. Est: 1996. Private premises. Internet and Postal. Spec: Company History; History - Industrial; Science - History of; Technology. PR: £5–100.

L.M.S. Books, 52 Westminster Court, St. Albans, AL1 2DX. Prop: Chris Fruin. Tel: 0208 679 2973. Web: www.lmsbooks.co.uk. Est: 1994. Office and/or bookroom; Internet and Postal. Appointment necessary. Medium stock. Spec: Author - Pratchett, Terry; Countries - Mexico; Fiction - General; Fiction - Women; First Editions; Literature; Modern First Editions; Mysteries. PR: £10–350. CC: MC; V; SW. Cata: Modern fiction especially Booker Prize1969-2007. Notes: *Publishers of Booker Prize 1969-2007 history and stock catalogue. 290 books listed. Stocks first editions of Booker Prize titles and signed recent literary fiction.*

RM Books, 18 Cornwall Road, St. Albans, AL1 1SH. Prop: Robert Moore. Tel: (01727) 830058. Web: www.rmbooks.co.uk. Est: 1988. Private premises. Postal only. Small stock. Spec: Anatomy; Bacteriology; Biochemistry; Biology - General; Chemistry; Crime (True); Criminology; Drugs. PR: £10–100. Cata: medicine & related sciences. Mem: ukbookworld.

WATFORD

Medievalbookshop, PO Box 2082, Watford, WD18 0AD. Prop: Nick Gorman. Tel: 01923 227323. Fax: 01923 227323. Web: www.medievalbookshop.co.uk. Est: 2001. Mail order only; Internet and Postal. Small stock. Spec: Academic/Scholarly; Archaeology; Author - Chaucer, Geoffrey; History - British; History - European; History - Middle Ages; History - Reformation; History - Renaissance, The. PR: £1–200. CC: PayPal. Cata: Medieval.

Moss Books Ltd., 4 Baird Court, Bushey, Watford, Hertfordshire, WD23 4UG. Tel: 0208 386 2707. Private premises. Internet and Postal. Appointment necessary. Open: **M:** 09:00–17:30; **T:** 09:00–17:30; **W:** 09:00–17:30; **Th:** 09:00–17:30; **F:** 09:00–17:30; **S:** 09:00–17:30; **Su:** 09:00–17:30. Medium stock. Spec: Antiquarian; Early Imprints; Illustrated - General; Non Fiction; Travel - General; Voyages & Discovery. PR: £5–100. Cata: General. Mem: PBFA. Notes: *General antiquarian.*

Peter Taylor & Son, 1 Ganders Ash, Leavesden, Watford, WD25 7HE. Prop: Peter Taylor. Tel: (01923) 663325. Web: www.http://ukbookworld.com/members/taylorbooks. Est: 1973. Storeroom; Postal only. Open in Summer. Medium stock. Spec: Antiquarian; Archaeology; Art History; Bibliography; Countries - France; Ecclesiastical History & Architecture; Fine & Rare; History - British. PR: £15–1,000. CC: MC; V. Cata: Medieval and early modern history in particular. Corresp: French. Notes: *Monographs and antiquarian books and pamphlets on British and European history from the Romans to the eighteenth century and with emphasis on the Middle Ages, the Renaissance and the Early Modern period. Catalogues and e-lists on request.*

Westons Booksellers Ltd., 44 Stratford Road, Watford, WD17 4NZ. Prop: Jeremy Weston. Tel: (01923) 229081. Fax: (01923) 243343. Web: www.westons.co.uk. Est: 1977. Private premises. Internet and Postal. Appointment necessary. Open: **M:** 09:30–17:30; **T:** 09:30–17:30; **W:** 09:30–17:30; **Th:** 09:30–17:30; **F:** 09:30–17:30. Very small stock. Spec: Aeronautics; Agriculture; Aids Crisis, The; Architecture; Astronautics; Astronomy; Autism; Bacteriology. PR: £3–300. CC: E; MC; V. Cata: monthly - on Science, Medicine, Architecture, Technology. VAT No: GB 225 0259 93. Notes: *Very recently published scientific, medical & technical books, all in new condition offered at substantial discounts, plus a very small number of older titles.*

WELWYN GARDEN CITY

Copperplate Antique Maps and Prints, Welwyn Garden City, AL7 2PP. Prop: Kevin and Caroline Welch. Tel: 01707 322940. Web: www.copperplate.co.uk. Est: 2006. Mail order only; Internet and Postal. Appointment necessary. Open: **M:** 09:00–17:30; **T:** 09:00–17:30; **W:** 09:00–17:30; **Th:** 09:00–17:30; **F:** 09:00–17:30; **S:** 09:00–17:30. Spec: Atlases; Countries - Great Britain; History - Local; Maps & Mapmaking; Topography - Local; Prints and Maps. CC: JCB; MC; V. Notes: *Specialising in antique atlases, plus books on Cambridge.*

ISLE OF WIGHT

COWES

Curtle Mead Books, 105 Curtle Mead, Baring Road, Cowes, PO31 8DS. Prop: John Lucas. Tel: (01983) 294312. Est: 1999. Private premises. Telephone First. Medium stock. Spec: Countries - Isle of Wight; General Stock; Maritime/Nautical; Maritime/Nautical - History; Maritime/Nautical - Log Books; Naval; Navigation; Navy, The. PR: £1–500. CC: Paypal. Cata: Maritime Yachting General. Corresp: German. Mem: PBFA. Notes: *The majority of our stock is maritime with an emphasis on recreational sailing. We do also have about 1500 general stock. Visitors are most welcome but please phone first. We are always interested in buying good yachting and sailing books.*

FRESHWATER

David G. Bancroft, Little Orchard Court Road, Freshwater, PO40 9NU. Tel: (01983) 759069. Est: 1995. Private premises. Postal only. Small stock. Spec: Aviation; Ephemera. PR: £3–150. Notes: *Most aspects of aviation including gliding and technical aspects of aviation. Also signed aviation books.*

Cameron House Books, ■Dimbola Lodge, Terrace Lane, Freshwater Bay, PO40 9QE. Prop: L.J. Sklaroff. Tel: 01983 754960. Web: www.cameronhousebooks.com. Est: 1994. Shop open: **T:** 10:00–16:00; **W:** 10:00–16:00; **Th:** 10:00–16:00; **F:** 10:00–16:00; **S:** 10:00–16:00; **Su:** 10:00–16:00. Spec: Art; Artists; Author - Ardizzone, Edward; Author - Cameron, Julia Margaret; Author - Clarke, Arthur C.; Author - Darwin, Charles; Author - Dickens, Charles; Author - Durrell, Lawrence. CC: Credit cards via PayPal. Cata: Modern firsts, illustrated, photography. Corresp: German, Spanish, French. Mem: PLA. Notes: *Specialist in Mervyn Peake, Charles Keeping, Julia Margaret Cameron & her circle (Darwin, Tennyson et al.), 20th Century illustrated books, early photography, modern first editions, Isle of Wight writers.*

NEWPORT

Marcus Niner, Willow Cottage, Marks Corner, Newport, PO30 5UD. Prop: Marcus Niner. Tel: (01983) 209473. Est: 1982. Private premises. Book fairs only. Appointment necessary. Small stock. Spec: Art; General; History - British; Literature; Topography - Local; Travel - General. PR: £10–2,000. CC: MC; V. Mem: PBFA.

RYDE

Heritage Books, ■ 7 Cross Street, Ryde, PO33 2AD. Prop: Rev. D.H. Nearn. Tel: (01983) 562933. Fax: (01983) 812634. Est: 1978. Shop open: **M:** 10:00–17:00; **T:** 10:00–17:00; **W:** 10:00–17:00; **F:** 10:00–17:00; **S:** 10:00–17:00. Large stock. Spec: Countries - Africa; Countries - Isle of Wight; Theology. PR: £1–500. CC: MC; V. Corresp: French, Portuguese. VAT No: GB 339 0615 58.

Kalligraphia, 66 Bettesworth Road, Ryde, PO33 3EJ. Prop: Louisa Mamakou. Tel: 00 44 (0) 1983 562702. Web: www.kalligraphia.com. Est: 2003. Private premises. Internet and Postal. Contactable. Spec: Countries - Cyprus; Countries - Great Britain; Countries - Greece; Earth Sciences; Evolution; Fossils; Geography; Geology. CC: MC; V; PayPal. Cata: Specialist subjects and others on request. Corresp: Greek; French. Notes: *Successful free booksearch service. Email catalogues issued on request. See us at Isle of Wight Book Fairs and mainland Fossil Fairs.*

The Ryde Bookshop, ■ 135 High Street, Ryde, PO33 2RJ. Prop: M.D. Sames. Tel: (01983) 565227. Est: 1988. Shop open: **M:** 09:00–17:00; **T:** 09:00–17:00; **W:** 09:00–17:00; **Th:** 09:00–17:00; **F:** 09:00–17:00; **S:** 09:00–17:00. Very large stock. PR: £1–200. CC: E; JCB; MC; V. Mem: BA. Notes: *Also, new books.*

ST. HELENS

Mothergoose Bookshop, ■West Green House, Upper Green Road, St. Helens, PO33 1XB. Prop: M.C. and V.F. Edmondson. Tel: 01983 874063. Est: 1980. Shop open at: Mothergoose Bookshop, Lower Green Road, St Helens I O W. Open: **M:** 10:30–17:00; **T:** 10:30–17:00; **W:** 10:30–17:00; **Th:** 10:30–17:00; **F:** 10:30–17:00; **S:** 10:30–17:00; **Su:** 10:30–16:30. Spec: Maritime/Nautical; Military; Prints and Maps. Notes: *Also at The Bookroom, Cross Street, Cowes I O W and The Bookroom, Jirah Place Yarmouth I O W and stocks cover most subjects.*

VENTNOR

Shirley Lane Books, St. Lawrence Dene,Undercliff Drive, Ventnor, PO38 1XJ. Prop: Shirley Lane. Tel: (01983) 852309. Web: www.abebook.co.uk. Est: 1976. Private premises. Internet and Postal. Appointment necessary. Small stock. Spec: Authors - Women; Feminism; Women. PR: £1–500. Corresp: French.

Ventnor Rare Books, ■ 32 Pier Street, Ventnor, PO38 1SX. Prop: Nigel & Teresa Traylen. Tel: (01983) 853706. Fax: (01983) 854706. Est: 1989. Shop open: **M:** 10:00–17:00; **T:** 10:00–17:00; **Th:** 10:00–17:00; **F:** 10:00–17:00; **S:** 10:00–17:00. Medium stock. Spec: Academic/Scholarly; Antiquarian; Antiques; Art Reference; Bibliography; Bindings; Fiction - General; Literature. PR: £1–500. CC: JCB; MC; V; UK Switch/Maestro. Corresp: French. Mem: ABA; PBFA; ILAB. VAT No: GB 566 5246 19.

YARMOUTH

Alan Argent, Two Ways, Sconce Road Norton, Yarmouth, PO41 0RT. Prop: Alan Argent. Tel: (01983) 760851. Storeroom; Appointment necessary. Small stock. Spec: Maritime/Nautical; Seamanship; Sport - Sailing. PR: £3–100. Notes: *Also, attends the occasional bookfair.*

The Bookroom, ■ Jirah Place, Yarmouth, PO33 1XB. Prop: M.C. & V.F. Edmondson. Tel: 01983 873897. Shop open: **M:** 10:30–16:30; **T:** 10:30–16:30; **W:** 10:30–16:30; **Th:** 10:30–16:30; **F:** 10:30–16:30; **S:** 10:30–16:30; **Su:** 10:30–16:30. Notes: *Also at Mothergoose Bookshop, Lower Green Road, St Helens, Isle of Wight. Closed Sunday. Good general stock, booksearch undertaken.*

KENT

ASHFORD

Stephen Dadd, 18 Dunkery Rise, Ashford, TN24 8QX. Prop: Stephen Dadd. Tel: 01233-638682. Fax: 01233-638682. Est: 2001. Private premises. Internet and Postal. Contactable. Open: **M:** 09:00–17:30; **T:** 09:00–17:30; **W:** 09:00–17:30; **Th:** 09:00–17:30; **F:** 09:00–17:30; **S:** 09:00–17:30; **Su:** 09:00–17:30. Spec: Directories - British. CC: PayPal. Notes: *General stock covering all topics. No personal callers as no books on display. Mail-order only. Always seeking Kent & SE London street directories for my personal collection.(Kelly's etc.)*

Riverside Books, Old Granary, Tally Ho Road, Ashford, TN26 1HL. Prop: Paul & Carole Lee. Tel: (01233) 620851). Est: 1990. Private premises. Internet and postal. Small stock. PR: £10 and upwards. CC: MC; V.

Woodside Books, 1 Woodside Cottages, Westwell Lane, Ashford, TN26 1JB. Prop: Ann Gipps. Tel: (01233) 624495. Est: 1991. Private premises. Internet and Postal. Appointment necessary. Small stock. Spec: Biology - General; Biology - Marine; Botany; Ecology; Entomology; Flora & Fauna; Forestry; Fungi. PR: £1–500. Cata: Botany, Entomology, Ornithology, Natural History. Notes: *Payment by cheque only.*

BECKENHAM

Julia Sesemann, 10 Kemerton Road, Beckenham, BR3 6NJ. Prop: Julia Sesemann. Tel: (020) 8658-6123. Est: 1977. Private premises. Postal only. Appointment necessary. Open: **M:** 09:30–21:00; **T:** 09:30–21:00; **W:** 09:30–21:00; **Th:** 09:30–21:00; **F:** 09:30–21:00; **S:** 09:30–21:00. Small stock. Spec: Author - Blyton, Enid; Children's; Comic Books & Annuals; Illustrated - General; Juvenile. PR: £2–250. Cata: one a year.

BEXLEY

Ruskin Books, 42 Red Lodge Road, Joydens Wood, Bexley, DA5 2JP. Prop: Frederick W. Lidyard. Tel: 01322 558291. Est: 2000. Private premises. Postal only. Telephone First. Spec: Booksearch. Notes: *Mainly a booksearch service.*

BIDDENDEN

P.R. & V. Sabin t/a Printed Works, Saxton House, The Nightingales, Biddenden, TN27 8HN. Prop: Paul and Vivien Sabin. Tel: (01580) 715603. Est: 1995. Private premises. Book fairs only. Appointment necessary. Medium stock. Spec: Illustrated - General; Limited Editions - General; Private Press. Mem: PBFA. Notes: *Private press specialist.*

BRENCHLEY

Anthony Whittaker, Four Seasons, Chill Mill Green, Brenchley, Tonbridge, TN12 7AL. Prop: Anthony Whittaker. Tel: 01892 723494. Est: 1980. Private premises. Telephone First. Open: **M:** 09:00–17:30; **T:** 09:00–17:30; **W:** 09:00–17:30; **Th:** 09:00–17:30; **F:** 09:00–17:30; **S:** 09:00–17:30; **Su:** 09:00–17:30; Closed for lunch: 13:00–14:00. Spec: Applied Art; Children's; Illustrated - General; Natural History; Topography - Local. CC: MC; V.

BROADSTAIRS

Albion Bookshop, ■ Albion Street, Broadstairs, CT10 1LX. Prop: Alan Kemp. Tel: 01843 862877. Fax: 01843 860084. Est: 1956. Shop open: **M:** 09:00–17:30; **T:** 09:00–17:30; **W:** 09:00–17:30; **Th:** 09:00–17:30; **F:** 09:00–17:30; **S:** 09:00–17:30; **Su:** 10:30–16:30. CC: MC; V.

CANTERBURY

The Canterbury Bookshop, ■ 37 Northgate, Canterbury, CT1 1BL. Prop: David Miles. Tel: (01227) 464773. Fax: (01227) 780073. Est: 1980. Shop open: **M:** 10:00–17:00; **W:** 10:00–17:00; **F:** 10:00–17:00; **S:** 10:00–17:00. Small stock. Spec: Children's; Illustrated - General; Juvenile; Typography; Prints and Maps. PR: £1–2,000. CC: MC; V. Mem: ABA; PBFA; ILAB. Notes: *Fairs attended: all London, ABA, Olympia, Chelsea and in USA.*

Chaucer Bookshop, ■6-7 Beer Cart Lane, Canterbury, CT1 2NY. Prop: Sir Robert Sherston-Baker, Bt. Tel: 01227 453912. Fax: 01227 451893. Web: www.chaucer-bookshop.co.uk. Est: 1956. Shop open: **M:** 10:00–17:00; **T:** 10:00–17:00; **W:** 10:00–17:00; **Th:** 10:00–17:00; **F:** 10:00–17:00; **S:** 10:00–17:00. Spec: Antiques; Art; Art History; Arts, The; Autobiography; Biography; Fiction - General; Gardening - General. CC: AE; E; JCB; MC; V; Switch / Solo. Mem: ABA; PBFA; BA; ILAB. Notes: *Within the city walls, less than 5 minutes walk from the Cathedral.*

Little Stour Books, North Court House, West Stourmouth, Nr Preston, Canterbury, CT3 1HT. Prop: Colin Button. Tel: (01227) 722371. Fax: (01227) 722021. Web: www.littlestourbooks.com. Est: 1996. Warehouse; Internet and Postal. Appointment necessary. Shop at: Book Depository Grove Road, Preston, Canterbury, Kent CT3 1EF. Open: **M:** 10:00–18:00; **T:** 10:00–18:00; **W:** 10:00–18:00; **Th:** 10:00–18:00; **F:** 10:00–18:00; **S:** 10:00–18:00; **Su:** 10:00–16:00. Very large stock. Spec: Author - Blyton, Enid; Author - Brent-Dyer, Elinor M.; Author - Buckeridge, A.; Author - Carroll, Lewis; Author - Crompton, Richmal; Author - Henty, G.A.; Author - Johns, W.E.; Author - Oxenham, Elsie. PR: £6–500. CC: E; JCB; MC; V; SW, SO. Cata: W. E. Johns, Spike Milligan, Kent, Military. Mem: PBFA. VAT No: GB 878 4455 69.

Oast Books, 1 Denstead Oast, Chartham Hatch, Canterbury, CT4 7SH. Prop: Bill & Jennie Reading. Tel: (01227) 730808. Web: www.http://members.aol.com/oastbooks/home.htm. Est: 1997. Market stand/ stall; Postal only. Small stock. Spec: Counselling; Psychoanalysis; Psychology/Psychiatry; Psychotherapy. PR: £2–40. CC: PayPal.

Periwinkle Press, ■ Bagham Barn Antiques Centre, Canterbury Road, Chilham, Cantebury CT4 8DU. Prop: Antony Swain. Tel: (01227) 732522. Web: www.baghambarn.com. Est: 1968. Open: **W:** 10:00–17:00; **Th:** 10:00–17:00; **F:** 10:00–17:00; **S:** 10:00–17:00; **Su:** 10:00–17:00. Small stock. Spec: Author - Ardizzone, Edward; General stock; Topography - Local; Prints and Maps. PR: £1–500. CC: MC; V. Mem: PBFA. Notes: *We have been antiquarian book and print sellers since 1968. Come and browse in our delightful shop in the heart of this wonderful antique centre in Chilham. We are also trade/ retail print picture framers, publishers and restorers.*

Tiger Books, Yew Tree Cottage, Westbere, Canterbury, CT2 0HH. Prop: Dr. Bryan & Mrs. Sylvia Harlow. Tel: (01227) 710030. Fax: (01227) 712066. Web: www.tigerbooks-online.com. Est: 1988. Private premises. Internet and Postal. Appointment necessary. Large stock. Spec: Academic/ Scholarly; Annuals; Antiquarian; Author - 19th Century; Author - Arnold, Matthew; Author - Austen, Jane; Author - Ballantyne, Robert M.; Author - Baring-Gould, S. PR: £10–5,500. CC: E; JCB; MC; V. Cata: literature. Mem: ABA; PBFA; ILAB. Notes: *Also, a booksearch service.*

CHATHAM

Roadmaster Books, P.O. Box 176, Chatham, ME5 9AQ. Prop: Malcolm & Sue Wright. Tel: (01634) 862843. Fax: (01634) 201555. Web: www.ukbookworld.com/members/ROADMASTER. Est: 1976. Private premises. Postal only. Medium stock. Spec: Automobilia/Automotive; Books about Books; Buses/Trams; Canals/Inland Waterways; Commercial Vehicles; Company History; Conservation; Dolls & Dolls' Houses. PR: £1–350. Cata: annually - transport & topography. Corresp: French. VAT No: GB 619 3009 52. Notes: *To contact publishing business info@roadmasterpublishing.co.uk*

Sandstone Books, 14 Seymour Road, Chatham, ME5 7AE. Prop: Verne Sanderson. Tel: 01634 306437. Web: www.sandstonebooks.co.uk. Est: 1989. Mail order only; Internet and Postal. Appointment necessary. Open: **M:** 09:00–17:30; **T:** 09:00–17:30; **W:** 09:00–17:30; **Th:** 09:00–17:30; **F:** 09:00–17:30; **S:** 09:00–17:30; **Su:** 09:00–17:30; Closed for lunch: 13:00–14:00. Cata: modern first editions.

CROCKENHILL

Lewis First Editions, 31 Cray Road, Crockenhill, Swanley, BR8 8LN. Prop: David Fordyce. Tel: (01689) 854261. Web: www.abebooks.com/home/davidfordyce/. Est: 2000. Internet and Postal. Small stock. Spec: Author - Lewis, C.S.; Author - Saville, M.; Author - Shute, Neville; Modern First Editions. PR: £5–2,000.

DEAL

Books, ■ 168 High Street, Deal, CT14 6BQ. Prop: Ann Ritchie. Tel: 01304 368662. Est: 2000. Shop. Open: **M:** 10:30–16:00; **W:** 10:30–16:00; **F:** 10:30–16:00; **S:** 10:30–14:00. Closed for lunch: 13:00–14:00. Spec: Architecture; Art; Artists; Autobiography; Ceramics; Motorbikes / motorcycles; Motoring; Railways and Railroads.

Inch's Books, 7 Western Road, Deal, CT14 6RX. Prop: Peter & Eleanor Inch. Tel: 01304 371752. Fax: 01304 375154. Web: www.inchsbooks.co.uk. Est: 1986. Private premises. Telephone First. Open: **M:** 09:00–17:00; **T:** 09:00–17:00; **W:** 09:00–17:00; **Th:** 09:00–17:00; **F:** 09:00–17:00; **S:** 09:00–13:00. Medium stock. Spec: Architecture; Building & Construction; Cities - General; Design; History - Design; Landscape; Town Planning; Urban History. PR: £10–2,000. CC: MC; V; SW. Cata: Architecture, Town Planning, Building, Design, Ph. Corresp: French. Mem: ABA; PBFA; ILAB. VAT No: GB 412 1286 94. Notes: *Also, architectural prints and drawings, international exhibitions. Visitors very welcome (please phone before calling).*

McConnell Fine Books, ■The Golden Hind, 85 Beach Street, Deal, CT14 6JB. Prop: Nick McConnell. Tel: (01304) 375086. Web: www.mcconnellfinebooks.com. Est: 1972. Telephone First. Shop open: **T:** 11:00–16:00; **W:** 11:00–16:00; **Th:** 11:00–16:00; **F:** 11:00–16:00; **S:** 11:00–16:00. Medium stock. Spec: Antiquarian; Bindings. PR: £2–1,000. CC: AE; MC; V. Corresp: French, Russian. Mem: ABA; PBFA; ILAB.

FARNINGHAM

Wadard Books, ■ 6 High Street, Farningham, DA4 0DG. Prop: Martin Finch. Tel: (01322) 863151. Est: 2001. Shop open: **M:** 10:00–13.00; **T:** 10:00–18:00; **W:** 10:00–13.00; **Th:** 10:00–18:00; **F:** 10:00–18:00; **S:** 10:00–18:00. Medium stock. Spec: Antiquarian; Art; Aviation; Children's; Children's - Early Titles; Children's - Illustrated; Churchilliana; Cookery/Gastronomy. PR: £1–5,000. CC: AE; JCB; MC; V. Mem: PBFA. VAT No: GB 586 5906 86. Notes: *www.wadardbooks.com Fully encrypted website for secure online shopping. Large proportion of stock currently illustrated.*

FAVERSHAM

Faversham Books, 49 South Road, Faversham, ME13 7LS. Prop: Mr. & Mrs. C.M. Ardley. Tel: (01795) 532873. Est: 1979. Private premises. Postal only. Spec: Author - Kipling, Rudyard. PR: £5–1,000. Cata: Rudyard Kipling; writings and critical works. Corresp: French. Notes: *Some stock on sale at the National Trust Shop at 'Bateman's', Burwash, East Sussex.*

Past Sentence, ■ 119 West Street, Faversham, ME13 7JB. Prop: Adrian and Kate Rowland. Tel: 01795 590000. Web: www.pastsentence.com. Est: 1996. Shop open: **T:** 10:00–17:00; **W:** 10:00–17:00; **Th:** 10:00–17:00; **F:** 10:00–17:00; **S:** 10:00–17:00. CC: MC; V; Maestro, Switch. VAT No: GB 781 8038 11. Notes: *A small number of our titles are listed on biblio.com and biblion.co.uk and we welcome enquiries.*

FOLKESTONE

Jenny Hurst, The Old Coach House, Rectory Lane, Lyminge, Folkestone, CT18 8EG. Prop: Jenny Hurst. Tel: (01303) 862693. Web: www.abebooks.com. Est: 1996. Private premises. Internet and Postal. Medium stock. Spec: Academic/Scholarly; Alternative Medicine; Architecture; Autobiography; Biography; Children's; Fiction - General; Film and Television Tie-ins. PR: £5–100. Notes: *Many books not listed on internet.*

MilitaryHistoryBooks.com, PO Box 590, Folkestone, CT20 2WX. Prop: Ian H. & Gillian M. Knight. Tel: (01303) 246500. Fax: (01303) 245133. Web: www.militaryhistorybooks.com. Est: 1970. Private premises. Internet and Postal. Appointment necessary. Open: **M:** 10:00–17:00; **T:** 10:00–17:00; **W:** 10:00–17:00; **Th:** 10:00–17:00; **F:** 10:00–17:00; **S:** 09:00–14:00. Spec: Aeronautics; Aircraft; Armed Forces - Australian Army; Arms & Armour; Army, The; Autobiography; Aviation; Coastal Defence. CC: AE; D; E; JCB; MC; V. Cata: Military. VAT No: GB 770 7124 36. Notes: *We specialise in all aspects of military history with specialist sections on Napoleonics, Colonial Wars, Regimental Histories, Uniforms, Insignia & Decorations, Third Reich, Aviation, Armoured Vehicles and Weapons and Naval & Maritime.*

Nick Spurrier, 27 Plain Road, Folkestone, CT20 2QF. Tel: (01303) 246100. Web: www.nick-spurrier.co.uk. Est: 1977. Private premises. Internet and Postal. Appointment necessary. Medium stock. Spec: Academic/Scholarly; Black Studies; Capitalism; Company History; Cultural Studies; Economics; Feminism; History - General. PR: £1–50. CC: AE; E; JCB; MC; V. VAT No: GB 362 1931 64.

HERNE BAY

Herne Bay Books, 22 Western Esplanade, Herne Bay, CT6 8RW. Prop: Mr. R.J.C. Eburne (Dick). Tel: (01227) 743201. Est: 1995. Private premises. Postal only. Appointment necessary. Small stock. Spec: Genealogy; General Stock. PR: £1–20. Corresp: French, German. Notes: *Normally I think of myself as retired but I am trading infrequently mainly searching wants for old customers.*

LYDD

Anthony Neville, New Hall, High Street, Lydd, TN29 9AJ. Tel: 01797 320180. Fax: 01797 320140. Est: 1985. Private premises. Appointment necessary. Spec: Art; Author - James, Henry; Foreign Texts; Illustrated - General; Private Press. CC: MC; V. Cata: 10 a year on specialities. Corresp: French, German and Russian. Mem: ABA; PBFA; BA. VAT No: GB 515 9087 34.

LYMINGE

Scott Brinded, 17 Greenbanks, Lyminge, CT18 8HG. Tel: (01303) 862258. Fax: (01303) 862660. Est: 1991. Private premises. Internet and Postal. Small stock. Spec: Antiquarian; Bibliography; Books about Books; Literature; Palaeography; Papermaking; Printing; Topography - General. PR: £1–5,000. CC: MC; V. Mem: ABA; PBFA. VAT No: GB 624 9315 38. Notes: *Also, UK distributors for Martin Publishing, Oak Knoll Press.*

Jenny Hurst, The Old Coach House, Rectory Lane, Lyminge, CT18 8EG. Prop: Jenny Hurst. Tel: 01303862693. Private premises. Internet and Postal. Telephone First. Open: **M:** 09:00–17:30; **T:** 09:00–17:30; **W:** 09:00–17:30; **Th:** 09:00–17:30; **F:** 09:00–17:30. Closed for lunch: 13:00–14:00. Spec: Animals and Birds; Architecture; Children's; Cookery/Gastronomy; Fiction - General; History - General; Humour; Military. CC: PayPal.

MAIDSTONE

Peter Blest, Little Canon Cottage, Wateringbury, Maidstone, ME18 5PJ. Prop: Peter & Jan Blest. Tel: (01622) 812940. Est: 1974. Private premises. Postal only. Very large stock. Spec: Agriculture; Animals and Birds; Botany; Cockfighting; Entomology; Flower Arranging; Gardening - General; Herbalism. PR: £5–5,000. CC: AE; JCB; MC; V. Cata: Natural History, Gardening & Botanical, Sporting. Corresp: French. Mem: PBFA.

Wealden Books, 39 Adisham Drive, Maidstone, ME16 0NP. Prop: Alfred & C.A. King. Tel: (01622) 762581. Est: 1980. Private premises. Book fairs only. Appointment necessary. Large stock. Spec: Fiction - General; History - Local; Topography - General; Topography - Local. PR: £2–1,000. Cata: on main subjects. VAT No: GB 304 1457 96. Notes: *Main stream subjects are on and about Kent, Surrey and Sussex.*

ORPINGTON

Roland Books, 60 Birchwood Road, Petts Wood, Orpington, BR5 1NZ. Prop: A.R. Hughes. Tel: (01689) 838872. Fax: (01689) 838872. Private premises. Internet and Postal. Appointment necessary. Open: **M:** 09:00–17:00; **T:** 09:00–17:00; **W:** 09:00–17:00; **Th:** 09:00–17:00; **F:** 09:00–17:00. Medium stock. Spec: Advertising; Animals and Birds; Annuals; Antiques; Archaeology; Architecture; Art; Autobiography. PR: £1–75.

PADDOCK WOOD

MSR Books, 16 Laxton Gardens, Paddock Wood, TN12 6BB. Prop: Ray Green. Tel: 01892 833648. Fax: 01892 833648. Mail order only; Internet and Postal. Open: **M:** 09:00–17:30; **T:** 09:00–17:30; **W:** 09:00–17:30; **Th:** 09:00–17:30; **F:** 09:00–17:30; **S:** 09:00–17:30; **Su:** 09:00–17:30; Closed for lunch: 13:00–14:00. CC: PayPal. Cata: Rail Transport, Bus Transport, Militaria, Music.

RAINHAM

G&S Books, 313 Lower Rainham Road, Rainham,ME7 2XH. Prop: Mr G. Winder. Tel: (01634) 360178. Est: 2004. Private premises. Book Fairs only. Appointment necessary. Small stock. Spec: PR: £1 –1,000. Cata: Military, Egyptology and Modern First beditions.

RAMSGATE

Michaelsbookshop.com, ■ 72 King St., Ramsgate, CT11 8NY. Prop: Michael Child. Tel: (01843) 589500. Web: www.michaelsbookshop.com. Est: 1984. Shop open: **M:** 09:30–17:30; **T:** 09:30–17:30; **W:** 09:30–17:30; **F:** 09:30–17:30; **S:** 09:30–17:30. Very large stock. Spec: Topography - Local. PR: £1–100. CC: MC; V. Cata: East Kent. Notes: *Mostley general modern secondhand with some remainders. We are also specialist publishers and stockists of books about south east England.*

Yesteryear Railwayana, Stablings Cottage, Goodwin Road, Ramsgate, CT11 0JJ. Prop: Patrick & Mary Mullen. Tel: 01843 587283. Fax: 01843 587283. Web: www.yesrail.com. Est: 1978. Private premises. Internet and Postal. Large stock. Spec: Buses/Trams; Model Engineering; Model Railways; Paddle Boats; Public Transport; Railways and Railroads; Shipbuilding and Shipping; Steam Engines. PR: £1–500. CC: AE; MC; V. Cata: Railways, all aspects. Notes: *Yesteryear Railwayana are also known as YesRail, we are trading by mail order in out of print and scarce railway books and all other kinds of printed material that relates to some aspect of world railway history and in any language.*

ROCHESTER

Baggins Book Bazaar, ■19 High Street, Rochester, ME1 1PY. Prop: Paul Minet, Godfrey & Bee George. Tel: 01634 811651. Fax: 01634 840591. Web: www.bagginsbooks.co.uk. Est: 1986. Shop open: **M:** 10:00–18:00; **T:** 10:00–18:00; **W:** 10:00–18:00; **Th:** 10:00–18:00; **F:** 10:00–18:00; **S:** 10:00–18:00; **Su:** 10:00–18:00. CC: AE; E; JCB; MC; V; plus all major debit cards. Cata: most subjects.

Stained Glass Books, 13 Parkfields, Rochester, ME2 2TW. Prop: K.R. & S.J. Hill. Tel: (01634) 719050. Web: www.glassconservation.com. Est: 1987. Private premises. Postal only. Contactable. Small stock. Spec: Glass; Stained Glass. PR: £5–500.

SEVENOAKS

Roderick M. Barron, P.O. Box 67, Sevenoaks, TN13 3WW. Tel: (01732) 742558. Fax: (01732) 742558. Web: www.barron.co.uk. Est: 1989. Private premises. Internet and Postal. Spec: Atlases; Prints and Maps. PR: £100–10,000. CC: AE; MC; V. Corresp: French, German. Mem: ABA; IMCoS. VAT No: GB 602 6465 60.

Garwood & Voigt, 55 Bayham Road, Sevenoaks, TN13 3XE. Prop: Nigel Garwood & Rainer G. Voigt. Tel: (01732) 460025. Fax: (01732) 460026. Web: www.garwood-voigt.com. Est: 1977. Office and/or bookroom; Appointment necessary. Small stock. Spec: Atlases; Cookery/Gastronomy; Gambling; Games; Maps & Mapmaking; Music - Opera; Performing Arts; Sport - General. CC: AE; E; MC; V. Cata: Antique Maps, Atlases, Prints, Cookery Books. Corresp: German, French. Mem: ABA; PBFA; ILAB; IMCoS. Notes: *Antique Maps, Atlases, Panoramas, Views, Decorative Prints & Engravings, Cookery & Gastronomy Books.*

Geophysical Books, 82 Granville Rd., Sevenoaks, TN13 1HA. Prop: Miss Bobbie Smith. Tel: 01732 456018. Web: www.geophysicalbooks.com. Est: 1986. Private premises. Telephone First. Open: **M:** 09:00–17:30; **T:** 09:00–17:30; **W:** 09:00–17:30; **Th:** 09:00–17:30; **F:** 09:00–17:30; **S:** 09:00–17:30; Closed for lunch: 13:00–14:00. Spec: Geology; Geophysics; Petroleum Geology; Petroleum Technology. CC: MC; V. Corresp: French.

Martin Wood Cricket Books, 1c Wickenden Road, Sevenoaks, TN13 3PJ. Tel: (01732) 457205. Fax: (01732) 457205. Web: www.martinwoodcricketbooks.co.uk. Est: 1970. Private premises. Appointment necessary. Small stock. Spec: Sport - Cricket; Ephemera. PR: £1–500.

SIDCUP

Mark W. Corder, 9 Townshend Close, Sidcup, DA14 5HY. Prop: Mark Corder. Tel: (020) 8309-5665. Web: www.mark.corder.btinternet.co.uk. Est: 1988. Private premises. Internet and Postal. Appointment necessary. Small stock. Spec: Academic/Scholarly; History - British; Reference; Theology; Topography - Local. PR: £10–500.

SITTINGBOURNE

John Collins, 8 Silverdale Grove, Sittingbourne ME10 1UY. Prop: John Collins. Tel: 01795 474957. Private premises. Book fairs only. Medium Stock. Spec: Aircraft; Antiquarian; Antiques; Architecture; Art; Art History; Author - Fleming; Ian; Classics, The. PR: £1–,000. Notes: *Please contact me for matters dealing with the Faversham Book Fairs.*

J. & J. Fox Books, 48 Woodstock Road, Sittingbourne, ME10 4HN. Prop: M.V. Fox. Tel: (01795) 470310. Fax: (01795) 470310. Est: 1981. Storeroom; Appointment necessary. Small stock. Spec: Antiquarian; Cookery/Gastronomy; Maritime/Nautical; Military; Typography; Ephemera. PR: £10–1,500. Corresp: French, Portugese, Spanish. Mem: PBFA.

SMARDEN

Mrs Janet Cameron, The Meeting House, Smarden, TN27 8NR. Tel: (01233) 770552. Est: 1992. Private premises. Postal only. Small stock.

TONBRIDGE

C. & A.J. Barmby, 140 Lavender Hill, Tonbridge, TN9 2AY. Prop: Chris & Angela Barmby. Tel: 01732 356479. Est: 1981. Storeroom; Internet and Postal. Appointment necessary. Large stock. Spec: Antiquarian; Antiques; Applied Art; Archaeology; Architecture; Art; Art Reference; Author - 20th Century. PR: £5–4,000. CC: MC; V; SW, DE. VAT No: GB 367 4200 58. Notes: *We specialise in books on antiques and collectables and signed editions. We are always looking to buy obscure early titles.*

Chas J. Sawyer, 46, The Haydens, Tonbridge, TN9 1NS. Prop: Richard Sawyer. Tel: 01732 353183. Fax: 01732 353183. VOIPpro: skype. Est: 1894. Private premises. Internet and Postal. Appointment necessary. Open: **M:** 09:00–17:30; **T:** 09:00–17:30; **W:** 09:00–17:30; **Th:** 09:00–17:30; **F:** 09:00–17:30; Closed for lunch: 13:00–14:00. Spec: Africana; Antique Paper; Author - Burton, R.F.; Author - Carroll, Lewis; Author - Chapman, Abel; Author - Churchill, Sir Winston; Autographs; Bibliography. CC: MC; V; PayPal. Cata: Churchilliana, Africana, inc Ephemera. Notes: *Insurance and Consultancy work undertaken based on 40 years experience of antiquarian booktrade. UK Representative and agent for auctionexplorerbooks.com - dedicated auction website for bookdealers and collectors. Also publisher of Bookdealer.*

Grant Demar Books, 15 White Cottage Road, Tonbridge, TN10 4PX. Prop: Grant Demar. Tel: (01732) 360208. Web: www.grantdemarbooks.co.uk. Est: 1974. Private premises. Appointment necessary. Small stock. Spec: Animals and Birds; Conservation; Entomology; Natural History; Nature; New Naturalist; Ornithology; Zoology. PR: £1–1,000. Cata: Birds and Natural History.

Invicta Booksearch, 63 Weald View Road, Tonbridge, TN9 2NQ. Prop: Mr. C. Easeman. Tel: (01732) 352684. Est: 1992. Private premises. Spec: Booksearch.

Mr. Books Bookshop, ■ 2 Bank Street, Tonbridge, TN9 1BL. Prop: Mark Richardson. Tel: 01732 363000. Web: www.mrbooks.co.uk. Est: 2004. Shop open: **T:** 10:00–18:00; **W:** 10:00–15:00; **Th:** 10:00–18:00; **F:** 10:00–15:00; **S:** 10:00–18:00. CC: AE; D; E; JCB; MC; V.

Tony Skelton, The Old School House, Shipbourne, Tonbridge, TN11 9PB. Prop: D.A.L. Skelton. Tel: (01732) 810481. Est: 1992. Private premises. Internet and Postal. Contactable. Open: **M:** 08:00–20:00; **T:** 08:00–20:00; **W:** 08:00–20:00; **Th:** 08:00–20:00; **F:** 08:00–20:00; **S:** 09:00–20:00; **Su:** 09:00–20:00. Small stock. Spec: Author - Heaney, Seamus; Countries - Ireland; First Editions; Literature; Literature - Irish; Modern First Editions; Plays; Poetry. PR: £5–500. CC: PayPal. Cata: Irish interest. Corresp: French, German. Mem: PBFA. VAT No: GB 796 5067 79.

P. & F. Whelan, 68 The Drive, Tonbridge, TN9 2LR. Prop: Tony & Mary Whelan. Tel: (01732) 354882. Fax: (01732) 354882. Est: 1986. Private premises. Postal only. Small stock. Spec: Countries - Ireland; History - National; Irish Interest. PR: £5–250. Cata: Irish interest.

TUNBRIDGE WELLS

Hall's Bookshop, ■ 20–22 Chapel Place, Tunbridge Wells, TN1 1YQ. Prop: Sabrina Izzard. Tel: (01892) 527842. Fax: (01892) 527842. Web: www.hallsbookshop.com. Est: 1898. Shop open: **M:** 09:30–17:00; **T:** 09:30–17:00; **W:** 09:30–17:00; **Th:** 09:30–17:00; **F:** 09:30–17:00; **S:** 09:30–17:00. Large stock. Spec: Archaeology; Architecture; Art; Art History; Aviation; Bindings; Biography; Books in Greek. Mem: PBFA.

Pantiles Bookshop, ■The Corn Exchange, The Pantiles, Tunbridge Wells, TN2 5TN. Prop: Steve and Val Marshall. Tel: 01892 618191. Web: www.pantilesbookshop.co.uk. Est: 2004. Shop open: **M:** 09:30–17:00; **T:** 09:30–17:00; **W:** 09:30–17:00; **Th:** 09:30–17:00; **F:** 09:30–17:00; **S:** 09:30–17:00; **Su:** 10:30–16:30. CC: AE; MC; V. Notes: *A well stocked mainly non-fiction bookshop specialising in Sport, Railway, Military, Cinema, Mind, Body, Spirit and books on Kent.*

The Secondhand Bookshop, ■ 13 Nevill Street, Tunbridge Wells, TN2 5RU. Prop: David Neal. Tel: (01892) 547005. Est: 1992. Shop open: **M:** 10:00–16:30; **T:** 10:00–16:30; **Th:** 10:00–16:30; **F:** 10:00–16:30; **S:** 10:00–16:30. Medium stock. Spec: Brewing. PR: £1–500. VAT No: GB 725 4573 27. Notes: *Attends Titlepage and HD Fairs.*

World War Books, Oaklands Camden Park, Tunbridge Wells, TN2 5AE. Prop: Tim Harper. Tel: (01892) 538465. Fax: (01892) 538465. Web: www.worldwarbooks.com. Est: 1993. Private premises. Internet and Postal. Contactable. Medium stock. Spec: Aviation; Holocaust; Maritime/Nautical; Military; Military - Modelling; Naval; School Registers/Rolls of Honour; War - General. PR: £10–5,000. CC: MC; V. Cata: Military and manuscripts/photograph albums. Mem: PBFA; OMRS. Notes: *We specialize in hard to find and rare Military, Aviation and Naval books, manuscripts and photograph albums etc. We also organise specialist Military, Naval and Aviation bookfairs at Tunbridge Wells, Chatham, London and Middle Wallop.*

WATERINGBURY

Cobnar Books, 567 Red Hill, Wateringbury, Maidstone, ME18 5BE. Prop: Lawrence Ilott. Tel: 01622 813230. Web: www.cobnarbooks.com. Est: 1995. Office and/or bookroom; Internet and Postal. Appointment necessary. Spec: Academic/Scholarly; Agriculture; Antiquarian; Bibles; Bindings; Cookery/Gastronomy; County - Local; Early Imprints. CC: JCB; MC; V. Cata: Antiquarian, bindings, Provincial Printing, Topog. Mem: PBFA. VAT No: GB 874 3008 26.

WESTERHAM

Barely Read Books, ■ 18 The Green, Westerham, TN16 1AX. Prop: Ross Williams. Tel: 01959 565854. Web: www.barelyreadbooks.co.uk. Est: 2001. Shop open: **T:** 10:00–18:00; **W:** 10:00–18:00; **Th:** 10:00–18:00; **F:** 10:00–18:00; **S:** 10:00–18:00; **Su:** 10:00–18:00. Spec: Author - Johns, W.E.; Aviation; Children's; Children's - Illustrated; Churchilliana.

Derek Stirling Bookseller, 1 Quebec Avenue, Westerham, TN16 1BJ. Tel: (01959) 561 822. Fax: (01959) 561822. Est: 1999. Private premises. Internet and Postal. Appointment necessary. Small stock. Spec: Academic/Scholarly; Advertising; Almanacs; Antiquarian; Author - 19th Century; Author - Churchill, Sir Winston; Author - Dickens, Charles; Author - Hardy, Thomas. PR: £10–2,000. Notes: *Purchases bound volumes, runs or quantities of newspapers and periodicals published pre-1850.*

The Design Gallery 1850-1950, ■ 5 The Green, Westerham, TN16 1AS. Prop: Chrissie Painell. Tel: (01959 561234. Web: www.designgallery.co.uk. Est: 2002. Shop open: **M:** 10:00–17:30; **T:** 10:00–17:30; **W:** 10:00–17:30; **Th:** 10:00–17:30; **F:** 10:00–17:30; **S:** 10:00–17:30; **Su:** 13:00–17:00. Spec: Aesthetic Movement; Art Deco; Art Nouveau; Arts & Crafts Era; Bindings; Crafts; Gothic Revival; Jewellery. CC: AE; MC; V. Mem: LAPADA. Notes: *Also, Victorian fine bindings, and original illustrations. Call in advance to see all stock. Also 19th & 20thC designer jewellery.*

WHITSTABLE

Alan & Margaret Edwards, 10 Meteor Avenue, Whitstable, CT5 4DH. Tel: (01227) 262276. Est: 1988. Private premises. Appointment necessary. Small stock. Spec: Ecclesiastical History & Architecture; Theology; Topography - General. PR: £2–500. Corresp: French, German. Cata: Regular.

LANCASHIRE

ASHTON-UNDER-LYNE

Marathon Books, 12 Lytham Close, Ashton-under-Lyne, Lancashire, OL6 9ER. Prop: Richard Bond. Tel: (0161) 343-2085. Est: 1980. Private premises. Postal only. Appointment necessary. Small stock. Spec: Psychology/Psychiatry; Sport - Athletics. Notes: *Also, a booksearch service.*

BLACKBURN

Neil Summersgill, Pigeon Hall, Abbott Brow, Mellor, Blackburn, BB2 7HT. Prop: Neil Summersgill. Tel: (01254) 813559. Est: 1984. Private premises. Appointment necessary. Small stock. Spec: Antiquarian; Atlases; Autographs; Bindings; Letters; Manuscripts; Natural History; Sport - Field Sports. PR: £10-5,000. CC: MC; V. Mem: PBFA.

BLACKPOOL

Blackpool Book Warehouse, 12 Spen Farm, Estate Ashworth Road, Blackpool, FY4 5LP. Prop: Nick Street. Tel: 01253-698364. Est: 1999. Warehouse; Shop open: **M:** 09:00–17:30; **F:** 10:00–17:00; **S:** 10:00–17:00; **Su:** 10:00–17:00. Spec: Adventure; Aircraft; Art Reference; History - British; History - Middle Ages; History - Napoleonic; Horology; Maritime/Nautical. Mem: PBFA. Notes: *Wide range of books in all classes, new, secondhand and remaindered titles. Good discounts for trade customers.*

Book Mad, ■ 151 Church Street, Blackpool, FY1 3NX. Prop: Nick Street. Tel: 01253 291969. Est: 1991. Shop open: **M:** 10:00–17:30; **T:** 10:00–17:30; **W:** 10:00–17:30; **Th:** 10:00–17:30; **F:** 10:00–17:30; **S:** 10:00–17:30; **Su:** 10:00–16:00; Closed for lunch: 10:00–16:00. Spec: out-of-print; Prints and Maps.

Bob Dobson, 3 Staining Rise, Staining, Blackpool, FY3 0BU. Tel: (01253) 895678. Fax: (01253) 895678. Est: 1969. Private premises. Appointment necessary. Large stock. Spec: History - Local; Topography - Local. PR: £1-100. VAT No: GB 534 3982 30. Notes: *Incl: books on Lancashire and Cheshire. Also publishes as Landy Publishing.*

John McGlynn, 173 Newton Drive, Blackpool, FY3 8ND. Tel: (01253) 300100. Fax: (01253) 300020. Web: www.vintagetechnology.org. Est: 1996. Private premises. Postal only. Medium stock. Spec: Motoring; Transport. PR: £10-200. Notes: *Rolls-Royce and Bentley Motor Cars material only.*

BRINSCALL

Modern Firsts Etc., Hilltops, Windsor Drive, Brinscall, PR6 8PX. Prop: R.J. Leek. Tel: (01254) 830861. Est: 1985. Private premises. Postal only. Small stock. Spec: Autographs; First Editions; Painting. PR: £1-500.

BURY

Richard Byrom Textile Bookroom, 3 Hawkshaw Lane, Bury, BL8 4JZ. Prop: Richard Byrom. Tel: (01204) 883110. Fax: (01204) 880155. Est: 1984. Private premises. Appointment necessary. Large stock. Spec: Carpets - General; Company History; Crochet; Embroidery; Fashion & Costume; Industry; Knitting; Lace. PR: £1-500.

CARNFORTH

The Carnforth Bookshop, ■ 38–42 Market Street, Carnforth, LA5 9JX. Prop: P. & G. Seward. Tel: (01524) 734588. Fax: (01524) 735893. Web: www.carnforthbooks.co.uk. Est: 1977. Internet and Postal. Shop open: **M:** 09:00–17:30; **T:** 09:00–17:30; **W:** 09:00–17:30; **Th:** 09:00–17:30; **F:** 09:00–17:30; **S:** 09:00–17:30. Very large stock. Spec: Alpinism/Mountaineering; Art; Art History; Biography; Classical Studies; Fiction - General; Fine & Rare; History - General. PR: £1-500. CC: AE; E; JCB; MC; V. Mem: BA. VAT No: GB 306 8293 93.

CHORLEY

Bowland Bookfinders, 88 Bury Lane, Withnell, Chorley, PR6 8SD. Prop: D.S. Suttie. Tel: (01254) 830619. Est: 1987. Private premises. Internet and Postal. Appointment necessary. Spec: Academic/Scholarly; Advertising; War - General; Booksearch.

CLITHEROE

Moorside Books Ltd, ■Moorside Cottage, Whalley Old Road, Billington, Clitheroe, BB7 9JF. Prop: David Sedgwick. Tel: (01254) 824104. Web: www.abebooks.com/home/DFSBOOKS/. Est: 1985. Internet and Postal. Shop at: 29 Moor Lane, Clitheroe, Lancs. Open: **T:** 10:00–17:00; **Th:** 10:00–17:00; **F:** 10:00–17:00; **S:** 10:00–17:00. Small stock. Spec: Antiquarian; Astronomy; Author - Lawrence, T.E.; Bindings; Cosmology; Countries - Arabian Peninsula; History - Science; Maps & Mapmaking. PR: £5–10,000. CC: MC; V; Maestro. Cata: T E Lawrence. Mem: PBFA. VAT No: GB 787 8011 92. Notes: *Plus my specialist stock of astronomy, early science, and T E Lawrence in bookroom open by appointment. Mobile 07890 980241.*

Roundstone Books, ■ 29 Moor Lane, Clitheroe, BB7 1BE. Prop: Jo Harding. Tel: 01200 444242. Web: www.roundstonebooks.co.uk. Est: 1995. Shop open: **T:** 09:00–17:00; **Th:** 09:00–17:00; **F:** 09:00–17:00; **S:** 09:00–17:00. Spec: Alternative Medicine; Biography; Children's; Drama; Fiction - General; Foreign Texts; Health; History - General. CC: JCB; MC; V; Debit.

FENCE

Pendleside Books, 359 Wheatley Lane Road, Fence, Nr. Burnley, BB12 9QA. Prop: E. & B. Sutcliffe. Tel: (01282) 615617. Est: 1974. Private premises. Postal only. Appointment necessary. Small stock. Spec: Entomology; Mycology; Topography - Local. PR: £5–500. Corresp: French, Italian.

HALTON

Mark Towers, 45 Beech Road, Halton, LA2 6QQ. Tel: (01524) 811556. Web: www.royoftherovers.com. Est: 1999. Private premises. Postal only. Contactable. Spec: Comic Books & Annuals; Comics. PR: £2–50.

HINDLEY

Wiend Books, Unit 1 Hindley Business Centre, Platt Lane, Hindley, Wigan, WN2 3PA. Prop: Paul Morris. Tel: (07976) 604203. Web: www.wiendbooks.co.uk. Est: 1997. Office and/or bookroom; Appointment necessary. Spec: Africana; Annuals; Archaeology - Industrial; Architecture; Art; Arthurian; Astronomy; Autobiography. PR: £2-250. Notes: *We used to be located in The Wiend & are also at Stalls 243 Bygone Times Eccleston near Charnock Richard on M6. We will be clearing whole warehouse at bargain prices. Always a discount for a personal visit-just quote Sheppards.*

LANCASTER

Interstellar Master Traders, ■ 33 North Road, Lancaster, LA1 1NS. Prop: P. Pinto. Tel: +44-1524-382181. Web: www.i-m-t.demon.co.uk/. Est: 1985. Internet and Postal. Shop open: **M:** 10:00–19:00; **T:** 10:00–19:00; **W:** 10:00–19:00; **Th:** 10:00–19:00; **F:** 10:00–19:00; **S:** 10:00–19:00. Large stock. Spec: Fiction - Fantasy, Horror; Fiction - Science Fiction. PR: £0–750. Notes: *Titles want-listed 'til found / deleted by customer.*

LEYLAND

Browse Books, 10 Silverdale Close, Worden Park, Leyland, Leyland, PR25 3BY. Prop: T.B. Bowe. Tel: (01772) 431608. Est: 1989. Display/stand; Internet and Postal. Telephone First. Shop at: Bygone Times, The Green, Eccleston, Lancashire. Open: **M:** 10:30–17:00; **T:** 10:30–17:00; **W:** 10:30–20:00; **Th:** 10:30–15:00; **F:** 10:30–17:00; **S:** 10:30–16:00; **Su:** 10:30–17:00. Spec: Antiques; Buses/Trams; Crafts; Crochet; Embroidery; Gardening - General; General; Humour. PR: £2–50. CC: V. Notes: *Extensive Sheet Music Stock. Credit card facilities at main counter where my unit is based. My unit is unmanned at most times. Bygone Times Tel: 01257 451889.*

Great Grandfather's, ■ 82 Towngate, Leyland, PR25 2LR. Prop: Greg D. Smith. Tel: (01772) 422268. Est: 1985. Shop open: **T:** 10:00–17:30 **Th:** 10:00–17:30; **F:** 10:00–17:30; **S:** 10:00–17:30. Large stock. Spec: General Stock. PR: £1–200. CC: pending. Corresp: French, German. Mem: PBFA. Notes: *Open other times by appointment. Large general stock. 5 mins from M6, Junction 28. Easy parking.*

LYTHAM ST. ANNES

Robert F. Butterworth, 33 Eldon Court, Glen Eldon Road, Lytham St. Annes, FY8 2BH. Prop: Robert F Butterworth. Tel: (01253) 729031. Fax: (01253) 729031. Est: 1982. Private premises. Internet and Postal. Appointment necessary. Small stock. Spec: Maritime/Nautical; Ephemera. PR: £1–750. Notes: *Antique Centre, St.George's Road, St.Annes.*

PRESTON

B D McManmon, 6 Sea View, Walmer Bridge, Preston, PR4 5GH. Prop: Barry McManmon. Tel: 01772 612727. Est: 1982. Private premises. Appointment necessary. Spec: Academic/Scholarly; Archaeology; Military; Travel - General. CC: AE; D; E; JCB; MC; V; Debit cards. Mem: ABA; PBFA; ILAB. Notes: *Stock includes books on academic history, travel and military history.*

Halewood & Sons, ■ 37 Friargate, Preston, PR1 2AT. Tel: (01772) 252603. Est: 1867. Shop open: **M:** 09:30–17:30; **T:** 09:30–17:30; **W:** 09:30–17:30; **Th:** 09:30–17:30; **F:** 09:30–17:30; **S:** 09:30–17:30. Very large stock. Spec: Countries - Africa; Countries - Americas, The; Countries - Australia; Booksearch; Prints and Maps. CC: AE; MC; V; Solo, Maestro. Corresp: French, German, Spanish. Mem: ABA; PBFA; BA. Notes: *Open Sunday by appointment.*

O'Connor Fine Books, 9 Garrison Road, Fulwood, Preston, PR2 8AL. Prop: John and Evelyn O'Connor. Tel: 01297 32431. Est: 2002. Private premises. Appointment necessary. Small stock. Spec: Bibliography; Folio Society, The; Printing. Corresp: French.

Pamona Books, Canberra Road, Preston, PR25 3JH. Prop: Mr. D. W. Heald. Tel: 01772 452198. Private premises. Postal only. Contactable. Spec: Fiction - General; First Editions; General Stock. Notes: *Free booksearch service.*

Preston Book Company, ■ 68 Friargate, Preston, PR1 2ED. Prop: M. Halewood. Tel: (01772) 252613. Est: 1960. Shop open: **M:** 10:00–17:00; **T:** 10:00–17:00; **W:** 10:00–17:00; **Th:** 10:00–17:00; **F:** 10:00–17:00; **S:** 10:00–17:00. Large stock. Spec: Africana; Americana - General; Anthropology; Antiquarian; Atlases; Australiana; Author - Conan Doyle, Sir Arthur; Author - Dickens, Charles. PR: £10–1,000. CC: JCB; MC; V.

ST. HELENS

Harvest Books, 25 Thickwood, Moss Lane, Rainford, St. Helens, WA11 8QL. Prop: Mrs. Janet Christie. Tel: (01744) 885747. Est: 1998. Private premises. Internet and Postal. Appointment necessary. Spec: Authors - British; Children's; Fairy/Folk Tales; Folklore; Illustrated - General; Literature; Rural Life; Social History. CC: PayPal. Mem: PBFA. Notes: *Attendance at Book Fairs, mainly in North West. Also selection of stock at Dales & Lakes Book Centre, Sedbergh, Cumbria.*

THORNTON CLEVELEYS

Seabreeze Books, 39 Woodfield Road, Thornton Cleveleys, FY5 4EQ. Prop: Martin L. Johnson. Tel: (01253) 850075. Est: 1994. Private premises. Appointment necessary. Medium stock. Spec: Antiquarian; Art; Books about Books; Children's; Churchilliana; Fiction - General; Limited Editions - General; Literature - Victorian. PR: £1–5,000. Notes: *Skipton Antiques Centre, Skipton (q.v.)*

WEETON

Fylde Books, 31 Knowsley Crescent, Weeton, Preston, PR4 3ND. Prop: Richard Eaves. Tel: 07984 701728. Web: www.ukbookworld.com/members/fyldebooks. Est: 1997. Private premises. Postal only. Appointment necessary. Spec: Aviation; Dogs; General Stock; Marque Histories (see also motoring); Motoring; Sport - Angling/Fishing; Sport - Field Sports; Sport - Shooting. CC: PayPal. Mem: PBFA. Notes: *Reasonably priced general stock with an emphasis on Northern Topography, Fishing, Shooting, Transport, Dogs & Technical. Books always wanted.*

WEIR

Neville Chapman, 3, Rochester Close, Weir, Bacup, OL13 8RN. Tel: 01706 879778. Web: www.abebooks.com/home/chapbooks. Est: 1992. Private premises. Internet and Postal. Appointment necessary. Small stock. Spec: Academic/Scholarly; Advertising; Author - du Maurier, Daphne; Countries - England; History - Local; Topography - Local. PR: £1–100.

LEICESTERSHIRE

EARLSDON

Armstrong's Books & Collectables, ■ 178 Albany Street, Earlsdon, Coventry, CV5 6NG. Prop: Colin Rowe Armstrong. Tel: 02476 714344. Est: 1983. Shop open: **T:** 10:00–17:00; **W:** 10:00–17:00; **Th:** 10:00–17:00; **F:** 10:00–17:00; **S:** 10:00–17:00. Spec: Annuals; Cinema/Film; Comics; Cookery/ Gastronomy; Fiction - Crime, Detective, Spy, Thrillers; Fiction - Fantasy, Horror; Fiction - Science Fiction; Law - General.

HINCKLEY

Caduceus Books, 28 Darley Road, Burbage, Hinckley, LE10 2RL. Prop: Ben Fernee. Tel: (01455) 250542. Fax: (0870) 055-2982. Web: www.caduceusbooks.com. Est: 1989. Private premises. Appointment necessary. Small stock. Spec: Alchemy; Astrology; Author - Crowley, Aleister; Esoteric; Folklore; Occult; Supernatural; Witchcraft. PR: £1–1,000. CC: MC; V; Switch. Cata: Esoteric, occult. Notes: *Also, manuscripts, association items.*

HUGGLESCOTE

Aucott and Thomas, 46 Dennis Street, Hugglescote, LE67 2FP. Prop: Roger Thomas. Tel: 01530 831604. Fax: 01530 831604. Web: www.aucott.com. Est: 1996. Office and/or bookroom; Internet and Postal. Appointment necessary. Open: **M:** 09:00–17:30; **T:** 09:00–17:30; **W:** 09:00–17:30; **Th:** 09:00–17:30; **F:** 09:00–17:30; **S:** 09:00–17:30; **Su:** 09:00–17:30; Closed for lunch: 13:00–14:00. Spec: General. CC: AE; E; JCB; MC; V; Maestro. Mem: Ibooknet. VAT No: GB 800 2360 90.

KIBWORTH HARCOURT

The Countryman Gallery, The Croft 14 Leicester Road, Kibworth Harcourt, LE8 0NN. Prop: Pamela M. Turnbull. Tel: (0116) 279-3211. Est: 1980. Private premises. Appointment necessary. Small stock. Spec: Children's; Dogs; Ornithology; Poultry; Sport - Angling/Fishing; Sport - Field Sports; Sport - Hunting; Sport - Shooting. PR: £1–500. CC: MC; V. Notes: *Shop also at above premises but appointment necessary.*

LEICESTER

Clarendon Books, ■ 144 Clarendon Park Road, Leicester, LE2 3AE. Prop: Julian Smith. Tel: (0116) 270-1856. Est: 1985. Shop open: **M:** 10:00–17:00; **T:** 10:00–17:00; **W:** 10:00–17:00; **Th:** 10:00–17:00; **F:** 10:00–17:00; **S:** 10:00–17:00. Medium stock. Spec: Academic/Scholarly; History - General; History - Local; Literary Criticism; Literature. PR: £1–1,000. CC: AE; E; JCB; MC; V. Mem: PBFA. VAT No: GB 890 0309 37.

Cottage Books, The Cottage, Rempstone Road, Gelsmoor, Coleorton, Leicester, LE67 8HR. Prop: Jennifer M. Boyd–Cropley. Tel: None. Est: 1970. Private premises. Postal only. Medium stock. Spec: Agriculture; Architecture; Canals/Inland Waterways; Crafts; Fairgrounds; Folklore; Gypsies; History - Local. PR: £1–2,000. Cata: Rural Life Past & Present. Gypsies. Mem: PBFA.

Rebecca Dearman Rare Books, 66 Gartree Road Stonygate, Leicester, LE2 2FW. Prop: Rebecca Dearman. Tel: (0116) 270-0469. Est: 1967. Private premises. Postal only. Shop open: **M:** 09:00–17:00; **T:** 09:00–17:00; **W:** 09:00–17:00; **Th:** 09:00–17:00; **F:** 09:00–17:00; **S:** 09:00–17:00. Medium stock. PR: £1–1,000. Cata: on various subjects. Notes: *Catalogues and occasional fairs. General stock.*

James M Pickard (Rare Books), 21 Grenfell Road, Leicester, LE2 2PA. Prop: James M Pickard. Tel: (0116) 2707169. Fax: (0116) 2702010. Web: www.jamesmpickard.com. Est: 1997. Private premises. Internet and Postal. Telephone First. Open: **M:** 09:00–17:30; **T:** 09:00–17:30; **W:** 09:00–17:30; **Th:** 09:00–17:30; **F:** 09:00–17:30; **S:** 09:00–17:30; **Su:** 09:00–17:30; Closed for lunch: 13:00–14:00. Spec: Author - Bellaires, George; Author - Blyton, Enid; Author - Carr, John Dickson; Author - Chandler, Raymond; Author - Charteris, Leslie; Author - Christie, Agatha; Author - Cornwell, Bernard; Author - Crofts, Freeman Wills. CC: MC; V. Cata: Modern First Editions. Mem: PBFA. Notes: *Specialise in Ian Fleming, Leslie Charteris, Georges Simenon, Agatha Christie and pre-war Detective Fiction from the Golden Age (1920-1940).*

Alfred Lenton, ■ 27 Saint Nicholas Place, Leicester, LE1 4LD. Prop: Philip Lenton. Tel: (0116) 262-7827. Est: 1942. Shop. Telephone First. Small stock. Spec: Art; Arts, The; Illustrated - General; Literature; Natural History; Science - General; Prints and Maps. PR: £1–100.

Bruce Main–Smith & Co. Ltd., 5 Lincoln Drive, Wigston, Leicester, LE18 4XU. Prop: (*) D.R. & M.E. Mitchell (Directors). Tel: (0116) 277-7669. Fax: (0116) 277-7669. Web: www.brucemainsmith.com. Est: 1972. Mail order only; Open: **M:** 08:00–17:00; **T:** 08:00–17:00; **W:** 08:00–17:00; **Th:** 08:00–17:00; **F:** 08:00–17:00; **S:** 08:00–17:00; **Su:** 08:00–17:00. Spec: Motorbikes / motorcycles. PR: £4–100. CC: MC; V; Switch. Cata: Motor Cycle Literature. Notes: *Also, virtually a complete stock of all new motor cycle books, plus 4,000 photocopied manuals, spares lists & brochures.*

Maynard & Bradley, ■ 1 Royal Arcade, Silver Street, Leicester, LE1 5YW. Prop: David Maynard & Stephen Bradley. Tel: (0116) 253-2712. Web: www.maynardandbradley.com. Est: 1971. Shop open: **M:** 09:15–17:15; **T:** 09:15–17:15; **W:** 09:15–17:15; **Th:** 09:15–17:15; **F:** 09:15–17:15; **S:** 09:00–17:00. Medium stock. Spec: Bindings; Colour-Plate; Cookery/Gastronomy; Illustrated - General; Private Press; Sport - Cricket; Sport - Field Sports; Topography - General. PR: £1–3,000. CC: E; MC; V; Solo, Maestro. Mem: PBFA. VAT No: GB 416 3807 58. Notes: *Also, booksearch, pictures, picture-framing, conservation services, print colouring & decorative mount cutting service (trade).*

Pooks Motor Books, ■ Unit 4 Victoria Road, Fowke Street, Rothley, Leicester, LE7 7PJ. Prop: (*) Barrie Pook & John Pook. Tel: (0116) 237-6222. Fax: (0116) 237-6491. Web: www.abebooks.com. Shop open: **M:** 09:00–17:00; **T:** 09:00–17:00; **W:** 09:00–17:00; **Th:** 09:00–17:00; **F:** 09:00–17:00. Very large stock. Spec: Biography; Marque Histories (see also motoring); Motorbikes / motorcycles; Motoring; Transport; Vintage Cars; Collectables; Ephemera. PR: £3–1,000. CC: MC; V. Mem: FSB. Notes: *Also, sales catalogues for cars & motorcycles. Open at other times by appointment.*

Rosanda Books, 11 Whiteoaks Road, Oadby, Leicester, LE2 5YL. Prop: David Baldwin BA, M. Phil, & Joyce Baldwin. Tel: (0116) 2713880. Est: 1994. Private premises. Appointment necessary. Spec: History - Ancient; History - British; History - Byzantine; History - European; History - Greek; History - Middle Ages; History - Modern; History - Roman. PR: £2–50. Cata: History (fiction & non-fiction).

Tin Drum Books, ■ 68 Narborough Road, Leicester, LE3 0BR. Prop: Valerie & Ian Smalley. Tel: (0116) 224-8409. Est: 1986. Shop open: **M:** 10:00–18:00; **T:** 10:00–18:00; **W:** 10:00–18:00; **Th:** 10:00–18:00; **F:** 10:00–18:00; **S:** 10:00–18:00. Medium stock. PR: £1–10. Notes: *Also, bookbinding.*

Treasure Trove Books, ■ 21 Mayfield Road, Leicester, LE2 1LR. Prop: Linda Sharman. Tel: (0116) 2755933. Est: 1993. Shop open: **M:** 09:30–16:30; **T:** 09:30–16:30; **Th:** 09:30–16:30; **F:** 09:30–16:30; **S:** 09:30–16:30. Very large stock. Spec: Annuals; Author - Bellaires, George; Author - Blyton, Enid; Author - Brent-Dyer, Elinor M.; Author - Buckeridge, A.; Author - Christie, Agatha; Author - Johns, W.E.; Author - Potter, Beatrix. PR: £1–500. CC: PayPal.

Tony Yates Antiquarian Books, 3 Melton Avenue, Leicester, LE4 7SE. Prop: Tony and June Yates. Tel: (0116) 266-1891. Est: 1989. Private premises. Book fairs only. Appointment necessary. Small stock. Spec: Academic/Scholarly; Almanacs; Antiquarian; Atlases; Bibliography; Bindings; Books about Books; Broadsides - Letterpress. PR: £5–1,000. Cata: On specialist areas. Mem: PBFA. Notes: *We attend bookfairs mainly in the Midlands and North of England. Specialisms include Leicestershire, Thomas Bewick and his apprentices, Joseph Crawhall, early children's books, fine bindings and antiquarian language, literature and history.*

LOUGHBOROUGH

Booklore, 6, The Green, East Leake, Loughborough, LE12 6LD. Prop: (*) Ralph & Simon Corbett. Tel: (01509) 820614. Est: 1994. Private premises. Internet and Postal. Appointment necessary. Open: **M:** 09:30–17:30; **T:** 09:30–17:30; **W:** 09:30–17:30; **Th:** 09:30–17:30; **F:** 09:30–17:30; **S:** 09:00–16:00. Large stock. Spec: Antiquarian; Bindings; Fine leather bindings (see also Fine & Rare). PR: £10–1,000. CC: MC; V; maestro. Mem: PBFA; Society of Bookbinders. VAT No: GB 815 6907 13. Notes: *We are always keen to buy and sell quality books. We deal with honesty and integrity.*

Eric Goodyer, Natural History, Hathern, Loughborough, LE12 5LE. Prop: Sue Duerdoth & Eric Goodyer. Tel: (01509) 844473. Fax: (01509) 844473. Web: www.abebooks.com/home/ ERICGOODYER/. Est: 1992. Private premises. Postal only. Telephone First. Small stock. Spec: Antiquarian; Natural History. PR: £5–300. CC: PayPal. VAT No: GB 61 65474 433.

Magis Books, 64 Leopold Street, Loughborough, LE11 5DN. Prop: Tom Clarke. Tel: 01509210626. Fax: 01509238034. Web: www.magis.co.uk. Est: 1975. Private premises. Internet and Postal. Telephone First. Open: **M:** 09:00–18:30; **T:** 09:00–18:30; **W:** 09:00–18:30; **Th:** 09:00–18:30; **F:** 09:00–18:30; **S:** 09:00–18:30; **Su:** 09:00–17:30; Closed for lunch: 13:00–14:00. Spec: Alchemy; Divining; Esoteric; Folklore; Ghosts; Graphology; Hermeticism; Homeopathy. CC: AE; MC; V. Cata: Esoteric, occult, Eastern & Western philosophies,. Mem: PBFA.

MARKET HARBOROUGH

Bowden Books, 14 Station Road Great Bowden, Market Harborough, LE16 7HN. Prop: Terry Bull. Tel: (01858) 466832. Est: 1986. Private premises. Book fairs only. Very small stock. Spec: Architecture; Art; Colour-Plate; Publishers - Black, A. & C.; Topography - General; Travel - General. PR: £1–1,000. Corresp: French, Italian. Mem: PBFA.

Christine's Book Cabin, ■ 7 Coventry Road, Market Harborough, LE16 9BX. Prop: Malcolm & Christine Noble. Tel: (01858) 433233. Web: www.bookcabin.co.uk. Est: 1992. Shop open: **M:** 10:00–16:30; **T:** 10:00–16:30; **Th:** 10:00–16:30; **F:** 10:00–16:30; **S:** 10:00–16:30. Small stock. Spec: Booksearch; Ephemera. PR: £1–400. CC: AE; JCB; MC; V. Notes: *General stock.*

MELTON MOWBRAY

Witmeha Productions, The Orchard Wymondham, Melton Mowbray, LE14 2AZ.

ROTHLEY

Whig Books Ltd., 11 Grangefields Drive, Rothley. Prop: Dr. J. Pollock & Mrs. A. Hinchliffe. Tel: (0116) 237-4420. Est: 1985. Private premises. Appointment necessary. Small stock. Spec: Art; History - General; Literature. PR: £1–500.

SHENTON

Michael D. Raftery (Books), Whitemoors Antique Centre Mill Lane, Shenton, CV13 0LA. Prop: Mike Raftery. Tel: Home (01455) 611017. Est: 1976. Office and/or bookroom; Shop open: **M:** 11:00–16:00; **T:** 11:00–16:00; **W:** 11:00–16:00; **Th:** 11:00–16:00; **F:** 11:00–16:00; **S:** 11:00–16:00; **Su:** 11:00–16:00. Small stock. Spec: Booksearch. PR: £1–30. CC: AE; D; E; JCB; MC; V. Corresp: French, German. Notes: *Tea Rooms, gardens visitor attractions (at Whitemoor only). Also at Leicester Antiques Warehouse, Leicester (q.v.).*

THURCASTON

Ian Kilgour (Sporting Books), 3 Hall Farm Road, Thurcaston, LE7 7JF. Prop: Ian Kilgour. Tel: (0116) 235-0025. Est: 1972. Private premises. Internet and Postal. Appointment necessary. Small stock. Spec: Cockfighting; Dogs; Farming & Livestock; Firearms/Guns; Rural Life; Sport - Angling/Fishing; Sport - Big Game Hunting; Sport - Coursing. PR: £2–500. Cata: fishing shooting hunting falconry.

WIGSTON

Michael D. Raftery (Books), Leicester Antiques Warehouse Clarkes Road, Wigston, Leicester, LE18 2BG. Prop: Mike Raftery. Display/stand. Notes: *Also at: Whitemoors Antique Centre, Shenton, Leicestershire (q.v.)*

Black Cat Bookshop, P O BOX 8662, Wigston, Leicester, LE18 9BB. Prop: Philip & Karen Woolley. Tel: (0116) 251-2756. Web: www.blackcatbookshop.com. Est: 1987. Mail order only; Internet and Postal. Contactable. Open: **M:** 09:30–17:00; **T:** 09:30–17:00; **W:** 9:30–17:00; **Th:** 09:30–17:00; **F:** 09:30–17:00; **S:** 09:30–17:00. Large stock. Spec: Author - Conan Doyle, Sir Arthur; Author - Crompton, Richmal; Author - Fleming, Ian; Author - Johns, W.E.; Children's; Children's - Illustrated; Comic Books & Annuals; Comics. PR: £1–500. CC: E; JCB; MC; V; SW, De. Cata: Crime, Sherlock Holmes James Bond, British Comics. Mem: PBFA. Notes: *Attends book fairs - Mostly Midlands and North. Worldwide mail order service, selling on Abe, Amazon, Books@pbfa, & eBay. Also bookstalls on Leicester Market Tues-Sat inc. Contact above number to see specific stock.*

LINCOLNSHIRE

BARTON–ON–HUMBER

Humber Books, Rozel House, 4 St. Mary's Lane, Barton–on–Humber, DN18 5EX. Prop: Peter M. Cresswell. Tel: (01652) 634958. Fax: (01652) 634965. Web: www.humberbooks.co.uk. Est: 1972. Private premises. Internet and Postal. Contactable. Spec: Antiquarian; Bibles; Hymnology; Manuscripts; Religion - Christian; Religion - Methodism; Religion - Non conformity; Religion - Protestantism. PR: £20–2,000. CC: AE; D; E; JCB; MC; V. Notes: *Humber Books is a leading UK Dealer in Antiquarian Theological Books and Bibles. We have been supplying rare books for over 30 years. Whilst selling antiquarian theology, we specialise in Protestant Reformation & English Puritanism up to 1700.*

BILLINGBOROUGH

Alan Redmond Books, 25 High Street, Billingborough, Sleaford, NG34 0QB. Prop: Mrs R. Redmond. Tel: 01529 240215. Est: 1981. Storeroom; Shop open: **S:** 10:00–17:00; **Su:** 10:00–17:00. Notes: *Also open on Bank Holidays but closed between 1 November and 1 March. Appointment may be possible outside these times.*

BILLINGHAY

Maggy Browne, 27-29 High Street, Billinghay, Lincoln, LN4 4AU. Prop: Maggy Browne. Tel: (01526) 860294. Fax: (0870) 7059623. Web: www.njbonline.com. Est: 1981. Private premises. Internet and Postal. Appointment necessary. Medium stock. Spec: Audio/Sound/Acoustics; Biography; Crime (True); Fiction - General; Fire & Fire Fighters; History - General; History - British; History - Modern. PR: £5–50. CC: JCB; MC; V; Switch. Mem: FSB. Notes: *Props for Theatre/Film/TV. Mailroom supplies, DJ sleeving, PB covers etc. Maps, Prints, Engravings, Vintage Adverts. Ephemera. Original Paintings. Largest stock Guinness titles in the WORLD! Audio Books + Tape Drops - solves tangled tapes.*

CLEETHORPES

Soccer Books Limited, 72 St Peter's Avenue, Cleethorpes, DN35 8HU. Prop: John, Michael & Glenys Robinson. Tel: 01472-696226. Fax: 01472-698546. Web: www.soccer-books.co.uk. Est: 1982. Office and/or bookroom; Postal only. Contactable. Open: **M:** 09:00–17:00; **T:** 09:00–17:00; **W:** 09:00–17:00; **Th:** 09:00–17:00; **F:** 09:00–12:00; Closed for lunch: 13:00–14:00. Spec: New Books; Railways and Railroads; Sport - Football (Soccer). CC: AE; E; JCB; MC; V; Maestro. Cata: soccer. Mem: PBFA. VAT No: GB 546 5008 49. Notes: *Publishers of 15 to 20 titles each year and mailorder suppliers of other publishers new and used football books throughout the world.*

CORBY GLEN

Anchor Books, 20 Walsingham Drive, Corby Glen, NG33 4TA. Prop: Mr. C.R. Dunn. Tel: 01476 550103. Web: www.abebooks.com/colindunn/home. Est: 1990. Private premises. Postal only. Appointment necessary. Medium stock. Spec: Aeronautics; Aircraft; Aviation; Canals/Inland Waterways; History - General; Maritime/Nautical; Maritime/Nautical - History; Maritime/Nautical - Log Books. CC: JCB; MC; V; Switch. Corresp: German. Notes: *We specialise in Maritime (particularly shipping company histories), Regimental History, Boer War, Naval, Combat Aeronautical, Canals.*

EAGLE

J and J Books, Holly Cottage, 14 Scale Lane, Eagle, Lincoln, LN6 9EJ. Prop: Jan and Jim Rayner. Tel: 01522 869597. Web: www.jandjbooks.com. Est: 1995. Private premises. Book fairs only. Appointment necessary. Open: **M:** 09:00–17:30; **T:** 09:00–17:30; **W:** 09:00–17:30; **Th:** 09:00–17:30. Spec: Countries - Great Britain; Fiction - Crime, Detective, Spy, Thrillers; Publishers - Penguin; Publishers - Shell Guides; Publishers - Warnes; Shell County Guides (UK only); Wayside and Woodland; Windmills & Watermills. Corresp: German, French. Mem: PBFA. Notes: *We mainly sell at fairs and on the internet and we also do booksearch.*

GAINSBOROUGH

Hemswell Antique Centre, Caenby Corner Estate Hemswell Cliff, Gainsborough, DN21 5TJ. Prop: Mr. R. Miller. Tel: (01427) 668389. Fax: (01427) 668935. Est: 1986. Shop and/or gallery; Shop open: **M:** 10:00–17:00; **T:** 10:00–17:00; **W:** 10:00–17:00; **Th:** 10:00–17:00; **F:** 10:00–17:00; **S:** 10:00–17:00; **Su:** 10:00–17:00. CC: AE; D; E; JCB; MC; V.

GRANTHAM

Gravity Books, 110 Harrowby Road, Grantham, NG31 9DS. Prop: Philip Emery. Tel: 01476 575682. Est: 1999. Private premises. Internet only. Spec: Architecture; Architecture - Theatre; Art; Art History; General; Music - Rock & Roll; Sport - General. CC: MC; V; Maestro, PayPal.

HOLBEACH

Bookshop at the Plain, 55 Fleet Street, Holbeach, PE12 7AU. Prop: M.D. Watts. Tel: (01406) 422 942. Est: 1987. Private premises. Internet only. Appointment necessary. Medium stock. Spec: Academic/Scholarly; Children's; History - General; History - Middle Ages; History - Modern; Literature; Religion - General; Religion - Christian. PR: £3–250. CC: MC; V.

HORNCASTLE

Good for Books, ■ 23 North Street, Horncastle, LN9 5DX. Prop: Richard & Sarah Ingram-Hill. Tel: 01507 525021. Fax: 01507 524415. Web: www.goodforbooks.co.uk. Est: 2004. Shop open: **M:** 10:00–16:30; **T:** 10:00–16:30; **W:** 10:00–16:30; **Th:** 10:00–16:30; **F:** 10:00–16:30; **S:** 10:00–16:30. Spec: Animals and Birds; Antiquarian; Architecture; Art; Author - 20th Century; Aviation; Biography; Calligraphy. Notes: *Shop divided into 3 rooms - Good for Books - eclectic mix! Books Two - All books 2.00 or under. Book 3 - All books 3 for 1.00. A coke burning stove adds to an ambient browsing atmosphere during the winter months!*

Jabberwock Books, ■ 14 - 16 St Lawrence Street, Horncastle, LN9 5BJ. Prop: Robert Flanagan and Pauline Flanagan. Tel: 01507 522112. Web: www.jabberwockbooks.co.uk. Est: 1986. Shop open: **M:** 10:30–16:30; **T:** 10:30–16:30; **W:** 10:30–16:30; **Th:** 10:30–16:30; **F:** 10:30–16:30; **S:** 10:30–16:30. Spec: Poetry.

Roger Lucas Booksellers, 44 Queen Street, Horncastle, LN9 6BG. Prop: Roger Lucas. Tel: 01507 522261. Web: www.rogerlucasbooks.com. Est: 1984. Private premises. Internet and Postal. Appointment necessary. Spec: General. CC: PayPal.

KIRTON

D.C. Books, 11 Hemington Way, Kirton, Boston, PE20 1EA. Prop: D.J. & C. Lidgett. Tel: (01205) 724507. Fax: (01205) 724507. Est: 1984. Private premises. Internet and Postal. Small stock. Spec: Travel - General; Booksearch. PR: £3–5.

LINCOLN

Aardvark Cricket Books, 19 Vanwell Drive, Waddington, Lincoln, LN6 9LT. Prop: Peter & Elizabeth Taylor. Tel: 01522 722671. Est: 1998. Private premises. Appointment necessary. Open: **M:** 09:00–17:00; **T:** 09:00–17:00; **W:** 09:00–17:00; **Th:** 09:00–17:00; **F:** 09:00–17:00; **S:** 09:00–17:00. Spec: Annuals; Sport - Cricket. Cata: Wisden Cricketers Almanacks. Mem: FSB. Notes: *A major dealer in Wisden Cricketers Almanacks. Also, book restoration.*

Arboretum Bookshop, ■ 123 Monks Road, Lincoln, LN2 5HT. Prop: Ms Cicely Heywood. Tel: 01522 520901. Est: 1995. Shop open: **M:** 09:00–17:00; **T:** 09:00–17:00; **W:** 09:00–17:00; **Th:** 09:00–17:00; **F:** 09:00–17:00; **S:** 09:00–17:00. Notes: *Also sells LPs, Videos, DVD, Cassettes, and bric-a-brac.*

Autumn Leaves, 14 Highfields, Nettleham, Lincoln, LN2 2SZ. Prop: Ian & Sue Young. Tel: (01522) 750314. Est: 1997. Private premises. Postal only. Shop open: **M:** 09:15–16:30; **T:** 09:15–16:30; **W:** 09:15–16:30; **Th:** 09:15–16:30; **F:** 09:15–17:00; **S:** 09:15–12:30. Medium stock. Spec: Antiques; Art; Cookery/Gastronomy; Drama; Entertainment - General; Fiction - General; Health; History - General. PR: £2–100. CC: Paypal. Corresp: French, German, Swedish. VAT No: GB 737 8648 80.

Begging Bowl Books, 25 Queens Crescent, Lincoln, LN1 1LR. Prop: Rob Bradley. Tel: (01522) 801132 (home). Web: www.abebooks.com. Est: 1998. Spec: Academic/Scholarly; Author - Graves, Robert; Author - Powys Family, The; Ecclesiastical History & Architecture; Esoteric; Fiction - General; Fiction - Crime, Detective, Spy, Thrillers; First Editions. PR: £1–1,000. CC: MC; V; credit cards via abebooks, PayPal. Notes: *Many titles not listed - please enquire for specific wants.*

Chapter & Verse, 17 Queensway, Lincoln, LN2 4AJ. Prop: Roy Fines. Tel: (01522) 523202. Est: 1977. Private premises. Internet and Postal. Appointment necessary. Open: **M:** 09:00–18:00; **T:** 09:00–18:00; **W:** 09:00–18:00; **Th:** 09:00–18:00; **F:** 09:00–18:00; **S:** 09:00–18:00; **Su:** 09:00–18:00. Small stock. Spec: Antiquarian; Architecture; Bindings; Books about Books; Cinema/Film; Directories - British; Engraving; First Editions. PR: £1–5,000. Cata: Lincolnshire Topography. Corresp: German. Notes: *Payment accepted by cheque, Postal order, or via PayPal.*

Gladstone Books, The Shambles 4 Westgate, Lincoln, LN1 3AS. Prop: Prof. Ben Mepham. Tel: 01636 813601. Est: 2005. Office and/or bookroom; Shop open: **Th:** 11:00–17:00; **F:** 11:00–17:00; **S:** 11:00–17:00; **Su:** 13:00–16:00. Spec: Academic/Scholarly; Agriculture; Archaeology; Architecture; Art; Biography; Biology - General; Chemistry. Notes: *Exhibit at some local fairs.*

Golden Goose Books, ■ 20–21 Steep Hill, Lincoln, LN2 1LT. Prop: Mrs Anna Cockram & Richard West–Skinn. Tel: (01522) 522589. Est: 1984. Internet only. Shop open: **M:** 11:00–17:30; **T:** 11:00–17:30; **Th:** 11:00–17:30; **F:** 11:00–17:30; **S:** 11:00–17:00. Spec: Antiques; Art; Illustrated - General. Notes: *Harlequin Gallery, 20-22, Steep Hill, Lincoln (q.v.)*

Harlequin Gallery, ■ 22 Steep Hill, Lincoln, LN2 1LT. Prop: Richard West–Skinn. Tel: (01522) 522589. Web: www.abe.books.com. Est: 1964. Shop open: **M:** 11:00–17:30; **T:** 11:00–17:30; **Th:** 11:00–17:30; **F:** 11:00–17:30; **S:** 11:00–17:00. Very large stock. Spec: Art; Maps & Mapmaking; Prints and Maps. PR: £1–20,000. Notes: *Antiquarian & secondhand books, antique maps & prints. Very wide general stock. Also at Golden Goose Books, 20-21, Steep Hill, Lincoln (R.W. West-Skinn & Anna Cockram) Internet sellers. Also, Golden Goose Globe Restorers.*

Lincolnshire Heritage Ltd, ■ Jew's Court, Steep Hill, Lincoln, LN2 1LS. Tel: 01522 532280. Web: www.lincolnshirepast.org.uk. Est: 1987. Shop open: **M:** 10:00–16:00; **T:** 10:00–16:00; **W:** 10:00–16:00; **Th:** 10:00–16:00; **F:** 10:00–16:00; **S:** 10:00–16:00. CC: AE; MC; V.

Orlando Booksellers, 1 Rasen Lane, Lincoln, LN1 3EZ. Prop: Alison Smith & Christopher McKee. Tel: 07771 650983. Web: www.abebooks.com/servlet/StoreFrontDisplay?. Est: 1994. Private premises. Internet and Postal. Contactable. Small stock. Spec: Beat Writers; Fine & Rare; Literature; Modern First Editions; Photography; Poetry; Publishers - Hogarth Press; Publishers - Pan. PR: £20–1,000. CC: PayPal. Cata: Modern Firsts. VAT No: GB 629 3707 21.

Readers Rest, ■ 13–14 Steep Hill, Lincoln, LN2 1LT. Prop: Nick Warwick. Tel: (01522) 543217. Est: 1982. Shop open: **M:** 11:00–15:00; **T:** 11:00–15:00; **W:** 11:00–15:00; **Th:** 11:00–15:00; **F:** 11:00–15:00; **S:** 10:00–16:00. Very large stock. PR: £1–50. Notes: *Readers Rest Hall of Books, Steep Hill, Lincoln. 40,000 in stock.*

LOUTH

Mostly Mysteries Bookstore, 64 Legbourne Road, Louth, LN11 8ER. Prop: Victor H. Brown & Mary Brown. Tel: 01507 354990. Est: 1985. Storeroom; Appointment necessary. Spec: Mysteries.

MARKET DEEPING

Cornucopia Books, 2 Godsey Crescent, Market Deeping, PE6 8HX. Prop: Roy Dennis. Web: www.cornucopiabooks.co.uk. Est: 1986. Mail order only; Internet and Postal. Contactable. Spec: Academic/Scholarly; Advertising; Aeronautics; Aircraft; Alternative Medicine; American Indians; Animals and Birds; Anthologies. CC: PayPal. Notes: *I am disabled and deal by Internet only. Most major credit cards can be accepted from my website using PayPal. Alternatively you may like to visit my eBay shop. Thank you. http://stores.ebay.co.uk/Cornucopia-Internet-Book-Shop*

MOULTON SEAS END

P. Cassidy (Bookseller), Warren Lodge, Common Road, Moulton Seas End, PE12 6LF. Prop: Patrick Cassidy. Tel: (01406) 370990. Web: www.cassidysbooks.co.nr. Est: 1974. Mail order only; Postal only. Medium stock. Spec: Agriculture; Art; County - Local; General; Military; Military History; Steam Engines; Topography - Local. PR: £1–250. CC: AE; MC; V; PayPal. Notes: *Postal business only. Enquiries and orders by telephone, e-mail or via my website.*

NORTH COTES

Savona Books, Savona Books 400 Seawall Lane, Haven Sands, North Cotes, DN36 5XE. Prop: William Krause. Tel: 01472 388994. Fax: 01472 389436. Web: www.savonabooks.free-online.co.uk. Est: 1992. Private premises. Postal only. Appointment necessary. Open: **M:** 08:00–21:00; **T:** 08:00–21:00; **W:** 08:00–21:00; **Th:** 08:00–21:00; **F:** 08:00–21:00; **S:** 08:00–21:00; **Su:** 08:00–21:00; Closed for lunch: 13:00–14:00. Spec: Agriculture; Anatomy; Arachnology; Autobiography; Bacteriology; Biography; Botany; Criminology. CC: AE; MC; V; Maestro PayPal. Cata: Microscopy & related, Life and Earth Sciences.

OSGODBY

Phototitles.com, Westwold, Main Street, Osgodby, LN9 3TA. Prop: Steve Taylor. Tel: 07802 887319. Web: www.phototitles.com. VOIPpro: Skype. VOIPnum: Phototitles. Est: 2005. Mail order only; Internet only. Contactable. Open: **M:** 08:00–20:00; **T:** 08:00–20:00; **W:** 08:00–20:00; **Th:** 08:00–20:00; **F:** 08:00–20:00; **S:** 08:00–20:00; **Su:** 08:00–20:00; Closed for lunch: 13:30–14:00. Spec: Photography. CC: E; JCB; MC; V. Cata: Photography. VAT No: GB 863 4039 23. Notes: *Specialising in Signed, Rare, and Out of Print Photographic Books.*

PETERBOROUGH (SEE ALSO UNDER CAMBRDGESHIRE)

Langford Press, 10 New Road, Peterborough, PE6 9LE. Prop: Angela Langford. Tel: 01778 341132. Fax: 01778 341132. Web: www.langford-press.co.uk. Est: 1996. Mail order only; Internet and Postal. Appointment necessary. Open: **M:** 09:00–17:30; **T:** 09:00–17:30; **W:** 09:00–17:30; **Th:** 09:00–17:30; **F:** 09:00–17:30; **S:** 09:00–17:30; **Su:** 09:00–17:30. Spec: Artists; Flora & Fauna; Gardening - General; Natural History; Nature; Ornithology. CC: JCB; MC; V. Cata: Wildlife Art, Natural history. VAT No: GB 761 8122 36.

SLEAFORD

Phillip Austen, 50 Main Street, Ewerby, Sleaford, NG34 9PJ. Tel: (01529) 461074. Est: 1989. Private premises. Postal only. Medium stock. Spec: Military; Military History. CC: D; E; JCB; MC; V. Mem: PBFA.

Mark Evans, 34 Northgate, Sleaford, NG34 7DA. Prop: Mark Evans. Tel: (0798) 1938165. Est: 1985. Private premises. Postal only. Small stock. Spec: Cinema/Film; Music - General; Sport - General; Television; Theatre; Booksearch. PR: £3–100.

Julian Roberts Fine Books, Hill House, Braceby, Sleaford, NG34 0TA. Tel: (01529) 497271. Fax: (01529) 497271. Web: www.jrfinebooks.com. Est: 1997. Private premises. Appointment necessary. Small stock. Spec: Antiquarian; Children's; Children's - Early Titles; Children's - Illustrated; Cookery/Gastronomy; Fiction - General; Literature; Modern First Editions. PR: £10–5,000. CC: MC; V. Mem: PBFA. Notes: *General stock including First Editions, Childrens & Antiquarian.*

Westgate Bookshop, ■ 45 Westgate, Sleaford, NG34 7PU. Prop: Geoffrey Almond. Tel: (01529) 304276. Web: www.abebooks.com/home/WESTGATEBOOKSHOP/. Est: 1986. Postal only. Shop open: **M:** 10:00–16:30; **T:** 10:00–16:30; **W:** 10:00–16:30; **F:** 10:00–16:30; **S:** 10:00–16:00. Small stock. PR: £1–15. CC: MC; V.

SOUTH KELSEY

Winghale Books Ltd., Grassmere Cottage, Brigg Road, South Kelsey, LN7 6PH. Prop: Directors: Irwin & Hilary Johnston. Tel: (01652) 678752. Est: 1984. Private premises. Internet and Postal. Appointment necessary. Medium stock. Spec: Academic/Scholarly; Americana - General; Archaeology; Classical Studies; Colonial; Ecclesiastical History & Architecture; Ecclesiology; European Studies. PR: £10–200. CC: AE; MC; V. Cata: academic history. Mem: PBFA. VAT No: GB 365 1833 46.

SPALDING

Robin Peake, 26 Balmoral Avenue, Spalding, PE11 2RN. Tel: (01775) 724050. Est: 1989. Postal only. Spec: Motorbikes / motorcycles; Motoring; Vintage Cars. PR: £2–250. CC: MC; V. Cata: motoring.

Michael Prior, 34 Fen End Lane, Spalding, PE12 6AD. Prop: Michael Prior. Tel: (01775) 761851. Est: 1970. Private premises. Internet and Postal. Appointment necessary. Medium stock. Spec: Advertising; Author - Churchill, Sir Winston; Author - Forester, C.S.; Author - Masefield, John; Aviation; Maritime/Nautical; Military; Military History. PR: £10–250. Cata: infrequent on maritime. Corresp: French. Notes: *Dealer in cigarette and other trade cards, continental chromo cards, postcards & printed maritime ephemera.*

STAMFORD

Andrew Burroughs Books, 3 Empingham Road, Stamford, PE9 2RH. Tel: (01780) 751363. Fax: (01780) 765140. Est: 1983. Private premises. Postal only. Spec: Armed Forces - Australian Army; Armed Forces - Australian Navy; Arms & Armour; Automobilia/Automotive; Espionage; French Foreign Legion, The; History - 19th Century; History - British Empire, The. PR: £5–500. Cata: Naval and military.

Robert Humm & Co, ■Station House, Gresley Drive, Stamford, PE9 2JN. Prop: Robert Humm and Clare Humm. Tel: 01780 766266. Fax: 01780 757929. Web: www.roberthumm.co.uk. Est: 1974. Shop. Open. Shop at: Alternative www.rhbooks.co.uk. Open: **M:** 09:30–17:00; **T:** 09:30–17:00; **W:** 09:30–17:00; **Th:** 09:30–17:00; **F:** 09:30–17:00; **S:** 09:30–17:00. Spec: Aeronautics; Aircraft; Archaeology - Industrial; Author - Rolt, L.T.C.; Aviation; Buses/Trams; Canals/Inland Waterways; Commerce - General. CC: JCB; MC; V. Cata: Railways and trams; industrial history. Corresp: French at a pinch. VAT No: GB 226 1728 73. Notes: *Specialists in railway, tramway, aviation, shipping, waterway, industrial and commercial history; no road transport or non-transport subjects stocked. We ship worldwide and welcome phone and email enquiries. Occasionally shut for lunch.*

St. Mary's Books & Prints, ■ 9 St. Mary's Hill, Stamford, PE9 2DP. Prop: N.A.M., M.G.D. P.A. Tyers. Tel: (01780) 763033. Fax: (01780) 763033. Web: www.stmarysbooks.com. Est: 1971. Shop open: **M:** 08:00–18:00; **T:** 08:00–18:00; **W:** 08:00–18:00; **Th:** 08:00–18:00; **F:** 08:00–18:00; **S:** 08:00–18:00; **Su:** 09:00–18:00. Large stock. Spec: Academic/Scholarly; Archaeology; Architecture; Author - Aldin, Cecil; Author - Fleming, Ian; Author - Rackham, Arthur; Author - Rowling, J.K.; Author - Watkins-Pitchford, Denys ('B.B.'). PR: £10–50,000. CC: AE; D; E; JCB; MC; V. Corresp: German, Latin, French, Spanish, Italian. Notes: *Open Sundays. Bookbinding, Valuations, Book Search & major stock of Wisdens. Fine Bindings.*

St. Paul's Street Bookshop, ■ 7, St. Paul's Street, Stamford, PE9 2BE. Prop: James Blessett. Tel: (01780) 482748. Fax: (01778) 380538. Est: 1986. Shop open: **M:** 10:00–17:00; **T:** 10:00–17:00; **Th:** 10:00–17:00; **F:** 10:00–17:00; **S:** 10:00–17:00. Medium stock. Spec: Motoring; Sport - Motor Racing; Topography - Local. PR: £1–500. CC: E; MC; V. Cata: Motor Sport. Corresp: French, German. Mem: PBFA. VAT No: GB 551 0471 74. Notes: *Also, catalogues on motorsport.*

Staniland (Booksellers), ■ 4/5 St. George's Street, Stamford, PE9 2BJ. Prop: B.J. Valentine Ketchum. Tel: (01780) 755800. Est: 1972. Shop open: **M:** 10:00–17:00; **T:** 10:00–17:00; **W:** 10:00–17:00; **F:** 10:00–17:00; **S:** 10:00–17:00; Closed for lunch: 13:00–14:00. Large stock. Spec: Academic/Scholarly; Antiquarian; Applied Art; Archaeology; Architecture; Art; Art History; Art Reference. PR: £1–3,000. CC: MC; V. Mem: PBFA. VAT No: GB 200 8434 08. Notes: *We specialize in architecture, music, literature (including library sets), philosophy and history.*

Undercover Books, ■ 30 Scotgate, Stamford, PE9 2YQ. Prop: Tony Dodson. Tel: 01780 480989. Fax: 01780 763963. Web: www.usedbooknews.com. Est: 1990. Internet and Postal. Shop open: **M:** 10:00–16:00; **T:** 10:00–16:00; **W:** 10:00–16:00; **Th:** 10:00–16:00; **F:** 10:00–16:00; **S:** 10:00–16:00. Very large stock. Spec: Crime (True); Criminology; Espionage; Law - General; Police Force Histories; Travel - Europe; Booksearch. CC: AE; D; E; JCB; MC; V; SW, De. Cata: Criminology and Police. Mem: Police History Ass. VAT No: GB 797 0827 78. Notes: *All titles available to be viewed through www.usedbooknews.com. Booksearch undertaken for rare and out-of-print titles on the following specialities including Police, True Crime, Espionage, Terrorism, Criminology, Court and Prison History.*

WINTERTON

Richard Williams (Bookdealer), 30 King Street, Winterton, DN15 9TP. Prop: Richard Williams. Tel: (01724) 737254. Web: http://ukbookworld.com/members/RichWilliams. Est: 1976. Private premises. Internet and Postal. Appointment necessary. Very large stock. Spec: Academic/Scholarly; Annuals; Author - Simenon, Georges; Author - Wallace, Edgar; Bibliography; Books about Books; Cinema/ Film; Cowboys. PR: £3–300. CC: MC; V. Corresp: French, German. Notes: *We are also the Dragonby Press, publishers of bibliographies and checklists.*

LONDON
EAST POSTAL DISTRICTS

Antique City Bookshop, ■2 - 3 Antique City Market, 98 Wood Street, Walthamstow, London, E17 3HX. Prop: Alan Stone. Tel: 020 8520 8300. Est: 1994. Shop open: **M:** 10:30–16:30; **T:** 10:30–17:30; **F:** 10:30–17:30; **S:** 10:30–16:30.

Bibliophile Books, Unit 5 Datapoint Business Centre, South Crescent, London, E16 4TL. Prop: A. Quigley. Tel: (0207) 474-2474. Fax: (0207) 474-8589. Web: www.bibliophilebooks.com. Est: 1978. Warehouse; Internet and Postal. Shop open: **M:** 08:30–17:30; **T:** 08:30–17:30; **W:** 08:30–17:30; **Th:** 08:30–17:30; **F:** 08:30–17:30. Very large stock. Spec: First Editions; Signed Editions; Social History. PR: £1–250. CC: AE; MC; V; Switch; Maestro. Cata: monthly on Art, Biography, War, Crafts, Erotica, History. Corresp: Spanish. Mem: BA. VAT No: GB 242 6934 55. Notes: *All books in mint condition unless otherwise described.*

Birchden Books, 3 Edith Road, East Ham, London, E1 1DE. Prop: Michael Vetterlein. Tel: (020) 8472-3654. Est: 2001. Private premises. Postal only. Appointment necessary. Small stock. Spec: Architecture; Art Reference; Bell-Ringing (Campanology); Cemeteries; Ecclesiastical History & Architecture; Illuminated Manuscripts; Music - Gregorian Chants; Needlework. PR: £2–500.

Crimes Ink, 35 Moreton Close, Upper Clapton, London, E5 9EP. Prop: Leigh.M.Piercy. Tel: (020) 8806-1895. Est: 1987. Private premises. Internet and Postal. Appointment necessary. Medium stock. Spec: Assassinations; Crime (True); Criminology; Espionage; Fiction - General; Fiction - Crime, Detective, Spy, Thrillers; Fiction - Fantasy, Horror; Fiction - Science Fiction. PR: £1–150. CC: Via abecom.

David Houston - Bookseller, 26 North Birkbeck Road, London, E11 4JG. Prop: David Houston. Tel: 020 8556 9048. Fax: 020 8556 9048. Web: www.abebooks.com/home/dghbooks. Est: 1997. Private premises. Internet and Postal. Open: **M:** 09:00–17:30; **T:** 09:00–17:30; **W:** 09:00–17:30; **Th:** 09:00–17:30; **F:** 09:00–17:30; **S:** 09:00–17:30; **Su:** 09:00–17:30; Closed for lunch: 13:00–14:00. Spec: Countries - Scotland; Literature - Scottish. CC: MC; V. Cata: Scottish Books, Scottish Literature. Notes: *Postal business only.*

I.D. Edrich, 17 Selsdon Road, Wanstead, London, E11 2QF. Prop: I. D. & S. Edrich. Tel: (020) 8989-9541. Fax: 020 8989 9541. Web: www.idedrich.co.uk. Est: 1966. Private premises. Postal only. Contactable. Open: **M:** 09:00–17:00; **T:** 09:00–17:00; **W:** 09:00–17:00; **Th:** 09:00–17:00; **F:** 09:00–17:00. Large stock. Spec: Literature; Poetry. PR: £3–1,000. CC: Paypal. Cata: Modern First Editions, Literary Periodicals. Corresp: French/German. VAT No: GB 410 1439 10. Notes: *On our website we itemise, in detail, issues of numerous literary periodicals. We are prepared to search, through our stock of periodicals, for individual authors. A detailed Wants List can be provided if requested.*

Keith Langford, Tredegar House, 97-99 Bow Road, London, E3 2AN. Prop: Keith Langford. Tel: 02089804326. Est: 1977. Private premises. Internet and Postal. Contactable. Open: **M:** 09:00–17:30; **T:** 09:00–17:30; **W:** 09:00–17:30; **Th:** 09:00–17:30; **F:** 09:00–17:30; **S:** 09:00–17:30; **Su:** 09:00–17:30; Closed for lunch: 13:00–14:00. Spec: Adventure; Antiquities; Applied Art; Canals/Inland Waterways; Caricature; Cities - General; Furniture; History - General. Cata: travel, mountaineering, antiquarian. Corresp: French. Notes: *Specialist in collectable books on all subjects.*

M.A. Stroh, Riverside House, Leaside Road, Upper Clapton, London, E5 9LU. Prop: M.A. Stroh. Tel: (0208) 806 3690. Fax: (0208) 806 3690. Web: www.webspawner.com/users/Buttonbook/. Est: 1956. Storeroom; Internet and Postal. Appointment necessary. Open: **M:** 10:00–17:30; **T:** 10:00–17:30; **W:** 10:00–17:30; **Th:** 10:00–17:30; **F:** 10:00–12:00. Very large stock. Spec: Aeronautics; Aircraft; Antique Stoves; Archives; Arms & Armour; Astronautics; Astronomy; Auction Catalogues. PR: £10–1,000. CC: paypal. Cata: science technology patents.

Dr Jeremy Parrott, 31A Beacontree Avenue, Walthamstow, E17 4BU. Tel: (0208) 5274315. Web: www.abebooks.com. Est: 1985. Private premises. Internet and Postal. Appointment necessary. Large stock. Spec: Author - Beckett, S.; Author - Benson, E.F.; Author - Conrad, Joseph; Author - Orczy, Baroness; Author - Stevenson, Robert Louis; Author - Twain, Mark; Author - Verne, Jules; Bibliography. PR: £5–1,000. Corresp: French, German, Spanish, Hungarian. Notes: *Book search for any book in Hungarian.*

LONDON
EAST CENTRAL POSTAL DISTRICT

Amwell Book Company, ∎53 Amwell Street, London, EC1R 1UR. Prop: Charlotte Robinson. Tel: 020 7837 4891. Web: www.amwellbookcompany.co.uk. Est: 1981. Shop open: **T:** 11:00–18:00; **Th:** 11:00–18:00; **F:** 11:00–18:00; **S:** 11:00–18:00. Spec: Applied Art; Architecture; Art; Art - Theory; Art History; Art Reference; Artists; Arts, The. CC: AE; MC; V. Cata: Architecture. Corresp: French, Italian. Mem: PBFA; FSB.

Camden Lock Books, 4 St. Agnes Well, Islington, London EC1Y 1BE. Prop: Jason Burley. Tel: (0207) 253 0666. Web: www.camdenlockbooks.co.uk. Est: 1984. Shop, open M: 08:30–19:00; **T:** 08:30–19:00; **W:** 08:30–19:00; **Th:** 08:30–19:00; **F:** 08:30–19:00. Medium stock. Spec: New books; Photography. PR: £1.99–150. CC: MC; V. Corresp: French. Mem: BA. VAT No. GB 735 6354 22. Notes: *Shop sells new books, out of print books avaialble only online at Amazon Marketplace.*

Elizabeth Crawford, 5 Owen's Row, London, EC1V 4NP. Prop: Elizabeth Crawford. Tel: (020) 7278-9479. Fax: (020) 7278-9479. Est: 1984. Private premises. Postal only. Appointment necessary. Small stock. Spec: Authors - Women; Women; Ephemera. PR: £5–5,000. Cata: Books and ephemera by and about women. Mem: PBFA.

IDEA, 104 Willoughby House, Barbican EC2Y 8BL. Prop: Angela Hill. Tel: (020) 7638 4608. Est: 1995. Private premises. Tellephone first. Very small stock. Spec: Advertising; Applied Art; Architecture; Art - British; Art - Theory; Art Reference; Artists, Arts, The. PR: £10–5,000. CC: AE; D; Eur; JCB; MC; V.

Andrew Sclanders (BeatBooks), 32 St Paul's View, 15 Amwell Street, London, EC1R 1UP. Prop: Andrew Sclanders. Tel: (020) 7278-5034. Fax: (020) 7278-5034. Web: www.beatbooks.com. Est: 1990. Private premises. Internet and Postal. Appointment necessary. Small stock. Spec: Art; Author - Bukowski, Charles; Author - Burroughs, William; Author - Kerouac, Jack; Avant-Garde; Beat Writers; Cinema/Film; Counterculture. PR: £5–2,500. CC: AE; E; JCB; MC; V. Cata: Beat Generation/60s CounterCulture/20th Century A.

LONDON
NORTH POSTAL DISTRICTS

Alpha Books, 60 Langdon Park Road, London, N6 5QG. Prop: Tony Maddock. Tel: (020) 8348-2831. Web: www.abebooks.com/home/alphabks. Est: 1983. Private premises. Internet and Postal. Contactable. Medium stock. Spec: Academic/Scholarly; Alchemy; Astrology; Egyptology; Esoteric; Folklore; Fourth Way; Freemasonry & Anti-Masonry. PR: £1–500. CC: MC; V; Maestro. Cata: Hermetica, Freemasonry, Folklore & Mythology.

G.W. Andron, 162a Brunswick Park Road, London, N11 1HA. Tel: (020) 8361-2409. Est: 1972. Private premises. Postal only. Medium stock. Spec: Books about Books; Military; Natural History; Naval; Printing; Topography - General; Travel - General. PR: £1–100.

Antique Prints of the World, 6 Livingstone Road, Palmers Green, London, N13 4SD. Prop: Mr Mel Menelaou. Tel: (020) 8292-0622. Fax: (020) 8292-0622. Web: www.antique19thcenturyprints.com. Est: 1994. Private premises. Appointment necessary. Spec: Antique Paper; Armenian; Australiana; Canadiana; Countries - General; Countries - Afghanistan; Countries - Albania; Countries - Armenia. CC: PayPal. Corresp: Greek. Notes: *Antique Prints of the World are the UK's foremost dealers specialising in original 19th Century prints (The Illustrated London News, Graphic, Le Petit Journal & other foreign publications. Contact us with your 'wants list'.*

Atlas, 17 Pitfield Street, London, N1 6HB. Prop: Alastair Brotchie. Tel: 07770 784 185. Fax: (020) 7490-8742. Est: 1996. Private premises. Postal only. Contactable. Spec: Art Reference; Counterculture; Foreign Texts; Literature in Translation; Surrealism. PR: £40–500. Cata: Surrealism/ Pataphysics. Notes: *Also, a publishers.*

Bannatyne Books, 6 Bedford Road, London, N8 8HL. Prop: Mr. & Mrs. Court. Tel: (020) 8340-1953. Est: 1980. Private premises. Postal only. Appointment necessary. Spec: Alpinism/Mountaineering; Author - Buchan, John. PR: £2–300. Notes: *Visitors welcome at any time by appointment.*

Black Gull Books, ■ 121 High Road, East Finchley, London, N2 8AG. Prop: C. Overfield. Tel: 0208 889 7112. Est: 2007. Shop open: **M:** 09:30–19:00; **T:** 09:30–19:00; **W:** 09:30–19:00; **Th:** 09:30–19:00; **F:** 09:30–19:00; **S:** 09:00–17:30; **Su:** 09:00–17:30; Closed for lunch: 13:00–14:00. CC: MC; V.

Cavendish Rare Books, 19 Chesthunte Road, London, N17 7PU. Prop: Barbara Grigor-Taylor. Tel: 0208 808 4595. Fax: 0208 808 4595. Est: 1976. Private premises. Postal only. Appointment necessary. Open: **M:** 09:00–17:30; **T:** 09:00–17:30; **W:** 09:00–17:30; **Th:** 09:00–17:30; **F:** 09:00–17:30; **S:** 09:00–17:30; **Su:** 09:00–17:30; Closed for lunch: 13:00–14:00. Spec: Alpinism/Mountaineering; Asian Studies; Countries - Alaska; Countries - Antarctic, The; Countries - Arctic, The; Countries - Asia; Countries - Australasia; Countries - Central Asia. Cata: Travel, Exploration, Alpine, Polar, Asia. Corresp: French. Spanish. Mem: ABA; PBFA; ILAB.

Church Street Bookshop, ■ 142 Stoke Newington Church Street, London, N16 0JU. Prop: Tim Watson. Tel: 0207 241 5411. Web: www.abebooks.com. Est: 1984. Shop open: **M:** 11:30–18:00; **T:** 11:30–18:00; **W:** 11:30–18:00; **Th:** 11:30–18:00; **F:** 11:30–18:00; **S:** 11:00–18:00; **Su:** 11:30–18:00. Spec: Academic/ Scholarly. CC: MC; V.

Decorum Books, 24 Cloudesley Square, London, N1 0HN. Prop: David Soames. Tel: 020 7278 1838. Est: 1971. Office and/or bookroom; Internet and Postal. Contactable. Spec: Applied Art; Architecture; Architecture - Theatre; Art; Art - Afro-American; Art - British; Art - Technique; Art - Theory. CC: MC; V; Maestro. VAT No: GB 230 3437 06. Notes: *For MUSIC Biographies, Historical & Subject Studies, Technica + SCORES & SHEET MUSIC - Classical, Light, Pop. FILM, TV, THEATRE Subject Studies, Directors & Actors Biographies. ART, DESIGN, ARCHITECTURE Subject Studies, Biographies.*

Erian Books, 24 Woodside Avenue, Highgate, London, N6 4SS. Prop: Dr. Eric Nieman. Tel: (020) 8444-9851. Est: 1992. Private premises. Postal only. Spec: Bridge; Illustrated - General; Medicine; Medicine - History of; Neurology; Poetry; Psychology/Psychiatry; Science - History of. PR: £15–750. Cata: Medicine. Corresp: French. Notes: *Catalogues are Medicine only, but I also stock art and illustrated books, modern poetry, bridge books, and modern 1st. editions - approach by email. Please quote for medical books, particularly neurology.*

Fantasy Centre, ■ 157 Holloway Road, London, N7 8LX. Prop: Ted Ball & Erik Arthur. Tel: (020) 7607-9433. Fax: (020) 7607-9433. Web: www.fantasycentre.biz. Est: 1972. Shop open: **M:** 10:00–18:00; **T:** 10:00–18:00; **W:** 10:00–18:00; **Th:** 10:00–18:00; **F:** 10:00–18:00; **S:** 10:00–18:00. Medium stock. Spec: Fiction - Fantasy, Horror; Fiction - Science Fiction. CC: E; MC; V. Cata: Science Fiction, Fantasy & Horror. VAT No: GB 227 3306 83. Notes: *We are the oldest science fiction book shop in the world.*

Fisher & Sperr, ■ 46 Highgate High Street, London, N6 5JB. Tel: (020) 8340-7244. Fax: (020) 8348-4293. Est: 1939. Shop open: **M:** 10:30–17:00; **T:** 10:30–17:00; **W:** 10:30–17:00; **Th:** 10:30–17:00; **F:** 10:30–17:00; **S:** 10:00–17:30. Very large stock. Spec: Art; Art History; Folio Society, The; Literary Criticism; Philosophy; Sets of Books; Topography - General; Collectables. PR: £1–100. CC: AE; D; E; JCB; MC; V. Corresp: French. Mem: ABA; ILAB. VAT No: GB 229 2603 70. Notes: *Bookbinding*.

Nicholas Goodyer, 8 Framfield Road, Highbury Fields, London, N5 1UU. Tel: (020) 7226-5682. Fax: (020) 7354-4716. Web: www.nicholasgoodyer.com. Private premises. Internet and Postal. Telephone First. Open: **M:** 10:00–17:00; **T:** 10:00–17:00; **W:** 10:00–17:00; **Th:** 10:00–17:00; **F:** 10:00–17:00. Small stock. Spec: Animals and Birds; Architecture; Art; Botany; Colour-Plate; Decorative Art; Fashion & Costume; Gardening - General. CC: MC; V. Cata: General. Corresp: French, German, Italian, Spanish, Portuguese. Mem: ABA; PBFA; ILAB. VAT No: GB 629 6750 05. Notes: *Business operates by appointment or by chance, weekdays. Specialising in Antiquarian Illustrated Books, Natural History, Arts and Architecture, Rare and Unusual Books.*

F. & J. Hogan, 31 Tranmere Road, Edmonton, London, N9 9EJ. Prop: Frederick & Joan Hogan. Tel: (020) 8360-6146. Est: 1969. Private premises. Postal only. Small stock. Spec: Atlases; Caricature; Cartography; Travel - General; Prints and Maps. PR: £5–1,000.

Idle Genius Books, 115 Cluse Court, St. Peter Street, London, N1 8PE. Prop: Philip Obeney. Tel: (020) 7704-3193. Est: 2000. Storeroom; Book fairs only. Appointment necessary. Small stock. Spec: Archaeology; Author - Christie, Agatha; Author - Wolfe, Thomas; Fiction - Science Fiction; Literature; Modern First Editions; Topography - Local. PR: £5–400. Notes: *Attends HD Book Fairs. Also, ephemera on London in wartime.*

InterCol London, 43 Templars Crescent, London, N3 3QR. Prop: Yasha Beresiner. Tel: (020) 8349-2207. Fax: (020) 8346-9539. Web: www.intercol.co.uk. Est: 1981. Private premises. Internet and Postal. Small stock. Spec: Caricature; Cartography; Cartoons; Cities - City of London; Collectables; Collecting; Erotica; Freemasonry & Anti-Masonry. PR: £5–500. CC: AE; E; JCB; MC; V; PayPal. Corresp: French, Italian, Spanish, Turkish, Hebrew. Mem: ANA; IBNS; IMCoS; IPCS. VAT No: GB 350 6069 69. Notes: *Specialising in Freemasonry; Playing Cards and Games; Currency, Paper Money Bonds and Shares and Maps, Atlases and Prints. Visitors are welcome by appointment.*

M. Eric Korn, 32 North Grove, London, N15 5QP. Prop: Eric Korn. Tel: 0208 800 1302. Fax: 0208 800 1302. Office and/or bookroom; Appointment necessary. Spec: Antiquarian; Author - Darwin, Charles; Juvenile; Languages - Foreign; Natural History. Cata: languages, Darwin, medicine, juvenile, biology. Corresp: French, Russian, Spanish. Mem: ABA; PBFA.

Leo Cadogan Rare Books Limited, 189 Corporation Street, London, N7 9EQ. Prop: Leo Cadogan. Tel: 02076073190. Web: www.leocadogan.com. VOIPpro: SKYPE. VOIPnum: leo.cadogan. Est: 2007. Private premises. Internet and Postal. Appointment necessary. Open: **M:** 09:00–19:30; **T:** 09:00–19:30; **W:** 09:00–19:30; **Th:** 09:00–19:30; **F:** 09:00–19:30; **S:** 09:00–19:30; **Su:** 15:00–18:30; Closed for lunch: 13:00–14:00. Spec: Antiquarian; Bibles; Biblical Studies; Commerce - General; Criminal Law; Early Imprints; Ecclesiastical History & Architecture; Ecclesiology. CC: JCB; MC; V. Cata: early and rare books and manuscripts. Corresp: French, Italian, Spanish. Mem: PBFA; FSB. VAT No: GB 921 1142 77.

Barrie Marks Limited, 24 Church Vale, Fortis Green, London, N2 9PA. Tel: (020) 8883-1919. Spec: Fine & Rare; Illustrated - General; Limited Editions - General; Literature; Private Press.

Ian McKelvie Bookseller, 45 Hertford Road, East Finchley, N2 9BX. Prop: Ian McKelvie. Tel: 020-8444-0567. Fax: 020-8444-0567. Web: www.ukbookworld.com/members/Dudley1. Est: 1969. Private premises. Postal only. Contactable. Large stock. Spec: Fiction - General; Fiction - Crime, Detective, Spy, Thrillers; Fine & Rare; First Editions; Literary Criticism; Literary Travel; Literature; Literature - Irish. CC: AE; MC; V; Maestro. Cata: annual on British, American & World Literature.

Mountaineering Books, 6 Bedford Road, London, N8 8HL. Prop: Mr. R. & Mrs. A. Court. Tel: (020) 8340-1953. Est: 1990. Private premises. Appointment necessary. Small stock. Spec: Alpinism/ Mountaineering. PR: £10–500.

Nicolas - Antiquarian Bookseller, 59 Fallowcourt Avenue, London, N12 0BE. Tel: (020) 8445-9835. Fax: (020) 8446-9615. Web: www.nicolasrarebooks.com. Est: 1971. Private premises. Internet and Postal. Small stock. Spec: Canals/Inland Waterways; Countries - Cyprus; Countries - Greece; Countries - Malta; Countries - Turkey; History - General; Topography - General; Travel - General. Mem: ABA; PBFA; BA; ILAB. Notes: *Also, pictures.*

Pendleburys Bookshop, ■Church House, Portland Avenue, Stamford Hill, London, N16 6HJ. Prop: Jonathan Pendlebury. Tel: +44 (0)20 8809-4922. Web: www.pendleburys.com. Est: 1984. Shop. Telephone First. Open: **M:** 10:00–17:00; **T:** 10:00–17:00; **Th:** 10:00–17:00; **F:** 10:00–17:00; **S:** 10:00–17:00. Very large stock. Spec: Bibles; Biblical Studies; Ecclesiastical History & Architecture; History - Reformation; History of Ideas; Missionaries & Missions; Mysticism; Philosophy. PR: £1–300. CC: MC; V; Paypal; Cheque; Cash. Cata: All aspects of the Christian faith. Corresp: English Afrikaans. Mem: PBFA; IOBA.

John Price, 8 Cloudesley Square, London, N1 0HT. Tel: (020) 7837-8008. Fax: (020) 7278-4733. Web: www.johnpriceantiquarianbooks.com. Est: 1988. Private premises. Internet and Postal. Appointment necessary. Small stock. Spec: Antiquarian; Antiquities; Art - Theory; Cookery/Gastronomy; Critical Theory; Curiosa; Dictionaries; Economics. PR: £45–4,500. CC: AE; E; MC; V. Cata: Philosophy, literature, musicology, aesthetics. Corresp: French, German. Mem: ABA; PBFA; BA; ILAB. Notes: *I specialize in books printed in the hand-press era (i. e., before c. 1820) on philosophy, literature, history, musicology, classics, theology, history of ideas, etc.*

Richard Thornton Books, 25 Beechdale, Winchmore Hill, London, N21 3QE. Prop: Richard Thornton. Tel: 020 8886 8202. Web: www.richardthorntonbooks.co.uk. Est: 1997. Shop and/or showroom; Telephone First. Open: **M:** 09:30–21:30; **T:** 09:30–21:30; **W:** 09:30–21:30; **Th:** 09:30–21:30; **F:** 09:30–21:30; **S:** 09:30–21:30; **Su:** 09:30–21:30. Spec: Animals and Birds; Antiquarian; Art; Arts, The; Author - Crompton, Richmal; Autobiography; Bindings; Children's. CC: AE; D; E; JCB; MC; V. Mem: PBFA. Notes: *We now have open 2 Large bookrooms to view with over 15,000 Books in many subjects Inc Modern 1st's, Childrens, Antiquarian, Military & Sporting Books. Impromptu callers are welcome, but it's best to ring Richard or Theresa on 020 8886 8202.*

Ripping Yarns, ■ 355 Archway Road, London, N6 4EJ. Prop: Celia Mitchell. Tel: (020) 8341-6111. Fax: (020) 7482-5056. Web: www.rippingyarns.co.uk. Est: 1984. Internet and Postal. Shop open: **T:** 11:00–17:00; **W:** 11:00–17:00; **Th:** 11:00–17:00; **F:** 11:00–17:00; **S:** 10:00–17:00; **Su:** 11:00–16:00. Very large stock. Spec: Children's; Children's - Early Titles; Children's - Illustrated; Comic Books & Annuals; Fiction - General; Illustrated - General; Literature; Magazines & Periodicals - General. PR: £1–500. CC: MC; V. Corresp: French, Spanish. Mem: PBFA. Notes: *Free parking up to 1 hour on Archway Rd close to shop. Highgate tube Northern Line across road.*

Robert Temple, 65 Mildmay Road, London, N1 4PU. Prop: P.J. Allen. Tel: (020) 7254-3674. Web: www.telinco.co.uk/RobertTemple/. Est: 1977. Warehouse; Internet and Postal. Appointment necessary. Medium stock. Spec: Academic/Scholarly; Anthologies; Antiquarian; Author - 19th Century; Author - 20th Century; Authors - Women; Autobiography; Belle-Lettres. PR: £5–6,000. CC: PayPal. Cata: occasionally e-mail only, Recent Acquisitions and others. Corresp: French. Mem: ABA; ILAB. VAT No: GB 292 2648 41. Notes: *Credit and Debit cards taken via the PayPal secure server only (VISA, non-corporate AmEx, MasterCard, Discover, Switch, Solo).*

Susanne Schulz-Falster Rare Books, 22 Compton Terrace, London, N1 2UN. Prop: Susanne Schulz-Falster. Tel: 020 7704 9845. Fax: 020 7354 4202. Web: www.schulz-falster.com. Est: 1998. Private premises. Internet and Postal. Appointment necessary. Spec: Accountancy; Aesthetics; Alchemy; Antiquarian; Arts, The; Auction Catalogues; Authors - Women; Banking & Insurance. CC: AE; MC; V. Cata: Economics, History of Ideas. Corresp: French, German, Italian. Mem: ABA; ILAB. VAT No: GB 714 4200 79. Notes: *Continental Books (17th & 18th Century), especially Italian, German and French imprints, Economics, History of Ideas, Law, Philosophy, Social Sciences, Language, History of the Book, History of Printing.*

John Trotter Books, 80 East End Road, London, N3 2SY. Prop: John Trotter. Tel: (020) 8349-9484. Web: www.bibliophile.net/John-Trotter-Books.htm. Est: 1973. Office and/or bookroom; Internet and Postal. Shop open: **M:** 08:30–17:00; **T:** 08:30–17:00; **W:** 09:30–17:00; **Th:** 08:30–17:00; **F:** 08:00–13.50; **Su:** 09:00–13:00. Large stock. Spec: Byzantium; Countries - Egypt; Countries - Germany; Countries - Holy Land, The; Countries - Lebanon; Countries - Middle East, The; Entomology; Hebraica. PR: £5–1,500. CC: MC; V. Corresp: French, German, Italian. Mem: PBFA.

Tyger Press, 41 Cheverton Road, London, N19 3BA. Prop: Alaric Bamping. Tel: (020) 7272-3234. Web: www.tygerpress.com. Est: 1984. Private premises. Internet and Postal. Appointment necessary. Spec: Genealogy; Guide Books; History - General; History - Family; History - Industrial; History - Local; Manuscripts; Maritime/Nautical - Log Books. PR: £1–750. CC: MC; V; Maestro/Switch. Delta. Cata: Topography. Mem: PBFA. VAT No: GB 646 2440 44.

Graham Weiner, 78 Rosebery Road, London, N10 2LA. Tel: (020) 8883-8424. Fax: (020) 8444-6505. Est: 1973. Private premises. Internet and Postal. Appointment necessary. Medium stock. Spec: Academic/Scholarly; Aeronautics; Aircraft; Alchemy; Almanacs; Anatomy; Antiquarian; Automata. PR: £20–2,500. CC: MC; V. Cata: Science, Technology, Medicine. Corresp: French. Mem: ABA; ILAB; IEE. VAT No: GB 230 6110 23.

P. H. Whetman, 42 Harberton Road, London N19. Tel: and Fax: 020 7263 1010. Private premises. Appointment necessary. Small stock. Spec: Topography - Local. PR: £10–5,000. Cata: annualy on History and Topography of London. Mem: P.B.F.A.

Woburn Books, 5 Caledonian Road, Islington, N1 9DX. Prop: Andrew Burgin. Tel: (020) 7263 5196. Fax: (020) 7263 5196. Web: www.andrewburgin.com. Est: 1991. Office and/or bookroom; Internet and Postal. Telephone First. Open: **M:** 10:00–18:00; **T:** 10:00–18:00; **W:** 10:00–18:00; **Th:** 10:00–18:00; **F:** 10:00–18:00; **S:** 10:00–18:00. Medium stock. Spec: Academic/Scholarly; African-American Studies; Africana; Anthropology; Antiquarian; Architecture; Art; Art - British. PR: £1–5,000. CC: JCB; MC; V; SW. Mem: PBFA.

Aurelian Books, 31 Llanvanor Road, London, NW2 2AR. Prop: David Dunbar. Tel: (020) 8455 9612. Fax: same. Web: www.aurelianbooks.co.uk. Est: 1970. Private premises. Appointment necessary. Small stock. Spec: Colour-Plate; Conservation; Entomology; Lepidoptera (butterflies, moths, insects); Lepidopterology; Natural History. PR: £5–5,000. CC: MC; V; SW. Mem: PBFA.

H. Baron, 121 Chatsworth Road, London, NW2 4BH. Prop: Christel Wallbaum. Tel: (020) 8459-2035. Fax: (020) 8459-2035. Est: 1949. Private premises. Postal only. Spec: Autographs; Iconography; Letters; Music - General. CC: E; MC; V. Corresp: French, German. Mem: ABA; ILAB.

Bibliopola, ■ 25 Church Street, London, NW8 8DT. Prop: Joseph Deagrossu. Tel: 020 7724 7231. Est: 1986. Shop open: **M:** 09:00–17:30; **T:** 09:00–17:30; **W:** 09:00–17:30; **Th:** 09:00–17:30; **F:** 09:00–17:30; **S:** 09:00–17:30; **Su:** 09:00–17:30; Closed for lunch: 13:00–14:00. Spec: Antiquarian; Modern First Editions; Private Press; Travel - General.

Biblipola, ■ 25 Church Street, London, NW8 8D7. Prop: Joseph Delgrosso. Tel: 020 7724 7231. Web: www.alfiesantiques.com. Est: 1986. Shop open at: Alfie's Antique Market, 25 Church Street, Marylebone, London NW8 8D7. Open: **T:** 10:00–17:30; **W:** 10:00–17:30; **Th:** 10:00–17:30; **F:** 10:00–17:30; **S:** 10:00–17:30. Spec: Antiquarian; Children's; Children's - Early Titles; Children's - Illustrated; First Editions; Modern First Editions; Natural History; Pop-Up, Movable & Cut Out. Notes: *Alternative e-mail address: delgro.bks@aol.com.*

The Book Depot, 111 Woodcote Avenue, Mill Hill, London, NW7 2PD. Prop: Conrad Wiberg. Tel: (020) 8906-3708. Est: 1980. Postal only. Spec: Booksearch. PR: £5–10.

Cranhurst Books, 20 Cranhurst Road, Willesden Green, NW2 4LN. Prop: Heidi Stransky. Tel: 0208 452 7845. Est: 1996. Private premises. Internet and Postal. Appointment necessary. Open: **M:** 09:00–17:30; **T:** 09:00–17:30; **W:** 09:00–17:30; **Th:** 09:00–17:30; **F:** 09:00–17:30; **S:** 09:00–17:30; **Su:** 09:00–17:30; Closed for lunch: 13:00–14:00. Small stock. Spec: Author - Ahlberg, Janet & Allan; Author - Aldin, Cecil; Author - Ardizzone, Edward; Author - Asimov, Isaac; Author - Bainbridge, Beryl; Author - Barrie, J.M.; Author - Burgess, A.; Author - Carroll, Lewis. PR: £5–2,000. CC: MC; V. Notes: *A mixture of old and new out of print children's books as well as a selection of modern firsts including, Rankin, Cornwall, Le Carre etc.*

Keith Fawkes, ■1–3 Flask Walk, Hampstead, London, NW3 1HJ. Prop: Keith Fawkes. Tel: (020) 7435-0614. Est: 1970. Shop open: **M:** 10:00–18:00; **T:** 09:00–18:00; **W:** 10:00–18:00; **Th:** 09:00–18:00; **F:** 10:00–18:00; **S:** 10:00–18:00; **Su:** 13:00–18:00. Large stock. PR: £1–100. VAT No: GB 232 0644 04. Notes: *Also, bric a brac.*

Fishburn Books, 43 Ridge Hill, London, NW11 8PR. Prop: Jonathan Fishburn. Tel: (0208) 455-9139. Fax: (0208) 922-5008. Web: www.fishburnbooks.com. Est: 2000. Private premises. Appointment necessary. Spec: Bibles; Biblical Studies; Countries - Israel; Countries - Middle East, The; Hebraica; Holocaust; Immigration; Judaica. PR: £15–5,000. CC: AE; MC; V. Cata: Judaica and Jewish Books. Mem: ABA; PBFA; ILAB. VAT No: GB 805 4965 16. Notes: *Specialists in Judaica, Hebraica and all items of Jewish interest, including Zionism, Holocaust, Jewish History, Synagogues etc.*

Fortune Green Books, 74 Fortune Green Road, London, NW6 1DS. Prop: Eric Stevens & Jane Bell. Tel: (020) 7435-7545. Est: 1992. Office and/or bookroom; Internet and Postal. Appointment necessary. Medium stock. Spec: Academic/Scholarly; Art; Belle-Lettres; Bibliography; Feminism; Fiction - General; Fiction - Women; Literary Criticism. PR: £1–50. CC: MC; V. Mem: PBFA. Notes: *Regular catalogues issued on 19th & early 20th Century literature, women writers & women's history including academic books in these fields.*

Stephen Foster, ■ 95 Bell Street, London, NW1 6TL. Prop: Stephen Foster. Tel: (020) 7724-0876. Fax: (020) 7724-0927. Web: www.95bellstreet.com. Est: 1987. Shop open: **M:** 10:30–18:00; **T:** 10:30–18:00; **W:** 10:30–18:00; **Th:** 10:30–18:00; **F:** 10:30–18:00; **S:** 10:30–18:00. Medium stock. Spec: Antiquarian; Antiques; Architecture; Art History; Art Reference; Artists; Arts, The; Decorative Art. PR: £1–1,000. CC: AE; JCB; MC; V; switch/ maestro. Cata: recent aquisitions. Mem: ABA; PBFA; ILAB; ibooknet. VAT No: GB 521 5504 81. Notes: *During July and August, the shop is closed Monday to Wednesday. Booksearch service; new books at a discount. See also Foster's Bookshop, London W4. (q.v.)*

Hellenic Bookservices, ■49–51 Fortess Road, Kentish Town, London, NW5 1AG. Prop: M. Williams & Andrew Stoddart. Tel: (020) 7267-9499. Fax: (020) 7267-9498. Web: www.hellenicbooks.com. Est: 1966. Shop open: **M:** 09:30–18:00; **T:** 09:30–18:00; **W:** 09:30–18:00; **Th:** 09:30–18:00; **F:** 09:30–18:00; **S:** 10:00–17:00. Large stock. Spec: Academic/Scholarly; Books in Greek; Byzantium; Classical Studies; Countries - Cyprus; Countries - Greece; Foreign Texts; Guide Books. PR: £1–500. CC: AE; JCB; MC; V. Corresp: Modern Greek. Mem: PBFA. Notes: *Also, a booksearch service, school supplies – all subjects.*

C.R. Johnson Rare Books, 4, Keats Grove, Hampstead, London, NW3 2RT. Prop: C.R. Johnson & C.A. Forster. Tel: (020) 7794-7940. Fax: (020) 7433-3303. Web: www.crjohnson.com. Est: 1970. Private premises. Internet and Postal. Appointment necessary. Very large stock. Spec: Authors - Women; Fiction - 18th Century; Fine & Rare; Literature; Social Economics. PR: £50–5,000. CC: MC; V. Cata: English Literature and Social Economics. Mem: PBFA; CERL.

Loretta Lay Books, 24 Grampian Gardens, London, NW2 1JG. Prop: Loretta Lay. Tel: 020 8455 3069. Web: www.laybooks.com. Est: 2001. Mail order only; Internet and Postal. Telephone First. Open: **M:** 09:00–17:30; **T:** 09:00–17:30; **W:** 09:00–17:30; **Th:** 09:00–17:30; **F:** 09:00–17:30; **S:** 09:00–17:30; **Su:** 09:00–17:30. Spec: Author - Tully, Jim; Author - Upfield, Arthur; Author - Wilson, Colin; Crime (True); Criminology; Espionage; Ghosts; Ku Klux Klan. CC: PayPal. Cata: all true crime. Notes: *A comprehensive stock of true crime including Notable British Trials, Organized Crime, Serial/Mass Murder, Fraud, Regional Crime, Collectors Items + much more, and specialising in Jack the Ripper.*

Richard Lucas, 114 Fellows Road, London, NW3 3JH. Prop: Richard Lucas. Tel: (020) 7449-9431. Est: 1975. Private premises. Appointment necessary. Medium stock. Spec: Brewing; Cookery/ Gastronomy; Etiquette; Food & Drink; Herbalism; Public Houses; Travel - General; Viticulture. PR: £10–1,000. Cata: lists.

Neil's Books, 151 Fordwych Road, London, NW2 3NG. Prop: Neil Aptaker. Tel: (020) 8452–0933. Est: 1990. Internet and Postal. Open: **M:** 10:00–18:45; **Th:** 10:00–18:45. Medium stock. Spec: Fiction - General; Modern First Editions. PR: £2–200.

Primrose Hill Books, 134 Regents Park Road, London, NW1 8XL. Tel: (0207) 586 2027. Fax: (0207) 722 9653. Est: 1987. Storeroom; Internet and Postal. Appointment necessary. Medium stock. Spec: Biography; First Editions; Poetry; Theatre. PR: £4–1,000. CC: AE; JCB; MC; V. VAT No: GB 523 4672 53.

Paul Rassam, Flat 5, 18 East Heath Road, London, NW3 1AJ. Tel: (020) 7794-9316. Est: 1972. Private premises. Internet and Postal. Appointment necessary. Small stock. Spec: Autographs; First Editions; Literature; Manuscripts. CC: MC; V. Cata: Late19th & 20th Century Literature. Mem: ABA; ILAB.

Robert G Sawers Ltd, No.5 Inglewood Road, London, NW6 1QT. Tel: (0207) 794 9618. Fax: (0207) 794 9571. Web: www.bobsawers.clara.net. Est: 1970. Private premises. Internet and Postal. Appointment necessary. Small stock. Spec: Countries - Far East, The; Countries - Japan. Corresp: French, Spanish, Japanese. Mem: ABA. VAT No: GB 233 701 02.

Sevin Seydi Rare Books, 13 Shirlock Road, London, NW3 2HR. Prop: Sevin Seydi & Maurice Whitby. Tel: (020) 7485 9801. Est: 1970. Private premises. Internet and Postal. Appointment necessary. Large stock. Spec: Antiquarian; Antiquities; Architecture; Architecture - Theatre; Art History; Art Reference; Bibliography; Bindings. CC: MC; V. PR: £20–10,000. Cata: occasionally on Antiquarian English and European. Corresp: French, Turkish. Mem: PBFA.

Terence Kaye - Bookseller, 52 Neeld Crescent, London, NW4 3RR. Prop: H Terence Kaye. Tel: (020) 8202-8188. Fax: (020) 8202-8188. Est: 1996. Office and/or bookroom; Appointment necessary. Open: **M:** 09:00–20:00; **T:** 09:00–20:00; **W:** 09:00–20:00; **Th:** 09:00–20:00; **F:** 09:00–18:00; **S:** 10:00–20:00; **Su:** 10:00–20:00; Spec: Architecture - Theatre; Cinema/Film; Circus; Drama; Entertainment - General; Fairgrounds; Music - Music Hall; Performing Arts. Corresp: Hebrew. Notes: *Also, a booksearch service (specialist subjects only), and library/collection development.*

Walden Books, ■ 38 Harmood Street, London, NW1 8DP. Prop: David Tobin. Tel: 020 7267 8146. Fax: 020 7267 8147. Web: www.ukbookworld.com/members/waldenbooks. Est: 1979. Shop open: **Th:** 10:30–18:30; **F:** 10:30–18:30; **S:** 10:30–18:30; **Su:** 10:30–18:30. Spec: Academic/Scholarly; Architecture; Art; Art - Technique; Art - Theory; Art History; Literature; Literature - 19th C. CC: AE; MC; V. Mem: PBFA.

Eva M. Weininger, Antiquarian Bookseller 79 Greenhill, London, NW3 5TZ. Tel: (020) 7435-2334. Est: 1979. Private premises. Appointment necessary. Small stock. Spec: Courtesy; Culture - Foreign; Culture - National; Etiquette; History of Ideas; Social History. PR: £10–150.

J. & S. Wilbraham, 1 Wise Lane Mill Hill, London, NW7 2RL. Prop: John and Shahin Wilbraham. Tel: (0208) 9593709. Web: www.wilbraham.demon.co.uk. Est: 1981. Private premises. Postal only. Contactable. Small stock. Spec: Antiquarian; Children's; Literature. PR: £10–1,000. CC: AE; MC; V. Cata: ANTIQUARIAN AND FOREIGN LITERATURE. Corresp: French.

White Eagle Books, 17 Rossall Crescent, Ealing (Park Royal), NW10 7HE. Prop: Andrew Szaflarski-Saidi. Tel: 020 8997 9894. Est: 2000. Private premises. Internet and Postal. Telephone First. Open: **M:** 09:00–19:30; **T:** 09:00–19:30; **W:** 09:00–19:30; **Th:** 09:00–19:30; **F:** 09:00–19:30; **S:** 10:00–19:30; **Su:** 10:00–19:30. Very small stock. Spec: Countries - Balkans, The; Countries - Central Asia; Countries - Cyprus; Countries - Himalayas, The; Countries - Iran; Countries - Middle East, The; Countries - Russia; Countries - Tibet. CC: PayPal and Personal cheque. Mem: PBFA. Notes: *White Eagle Books exibit at The Royal National, Gerrards Cross, Cookham and Duxford Book Fairs. White Eagle Books is also on ABE and the PBFA websites*

LONDON
SOUTH EAST POSTAL DISTRICTS

Beaumont Travel Books, 33 Couthurst Road, Blackheath, London, SE3 8TN. Prop: Gabriel Beaumont. Tel: 0208 293 4271. Web: www.abebooks.com/home/beaumont. Est: 1969. Private premises. Appointment necessary. Spec: Africana; Alpinism/Mountaineering; Anthropology; Archaeology; Countries - Central Asia; Countries - Far East, The; Countries - India; Countries - Middle East, The. CC: AE; D; E; MC; V; Switch. Cata: 5, General, Middle East, Africa, India, Asia. Corresp: French. Mem: ABA; ILAB.

Bermondsey Basement Bookstore, PO Box 3158, London, SE1 4RA. Prop: Peter Marcan. Tel: 020 7357 0368. Est: 2006. Office and/or bookroom; Appointment necessary. Open: **M:** 10:00–19:00; **T:** 10:00–19:00; **W:** 10:00–19:00; **Th:** 10:00–19:00; **F:** 10:00–19:00; **S:** 10:00–19:00. Spec: Architecture; Art - British; History - Sports; Illustrated - General; Music - Classical; Parks and gardens; Photography; Social History. Notes: *Also publishers 'Peter Marcan Publications' London SE. Issues up to 3 catalogues a year. (q.v.)*

The Book Palace, Jubilee House Bedwardine Road, Crystal Palace, London, SE19 3AP. Prop: G West. Tel: 020 8768 0022. Fax: 020 8768 0563. Web: www.bookpalace.com. Est: 1997. Warehouse; Internet and Postal. Appointment necessary. Open: **M:** 10:00–18:00; **T:** 10:00–18:00; **W:** 10:00–18:00; **Th:** 10:00–18:00; **F:** 10:00–18:00. Spec: Annuals; Art; Art - British; Art - Theory; Art History; Art Reference; Artists; Arts, The. CC: AE; MC; V; Maestro. Cata: Popular culture. Corresp: Dutch, French. VAT No: GB 756 4588 84. Notes: *Wholesale on many titles.*

The Bookshop on the Heath Ltd, ■74 Tranquil Vale, Blackheath, London, SE3 0BW. Prop: Richard Platt, Jasmine Platt. Tel: (020) 88524786. Fax: (020) 83189875. Web: www. bookshopontheheath.co.uk. Est: 2003. Shop open: **M:** 10:00–17:00; **T:** 10:00–17:00; **W:** 10:00–17:00; **Th:** 10:00–17:00; **F:** 10:00–17:00; **S:** 10:00–18:00. Medium stock. Spec: Art; Astronomy; Auction Catalogues; Author - Bates, H.E.; Author - Bennett, (Enoch) Arnol; Author - Blyton, Enid; Author - Churchill, Sir Winston; Author - Fleming, Ian. PR: £1–5,000. CC: MC; V; Switch, Maestro. Corresp: German, Mandarin. Mem: BA. VAT No: GB 831 1125 78. Notes: *We also sell many original posters incl. James Bond & The Beatles. Book Investments, Bookbinding & Restoration.*

Fiona Campbell, 158 Lambeth Road, London, SE1 7DF. Tel: (020) 7928-1633. Fax: (020) 7928-1633. Est: 1970. Private premises. Appointment necessary. Small stock. Spec: Countries - Italy; Travel - General; Travel - Europe. Corresp: French, German and Italian. Mem: ABA; PBFA; ILAB.

Marcus Campbell Art Books, ■ 43 Holland Street, Bankside, London, SE1 9JR. Prop: Marcus Campbell. Tel: (020) 7261-0111. Fax: (020) 7261-0129. Web: www.marcuscampbell.co.uk. Est: 1998. Internet and Postal. Shop open: **M:** 10:30–18:30; **T:** 10:30–18:30; **W:** 10:30–18:30; **Th:** 10:30–18:30; **F:** 10:30–18:30; **S:** 10:30–18:30; **Su:** 12:00–18:00. Very large stock. Spec: Art; Art - Afro-American; Art - British; Art - Technique; Art - Theory; Art History; Art Reference; Artists. PR: £2–2,000. CC: AE; E; MC; V; Switch. Cata: Modern Art. Corresp: French. Mem: PBFA. VAT No: GB 605 8695 15.

Chapter Two, Fountain House, Conduit Mews, Woolwich, London, SE18 7AP. Prop: Manager: Miss P. Brachotte. Tel: (020) 8316-5389. Fax: (020) 8854-5963. Web: www.chaptertwobooks.org.uk. Est: 1976. Office and/or bookroom; Internet and Postal. Telephone First. Open: **M:** 09:00–17:00; **T:** 09:00–17:00; **W:** 09:00–17:00; **Th:** 09:00–17:00; **F:** 06:00–17:00; Closed for lunch: 13:00–14:30. Medium stock. Spec: Amish; Author - Baring-Gould, S.; Author - Blyton, Enid; Author - Bunyan, John; Author - Johns, W.E.; Author - Lewis, C.S.; Authors - Local; Bibles. PR: £2–3,500. CC: AE; MC; V. Cata: Plymouth Brethren, Fundemental Christianity. Corresp: Afrikaans, French, German, Dutch, Spanish. Mem: CBA. Notes: *Chapter Two Christian Bookshop, 199 Plumstead Common Rd Plumstead Common, London SE18 2UJ. Also publisher/retailer of new books & foreign language Christian literature, Bible distributor, archive & booksearch service.*

Nigel A. Clark, 28 Ulundi Road, Blackheath, London, SE3 7UG. Prop: Sole Propreietor. Tel: (020) 8858-4020. Est: 1975. Private premises. Postal only. Appointment necessary. Small stock. Spec: Antiques; Art History; Art Reference; Artists; Auction Catalogues; Ceramics; Collectables; Collecting. PR: £1–100. Cata: Numismatic Publications. VAT No: GB 311 6080 06. Notes: *Also, British coins & Tokens.*

Collectable Books, 15 West Park, London, SE9 4RZ. Prop: Partners: Tom & Sue Biro. Tel: (020) 8851-8487. Web: www.collectablebooks.co.uk. Est: 1992. Private premises. Appointment necessary. Small stock. Spec: Antiquarian; Architecture; Architecture - Theatre; Arts, The; Food & Drink; Health; Medicine; Natural History. PR: £10–20,000. CC: E; JCB; MC; V; SO, SW. Corresp: French, German, Italian, Hungarian, Portuguese. Mem: ABA; PBFA; ILAB. VAT No: GB 299 3282 10.

Eclectica, 48 Rosendale Road West Dulwich, London, SE21 8DP. Prop: Michael Coupe. Tel: (0208) 761-4138. Office and/or bookroom; Appointment necessary. Small stock. Spec: Antiquarian; Author - Henty, G.A.; Author - Lang, Andrew; Author - MacDonald, George; Author - Searle, Ronald; Author - Yee, Chiang; Bindings; Children's. PR: £1–2,000. Mem: PBFA. Notes: *General antiquarian, decorated/pictorial cloth bindings (especially Victorian and Edwardian children's), illustrated books and ephemera.*

Enscot Books, 17 Crantock Road, Catford, London, SE6 2QS. Prop: Michael Enscot and Philip Enscot. Tel: (020) 8698 1976. Fax: (020) 8698 1976. Est: 1998. Private premises. Small stock. Spec: Fiction - Historical; Modern First Editions. PR: £2–50. Corresp: French, German.

Jane Gibberd, ■ 20 Lower Marsh, London, SE1 7RJ. Tel: (020) 7633-9562. Est: 1968. Shop open: **W:** 11:00–19:00; **Th:** 11:00–19:00; **F:** 11:00–19:00. Small stock. PR: £1–25.

Hava Books, 110 Aspinall Road, Brockley, London, SE4 2EG. Prop: J. Havercroft. Tel: (020) 76398339. Est: 1998. Private premises. Internet only. Appointment necessary. Medium stock. Spec: Antiquarian; Antique Paper; Antiquities; Archaeology; Atlases; Author - Dickens, Charles; Bibles; Bindings. PR: £5–5,000. CC: PayPal. Corresp: French, Spanish. Mem: PBFA. VAT No: GB 782 4918 92. Notes: *We specialise in rare, out of print and collectible books. Only part of our stock is on the net- the books we sell at fairs are not yet catalogued and are not for sale elsewhere. Good general stock booksearch undertaken.*

James Hawkes, Flat One, 63 East Dulwich Road, London, SE22 9AP. Tel: (0208) 299 2995. Private premises. Postal only. Appointment necessary. Spec: Academic/Scholarly; Antiquarian; Literary Criticism; Literature. PR: £20–1,500. Cata: bi-annually on English Literature: Academic & Scholarly. Notes: *English Literature specialists: Academic, Scholarly, and selected Antiquarian. Emphasis on authors 1500-1900. Our stock is not listed online. Catalogues issued. Enquiries & wants lists welcomed (please phone or e-mail for fastest response).*

Junk & Spread Eagle, ■9 Greenwich South Street, Greenwich, London, SE10 8NW. Prop: Tobias Moy. Tel: (020) 8305-1666. Est: 1960. Shop open: **M:** 10:00–18:00; **T:** 10:00–18:00; **W:** 10:00–18:00; **Th:** 10:00–18:00; **F:** 10:00–18:00; **S:** 10:00–18:00; **Su:** 10:00–18:00; Closed for lunch: 13:00–14:00. Medium stock. Spec: Advertising; Animals and Birds; Antiquarian; Arts, The; Author - Churchill, Sir Winston; Bindings; Children's; Children's - Illustrated. PR: £3–100. CC: D; E; JCB; MC; V; SW. Notes: *Also, ephemera, collectables and antiques.*

Kirkdale Bookshop, ■ 272 Kirkdale, Sydenham, SE26 4RS. Prop: Ms. Geraldine A. Cox. Tel: (020) 8778-4701. Fax: (020) 8776-6293. Est: 1966. Shop open: **M:** 09:00–17:30; **T:** 09:00–17:30; **W:** 09:00–17:30; **Th:** 09:00–17:30; **F:** 09:00–17:30; **S:** 09:00–17:30. Medium stock. CC: MC; V. Mem: BA. Notes: *Also, new books, greetings cards, selected gift items and a small art gallery showing work by local artists.*

Peter Marcan, Bookseller, P.O. Box 3158, London, SE1 4RA. Prop: Peter Marcan. Tel: (020) 7357 0368. Est: 2000. Private premises. Appointment necessary. Open: **M:** 10:00–19:00; **T:** 10:00–19:00; **W:** 10:00–19:00; **Th:** 10:00–19:00; **F:** 10:00–19:00; **S:** 10:00–19:00. Small stock. Spec: Music - Classical; Social History; Topography - General; Topography - Local. PR: £3–50. Notes: *Small stock of books on 18th - 20th C British art, Greater London and S. East England topography. Publishing (est 1978) - reprints, handbooks, catalogues and Art - British. Also trades as Bermondsey Basement Bookstore.*

Marcet Books, ■The Bookshop, 4a Nelson Road, Greenwich, London, SE10 9JB. Prop: Martin Kemp. Tel: 020 8853 5408. Web: www.marcetbooks.co.uk. Est: 1980. Shop open: **M:** 10:00–17:30; **T:** 10:00–17:30; **W:** 10:00–17:30; **Th:** 10:00–17:30; **F:** 10:00–17:30; **S:** 09:00–17:30; **Su:** 10:00–17:30. Spec: Africana; Aircraft; Arabica; Art History; Canals/Inland Waterways; Cartography; Cities - City of London; Cookery - Professional. CC: AE; MC; V; PayPal. Cata: Foreign Travel.

Military Bookworm, P.O. Box 235, London, SE23 1NS. Prop: David W. Collett. Tel: (020) 8291-1435. Web: www.militarybookworm.co.uk. Est: 1975. Storeroom; Internet only. Contactable. Medium stock. Spec: Military; Military History; School Registers/Rolls of Honour; Collectables. PR: £5–300. CC: MC; V.

Herbert Murch Booksend, 258/260 Creek Road, Greenwich, London, SE10 9SW. Prop: D. Herbert. Tel: (020) 8858 2414. Est: 1974. Private premises. Postal only. Spec: Arts, The; Biography; Literature; Media. PR: £8–25. Cata: Poetry, Sex & Gender, Biography. Notes: *Business being re-organised spring 2006. Has large stock of biographies, especially first half 20th Century.*

Print Matters, 23 Phoenix Road, Penge, SE20 7BT. Prop: Paul Tanner. Tel: 020 8778 8580. Fax: 020 8776 8476. Web: www.printmatters.com. Est: 1997. Warehouse; Internet and Postal. Telephone First. Open: **M:** 10:30–17:30; **T:** 10:30–17:30; **W:** 10:30–17:30; **Th:** 10:30–17:30; **F:** 10:30–17:30; **S:** 10:30–17:30; Closed for lunch: 13:00–14:00. Large stock. Spec: Art; Art - Technique; Art Deco; Art Nouveau; Art Reference; Artists; Arts, The; Calligraphy. PR: £5 – 500. CC: AE; MC; V; PayPal. Cata: on-line - graphic novels; british comics; illustrated books. Corresp: French, Spanish. Notes: *Huge range of GRAPHIC NOVELS and illustrated books on many aspects of POPULAR CULTURE. World's largest stock of BRITISH COMICS and ANNUALS! Also American and European comic books. ORIGINAL ART for books, comics, newspaper strips and mags.*

Rogers Turner Books, 87 Breakspears Road, London, SE4 1TX. Prop: P.J. Rogers & A.J. Turner. Tel: (0208) 692-2472. Fax: (0208) 692- 2472. Est: 1976. Private premises. Internet and Postal. Appointment necessary. Open: **Th:** 10:00–18:00; **F:** 10:00–18:00. Small stock. Spec: Horology; Science - General; Science - History of; Scientific Instruments; Technology. CC: AE; D; JCB; MC; V. Cata: Horology, science, scientific instruments. Corresp: French, German, Spanish. Mem: ABA; PBFA.

John Rolfe, 39 Combe Avenue, Blackheath, London, SE3 7PZ. Prop: John Rolfe. Tel: (020) 8858-3349. Web: www.abebooks.com/home/johnrolfe. Est: 1990. Private premises. Internet and Postal. Appointment necessary. Small stock. Spec: Dogs. PR: £5–500. Cata: Dogs.

Michael Silverman, P.O. Box 350, London, SE3 0LZ. Tel: (020) 8319-4452. Fax: (020) 8856-6006. Web: www.michael-silverman.com. Est: 1989. Private premises. Internet and Postal. Appointment necessary. Medium stock. Spec: Art; Autographs; Documents - General; History - General; Letters; Literature; Manuscripts. CC: AE; MC; V. Cata: literary & historical autographs & manuscripts. Mem: ABA; ILAB. VAT No: GB 532 9017 59.

Anthony J. Simmonds, ■66 Royal Hill, Greenwich, London, SE10 8RT. Prop: Anthony & Setitia Simmonds. Tel: (020) 8692 1794. Web: www.navalandmaritimebooks.com. Est: 1974. Shop open: **M:** 10:00–18:00; **T:** 10:00–18:00; **W:** 10:00–18:00; **Th:** 10:00–18:00; **F:** 10:00–18:00; **S:** 10:00–18:00. Spec: Maritime/Nautical; Naval; Booksearch. PR: £1–5,000. CC: JCB; MC; V. Cata: on specialities, naval and maritime history. Corresp: French and German. Mem: PBFA. VAT No: GB 231 0328 20.

Stephen E. Tilston, 7 Dartmouth House, Dartmouth Row, Greenwich, London, SE10 8BF. Prop: Steve & Frances Tilston. Tel: (020) 8691 3108. Web: www.ukbookworld.com/members/tilston. Est: 1985. Private premises. Internet and Postal. Appointment necessary. Medium stock. Spec: Architecture; Architecture - Theatre; Art; Author - Lawrence, D.H.; Aviation; Biography; Bridge; Cookery/Gastronomy. PR: £5–1,000. CC: AE; MC; V; Maestro. VAT No: GB 626418535.

Warwick Leadlay Gallery, 5 Nelson Road, Greenwich, London, SE10 9JB. Tel: (020) 8858-0317. Web: www.warwickleadlay.com. Est: 1974. Shop and/or gallery; Shop open: **M:** 09:30–17:30; **T:** 09:30–17:30; **W:** 09:30–17:30; **Th:** 09:30–17:30; **F:** 09:30–17:30; **S:** 09:30–17:30; **Su:** 11:00–17:30. Small stock. Spec: Naval. PR: £5–500. CC: AE; D; JCB; MC; V.

LONDON
SOUTH WEST POSTAL DISTRICTS

Allsworth Rare Books, P.O.Box 134, 235 Earls Court Road, London, SW5 9FE. Tel: (020) 7377-0552. Fax: (020) 7377-0552. Web: www.allsworthbooks.com. Est: 2002. Office and/or bookroom; Appointment necessary. Spec: Africana; Countries - Africa; Countries - Arabia; Countries - Asia; Countries - Caribbean, The; Countries - Central Asia; Countries - China; Countries - Hong Kong. PR: £50–50,000. CC: MC; V; Maestro. Cata: Travel & Exploration. Mem: ABA; PBFA; ILAB. VAT No: GB 798 7327 57. Notes: *Stock may be viewed (by appt.) at central London office. Valuation service.*

Ancient Art Books, 34 East Sheen Ave., East Sheen, London, SW14 8AS. Prop: D.G. Giles. Tel: (020) 8878-8951. Fax: (020) 8878-9201. Web: www.gilesancientart.com. Est: 1999. Shop and/or gallery; Internet and Postal. Appointment necessary. Small stock. Spec: Antiques; Applied Art; Archaeology; Collecting; Glass; Pottery & Glass. PR: £10–15,000. CC: AE; D; MC; V. Cata: ancient, old and antique glass. Mem: PBFA.

Andrew Hunter Rare Books, Box 9, 34 Buckingham Palace Road, London, SW1V 4DF. Prop: Andrew Hunter. Tel: 02078344924. Fax: 02078344924. Web: www.rarebookhunter.com. Est: 2001. Private premises. Postal only. Appointment necessary. Open: **M:** 09:00–17:30; **T:** 09:00–17:30; **W:** 09:00–17:30; **Th:** 09:00–17:30; **F:** 09:00–17:30; **S:** 09:00–17:30; **Su:** 09:00–17:30; Closed for lunch: 13:00–14:00. Spec: Earth Sciences; Incunabula; Literature; Manuscripts; Mathematics; Medicine; Medicine - History of; Pharmacy/Pharmacology. Cata: science, medicine. Mem: ABA; ILAB. VAT No: GB 782 2863 04.

Ash Rare Books, 43 Huron Road, London, SW17 8RE. Prop: Laurence Worms. Tel: (020) 8672-2263. Web: www.ashrare.com. Est: 1946. Private premises. Internet and Postal. Appointment necessary. Open: **M:** 10:00–17:00; **T:** 10:00–17:00; **W:** 10:00–17:00; **Th:** 10:00–17:00; **F:** 10:00–17:00. Medium stock. Spec: Author - 19th Century; Author - 20th Century; Author - Bennett, (Enoch) Arnol; Author - Dickens, Charles; Author - Trollope, Anthony; Bibliography; Cities - City of London; First Editions. PR: £20–5,000. CC: JCB; MC; V. Cata: Literary First Editions; Modern Poetry; London. Mem: ABA; ILAB. VAT No: GB 244 2896 45.

Book Mongers, ■ 439 Coldharbour Lane, London, SW9 8LN. Prop: Patrick Kelly. Tel: (020) 7738-4225. Fax: (020) 7738-4225. Web: www.freespace.virgin.net/book.mongers. Est: 1992. Shop open: **M:** 10:30–18:30; **T:** 10:30–18:30; **W:** 10:30–18:30; **Th:** 10:30–18:30; **F:** 10:30–18:30; **S:** 10:30–18:30. Very large stock. PR: £1–10. CC: D; E; JCB; MC; V; Mae. So.

Classic Bindings Ltd, ■ 61 Cambridge Street, Pimlico, London, SW1V 4PS. Prop: Mr. Sasha Poklewski–Koziell. Tel: (020) 7834-5554. Fax: (020) 7630-6632. Web: www.classicbindings.net. Est: 1988. Shop open: **M:** 09:30–17:30; **T:** 09:30–17:30; **W:** 09:30–17:30; **Th:** 09:30–17:30; **F:** 09:30–17:30. Large stock. Spec: Architecture; Art; Bindings; Biography; Foreign Texts; History - General; Poetry; Religion - Christian. PR: £10–5,000. CC: E; MC; V. VAT No: GB 562 2080 66.

Robin de Beaumont, 25 Park Walk, Chelsea, London, SW10 0AJ. Tel: (0207) 352-3440. Fax: (0207) 352-1260. Web: www.abebooks.com/home/RDEBOOKS. Est: 1980. Private premises. Internet and Postal. Telephone First. Small stock. Spec: Art; Bindings; Illustrated - General; Victoriana. PR: £20–3,000. CC: MC; V. Corresp: French. Mem: BA.

Earlsfield Bookshop, ■513 Garratt Lane,Wandsworth, London, SW18 4SW. Prop: Charles Dixon. Tel: (020) 8946-3744. Est: 1995. Shop open: **M:** 16:00–18:00; **T:** 16:00–18:00; **W:** 16:00–18:00; **Th:** 16:00–18:00; **F:** 11:00–16:00; **S:** 10:00–17:00. Small stock. PR: £1–50.

Harfield Books of London, 1 Engadine Street, Southfields, London, SW18 5BJ. Prop: P.H. Eastman. Tel: (020) 8871-0880. Fax: (020) 8871-0880. Web: www.harfieldbooks.com. Est: 1989. Warehouse; Internet and Postal. Appointment necessary. Very large stock. Spec: Academic/Scholarly; Booksearch. CC: AE; E; MC; V; Paypal. Notes: *Also, a booksearch service & academic publishing.*

Edmund Pollinger Rare Books, Flat D, 27 Bramham Gardens, London, SW5 0JE. Prop: Edmund Pollinger. Tel: 07834 601432. Fax: 0207 244 8498. Web: www.etpollinger.com. Est: 2004. Office and/or bookroom; Contactable. Open: **M:** 10:00–17:30; **T:** 10:00–17:30; **W:** 10:00–17:30; **Th:** 10:00–17:30; **F:** 10:00–17:30; Closed for lunch: 12:00–14:00. Spec: Adventure; Africana; Animals and Birds; Apiculture; Author - Selous, Frederick; Curiosa; Entomology; Erotica. CC: MC; V. Cata: Natural History, game hunting, fishing, food, drink. Corresp: French. Mem: PBFA. Notes: *Usually somebody here all the time, but call first to be sure.*

Folios Limited, Flat 5 193/195 Brompton Road, London, SW3 1LZ. Prop: Mr. Badr El–Hage. Tel: (020) 7581-2706. Fax: (020) 7581-2563. Est: 1990. Office and/or bookroom; Internet and Postal. Appointment necessary. Open: **M:** 9:30–5:30; **T:** 9:30–5:30; **W:** 9:30–5:30; **Th:** 9:30–5:30; **F:** 9:30–5:30. Spec: Countries - Africa; Countries - Arabia; Countries - Holy Land, The; Religion - Islam; Prints and Maps. PR: £5–1,000. CC: MC; V. Corresp: Arabic, French.

Paul Foster Books, 49 Clifford Avenue, London, SW14 7BW. Tel: (020) 8876-7424. Fax: (020) 8876 7424. Web: www.paulfosterbooks.com. Est: 1990. Office and/or bookroom; Internet and Postal. Appointment necessary. Open: **M:** 10:00–18:00; **T:** 10:00–18:00; **W:** 10:00–18:00; **Th:** 10:00–18:00; **F:** 10:00–18:00; **S:** 10:00–18:00. Medium stock. Spec: Antiquarian; Art; Author - 19th Century; Author - 20th Century; Author - Austen, Jane; Author - Carroll, Lewis; Author - Churchill, Sir Winston; Author - Dickens, Charles. PR: £5–10,000. CC: JCB; MC; V. Mem: ABA; PBFA; ILAB.

Robert Frew Ltd, ■ 8 Thurloe Place, London, SW7 2RX. Prop: Robert Frew. Tel: 020 7590 6650. Fax: 020 7590 6651. Web: www.robertfrew.com. Est: 1993. Shop open: **M:** 10:00–18:00; **T:** 10:00–18:00; **W:** 10:00–18:00; **Th:** 10:00–18:00; **F:** 10:00–18:00; **S:** 11:00–17:00. Spec: Antiquarian; Atlases; Author - Churchill, Sir Winston; Bindings; Cartography; Colour-Plate; Encyclopaedias; History - General. PR: £10–30,000. CC: AE; D; E; JCB; MC; V. Mem: ABA; PBFA; ILAB. VAT No: GB 625 8877 92. Notes: *Sister company RF Shipping Ltd, offers a bespoke packing and shipping service to trade and private clients.*

Gardener & Cook, 90 Clancarty Road, London, SW6 3AA. Prop: Jonathan Tootell & Simon Cobley. Tel: 020 7751 3377. Fax: 020 7731 8400. Web: www.gardenerandcook.com. Est: 2005. Office and/or bookroom; Appointment necessary. Open: **M:** 09:00–17:30; **T:** 09:00–17:30; **W:** 09:00–17:30; **Th:** 09:00–17:30; **F:** 09:00–17:30; **S:** 09:00–17:30. Spec: Antiquarian; Catering & Hotel Management; Cookery - Professional; Cookery/Gastronomy; Fine & Rare; Food & Drink; Fungi; Gardening - General. CC: MC; V. Cata: Gardening & Cookery.

Geneva Books, 58 Elms Road, London, SW4 9EW. Tel: (020) 7627-4070. Est: 1985. Private premises. Appointment necessary. Spec: Religion - General. PR: £1–350.

Gloucester Road Bookshop, ■ 123 Gloucester Road, London, SW7 4TE. Prop: Nick Dennys. Tel: (020) 7370-3503. Fax: (020) 7373-0610. Est: 1983. Shop open: **M:** 09:30–22:30; **T:** 09:30–22:30; **W:** 09:30–22:30; **Th:** 09:30–22:30; **F:** 09:30–22:30; **S:** 10:30–18:30; **Su:** 10:30–18:30. Large stock. Spec: Applied Art; Architecture; Art; Art - British; Art - Theory; Art Deco; Art History; Art Nouveau. PR: £0–5,000. CC: MC; V. Cata: Modern First Editions, Children's/Illustrated. VAT No: GB 394 5021 50.

Grays of Westminster, ■40 Churton Street Pimlico, London, SW1V 2LP. Prop: Gray Levett & Nick Wynne. Tel: (020) 7828-4925. Fax: (020) 7976-5783. Web: www.graysofwestminster.co.uk. Est: 1985. Internet and Postal. Shop open: **M:** 10:00–17:30; **T:** 10:00–17:30; **W:** 10:00–17:30; **Th:** 10:00–17:30; **F:** 10:00–17:30; **S:** 10:00–13:00. Spec: Photography. PR: £10–200. CC: AE; D; E; MC; V; Maestro. Corresp: Japanese, Italian, Polish, German. VAT No: GB 503 1317 05. Notes: *Also, new, secondhand and vintage Nikon cameras.*

Robin Greer, 434 Fulham Palace Road, London, SW6 6HX. Prop: Robin Greer. Tel: (020) 7381-9113. Web: www.rarerobin.com. Est: 1966. Private premises. Appointment necessary. Small stock. Spec: Arthurian; Author - Lang, Andrew; Children's; Children's - Illustrated; Illustrated - 19th & 20th Century; Illustrators. PR: £1–5,000. CC: MC; V. Cata: Children's & Illustrated Book. Corresp: Spanish. Mem: ABA; PBFA; ILAB.

Hanshan Tang Books, Unit 3, Ashburton Centre, 276 Cortis Road, London, SW15 3AY. Prop: John Cayley, John Constable, Myrna Chua. Tel: 0208 788 4464. Fax: 02087801565. Web: www.hanshan.com. Est: 1973. Office and/or bookroom; Internet and Postal. Appointment necessary. Open: **M:** 10:00–17:00; **T:** 10:00–17:00; **W:** 10:00–17:00; **Th:** 10:00–17:00; **F:** 10:00–17:00. Spec: Antiquarian; Antiques; Antiquities; Archaeology; Architecture; Art; Art History; Art Reference. CC: AE; MC; V. Cata: East Asian Art and Archaeology. Mem: ABA; BA. VAT No: GB 749 5193 91.

Peter Harrington Antiquarian Bookseller, ■100 Fulham Road, London, SW3 6HS. Prop: Peter Harrington. Tel: 020 7591 0220. Fax: 020 7225 7054. Web: www.peter-harrington-books.com. Est: 1969. Shop open: **M:** 10:00–18:00; **T:** 10:00–18:00; **W:** 10:00–18:00; **Th:** 10:00–18:00; **F:** 10:00–18:00; **S:** 10:00–18:00. Very large stock. Spec: Aeronautics; Antiquarian; Architecture; Atlases; Autographs; Bibles; Bindings; Botany. PR: £10–100,000. CC: AE; E; JCB; MC; V. Cata: General, Literature, Travel, Children's. Corresp: Spanish, Polish. Mem: ABA; PBFA; ILAB. VAT No: GB701 5578 50.

Thomas Heneage Art Books, ■ 42 Duke Street, St. James's, London, SW1Y 6DJ. Tel: (020) 7930-9223. Fax: (020) 7839-9223. Web: www.heneage.com. Est: 1977. Shop open: **M:** 09:30–18:00; **T:** 09:30–18:00; **W:** 09:30–18:00; **Th:** 09:30–18:00; **F:** 09:30–18:00. Medium stock. Spec: Antiques; Applied Art; Arms & Armour; Art; Art History; Carpets - General; Catalogues Raisonnes; Ceramics. PR: £2–30,000. CC: MC; V. Mem: ABA; ILAB; LAPADA. VAT No: GB 242 1045 14. Notes: *Also, a booksearch service and publishers of Art Book Survey. Open at other times by appointment.*

Hesketh & Ward Ltd., 31 Britannia Road, London, SW6 2HJ. Prop: Viscount Bangor. Tel: (020) 7736-5705. Fax: (020) 7736-1089. Est: 1985. Private premises. Appointment necessary. Small stock. Spec: Foreign Texts. PR: £80–5,000. CC: MC; V. Cata: Early continental. Corresp: French, Italian. VAT No: GB 394 8008 27. Notes: *Stock is mainly 16th Century Continental, especially Italian.*

Hünersdorff Rare Books, P.O. Box 582, London, SW10 9RP. Prop: Richard von Hünersdorff. Tel: (020) 7373-3899. Fax: (020) 7370-1244. Web: www.abebooks.com/hunersdorff/home. Est: 1969. Private premises. Appointment necessary. Spec: Architecture; Architecture - Theatre; Countries - Latin America; Countries - South America; Gardening - General; Horses; Horticulture; Landscape. PR: £25–500,000. CC: MC; V. Corresp: German, Spanish, French. Mem: ABA; ILAB. Notes: *Science, medicine, Latin Americana, early European books. Small stock of travel, architecture,horticulture, near eastern books.*

Indoislamica, 17 Anselm Road, London, SW6 1LH. Prop: Mr. K.S. Hosain and Mr S. Brandenburger. Tel: (020) 7835 5772. Web: www.indoislamica.com. Est: 1979. Storeroom; Internet only. Spec: Oriental; Ottoman Empire; Travel - Africa; Voyages & Discovery; Prints and Maps. PR: £100–5,000. CC: MC; V. Cata: bi-annual.

J.C. Deyong Books, 17 Cadogan Court Draycott Avenue, London, SW3 3BX. Prop: J.C. Deyong (Previously of Snowden Smith Books). Tel: 020 7581 8665. Fax: 020 7581 0031. Web: www.jcdeyong.co.uk. Est: 1973. Private premises. Internet and Postal. Contactable. Spec: Aboriginal; Anthropology; Countries - Middle East, The; Ethnography; Ethnology; Languages - African; Travel - Africa; Travel - Asia. CC: MC; V. Cata: Travel & Related Subjects. Corresp: French. Mem: PBFA.

Romilly Leeper, 12 Bolton Garden Mews, London, SW10 9LW. Prop: Romilly Leeper. Tel: (020) 7373-8370. Fax: (020) 7370-3226. Est: 1986. Private premises. Appointment necessary. Small stock. Spec: Sport - Horse Racing (inc. Riding/Breeding/Equestrian); Travel - Asia, South East. PR: £6–100. Corresp: French, German, Portuguese.

Mandalay Bookshop, 36c Sisters Avenue, London, SW11 5SQ. Prop: Nicholas Greenwood. Web: www.mandalaybookshop.com. Est: 1994. Private premises. Internet and Postal. Small stock. Spec: Animals and Birds; Anthropology; Antiquarian; Architecture; Army, The; Art; Asian Studies; Author - Orwell, George. PR: £5–1,500. Corresp: French, German, Burmese, Thai. Notes: *WWII includes the Burma Campaign.*

Michael Graves-Johnston, 54 Stockwell Park Road, London, SW9 0DA. Prop: Michael Graves-Johnston. Tel: 020-7274-2069. Fax: 020-7738-3747. Web: www.Graves-Johnston.com. Est: 1978. Private premises. Postal only. Appointment necessary. Open: **M:** 09:00–17:30; **T:** 09:00–17:30; **W:** 09:00–17:30; **Th:** 09:00–17:30; **F:** 09:00–17:30; **S:** 09:00–17:30; **Su:** 09:00–17:30; Closed for lunch: 13:00–14:00. Spec: Aboriginal; Academic/Scholarly; African-American Studies; Africana; American Indians; American Northwest; Anthropology; Antiquarian. CC: AE; E; MC; V. Cata: Africa, Oceania, Egyptology, Tribal, Archaeology. Mem: ABA; ILAB. Notes: *Buying and selling rare, antiquarian and scholarly books for over 25 years, specializing in tribal and ancient cultures, we carry stock of many thousands of works on Africa, Oceania, travel, anthropology, ethnology, Egyptology, Archaeology,*

My Back Pages, ■ 8-10 Balham Station Road, London, SW16 6RT. Prop: Douglas Jeffers. Tel: 0208 675 9346. Fax: 0208 769 9741. Est: 1990. Shop open: **M:** 10:10–20:00; **T:** 10:00–20:00; **W:** 10:00–20:00; **Th:** 10:00–20:00; **F:** 10:00–20:00; **S:** 10:00–19:00; **Su:** 11:00–18:00. Very large stock. Spec: Academic/Scholarly; Architecture; Art; Art - British; Art Reference; Cinema/Film; Countries - India; Egyptology. CC: AE; JCB; MC; V. VAT No: GB 562 0221 84.

Nibris Books, 14 Ryfold Road Wimbledon Park, London, SW19 8BZ. Prop: Nigel Israel. Tel: (020) 8946-7207. Fax: (020) 8946-7207. Est: 1980. Private premises. Postal only. Appointment necessary. Small stock. Spec: Antiquarian; Antiques; Gemmology; Horology; Jewellery; Mineralogy; Precious Metals - Silver; Silversmiths. PR: £10–500. Cata: As per classifications. VAT No: GB446 2021 80. Notes: *Included in clasifications: Jewellery,gem stones, engraved gems, crown jewels, regalia & ceremony, silver, horology.*

Paul Orssich, 2 St. Stephen's Terrace South, Lambeth, London, SW8 1DH. Tel: (020) 7787-0030. Fax: (020) 7735-9612. Web: www.orssich.com. Est: 1980. Private premises. Internet and Postal. Telephone First. Very large stock. Spec: Author - Cervantes Saavedra, Miguel de; Author - Lorca, Garcia; Braziliana; Bull Fighting; Countries - Andorra; Countries - Central America; Countries - Gibraltar; Countries - Guatemala. PR: £25–5,000. CC: AE; MC; V. Cata: Hispanic Studies in general. Corresp: Spanish, Catalan, French, German, Italian. Mem: PBFA. VAT No: GB 442 4102 94. Notes: *Open any time by appointment. Nearest tube is Stockwell (Victoria Line & Northern Line).*

Pimpernel Booksearch, 90 Clencarty Road, London, SW6 3AA. Prop: Jonathan Tootell. Tel: (020) 7731-8500. Fax: (020) 7731-8400. Web: www.pimpernelbooks.co.uk. Est: 1999. Private premises. Postal only. Contactable. Open: **M:** 09:00–18:00; **T:** 09:00–18:00; **W:** 09:00–18:00; **Th:** 09:00–18:00; **F:** 09:00–18:00; **S:** 09:00–14:00. Small stock. Spec: Booksearch. CC: MC; V. Corresp: French.

Russell Rare Books, ■239A Fulham Road, Chelsea, London, SW3 6HY. Tel: (020) 7351-5119. Fax: (020) 7376-7227. Web: www.russellrarebooks.com. Est: 1977. Shop open: **M:** 14:00–18:00; **T:** 14:00–18:00; **W:** 14:00–18:00; **Th:** 14:00–18:00; **F:** 14:00–18:00. Small stock. Spec: Atlases; Bindings; Natural History; Social History; Travel - General; Prints and Maps. PR: £200–10,000. CC: V. Mem: ABA; PBFA; ILAB. Notes: *WHEN CLOSED: telephone 07768 004152 usually open but appointment advisable.*

SaBeRo Books, 27 Cavendish Road, Colliers Wood, London, SW19 2ET. Prop: Ron, Bethani and Sarah Travis. Tel: 44 (0) 20 85 40 60 2. Est: 2002. Private premises. Internet and Postal. Contactable. Open: **M:** 09:00–17:00; **T:** 09:00–17:00; **W:** 09:00–17:00; **Th:** 09:00–17:00; **F:** 09:00–17:00; **S:** 09:00–17:00. Medium stock. Spec: Africana; Author - 20th Century; Author - Pratchett, Terry; Drama; Fiction - Fantasy, Horror; Fiction - Science Fiction; Irish Interest; Music - Jazz & Blues. PR: £2–500. CC: PayPal. Cata: Various, as requested.

Sandpiper Books Ltd., 24 Langroyd Road, London, SW17 7PL. Prop: Robert Collie. Tel: (020) 8767-7421. Fax: (020) 8682-0280. Web: www.sandpiper.co.uk. Est: 1983. Office and/or bookroom; Internet and Postal. Appointment necessary. Open: **M:** 09:00–17:00; **T:** 09:00–17:00; **W:** 09:00–17:00; **Th:** 09:00–17:00; **F:** 09:00–17:00. Medium stock. Spec: Academic/Scholarly; Classical Studies; Medieval. PR: £1–100. CC: MC; V. Mem: BA. Notes: *Trade and scholarly remainders from general history, religion and reference to classical studies. Visit our wholesale website at www.sandpiper.co.uk or our mail order Postscript selling to individuals at www.psbooks.co.uk.*

Sims Reed Limited, ■ 43a Duke Street, London, SW1Y 6DD. Prop: John Sims. Tel: 020 7930 5566. Fax: 020 7925 0825. Web: www.simsreed.com. Est: 1978. Shop open: **M:** 10:00–18:00; **T:** 10:00–18:00; **W:** 10:00–18:00; **Th:** 10:00–18:00; **F:** 10:00–18:00. Spec: Antiquarian; Art; Artists; Illustrated - General; Prints and Maps. CC: AE; E; MC; V; Maestro. Cata: about a year. Mem: ILAB. VAT No: GB 242 9715 52. Notes: *Open at other times by appointment.*

tsbbooks, 214 Ferndale Road, London, SW9 8AG. Tel: (0207) 7330965. Est: 1989. Mail order only; Internet and Postal. Small stock. Spec: Adult; Author - Benson, E.F.; Author - Isherwood, Christopher; Author - Paul Bowles; Author - Williams, Tennessee; Comics; Erotica; Fiction - Gay Fiction. PR: £4–450.

Mary Wells, 24 Minehead Road, London, SW16 2AW. Prop: Mary Wells. Tel: (020) 8769-0778. Fax: (020) 8769-0778. Est: 1980. Private premises. Book fairs only. Small stock. Spec: Booksearch. PR: £1–500. Notes: *Attends Bloomsbury Fair, Royal National.*

Whistler's Books, 11 Ashbourne Terrace, Wimbledon, London, SW19 1QX. Prop: Ronald H. Ashworth. Tel: (020) 8540-7370. Est: 1993. Private premises. Appointment necessary. Small stock. Spec: Building & Construction; Chess; Company History; Electronics; Engineering; Industry; Mathematics; Music - Composers. PR: £5–50.

Worlds End Bookshop, ■357 Kings Road, London, SW3 5ES. Prop: Stephen Dickson. Tel: 020 7352 9376. Est: 1990. Shop open: **M:** 10:00–18:30; **T:** 10:00–18:30; **W:** 10:00–18:30; **Th:** 10:00–18:30; **F:** 10:00–18:30; **S:** 10:00–18:30; **Su:** 10:00–18:30. Spec: Antiquarian; Antiques; Architecture; Art; Avant-Garde; Beat Writers; Biography; Children's - Illustrated. CC: AE; JCB; MC; V; Switch. Notes: *20% discounts every Saturday, Sunday & Monday. 40% discounts every Bank Holiday.*

Wykeham Books, 64 Ridgway, Wimbledon, London, SW19 4RA. Prop: H.S.G. Mather. Tel: (020) 8879-3721. Web: www.bibliographies.co.uk. Est: 1976. Private premises. Internet and Postal. Medium stock. Spec: Author - Kipling, Rudyard; Bibliography; Book Arts; Bookbinding; Books about Books. PR: £5–15,000. Mem: PBFA.

LONDON
WEST POSTAL DISTRICTS

Rebecca Hardie Rare Books, 28 Pavilion Terrace Wood Lane, London, W12 0HT. Prop: Rebecca Hardie. Tel: 020 8749 3675. Fax: 020 8749 3675. Est: 2001. Private premises. Appointment necessary. Spec: Alternative Medicine; Anatomy; Astronomy; Dentistry; Feminism; Food & Drink; Gynaecology; Health. CC: MC. Cata: Medicine, Science. Mem: ABA; ILAB. VAT No: GB 782 7561 92. Notes: *All eras and languages covered. Women's and Children's Medicine, Public Health and Popular Medicine a particular speciality.*

Al Saqi Books, ■ 26 Westbourne Grove, London, W2 5RH. Prop: Arab Books Ltd. Tel: (020) 7229-8543. Fax: (020) 7229-7492. Est: 1978. Shop open: **M:** 10:00–18:00; **T:** 10:00–18:00; **W:** 10:00–18:00; **Th:** 10:00–18:00; **F:** 10:00–18:00; **S:** 10:00–18:00. Medium stock. Spec: Academic/Scholarly; Antiquarian; Arabica; Architecture; Art; Authors - Women; Canals/Inland Waterways; Cookery/Gastronomy. PR: £5–800. CC: AE; D; E; JCB; MC; V. Cata: Middle East. Corresp: French, Arabic. Mem: BA. VAT No: GB 242 6953 51. Notes: *Also, important stock of Arabic books, also new books.*

Altea Gallery, 35 Saint George St., London, W1S 2FN. Prop: Mr. Massimo De Martini. Tel: (020) 7491 0010. Fax: (020) 7491 0015. Web: www.alteagallery.com. Est: 1993. Shop and/or gallery; Shop open: **M:** 10:00–18:00; **T:** 10:00–18:00; **W:** 10:00–18:00; **Th:** 10:00–18:00; **F:** 10:00–18:00; **S:** 11:00–16:00. Medium stock. Spec: Antiquarian; Astronomy; Atlases; Cartography; Cities - City of London; Geography; Maps & Mapmaking; Maritime/Nautical. PR: £50–10,000. CC: AE; E; JCB; MC; V. Cata: Antiquarian Maps & Atlases. Corresp: Italian, Spanish. Mem: ABA; PBFA; ILAB; IMCoS. VAT No: GB 649 5809 86.

David Batterham, 36 Alexander Street, London, W2 5NU. Tel: (020) 7229-3845. Est: 1965. Private premises. Internet and Postal. Appointment necessary. Small stock. Spec: Advertising; Applied Art; Architecture; Art Deco; Art Nouveau; Arts, The; British Art & Design; Caricature. PR: £5–5,000. CC: V; Paypal. Cata: Applied Arts Trade Catalogues, Fashion. Corresp: French. Mem: PBFA. VAT No: GB 241 1361 10. Notes: *Subjects (continued from short space above) Caricature Magazines.*

Nicholas Bernstein, 2 Vaughan Avenue, London, W6 0XS. Prop: Nicholas Bernstein. Tel: (020) 874 17140. Est: 1986. Private premises. Appointment necessary. Medium stock. Spec: Antiquarian; Bibles; Bindings; Curiosities; Dictionaries; Economics; Fiction - General; History of Ideas. PR: £25–5,000. Corresp: French. Mem: PBFA. Notes: *Appointments: 7 days a week. Exhibits at monthly PBFA fairs at Holiday Inn Bloomsbury.*

J. & S.L. Bonham, Flat 14, 84 Westbourne Terrace, London, W2 6QE. Prop: John & Suzanne Bonham. Tel: (020) 7402-7064. Fax: (020) 7402-0955. Web: www.bonbooks.dial.pipex.com. Est: 1976. Private premises. Internet and Postal. Appointment necessary. Medium stock. Spec: Africana; Alpinism/Mountaineering; Arabica; Australiana; Author - Burton, Sir Richard F.; Countries - Africa; Countries - Antarctic, The; Countries - Arabia. PR: £10–2,000. CC: MC; V; SW, SO. Corresp: German. Mem: ABA; PBFA; ILAB. VAT No: GB 362 1962 53. Notes: *Valuations.*

The Book Business, 90 Greenford Avenue, London, W7 3QS. Prop: Giles Levete. Tel: (020) 8840-1185. Est: 1990. Private premises. Internet and Postal. Appointment necessary. Small stock. Spec: Academic/Scholarly; Antiquarian; Architecture; Arts, The; Autographs; Children's; Fiction - Crime, Detective, Spy, Thrillers; First Editions. PR: £10–2,000. Mem: PBFA.

Books & Things, P.O. Box 17768, London, W8 6ZD. Prop: M.M. Steenson. Tel: (020) 7370-5593. Fax: (020) 7370-5593. Web: www.booksandthings.co.uk. Est: 1972. Warehouse; Internet and Postal. Small stock. Spec: Advertising; Aesthetic Movement; Applied Art; Art - British; Art Nouveau; Art Reference; Arts & Crafts Era; Author - Beardsley, Aubrey. PR: £20–1,000. CC: JCB; MC; V. Mem: ABA; PBFA; ILAB. Notes: *Also a selection of original posters & prints.*

Don Kelly Books, Admiral Vernon L16-20 141-149 Portobello Rd, London, W11. Prop: Don Kelly. Tel: 020 7731 0482. Fax: 020 7731 0482. Est: 1978. Market stand/stall. Open: S: 07.30–15:30. Spec: Antiques; Antiquities; Art Deco; Art History; Art Nouveau; Art Reference; Arts, The; Carpets - General. CC: MC; V. Cata: Reference books for the Art & Antique trade. Mem: Also at: P.O.Box 44132 London SW6 2RP. VAT No: GB 563 2239 49. Notes: *I also exhibit at The Olympia Fine Art and Antique Fair three times a year. Although I am only open on Saturdays, a selection of my stock can be viewed by appointment, throughout the week.*

Marc-Antoine du Ry Medieval Art, 13 New Burlington Street, London, W1S 3BG. Prop: Marc du Ry. Tel: 0044 (0) 207 287 905. Fax: (cell) 0044 (0) 777 0888 116. Web: www.earlyart.net. Est: 1997. Office and/or bookroom; Telephone First. Spec: Bibles; Book of Hours; Illuminated Manuscripts; Medieval. PR: £100–100,000. Corresp: French, Italian. VAT No: GB 735 7640 16. Notes: *Also contactable in Belgium on 0032 (0) 475 866073.*

Elton Engineering Books, 32 Fairfax Road, London, W4 1EW. Prop: Julia Elton. Tel: (0208) 747 0967. Est: 1985. Private premises. Internet and Postal. Appointment necessary. Small stock. Spec: Architecture; Building & Construction; Electricity & Gas; Engineering; Engineering - Electrical; Industry; Inventors & Inventions; Maritime/Nautical. PR: £30–8,000. CC: MC; V. Corresp: French, German. Mem: ABA; ILAB. VAT No: GB 429 7966 90.

Simon Finch Rare Books Ltd., ■ 53 Maddox Street, London, W1S 2PN. Tel: (020) 7499-0974. Fax: (020) 7499-0799. Web: www.simonfinch.com. Est: 1981. Shop open: M: 11:00–18:00; T: 11:00–18:00; W: 11:00–18:00; Th: 11:00–18:00; F: 11:00–18:00. Spec: Antiquarian; Art; Autographs; Bindings; Design; Early Imprints; Literature; Manuscripts. PR: £1–500,000. CC: AE; MC; V; SW.

Fine Books Oriental, 94 Addison Gardens, London W14. Prop: Geoffrey Somers. Tel: (0207) 603-9797. Very small stock. Spec: Countries - China; Countries - Iceland; Countries - Japan; Countries - Korea. Corresp: Japanese.

First State Books, 35 Talbot Road, London, W2 5JG. Prop: Euan Stuart. Tel: (020) 7792-2672. Fax: (020) 7792-2672. Web: www.firststatebooks.com. Est: 2001. Private premises. Internet and Postal. Spec: Children's; Fiction - General; First Editions; Modern First Editions. PR: £15–100. CC: AE; D; E; JCB; MC; V; Maestro, Solo.

Sam Fogg Ltd, ■ 15d Clifford Street, London, W1S 4JZ. Tel: (020) 7534-2100. Fax: (020) 7534-2122. Web: www.samfogg.com. Est: 1978. Shop. Appointment necessary. Open: M: 09:30–17:30; T: 09:30–17:30; W: 09:30–17:30; Th: 09:30–17:30; F: 09:30–17:30. Small stock. Spec: Manuscripts. CC: MC; V. Corresp: French, German,. Mem: ABA. VAT No: GB 467 6893 80.

Richard Ford, 70 Chaucer Road, London, W3 6DP. Tel: (020) 8993-1235. Fax: (020) 8752-1431. Est: 1982. Private premises. Internet and Postal. Appointment necessary. Small stock. Spec: Autographs; Bibliography; Bibliophily; Book Arts; Books about Books; Documents - General; Manuscripts; Publishers - General. PR: £10–1,000. Cata: Bookselling & Publishing. Corresp: French, Italian. Mem: ABA; ILAB. Notes: *Printed ephemera, manuscripts, autograph letters. Any subject.*

Fosters Bookshop, ■ 183 Chiswick High Road, London, W4 2DR. Prop: Stephen Foster. Tel: (020) 8995-2768. Web: www.fostersbookshop.co.uk. Est: 1968. Shop. Open: T: 10:30–17:00; W: 10:30–17:00; Th: 10:30–17:00; F: 10:30–17:00; S: 10:30–17:00. Medium stock. Spec: Antiquarian; Applied Art; Architecture; Art; Bindings; Children's; Children's - Illustrated; Cities - City of London. PR: £2–1,000. CC: AE; MC; V; Switch / Maestro. Mem: ABA; PBFA; ILAB; ibooknet. Notes: *Family run bookshop, now with the 2nd generation. See also Stephen Foster, London NW (q.v.).*

Fuller D'Arch Smith, 37b New Cavendish Street, London, W1G 8JR. Prop: Jean Overton Fuller & Timothy D'Arch Smith. Tel: (020) 7722-0063. Fax: (020) 7722-0063. Est: 1969. Private premises. Postal only. Appointment necessary. Small stock. PR: £5–500. Corresp: French, German, Italian, Russian.

Golfiana, ■ Grays Antique Centre B12. South Davis Mews, off Brook Street, Mayfair, London W.l, W1. Prop: Sarah Fabian-Baddiel. Tel: 0207 408 1239 or 0208 437 3487. Est: 1977. Shop open: M: 09:00–17:30; T: 09:00–17:30; W: 09:00–17:30; Th: 09:00–17:30; F: 09:00–17:30; S: 09:00–17:30; Su: 09:00–17:30; Closed for lunch: 13:00–14:00. Spec: Sport - Golf. CC: MC; V. Cata: Golfiana. Tin and Dinky toys. Notes: *Please telephone first if you would like to see me personally.*

Hab Books, 35 Wellington Road Ealing, London, W5 4UJ. Prop: T. Habraszewski. Tel: (020) 8932-5058. Fax: (020) 8932-5058. Est: 1981. Private premises. Postal only. Spec: Annuals; Autobiography; Biography; Communism; Countries - East Europe; Countries - Russia; Fiction - General; Folio Society, The. Notes: *Stock includes books in Polish.*

Adrian Harrington, 64a Kensington Church Street Kensington, London, W8 4DB. Tel: (020) 7937-1465. Fax: (020) 7368-0912. Web: www.harringtonbooks.co.uk. Est: 1971. Spec: Aesthetic Movement; Antiquarian; Art; Author - General; Author - Aickman, R.; Author - Churchill, Sir Winston; Author - Conan Doyle, Sir Arthur; Author - Cornwell, Bernard. PR: £10–50,000. CC: AE; MC; V. Mem: ABA; PBFA; ILAB. Notes: *Also, bookbinding, library sets, decorative bindings.*

G. Heywood Hill Limited, ■ 10 Curzon Street, London, W1J 5HH. Tel: (020) 7629-0647. Fax: (020) 7408-0286. Web: www.heywoodhill.com. Est: 1936. Shop open: **M:** 09:00–17:30; **T:** 09:00–17:30; **W:** 09:00–17:30; **Th:** 09:00–17:30; **F:** 09:00–17:30; **S:** 09:00–12:30. Medium stock. Spec: Architecture; Children's; History - General; Illustrated - General; Literature; Natural History; Booksearch. PR: £5–10,000. CC: MC; V; Switch. Corresp: French, German, Spanish, Italian. Mem: ABA; BA. VAT No: GB 239 4090 56. Notes: *Also, new books & a booksearch service.*

P.J. Hilton (Books), ■ 12 Cecil Court Charing Cross Road, London, WC2N 4HE. Prop: Paul John Hilton. Tel: (020) 7379-9825. Est: 1988. Shop. Open: **M:** 11:00–1730; **T:** 11:00–1730; **W:** 11:00–1730; **Th:** 11:00–1730; **F:** 11:00–1730; **S:** 11:00–1730. Spec: Antiquarian; Bibles; Bibliophily; Biography; Fiction - General; Prayer Books; Religion - Catholic; Religion - Christian. PR: £1–1,000. CC: MC; V. Cata: Antiquarian, Literature, Religion. Notes: *We are always pleased to deal with enquiries by telephone or email and to make a note of your interests if we may be able to help. We can also provide larger quantities of books if required.*

Judith Hodgson, 11 Stanwick Road, London, W14 8TL. Tel: (020) 7603-7414. Fax: (020) 7602-1431. Est: 1986. Private premises. Internet and Postal. Appointment necessary. Small stock. Spec: Antiquarian; Braziliana; Countries - Americas, The; Countries - Argentina; Countries - Azores, The; Countries - Bolivia; Countries - Brazil; Countries - Cuba. Cata: Spain, Portugal, Latin America. Corresp: French, Spanish, Portuguese. Mem: ABA; ILAB. VAT No: GB 446 0649 44.

James Fergusson Books & Manuscripts, 39 Melrose Gardens, London, W6 7RN. Tel: 020 7602 3536. Fax: 020 7602 0502. Est: 1986. Private premises. Postal only. Appointment necessary. Spec: Letters; Manuscripts. Notes: *Also, 19th & 20th Century literary association copies, autographs and photographs.*

Kay Books, Roger's Arcade, 65 Portobello Road, London, W11 2QB. Prop: Peter Degnan. Tel: (020) 8640-7779. Fax: (Mobile) 07940 833870. Est: 1968. Storeroom; Telephone First. Spec: Antiquarian; Bindings; Topography - General; Travel - General.

Robert J. Kirkpatrick, 6 Osterley Park View Road, Hanwell, W7 2HH. Tel: (020) 8567-4521. Est: 1986. Private premises. Postal only. Appointment necessary. Very small stock. Spec: Children's; Education & School; Juvenile; Memoirs; Public Schools; Schools - General. PR: £1–100. Cata: Boys school fiction, school memoirs & histories.

Maggs Brothers Limited, ■ 50 Berkeley Square, London, W1J 5BA. Tel: (020) 7493-7160. Fax: (020) 7499-2007. Web: www.maggs.com. Est: 1853. Shop open: **M:** 09:30–17:00; **T:** 09:30–17:00; **W:** 09:30–17:00; **Th:** 09:30–17:00; **F:** 09:30–17:00. Very large stock. Spec: Autographs; Bibliography; Bindings; Cookery/Gastronomy; Early Imprints; Fine Printing; Geology; Illuminated Manuscripts. PR: £5–5,000,000. CC: MC; V. Corresp: Japanese, Mandarin, German, French, Italian, Spanish. Mem: ABA; PBFA; BA; ILAB; BADA.

Marlborough Rare Books Ltd, ■ 144/146 New Bond Street, London, W1S 2TR. Prop: Jonathan Gestetner. Tel: (020) 7493-6993. Fax: (020) 7499-2479. Est: 1948. Shop open: **M:** 09:30–17:30; **T:** 09:30–17:30; **W:** 09:30–17:30; **Th:** 09:30–17:30; **F:** 09:30–17:30. Medium stock. Spec: Architecture; Bibliography; Bindings; Cities - City of London; Cities - General; Colour-Plate; Country Houses; Fine Art. PR: £50–50,000. CC: E; MC; V. Cata: Art, Architecture, London, Travel, Topography. Corresp: French, German. Mem: ABA; ILAB. VAT No: GB 341 2642 86.

Mayfly Ephemera, 38 Rusthall Avenue, London, W4 1BP. Prop: C Martin. Tel: 020 8994 2258. Est: 1981. Private premises. Internet and Postal. Open: **M:** 09:00–17:30; **T:** 09:00–17:30; **W:** 09:00–17:30; **Th:** 09:00–17:30; **F:** 09:00–17:30; **S:** 09:00–17:30; **Su:** 09:00–17:30; Closed for lunch: 13:00–14:00. Spec: Documents - General; Ephemera. CC: MC; V. Cata: Ephemera, Documents. Ms , Archives. Corresp: French. Mem: PBFA; Ephemera Society. Notes: *we buy and sell a wide range of printed and manuscript ephemera documents and archives. We like the unusual.*

Melvin Tenner, 51 Gayford Road, London, W12 9BY. Prop: Melvin Tenner. Tel: 020 8740 6677. Fax: 010 8740 6960. Est: 1980. Private premises. Appointment necessary. Spec: International Affairs; Booksearch. Notes: *Also, a booksearch service.*

Orbis Books (London) Ltd., ■ 206 Blythe Road, London, W14 0HH. Prop: Dir: Mr. Jerzy Kulczycki & Dr. Aleksandra Kulczycka. Tel: 020 7602 5541. Fax: (020) 8742-7686. Est: 1944. Spec: Countries - East Europe; Countries - Poland; Countries - Russia; Foreign Texts; Booksearch. PR: £2–20,000. Notes: *Also, new books, booksearch, large print books, CDs & cassettes of Polish music.*

Diana Parikian, Rare Books, 3 Caithness Road, London, W14 0JB. Tel: (020) 7603-8375. Fax: (020) 7602-1178. Web: www.bibliopoly.com/parikian. Est: 1960. Private premises. Appointment necessary. Spec: Emblemata; Fine & Rare; Foreign Texts; Iconography. PR: £200–10,000. Corresp: French, Italian. Mem: ABA; ILAB. VAT No: GB 194 5853 21.

Pickering & Chatto, ■ 144-146 New Bond Street, London, W1S 2TW. Tel: (020) 7491-2656. Fax: (020) 7499-2479. Web: www.pickering-chatto.com. Est: 1820. Shop open: **M:** 09:30–17:30; **T:** 09:30–17:30; **W:** 09:30–17:30; **Th:** 09:30–17:30; **F:** 09:30–17:30. Small stock. Spec: Chemistry; Early Imprints; Economics; Education & School; Health; Humanities; Incunabula; Literature. PR: £100–10,000. CC: AE; MC; V. Corresp: French. Mem: ABA; PBFA; ILAB. VAT No: GB 896 1174 90.

William Poole, 97 New Bond Street, London, W1S 1SL. Tel: (020) 7629-8738. Est: 1979. Private premises. Appointment necessary. Small stock. Spec: Academic/Scholarly; Classical Studies; Fine & Rare; Foreign Texts; Humanism; Publishers - General. Notes: *Also books by Foulis Press.*

Portobello Books, ■ 328 Portobello Road, London, W10 5RU. Prop: Lawrence Thompson. Tel: 020 8964 3166. Fax: 020 8964 3166. Web: www.portobello-books.com. Est: 1985. Shop open: **T:** 11:00–17:00; **W:** 11:00–17:00; **Th:** 11:00–17:00; **F:** 11:00–17:00; **S:** 09:00–17:00. Spec: Anthropology; Architecture; Art - Technique; Art History; Astronomy; Biography; Children's - Illustrated; Cinema/Film. CC: AE; D; E; JCB; MC; V. Cata: Various. Notes: *We are a second hand book shop, specialising in out of print books. Not open on Mondays or Sundays.*

Quadrille at Delehar, ■ 146 Portobello Road, London, W11 2DZ. Prop: Valerie Jackson–Harris. Tel: (01923) 829079. Fax: (01923) 825207. Est: 1965. Shop. Open: **S:** 09:00–16:00. Medium stock. Spec: Antiques; Dance; Performing Arts; Royalty - General; Ephemera. PR: £5–5,000. CC: AE; MC; V. Mem: ABA; PBFA; ES. Notes: *Also, Valentines, Christmas cards.*

Bernard Quaritch Ltd., ■ 50 South Audley Street, London, W1K 2PR. Prop: John Koh. Tel: (020) 7297-4888. Fax: (020) 7297-4866. Web: www.quaritch.com. Est: 1847. Shop open: **M:** 09:00–18:00; **T:** 09:00–18:00; **W:** 09:00–18:00; **Th:** 09:00–18:00; **F:** 09:00–18:00. Large stock. Spec: Accountancy; Africana; Agriculture; Alchemy; Alpinism/Mountaineering; Americana - General; Anatomy; Antiquarian. PR: £100–500,000. CC: AE; MC; V; SW. Cata: rare books and manuscripts in most fields. Corresp: French, German, Italian, Spanish, Russian, Arabic. Mem: ABA; PBFA; ILAB; SLAM, VDA, BADA. VAT No: GB 840 1358 54. Notes: *We also offer Valuations and representation at auction.*

Leslie Robert, t/a Hyde Park Books, 74 Devonport, 23 Southwick Street, London, W2 2QH. Tel: (020) 7402-9567. Est: 1978. Private premises. Internet and Postal. Appointment necessary. Spec: Fiction - General; Fiction - Crime, Detective, Spy, Thrillers; Fiction - Historical; Fiction - Young Adult Mystery & Adventure Series; First Editions; Modern First Editions; Sexology; Signed Editions. PR: £20–500. CC: Cheques in sterling. Cata: Modern First Editions both literary and many crim. Notes: *We specialise in modern first editions of which many are signed by the author. We are situated near to Paddington station so it is easy to call in by appointment only. Most of our books are in fine condition.*

Saint Swithin's Illustrated & Children's Books, 87 Portobello Road London, London, W11 2QB. Prop: Mrs. Margaret Davies. Tel: (020) 8573-8556. Shop and/or showroom; Appointment necessary. Spec: Advertising; Artists; Cats; Children's; Children's - Illustrated; Christmas; Circus; Decorative Art. Notes: *None of the stock is shown on the Internet.*

A.F. Sephton, 16 Bloemfontein Avenue Shepherds Bush, London, W12 7BL. Prop: A.F. Sephton. Tel: (020) 8749-1454. Est: 1966. Private premises. Appointment necessary. Small stock. Spec: Artists; Colour-Plate; Illustrated - General; Social History; Prints and Maps. PR: £10–100. Notes: *Work by W Hogart included.*

Bernard J. Shapero Rare Books, ■ 32 St. George Street, London, W1S 2EA. Tel: (020) 7493-0876. Fax: (020) 7495-5010. Web: www.shapero.com. Est: 1979. Internet and Postal. Shop open: **M:** 09:30–18:30; **T:** 09:30–18:30; **W:** 09:30–18:30; **Th:** 09:30–18:30; **F:** 09:30–18:30; **S:** 11:00–17:00. Large stock. Spec: Atlases; Author - Baedeker, Karl Travel - Antiquarian; Cartography; Colour-Plate; Guide Books; Maps & Mapmaking; Modern First Editions; Travel - General. PR: £50–100,000. CC: AE; E; MC; V. Cata: Travel, colour-plate, cartography, baedekers,. Corresp: French, German. Mem: ABA; PBFA; ILAB; BADA; IMCOS; VDA. VAT No: GB 466 5294 16. Notes: *catalogues continued: photography, modern literature.*

Henry Sotheran Limited, ■2–5 Sackville Street Piccadilly, London, W1S 3DP. Tel: (020) 7439-6151. Fax: (020) 7434-2019. Web: www.sotherans.co.uk. Est: 1761. Shop open: **M:** 09:30–18:00; **T:** 09:30–18:00; **W:** 09:30–18:00; **Th:** 09:30–18:00; **F:** 09:30–18:00; **S:** 10:00–16:00. Very large stock. Spec: Architecture; Art; Bindings; Children's; Churchilliana; Illustrated - General; Literature; Natural History. PR: £20–100,000. CC: AE; D; MC; V. Mem: ABA; PBFA; ILAB. VAT No: GB 689 7172.

Sue Lowell Natural History Books, 101 Cambridge Gardens, London, W10 6JE. Prop: Sue Lowell. Tel: (020) 8960-4382. Web: www.abebooks.com. Est: 1972. Private premises. Internet and Postal. Appointment necessary. Open: **M:** 10:00–17:00; **T:** 10:00–17:00; **W:** 10:00–17:00; **Th:** 10:00–17:00; **F:** 10:00–18:00; **S:** 10:00–13.00; **Su:** 10:00–12:00. Medium stock. Spec: Academic/Scholarly; Animals and Birds; Art Reference; Artists; Bibliography; Bookbinding; Botany; Egyptology. PR: £10–4,000. CC: MC; V. Corresp: French. Notes: *Callers are asked to telephone first just to make sure we are available. Also, booksearch.*

The Travel Bookshop, 13-15 Blenheim Crescent Notting Hill, London, W11 2EE. Prop: Sarah Anderson. Tel: (020) 7229-5260. Fax: (020) 7243-1552. Web: www.thetravelbookshop.co.uk. Est: 1979. Shop open: Open: **M:** 10:00–18:00; **T:** 10:00–18:00; **W:** 10:00–18:00; **Th:** 10:00–18:00; **F:** 10:00–18:00; **S:** 10:00–18.00; **Su:** 12:00–17:00. Spec: New Books; Travel - General. PR: £1–200. Notes: *Also, new books on travel.*

Valentine Rare Books, 20 Fitzroy Square, London, W1T 6EJ. Prop: Gaston Chappell. Tel: 020 7387 5454. Est: 1983. Office and/or bookroom; Appointment necessary. Spec: Author - Austen, Jane; Author - Dickens, Charles; Author - Hardy, Thomas; Author - James, Henry; Authors - British; Fiction - 18th Century; Fine & Rare; Literature. PR: £20–10,000. Cata: Fiction (mostly 19th Century). Mem: ABA; ILAB. VAT No: GB 504 6399 43.

C.R. White, 22 Denbigh Terrace, London, W11 2QJ. Tel: (020) 7727 8381. Fax: (020) 7598-1248. Est: 1989. Private premises. Postal only. Small stock. Spec: Africana; Author - Baden-Powell, Lord Robert; Author - Churchill, Sir Winston; Author - Dinesen, Isak; Churchilliana; Colonial; Countries - East Africa; Countries - Kenya. Notes: *Travel stock is mainly East and Central Africa. Small stock of Polar exploration.*

Mrs. Teresa White, Flat 4, 79 St. Helen's Gardens, London, W10 6LJ. Prop: Mrs. Teresa White. Private premises. Postal only. Small stock. Spec: Ephemera. PR: £1–100. Notes: *General non-fiction.*

LONDON
WEST CENTRAL POSTAL DISTRICTS

Any Amount of Books, ■ 56 Charing Cross Road, London, WC2H 0QA. Prop: Nigel Burwood. Tel: (020) 7836-3697. Fax: (020) 7240-1769. Web: www.anyamountofbooks.com. Est: 1975. Shop open: **M:** 10:30–21:30; **T:** 10:30–21:30; **W:** 10:30–21:30; **Th:** 10:30–21:30; **F:** 10:30–21:30; **S:** 10:30–21:30; **Su:** 11:30–20:30. Spec: Academic/Scholarly; Antiquarian; Art Reference; General Stock; Collectables; Ephemera. PR: £1–25,000. CC: AE; JCB; MC; PayPal. Cata: Literature. Mem: ABA; PBFA; ILAB. VAT No: GB 662 6656 11. Notes: *Also, books by the yard, i.e. for furnishing, film sets etc. & we offer valuations/appraisals for probate, insurance etc.,*

The Atlantis Bookshop, ■ 49a Museum Street, London, WC1A 1LY. Prop: Bali Beskin & Geraldine Beskin. Tel: (020) 7405-2120. Web: www.theatlantisbookshop.com. Est: 1922. Shop open: **M:** 10:30–18:00; **T:** 10:30–18:00; **W:** 10:30–18:00; **Th:** 10:30–18:00; **F:** 10:30–18:00; **S:** 10:30–18:00. Small stock. Spec: Alchemy; Archaeology; Author - Crowley, Aleister; Author - Spare, Austin Osman; Celtica; Countries - Egypt; Cryptozoology; Earth Mysteries. PR: £4–40. CC: AE; E; MC; V; SW. Notes: *Crowley, Spare, Grant, Alchemy, Qabalah, Witchcraft, Druidism, Mystery History, all the Esoteric Sciences new and secondhand. Please send your wants lists or phone.*

Baconboooks, ■ 197 Kings Cross Road, London, WC1X 9DB. Prop: Josephine Bacon. Tel: 020 7278 9490. Fax: 020 7278 2447. Web: www.baconbooks.co.uk. Est: 2007. Shop. Open: **M:** 11:00–15:00; **T:** 11:00–15:00; **W:** 11:00–15:00; **Th:** 11:00–15:00; **F:** 11:00–15:00; **S:** 11:00–15:00. Spec: Antiques; Artists; Biography; Children's; Comedy; Cookery - Professional; Cookery/Gastronomy; Counties in England. CC: Paypal. Corresp: any language (we also run a translation agency). VAT No: GB –. Notes: *We also deal over the internet and by post. We are currently making arrangements to take credit cards.*

Bertram Rota Ltd., ■31 Long Acre, Covent Garden, London, WC2E 9LT. Tel: (020) 7836 0723. Fax: (020) 7497 9058. Web: www.bertramrota.co.uk. Est: 1923. Shop. Contactable. Open: **M:** 09:30–17:30; **T:** 09:30–17:30; **W:** 09:30–17:30; **Th:** 09:30–17:30; **F:** 09:30–17:30. Medium stock. Spec: Antiquarian; Autographs; Book Arts; First Editions; Literature; Manuscripts; Modern First Editions; Private Press. CC: E; JCB; MC; V. Mem: ABA; ILAB. VAT No: GB 239 6020 67. Notes: *Also, a booksearch service, valuations.*

Steve Burak, ■18 Leigh Street, off Judd Street, London, WC1H 9EW. Prop: Steve Burak. Tel: (020) 7388-1153. Est: 2002. Telephone First. Shop open: **M:** 11:00–19:00; **T:** 11:00–19:00; **W:** 11:00–19:00; **Th:** 11:00–19:00; **F:** 11:00–19:00; **S:** 11:00–19:00. Large stock. Spec: Academic/Scholarly; Antiquarian; Ephemera; Prints and Maps. PR: £5–1,000. Corresp: French. Notes: *Also, ephemera artwork and various eclectica.*

Collinge & Clark, ■The Bookshop, 13 Leigh Street, London, WC1H 9EW. Prop: Oliver Clark. Tel: 0207 387 7105. Fax: 0207 388 1315. Est: 1987. Shop open: **M:** 11:00–18:30; **T:** 11:00–18:30; **W:** 11:00–18:30; **Th:** 11:00–18:30; **F:** 11:00–18:30. Spec: Author - Gill, Eric; Author - Morris, William; Book Arts; Books about Books; Calligraphy; Engraving; Fine Printing; Limited Editions - General. CC: AE; MC; V. Cata: Private Press & Typography. Corresp: Francais, Deutsch. Mem: PBFA. VAT No: GB 523 1738 64.

Delectus Books, 27 Old Gloucester Street, London, WC1N 3XX. Prop: Michael R. Goss. Tel: (020) 8963-0979. Fax: (020) 8963-0502. Web: www.delectusbooks.co.uk. Est: 1987. Private premises. Internet and Postal. Very large stock. Spec: Academic/Scholarly; Adult; Aesthetic Movement; Africana; Alcoholics Anonymous; Animals and Birds; Anthropology; Antiques. PR: £20–5,000. CC: E; JCB; MC; V; Switch, Solo, Delta, Maestro. Corresp: French, German, Spanish, Dutch. VAT No: GB 532 3080 82. Notes: *Amex, Discover and Diners can also be accepted but only via our website.*

David Drummond at Pleasures of Past Times, 11 Cecil Court, Charing Cross Road, London, WC2N 4EZ. Prop: David Drummond. Tel: (020) 7836-1142. Fax: (020) 7836-1142. Est: 1967. Open: **M:** 11:00–17:45; **S:** 11:00–14:30; Closed for lunch: 02:30–15:30. Spec: Children's; Circus; Illustrated - General; Magic & Conjuring; Performing Arts. PR: £10–500. Notes: *Also, juvenile illustrated.*

Francis Edwards (London), ■13 Great Newport Street Charing Cross Road, London, WC2H 7JA. Tel: (020) 7240 7279. Fax: (020) 7836-5977. Web: www.francisedwards.co.uk. Est: 1983. Shop open: **M:** 10:00–19:00; **T:** 10:00–19:00; **W:** 10:00–19:00; **Th:** 10:00–19:00; **F:** 10:00–19:00; **S:** 10:00–19:00; **Su:** 12:00–19:00. Small stock. Spec: Architecture; Art; Aviation; Bindings; Economics; Folklore; History - General; Law - General. PR: £15–5,000. CC: AE; D; E; JCB; MC; V. Corresp: Dutch German French. Mem: ABA; PBFA; ILAB. VAT No: GB 594 2720 23.

Peter Ellis, Bookseller, ■ 18 Cecil Court, London, WC2N 4HE. Tel: (020) 7836 8880. Web: www.peter-ellis.co.uk. Est: 1999. Shop open: **M:** 10:30–19:00; **T:** 10:30–19:00; **W:** 10:30–19:00; **Th:** 10:30–19:00; **F:** 10:30–19:00; **S:** 10:30–17:30. Medium stock. Spec: Academic/Scholarly; Art; Art History; Artists; Arts, The; Author - Betjeman, Sir John; Author - Brooke, Rupert; Author - Buchan, John. PR: £10–1,000. CC: AE; MC; V. Cata: Modern Firsts, Illustrated, Literature. Corresp: French, German. Mem: ABA; ILAB. VAT No: GB 751 8751 12.

Gay's The Word, ■ 66 Marchmont Street, London, WC1N 1AB. Prop: Noncyp Ltd. Tel: (020) 7278-7654. Web: www.gaystheword.co.uk. Est: 1979. Shop open: **M:** 10:00–18:30; **T:** 10:00–18:30; **W:** 10:00–18:30; **Th:** 10:00–18:30; **F:** 10:00–18:30; **S:** 10:00–18:30; **Su:** 14:00–18:00. Spec: Homosexuality & Lesbianism; New Books. PR: £1–60. CC: AE; D; E; JCB; MC; V; Switch. Notes: *Also, new books.*

Gekoski Booksellers, ■Pied Bull Yard 15a Bloomsbury Square, London, WC1A 2LP. Prop: R.A. Gekoski & P.A. Grogan. Tel: (020) 7404-6676. Fax: (020) 7404-6595. Web: www.gekoski.com. Est: 1982. Shop open: **M:** 10:00–17:30; **T:** 10:00–17:30; **W:** 10:00–17:30; **Th:** 10:00–17:30; **F:** 10:00–17:30. Small stock. Spec: First Editions; Letters; Manuscripts. PR: £100–1,000. CC: MC; V. Mem: ABA. VAT No: GB 418 5464 40.

Grosvenor Prints, 19 Shelton Street, London, WC2H 9JN. Prop: Nigel C. Talbot. Tel: 020 7836 1979. Fax: 020 7379 6695. Web: www.grosvenorprints.com. Est: 1976. Shop and/or gallery open: **M:** 10:00–18:00; **T:** 10:00–18:00; **W:** 10:00–18:00; **Th:** 10:00–18:00; **F:** 10:00–18:00; **S:** 11:00–16:00. Very large stock. Spec: Animals and Birds; Art Reference; Fine Art; Painting; Printing. PR: £5-10,000. CC: AE; MC; V. Cata: quarterly on antiquarian books and prints. Mem: ABA; BA. VAT No: GB 217 6907 49. Notes: *London's largest selection of anitquarian prints.*

Jarndyce Antiquarian Booksellers, 46 Great Russell Street (opp. British Museum), London, WC1B 3PA. Prop: Brian Lake & Janet Nassau. Tel: (020) 7631-4220. Fax: (020) 7631-1882. Web: www.jarndyce.co.uk. Est: 1969. Shop and/or showroom; Internet and Postal. Shop open: **M:** 10:30–17:30; **T:** 10:30–17:30; **W:** 10:30–17:30; **Th:** 10:30–17:30; **F:** 10:30–17:30. Large stock. Spec: Antiquarian; Author - Arnold, Matthew; Author - Austen, Jane; Author - Byron, Lord; Author - Coleridge, Samuel T.; Author - Dickens, Charles; Author - Eliot, G.; Author - Gissing, George. PR: £5–5,000. CC: MC; V. Cata: 18thC & 19thC English Literature & Social History. Corresp: French. Mem: ABA; PBFA; ILAB. VAT No: GB 524 0890 57. Notes: *Valuations and book search within our specialist areas.*

Judd Books, ■ 82 Marchmont Street, London, WC1N 1AG. Prop: Nigel Kemp & A. Donaldson. Tel: (020) 7387-5333. Web: www.juddbooks.com. Est: 1995. Shop open: **M:** 11:00–19:00; **T:** 11:00–19:00; **W:** 11:00–19:00; **Th:** 11:00–19:00; **F:** 11:00–19:00; **S:** 11:00–19:00; **Su:** 12:00–18:00. Large stock. Spec: Architecture; Art; Cinema/Film; Drama; Feminism; History - General; Homosexuality & Lesbianism; Interior Design. PR: £1–100. CC: AE; E; MC; V. Corresp: French, Spanish.

The Maghreb Bookshop, ■ 45 Burton Street, London, WC1H 9AL. Prop: Mohamed Ben Madani. Tel: (020) 7388-1840. Fax: (020) 7388-1840. Web: www.maghrebboshop.com. Est: 1981. Appointment necessary. Shop open: **M:** 09:00–18:00; **T:** 09:00–18:00; **W:** 08:00–18:00; **Th:** 09:00–18:00; **F:** 09:00–18:00; **S:** 09:00–18:00. Spec: Academic/Scholarly; Anthropology; Archaeology; Architecture; Authors - Women; Colonial; Countries - Middle East, The; Countries - North Africa. CC: AE; D; MC; V. Cata: Maghreb, Middle East, Africa and Islam. Corresp: Arabic, French. VAT No: GB 735 8794 81. Notes: *Please note: We do not accept credit cards in the shop. However, we do accept credit cards on line.*

Marchpane, ■ 16 Cecil Court, Charing Cross Road, London, WC2N 4HE. Prop: Kenneth R. Fuller. Tel: (020) 7836-8661. Fax: (020) 7497-0567. Web: www.marchpane.com. Est: 1989. Shop open: **M:** 11:00–18:00; **T:** 11:00–18:00; **W:** 11:00–18:00; **Th:** 11:00–18:00; **F:** 11:00–18:00; **S:** 11:00–18:00. Spec: Author - Carroll, Lewis; Children's; Illustrated - General; Punk Fanzines; War - WWII Home Front UK (1939-45). PR: £1–2,000. CC: AE; E; JCB; MC; V; Debit. Mem: ABA; PBFA; ILAB.

Photo Books International, ■ 99 Judd Street, London, WC1H 9NE. Prop: Bill Herbert & Jasper Howard. Tel: (020) 7813-7363. Web: www.pbi-books.com. Est: 1998. Shop open: **W:** 11:00–18:00; **Th:** 11:00–18:00; **F:** 11:00–18:00; **S:** 11:00–18:00. Medium stock. Spec: Fashion & Costume; Photography. PR: £5–200. CC: AE; MC; V. Mem: PBFA; BA. Notes: *With more than 5,000 different photography books in stock at any time we are able to offer a wide selection of new & used books from around the world.*

Henry Pordes Books Ltd., ■ 58-60 Charing Cross Road, London, WC2H 0BB. Prop: Gino Della-Ragione. Tel: (020) 7836 9031. Fax: (020) 7240 4232. Web: www.henrypordesbooks.com. Est: 1980. Shop open: **M:** 10:00–19:00; **T:** 10:00–19:00; **W:** 10:00–19:00; **Th:** 10:00–19:00; **F:** 10:00–19:00; **S:** 10:00–19:00; **Su:** 13:00–18:00. Spec: Academic/Scholarly; Advertising; Aeronautics; Africana; Antiques; Archaeology; Architecture; Art. PR: £1–2,000. CC: AE; MC; V. Mem: PBFA.

Arthur Probsthain, ■ 41 Great Russell Street, London, WC1B 3PE. Prop: Arthur Probsthain. Tel: (020) 7636-1096. Fax: (020) 7636-1096. Web: www.oriental-african-books.com. Est: 1902. Shop open: **M:** 09:30–17:30; **T:** 09:30–17:30; **W:** 09:30–17:30; **Th:** 09:30–17:30; **F:** 09:30–17:30; **S:** 12:00–16:00. Spec: Countries - Africa; Oriental. CC: AE; D; E; JCB; MC; V. Cata: on specialised subjects. Notes: *Collection of music and artworks from around the world.*

Quinto of Charing Cross Road, ■ 48a Charing Cross Road, London, WC2H 0BB. Prop: Hay Cinema Bookshop Ltd. Tel: (0207) 379 7669. Fax: (0207) 836-5977. Web: www.haycinemabookshop.co.uk. Est: 1905. Shop open: **M:** 09:00–21:00; **T:** 09:00–21:00; **W:** 09:00–21:00; **Th:** 09:00–21:00; **F:** 09:00–21:00; **S:** 09:00–21:00; **Su:** 12:00–20:00. Very large stock. Spec: Art; Fiction - General; History - General; Literature; Medicine; Military History; Music - General; Philosophy. PR: £1–100. CC: AE; D; E; JCB; MC; V. Corresp: Spanish. VAT No: GB 594 2720 23.

Omega Bookshop, 31 Long Acre, London, WC2E 9LA. Prop: Angus O'Neill. Tel: (020) 7836-3336. Web: www.omegabookshop.com. Est: 1984. Mail order only; Internet and Postal. Appointment necessary. Spec: Antiques; Applied Art; Architecture; Art; Illustrated - General; Literature; Modern First Editions. CC: E; MC; V. Mem: ABA; ILAB. Notes: *Valuations, consultancy, logistics.*

Skoob Books, ■66 The Brunswick Off Marchmont Street, London, WC1N 1AE. Prop: Chris Edwards. Tel: 020 7278 8760. Web: www.skoob.com. Est: 1979. Shop open: **M:** 10:00–20:00; **T:** 10:00–20:00; **W:** 10:00–20:00; **Th:** 10:00–20:00; **F:** 10:00–20:00; **S:** 10:00–20:00; **Su:** 11:00–18:00. CC: AE; E; MC; V. VAT No: GB 824 8827 00. Notes: *Newly re-opened in extensive book basement in Bloomsbury. Lift access, air-conditioned, excellent staff. Over 60,000 titles in stock plus and additional similar number in our warehouse on one day delivery.*

Spink, Southampton Row, London, WC1B 4ET. Prop: Olivier Stocker. Tel: 020 7563 4000. Fax: 020 7563 4066. Web: www.spink.com. Est: 1666. Shop and/or gallery; Shop open: **M:** 09:00–17:30; **T:** 09:00–17:30; **W:** 09:00–17:30; **Th:** 09:00–17:30; **F:** 09:00–17:30. Spec: Collectables; Collecting; Military; Numismatics. CC: AE; MC; V. Cata: Numismatics. Corresp: Any. Mem: BNTA. VAT No: GB 791 6271 08. Notes: *Specialists in books relating to coins, medals, tokens, banknotes, commemorative medals.*

Tim Bryars Ltd, ■ 8 Cecil Court, London, WC2N 4HE. Prop: Tim Bryars. Tel: (020) 7836-1901. Fax: (020) 7836-1910. Web: www.timbryars.co.uk. Est: 2004. Shop open: **M:** 11:00–18:00; **T:** 11:00–18:00; **W:** 11:00–18:00; **Th:** 11:00–18:00; **F:** 11:00–18:00; **S:** 12:00–17:00. Very large stock. Spec: Antiquarian; Atlases; Cartography; Classical Studies; Early Imprints; Fine & Rare; Maps & Mapmaking; Natural History. PR: £10–30,000. CC: MC; V. Mem: ABA; ILAB; IAMA. VAT No: GB 839 6884 58.

Tindley & Chapman, ■ 4 Cecil Court, London, WC2N 4HE. Prop: James Tindley, Ron Chapman. Tel: (0207) 240-2161. Fax: (0207) 379-1062. Est: 1975. Shop open: **M:** 10:00–17:30; **T:** 10:00–17:30; **W:** 10:00–17:30; **Th:** 10:00–17:30; **F:** 10:00–17:30; **S:** 11:00–17:00. Medium stock. Spec: Fiction - General; Fiction - Crime, Detective, Spy, Thrillers; Fiction - Women; First Editions; Literature; Poetry. PR: £10–5,000. CC: MC; V. Mem: PBFA. Notes: *Ron Chapman, London SW10 9LW (q.v.)*

Travis & Emery Music Bookshop, ■17 Cecil Court, off Charing Cross Road, London, WC2N 4EZ. Tel: (020) 7240-2129. Fax: (020) 7497-0790. Web: www.travis-and-emery.com. Est: 1960. Shop open: **M:** 10:15–18:45; **T:** 10:15–18:45; **W:** 10:15–18:45; **Th:** 10:15–18:45; **F:** 10:15–18:45; **S:** 10:15–18:45; **Su:** 11:30–16:30. Very large stock. Spec: Dance; Drama; Hymnology; Music - General; Music - Chart Histories & Research; Music - Classical; Music - Composers; Music - Country & Western. PR: £0 - 5,000. CC: AE; MC; V. Cata: Music, Books on music. Mem: ABA; PBFA; ILAB. VAT No: GB 239 5258 39. Notes: *Also, secondhand sheet music & new music books, plus prints.*

Treadwell's Books, ■ 34 Tavistock Street, Covent Garden, London, WC2E 7PB. Prop: Christina Harrington. Tel: 0207 240 8906. Web: www.treadwells-london.com. Est: 2003. Shop open: **M:** 12:00–19:00; **T:** 12:00–19:00; **W:** 12:00–19:00; **Th:** 12:00–19:00; **F:** 12:00–19:00; **S:** 12:00–19:00; **Su:** 12:00–19:00. Spec: History of Civilisation; History of Ideas; Mythology; Occult; Travel - General. CC: AE; MC; V; Switch. Cata: Esoterica, cultural history. VAT No: GB 810 3399 51.

Unsworth's Antiquarian Books, ■ 36 St. Martin's Court, London, WC2N 04AL. Prop: Charlie Unsworth. Tel: 020 7836 6622. Fax: 020 7836 5044. Web: www.unsworths.com. Est: 1986. Shop open: **M:** 10:30–19:00; **T:** 10:30–19:00; **W:** 10:30–19:00; **Th:** 10:30–19:00; **F:** 10:30–19:00; **S:** 10:30–19:00. Spec: Academic/Scholarly; Antiquarian; Bibliography; Books about Books; Byzantium; Classical Studies; Classics, The; Early Imprints. CC: AE; D; E; JCB; MC; V. Corresp: Latin. Mem: ABA; ILAB. VAT No: GB 480 1145 75.

Waterstone's, ■ 82 Gower Street, London, WC1E 6EQ. Prop: HMV Media Group. Tel: (020) 7636-1577. Fax: (020) 7580-7680. Web: www.waterstones.com/. Est: 1936. Shop open: **M:** 09:30–20:00; **T:** 10:00–20:00; **W:** 09:30–20:00; **Th:** 09:30–20:00; **F:** 09:30–20:00; **S:** 09:30–19:00; **Su:** 12:00–18:00. Medium stock. Spec: Academic/Scholarly. CC: AE; D; JCB; MC; V. Notes: *Dept. also sells academic remainders and is situated within large, well-known bookshop.*

Watkins Books Ltd., ■19–21 Cecil Court, off Charing Cross Road, London, WC2N 4EZ. Tel: (020) 7836-2182. Fax: (020) 7836-6700. Web: www.watkinsbooks.com. Est: 1894. Shop open: **M:** 11:00–19:00; **T:** 11:00–19:00; **W:** 11:00–19:00; **Th:** 11:00–19:00; **F:** 11:00–19:00; **S:** 11:00–19:00. Large stock. Spec: Aboriginal; Academic/Scholarly; Acupuncture; African-American Studies; Alchemy; Almanacs; Alternative Medicine; American Indians. PR: £50–500. CC: MC; V; Sw.

Wildy & Sons Ltd, ■Lincoln's Inn Archway, Carey Street, London, WC2A 2JD. Prop: John Sinkins. Tel: 02072425778. Fax: 02074300897. Web: www.wildy.co.uk. Est: 1830. Shop open: **M:** 09:00–18:00; **T:** 09:00–18:00; **W:** 09:00–18:00; **Th:** 09:00–18:00; **F:** 09:00–18:00. Spec: Law - General; Law - Constitutional. CC: AE; D; MC; V. Cata: Law. VAT No: GB 233 5262 84. Notes: *Exclusively sell law books and sets, new and secondhand (including antiquarian).*

Nigel Williams Rare Books, ■25 Cecil Court, Charing Cross Road, London, WC2N 4EZ. Tel: (020) 7836-7757. Fax: (020) 7379-5918. Web: www.nigelwilliams.com. Est: 1989. Shop open: **M:** 10:00–18:00; **T:** 10:00–18:00; **W:** 10:00–18:00; **Th:** 10:00–18:00; **F:** 10:00–18:00; **S:** 10:00–18:00. Large stock. Spec: Author - Christie, Agatha; Author - Fleming, Ian; Author - Greene, Graham; Author - Joyce, James; Author - Wodehouse, P.G.; Fables; Fiction - General; Fiction - Historical. PR: £5–10,000. CC: AE; D; E; JCB; MC; V. Cata: First editions, P.G. Wodehouse. Mem: ABA; PBFA; ILAB. VAT No: GB 574 3776 05.

GREATER LONDON OUTER

CARSHALTON

Croydon Bookshop, ■ 304 Carshalton Road, Carshalton, SM5 3QB. Prop: Mrs. P.F. Reding & P.J. Rogers. Tel: (020) 8643-6857. Est: 1954. Shop open: **T:** 10:30–17:30; **W:** 10:30–17:30; **Th:** 10:30–17:30; **F:** 10:30–17:30; **S:** 10:30–17:30. Medium stock. PR: £2–100. Corresp: French, German, Spanish.

Crosby Nethercott Books, 16 Kings Avenue, Carshalton, Surrey, SM5 4NX. Prop: (*) D.W. Beer. Tel: (020) 8643 4124. Est: 1991. Private premises. Internet and Postal. Appointment necessary. Small stock. Spec: Author - Raistrick, Arthur; Author - Rolt, L.T.C.; Canals/Inland Waterways; Company History; History - Industrial; History - Mining; Publishers - David & Charles; Publishers - Oakwood Press. PR: £5–100. Corresp: French, German. Notes: *Also, a booksearch service.*

CROYDON

Steve Archer, 11 Bedford Place, Croydon, Surrey, CR0 2BS. Prop: (*). Tel: (020) 8686 3736. Web: www.ukbookworld.com/members/stevearcher. Est: 2000. Private premises. Internet and Postal. Small stock. Spec: Autobiography; Biography; Canals/Inland Waterways; Literary Travel; Literature; Modern First Editions; Booksearch. PR: £2–200. CC: PayPal.

EASTCOTE

The Eastcote Bookshop, ■ 156/160 Field End Road, Eastcote, Middlesex, HA5 1RH. Prop: Eileen & David May. Tel: (020) 8866-9888. Fax: (020) 8905-9387. Est: 1993. Shop open: **T:** 12:00–16:00; **Th:** 12:00–16:00; **F:** 12:00–16:00; **S:** 10:00–17:00. Very large stock. Spec: Alpinism/Mountaineering; American Indians; Annuals; Antiques; Art; Canals/Inland Waterways; Children's; Cinema/Film. PR: £2–500. CC: MC; V. Mem: PBFA. Notes: *Occasional fairs.*

EDGWARE

Two Jays Bookshop, ■ 119 High Street, Edgware, HA8 7DB. Prop: Mark Matthews. Tel: (020) 8952-1349. Est: 1977. Shop open: **T:** 09:00–17:00; **W:** 09:00–17:00; **Th:** 09:00–17:00; **F:** 09:00–17:00; **S:** 09:00–17:00. Very large stock.

ENFIELD

Terence J. McGee, 20 Slades Close, Enfield, Middlesex, EN2 7EB. Prop: T.J. & J.I. McGee. Tel: (020) 8366-5727. Est: 1972. Private premises. Appointment necessary. Open: **S:** 09:00–19:00; **Su:** 09:00–19:00. Small stock. Spec: Author - Betjeman, Sir John; Author - Christie, Agatha; Author - Conan Doyle, Sir Arthur; Author - Wallace, Edgar; Cinema/Film; Comedy; Comics; Counterculture. PR: £1–500. Corresp: French, German, Italian, Spanish. Mem: Brit. Ephemera Society. Notes: *Also, sound and video recordings & record tapes (inc. 16s, 33s, 45s, 78s, CDs and DVDs).*

Felicity J. Warnes, ■The Old Bookshop 36 Gordon Road, Enfield, Middlesex, EN2 0PZ. Prop: F. J. Warnes. Tel: (020) 8366 0722. Fax: (020) 8372-1035. Web: www.fjwarnes.u-net.com. Est: 1978. Shop. Appointment necessary. Large stock. Spec: Embroidery; Fashion & Costume; Jewellery; Knitting; Knitting; Lace; Military; Social History. PR: £5–200. CC: MC; V. Mem: PBFA; ES. Notes: *I also provide a fashion research facility for designers, teachers, students. Please phone for details.*

GREENFORD

Jack Ben–Nathan, 22 Teignmouth Gardens, Perivale, Greenford, UB6 8BX. Prop: (*). Tel: (020) 8997-6574. Est: 1980. Private premises. Appointment necessary. Small stock. Spec: Games; Sport - Billiards/Snooker/Pool; Booksearch. PR: £3–300. Cata: Billiards and related games.

Books B.C., 58 Elton Avenue, Greenford, Middlesex, UB6 0PP. Prop: Martin McCrory. Tel: (020) 8864-0580. Est: 1987. Private premises. Postal only. Appointment necessary. Small stock. Spec: Archaeology; Egyptology; Fiction - Fantasy, Horror; Fiction - Science Fiction; History - Ancient. PR: £1–500.

HAMPTON HILL

Bates Books, 95 High Street, Hampton Hill, Middlesex, TW12 1NH. Prop: Garry and Jackie Bates. Tel: (020) 8941-6782. Est: 2002. Private premises. Postal only. Telephone First. Small stock. Spec: Books about Books; Children's; Children's - Illustrated; Collectables; Comic Books & Annuals; Comics; Countries - Vietnam; Fairy/Folk Tales. PR: £2–30. CC: Cheque/money order/cash.

HAMPTON

R. W. Clements, 114 High Street, Hampton, Middlesex, TW12 2ST. Prop: R. W. Clements. Tel: (020) 8979-3069. Est: 1992. Private premises. Appointment necessary. Large stock. Spec: Archaeology; Art; Autobiography; Biography; Children's; Drama; Fiction - General; History - General. PR: £5–1,000. Notes: *All speciality subjects shown relate to Ireland. Also, ephemera and prints related to Ireland.*

R. S. & P. A. Scowen, 9 Birchwood Grove, Hampton, Middlesex, TW12 3DU. Prop: Roger Scowen. Tel: +44 (0) 20 8979 7429. Est: 1987. Private premises. Internet and Postal. Appointment necessary. Open: **M:** 09:00–17:30; **T:** 09:00–17:30; **W:** 09:00–17:30; **Th:** 09:00–17:30; **F:** 09:00–17:30; **S:** 09:00–17:30; **Su:** 09:00–17:30; Closed for lunch: 13:00–14:00. Spec: Bridge; Chess; Games; Sport - Billiards/Snooker/Pool. Notes: *We specialise in indoor games of skill, for example: chess, bridge, draughts, checkers, snooker, billiards.*

ILFORD

Bloomsbury Bookshop, 41 Eton Road, Ilford, IG1 2UD. Prop: Mike Thompson. Tel: 0208-262-5729. Est: 1989. Private premises. Postal only. Telephone First. Open: **M:** 09:00–17:30; **T:** 09:00–17:30; **W:** 09:00–17:30; **Th:** 09:00–17:30; **F:** 09:00–17:30. Spec: Academic/Scholarly; Africana; Economics; History - Ancient; History - European; History - Irish; History - Labour/ Radical Movements; History - Middle Ages. CC: JCB; MC; V. Cata: History. Corresp: French.

Porcupine Books, 37 Coventry Road, Ilford, Essex, IG1 4QR. Prop: (*) Brian Ameringen. Tel: 020 8554-3799. Web: www.porcupine.demon.co.uk. Est: 1998. Private premises. Internet and Postal. Appointment necessary. Open: **M:** 08:00–21:00; **T:** 08:00–21:00; **W:** 18:00–21:00; **Th:** 18:00–21:00; **F:** 20:00–21:00; **S:** 18:00–21:00; **Su:** 08:00–21:00. Medium stock. Spec: Children's; Fiction - Crime, Detective, Spy, Thrillers; Fiction - Fantasy, Horror; Fiction - Science Fiction; Fiction - Supernatural; Fiction - Young Adult Mystery & Adventure Series. PR: £1–2,500. CC: MC; V. Cata: Science Fiction, Fantasy, Horror, Young Adult.

ISLEWORTH

Chaters Motoring Booksellers, ■ 8 South Street, Isleworth, Middlesex, TW7 7DH. Prop: C. Stroud. Tel: (020) 8568-9750. Fax: (020) 8569-8273. Web: www.chaters.co.uk. Est: 1957. Shop open: **M:** 09:00–17:30; **T:** 09:00–17:30; **W:** 09:00–17:30; **Th:** 09:00–17:30; **F:** 09:00–17:30; **S:** 10:00–17:00. Spec: Motorbikes / motorcycles; Motoring; New Books; Booksearch. PR: £1–500. CC: JCB; MC; V; plus Debit cards. Mem: BA. Notes: *Also, new books in specialities & a booksearch service.*

Patrick Tuft, 68 Worple Road, London, TW7 7HU. Prop: Patrick Tuft. Tel: (withheld). Private premises. Postal only. Small stock. Spec: Bibles; Bibliography; History - General; Religion - Christian; Vatican and Papal History, The.

KENLEY

David & Lynn Smith, The Hermitage, 21 Uplands Road, Kenley, Surrey, CR8 5EE. Prop: David & Lynn Smith. Tel: (020) 8660-9908. Est: 1980. Storeroom; Appointment necessary. Small stock. Spec: Biology - General; Medicine; Medicine - History of; Pharmacy/Pharmacology; Science - General; Science - History of; Scientific Instruments. PR: £10–500. CC: JCB; MC; V. Cata: Medicine and its history. Mem: PBFA.

KEW

Criterion Books, 6 Nylands Avenue, Kew, Richmond, TW9 4HH. Prop: (*) Terence Crimmings. Tel: (020) 8876-1773. Fax: (020) 8876-1773. VOIPpro: Skype. Est: 1992. Private premises. Postal only. Telephone First. Small stock. Spec: Art Reference; Author - Ardizzone, Edward; Author - Barrie, J.M.; Author - Bloomsbury Group, The; Author - Bowles, Paul; Author - Coetzee, J.M.; Author - Durrell, Lawrence; Author - Forester, C.S. PR: £10–350.

KINGSTON

Coombe-Hill-Books, 32 Woodlands Avenue New Malden, Surrey, Kingston, KT3 3UQ. Prop: (*) Nicholas & Helen Burrows. Tel: (020) 8942-2677. Est: 1993. Private premises. Internet and Postal. Appointment necessary. Small stock. Spec: Author - Coetzee, J.M.; Author - Heaney, Seamus; Award Winners; Countries - Melanesia; Countries - Mexico; Fiction - General; Fiction - Fantasy, Horror; Fiction - Science Fiction. PR: £5–500. CC: AE; MC; V; Paypal. Notes: *Email lists of new SIGNED First editions provided monthly upon request to nick@burrbook.demon.co.uk.*

MORDEN

A. Burton–Garbett, 35 The Green, Morden, Surrey, SM4 4HJ. Tel: (020) 8540-2367. Fax: (020) 8540-4594. Est: 1959. Private premises. Appointment necessary. Small stock. Spec: Countries - Caribbean, The; Countries - Central America; Countries - Mexico; Countries - South America. PR: £5–1,000.

OSTERLEY

Osterley Bookshop, ■ 168a Thornbury Road, Osterley, Middlesex, TW7 4QE. Prop: Pennie Smith & Tony Vesely. Tel: (020) 8560-6206. Est: 1973. Internet and Postal. Shop open: **M:** 09:30–17:30; **T:** 09:30–17:30; **W:** 09:30–17:30; **Th:** 09:30–17:30; **F:** 09:30–17:30; **S:** 09:30–17:30; **Su:** 09:30–17:30. Medium stock. PR: £3–150. CC: AE; JCB; MC; V; Maestro. Notes: *Large general stock.*

RUISLIP MANOR

Dr Bernard Dixon and Kath Adams, 130 Cornwall Rd, Ruislip Manor, Middlesex, HA4 6AW. Prop: Dr Bernard Dixon and Kath Adams. Tel: 01895 632390. Fax: 01895 678645. Est: 2000. Private premises. Postal only. Telephone First. Open: **M:** 09:00–17:30; **T:** 09:00–17:30; **W:** 09:00–17:30; **Th:** 09:00–17:30; **F:** 09:00–17:30; **S:** 09:00–17:30; **Su:** 09:00–17:30; Closed for lunch: 13:00–14:00. Small stock. Spec: Bacteriology; Biochemistry; Biology - General; Botany; Brewing; Chemistry; Drugs; Ecology. Cata: annually on medicine, science, biology, biography, history. PR: US$ 5–100. Notes: *We deal in all biomedical sciences, especially microbiology and infectious diseases. As well as offering catalogues at least annually, we retain details of customers' specific wants. We are also interested in buying books.*

ST MARGARETS

Marble Hill Books, 35 Napoleon Road, St Margarets, TW1 3EW. Prop: Philip Dawson. Tel: 020 8892 0511. Web: www.marblehillbooks.com. Est: 1999. Mail order only; Internet and Postal. Telephone First. Spec: American Indians; Antiquarian; Architecture; Author - 20th Century; Countries - Africa; Countries - Antarctic, The; Countries - Far East, The; Countries - Latin America. CC: AE; JCB; MC; V; Maestro/Switch. Cata: Modern First Editions; Antiquarian; General. Corresp: French; German. Mem: Title Page Book Fairs. Notes: *Stock also stored in and shipped from Connecticut, USA. Books listed on ABE, Alibris, Biblio etc. Also on www.marblehillbooks.com.*

SUTTON

Mike Park, 351 Sutton Common Road, Sutton, Surrey, SM3 9HZ. Prop: Mike Park & William To. Tel: (020) 8641-7796. Fax: (020) 8641-3330. Est: 1974. Private premises. Appointment necessary. Open: **M:** 09:00–17:00; **T:** 09:00–17:00; **W:** 09:00–17:00; **Th:** 09:00–17:00; **F:** 09:00–17:00. Small stock. Spec: Agriculture; Bamboo; Botany; Countries - British North Borneo; Countries - Indonesia; Ethnobotany; Flower Arranging; Forestry. PR: £1–1,000. CC: E; MC; V. Cata: Gardening, Botany. Natural History. Mem: PBFA. Notes: *Search service available for books within our speciality. Catalogues are available by email as well as by post.*

TEDDINGTON

Chris Hollingshead Horticulture, 10 Linden Grove, Teddington, TW11 8LT. Tel: (0208) 977 6051. Est: 1995. Private premises. Shop open: **M:** 09:30–17:00; **T:** 09:30–17:00; **W:** 09:30–17:00; **Th:** 09:30–17:00; **F:** 09:30–17:00. Small stock. Spec: Agriculture; Botany; Gardening - General; Herbalism; Horticulture; Landscape; Mycology; Natural History. PR: £5–3,000. CC: MC; V. Notes: *Garden history, design landscape and architecture; farming, botanical academic & antiquarian.*

TWICKENHAM

Books on Spain, P.O. Box 207, Twickenham, TW2 5BQ. Prop: (*) Keith Harris. Tel: (020) 8898-7789. Fax: (020) 8898-7789 (24 hours). Est: 1993. Private premises. Internet and Postal. Contactable. Large stock. Spec: Antiquarian; Bull Fighting; Countries - Andorra; Countries - Central America; Countries - Cuba; Countries - Gibraltar; Countries - Latin America; Countries - Mexico. PR: £5–1,000. CC: AE; JCB; MC; V; Switch. Corresp: Spanish, Portuguese, French. Mem: PBFA. VAT No: GB 720 5623 63.

Anthony C. Hall, Antiquarian Bookseller, ■ 30 Staines Road, Twickenham, TW2 5AH. Prop: Anthony C. Hall. Tel: (020) 8898-2638. Fax: (020) 8893-8855. Web: www.hallbooks.co.uk. Est: 1966. Shop open: **M:** 10:00–17:00; **Th:** 10:00–17:00; **F:** 10:00–17:00; Closed for lunch: 12:30–01:30. Small stock. Spec: Countries - Africa; Countries - Asia; Countries - East Europe; Countries - Middle East, The; Countries - Russia; History - Industrial; Travel - Africa; Travel - Asia. PR: £10–1,000. CC: MC; V. Cata: Russian & East European Studies. Corresp: French, German, Russian, Spanish. Mem: ABA; PBFA. Also at: alternative web address: ukbookworld.com/members/achallbooks. VAT No: GB 224 2699 61. Notes: *Large specialist stock on Russian & East European Studies (including scarce books in Russian) the Middle East, Africa, Asia, Business & Industrial History, seen by appointment.*

Stephen Miller, 19 Clifden Road, Twickenham, Middlesex, TW1 4LU. Tel: (020) 8892-0331. Est: 1981. Private premises. Small stock. Spec: Antiquarian. PR: £1–500. Corresp: French.

WELLING

Falconwood Transport & Military Bookshop, ■5 Falconwood Parade, The Green, Welling, DA16 2PL. Prop: Andy Doran. Tel: (020) 8303-8291. Fax: (020) 8303-8291. Est: 1985. Shop open: **Th:** 09:30–17:30; **F:** 09:30–17:30; **S:** 09:30–17:30. Medium stock. Spec: Automobilia/Automotive; Aviation; Buses/Trams; Engineering; Maritime/Nautical; Maritime/Nautical - History; Marque Histories (see also motoring); Military. PR: £5–50. CC: E; JCB; MC; V. VAT No: GB427 0309 76. Notes: *Easy parking. No yellow lines. Falconwood Station 10 minute walk away or from Falconwood Station B16 bus passes door. No general stock.*

MERSEYSIDE

BOOTLE

Ahbooks, 65 Springwell Road, Bootle, L206LU. Prop: Andrew Harty. Tel: 0151 2862745 (M. 0785 1128145). Web: www.ahbooks.co.uk. Est: 2000. Storeroom; Internet and Postal. Appointment necessary. Shop at: Unit 5 Parrs Corner, Marsh Lane/Stanley Rd., Bootle, L20. Spec: Fiction - General; Modern First Editions. CC: Paypal. VAT No: GB 867 1615 04.

BIRKENHEAD

Interesting Books, Grayson Mews, John Street, Birkenhead, Wirral CH41 1LU. Prop: Andrew Forsey. Tel: (07787) 960073. Est: 1998. Private premises. Internet and postal. Medium stock. PR: 3–500. CC: MC; V. Cata: online/internet - general - mainly non-fiction.

HESWELL

Acanthophyllum Books, 243 Pensby Road, Heswell, Wirral CH61 5UA. Prop: Dr John Edmondson. Tel: (0151) 342 8287. Web: www.heswellbooks.co.uk. Est: 2009. Office and/or bookroom at 121 Telegraph Road, Heswell, Wirral CH60 0AF. Internet and postal. Small stock. Spec: Architecture; Bibliography; Botany; Conchology (see also Malacology); Conservation; Countries - Africa; Countries - Arabian Peninsula; Countries - Asia. PR: £5–2,000. CC: PayPal. Cata: occasionally on Botany. Nen: PBFA. Notes: Mobile 0775 858 3706.

LIVERPOOL

Black Voices, 2, Saville Road, Liverpool, L13 4DP. Prop: T. Aitman. Tel: (0151) 475 2936. Est: 1992. Private premises. Internet and Postal. Appointment necessary. Small stock. Spec: African-American Studies; Africana; Author - Baldwin, James; Black Studies; Countries - Africa; Countries - Caribbean, The; Literature - African-American; Literature - South African. PR: £3–2,000. Notes: *Also booksearches in specialist subjects.*

Hylton Booksearch, 23 Chelsea Court, West Derby, Liverpool, L12 6RS. Prop: Mr. R.A. Hylton. Tel: (0151) 259-5163. Web: www.rahylton@btinternet.com. Est: 1992. Private premises. Postal only. Appointment necessary. Very small stock. Spec: Author - General; Author - Hunter, Alan; Black Studies; Books about Books; Children's; Collectables; Communism; Countries - Central America. PR: £5–500. CC: V; PayPal. Notes: *Also trade as "liverpoolbooqshop" on Amazon Internet Site. For further details go to www.liverpoolbooqshop.com.*

Modern Welsh Publications Ltd., 32 Garth Drive, Liverpool, L18 6HW. Prop: Professor D. Ben Rees. Tel: (0151) 724 1989. Fax: (0151) 724-5691. Est: 1962. Private premises. Postal only. Telephone First. Medium stock. Spec: Countries - Wales; History - General; Literature in Translation; Politics; Theology; Ephemera. CC: Cheque. Corresp: Welsh.

Reid of Liverpool, ■ 105 Mount Pleasant, Liverpool, L3 5TB. Prop: Gerard Fitzpatrick. Tel: (0151) 709-2312. Est: 1980. Shop open: **M:** 10:30–17:30; **T:** 10:30–17:30; **W:** 10:30–17:30; **Th:** 10:30–17:30; **F:** 10:30–17:30; **S:** 10:30–17:30. Spec: Academic/Scholarly; Culture - Popular; Esoteric; Fiction - Science Fiction; Finance - General; Mysticism; Odd & Unusual; Psychology/Psychiatry. CC: PayPal.

PRENTON

Thin Read Line, 11 St. Andrews Road, Prenton, CH43 1TB. Tel: 0151 652 4483. Est: 1995. Private premises. Postal only. Contactable. Open: **M:** 09:00–17:30; **T:** 09:00–17:30; **W:** 09:00–17:30; **Th:** 09:00–17:30; **F:** 09:00–17:30; **S:** 09:00–17:30; **Su:** 09:00–17:30; Closed for lunch: 13:00–14:00. Spec: Aeronautics; Africana; Agriculture; Aircraft; Animals and Birds; Antiques; Arms & Armour; Army, The. Corresp: Dutch. Notes: *We are principally dealers in military collectibles reference books (guns, swords, badges, medals, uniforms etc., but also stock a wide range of military history titles to with special emphasis on colonial wars, WW1 & WW2.*

PRESCOT

Nostalgia Unlimited, 19 Dunbeath Avenue, Rainhill, Prescot, L35 0QH. Tel: (0151) 426-2046. Est: 1988. Private premises. Postal only. Small stock. Spec: Christmas; Collecting; Comic Books & Annuals; Comics; Magazines & Periodicals - General; Newspapers; Nostalgia. PR: £1–35.

SOUTHPORT

Broadhursts of Southport Ltd., ■ 5 & 7 Market Street, Southport, PR8 1HD. Prop: Laurens R. Hardman. Tel: (01704) 532064 & 534110. Fax: (01704) 542009. Web: www.ckbroadhurst.co.uk. Est: 1926. Shop open: **M:** 09:00–17:30; **T:** 09:00–17:30; **W:** 09:00–17:30; **Th:** 09:00–17:30; **F:** 09:00–17:30; **S:** 09:00–17:30. Very large stock. Spec: Aircraft; Architecture; Art; Aviation; Bibliography; Biography; Children's; Comic Books & Annuals. PR: £5–10. CC: AE; MC; V. Corresp: French. Mem: ABA; PBFA; BA; ILAB. VAT No: GB 164288054. Notes: *Also, bookbinding & restoration service. New books on all subjects. Specialist childrens department. Booksearch service. Prints and paintings.*

Cover to Cover, 252 Balmoral Drive, Southport, PR9 8QA. Prop: Arthur Reeve. Tel: (01704) 231443. Web: www.covers.freeuk.com. VOIPpro: skype. VOIPnum: coversuk. Est: 1996. Private premises. Internet and Postal. Telephone First. Open: **M:** 09:00–19:00; **T:** 09:00–19:00; **Th:** 09:00–19:00; **F:** 09:00–19:00; **S:** 12:00–19:00; **Su:** 12:00–19:00. Spec: Applied Art; Architecture; Architecture - Theatre; Art; Art - Encaustic; Art - Technique; Art - Theory; Art Deco. PR: £1–300.

Kernaghans, ■57–65 Wayfarers, Arcade Lord Street, Southport, PR8 1NT. Prop: Alwyn & Bryan Kernaghan. Tel: (01704) 546329. Fax: (01704) 546329. Est: 1972. Shop open: **M:** 10:00–17:00; **T:** 10:00–17:00; **W:** 10:00–17:00; **Th:** 10:00–17:00; **F:** 10:00–17:00; **S:** 10:00–17:00. Very large stock. Spec: Children's - Illustrated; Countries - Ireland; Countries - Isle of Man; Fine & Rare; Irish Interest; Natural History; Pop-Up, Movable & Cut Out; Religion - Christian. PR: £5–5,000. CC: AE; MC; V. Mem: PBFA.

Merseyside Books, 12 Maple Street, Southport PR8 6BY. Prop: Craig Thomas & Linda Abberley. Tel: 0776 2149326. Web: www.merseysidebooks.co.uk. Private premises. Internet and postal. Very small stock. Spec: Automobilia/Automotive; Canals/Inland Waterways; Sport - Caving (Spelaeology); Sport - Potholing; Topography - General. PR: £3-50.

Parkinsons Books, ■ In Parkinson's Ginnel, between Monsoon & Lakeland 359-363 Lord Street, Southport, PR8 1NH. Prop: K.A. & J. Parkinson. Tel: 01704-547016. Web: www.parki.co.uk. Shop open: **M:** 10:00–17:00; **T:** 10:00–17:00; **W:** 10:00–17:00; **Th:** 10:00–17:00; **F:** 10:00–17:00; **S:** 10:00–17:00; **Su:** 13:00–17:00. Spec: Aesthetics; Agriculture; Alchemy; Animals and Birds; Antiquarian; Antiquities; Aquatics; Arachnology. CC: AE; JCB; MC; V; Most major cards. Notes: *We occupy three floors on the main shopping street, between Monsoon & Lakeland. The stock is is well classified, with a leaning towards the academic. We also sell coins, antiquities, tropical shells, fossils, mineral specimens & crystals.*

WALLASEY

J.E. Burns Booksellers, 11 Sandfield Road, Wallasey, Merseyside CH45 1JQ. Prop: J. E. Burns. Private premises. Appointment necessary. Book Fairs only.

WEST KIRBY

Don Mulyan, 5 Redhouse Lane, West Kirby, CH48 5ED. Prop: Don Mulyan. Tel: 0151 625 7525. Est: 1970. Private premises. Internet and Postal. Appointment necessary. Open: **M:** 10:00–20:00; **T:** 10:00–20:00; **W:** 10:00–20:00; **Th:** 10:00–20:00; **F:** 10:00–20:00; **S:** 10:00–20:00. Small stock. Spec: Adventure; Advertising; Archaeology; Architecture; Art; Bibliography; Countries - Isle of Man; Countries - Norway. Notes: *Specialist in Norway pre 1940, Isle of Man, Liverpool. Wirral, Merseyside.*

NORFOLK

AYLSHAM

Burebank Books, ■44 Red Lion Street, Aylsham, NR11 6ER. Prop: Roger M Crouch. Tel: 01263 735710. Fax: 01263 735703. Est: 1993. Shop. Open: **M:** 10:00–17:00; **T:** 10:00–17:00; **W:** 10:00–13:00; **Th:** 10:00–17:00; **F:** 10:00–17:00; **S:** 09:00–17:00; Closed for lunch: 13:00–14:00. Spec: Archaeology; Countries - Japan; History - Local; Landscape; Maritime/Nautical. CC: MC; V; Solo, Switch. Corresp: Italian, Japanese.

BINHAM

John Hart, Doe Barn, Front Street, Binham, NR21 0AL. Tel: 01328 830877. Fax: 01328 830266. Est: 1987. Private premises. Appointment necessary. Small stock. Spec: Literature. PR: £20–2,000. CC: MC; V. Cata: English Literature. Corresp: French. Mem: ABA; PBFA. VAT No: GB 529 2455 28.

BUXTON

Chris Porter Books, Alwoodley House, Mill Street, Buxton, Norwich, NR10 5JE. Prop: Chris Porter. Tel: 01603 273219. Web: www.ukbookworld.com/members/chrisporter. Est: 1996. Private premises. Appointment necessary. Open: **M:** 09:00–17:30; **T:** 09:00–17:30; **W:** 09:00–17:30; **Th:** 09:00–17:30; **F:** 09:00–17:30; **S:** 09:00–17:30; **Su:** 09:00–17:30; Closed for lunch: 13:00–14:00. Spec: Banking & Insurance; Fire & Fire Fighters; Industry; Motoring; Transport; Booksearch. CC: PayPal. Corresp: Italian.

CAISTER–ON–SEA

Brian Beighton, Garfield Villa, Garfield Terrace, Caister–on–Sea, NR30 5DQ. Tel: 01493 728114. Private premises. Postal only. Appointment necessary. Small stock. Spec: Almanacs; Sport - Cricket.

CROMER

Bookworms, ■ 9 New Street, Cromer, NR27 9HP. Prop: Susan & Ted Liddell & I.R. Petrie. Tel: (01263) 515078. Fax: (01263) 519008. Web: www.susanlid.freeserve.co.uk. Est: 1987. Shop open: **M:** 10:00–17:00; **T:** 10:00–17:00; **W:** 10:00–17:00; **Th:** 10:00–17:00; **F:** 10:00–17:00; **S:** 10:00–17:00; **Su:** 10:00–17:00. Large stock. Spec: Art; Aviation; Biography; Children's; History - General; Literature; Music - General; Natural History. PR: £1–100. CC: AE.

Much Binding, ■ 36 Church Street, Cromer, NR27 9ES. Prop: Susan and Andy Slovak. Tel: 01263 517194. Est: 2005. Shop open: **T:** 10:00–16:00; **W:** 10:00–16:00; **Th:** 10:00–16:00; **F:** 10:00–16:00; **S:** 10:00–16:00; **Su:** 11:00–16:00. Spec: Antiquarian; Classical Studies; History - General; Medicine; Religion - General; Science - General; Vintage Paperbacks; War - General. Corresp: French, Spanish, German, Slovak. Notes: *Opening hours apply between 1 May and first weekend in October. Thereafter - please contact by telephone.*

DEREHAM

Village Books, 7 Middle March Road, Dereham, NR19 1EQ. Prop: Mr Jack James. Tel: (01362) 853066. Fax: (01362) 853066. Est: 1996. Private premises. Internet and Postal. Very large stock. Spec: Art; History - General; Medicine; Military History. PR: £1–100. CC: PayPal.

DISS

Church Street Books, ■ 6 Church Street, Diss, IP22 4DD. Prop: Andy Vidion. Tel: 01379 652020. Est: 2005. Shop open: **M:** 10:00–17:30; **T:** 10:00–17:30; **Th:** 10:00–17:30; **F:** 10:00–17:30; **S:** 10:00–17:30. Spec: Alpinism/Mountaineering; Autobiography; Aviation; Biography; Counterculture; Dictionaries; Fiction - General; Free Thought.

Riderless Horse Books, Oakfields, Redgrave Road, Blo Norton, Diss, IP22 2JA. Prop: (*) Richard B. Hamburger. Tel: (01379) 898481. Fax: 01379 898481. Est: 1991. Private premises. Internet and Postal. Appointment necessary. Small stock. Spec: Author - Anna Kavan; Author - Bowles, Paul; Author - Gurdjieff, W.I.; Author - Paul Bowles; Author - Watkins, Vernon; Author - Williams, Charles; Autographs; Avant-Garde. PR: £2–1,000. CC: MC; V. Cata: Literature, Modern Poetry, First Editions. Corresp: French, German. Mem: PBFA.

Michael Taylor Rare Books, Hoblins, One Eyed Lane Weybread, Diss, IP21 5TT. Tel: (01379) 853889. Fax: (01379) 853889. Est: 1984. Private premises. Appointment necessary. Small stock. Spec: Bibliography; Calligraphy; Fine Printing; Illustrated - General; Illustrated - 19th & 20th Century; Lettering; Private Press; Typography. PR: £5–1,000. CC: MC; V. Cata: Private, Illustrated Books, Typography. Mem: PBFA.

DOWNHAM MARKET

Richard Everett, Sandfield House, 58 Lynn Road, Downham Market, PE38 9NN. Prop: Richard & Jenny Everett. Tel: (01366) 382074. Est: 1983. Office and/or bookroom; Appointment necessary. Large stock. Spec: Children's; Illustrated - General; Publishers - Warnes; Topography - Local; Collectables. PR: £2–400. Mem: PBFA. Notes: *Also at: Southwold Antiques Centre, Suffolk (q.v.).*

EAST RUDHAM

Victor Sutcliffe, Mulberry Coach House, East Rudham, PE31 8RD. Prop: Victor Sutcliffe. Tel: (01485) 528463. Web: www.victorsutcliffe.demon.co.uk. Est: 1970. Private premises. Internet and Postal. Appointment necessary. Small stock. Spec: History - Napoleonic; Military; Military History; Travel - Africa; Travel - India; War - Boer, The; War - Napoleonic; War - Zulu. PR: £15–5,000. CC: MC; V. Cata: military.

FAKENHAM

The Dancing Goat Bookshop, ■ 5 Oak Street, Fakenham, NR21 9DX. Prop: Michael Goss. Tel: (01328) 855757. Est: 1998. Shop open: **M:** 10:00–16:00; **T:** 10:00–16:00; **W:** 10:00–16:00; **Th:** 10:00–16:00; **F:** 10:00–16:00; **S:** 10:00–16:00. Medium stock. Spec: American Indians; Americana - General; Folklore; Music - Folk & Irish Folk; Music - Popular; Music - Rock & Roll; Ornithology; Poetry. PR: £1–100. CC: none. Notes: *Also a coffee shop (coffee, tea, home made cakes & light lunches).*

GORLESTON-ON-SEA

C. & J. Read - Gorleston Bookstore, Unit 10 Longs Industrial Estate Englands Lane, Gorleston-on-Sea, NR31 6NE. Prop: Cynthia & John Read. Tel: (01493) 656511. Est: 1993. Storeroom; Internet and Postal. Telephone First. Medium stock. Spec: Aeronautics; Architecture; Artists; Arts, The; Collectables; Collecting; Countries - England; Countries - Scotland. PR: £1–1,000. CC: MC; V; Maestro, PayPal. Notes: *We welcome visitors and are here most days between about 10:30 and 5.00, but please ring first as we are sometimes out buying.*

GREAT ELLINGHAM

John Knowles, Brick Kiln Farm, Hingham Road, Great Ellingham, Nr. Attleborough, NR17 1JE. Prop: John Knowles. Tel: (01953) 452257. Fax: (01953) 452733. Est: 1985. Private premises. Internet and Postal. Appointment necessary. Open: **M:** 09:00–19:00; **T:** 09:00–19:00; **W:** 09:00–19:00; **Th:** 09:00–19:00; **F:** 09:00–19:00; **S:** 09:00–19:00; **Su:** 09:00–19:00. Small stock. Spec: Buses/Trams; Marque Histories (see also motoring); Motorbikes / motorcycles; Motoring; Sport - Motor Racing; Transport; Vintage Cars. PR: £5–1,000. CC: E; JCB; MC; V; SW. Cata: Motoring, Motor Sport and other road transport. Corresp: French, German.

GREAT YARMOUTH

R.F. & C. Ward, 27, Great Yarmouth, NR30 2EX. Prop: Frank & Carol Ward. Tel: (01493) 856280. Fax: (01493) 853909. Web: www.ashbook.co.uk. Est: 1985. Private premises. Postal only. Very large stock. Spec: Fiction - General; Fiction - Crime, Detective, Spy, Thrillers; Fiction - Science Fiction; Fiction - Westerns; First Editions; War - General. PR: £1–500. CC: AE; JCB; MC; V. Cata: All. Notes: *We have a stock of 25,000 plus titles priced from 50 pence to £500.00. If we do not have it we can normally get it. We have sold books world wide since 1985. Try our website at www.ashbook.co.uk there you will find over 30 catalogues.*

HARLESTON

Black Cat Books, Meadow Cottage High Road, Wortwell, Harleston, IP20 0EN. Prop: Ann Morgan–Hughes. Tel: (01986) 788826. Fax: (01986) 788826. Web: www.blackcatbooks.co.uk. Est: 1984. Office and/or bookroom; Telephone First. Small stock. Spec: Colour-Plate; Cookery/Gastronomy; Courtesy; Embroidery; Etiquette; Fashion & Costume; Food & Drink; Hairdressing. PR: £10–2,000. CC: MC; V; PayPal. Corresp: French, German, Greek. Mem: ABA; PBFA; ILAB. VAT No: GB 446 3847 25. Notes: *Visitors are most welcome, but please telephone first to make sure I am at home and to ask for directions.*

Riviera Books, ■ 9 Market Place, Harleston, IP20 9AD. Prop: David Chatten. Tel: (01379) 855123. Web: www.rivierabooks.co.uk. Est: 1999. Shop open: **T:** 10:00–16:30; **W:** 10:00–16:30; **F:** 10:00–16:30; **S:** 10:00–16:30. Large stock. PR: £2–200. Corresp: French.

HINDRINGHAM

Fullerton's Booksearch, The Dukes House, Moorgate Road, Hindringham, Fakenham, NR21 0PT. Prop: Humphrey Boon. Tel: 01328 87 87 81. Fax: 01328 87 87 82. Web: www.glavenvalley.co.uk/fullertons/. Est: 1991. Mail order only; Internet and Postal. Appointment necessary. Open: **M:** 09:00–17:00; **T:** 09:00–17:00; **W:** 09:00–17:00; **Th:** 09:00–17:00; **F:** 09:00–17:00. Spec: Booksearch. PR: £18–2,000. CC: JCB; MC; V; Most UK debit cards. VAT No: GB 631 8838 22. Notes: *Fullerton's Booksearch are leading book searchers within the U.K; looking for around 7,800 titles for 6,500 customers per annum.We will look for almost any book, published in the English language, on any subject, anywhere in the world!*

HOLT

Simon Finch Norfolk, ■ 3-5 Fish Hill, Holt, NR25 6BD. Prop: Simon Finch Rare Books Limited. Tel: 01263 712650. Fax: 01263 711153. Web: www.simonfinchnorfolk.com/. Est: 1980. Shop open: **M:** 10:00–17:00; **T:** 10:00–17:00; **W:** 10:00–17:00; **Th:** 10:00–17:00; **F:** 10:00–17:00; **S:** 10:00–17:00. CC: AE; JCB; MC; V. Cata: General. VAT No: GB 867 8126 81.

Jackdaw Books, 10 New Street, Holt, NR25 6JJ. Prop: Eleanor and Mick Finn. Tel: 01263 711658. Fax: 01263 710056. Web: www.jackdawbooks.co.uk. Est: 1997. Private premises. Internet and Postal. Appointment necessary. Spec: Academic/Scholarly; Anthologies; Archaeology; Architecture; Architecture - Theatre; Art; Art Reference; Author - General. CC: MC; V; Paypal. VAT No: GB 700 1936 76. Notes: *Specialists in Norfolk history and topography.*

HUNSTANTON

Musicalania, 8B Melton Drive, Hunstanton, PE36 5DD. Prop: David Burkett. Tel: (01485) 534282. Est: 1973. Private premises. Internet and Postal. Telephone First. Small stock. Spec: Music - Classical; Music - Composers; Music - Gilbert & Sullivan; Music - Opera; Music - Popular; Music - Printed, Sheet Music & Scores; Music - Songs & Ballads. PR: £1–50. Cata: Piano solo; organ; songs; wind, brass & strings. Corresp: French and German. Notes: *Secondhand music bought and sold. We also sell secondhand classical compact discs and concert programmes. Music by British composers our speciality.*

KING'S LYNN

Bookends, ■ 4 King Street, King's Lynn, PE30 1ES. Prop: Iain Dempster. Tel: 01553 774374. Est: 2002. Shop open: **M:** 10:00–16:00; **T:** 10:00–16:00; **Th:** 10:00–16:00; **F:** 10:00–16:00; **S:** 10:00–16:00. CC: AE; MC; V; Meastro. Notes: *Also, prints and fine art cards.*

Brazenhead Ltd., The Brazen Head Bookshop, Market Place ,Burnham Market, King's Lynn, PE31 8HD. Prop: H.S. Kenyon David Kenyon. Tel: (01328) 730700. Web: www.brazenhead.co.uk. Est: 1996. Shop and/or gallery; Internet and Postal. Shop open: **M:** 09:30–17:00; **T:** 09:30–17:00; **W:** 09:30–17:00; **Th:** 09:30–17:00; **F:** 09:30–17:00; **S:** 09:30–17:00. Very large stock. Spec: Architecture; Art; Children's; Children's - Illustrated; History - Local; Illustrated - 19th & 20th Century; Literature; Military. PR: £1–10,000. CC: MC; V; Maestro.

John Lowe, 7 Orchard Grove, West Lynn, King's Lynn, PE34 3LE. Tel: (01553) 661271. Est: 1982. Spec: Academic/Scholarly; Advertising; Aeronautics; Alternative Medicine; Archaeology; Folklore; History - British; Topography - General. PR: £2–200. Mem: PBFA.

Torc Books, ■9 Hall Road, Snettisham, King's Lynn, PE31 7LU. Prop: Heather Shepperd. Tel: 01485 541188. Est: 1977. Shop open: **F:** 10:00–16:00; **S:** 10:00–16:00.

LYNG

Lyngheath Books, 51 Pightle Way, Lyng, Norwich, NR9 5RL. Prop: Tim Holt. Tel: 01603 879037. Web: www.lyngheathbooks.co.uk. Est: 1999. Private premises. Internet and Postal. Appointment necessary. Open: **M:** 09:00–17:30; **T:** 09:00–17:30; **W:** 09:00–17:30; **Th:** 09:00–17:30; **F:** 09:00–17:30; **S:** 09:00–17:30; **Su:** 09:00–17:30; Closed for lunch: 13:00–14:00. Spec: Autobiography; Biography; Sport - General. CC: UK Bank sterling cheque. Corresp: French. Notes: *The main focus of LyngHeath Books is book searching. Only a small stock of books is held - mainly biography and autobiography. Website being updated.*

NEW BUCKENHAM

John Underwood Antiquarian Books, Hill House, Chapel Street, New Buckenham, NR16 2BB. Prop: John Underwood. Tel: 01953 860746. Web: www.abebooks.com. Est: 1991. Office and/or bookroom; Telephone First. Open: **Th:** 14:00–17:30; **F:** 09:00–17:30; **S:** 09:00–17:30; **Su:** 09:00–17:30. Spec: Antiquarian; Author - Norton, Mary; Author - White, T.H.; Book of Hours; Calligraphy; Children's; Children's - Illustrated; Crime (True). CC: Cheques /Cash/Paypal. Mem: PBFA. Notes: *Book Fairs with PBFA. London Fair most months. Bookroom open by appointment, telephone, leave message, or e-mail. Small quality stock of Antiquarian, Children's, Newspapers, Manuscripts, Medieval leaves, True Crime, some Modern Firsts.*

NORTH WALSHAM

C.J. Murphy, 5 Burton Avenue, North Walsham, NR28 0EW. Tel: (01692) 402831. Est: 1999. Private premises. Postal only. Telephone First. Medium stock. Spec: Academic/Scholarly; Annuals; Antiquarian; Art Reference; Atlases; Author - General; Autobiography; Children's. PR: £1–1,000. Corresp: English only. Notes: *Also, a booksearch service.*

NORWICH

Ampersand Books, ■ 64 St. Benedicts Street, Norwich, NR2 4AR. Prop: Mr. W. Green. Tel: 01603 663169. Est: 1989. Shop open: **T:** 10:00–17:00; **W:** 10:00–17:00; **Th:** 10:00–17:00; **F:** 10:00–17:00; **S:** 10:00–16:00. Medium stock. Spec: Bicycles and Cycling; History - Local; Sport - Cycling; Topography - Local; Booksearch. PR: £1–500. Cata: bicycles and cycling. Mem: PBFA.

Carlton Books, 44 Langley Road, Chedgrave, Norwich, NR14 6HD. Prop: A.P. Goodfellow. Tel: (01508) 520124. Est: 1974. Private premises. Postal only. Appointment necessary. Small stock. Spec: History - Local; Natural History; Ornithology; Topography - Local. PR: £1–500. Mem: PBFA. Notes: *also attends book fairs.*

John Debbage, 28 Carterford Drive, Norwich, NR3 4DW. Tel: (01603) 488015. Fax: (01603) 788933. Est: 1954. Private premises. Internet and Postal. Telephone First. Spec: Advertising; Agriculture; Antiquarian; Archaeology - Industrial; Architecture; Author - Bell, Adrian; Author - Borrow, George; Author - Cobbett, William. Cata: Norfolk history and Nelson.

The Dormouse Bookshop, ■ 29 Elm Hill, Norwich, NR3 1HG. Prop: Philip Goodbody. Tel: 01603 621021. Est: 1985. Shop open: **M:** 10:00–16:00; **T:** 10:00–16:00; **W:** 10:00–16:00; **Th:** 10:00–16:00; **F:** 10:00–16:00; **S:** 10:00–17:00. Spec: Children's; Fiction - General; History - General; History - Local; Military History; Modern First Editions; Naval; Publishers - Ladybird Books. CC: MC; V. Notes: *Book lovers welcomed. Prefer telephone enquiries as e-mail not always responded to.*

J.R. & R.K. Ellis, ■ 53 St. Giles Street, Norwich, NR2 1JR. Prop: John Ellis and Robert Ellis. Tel: (01603) 623679. Est: 1960. Shop open: **M:** 08:30–18:00; **T:** 08:30–18:00; **W:** 08:30–18:00; **Th:** 08:30–18:00; **F:** 08:30–18:00; **S:** 08:30–18:00. Large stock. PR: £1–100. Notes: *also, Market Stalls. 25,000 books in stock.*

firstpagebooks, Oakdale House, Church Road Bergh Apton, Norwich, NR15 1BP. Prop: Mr Kim Sergeant. Tel: 01508 558484. Fax: 01508 558484. Web: www.firstpagebooks.com. Est: 2002. Mail order only; Internet and Postal. Contactable. Open: **M:** 09:30–17:00; **T:** 09:30–17:00; **W:** 09:30–17:00; **Th:** 09:30–17:00; **F:** 09:30–17:00; **S:** 09:30–17:00. Spec: Annuals; Author - Francis, Dick; Author - Greene, Graham; Autobiography; Autographs; Children's; Cinema/Film; Comedy. Cata: Modern First Editions, Giles, Rupert, Cricket. Corresp: Japanese. Notes: *General booksellers, specialising in Modern First Editions, Rock/Pop music, Cricket, Rupert, Football, Giles, Military, TV/Sci-Fi, Westerns as well as stockists in Sport & Pop memorabilia.*

Tombland Bookshop, ■ 8 Tombland, Norwich, NR3 1HF. Prop: J.G. & A.H. Freeman. Tel: 01603 490000. Fax: 01603 760610. Est: 1973. Shop open: **M:** 09:30–17:00; **T:** 09:30–17:00; **W:** 09:30–17:00; **Th:** 09:30–17:00; **F:** 09:30–17:00; **S:** 09:30–16:30. Spec: Antiquarian; Archaeology; Architecture; Art; Books about Books; Countries - General; Fiction - General; Fine leather bindings (see also Fine & Rare). CC: MC; V. Corresp: Italian, Spanish, German and French. VAT No: GB 366 6678 01. Notes: *short term parking is available and legal directly outside the shop on the double yellow lines!*

Freya Books & Antiques, St. Mary's Farm, Cheney's Lane, Tacolneston, Norwich, NR16 1DB. Prop: Colin Lewsey. Tel: (01508) 489252. Web: www.freyaantiques.co.uk. Est: 1971. Shop and/or showroom; Telephone First. Medium stock. Spec: Children's; Fiction - General; Juvenile; Booksearch; Collectables; Ephemera. PR: £1–50. CC: MC; V. Corresp: French, Danish. Notes: *Also, 3,000sq ft antique furniture. Organiser of book and antiques fairs.*

Hawes Books, 8 Keswick Road, Cringleford, Norwich, NR4 6UG. Prop: T.L.M. & H.J. Hawes. Tel: (01603) 452043. Est: 1980. Private premises. Postal only. Appointment necessary. Large stock. Spec: Genealogy; History - Local; History - National; Topography - General. PR: £2–200. VAT No: GB 342 4870 57.

Katnap Arts, 1 Whitefields, Norwich Road, Saxlingham Nethergate, Norwich, NR15 1TP. Prop: Margaret Blake. Tel: 01508 498323. Fax: 01508 498323. Web: www.katnap.co.uk. Est: 1999. Private premises. Internet and Postal. Contactable. Open: **M:** 09:00–17:30; **T:** 09:00–17:30; **W:** 09:00–17:30; **Th:** 09:00–17:30; **F:** 09:00–17:30; **S:** 09:00–17:30; **Su:** 09:00–17:30; Closed for lunch: 13:00–14:00. Spec: Annuals; Architecture; Art; Art History; Art Reference; Children's; Entertainment - General; First Editions.

David Lake, 36 Colney Lane, Cringleford, Norwich, NR4 7RE. Tel: 07909 896 809. Web: www.ukbookworld.com/members/davidlake. Est: 1990. Private premises. Postal only. Small stock. Spec: Antiquarian; Author - Blyton, Enid; Author - Crompton, Richmal; Author - Johns, W.E.; Children's; Children's - Early Titles; Children's - Illustrated; Colour-Plate. PR: £5–500. CC: PayPal.

Lyng Heath Books, 51 Pightle Way, Lyng, Norwich, NR9 5RL. Prop: Tim Holt. Tel: 01603 879037. Est: 1997. Private premises. Internet and Postal. Open: **M:** 09:00–20.00; **T:** 09:00–20.00; **W:** 09:00–20.00; **Th:** 09:00–20.00; **F:** 09:00–20.00; **S:** 09:00–20.00; **Su:** 10:00–18:00. Spec: Autobiography; Biography; Sport - Football (Soccer). CC: PayPal. cheque. Corresp: French. Notes: *Booksearch a speciality. Autobiography and Biography always in stock.*

National Trust Second Hand Bookshop, ■Blickling Hall, Blickling, Norwich, NR11 6NF. Prop: National Trust. Tel: 1263 738030. Est: 1996. Shop open: **M:** 10:30–17:30; **W:** 10:30–17:30; **Th:** 10:30–17:30; **F:** 10:30–17:30; **S:** 10:30–17:30; **Su:** 10:30–17:30. CC: MC; V. Notes: *Open in winter: Wednesday to Sundays 11:00 - 17.30.*

Steven Simpson Books, 5 Hardingham Road, Hingham, Norwich, NR9 4LX. Prop: S.J. Simpson. Tel: 01953-850-471. Fax: 01953-850-471. Web: www.stevensimpsonbooks.com. Est: 1986. Warehouse; Internet and Postal. Open: **M:** 08:00–16:30; **T:** 08:00–16:30; **W:** 08:00–16:30; **Th:** 08:00–16:30; **F:** 08:00–16:00; **S:** 08:00–12:00; Closed for lunch: 13:00–14:00. Spec: Aquatics; Botany; Fisheries; Fishes; Herpetology; Ichthyology; Marine Biology; Mycology. CC: E; MC; V. Cata: Aquaculture, Fisheries, Ichthyology, Aquaria. Corresp: German, French, Spanish, Portuguese. VAT No: GB711 6055 70. Notes: *Exclusive UK book trade distributors for Aqualog Verlag A.C.S. GmbH., Aquapress, Hans A Baensch/Mergus Verlag, Birgit Schmettkamp Verlag, NTV., & Eugen Ulmer KG. Sales Agent for FAO (Food and Agriculture Organisation of the United Nations.*

Tasburgh Books, 20 Henry Preston Road, Tasburgh, Norwich, NR15 1NU. Prop: Janet Lamb & David Newton. Tel: (01508) 471921. Est: 1995. Private premises. Internet and Postal. Telephone First. Small stock. Spec: Applied Art; Architecture; Art; Art - British; Art History; Art Reference; Decorative Art; Fine Art. CC: AE; MC; V. Cata: Architectuure, Art. Folio Society. Mem: PBFA.

Tombland Bookshop, ■8, Tombland, Norwich, NR3 1HF. Prop: J.G. & A.H. Freeman. Tel: 01603 490000. Fax: 01603 760610. Est: 1973. Shop open: **M:** 09:30–17:00; **T:** 09:30–17:00; **W:** 09:30–17:00; **Th:** 09:30–17:00; **F:** 09:30–17:00; **S:** 09:30–16:30. Spec: Academic/Scholarly; Antiquarian; Archaeology; Architecture; Art; Biography; Literary Criticism; Military. CC: E; MC; V; PayPal. VAT No: GB 366 6678 01. Notes: *Short term parking is available on double yellow lines directly outside shop.*

OLD COSTESSEY

Wensumbooks, 113 The Street, Old Costessey, NR8 5DF. Prop: Elke Katherina McKinlay. Tel: 01603 742957. Web: www.abebooks.com. Est: 2005. Private premises. Shop open: **T:** 10:00–17:00; **W:** 10:00–17:00; **Th:** 10:00–17:00; **F:** 10:00–17:00; **S:** 10:00–17:00; Closed for lunch: 13:00–14:00. Spec: Ornithology; Ephemera; Prints and Maps. CC: PayPal. Corresp: German.

SHERINGHAM

Peter Pan Bookshop, ■5 The Courtyard Station Road, Sheringham, NR26 8RF. Prop: Peter Cox. Tel: (01263) 824411. Est: 1994. Shop open: **M:** 10:30–16:30; **T:** 10:30–16:30; **W:** 10:30–16:30; **Th:** 10:30–16:30; **F:** 10:30–16:30; **S:** 10:30–16:30; **Su:** 12:00–16:00. Small stock. PR: £1–20. Notes: *Peter's Bookshop, 19 St Peter's Road (q.v.) Secondhand books published after 1990.*

Peter's Bookshop, ■ 19 St. Peter's Road, Sheringham, NR26 8QY. Prop: Peter Cox. Tel: (01263) 823008. Est: 1984. Shop open: **M:** 10:30–17:00; **T:** 10:30–17:30; **W:** 10:30–17:30; **Th:** 10:30–17:30; **F:** 10:30–17:30; **S:** 10:30–17:30; **Su:** 13:00–16:30. Very large stock. Spec: Children's; Fiction - General; Literature; Ephemera; Large Print Books. PR: £1–100. Notes: *The Peter Pan Bookshop, Sheringham, Norfolk (q.v.) Winter hours: (Nov. to Mar.) Mon./Tue. & Thurs. to Sat. 10:30–16:30.*

SOUTH BURLINGHAM

Mermaid Books (Burlingham), Old Hall, Norwich Road, South Burlingham, NR13 4EY. Prop: (*) Peter Scupham. Tel: (01493) 750804. Fax: (01493) 750804. Est: 1991. Private premises. Appointment necessary. Spec: Antiquarian; Literature; Poetry. PR: £5–500. Mem: PBFA.

SWANTON ABBOT

Hamish Riley-Smith, Swanton Abbot Hall , Swanton Abbot, NR10 5DJ. Prop: Hamish Riley-Smith. Tel: 01692538244. Web: www.riley-smith.com. Est: 1974. Private premises. Internet and Postal. Appointment necessary. Open: **M:** 09:00–17:30; **T:** 09:00–17:30; **W:** 09:00–17:30; **Th:** 09:00–17:30; **F:** 09:00–17:30; **S:** 09:00–17:30; **Su:** 09:00–17:30; Closed for lunch: 13:00–14:00. Spec: Antiquarian; Arabica; Economics; History - Economic Thought; Philosophy; Printing and Mind of Man; Science - History of; Scottish Enlightenment. Cata: Economics, Philosophy, PMM, Sciences, Arithmetic.

WATTON

J.C. Books, ■ 55 High Street, Watton, IP25 6AB. Prop: C.F. & J.A. Ball & T.F. Robinson. Tel: (01953) 883488. Est: 1992. Shop open: **M:** 10:00–16:30; **T:** 10:00–16:30; **W:** 10:00–16:30; **Th:** 10:00–12:30; **F:** 10:00–16:30; **S:** 10:00–16:30. Medium stock. Spec: Theatre. PR: £1–1,000. CC: MC; V. Mem: PBFA. Notes: *Exhibits at PBFA fairs.*

WELLS-NEXT-THE-SEA

The Old Station Pottery & Bookshop, The Old Station, Wells-next-the-Sea, NR23 1LY. Prop: Thom Borthwick. Tel: 01328 710847. Est: 1975. Shop and/or gallery; Shop open: **M:** 09:00–17:30; **T:** 14.00–17:30; **W:** 09:00–17:30; **F:** 09:00–17:30; **S:** 09:00–17:30; **Su:** 09:00–17:30; Closed for lunch: 12.30–13.30. Large stock. Spec: Annuals; Archaeology; Art; Author - Ardizzone, Edward; Author - Ransome, Arthur; Author - Read, Miss; Author - Saville, M.; Author - Williamson, Henry. PR: £1–50. CC: PayPal, Cash & Cheques only. Notes: *General stock including a large range of children's, Edwardian / Victorian 'ripping yarns' and Penguins.*

WYMONDHAM

The Bookshop, ■ 1 Town Green, Wymondham, NR18 0PN. Prop: M. & A.C. Thompson. Tel: (01953) 602244. Web: www.abebooks.com/home/MANDACTHOMPSON. Est: 1975. Shop open: **M:** 10:45–16:45; **T:** 10:30–1645; **Th:** 10:30–16:45; **F:** 10:30–16:45; **S:** 10:00–17:00. Medium stock. Spec: Autographs; Aviation; Cinema/Film; Comics; Entertainment - General; Literature; Music - General; Music - Folk & Irish Folk. PR: £1–300.

Turret House, ■ 27 Middleton Street, Wymondham, NR18 0AB. Prop: Dr. D.H. & R.A. Morgan. Tel: (01953) 603462. Est: 1972. Shop open: **M:** 10:00–17:00; **T:** 10:00–17:00; **W:** 00.00–00.00; **Th:** 10:00–17:00; **F:** 10:00–17:00; **S:** 10:00–17:00. Small stock. Spec: Astronomy; Bacteriology; Biochemistry; Biology - General; Chemistry; Evolution; Genetics; History - Science. PR: £1–1,000. Cata: lists of science & medicine. Mem: PBFA. Notes: *Usually open Monday – Saturday 09:00–17:00 but telephone first to save a wasted journey. Please ring the bell even if apparently closed.*

M. and A.C. Thompson, ■The Bookshop 1 Town Green, Wymonham, NR18 0PN. Prop: Allan C. Thompson. Tel: 01953 602244. Est: 1975. Shop open: **M:** 10:30–16:45; **T:** 10:30–16:45; **Th:** 10:30–16:45; **F:** 10:30–16:45; **S:** 10:00–17:00. Spec: Autographs; Aviation; Children's; Comic Books & Annuals; Comics; Entertainment - General; Fiction - General; Folklore.

NORTH YORKSHIRE

AUSTWICK

Austwick Hall Books, Austwick Hall Town Head, Austwick, Lancaster, LA2 8BS. Prop: Michael Pearson. Tel: 015242 51794. Est: 2000. Private premises. Internet only. Appointment necessary. Open: **M:** 09:00–17:30; **T:** 09:00–17:30; **W:** 09:00–17:30; **Th:** 09:00–17:30; **F:** 09:00–17:30; **S:** 09:00–17:30; **Su:** 09:00–17:30; Closed for lunch: 13:00–14:00. Spec: Academic/Scholarly; Antiquarian; Biology - General; Botany; Evolution; Exploration; Farriers; Geology. CC: V; Paypal.

AYSGARTH

Richard Axe Rare & Out of Print Books, The Old Youth Hostel, Aysgarth, DL8 3SR. Prop: Richard Axe. Est: 2006. Office and/or bookroom; Appointment necessary. Open: **M:** 09:00–17:30; **T:** 09:00–17:30; **W:** 09:00–17:30; **Th:** 09:00–17:30; **F:** 09:00–17:30; **S:** 09:00–17:30; **Su:** 09:00–17:30; Closed for lunch: 13:00–14:00. CC: AE; D; E; JCB; MC; V. Notes: *35 rooms of books to be developed over next two years. Open strictly by appointment. Also at 12 Cheltenham Crescent, Harrogate North Yorkshire (q.v.)*

BILLINGHAM

Norton Books, 18 Wolviston Road, Billingham, TS22 5AA. Prop: C. Casson. Tel: (01642) 553965. Fax: (01642) 553965. Est: 1981. Private premises. Internet and Postal. Appointment necessary. Spec: Antiquarian; Author - Barnes, Djuna; Author - Beckett, S.; Author - Cocteau, Jean; Author - Crosby, Harry & Caresse; Author - Cunard, Nancy; Author - Durrell, Lawrence; Author - Hemingway, Ernest. PR: £10–2,000. CC: PayPal. Cata: Ex=patriate literature 1920-1940.

Spike's Books, 23 Roseberry Flats The Causeway, Billingham, TS23 2LD. Prop: Stephen Phelps. Tel: 01642 643651. Est: 2003. Private premises. Internet only. Spec: Adult; Fiction - Adventure; Fiction - Crime, Detective, Spy, Thrillers; Fiction - Fantasy, Horror; Fiction - Historical; Fiction - Romantic; Fiction - Science Fiction; Fiction - Westerns. CC: Paypal, Nochex, Moneybookers. Notes: *Credit Card payments accepted through Paypal, Nochex, Moneybookers.*

CATTERICK VILLAGE

Brock Books, 43 High Street, Catterick Village, DL10 7LL. Prop: Jude Haslam. Tel: (01748) 818729. Web: www.brockbooks.com. Est: 2002. Private premises. Internet and Postal. Appointment necessary. Open: **M:** 09:00–21.00; **T:** 09:00–16:00; **W:** 09:00–20.00; **Th:** 09:00–21.00; **F:** 13:00–18:00; **S:** 09:00–17:00; **Su:** 10:00–16:00. Very small stock. Spec: Animals and Birds; Annuals; Antiquarian; Archaeology; Art; Art - British; Art History; Art Reference. PR: £1–500. CC: PayPal. Corresp: Espanol. Mem: Society of Bookbinders and the Federation of Small Businesses. Notes: *Book Restoration service offered. Individual book repair assessment carried out free of charge. Communication also in Spanish.*

DACRE

Theatreshire Books, Dacre Hall, Dacre, HG3 4ET. Prop: Catherine Shire. Tel: (01423) 780497. Fax: (01423) 781957. Est: 2000. Private premises. Internet and Postal. Telephone First. Small stock. Spec: Architecture; Cinema/Film; Drama; Engineering; Fire & Fire Fighters; Music - Gilbert & Sullivan; Performing Arts; Theatre. PR: £1–5,000. CC: Paypal. Cata: Theatre. Notes: *Specialising in theatre, performing arts, cinema, theatre prints and engravings, theatre postcards.*

GIGGLESWICK

Post Horn Books, Belle Hill, Giggleswick, BD24 0BA. Prop: Patricia & Edward Saunders. Tel: (01729) 823438. Est: 1979. Private premises. Spec: Alpinism/Mountaineering; Countries - Africa; Countries - Asia; County - Local; Environment, The; Religion - Quakers; Sport - Caving (Spelaeology); Topography - Local.

GUISBOROUGH

The Guisborough Bookshop, ■ 4 Chaloner Street, Guisborough, TS14 6QD. Tel: (01287) 639018. Shop open: **M:** 09:00–17:15; **T:** 09:00–17:15; **W:** 09:00–17:15; **Th:** 09:00–17:15; **F:** 09:00–17:15; **S:** 09:00–17:15. Spec: History - Local; Topography - Local. CC: D; E; JCB; MC; V. Cata: at Christmas time.

K.A. McCaughtrie, 7 Grosvenor Square, Guisborough, TS14 6PB. Tel: (01287) 633663. Est: 1986. Private premises. Postal only. Appointment necessary. Small stock. Spec: Biography; Crime (True); Fiction - Crime, Detective, Spy, Thrillers. PR: £1–50.

HARROGATE

Richard Axe Rare & Out of Print Books, ■ 12 Cheltenham Crescent, Harrogate, HG1 1DH. Prop: Richard Axe. Tel: (01423) 561867. Fax: (01423) 561837. Est: 1981. Shop open at: The Old Youth Hostel, Aysgarth, Nth Yorkshire DL8 3SR. Open: **T:** 10:00–17:30; **W:** 10:00–17:30; **Th:** 10:00–17:30; **F:** 10:00–17:30; **S:** 10:00–17:30. Very large stock. Spec: Antiquarian; Antiques; Art History; Ceramics; Cookery/Gastronomy; History - General; Literary Criticism; Literature. PR: £2–1,000. CC: AE; D; E; JCB; MC; V. Mem: PBFA. Notes: *Libraries purchased throughout UK and worldwide. Open at other times by appointment. 100,000 books in stock. Viewing at alternative premises by appointment only (q.v.)*

Books For All, ■ 23a Commercial Street, Harrogate, HG1 1UB. Prop: Jenny Todd. Tel: (01423) 561982. Est: 1997. Shop open: **M:** 10:30–17:00; **T:** 10:30–17:00; **W:** 10:30–17:00; **Th:** 10:30–17:00; **F:** 10:30–17:00; **S:** 10:30–17:00. Large stock. Spec: Art History; Biography; Children's; Cookery/Gastronomy; Esoteric; Fiction - Science Fiction; History - General; Horticulture. PR: £1–150. CC: MC; V; SW.

Macbuiks, 7 Leadhall Crescent, Harrogate, HG2 9NG. Prop: Sally Mackenzie. Tel: 01423 870978. Est: 1997. Private premises. Internet and Postal. Appointment necessary. Spec: Author - Kipling, Rudyard; Children's; Children's - Illustrated; Crafts; Gardening - General; Gardening - Organic; Wine. CC: Paypal. Mem: Ibooknet.

HELMSLEY

Helmsley Antiquarian & Secondhand Books, ■The Old Fire Station, Borogate, Helmsley, YO62 5BN. Prop: Myles Moorby. Tel: (01439) 770014. Est: 1985. Shop open: **M:** 10:00–17:00; **T:** 10:00–17:00; **W:** 09:00–17:00; **Th:** 10:00–17:00; **F:** 10:00–17:00; **S:** 10:00–17:00; **Su:** 12:00–17:00. Medium stock. Spec: Architecture; Art; Topography - Local. PR: £1–100. CC: MC; V. VAT No: GB 390 4976 18.

INGLETON

John Killeen, Pendragon 16 Main Street, Ingleton, LA6 3HF. Prop: John Killeen. Tel: (015242) 41021. Est: 1974. Private premises. Shop open: **M:** 09:00–17:00; **T:** 09:00–17:00; **W:** 09:00–17:00; **Th:** 09:00–17:00; **F:** 09:00–17:00. Medium stock. Spec: Literature; Marxism; Philosophy; Religion - Catholic; Topography - Local; Travel - General. PR: £4–1,000. Corresp: French. Mem: PBFA. Notes: *Attends fairs in Northern England. Irregular opening hours.*

KIRKBY FLEETHAM

Sugen & Co., Meadowside Lumley Lane, Kirkby Fleetham, DL7 0SL. Prop: Mark. Tel: 01609748582. Web: www.film-tvtieins.com. Est: 1993. Private premises. Internet and Postal. Medium stock. Spec: Cinema/Film; Television. PR: £3–100. CC: PayPal. Mem: IOBA. Notes: *Mail Order only - no shop premises. Book stock includes Film and TV tie ins.*

KNARESBOROUGH

Pennymead Books, 1 Brewerton Street, Knaresborough, HG5 8AZ. Prop: David Druett. Tel: (01423) 865962. Fax: (01423) 547057. Web: www.pennymead.com. Est: 1984. Private premises. Internet and Postal. Telephone First. Small stock. Spec: Carriages & Driving; Cartography; Colonial; Countries - Bahamas, The; Countries - Bermuda; Countries - Caribbean, The; Countries - Cuba; Countries - Dominican Republic. PR: £5–5,000. CC: JCB; MC; V. Mem: PBFA. VAT No: GB 387 9262 94. Notes: *Also, postage stamp auctioneer.*

LEALHOLM

Stepping Stones Bookshop, ■ Stepping Stones, Lealholm, near Whitby, YO21 2AJ. Prop: Judith & Lawrence Davies. Tel: (01947) 897382. Est: 1970. Shop open: **M:** 10:00–17:00; **T:** 10:00–17:00; **W:** 10:00–17:00; **Th:** 09:00–17:00; **F:** 10:00–17:00; **S:** 10:00–17:00; **Su:** 10:00–17:00. Medium stock. Spec: Children's; Children's - Illustrated. PR: £1–100.

LONG PRESTON

Jo Lunt, Barn Cottage Church Street, Long Preston, BD23 4NJ. Prop: Jo Lunt. Tel: (01729) 840152. Est: 1993. Private premises. Postal only. Appointment necessary. Medium stock. Spec: Publishers - Pelican; Publishers - Penguin; Publishers - Puffin; Ephemera. PR: £1–100. Cata: Penguin Books, all series. Corresp: French, German.

PICKERING

Alan Avery, 15 Middleton Road, Pickering, YO18 8AL. Prop: Alan Avery. Tel: (01751) 476863. Web: www.abebooks.com/home/avery. Est: 1988. Private premises. Postal only. Appointment necessary. Open: **M:** 09:00–17:00; **T:** 09:00–17:17; **W:** 09:00–17:00; **Th:** 09:00–17:00; **F:** 09:00–17:00; **S:** 09:00–13:00. Small stock. Spec: Folio Society, The. PR: £5–60. CC: AE; MC; V. Notes: *Specialist in Folio Society books. Issues 'Avery's Folio Society Catalogue, 1947 - 2007' which lists all known Folio Society books and their used values. Available via the website or direct from the dealer. £5-50 in the UK, including P&P.*

Sybil Buckley, ■Pickering Antique Centre, Southgate, Pickering, YO18 8BN. Tel: (01751) 477210. Est: 1998. Shop open: **M:** 10:00–17:00; **T:** 10:00–17:00; **W:** 10:00–17:00; **Th:** 10:00–17:00; **F:** 10:00–17:00; **S:** 10:00–17:00; **Su:** 11:00–17:00. Small stock. PR: £1–200. CC: MC; V; DELTA.

Cobweb Books, ■Ye Olde Corner Shoppe, 1 Pickering Road, Thornton–Le–Dale, Pickering, YO18 7LG. Prop: Robin & Sue Buckler. Tel: (01751) 476638. Web: www.cobwebbooks.co.uk. Est: 1989. Shop open: **M:** 10:00–17:00; **T:** 10:00–17:00; **W:** 10:00–17:00; **Th:** 10:00–17:00; **F:** 10:00–17:00; **S:** 10:00–17:00; **Su:** 10:00–17:00. Very large stock. Spec: Antiquarian; Art; Aviation; Biography; Children's; Children's - Illustrated; Fine & Rare; First Editions. PR: £1–1,000. CC: AE; E; JCB; MC; V; SW.

RAINTON

Pandion Books, 10 Carr Close, Rainton, Thirsk, YO7 3QE. Prop: Les Wray. Tel: 01845 578224. Est: 1980. Private premises. Internet and Postal. Appointment necessary. Spec: Natural History; Ornithology. Mem: PBFA.

RICHMOND

Richmond Books, ■ 20 Trinity, Church Square, Richmond, DL10 4QN. Prop: Bob & Gail Ions. Tel: (01325) 377332. Est: 1995. Shop open: **M:** 09:30–16:30; **T:** 09:30–16:30; **W:** 09:30–16:30; **Th:** 09:30–16:30; **F:** 09:30–16:30; **S:** 09:30–16:30; **Su:** 10:00–16:30. Medium stock. Spec: Art; Autobiography; Aviation; Biography; Countries - Great Britain; Fiction - General; Fiction - Crime, Detective, Spy, Thrillers; History - General. PR: £1–200. Cata: 8 a year.

J.P. Vokes, Linton House, 43 Bargate, Richmond. Prop: Jonathan Peter Vokes. Tel: (01748) 824946. Fax: (01748) 824946. Est: 1972. Private premises. Postal only. Small stock. Spec: Fiction - General; Gardening - General; Horticulture; Military History; Natural History; Topography - General; Travel - General; Booksearch. PR: £1–500.

RIPON

Hornseys' of Ripon, ■The Gallery, 3 Kirkgate, Ripon, HG4 1PA. Prop: Bruce, Susan & Daniel Hornsey. Tel: (01765) 602878. Web: www.hornseys,com. Est: 1976. Shop open: **M:** 10:00–17:30; **T:** 10:00–17:30; **W:** 10:00–17:30; **Th:** 10:00–17:30; **F:** 10:00–17:30; **S:** 10:00–17:30; **Su:** 12:00–4:00. Very large stock. Spec: Antiques; Architecture; Art - British; Art Reference; Arts & Crafts Era; Arts, The; Children's; History - British. PR: £1–8,000. CC: MC; V; Switch. VAT No: GB 809 4995 80. Notes: *Our fine gallery space includes Modern and Contemporary Art, Ceramics by members of the Northern Potters Association, Jewellery and Glass. We focus on good quality books on the Arts, Design, Architecture, Yorkshire and Childrens' Books.*

SALTBURN–BY–THE–SEA

Saltburn Bookshop, ■ 3 Amber Street, Saltburn–by–the–Sea, TS12 1DT. Prop: Josef Thompson. Tel: (01287) 623335. Est: 1978. Shop open: **W:** 11:00–16:00; **Th:** 11:00–16:00; **F:** 11:00–16:00; **S:** 11:00–16:00; Closed for lunch: 13:00–14:00. Medium stock. Spec: Booksearch. PR: £1–100. Corresp: French.

SCARBOROUGH

Antiquary Ltd., (Bar Bookstore), ■ 4 Swanhill Road, Scarborough, YO11 1BW. Prop: Michael Chaddock. Tel: (01723) 500141. Web: www.ukbookworld.com/members/Barbooks. Est: 1976. Shop open: **T:** 10:30–17:00; **W:** 10:30–17:00; **Th:** 10:30–17:00; **F:** 10:30–17:00; **S:** 10:30–17:00. Medium stock. Spec: Academic/Scholarly; Antiquarian; Archaeology; Architecture; Art; Author - Housman, A.E.; Biography; History - General. PR: £1–450. Mem: PBFA. Notes: *Booksearch.*

Book Emporium, ■2, Queen Street, Scarborough, YP11 1HA. Prop: Shaun Lofthouse. Tel: 01723506057. Fax: 01723506057. Est: 1989. Shop open: **M:** 10:00–17:00; **T:** 10:00–17:00; **W:** 10:00–17:00; **Th:** 10:00–17:00; **F:** 10:00–17:00; **S:** 10:00–17:00; **Su:** 10:00–17:00. CC: MC; V. Notes: *We believe that each customer is important. Close at 4pm from Oct to March.*

The Bookshelf, ■ 6 Victoria Road, Scarborough, YO11 1SD. Prop: Mrs. Leslie Anne Stones. Tel: (01723) 381677. Web: www.bookshelf.scarborough.co.uk. Est: 2000. Shop open: **M:** 10:00–17:00; **T:** 10:00–17:00; **W:** 10:00–17:00; **Th:** 10:00–17:00; **F:** 10:00–17:00; **S:** 10:00–17:00. Small stock. PR: £1–100. Corresp: Some French.

Richard Dalby, 4 Westbourne Park, Scarborough, YO12 4AT. Tel: (01723) 377049. Est: 1976. Private premises. Postal only. Small stock. Spec: Fiction - Fantasy, Horror; Fiction - Supernatural; Ghosts; Literature. Mem: PBFA.

Doodles Bookshop, ■ 45 Newborough, Scarborough, YO11 1NF. Prop: Nicholas Paul Ironside. Tel: 01723 379079. Est: 2004. Shop open: **M:** 10:00–17:00; **T:** 10:00–17:00; **W:** 10:00–17:00; **Th:** 10:00–17:00; **F:** 10:00–17:00; **S:** 10:00–17:00; **Su:** 10:00–17:00. CC: AE; MC; V. Notes: *Open in winter: 11:00 – 16:00.*

Ramrod Antiques, ■15 Market Vaults, St Helen Square, Scarborough, YO11 1EU. Prop: David John William Stroud. Tel: 01723 376070. Fax: 01723 376070. Web: www.ramrodantiques.co.uk. Est: 2004. Shop open: **T:** 10:00–16:00; **W:** 10:00–16:00; **Th:** 12:00–16:00; **F:** 10:00–16:00; **S:** 10:00–16:00. Spec: Arms & Armour; Firearms/Guns; Military; Rural Life; Sport - Field Sports; Booksearch.

Reeves Technical Books, Flat O, Dr. Smarts Homes, Woodland Grove, Scarborough, YO12 6NE. Prop: W.H. & L.I. Reeves. Tel: 01723 503276. Fax: 01723 503276 (Ring First). Web: www.reevestechnicalbooks.co.uk. Est: 1975. Private premises. Telephone First. Open: **M:** 09:00–17:30; **T:** 09:00–17:30; **W:** 09:00–17:30; **Th:** 09:00–17:30; **F:** 09:00–17:30; **S:** 09:00–17:30; **Su:** 09:00–17:30; Closed for lunch: 13:00–14:00. Spec: Academic/Scholarly; Annuals; Architecture; Arts & Crafts Era; Botany; Bridge; Building & Construction; Catalogues Raisonnes. CC: Paypal. Cata: Carpentry, Wood Machining, Furniture, Building Co. Notes: *I specialise in Books mainly for the Building Industry (Woodworking in all its forms). With a few exceptions all my Books are of a technical nature with no fiction.*

SELBY

Anthony Vickers Books, 23 Baffam Gardens, Selby, Y08 9AY. Prop: Anthony Vickers. Tel: 01757 705949. Est: 1994. Private premises. Internet and Postal. Telephone First. Spec: Aeronautics; Alpinism/Mountaineering; Antiques; Archaeology - Industrial; Architecture; Author - Raistrick, Arthur; Author - Rolt, L.T.C.; Author - Wainwright, Alfred. Cata: Topography, Transport, Mountaineering. Industrial. Mem: PBFA. Notes: *Stock includes books on Yorkshire.*

SETTLE

Peter M. Thornber, 3 School Hill, Settle, BD24 9HB. Tel: (01729) 824067. Est: 1997. Private premises. Appointment necessary. Small stock. Spec: Agriculture; Antiquarian; Archives; Auction Catalogues; Bibliography; Bibliophily; Books about Books; Ecclesiastical History & Architecture. PR: £5–500. Corresp: French. Notes: *Also, valuations, consultancy and research, commissions at auctions, bookhunting, talks and masterclasses on all aspects of bookmanship.*

SKIPTON

Grove Rare Books, ■The Old Post Office Bolton Abbey, Skipton, BD23 6EX. Prop: Andrew & Janet Sharpe, Adam Yates. Tel: (01756) 710717. Fax: (01756) 711098. Web: www.grovebookshop.co.uk. Est: 1984. Shop open: **T:** 10:00–17:00; **W:** 10:00–17:00; **Th:** 10:00–17:00; **F:** 10:00–17:00; **S:** 10:00–17:00; Closed for lunch: 13:00–14:00. Medium stock. Spec: Antiquarian; Architecture; Author - Brontes, The; Author - Raistrick, Arthur; Author - Ratcliffe, Dorothy Una; Author - Williamson, Henry; Bindings; Countries - England. PR: £10–3,000. CC: JCB; MC; V; SW, SO. Cata: Sporting, Yorkshire ,Topography. Mem: ABA; PBFA; ILAB. VAT No: GB 756 1269 18. Notes: *Charming 18th Century building on The Duke of Devonshire's estate in the Yorkshire Dales National Park. Specialising in Yorkshire Topography, Hunting, Shooting, Fishing, Fine Bindings and Library sets. Trade callers welcome.*

C. L. Hawley, 26 Belgrave Street, Skipton, BD23 1QB. Prop: Catherine Hawley. Tel: (01756) 792380. Web: www.clhawley.co.uk. Est: 2000. Private premises. Postal only. Contactable. Small stock. Spec: Academic/Scholarly; Arts, The; Biography; Children's; Ecology; English; Ethics; History - General. PR: £2–250. CC: JCB; MC; V; debit cards. Cata: literary criticism of children's works. Mem: Ibooknet. Notes: *Academic books especially literary criticism, literary and cultural theory, as well as history, psychology, etc. Small selection of Yorkshire local history. Some children's books including Fidra reprints. No-obligation booksearch service.*

Skipton Antiques Centre, ■ Cavendish Street, Skipton, BD23 2AB. Tel: (01756) 797667. Shop open: **M:** 10:30–16:30; **T:** 10:30–16:30; **W:** 10:30–16:30; **Th:** 10:30–16:30; **F:** 10:30–16:30; **S:** 10:30–16:30; **Su:** 10:30–16:00. PR: £1–5,000.

STAITHES

John L Capes (Books Maps & Prints), Church Street, Staithes, TS13 5DB. Prop: John Capes. Tel: 01947 840790. Web: www.johncapes.com. VOIPpro: BT. VOIPnum: 05600739120. Est: 1969. Private premises. Internet and Postal. Appointment necessary. Spec: Author - 19th Century; Author - Haggard, Sir Henry Rider; Author - Jefferies, R.; Authors - Women; Fiction - General; Fiction - Crime, Detective, Spy, Thrillers; Fiction - Historical; Fiction - Supernatural. CC: Paypal. Mem: PBFA. Notes: *Specialising VICTORIAN FICTION Yorkshire Topograpy. Sheffield Local & Industrial History, Fishing Industry. Staithes Group Painters.*

STOCKTON-ON-THE-FOREST

York Modern Books, 14 The Bull Centre, Stockton-on-the-Forest, York. Prop: Philip Barraclough. Tel: 01904 400 331. Fax: 01904 400 331. Web: www.yorkbooks.com. Est: 2005. Storeroom; Appointment necessary. Open: **T:** 10:00–18:00; **W:** 10:00–18:00; **Th:** 10:00–18:00; **F:** 10:00–18:00; **S:** 10:00–18:00. Spec: History - 20th Century; History - British; Illustrated - General; Literary Travel; Modern First Editions; Private Press. CC: AE; MC; V; PayPal. Cata: on modern firsts, private press, illustrated. Mem: PBFA. VAT No: GB 859 9635 50.

THIRSK

Hambleton Books, ■ 43 Market Place, Thirsk, YO7 1HA. Prop: Terry & Vicki Parr. Tel: 01845 522343. Est: 1997. Shop open: **M:** 09:00–17:30; **T:** 09:00–17:30; **W:** 09:00–17:30; **Th:** 09:00–17:30; **F:** 09:00–17:30; **S:** 09:00–17:30; **Su:** 10:30–16:30. Spec: Annuals; Author - Herriot, James; Autobiography; Biography; Children's; Children's - Early Titles; Cinema/Film; Comic Books & Annuals. CC: MC; V; Maestro, American Express. Mem: BA. Notes: *Books available online at Panda Books on www.abebooks.co.uk.*

Pickering Bookshop, ■ 43 Market Place, Thirsk, YO7 1HA. Prop: Terry & Vicki Parr. Tel: 01845 522343. Est: 1997. Shop open: **M:** 09:00–17:00; **T:** 09:00–17:00; **W:** 09:00–17:00; **Th:** 09:00–17:00; **F:** 09:00–17:00; **S:** 09:00–17:00. Spec: Annuals; Children's; Cinema/Film; Comic Books & Annuals; Fiction - General; First Editions; History - General. CC: MC; V; Maestro. Mem: BA. Notes: *See also Hambleton Books (q.v.)*

Potterton Books, The Old Rectory Sessay, Thirsk, YO7 3LZ. Prop: Clare Jameson. Tel: (01845) 501218. Fax: (01845) 501439. Web: www.pottertonbooks.co.uk. Est: 1982. Office and/or bookroom; Internet and Postal. Spec: Antiquarian; Antiques; Applied Art; Architecture; Art Reference; Carpets - General; Ceramics; Decorative Art. PR: £5–5,000. CC: AE; D; MC; V. Notes: *Also, booksearch.*

WHITBY

Clewlow Books of Whitby, ■ Sandringham House 6 & 8 Skinner Street, Whitby, YO21 3AJ. Prop: Allan Clewlow. Tel: (01947) 821655. Est: 1979. Shop open: **F:** 11:00–17:00; **S:** 11:00–17:00. PR: £5–500. CC: MC; V. Corresp: French. Mem: PBFA. Notes: *Often open at other times than those specified, but perhaps ring first before calling.*

Endeavour Books, ■ 1 Grape Lane, Whitby, YO22 4BA. Tel: (01947) 821331. Web: www.endeavourbooks.co.uk. Est: 1989. Shop open: **M:** 10:30–17:00; **T:** 10:30–17:00; **W:** 10:30–17:00; **Th:** 10:30–17:00; **F:** 10:30–17:00; **S:** 10:30–17:00; **Su:** 10:30–17:00. Large stock. PR: £3–50. CC: MC; V.

YARM

Richard J. Hodgson (Books), Manor Farm, Kirklevington, Yarm, TS15 9PY. Prop: Richard Hodgson. Tel: 07950 647377. Est: 1989. Private premises. Book fairs only. Appointment necessary. Medium stock. Spec: Agriculture; Author - Baedeker, Karl Travel - Antiquarian; Author - Darwin, Charles; Cattlemen; Colour-Plate; Ex-Libris; Farming & Livestock; Guide Books. PR: £1–1,000. Mem: PBFA. Notes: *Visitors are welcome, by appointment, to view items specific to their previous requests.*

YORK

Barbican Bookshop, ■ 24 Fossgate, York, YO1 9TA. Prop: Wesley Owen Books and Music. Tel: (01904) 653643. Fax: (01904) 653643. Web: www.barbicanbookshop.co.uk. Est: 1960. Shop open: **M:** 09:30–17:30; **T:** 09:30–17:30; **W:** 09:15–17:30; **Th:** 09:15–17:30; **F:** 09:15–17:30; **S:** 09:15–17:30. Large stock. Spec: Aeronautics; Aviation; Bibles; Buses/Trams; Canals/Inland Waterways; Ecclesiastical History & Architecture; Folio Society, The; History - General. PR: £1–500. CC: E; JCB; MC; V. Cata: Aviation, Railway, Yorkshire, Theology. Mem: PBFA; BA; York Tourism Bureau. Notes: *Also, new books, remainders, cards, CDs, DVDs and gift items. Our shop has 10 rooms and browsers are welcome. Mail Order available. Lists of secondhand books on core subjects are available on request.*

Boer War Books, 8 Mill Lane, Heworth, York, YO31 7TE. Prop: E. A. Hackett. Tel: 01904 415829. Fax: 01904 415829. Est: 1969. Private premises. Postal only. Appointment necessary. Spec: Countries - South Africa; History - South Africa; Military; Military History; War - Boer, The.

Courtney & Hoff, Hutton Hall Farm Hutton Wendasley, York, YO26 7LZ. Prop: Gerrit van Hoff. Tel: (01904) 738885. Fax: Mob: 07762 378540. Est: 1986. Storeroom; Appointment necessary. Small stock. Spec: Antiquarian; Architecture; Bindings; Ecclesiastical History & Architecture; Stone Masonry. PR: £1–900. Corresp: Dutch. Mem: PBFA. Notes: *Abstract & figurative sculpture; also vellum and leather.*

Empire Books, 12 Queens Staith Mews, York, YO1 6HH. Prop: Colin Hinchcliffe. Tel: (01904) 610679. Fax: (01904) 641664. Web: www.empirebooks.org.uk. Est: 1990. Private premises. Internet and Postal. Appointment necessary. Large stock. Spec: Academic/Scholarly; Africana; Architecture; Australiana; Colonial; Countries - Africa; Countries - Asia; Countries - Atlantic Ocean. PR: £3–1,000. CC: AE; MC; V; PayPal. Cata: Pacific Islands. VAT No: GB 647 2977 92. Notes: *We specialise in books, maps & engravings on Pacific Islands and British Parliamentary Papers on all subjects.*

Fossgate Books, ■36 Fossgate, York, YO1 9TF. Prop: Alexander Helstrip. Tel: 01904 641389. Est: 1992. Shop open: **M:** 10:00–17:30; **T:** 10:00–17:30; **W:** 10:00–17:30; **Th:** 10:00–17:30; **F:** 10:00–17:30; **S:** 10:00–17:30. Spec: Academic/Scholarly; Arts, The; Auction Catalogues; Cinema/Film; Fiction - General; Folio Society, The; History - General; Literature. CC: MC; V. Cata: Folio Society. Corresp: Spanish.

Second Nature at Knapton Bookbarn, Back Lane Knapton, York, YO26 6QJ. Prop: Tom and Julia Lawson. Tel: (01904) 339493. Web: www.secondnaturebooks.com. Est: 1996. Private premises. Postal only. Medium stock. Spec: Natural History; Nature, New Naturalist, Scottish Interest; Zoology. PR: £5–500. Notes: *Specialist stock of natural history and travel with a natural history interest.*

Lucius Books, ■ 41 Fossgate, York, YO1 9TF. Prop: James Hallgate & Georgina Harris. Tel: 01904 640111. Fax: 01904 640444. Web: www.luciusbooks.com. Est: 1993. Shop open: **T:** 10:00–18:00; **W:** 10:00–18:00; **Th:** 10:00–18:00; **F:** 10:00–18:00; **S:** 10:00–18:00. Small stock. Spec: Author - Aldin, Cecil; Author - Barker, Cecily M.; Author - Blyton, Enid; Author - Bramah, Ernest; Author - Brent-Dyer, Elinor M.; Author - Burroughs, William; Author - Carr, John Dickson; Author - Chandler, Raymond. PR: £30–20,000. CC: D; E; JCB; MC; V; Debit. Corresp: French. Mem: ABA; PBFA; ILAB. VAT No: GB 766 9110 08.

Nostalgia Publciations Ltd, 91-93 Nunnery Lane, York, YO23 1AH. Tel: (01904) 624901. Prop: Jim Barker. Fax: (01904) 654925. Web: www.nostalgia-publications.co.uk. Est: 1983. Shop, Internet and Postal. **T:** 11:00–17:30; **W:** 11:00–17:30; **Th:** 11:00–17:30; **F:** 11:00–17:30; **S:** 11:00–17:30. Medium stock. Spec: Glamour; Magazines & Periodicals; Ephemera. PR: £1–100. CC: MC; V. Notes: *Mail order.*

Philip Martin Music Books, ■ 22 Huntington Road (Office), York, YO31 8RL. Prop: Martin & Eleanor Dreyer. Tel: (01904) 636111. Fax: (01904) 658889. Est: 1975. Shop open at: 38 Fossgate, York YO1 9TF. Open: **T:** 10:00–17:30; **W:** 10:00–17:30; **Th:** 10:00–17:30; **F:** 10:00–17:30; **S:** 10:00–17:30; Closed for lunch: 13:00–14:00. Spec: Music - General; Music - Classical; Music - Composers; Music - Gilbert & Sullivan; Music - Jazz & Blues; Music - Musicians; Music - Opera; Music - Orchestral. PR: £1–75. CC: AE; MC; V; most debit and credit cards. Cata: 3 per year. Corresp: French. VAT No: GB 332 3786 58. Notes: *As well as secondhand books, we have a comprehensive display of new books about music. We also stock secondhand music for most instruments and orchestral scores.*

Minster Gate Bookshop, ■ 8 Minster Gates, York, YO1 7HL. Prop: Nigel Wallace. Tel: (01904) 621812. Fax: (01904) 622960. Web: www.minstergatebooks.co.uk/ minstergatebooks.com. Est: 1970. Shop open: **M:** 10:00–17:30; **T:** 10:00–17:30; **W:** 10:00–17:30; **Th:** 10:00–17:30; **F:** 10:00–17:30; **S:** 10:00–17:30; **Su:** 11:00–17:00. Large stock. Spec: Antiquarian; Archaeology; Architecture - Theatre; Art; Arthurian; Author - Dickens, Charles; Author - Dulac, Edmund; Author - Rackham, Arthur. PR: £1–500. CC: MC; V. Cata: Folklore, Illustrated & Children's books. Corresp: French, German, Spanish. Mem: PBFA. VAT No: GB 450 7122 78.

O'Flynn Books, 2 Dalguise Grove, Heworth Green, York, YO31 7SY. Prop: D. Francis O'Flynn. Tel: 01904-414925. Web: www.oflynnbooks.com. Est: 1969. Private premises. Internet and Postal. Appointment necessary. Shop at: Red House Antique Centre, Duncombe Place, York. Large stock. Spec: Animals and Birds; Antiquities; Art Reference; Atlases; British Books; Cartography; Cities - General; Classical Studies. CC: MC; V. Cata: Miscellaneous subjects with maps and prints. Mem: BA. Notes: *We have a large stock of maps and prints of the UK and the rest of the World.*

O'Flynn Books, Red House Antiques Centre Duncombe Place, York. Prop: Francis O'Flynn. Tel: 01904 637000. Est: 2007. Office and/or bookroom; Shop open: **M:** 09:30–17:30; **T:** 09:30–17:30; **W:** 09:30–17:30; **Th:** 09:30–17:30; **F:** 09:30–17:30; **S:** 09:30–17:30; **Su:** 10:30–17:30. Spec: Academic/Scholarly; Antiquarian; Antiques; Cartography; Exploration; Fiction - General; Fine & Rare; Flora & Fauna. CC: AE; MC; V. Cata: Miscellaneous, Antiquarian and Topography. Notes: *Also at Heworth Green, York*

Janette Ray Rare and Out of Print Books, ■ 8 Bootham, York, YO30 7BL. Prop: Janette Ray. Tel: (01904) 623088. Fax: (01904) 620814. Web: www.janetteray.co.uk. Est: 1995. Internet and Postal. Shop open: **W:** 09:30–17:30; **Th:** 09:30–17:30; **F:** 09:30–17:30; **S:** 09:30–17:30. Medium stock. Spec: Applied Art; Architecture; Art; Art History; Artists; Arts, The; Design; Fine Art. PR: £20–8,000. CC: E; MC; V. Cata: Architecture, Design, Gardens, Art, Photography. Corresp: French, Spanish. Mem: ABA; PBFA; ILAB. VAT No: GB 698 7195 56. Notes: *We also sell original drawings & photographs Valuations undertaken. Our website has secure ordering and is regularly updated with new books for sale.*

Ken Spelman, ■ 70 Micklegate, York, YO1 6LF. Prop: Peter Miller & Tony Fothergill. Tel: (01904) 624414. Fax: (01904) 626276. Web: www.kenspelman.com. Est: 1948. Shop open: **M:** 09:00–17:30; **T:** 09:00–17:30; **W:** 09:00–17:30; **Th:** 09:00–17:30; **F:** 09:00–17:30; **S:** 09:00–17:30. Very large stock. Spec: Academic/Scholarly; Antiquarian; Applied Art; Architecture; Art; Author - Sterne, L; Countries - Italy; Fine Art. PR: £1–10,000. CC: E; MC; V; Paypal. Cata: Art, Arch, Lit, Manuscripts, Italy, 18th century. Mem: ABA; PBFA; BA; ILAB. Notes: *Books bought in all quantities, major items handled on commission if required. Insurance valuations. Full on-line ordering via our website.*

Jeffrey Stern Antiquarian Books, Little Hall, Heslington, York, YO10 5EB. Tel: (01904) 413711. Fax: (01904) 412761. Web: www.abebooks.com/home/STARLIN. Est: 1971. Internet and Postal. Spec: Academic/Scholarly; Anthropology; Antiquarian; Architecture; Art; Biography; Business Studies; Computing. PR: £25–2,000. CC: MC; V.

Stone Trough Books, ■ 38 Fossgate, York, YO1 9TF. Prop: George Ramsden. Tel: (01904) 670323. Fax: (01944) 768465. Est: 1981. Shop open: **T:** 10:00–17:30; **W:** 10:00–17:30; **Th:** 10:00–17:30; **F:** 10:00–17:30; **S:** 10:00–17:30. Small stock. Spec: Art; Literature. PR: £2–200. CC: MC; V. Corresp: French, German. Mem: PBFA. VAT No: GB 237 5500 70.

Westfield Books, 28 Easthorpe Drive, York, YO26 6NR. Prop: A E Cunningham. Tel: 01904 794711. Est: 1992. Mail order only; Internet and Postal. Contactable. Spec: Antiquarian; Law - General. CC: Paypal. Mem: PBFA. VAT No: GB 827 4126 32. Notes: *General antiquarian booksellers.*

NORTHAMPTONSHIRE

BRACKLEY

The Old Hall Bookshop, ■ 32 Market Place, Brackley, NN13 7DP. Prop: John & Lady Juliet Townsend. Tel: 01280 704146. Web: www.oldhallbooks.com. Est: 1977. Shop open: **M:** 09:30–17:30; **T:** 09:30–17:30; **W:** 09:30–17:30; **Th:** 09:30–17:30; **F:** 09:30–17:30; **S:** 09:30–17:30. Medium stock. Spec: Children's; Topography - Local; Travel - General. PR: £1–10,000. CC: AE; JCB; MC; V; Maestro. Mem: ABA; PBFA; BA; ILAB. Notes: *New books, Ordnance Survey Mapping & Data Centre, fast order service, Book Tokens, book search etc.*

IRCHESTER

Jane Badger Books, The Manor House, High St, Irchester, Wellingborough, NN29 7AA. Prop: Jane Badger. Tel: (01933) 410943. Web: www.janebadgerbooks.co.uk. Est: 2002. Mail order only; Internet and Postal. Appointment necessary. Open: **M:** 09:00–17:00; **T:** 09:00–17:00; **Th:** 09:00–17:00; **F:** 09:00–17:00. Spec: Children's; Horses; Sport - Horse Racing (inc. Riding/Breeding/Equestrian); Sport - Hunting. CC: PayPal. Cata: Pony Books and Equine Non-Fiction. Mem: Ibooknet. Notes: *Specialising in British children's pony fiction.*

NORTHAMPTON

Occultique, 30 St. Michael's Avenue, Northampton, NN1 4JQ. Prop: Michael John Lovett. Tel: (01604) 627727. Fax: (01604) 603860. Web: www.occultique.co.uk. Est: 1973. Private premises. Internet and Postal. Appointment necessary. Medium stock. Spec: Acupuncture; Alchemy; Alternative Medicine; American Indians; Astrology; Author - Crowley, Aleister; Author - Spare, Austin Osman; Countries - Egypt. PR: £1–1,000. CC: PayPal. Notes: *Also, new books, essential oils, herbs & occult paraphernalia.*

Roosterbooks, 7 Elysium Terrace, Northampton, NN2 6EN. Tel: 01604 720983. Fax: 01604 720983. Web: www.ukbookworld.com/members/rooster. Est: 1997. Private premises. Internet and Postal. Telephone First. Large stock. Spec: Aircraft; Biology - General; Chemistry; Engineering; Esoteric; Mathematics; Mind, Body & Spirit; Philosophy. PR: £3–3,000. CC: MC; V. VAT No: GB 655 1461 40. Notes: *Free booksearch service.*

Alan and Joy Riley, Bookdealers, 18 St George's Place, Northampton, NN2 6EP. Tel: 01604 716901. Est: 1998. Private premises. Small stock. PR: £5 – 1,000. Notes: General quality stock. Notes: *Strong in Church architecture, Northants topography, U.S. Forces in Britain and Europe, T.E. Lawrence, Freya Stark.*

Ryeland Books, 18 St. George's Place, Northampton, NN2 6EP. Prop: Alan & Joy Riley. Tel: (01604) 716901. Est: 1998. Private premises. Appointment necessary. Small stock. Spec: Architecture; Art History; Children's; Countries - Middle East, The; Natural History. PR: £3–1,000. Mem: PBFA.

RUSHDEN

Booksmart, 4 Manning Rise, Rushden, NN10 0LY. Prop: Andy Wagstaff. Tel: (01933) 357416. Web: www.booksmart.co.uk. Est: 1990. Postal only. Spec: Ephemera. PR: £1–10. CC: Paypal.

SILVERSTONE

Collectors Carbooks, ■2210 Silverstone, Technology Park, Silverstone Circuit, Silverstone, NN12 8GX. Prop: Chris Knapman. Tel: (01327) 855888. Web: www.collectorscarbooks.com. Est: 1993. Internet and Postal. Shop open: **M:** 10:00–17:00; **T:** 10:00–17:00; **W:** 10:00–17:00; **Th:** 10:00–17:00; **F:** 10:00–17:00. Large stock. Spec: Collectables; History - Sports; Maritime/Nautical; Marque Histories (see also motoring); Memorabilia; Motorbikes / motorcycles; Motoring; Sport - Motor Racing. PR: £1–1,200. CC: MC; V. VAT No: GB 649 2588 91. Notes: *Open certain race Saturdays 08:30–14:30. Also, a free booksearch service.*

TOWCESTER

Mr. Pickwick of Towcester, Lavender Cottage, Shutlanger, Towcester, NN12 7RR. Prop: William Mayes. Tel: (01604) 862006. Fax: (01604) 862006. Web: www.yell.co.uk.sites/pickwickbookfinders. Est: 1963. Private premises. Internet and Postal. Very large stock. Spec: Author - Dickens, Charles; Biography; Books about Books; Fiction - General; Literature; Magazines & Periodicals - General; Memoirs; Newspapers. PR: £3–300.

WELLINGBOROUGH

Harrowden Books of Finedon, ■ 61 High Street, Finedon, Wellingborough, NN9 5JN. Prop: Mike Sumner. Tel: 01933 681522. Web: www.harrowdenbooks.com. Est: 2003. Shop open: **M:** 10:00–18:00; **T:** 10:00–18:00; **W:** 10:00–18:00; **Th:** 10:00–18:00; **F:** 10:00–18:00; **S:** 10:00–18:00. CC: AE; JCB; MC; V.

Lost Books, 103 Leyland Trading Estate, Wellingborough, NN8 1RT. Prop: Meisterco Limited. Tel: 01933 228828. Fax: 01933 228828. Web: www.lostbooks.net. Est: 2000. Warehouse; Internet and Postal. Telephone First. Open: **M:** 09:30–17:00; **T:** 09:30–17:00; **W:** 09:30–17:00; **Th:** 09:30–17:00; **F:** 09:30–17:00. Spec: Aeronautics; Aircraft; Arms & Armour; Army, The; Author - Churchill, Sir Winston; Aviation; Deep Sea Diving; Espionage. CC: AE; MC; V; Debit Cards. Cata: Over 100 military, history & exploration subjects. Corresp: Basic French & German. Mem: PBFA. VAT No: GB 818 7468 87. Notes: *We specialise in the sale of books covering military, history and exploration.*

The Park Gallery & Bookshop, ■ 16 Cannon Street, Wellingborough, NN8 4DJ. Prop: J.A. Foster. Tel: (01933) 222592. Web: www.ukbookworld.com/members/parkbookshop. Est: 1979. Internet and Postal. Shop open: **M:** 10:00–17:30; **T:** 10:00–17:30; **W:** 10:00–17:30; **Th:** 10:00–14:30; **F:** 10:00–17:30; **S:** 10:00–16:00. Medium stock. Spec: Aircraft; Animals and Birds; Annuals; Antiquarian; Antiques; Author - 19th Century; Author - 20th Century; Author - Bates, H.E. PR: £1–500. Notes: *Large general stock, some antiquarian, a booksearch service, collectables, ephemera, prints & maps, plus picture framing.*

NORTHUMBERLAND

ALNWICK

Barter Books, ■ Alnwick Station, Alnwick, NE66 2NP. Prop: Stuart and Mary Manley. Tel: 01665 604888. Fax: 01665 604444. Web: www.barterbooks.co.uk. Est: 1991. Shop open: **M:** 09:00–19:00; **T:** 09:00–19:00; **W:** 09:00–19:00; **Th:** 09:00–19:00; **F:** 09:00–19:00; **S:** 09:00–19:00; **Su:** 09:00–19:00. CC: AE; MC; V. Notes: *One of the largest secondhand bookshops in Britain. Complete with Station Buffet and many other features. Open every day: 09:00 - 19:00 summer and 09:00 to 17:00 winter.*

BEADNELL

Shearwater Books, Shearwater, 78 Harbour Road, Beadnell, NE67 5BE. Prop: John Lumby. Tel: 01665 720654. Web: www.shearwaterbooks.co.uk. Est: 1964. Private premises. Internet and Postal. Appointment necessary. Spec: Animals and Birds; Ecology; Entomology; Flora & Fauna; Hand bookbinding; Natural History; New Naturalist; Ornithology. Cata: Ornithology, New Naturalist, Poyser, Wayside. Notes: *E-mail for Catalogues on New Naturalist, Poysers, Wayside & Woodland, Bird art & artists, Pre-1950, etc. Bookbinding/repair service & booksearch. Also B&B. Small stock of other branches of natural history.*

HATLWHISTLE

Newcastle Bookshop At Haltwhistle, ■ Market Square, Hatlwhistle, NE49 0BG. Prop: Valerie Levitt. Tel: 01434 320103. Web: www.Newcastlebookshop.com. Est: 1973. Contactable. Spec: Architecture; Art; Art - British; Art - Theory; Art History; Art Reference; Artists; Arts, The. CC: AE; MC; V; PayPal. Notes: *We have a fully equipped bindery in the bookshop where we repair books and make new books and boxes. The bindery is open most days and customers are welcome to browse or call and discuss bookbinding. Our mobile number is 07837 982809.*

HEXHAM

Alex Fotheringham, East Chesterhope, West Woodburn, Hexham, NE48 2RQ. Tel: (01434) 270046. Fax: (01434) 632931. Est: 1975. Private premises. Internet and Postal. Appointment necessary. Small stock. Spec: Antiquarian; Architecture; Art; Bibliography; Literature; Theology. PR: £20–2,500. Mem: ABA; PBFA. VAT No: GB 646 1882 17. Notes: *Also attends bookfairs.*

Hencotes Books & Prints, ■ 8 Hencotes, Hexham, NE46 2EJ. Prop: Penny Pearce. Tel: (01434) 605971. Web: www.hencotes.com. Est: 1981. Shop open: **M:** 10:30–17:00; **T:** 10:30–17:00; **W:** 10:30–17:00; **F:** 10:30–17:00; **S:** 10:30–17:00. Medium stock. Spec: Booksearch. PR: £1–1,000. CC: JCB; MC; V; SW. Mem: PBFA. VAT No: GB 796 9893 26. Notes: *Also attends P.B.F.A. and local fairs.*

Newgate Books and Translations, 3 Quatre Bras, Hexham, NE46 3JY. Prop: Davina and John Dwyer. Tel: (01434) 607650. Fax: (01434) 607650. Est: 1987. Private premises. Postal only. Contactable. Open: **M:** 09:00–17:30; **T:** 09:00–17:30; **W:** 09:00–16:00; **Th:** 09:00–17:30; **F:** 09:00–17:30; **S:** 09:00–12:00; Closed for lunch: 12:45–14:00. Small stock. Spec: Conservation; Environment, The; Fiction - Crime, Detective, Spy, Thrillers; Music - General; Music - Classical. PR: £5–300. Corresp: French, German. Notes: *French - English Translation Service. Small stock of books available to purchase online through ABE and UKBookWorld.*

Priestpopple Books, ■ 9b Priestpopple, Hexham, NE46 1PF. Prop: John B. Patterson. Tel: (01434) 607773. Est: 1997. Shop open: **M:** 09:00–17:00; **T:** 09:00–17:00; **W:** 09:00–17:00; **Th:** 09:00–17:00; **F:** 09:00–17:00; **S:** 09:00–17:00. Very large stock. Spec: Academic/Scholarly; Art Reference; Author - General; Author - Carlyle, Thomas; Children's; Cinema/Film; Crafts; Dogs. PR: £1–500. Notes: *Also, sheet music and used LPs.*

MORPETH

Intech Books, 14 Bracken Ridge, Morpeth, NE61 3SY. Prop: Mr. D. J. Wilkinson. Tel: (01670) 519102. Fax: (01670) 515815. Est: 1981. Private premises. Internet and Postal. Appointment necessary. Small stock. Spec: American Indians; Annuals; Author - Ahlberg, Janet & Allan; Author - Bainbridge, Beryl; Author - Barker, Cecily M.; Author - Bates, H.E.; Author - Beardsley, Aubrey; Author - Belloc, Hilaire. PR: £1–100. Notes: *We also trade at many independent book fairs, including Pudsey, Keswick, Tynemouth Station, Bedale and Ingleton. A booksearch service is also offered.*

STOCKSFIELD

Leaf Ends, Leaf End, Ridley Mill, Stocksfield, NE43 7QU. Prop: Moira Tait. Tel: 01661 842423. Fax: 01661 842423. Web: www.abebooks.com. Est: 1995. Mail order only; Internet and Postal. Appointment necessary. Spec: Children's. CC: MC; V; Paypal and Visa, Mastercard, debit cards via PayPal. VAT No: GB 747 2468 08. Notes: *No set opening hours but contactable at any time, mixed general stock, including over 5,000 childrens' books, stock listed on abebooks.com.*

WOOLER

Hamish Dunn Antiques & Books, ■ 17 High Street, Wooler, NE71 6BU. Tel: (01668) 281341. Est: 1986. Shop open: **M:** 09:00–16:00; **T:** 09:00–16:00; **W:** 09:00–16:00; **F:** 09:00–16:00; **S:** 09:00–16:00. Small stock. Spec: Collectables; Ephemera; Prints and Maps. PR: £1–100. CC: D; JCB; MC; V.

NOTTINGHAMSHIRE

BALDERTON

Anthony W. Laywood, Kercheval House 79 Main Street, Balderton, Newark, NG24 3NN. Prop: Anthony William Laywood. Tel: 01636 659031. Est: 1964. Private premises. Internet and Postal. Open: **M:** 09:00–17:30; **T:** 09:00–17:30; **W:** 09:00–17:30; **Th:** 09:00–17:30; **F:** 09:00–17:30; **S:** 09:00–17:30; **Su:** 09:00–17:30; Closed for lunch: 13:00–14:00. Spec: Antiquarian. CC: MC; V. Cata: Books in English before 1850. Notes: *Books in English before 1850.*

BOTTESFORD

Belfry Books, Barkestone Lane, Bottesford, NG13 0FH. Tel: (01949) 843559. Est: 1989. Private premises. Internet only. Small stock. Spec: Animals and Birds; Art History; Bell-Ringing (Campanology); Countries - New Zealand; Gardening - General. PR: £20–20,000.

BULLWELL

A Holmes Books, 82 Highbury Avenue, Bullwell, Nottingham, NG6 9DB. Prop: Andrew Holmes. Tel: 0115 9795603. Web: www.amazon.co.uk/shops/aholmesbooks. Est: 1989. Private premises. Internet and Postal. Contactable. Open: **M:** 09:00–17:30; **T:** 09:00–17:30; **W:** 09:00–17:30; **Th:** 09:00–17:30; **F:** 09:00–17:30; **S:** 09:00–17:30; **Su:** 09:00–17:30; Closed for lunch: 13:00–14:00. Spec: General Stock; Gypsies. Notes: *General stock most subjects.*

GUNTHORPE

Letterbox Books, The Coach House, Gunthorpe, NG14 7ES. Prop: Bob Dakin. Tel: (0115) 966-4349. Est: 1993. Private premises. Internet and Postal. Small stock. Spec: Alpinism/Mountaineering; History - Local; Sport - Caving (Spelaeology); Sport - Potholing; Topography - General; Topography - Local; Booksearch; Ephemera. PR: £1–200.

KIRKBY–IN–ASHFIELD

Kyrios Books, ■ 11 Kingsway, Kirkby–in–Ashfield, NG17 7BB. Prop: Keith Parr. Tel: (01623) 452556 answerphone. Web: www.kyriosbooks.co.uk. Est: 1989. Internet and Postal. Telephone First. Open: **M:** 09:00–16:30; **T:** 09:00–16:30; **W:** 09:00–16:00; **Th:** 09:00–16:30; **F:** 09:00–16:30; **S:** 09:00–16:30; Closed for lunch: 12:00–13:00. Large stock. Spec: Autobiography; Ecclesiastical History & Architecture; Philosophy; Prayer Books; Religion - General; Religion - Christian; Theology. PR: £1–100. Mem: FSB.

MANSFIELD

Fiona Edwards, 33 Crompton Road, Mansfield, NG19 7RG. Tel: 07710 410325. Est: 1992. Private premises. Internet and Postal. Appointment necessary. Spec: Art; Cookery - Professional; Cookery/Gastronomy; Embroidery; Food & Drink; General Stock; Music - General; Needlework. CC: MC; V. Mem: PBFA. Notes: *A small general stock with a strong emphasis on cookery. Booksearches carried out. Books for sale on PBFA website and ABE. Book Fairs attended. Good general stock; booksearch undertaken.*

R. W. Price, 19 Park Avenue, Mansfield, NG18 2AU. Prop: Mr G.D. Price. Tel: (01623) 629858. Web: www.gdprice.com. Est: 1986. Private premises. Internet and Postal. Very large stock. Spec: Beat Writers; Children's; Comedy; Erotica; Espionage; Fiction - General; Fiction - Crime, Detective, Spy, Thrillers; Fiction - Fantasy, Horror. PR: £1–100.

NEWARK–ON–TRENT

Lawrence Books, Newark Antiques Centre, Lombard Street, Newark–on–Trent, NG24 1XP. Prop: Arthur Lawrence. Tel: (01636) 605865. Est: 1987. Warehouse; Shop open: **M:** 09:30–17:00; **T:** 09:30–17:00; **W:** 09:30–17:00; **Th:** 09:30–17:00; **F:** 09:30–17:00; **S:** 09:30–17:00; **Su:** 11:00–16:00. Small stock. Spec: Aviation; Diaries; History - General; Letters; Maritime/Nautical; Military; Poetry; Topography - Local. PR: £1–200. Mem: Bookbinding Society. Notes: *Exhibits at book fairs; bookbinding. Trades from bookroom/warehouse. Alternative tel: (01636) 701619.*

NOTTINGHAM

Artco, 6 Grantham Road, Radcliffe on Trent, Nottingham, NG12 2HD. Prop: Mr. H. Boehm. Tel: (0115) 933-3530. Fax: (0115) 911-9746. Est: 1970. Private premises. Appointment necessary. Small stock. Spec: Applied Art; Art; Art Reference; Artists; Arts, The; Colour-Plate; Foreign Texts; Illustrated - General. PR: £10–1,000. CC: MC; V. Corresp: German.

Geoffrey Blore's Bookshop, ■484 Mansfield Road, Sherwood, Nottingham, NG5 2BF. Tel: (0115) 969-1441. Est: 1987. Shop open: **M:** 10:30–17:00; **T:** 10:30–17:00; **W:** 10:30–17:00; **Th:** 10:30–17:00; **F:** 10:30–17:00; **S:** 10:30–17:00. Very large stock. Spec: History - Local; Topography - Local. Notes: *Stock includes books on Nottinghamshire history and topography.*

Guy Davis, Antiquarian Books, 61 Bakerdale Road, Bakersfield, Nottingham, NG3 7GJ. Tel: (0115) 940-3835. Fax: (0115) 940-0093. Est: 1970. Spec: Bindings; Fore-Edge Paintings; Prints and Maps. PR: £50–5,000.

Jermy & Westerman, ■ 203 Mansfield Road, Nottingham, NG1 3FS. Prop: G.T. Blore. Tel: (0115) 947-4522. Est: 1977. Shop open: **M:** 11:00–17:00; **T:** 11:00–17:00; **W:** 11:00–17:00; **Th:** 11:00–17:00; **F:** 11:00–17:00; **S:** 11:00–17:00. Medium stock. Spec: Illustrated - General; Literature; Topography - Local. Notes: *Geoffrey Blore's Bookshop, Nottingham. Stocks books on Nottingham history and topography.*

Frances Wakeman Books, 103 Austin Street, Nottingham, NG6 9HE. Prop: Frances & Paul Wakeman. Tel: (0115) 875 3944. Web: www.fwbooks.com. Est: 1970. Private premises. Internet and Postal. Appointment necessary. Small stock. Spec: Bibliography; Books about Books; Papermaking; Printing; Private Press; Publishing; Typography. PR: £100–6,000. CC: AE; E; JCB; MC; V. Mem: PBFA. VAT No: GB 685 4226 14. Notes: *Also, publishing books about books.*

REDMILE

Forest Books, Overfields, 1 Belvoir Road, Redmile, NG13 0GL. Prop: William Laywood. Tel: (01949) 842360. Fax: (01949) 844196. Web: www.forestbooks.co.uk. Est: 1979. Private premises. Internet and Postal. Appointment necessary. Medium stock. Spec: Antiquarian; Bibliography; Bindings; Bookbinding; Books about Books; Papermaking; Printing; Typography. PR: £5–5,000. CC: MC; V. Cata: Antiquarian Books, Bibliography & Bookbinding. Mem: PBFA.

SANDIACRE

A.E. Beardsley, 14 York Avenue, Sandiacre, NG10 5HB. Prop: Tony and Irene Beardsley. Tel: (0115) 917-0082. Web: www.ukbookworld.com/members/aebbooks. Est: 1991. Private premises. Appointment necessary. Small stock. Spec: Countries - Malaysia; Topography - General; Travel - General; Booksearch. PR: £4–400. Notes: *Exhibits at Buxton Book Fair - 1,000 books on www.abebooks.com.*

SUTTON IN ASHFIELD

Fackley Services, 6 Ash Grove Skegby, Sutton in Ashfield, NG17 3FH. Prop: Malcolm Walters. Tel: (01623) 552530. Fax: (01623) 552530. Web: www.fackley.co.uk. Est: 1991. Private premises. Postal only. Small stock. Spec: Aircraft; Animals and Birds; Antiques; Children's; Crime (True); Fiction - General; General Stock; History - Local. PR: £3–100. CC: AE; E; JCB; MC; V. Notes: *Specialising mainly on Booksearch, Observer's Pocket Series, Military and General stock.*

OXFORDSHIRE

ABINGDON

Bennett & Kerr Books, Millhill Warehouse, Church Lane, Steventon, Abingdon, OX13 6SW. Prop: (*) Edmund Bennett & Andrew Kerr. Tel: (01235) 820604. Fax: (01235) 821047. Web: www.abebooks.com/home/bennettkerr. Est: 1982. Office and/or bookroom; Internet and Postal. Telephone First. Open: **M:** 09:30–17:30; **T:** 09:30–17:30; **W:** 09:30–17:30; **Th:** 09:30–17:30; **F:** 09:30–17:30; **S:** 10:00–13:00; Closed for lunch: 13:15–14:15. Medium stock. Spec: Academic/Scholarly; Architecture; Art History; Arthurian; Author - Chaucer, Geoffrey; Author - James, M.R.; Author - Shakespeare, William; Byzantium. PR: £5–1,000. CC: MC; V; Switch. Cata: Medieval & Renascence studies. Corresp: French, Italian. Mem: ABA; PBFA; ILAB. VAT No: GB 348 7058 28. Notes: *We specialise in books on the European Middle Ages, from late antiquity to the renascence, including art, architecture, history & literature.*

Courtenay Bookroom, Appleford, Abingdon, OX14 4PB. Prop: G. Duffield. Tel: (01235) 848319. Est: 1960. Spec: Academic/Scholarly; Antiquarian; Bibles; Dictionaries; History - General; Theology; Ephemera; Prints and Maps. PR: £1–10,000.

B. & N. Kentish, Old Farmhouse, Longworth, Abingdon, OX13 5ET. Tel: (01865) 820711. Private premises. Postal only. Spec: Atlases. Notes: *Also see under Prints & Map Sellers on Sheppard's World.*

Mary Mason, 55 Winterborne Road, Abingdon, OX14 1AL. Prop: Mary Mason. Tel: (01235) 559929. Web: www.masonpeett.co.uk. Est: 1988. Private premises. Internet and Postal. Appointment necessary. Medium stock. Spec: Art; Author - Ardizzone, Edward; Children's; Illustrated - General; Juvenile. PR: £1–1,000. CC: PayPal. Corresp: French. Notes: *Booksearch.*

PsychoBabel Books & Journals, 56b Milton Park, Abingdon, OX14 4RX. Prop: Chris Edwards. Tel: 01235 861411. Fax: 01235 861422. Web: www.psychobabel.co.uk. VOIPpro: Skype. VOIPnum: psychobabel. Est: 2003. Warehouse; Internet and Postal. Contactable. Open: **M:** 08:30–18:00; **T:** 08:30–18:00; **W:** 08:30–18:00; **Th:** 08:30–18:00; **F:** 08:30–18:00; **S:** 10:00–14:00; **Su:** 10:00–14:00. Very large stock. Spec: Academic/Scholarly; Antiquarian; Architecture; Arms & Armour; Art; Art History; Asian Studies; Author - Crowley, Aleister. PR: £1 – 5,000. CC: AE; MC; V; PayPal, £ or $ cheques. Cata: online/internet. Corresp: German, French, Spanish. VAT No: GB 824 8827 00. Notes: *PsychoBabel specialises in academic texts, with a large stock of general literature, antiquarian and non-fiction titles. Sameday despatch. You can browse/buy from our homepage on www.psychobabel.eu. In partnership with Skoob Books, London.*

BANBURY

Books, The Old Forge, Upper Brailes, Banbury, OX15 5AT. Prop: Mrs E.M. Pogmore. Tel: (01608) 685260. Web: www.pogmore@marg3.freeserve.co.uk. Est: 1985. Private premises. Postal only. Contactable. Open: **M:** 09:00–17:00; **T:** 09:00–17:00; **W:** 09:00–17:00; **Th:** 09:00–17:00; **F:** 09:00–17:00; **S:** 09:00–12:00. Small stock. Spec: Author - Fleming, Ian; Autobiography; Cookery/Gastronomy; Modern First Editions; Poetry; Tapestry. PR: £1–200. CC: Cheques. Cata: Modern Firsts, Cookery, Poetry.

Books & Ink Bookshop, ■ 4 White Lion Walk, Banbury, OX16 5UD. Prop: Samantha Barnes & Sheryl Root. Tel: 01295 709769. Web: www.booksandink.co.uk. Est: 2005. Shop open: **M:** 09:00–17:30; **T:** 09:00–17:30; **W:** 09:00–17:30; **Th:** 09:00–17:30; **F:** 09:00–17:30; **S:** 09:00–17:30. CC: AE; MC; V. Mem: BA; Ibooknet. VAT No: GB 868 2729 75. Notes: *Old & new books. We also stock a range of gifts, cards and prints. Self-service tea/coffee available.*

BURFORD

The Classics Bookshop, Greyhounds, 23 Sheep Street, Burford, OX18 4LS. Prop: Anne Powell-Jones. Tel: 01993 822969. Fax: 01993 822969. Web: www.classicsbookshop.co.uk. Est: 1975. Office and/or bookroom; Shop open: **W:** 10:00–17:00; **S:** 10:00–17:00; Closed for lunch: 13:00–14:00. Spec: Archaeology; Classical Studies; History - Ancient; Languages - Ancient; Philosophy; Sport - Angling/Fishing. CC: AE; MC; V. Cata: Latin and Greek Classics. Mem: PBFA. VAT No: GB 298 2963 94. Notes: *Subject listed 'Philosophy' includes Ancient Philosophy.*

CHIPPING NORTON

Greensleeves, P.O. Box 156, Chipping Norton, OX7 3XT. Prop: P.R. & C. Seers. Tel: 01993 832423. Fax: 01993 832423. Web: www.greensleevesbooks.co.uk. Est: 1982. Private premises. Internet and Postal. Medium stock. Spec: Alternative Medicine; Anthroposophy; Astrology; Esoteric; Health; Herbalism; Homeopathy; Metaphysics. PR: £1–500. CC: MC; V; Switch. Cata: on specialised subjects. Mem: BA. VAT No: GB 596 3357 96. Notes: *Also, new books and booksearch service.*

Kellow Books, ■ 6 Market Place, Chipping Norton, OX7 5NA. Prop: Peter & Jan Combellack. Tel: (01608) 644293. Est: 1998. Shop open: **M:** 10:00–16:30; **T:** 10:00–16:30; **W:** 10:00–16:30; **Th:** 10:00–16:30; **F:** 10:00–16:30; **S:** 10:00–16:30. Medium stock. Spec: Children's; Company History; Fiction - General; Maritime/Nautical; Military History; Natural History; Ornithology; Topography - General. PR: £2–800. CC: D; E; JCB; MC; V; All cards.

DIDCOT

The Parlour Bookshop, ■ 30 Wantage Road, Didcot, OX11 0BT. Prop: Roy Burton. Tel: (01235) 818989. Fax: (01235) 814494. Est: 1995. Shop open: **W:** 10:00–16:00; **Th:** 10:00–16:00; Closed for lunch: 12:45–13:45. Small stock. Spec: Military; Railways and Railroads; Topography - General. PR: £1–50. Notes: *Closed Bank Holidays, Good Friday: Easter Monday, Christmas Eve to 4 January.*

Wayside Books & Cards, Wayside, Wellshead Harwell, Didcot, OX11 0HD. Prop: J.A.B. & J.L. Gibson. Tel: (01235) 835256. Est: 1985. Private premises. Postal only. Open in Summer. Medium stock. Spec: Astronomy; Atomic; Author - Asimov, Isaac; Author - Cecil, H.; Author - Christie, Agatha; Author - Clarke, Arthur C.; Author - Cornwell, Bernard; Author - Greene, Graham. PR: £1–100.

DORCHESTER ON THAMES

Pablo Butcher, Overy Mill, Dorchester on Thames, OX10 7JU. Tel: (01865) 341445. Fax: (01865) 340180. Est: 1974. Private premises. Appointment necessary. Small stock. Spec: Art; Ethnography; Photography; Travel - Africa; Travel - Americas; Travel - Asia, South East; Travel - India; Travel - Islamic World. Corresp: French. Mem: ABA; PBFA; ILAB. Notes: *Book fairs and postal.*

DUCKLINGTON

Demetzy Books, Manor House, 29 Standlake Road, Ducklington, OX29 7UX. Prop: Paul & Marie Hutchinson. Tel: 01993 702209. Fax: 01993 702209. Est: 1971. Market stand/stall; Shop at: 113 Portobello Road, London W.11. Open: **S:** 07:00–15.00. Spec: Bibles; Bindings; Children's - Illustrated; Miniature Books; Natural Sciences; Surgery; Travel - General. CC: JCB; MC; V. Mem: ABA; PBFA; ILAB.

EAST HAGBOURNE

E.M. Lawson & Company, Kingsholm, Main Street, East Hagbourne, OX11 9LN. Prop: W.J. & K.M. Lawson. Tel: (01235) 812033. Est: 1921. Private premises. Appointment necessary. Small stock. Spec: Antiquarian; Countries - Africa; Countries - Americas, The; Countries - Australasia; Economics; Literature; Medicine; Science - General. Cata: on general subjects. Mem: ABA; ILAB.

FARINGDON

N.W. Jobson, 8 Weston Cottages, Buscot Wick, Faringdon, SN7 8DN. Prop: Nigel Jobson. Tel: (01367) 252240. Est: 1981. Private premises. Internet and Postal. Small stock. Spec: Booksearch. PR: £1–100. Mem: National Federation of Market Traders. Notes: *Also, a booksearch service. Secondhand Bookstall, Shambles Market, Devizes, Wiltshire Every Tuesday, 7.30am - 3pm.*

Thornton's Bookshop, The Old Barn, Walnut Court, Faringdon, SN7 7JH. Prop: W.A. Meeuws. Tel: (01367) 240056. Fax: (01367) 241544. Web: www.thorntonsbooks.co.uk. VOIP: Skype VOIPnum: skype search for Meeuws. Est: 1835. Shop and/or gallery; Internet and Postal. Contactable. Shop at: 65, St. Luke's Road/Cowley/Oxford OX4 3JE. Bookshop: 10A Marlborough Street, Faringdon SN7 7JP. Open: **T:** 10:00–17:00; **W:** 10:00–17:00; **Th:** 10:00–17:00; **F:** 10:00–17:00; **S:** 10:00–13:00. Medium stock. Spec: Academic/Scholarly; Africana; Antiquarian; Antiquities; Arabica; Archaeology; Architecture - Theatre; Art - British. PR: £15–1,000. CC: E; MC; V; Maestro. Corresp: French, Dutch, German, Spanish. Mem: ABA; BA; ILAB. VAT No: GB 194 4663 31. Notes: *Business now in Faringdon in partnership with the Whitehorse Bookshop and rare books located at the Old Barn.*

FYFIELD

Oak Tree Press, Fyfield Grange, Fyfield, OX13 5LR. Prop: Bruce Howard. Tel: 07796 174733. Fax: 01865 390161. Web: www.oaktreepress.co.im. Est: 2005. Private premises. Internet and Postal. Appointment necessary. Open: **M:** 09:00–17:30; **T:** 09:00–17:30; **W:** 09:00–17:30; **Th:** 09:00–17:30; **F:** 09:00–17:30; **S:** 09:00–17:30; **Su:** 09:00–17:30; Closed for lunch: 13:00–14:00. Spec: Author - 20th Century; Author - Coetzee, J.M.; Author - Le Carre, John; Booker Prize; Charity; Collectables; Limited Editions - General; Literature - South African. CC: MC; V. Mem: The Publishers Association. Notes: *Publishers of The First Chapter Series, a contribution by authors of the opening chapters of their Booker Prize winning novels in support of children living with HIV/AIDS. Also specialising in prize winning modern first editions.*

GORING–ON–THAMES

Nevis Railway Books, ■ Barbara's The Orchard, Goring–on–Thames, RG8 9HB. Prop: N.J. Bridger. Tel: 01635 200507. Web: www.nevis-railway-bookshops.co.uk. Est: 1992. Shop open: **M:** 10:00–17:00; **T:** 10:00–17:00; **W:** 10:00–17:00; **Th:** 10:00–17:00; **F:** 10:00–17:00; **S:** 10:00–17:00; Closed for lunch: 13:00–14:15. Small stock. Spec: Railways and Railroads. PR: £1–50. Notes: *Railway Book & Magazine Search, Newbury, Berks. (qv.) Nevis railway Bookshops, Marlborough, Wilts (q.v). Alt tel: 01635 200507.*

HENLEY ON THAMES

Jonkers Rare Books, 24 Hart Street, Henley on Thames, RG9 2AU. Tel: (01491) 576427. Web: www.jonkers.co.uk. Est: 1990. Shop and/or showroom; Shop open: **M:** 10:00–17:30; **T:** 10:00–17:30; **W:** 10:00–17:30; **Th:** 10:00–17:30; **F:** 10:00–17:30; **S:** 10:00–17:30. Small stock. Spec: Arthurian; Author - 19th Century; Author - 20th Century; Author - Aldin, Cecil; Author - Betjeman, Sir John; Author - Blyton, Enid; Author - Brontes, The; Author - Christie, Agatha. PR: £25–1,000,000. CC: AE; E; MC; V. Cata: on specialist subjects. Corresp: Italian, French, Spanish. Mem: ABA; PBFA; BA; ILAB.

Way's Bookshop, ■54 Friday Street, Henley on Thames, RG9 1AH. Prop: Diana Cook and Richard Way. Tel: 01491 576663. Fax: 01491 576663. Est: 1977. Shop. Open: **M:** 10:00–17:15; **T:** 10:00–17:15; **W:** 10:00–17:15; **Th:** 10:00–17:15; **F:** 10:00–17:15; **S:** 10:00–17:15. CC: MC; V; Debit. Mem: ABA; ILAB. Notes: *Traditional Secondhand & Antiquarian shop. Most subjects except sciences, at all levels of value. Phone first if coming any distance with books for sale. Car park available at rear during weekdays - on Saturday park in wide driveway.*

HOOK NORTON

Orangeberry Books, Rowan House, Queens Street, Hook Norton, Banbury, OX15 5PH. Prop: Paul Tranter. Tel: (01608) 737928. Fax: (01608) 730810. Web: www.orangeberry.co.uk. Est: 1995. Private premises. Internet and Postal. Telephone First. Medium stock. Spec: Literature; Poetry; Science - General; Technology; Travel - General. PR: £5–1,000. CC: E; MC; V; Maestro/Switch. Corresp: French. Mem: IBN. VAT No: GB 800 0734 85. Notes: *Visitors welcomed - it is advisable to phone first.*

OXFORD

Adrian Greenwood, 25 Iffley Road, Oxford, OX4 1EA. Tel: 01865 202691. Web: www.adriangreenwoodbooks.co.uk. Est: 1996. Private premises. Internet and Postal. Appointment necessary. CC: MC; V. Mem: PBFA. Notes: *A highly selective stock of top quality antiquarian, rare and first edition volumes with particular strengths in 15th and 16th Centuries works. Natural Philosophy and Early Science, Bibles, and selected modern firsts.*

Antiques on High, ■ 85 High Street, Oxford, OX1 4BG. Prop: Tony Sloggett and Joan Lee. Tel: (01865) 251075. Web: www.antiquesonhigh.co.uk. Est: 1997. Shop open: **M:** 10:00–17:00; **T:** 10:00–17:00; **W:** 10:00–17:00; **Th:** 10:00–17:00; **F:** 10:00–17:00; **S:** 10:00–17:00; **Su:** 11:00–17:00. Medium stock. Spec: Antiques; Architecture; Art; Art History; Autobiography; Biography; Children's; Collecting. PR: £1–200. CC: AE; E; MC; V. Mem: TVADA. Notes: *Has stock for 'Books on High' and 'Music Bookshop'.*

Arcadia, ■ 4 St. Michael's Street, Oxford, OX1 2DU. Tel: (01865) 241757. Est: 1975. Shop open: **M:** 10:00–17:30; **T:** 10:00–17:30; **W:** 10:00–17:30; **Th:** 10:00–17:30; **F:** 10:00–17:30; **S:** 10:00–18:00. Small stock. Spec: Publishers - Penguin; Ephemera; Prints and Maps. PR: £1–50. CC: AE; D; E; JCB; MC; V. Mem: PBFA. Notes: *Mainly prints and postcards.*

Ars Artis, 31 Abberbury Road, Oxford, OX4 4ET. Prop: G.B. & H.J. Lowe. Tel: 01865 770714. Est: 1976. Private premises. Appointment necessary. Spec: Applied Art; Architecture; Art History; Art Reference; Artists; Catalogues Raisonnes; Fine Art; Photography. VAT No: GB 119 1785 58.

Blackwell's Music Shop, ■ 23-25 Broad Street, Oxford, OX1 3AX. Tel: (01865) 333580. Fax: (01865) 728020. Web: www.blackwell.co.uk/printedmusic. Est: 1955. Internet and Postal. Shop open: **M:** 09:00–18:00; **T:** 09:30–18:00; **W:** 09:00–18:00; **Th:** 09:00–18:00; **F:** 09:00–18:00; **S:** 09:00–18:00; **Su:** 11:00–17:00. Very large stock. Spec: Music - General; Music - Classical; Music - Composers; Music - Musicians; Music - Opera. PR: £2–175. CC: MC; V.

Blackwell Rare Books, ■ 48 - 51 Broad Street, Oxford, OX1 3BQ. Tel: (01865) 333555. Fax: (01865) 794143. Web: www.rarebooks.blackwell.co.uk. Est: 1879. Internet and Postal. Shop open: **M:** 09:00–18:00; **T:** 09:30–18:00; **W:** 09:00–18:00; **Th:** 09:00–18:00; **F:** 09:00–18:00; **S:** 09:00–18:00. Medium stock. Spec: Antiquarian; British Books; Children's - Early Titles; Children's - Illustrated; Countries - General; County - Local; Early Imprints; Fiction - General. PR: £20–20,000. CC: MC; V. Cata: Quarterly on wide range of subjects. Corresp: French, German. Mem: ABA; PBFA; BA; ILAB. Notes: *Blackwell Rare Books is situated within the famous Blackwell Bookshop, which houses a huge range of new books, often in great depth, particularly in academic subjects. There is also a large secondhand books section in the same building.*

Roy Davids Ltd., The Old Forge, Rectory Road, Great Haseley, Oxford, OX44 7JG. Prop: Roy Davids. Tel: (01844) 279154. Fax: (01844) 278221. Web: www.roydavids.com. Est: 1994. Private premises. Spec: Autographs; History - General; Letters; Manuscripts; Music - General; Collectables; Ephemera. PR: £50–100,000. CC: MC; V. Mem: ABA; ILAB. Notes: *Also, portraits and related artefacts.*

Game Advice, 71 Rose Hill, Oxford, OX4 4JR. Prop: Alick Elithorn & Karen Stevenson. Tel: (01865) 777317/433050. Fax: (01865) 433050. Web: www.game-advice.com. Mobile 07912115310. Est: 1975. Private premises. Internet and Postal. Telephone First. Large stock. Spec: Academic/Scholarly; Alternative Medicine; Anthropology; Children's; Computing; Education & School; Feminism; Fore-Edge Paintings. PR: £3–9,000. Corresp: French. Notes: *Also, chess sets, antique games & puzzles, chess prints, educational software, computer & personal consultancy, booksearch & loan computing and Business Consultancy.*

Hanborough Books, The Foundry Church, Hanborough, Nr. Witney, Oxford, OX29 8AB. Prop: Dennis Hall. Tel: (01993) 881260. Fax: (01993) 883080. Web: www.parrotpress.co.uk. Est: 1970. Private premises. Telephone First. Small stock. Spec: Antiquarian; Illustrated - General; Limited Editions - General; Private Press; Typography. PR: £5–650. CC: MC; V. Cata: twentieth century book illustration. VAT No: GB 490 6827 17.

The Inner Bookshop, ■ 111 Magdalen Road, Oxford, OX4 1RQ. Prop: R.E. Ashcroft & A.S. Cheke. Tel: (01865) 245301. Fax: (01865) 245521. Web: www.innerbookshop.com. Est: 1982. Internet and Postal. Shop open: **M:** 10:00–17:45; **T:** 10:00–17:45; **W:** 10:00–17:45; **Th:** 10:00–17:45; **F:** 10:00–17:45; **S:** 10:00–17:45. Large stock. Spec: Aboriginal; Academic/Scholarly; Acupuncture; Alchemy; Alternative Medicine; American Indians; Animals and Birds; Anthroposophy. PR: £1–1,000. CC: MC; V; SW, SO. Corresp: French. Mem: BA; FSB. Notes: *Also, new books on specialities & tarot cards, New Age music, bargain books and a passive booksearch service.*

Leabeck Books, Meadowbrook Farm, Sheepwash Lane, Steventon, Oxford, OX13 6SD. Prop: Tony Sloggett. Tel: (01235) 820914. Est: 1993. Private premises. Internet and Postal. Appointment necessary. Small stock. Spec: Antiques; Art; Children's; First Editions; History - General; Illustrated - General; Literature; Travel - General. PR: £5–200. Corresp: French, German. Notes: *Antiques on High, 85 High Street, Oxford, OX1 4BG.*

Chris Morris Secondhand & Antiquarian Books, 67 Home Close, Wolvercote, Oxford, OX2 8PT. Tel: (01865) 557806. Est: 1992. Private premises. Internet and Postal. Small stock. Spec: Automobilia/Automotive; Broadcasting; Cinema/Film; Countries - Greece; Film and Television Tie-ins; Media; Memorabilia; Motoring. PR: £1–75. Notes: *Also, a booksearch service.*

St Philip's Books, ■ 82 St. Aldates, Oxford, OX1 1RA. Prop: Christopher James Zealley. Tel: (01865) 202182. Fax: (01865) 202184. Web: www.stphilipsbooks.co.uk. Est: 1995. Internet and Postal. Shop open: **M:** 10:00–17:00; **T:** 10:00–17:00; **W:** 10:00–17:00; **Th:** 10:00–17:00; **F:** 10:00–17:00; **S:** 10:00–17:00. Large stock. Spec: Academic/Scholarly; Antiquarian; Art History; Author - Belloc, Hilaire; Author - Benson, R.H.; Author - Chesterton, G.K.; Author - Inklings, The; Author - Lewis, C.S. PR: £1–2,000. CC: MC; V; SO, SW, Maestro. Cata: Theology, Church History. Mem: PBFA; BA. VAT No: GB 717 9250 21. Notes: *Religious books bought nationwide. Our special interests include Roman Catholicism, Eastern Christianity, Newman and Oxford Movement, C.S. Lewis and Inklings, Biblical studies, Patristics, Chesterton & Distributism, Latin liturgy & chant.*

Waterfield's, ■ 52 High Street, Oxford, OX1 4AS. Prop: Robin Waterfield Ltd. Tel: (01865) 721809. Est: 1973. Shop open: **M:** 09:45–17:45; **T:** 09:45–17:45; **W:** 09:45–17:44; **Th:** 08:45–17:45; **F:** 09:45–17:45; **S:** 09:45–17:45. Large stock. Spec: Academic/Scholarly; Antiquarian; Arts, The; First Editions; History - General; Humanities; Literary Criticism; Literature. PR: £1–5,000. CC: MC; V. Corresp: French. Mem: ABA; PBFA. VAT No: GB 195 8007 39. Notes: *Catalogues also on 17th and 18thC books.*

STONESFIELD

Karen Thomson, Fowler's Cottage, Witney Lane, Stonesfield, OX29 8DN. Tel: 01993 898734. Est: 1987. Private premises. Postal only. Appointment necessary. Spec: Antiquarian; Dictionaries; Medieval; Philology; Philology - German. CC: MC; V. Cata: Antiquarian books on Language, Old English. Corresp: French, German. Mem: ABA; ILAB. VAT No: GB 527 7505 33.

Austin Sherlaw-Johnson, Woodland View, Churchfields, Stonesfield, OX29 8PP. Tel: (01993) 898223. Web: www.austinsj.co.uk. Est: 2001. Private premises. Appointment necessary. Open: **M:** 09:00–17:00; **T:** 09:00–17:00; **W:** 09:00–17:00; **Th:** 09:00–17:00; **F:** 09:00–17:00. Medium stock. Spec: Music - General; Music - Classical; Music - Composers; Music - Folk & Irish Folk; Music - Gilbert & Sullivan; Music - Gregorian Chants; Music - Illustrated Sheet Music; Music - Jazz & Blues. PR: £1–500. Cata: printed music. Notes: *Malvern Bookshop, Malvern, Worcestershire (q.v.) Antiques on High, 85 High Street, Oxford.*

WALLINGFORD

Christopher Edwards, 8 St Leonard's Square, Wallingford, OX10 0AR. Prop: Christopher Edwards & Margaret Erskine. Tel: 01491 833682. Est: 1992. Office and/or bookroom; Internet only. Appointment necessary. Small stock. Spec: Early Imprints; History - General; Literature. CC: MC; V. Corresp: French. Mem: ABA; ILAB. VAT No: GB 563 0529 50.

Toby English, ■ 10 St. Mary's Street, Wallingford, OX10 0EL. Tel: (01491) 836389. Fax: (01491) 836389. Web: www.tobyenglish.com. Est: 1981. Shop open: **M:** 09:30–17:00; **T:** 09:30–17:00; **W:** 09:30–17:00; **Th:** 09:30–16:45; **F:** 09:30–16:45; **S:** 09:30–17:00. Large stock. Spec: Academic/Scholarly; Architecture; Art; Art Reference; Author - Inklings, The; First Editions; Private Press; Topography - Local. PR: £1–500. CC: AE; JCB; MC; V; SW. Corresp: French, German. Mem: PBFA. Notes: *General stock, specialities art and architecture, Thames books, also provide a booksearch service.*

Tooley, Adams & Co, PO Box 174, Wallingford D.O., OX10 0RB. Prop: Steve Luck. Tel: 01491 838298. Fax: 01491834616. Web: www.tooleys.co.uk. Est: 1979. Private premises. Internet and Postal. Telephone First. Open: **M:** 09:00–17:00; **T:** 09:00–17:00; **W:** 09:00–17:00; **Th:** 09:00–17:00; **F:** 09:00–17:00. Spec: Antiquarian; Caricature; Cartography; Geography; Reference; River Thames. CC: AE; D; E; MC; V. Cata: Maps, Atlases, Views, Cartobibliographies. Corresp: French, Spanish. Mem: ABA; ILAB; International Antiquarian Mapdealers Assoc. VAT No: GB 371 2110 01.

WANTAGE

Parrott Books, ■Regent Mall, Town Centre, Wantage, OX12 8BU. Tel: (01367) 820251. Fax: (01367) 820210. Est: 1997. Shop open: **M:** 08:30–17:30; **T:** 08:30–17:30; **W:** 08:30–17:30; **Th:** 08:30–17:30; **F:** 08:30–17:30; **S:** 08:30–17:00. Very large stock. Spec: Aircraft; Alpinism/Mountaineering; Animals and Birds; Archaeology; Architecture; Art Reference; Biography; Children's. PR: £2–50. Notes: *Parrott Books try to offer an eclectic mix of secondhand and antiquarian books.*

Regent Furniture, ■Regent Shopping Mall, Newbury Street, Wantage, OX12 8BU. Prop: W.O. & S. Mudway. Tel: 01235 766625. Est: 1995. Shop open: **M:** 08:30–17:00; **T:** 08:30–17:00; **W:** 08:30–17:00; **Th:** 08:30–17:00; **F:** 08:30–17:00; **S:** 08:30–17:00. VAT No: GB 685 6589 65.

WARBOROUGH

Nineteenth Century Books, St. Mary's Cottage, 61 Thame Road, Warborough, Wallingford, OX10 7EA. Prop: Dr. Ann M. Ridler. Tel: (01865) 858379. Fax: (01865) 858575. Web: www.ukbookworld.com/members/papageno. Est: 1984. Private premises. Internet and Postal. Small stock. Spec: Author - Borrow, George; Biography; Books about Books; History - General; Literary Criticism; Literary Travel; Literature; Natural History. PR: £5–500. CC: MC; V. Cata: Nineteenth century. Corresp: French, Spanish. Mem: PBFA.

WITNEY

Brian Carter, 8 Swan Court, Corn Street, Witney, OX28 6EA. Prop: Brian Carter. Tel: (01993) 866627. Est: 1974. Private premises. Postal only. Contactable. Small stock. Spec: Ecclesiastical History & Architecture; Oxford Movement; Philosophy; Theology. PR: £5–500. CC: MC; V. Cata: Theology/ Church History. Notes: *We take telephone calls from 09:00 to 21:00 all week.*

Church Green Books, ■ 46 Market Square, Witney, OX28 6AL. Prop: Roger & Margaret Barnes. Tel: (01993) 700822. Web: www.churchgreen.co.uk. Est: 1992. Shop open: **M:** 10:00–16:00; **T:** 10:00–16:00; **W:** 10:00–16:00; **Th:** 10:00–16:00; **F:** 10:00–16:00. Medium stock. Spec: Bell-Ringing (Campanology); Music - Folk & Irish Folk; Music - Political Songs & Ballads; Rural Life; Topography - Local; Booksearch. PR: £1–300. CC: MC; V. Cata: Church Bells & Bell-ringing. Mem: PBFA. Notes: *Valuations of Bell-ringing books. Closed in September for annual holiday. For urgent enquiries call 07891 633429.*

RUTLAND

UPPINGHAM

The Rutland Bookshop, ■ 13 High Street West, Uppingham, LE15 9QB. Prop: Mr & Mrs Edward Baines. Tel: 01572 823450 (24 hr answerphone). Est: 1979. Shop open: **T:** 11:00–17:00; **W:** 11:00–17:00; **Th:** 11:00–17:00; **F:** 11:00–17:00; **S:** 11:00–17:00. Medium stock. Spec: Education & School; Farming & Livestock; Farriers; Fiction - General; Fine & Rare; Gardening - General; Literary Criticism; Natural History. PR: £1–500. Corresp: French, German. Mem: PBFA. Notes: *Attends: Burghley Horse Trials, Rutland Water Bird Fair, Rutland & Leicester Agricultural - and Lincoln Shows. Lists on request.*

Forest Books, ■ 7 High Street West, Uppingham, Rutland, LE15 9QB. Prop: David Siddons. Tel: (01572) 821173. Fax: (0870) 1326314. Web: www.homepages.primex.co.uk/~forest. Est: 1986. Shop open: **M:** 10:30–17:00; **T:** 10:30–17:00; **W:** 10:30–17:00; **Th:** 10:30–17:00; **F:** 10:30–17:00; **S:** 10:30–17:00; **Su:** 13:30–16:30. Very large stock. Spec: Music - Sheet Music; Booksearch; Ephemera. PR: £1–500. CC: JCB; MC; V; Solo; Maestro. Corresp: French. VAT No: GB 424 4691 51. Notes: *We also organise book fairs - 2 a year in Farndon, Nottinghamshire. Also, full copying service in the shop (including A3 colour copying). Secondhand sheet music, postcards. We also sell local new OS maps.*

SHROPSHIRE

BISHOP'S CASTLE

Autolycus, ■ 10 Market Square, Bishop's Castle, SY9 5BN. Prop: David & Jay Wilkinson. Tel: (01588) 630078. Fax: (01588) 630078. Web: www.booksonline.uk.com. Est: 1996. Internet and Postal. Shop open: **M:** 11:00–16:30; **T:** 11:00–16:30; **W:** 11:00–16:30; **Th:** 11:00–16:30; **F:** 11:00–17:00; **S:** 10:30–17:00. Medium stock. Spec: Antiquarian; Children's; Children's - Early Titles; Children's - Illustrated; First Editions; Illustrated - General; Literature; Modern First Editions. PR: £1–1,500. CC: MC; V; Maestro, also Paypal. Cata: Lists on request. Corresp: French, German. VAT No: GB 771 9717 90. Notes: *Please telephone if travelling from afar as opening hours may vary.*

Yarborough House Bookshop, ■ Yarborough House, The Square, Bishop's Castle, SY9 5BN. Prop: Carol Wright. Tel: (01588) 638318. Est: 1980. Shop open: **T:** 10:00–17:30; **Th:** 10:00–17:30; **F:** 10:00–17:30; **S:** 09:00–17:30; **Su:** 10:00–17:30. Medium stock. Spec: Fiction - General; Collectables. PR: £1–20. CC: AE; D; E; JCB; MC; V. Notes: *Also, 4,000 secondhand classic records, 4,000 classic CDs and coffee house serving home made cakes, coffees, and teas.*

BRIDGNORTH

The Bookpassage, ■ 57a High Street, Bridgnorth, WV16 4DX. Prop: David Lamont. Tel: (01746) 768767. Web: www.thebookpassage.co.uk. Est: 1990. Shop open: **M:** 09:00–17:15; **T:** 09:00–17:15; **W:** 08:00–17:15; **Th:** 09:00–17:15; **F:** 09:00–17:15; **S:** 09:00–17:15. Large stock. Spec: Author - General; Author - 20th Century; Author - Saville, M.; Authors - Local; County - Local; Fiction - General; Fiction - Adventure; Fiction - Crime, Detective, Spy, Thrillers. PR: £1–500. Notes: *Open occasionally on Sundays, specialists in local history and local authors.*

CLUN

Bodders Books, Heather Cottage, Ford Street, Clun, SY7 8LD. Prop: Andy Boddington. Tel: 0771 801681. Est: 2008. Postal business. Appointment necessary. Small stock. Spec: Academic/Scholarly; Adventure; Autobiography; Biography; Heritage; History - General; History - Science. PR: £7.50 – £300.

ELLESMERE

Glyn's Books, 6 The Avenue, Lyneal, Ellesmere, SY12 OQJ. Prop: Glyn Watson. Tel: (01948) 710591. Fax: (01948) 710442. Web: www.glynsbooks.com. Est: 1986. Private premises. Internet and Postal. Spec: Astrology; First Editions; History - General; Literature; Booksearch. CC: AE; E; JCB; MC; V. Notes: *Major international booksearch service. Successfully sourcing hard to find books for over 20 years. Website : www.glynsbooks.com.*

JACKFIELD

The Boox-Box, 10 Chapel View, Chapel Road, Jackfield, TF8 7LU. Tel: 07976 579848. Private premises. Internet only. Telephone First. Open: **M:** 09:00–17:30; **T:** 09:00–17:30; **W:** 09:00–17:30; **Th:** 09:00–17:30; **F:** 09:00–17:30; Closed for lunch: 13:00–14:00. Spec: Author - Rolt, L.T.C.; Steam Engines.

LUDLOW

Lyndon Barnes - Books, 3 Mortimer Drive, Ludlow, SY8 4JW. Prop: Lyndon Barnes. Tel: (01568) 780641. Web: www.abebooks.co.uk. Est: 1988. Private premises. Internet and Postal. Contactable. Open: **M:** 09:00–20:00; **T:** 09:00–20:00; **W:** 09:00–20:00; **Th:** 09:00–20:00; **F:** 09:00–20:00; **S:** 09:00–20:00; **Su:** 09:00–20:00. Small stock. Spec: Music - General; Music - Classical; Music - Composers; Music - Country & Western; Music - Jazz & Blues; Music - Musicians; Music - Opera; Music - Orchestral. PR: £2–100. CC: PayPal. Cata: mostly non-fiction. Notes: *All stock on abebooks.*

Innes Books, 22 Julian Road, Ludlow, SY8 1HA. Prop: Pat Innes. Tel: (01584) 878146. Web: www.innesbooks.co.uk. Est: 1997. Private premises. Internet and Postal. Appointment necessary. Open: **M:** 09:00–10:00; **T:** 09:00–10:00; **W:** 09:00–10:00; **Th:** 09:00–10:00; **F:** 09:00–10:00; **S:** 10:00–06:00; **Su:** 10:00–05:00. Small stock. Spec: Academic/Scholarly; Children's; Fiction - General; Fiction - Adventure; Fiction - Crime, Detective, Spy, Thrillers; First Editions; General Stock; Illustrated - General. PR: £3–600. CC: PayPal. VAT No: GB 812 5174 53.

Offa's Dyke Books, Old School House, Downton-on-the-Rock, Ludlow, SY8 2HX. Prop: S.R. Bainbridge. Tel: (01584) 856212. Fax: (01584) 856757. Est: 1974. Private premises. Telephone First. Spec: Academic/Scholarly; Antiquarian; Antiques; Art; Bindings; Fine & Rare; Literature. CC: Paypal. VAT No: GB 393 9270 15.

Olynthiacs, 19 Castle View Terrace, Ludlow, SY8 2NG. Prop: Neil MacGregor. Tel: (01584) 872671. Web: www.ukbookworld.com/members/olynthiacs. Est: 1735. Private premises. Postal only. Contactable. Open: **M:** 09:00–18:00; **T:** 09:00–18:00; **W:** 09:00–18:00; **Th:** 09:00–18:00; **F:** 09:00–18:00; **S:** 09:00–18:00; Closed for lunch: 13:00–14:00. Medium stock. Spec: Author - Burgess, A.; Author - Stevenson, Robert Louis; Author - Wodehouse, P.G.; Biography; Classical Studies; Ecclesiastical History & Architecture; English; Fiction - General. PR: £5–500. Cata: English Language, History, Eton, Oxford, Theology.

Madelay

C. R. Moore, Park House, Park Lane, Madeley, TF7 5HF. Prop: C. R. Moore. Tel: 01952 585231. Est: 1995. Private premises. Appointment necessary. Spec: Antiquarian; Bindings; Genealogy; Heraldry; Printing; Sport - General; Sport - Football (Soccer); Topography - Local. Notes: *Exhibits at bookfairs.*

MUCH WENLOCK

Good Books, Hill Top Farm, Hill Top, Much Wenlock, TF13 6DJ. Prop: Judith Goodman. Tel: (01746) 785250. Web: www.abebooks.com. Est: 1996. Private premises. Appointment necessary. Spec: Children's; Private Press; Railways and Railroads; Sport - Angling/Fishing; Sport - Field Sports. PR: £1–200.

Wenlock Books, ■ 12 High Street, Much Wenlock, TF13 6AA. Prop: Anna Dreda. Tel: (01952) 727877. Fax: (01952) 727877. Web: www.wenlockbooks.co.uk. Est: 1985. Shop open: **M:** 10:00–17:00; **T:** 10:00–17:00; **W:** 10:00–17:00; **Th:** 10:00–17:00; **F:** 10:00–17:00; **S:** 10:00–17:00. Medium stock. PR: £10–25. CC: MC; V. Mem: BA. VAT No: GB 823 8745 08. Notes: *March to December 09:00 to 17:30 Sundays 11:00 - 17:00. British Book Trade Award awarded Wenlock Books the 'Independent Bookseller of the Year 2006'.*

NEWPORT

Newport Book Shop, ■ 16 Upper Bar, Newport, TF10 7EJ. Prop: Mike Barwell. Tel: 01952 813900. Est: 2007. Shop open: **Th:** 11:30–17:30; **F:** 11:30–17:30; **S:** 11:30–17:30; **Su:** 11:30–17:30.

OSWESTRY

Bookworld, ■ 32 Beatrice Street, Oswestry, SY11 1QG. Prop: John Cranwell. Tel: (01691) 657112. Fax: (01691) 657112. Web: www.tgal.co.uk/bookworld. Est: 1993. Shop open: **M:** 09:00–17:00; **T:** 09:00–17:00; **W:** 09:00–17:00; **Th:** 09:00–17:00; **F:** 09:00–17:00; **S:** 09:00–17:00. Medium stock. Spec: Booksearch. PR: £1–1,500. CC: E; JCB; MC; V.

John Read Antiques, 59 Church Street, Oswestry, SY11 2SZ. Prop: John Read. Tel: (01691) 672914. Est: 1964. Open: **T:** 10:00–17:00; **W:** 10:00–17:00; **F:** 10:00–17:00; **S:** 10:00–17:00. PR: £1–150. Notes: *Also antiques. Mobile No: 07802 844891.*

SHREWSBURY

Candle Lane Books, ■ 28 & 29 Princess Street, Shrewsbury, SY1 1LW. Prop: John & Margaret Thornhill. Tel: (01743) 365301. Est: 1974. Shop open: **M:** 09:30–17:00; **T:** 09:00–17:00; **W:** 09:00–17:00; **Th:** 09:00–17:00; **F:** 09:00–17:00; **S:** 09:00–17:00. Very large stock. Spec: Booksearch. PR: £1–3,000. CC: MC; V.

Gemini-Books, The Old Post Office, Main Road, Pontesbury, Shrewsbury, SY5 0PS. Prop: Geoff and Rosalie Davies. Tel: 01743 790999/792721. Est: 2000. Storeroom; Internet and Postal. Appointment necessary. Open: **M:** 10:00–16:00; **T:** 10:00–16:00; **W:** 10:00–16:00; **Th:** 10:00–16:00; **F:** 10:00–16:00; **S:** 10:00–16:00; **Su:** 10:00–16:00. Medium stock. Spec: Children's; Fiction - General. PR: £4–300. CC: AE; JCB; MC; V; Maestro. Notes: *Exhibits at Kinver Book Fair in Staffordshire (3rd Sunday every month).*

Roundwood Books, ■ 24 Claremont Hill, Shrewsbury, SY1 1RD. Prop: Andrew Cork. Tel: (01743) 244833. Web: www.roundwoodbooks.com. Est: 1995. Shop open: **T:** 10:00–16:00; **W:** 10:00–16:00; **Th:** 10:00–16:00; **F:** 10:00–16:00; **S:** 10:00–16:00. Medium stock. PR: £1–50. CC: MC; V. Mem: DTMFC.

The Victorian Gallery, ■ 40 St. John's Hill, Shrewsbury, SY1 1JQ. Prop: R.D. Vernon. Tel: (01743) 356351. Fax: (01743) 356351. Est: 1987. Shop open: **M:** 09:00–17:00; **T:** 09:00–17:00; **W:** 09:00–17:00; **Th:** 09:00–17:00; **F:** 09:00–17:00. Very large stock. PR: £6–600. CC: accepted.

TELFORD

Andrew Cox, 16 Garbett Road Aqueduct, Telford, TF4 3RX. Prop: Andrew Cox. Tel: (01952) 590630. Est: 2000. Private premises. Postal only. Telephone First. Small stock. Spec: Antiquarian; Author - Austen, Jane; Author - Verne, Jules; Children's - Illustrated; County - Local; Fairy/Folk Tales; Fossils; Geology. PR: £10–10. Mem: PBFA.

WEM

Black 5 Books, ■ 54 High Street, Wem, SY4 5DW. Prop: Ken Simpson. Tel: 0845 166 4084. Web: www.black5books.com. Est: 1984. Internet and Postal. Shop open: **M:** 10:00–17:00; **T:** 10:00–17:00; **Th:** 10:00–17:00; **F:** 10:00–17:00; **S:** 10:00–13:00; Closed for lunch: 13:30–15:00. Very large stock. Spec: Army, The; Autobiography; Aviation; Biography; Children's; Education & School; Fiction - General; Fiction - Historical. PR: £1–200. CC: MC; V; Maestro. Mem: BA. VAT No: GB 701 2786 58. Notes: *If travelling any distance, you are advised to check availability first, as other priorities could lead to temporary closure or early closing.*

Booksets, Unit 5, Wem Business Park, New Street, Wem SY4 5JX. Prop: Booksets Ltd. Web: www.booksets.com. Est: 1974. Prem: Warehouse. Internet and postal.Very large stock. PR: £10–500. CC: PayPal. Cata: online/internet on English Language Antiquarian in all subjects. VAT No: GB 696 1311 25. Notes: *Booksets.com is today perhaps better known as the internet business 'BooksetsExtra', with over 250,000 new and near-new books for sale on popular internet sites, but we still have an active interest in antiquarian pamphlets and journals.*

Kabristan Archives, 19 Foxleigh Grove, Wem, SY4 5BS. Prop: Eileen Hewson FRGS. Tel: (01939) 234061. Web: www.kabristan.org.uk. Est: 2004. Private premises. Internet and Postal. Small stock. Spec: Countries - Himalayas, The; Countries - India; Countries - Ireland; Countries - Ladakh; Genealogy; Geography; Graveyards; Himalayan Kingdoms. PR: £5–100. CC: MC; V. Cata: Irish & Indian graveyards. Notes: *Stock include books on Indian and Irish graveyards. Irish genealogy search engine on website.*

WHITCHURCH

Barn Books, ■Pear Tree Farm, Norbury, Whitchurch, SY13 4HZ. Prop: Mary Perry. Tel: (01948) 663742. Fax: (01948) 663742. Web: www.barnbooks.co.uk. Est: 1985. Internet and Postal. Shop open: **F:** 10:00–17:30; **S:** 10:00–17:30; **Su:** 10:00–17:30. Spec: Agriculture; Countries - England; County - Local; Farming & Livestock; Gardening - General; Gardening - Organic; History - Local; Horticulture. PR: £1–500. CC: MC; V. Cata: Gardening, & Local History. Notes: *Also, open on Bank Holidays.*

SOMERSET

BARRINGTON

R.G. Watkins, Books and Prints, 7 Water Street, Barrington, Ilminster, TA19 0JR. Prop: Richard Watkins. Tel: (01460) 54188. Web: www.rgwatkins.co.uk. Est: 1985. Mail order only; Internet and Postal. Contactable. Small stock. Spec: Art Reference, Auction Catalogues, Author - Lawrence, T.E.; Autographs; Countries - Arabian Peninsula; Ephemera; Travel - Middle East; Appraisals & Valuations. PR: £1–500. CC: AE; MC; V. Cata: Lawrence of Arabia, Engraved Portraits. Corresp: French. Notes: *Specialist stock concentrating on Art, Collecting, Lawrence of Arabia. Prints including Engraved Portraits and Country House views. Maps: Valuations for insurance and probate.*

BATH

Bath Book Exchange, ■ 35 Broad Street, Bath, BA1 5LP. Tel: (01225) 466214. Est: 1959. Shop open: **M:** 09:30–17:00; **T:** 09:30–17:00; **W:** 09:30–17:00; **Th:** 09:30–17:00; **F:** 09:30–17:00; **S:** 09:30–17:00; Closed for lunch: 13:00–14:00. Medium stock. Spec: Booksearch. PR: £1–10.

Bath Old Books, ■ 9c Margarets Buildings, Bath, BA1 2LP. Prop: Chris Crook, Steven Ferdinando, Chris Phillips, Richard Selby, John Williams. Tel: (01225) 422244. Fax: 0870 8312098. Est: 1990. Shop open in Summer: **M:** 10:00–17:00; **T:** 10:00–17:00; **W:** 10:00–17:00; **Th:** 10:00–17:00; **F:** 10:00–17:00; **S:** 10:00–17:00. Large stock. Spec: Antiquarian; Art; Children's - Illustrated; County - Local; First Editions; Folio Society, The; General Stock; History - General. CC: JCB; MC; V; All Major cards. Corresp: French. Mem: PBFA. Notes: *Booksearch service, Valuations for probate and Insurance purposes. Books bought.*

George Bayntun, ■ Manvers Street, Bath, BA1 1JW. Prop: E.W.G. Bayntun–Coward. Tel: (01225) 466000. Fax: (01225) 482122. Web: www.georgebayntun.com. Est: 1894. Shop open: **M:** 09:00–17:30; **T:** 09:00–17:30; **W:** 09:00–17:30; **Th:** 09:00–17:30; **F:** 09:00–17:30; **S:** 09:30–13:00; Closed for lunch: 13:00–14:00. Small stock. Spec: Bindings; Children's; Children's - Illustrated; Classics, The; Fine leather bindings (see also Fine & Rare); First Editions; Illustrated - General; Literature. PR: £10–5,000. CC: MC; V; SW, SO. Corresp: French. Mem: ABA; PBFA; ILAB. VAT No: GB 137 5073 71. Notes: *Also, bindery incorporating the famous binding firm of Robert Riviere & Son, est. 1829.*

Camden Books, Bath, BA15JD. Prop: Elizabeth Suchar. Tel: (01225) 337026. Fax: none. Web: www.camdenbooks.com. Est: 1984. Private premises. Internet and Postal. Small stock. Spec: Academic/Scholarly; Antiquarian; Architecture; Art History; Civil Engineering; Classical Studies; Economics; Fine & Rare. PR: £10–2,000. CC: Cheque. Mem: PBFA. Notes: *Online business on abebooks only.*

Janet Clarke, 3 Woodside Cottages, Freshford, Bath, BA2 7WJ. Prop: Janet Clarke. Tel: (01225) 723186. Fax: (01225) 722063. Web: www.janetclarke.com. Est: 1973. Private premises. Postal only. Small stock. Spec: Author - David, Elizabeth; Author - Heath, Ambrose; Cookery/Gastronomy; Food & Drink; Wine; Ephemera. PR: £5–3,000. CC: PayPal. Cata: on specialities. Mem: ABA; BA; ILAB.

George Gregory, Manvers Street, Bath, BA1 1JW. Prop: Charlotte Bayntun-Coward. Tel: (01225) 466000. Fax: (01225) 482122. Est: 1846. Shop and/or gallery; Shop open: **M:** 09:00–17:30; **T:** 09:00–17:30; **W:** 09:00–17:30; **Th:** 09:00–17:30; **F:** 09:00–17:30; **S:** 09:30–13:00; Closed for lunch: 13:00–14:00. Large stock. Spec: Literature; Prints and Maps. PR: £1–200. CC: MC; V. Notes: *Engraved portraits and views.*

Peter Goodden Books Ltd, 7 Clarendon Villas, Widcombe Hill, Bath, BA2 6AG. Prop: Peter Goodden. Tel: (01225) 310986. Est: 1976. Mail order only; Internet and Postal. Open: **M:** 09:00–18:00; **T:** 09:00–18:00; **W:** 09:00–18:00; **Th:** 09:00–18:00; **F:** 09:00–18:00; **S:** 09:00–18:00; **Su:** 09:00–18:00. Small stock. Spec: Music - General; Music - Classical; Music - Composers; Music - Gilbert & Sullivan; Music - Gregorian Chants; Music - Musicians; Music - Theory; Musical Instruments. PR: £5–1,500. CC: JCB; MC; V. Cata: Music; some general. Corresp: Simple French !. Mem: PBFA. VAT No: GB 195 9854 90. Notes: *Please, no casual callers: much of the stock is not easily viewed.*

Hugh Ashley Rayner, 4 Malvern Buildings Fairfield Park, Bath, BA1 6JX. Prop: Hugh A. Rayner. Tel: (01225) 463552. Fax: (01225) 463552. Web: www.indiabooks.co.uk. Est: 1986. Private premises. Telephone First. Open: **M:** 10:00–19:00; **T:** 10:00–19:00; **W:** 10:00–19:00; **Th:** 10:00–19:00; **F:** 10:00–19:00; **S:** 10:00–19:00; **Su:** 12:00–18:00. Small stock. Spec: Antiquarian; Asian Studies; Countries - Asia; Countries - Bhutan; Countries - Burma; Countries - Central Asia; Countries - Himalayas, The; Countries - India. PR: £35–500. CC: AE; D; JCB; MC; V. Cata: India and South Asia. Corresp: German. Mem: PBFA. Notes: *Valuations, Library Cataloguing.*

Solitaire Books, Holly Lawn, Prospect Place, Bath, BA2 4QP. Prop: Martyn Thomas. Tel: 01225 469441. Fax: 0870 135 8843. Web: www.solitairebooks.co.uk. Est: 1994. Private premises. Postal only. Appointment necessary. Spec: Author - Ruskin, John; Bibliography; Books about Books; Fine Printing; Printing; Private Press; Publishers - Curwen Press; Publishers - Incline Press. CC: Paypal. Cata: Fine Press and Books about Books. Notes: *I usually have many Whittington Press, Old School Press and other UK private press items available. Please email details of books sought to sales@solitairebooks.co.uk.*

BATHEASTON

Libris (Weston) Books, 68 London Road West, Batheaston, BA1 7DA. Tel: (01225) 858809. Private premises. Book fairs only. Spec: Aviation; Countries - Antarctic, The; History - General; Performing Arts; Poetry; Topography - General. Mem: PBFA.

BRIDGEWATER

Wembdon Books, 112 Wembdon Hill, Bridgewater, TA6 7QA. Prop: Ray Millard. Tel: (01278) 424060. Est: 1987. Private premises. Internet and Postal. Small stock. Spec: Antiquarian; Diaries; Military; Topography - Local; Travel - General; War - World War II; Booksearch. PR: £3–150.

BURNHAM-ON-SEA

Boris Books, 19 Lynton Road, Burnham-on-Sea, TA8 1PW. Prop: Pam Stevenson. Tel: 0845 398 5771. Web: www.borisbooks.co.uk. Est: 1997. Private premises. Internet and Postal. Appointment necessary. Spec: Author - Austen, Jane; Author - Bennett, (Enoch) Arnol; Author - Benson, E.F.; Author - Betjeman, Sir John; Author - Blyton, Enid; Author - Brent-Dyer, Elinor M.; Author - Brontes, The; Author - Crompton, Richmal. CC: Paypal. VAT No: GB 717 6806 15. Notes: *Bookroom in private premises. Local sales and internet business. Books bought within our specialist areas: children's; historical fiction; literature.*

CASTLE CARY

Avedikian Rare Books, Bank House, Castle Cary, BA7 7AW. Prop: Stephen James Avedikian. Tel: 01963 359680. Web: www.militarybookshop.com. Open: **M:** 09:00–17:30; **T:** 09:00–17:30; **W:** 09:00–17:30; **Th:** 09:00–17:30; **F:** 09:00–17:30; **S:** 09:00–17:30; **Su:** 09:00–17:30; Closed for lunch: 13:00–14:00. Spec: Author - Lawrence, T.E.; Aviation; Military History; Voyages & Discovery; War - World War I. Mem: ABA.

CHARD

P.J. Baron - Scientific Book Sales, Lakewood, Chard, TA20 4AJ. Prop: Dr. P. Baron. Tel: (01460) 66319. Fax: (01460) 66319. Web: www.books.free-online.co.uk. Est: 1975. Private premises. Internet and Postal. Small stock. Spec: Academic/Scholarly; Biology - General; Botany; Chemistry; Ecology; Engineering; Mathematics; Medicine. PR: £5–150. CC: MC; V; SW, Delta, PayPal. Cata: all science, engineering, medicine. Corresp: French. VAT No: GB 549 4779 82.

CLAPTON–IN–GORDANO

Avonworld Books, 1 Swancombe, Clapton–in–Gordano, BS20 7RR. Prop: Michael C. Ross. Tel: (01275) 842531. Fax: (01275) 849221. Web: www.avonworld-booksource.co.uk. VOIPpro: Skype. VOIPnum: michaelross70. Est: 1984. Office and/or bookroom; Internet and Postal. Appointment necessary. Open: **M:** 09:00–18:00; **T:** 09:00–18:00; **W:** 09:00–18:00; **Th:** 09:00–18:00; **F:** 09:00–18:00; Closed for lunch: 13:00–14:00. Small stock. Spec: Art; Author - Buchan, John; Author - Coward, Noel; Author - Durrell, Lawrence; Author - Graves, Robert; Author - Kipling, Rudyard; Author - Masters, John; Author - Michener, James. PR: £1–500. CC: MC; V. Corresp: German (post only, not e-mail). Mem: PBFA. VAT No: GB 496 6867 66. Notes: *Valuations for insurance or probate of private collections in our author specialities.*

Read Sheppard's Confidential

a weekly newsletter with trade news, forthcoming auctions, book fairs, and other events
Free to everyone registered on Sheppard's

CLEVEDON

Clevedon Books, ■Cambourne Cottage, 6 Seavale Road, Clevedon, BS21 7QB. Prop: George & Wendy Douthwaite. Tel: (01275) 872304. Fax: (01275) 342817. Est: 1970. Internet and Postal. Open: **Th:** 11:00–16:30; **F:** 11:00–16:30; **S:** 11:05–16:30; Closed for lunch: 13:00–14:30. Very large stock. Spec: Academic/Scholarly; Aeronautics; Architecture; Art History; Atlases; Aviation; Canals/Inland Waterways; Cartography. PR: £10–3,000. CC: JCB; MC; V; Debit, PayPal. Cata: science, geology, travel, maps, topography. Mem: PBFA. Notes: *Alternative tel. no: 01275 790579. Also at: 27 Copse Road, Clevedon. (q.v.) Also, colouring & mounting service. Attends fairs occasionally.*

K.W. Cowley, Bookdealer, Trinity Cottage, 153 Old Church Road, Clevedon, BS21 7TU. Prop: Ken Cowley. Tel: (01275) 872247. Est: 1987. Private premises. Postal only. Telephone First. Small stock. Spec: Anthologies; Books about Books; Cinema/Film; Fiction - Crime, Detective, Spy, Thrillers; Fiction - Fantasy, Horror; Fiction - Science Fiction; Ghosts; Pulps. PR: £1–100. Cata: S/F, Fantasy, Horror, Crime, Supernatural. Notes: *Small presses a speciality.*

CREWKERNE

Gresham Books, ■ 31 Market Street, Crewkerne, TA18 7JU. Prop: James Hine. Tel: (01460) 77726. Fax: (01460) 52479. Web: www.greshambooks.co.uk. Est: 1972. Shop open: **M:** 10:00–17:00; **T:** 10:00–17:00; **W:** 10:00–17:00; **Th:** 10:00–17:00; **F:** 10:00–17:00; **S:** 10:00–17:00. Medium stock. Spec: Antiquarian; Antiques; Architecture; Cookery/Gastronomy; Fashion & Costume; Food & Drink; Needlework; Sport - Golf. PR: £1–1,000. CC: AE; MC; V; Switch. Mem: PBFA.

Anne Hine / Gresham Books, ■ 31 Market Street, Crewkerne, TA18 7JU. Tel: (01460) 77726. Fax: (01460) 52479. Est: 1994. Shop open: **M:** 10:00–17:00; **T:** 10:00–17:00; **W:** 10:00–17:00; **Th:** 10:00–17:00; **F:** 10:00–17:00; **S:** 10:00–17:00. Small stock. Spec: Publishers - Warnes. CC: AE; MC; V. Notes: *Also, provides a bookseach service for all plant related books, and Japanese gardening.*

DULVERTON

Rothwell & Dunworth, ■ 2 Bridge Street, Dulverton, TA22 9HJ. Tel: 01398 323169. Est: 1975. Shop open: **M:** 10:30–17:15; **T:** 10:30–17:15; **W:** 10:30–17:15; **Th:** 10:30–17:15; **F:** 10:30–17:15; **S:** 10:30–17:15; **Su:** 11:00–16:00. Spec: Aircraft; Antiquarian; Architecture; Army, The; Art History; Author - Aldin, Cecil; Autobiography; History - General. CC: MC; V; Debit. Mem: ABA.

DUNSTER

Cobbles Books, ■ 14 - 16 Church Street, Dunster, TA24 6SH. Prop: Adrian Corley. Tel: 01643 821305. Fax: 01643 821305. Est: 2003. Shop open: **M:** 10:30–17:00; **T:** 10:30–17:00; **W:** 10:30–17:00; **F:** 10:30–17:00; **S:** 10:30–17:00; **Su:** 10:30–17:00. Spec: Antiques; Art; Aviation; Biography; Fiction - General; Folio Society, The; History - General; History - British. CC: MC; V. Notes: *Opening times may vary between November and March. Please telephone for details.*

FROME

Upper–Room Books, ■Above Antiques & Country Living, 43 - 44 Vallis Way, Babcox, Frome, BA11 3BA. Prop: Victor Adams. Tel: (01373) 467125. Fax: (01373) 467125. Web: www.vabooks.co.uk. Est: 1990. Internet and Postal. Shop open: **M:** 09:30–17:30; **T:** 09:30–17:30; **W:** 09:30–17:30; **Th:** 09:30–17:30; **F:** 09:30–17:30; **S:** 09:30–17:30. Medium stock. Spec: Art; Artists; Author - Morris, William; Building & Construction; Crafts; Furniture; Furniture and Cabinet making; Woodwork. PR: £5–1,000. CC: JCB; MC; V. Mem: PBFA. Notes: *2 hours free parking 30 yards from shop.*

HENSTRIDGE

March House Books, 38 Old Station Gardens, Henstridge, BA8 0PU. Prop: Mrs. Barbara Fisher. Tel: (01963) 364403. Fax: (01963) 364476. Web: www.marchhousebooks.com/. Est: 1997. Private premises. Internet and Postal. Small stock. Spec: Annuals; Children's; Children's - Early Titles; Children's - Illustrated; Illustrated - General; Collectables. PR: £5–650. CC: MC; V; PayPal. Mem: PBFA; ibooknet.

ILMINSTER

Ile Valley Bookshop, ■ 10 Silver Street, Ilminster, TA19 0DJ. Prop: Chris Chapman. Tel: (01460) 57663. Fax: (01460) 57188. Est: 1985. Shop. Small stock.

LANGPORT

David Clarke Books, Flat 2, Earnshill House, Hambridge, Langport, TA10 0AX. Prop: David Clarke. Tel: (01460) 281874. Est: 1999. Private premises. Internet and Postal. Appointment necessary. Medium stock. Spec: Aeronautics; Agriculture; Aircraft; Counties in England; Countries - Arabia; Countries - Arabian Peninsula; Countries - Great Britain; Countries - Middle East, The. PR: £4–300. Cata: England-regional material, farming, Middle East. Corresp: French.

Keeble Antiques, ■ Cheapside, Langport, TA10 9PW. Prop: Clive Keeble. Tel: (01458) 259627. Fax: (01458) 259627. Web: www.keebleantbks.co.uk. Est: 1998. Internet and Postal. Shop open: **M:** 09:00–18:00; **T:** 09:00–18:00; **W:** 09:00–18:00; **Th:** 09:00–18:00; **F:** 09:00–18:00; **S:** 09:00–18:00; **Su:** 10:00–16:30. Medium stock. Spec: Antiques; Art; Carriages & Driving; Natural History; Private Press; Rural Life; Topography - Local; Travel - General. PR: £1–1,000.

MIDSOMER NORTON

Tom Randall, Welton Hill Cottage, Welton Grove, Midsomer Norton, Radstock, BA3 2TS. Prop: Tom Randall. Tel: (01761) 418926. Web: www.ukbookworld.com/members/folklorist. Est: 1987. Private premises. Internet and Postal. Contactable. Spec: Agriculture; Antique Stoves; Archaeology - Industrial; Arthurian; Author - Baring-Gould, S.; Author - Lang, Andrew; Author - Rolt, L.T.C.; Automata. PR: £2–500. Cata: folklore & folkmusic. Notes: *Also, a booksearch service.*

MILVERTON

Cat Lit, Loundshay Manor Cottage, Preston Bowyer, Milverton, TA4 1QF. Tel: (01823) 401527. Fax: (01823) 401527. Est: 2002. Private premises. Postal only. Appointment necessary. Spec: Cats; Dogs; Sport - Field Sports.

MINEHEAD

Rare Books & Berry, ■ 1Lowerbourne House High Street, Porlock, Minehead, TA24 8PU. Prop: Helen & Michael Berry. Tel: (01643) 863255. Fax: (01643) 863092. Web: www.rarebooksandberry.co.uk. Est: 1992. VAT No: GB 801 1222 04.

NORTH CHERITON

Paper Pleasures, Holt Farm, North Cheriton, BA8 0AQ. Prop: Lesley Tyson. Tel: (01963) 33718. Web: www.paperpleasures.com. Est: 1998. Private premises. Postal only. Appointment necessary. Small stock. Spec: Art; Bookbinding; Erotica; Ex-Libris; Glamour; Homosexuality & Lesbianism; Literature; Magazines & Periodicals - General. PR: £5–2,000. CC: MC; V; Switch. Cata: Erotica. Mem: PBFA. Notes: *To receive my illustrated Erotica catalogue, three times a year, just phone, email or write to me and I will place you on my exclusive and confidential mailing list.*

PEASEDOWN ST. JOHN

BookLovers.co.uk, ■The Post Office, 12 Bath Road, Peasedown St. John, BA2 8DH. Prop: David Gower-Spence. Tel: 0845 009 4455. Fax: 0845 009 1786. Web: www.booklovers.co.uk. VOIPpro: skype. VOIPnum: david.gower.spence. Est: 1994. Internet and Postal. Shop open: **M:** 09:00–17:30; **T:** 09:00–17:30; **W:** 09:00–13:00; **Th:** 09:00–17:30; **F:** 09:00–17:30; **S:** 09:00–12:30; Closed for lunch: 13:00–14:00. CC: AE; D; JCB; MC; V. Notes: *A small eclectic selection of 500+ books in the shop only - majority of stock is available mail order only.*

PEN SELWOOD

The Traveller's Bookshelf, Holly Lodge, Pear Ash Lane, Pen Selwood, BA9 8LX. Prop: Jenny Steadman. Tel: 01747 841041. Est: 1991. Private premises. Internet and Postal. Spec: Countries - Afghanistan; Countries - Albania; Countries - Arabia; Countries - Armenia; Countries - Asia; Countries - Asia Minor; Countries - Balkans, The; Countries - Baltic States. PR: £20–5,000. CC: MC; V. Cata: Travel & Exploration. Mem: PBFA. VAT No: GB 779 2193 85. Notes: *We specialise in books of travel, exploration and scholarship on the Balkans, North Africa, the Middle East, Central Asia, the Himalayan region, South East Asia and the Far East.*

QUEEN CAMEL

Steven Ferdinando, The Old Vicarage, High Street, Queen Camel, Nr. Yeovil, BA22 7NG. Tel: (01935) 850210. Est: 1977. Office and/or bookroom; Telephone First. Medium stock. Spec: Agriculture; Author - Hardy, Thomas; Author - Powys Family, The; Illustrated - General; Irish Interest; Literature; Topography - Local; Travel - General. PR: £10–800. CC: MC; V; Maestro, Delta. Mem: PBFA. Notes: *Bath Old Books, Bath. (q.v.)*

SIMONSBATH

Spooner & Co, Mead Cottage, Honeymead, Simonsbath, TA24 7JX. Prop: Brian John Spooner. Tel: (01643) 831562. Est: 1985. Private premises. Internet and Postal. Appointment necessary. Small stock. Spec: Antiquarian; Archaeology; Architecture; Bibles; Biblical Studies; Bibliography; Bookbinding; Books about Books. PR: £3–230. Notes: *Also, booksearch, bookbinding and repairs.*

SOMERTON

Simon's Books, ■ Broad Street, Somerton, TA11 7NH. Prop: Bryan Ives. Tel: (01458) 272313. Est: 1978. Shop open: **M:** 10:00–16:00; **T:** 10:00–16:00; **W:** 10:00–16:00; **Th:** 10:00–16:00; **F:** 10:00–16:00; **S:** 10:00–16:00. Large stock. PR: £1–100.

TAUNTON

Badger Books, 2 The Orchard, Dowell Close, Taunton, TA2 6BN. Prop: Janet & Nic Tall. Tel: (01823) 323180. Web: www.badgerbooks.co.uk. Est: 2002. Private premises. Internet and Postal. Appointment necessary. Small stock. Spec: Author - Brent-Dyer, Elinor M.; Author - Forest, A.; Author - Hill, Lorna; Author - Oxenham, Elsie; Children's. PR: £1–200. Corresp: German.

Boxwood Books & Prints, Ashbrook House, Winsford, Minehead, Taunton, TA24 7HN. Prop: (*) Peter & Catherine Nicholls. Tel: (01643) 851588. Fax: (01643) 851588. Est: 1995. Private premises. Appointment necessary. Small stock. Spec: Art Reference; Illustrated - General; Printing; Private Press; Prints and Maps. PR: £50–1,500. CC: MC; V. Mem: PBFA. Notes: *Attends Oxford Fine Press Fair only.*

Dene Barn Books & Prints, Brackenbury, Ash Priors, Taunton, TA4 3NF. Prop: Derek Cundy. Tel: (01823) 433103. Est: 1990. Private premises. Appointment necessary. Small stock. Spec: Botany; Natural History; Topography - Local; Prints and Maps. PR: £10–500. Notes: *Picture Framing and mounting.*

The Eastern Traveller, 52 Mountway Road, Bishops Hull, Taunton, TA1 5LS. Prop: Anna Mullett. Tel: (01823) 327012. Est: 1979. Private premises. Book fairs only. Spec: Adventure; Antiquities; Asian Studies; Countries - Arabia; Countries - Asia; Countries - Egypt; History - General; Travel - General. PR: £5–50. Cata: Travel esp. Eastern. Corresp: French. Mem: PBFA.

Firsts in Print, Unit 3, Apple Business Centre, Frobisher Way, Taunton, TA2 6BB. Prop: Peter Elliston. Tel: 07970260073. Web: www.firsts-in-print.co.uk. Est: 1984. Private premises. Internet and Postal. Appointment necessary. Open: **M:** 09:00–17:00; **T:** 09:00–17:00; **W:** 09:00–17:00; **Th:** 09:00–17:00; **F:** 09:00–17:00. Medium stock. Spec: Booker Prize; Children's; Fiction - General; Fiction - Crime, Detective, Spy, Thrillers; Fiction - Fantasy, Horror; Fiction - Historical; First Editions; Literature. PR: £3–1,000. CC: MC; V; Switch/Mae. VAT No: GB 768 9507 66.

Russell Needham Books, 5 Silver St., Milverton, Taunton, TA4 1LA. Prop: (*). Tel: (01823) 400470. Fax: (0870) 0561167. Web: www.needhambooks.demon.co.uk. Private premises. Internet and Postal. Telephone First. Small stock. Spec: Academic/Scholarly; Alchemy; Alternative Medicine; American Indians; Arabica; Author - Bennett, J.G.; Author - Gurdjieff, W.I.; Author - Nicoll, Maurice. PR: £5–300. CC: PayPal. Corresp: French, Francais. Notes: *Specialist in the works of JG Bennett, Ouspensky, Gurdjieff and other Fourth Way writers. UK representative for Bennett Books and Chalice Books, the works of Reshad Feild.*

TICKENHAM

R.A. Gilbert, 215 Clevedon Road, Tickenham, Clevedon, BS21 6RX. Tel: 01275 854486. Est: 1963. Private premises. Appointment necessary. Small stock. Spec: Alchemy; Folklore; Freemasonry & Anti-Masonry; Gnostics / Gnosticism; Occult; Psychic; Religion - General; Theology. PR: £5–1,000. Corresp: French. VAT No: GB 138 9728 22.

WELLINGTON

Peter J. Ayre, Greenham Hall, Greenham, Wellington, TA21 0JJ. Tel: (01823) 672603. Fax: (01823) 672307. Est: 1980. Private premises. Internet and Postal. Appointment necessary. Small stock. Spec: Africana; Countries - Africa; Countries - Kenya; Countries - Tanzania; Natural History; Sport - Big Game Hunting; Travel - Africa; Booksearch. PR: £10–5,000. CC: JCB; MC; V. Cata: East Africa. Mem: PBFA. Notes: *Also, a booksearch service.*

Mary Sharpe, 55 Twitchen, Holcombe Rogus, Wellington, TA21 0PS. Tel: (01823) 672304. Est: 1995. Private premises. Postal only. Small stock. Spec: Author - Austen, Jane; Author - Brontes, The; Author - Burney, Fanny; Author - Eliot, G.; Author - Gaskell, E.; Author - Hardy, Thomas; Children's; Illustrated - General. PR: £5–200. Notes: *Exhibits at bookfairs.*

WEST PENNARD

Eddie Baxter - Books, The Old Mill House, West Pennard, BA6 8ND. Prop: Josie Matthews. Tel: (01749) 890369. Fax: (01749) 890369. Est: 1956. Private premises. Postal only. Small stock. Spec: Dance; Music - General; Music - Jazz & Blues; Booksearch.

WESTON–SUPER–MARE

Manna Bookshop, ■ 30 Orchard Street, Weston–Super–Mare, BS23 1RQ. Prop: Peter Fairnington. Tel: (01934) 636228. Est: 1981. Shop open: **M:** 10:00–17:00; **T:** 10:00–17:00; **W:** 10:00–17:00; **Th:** 10:00–17:00; **F:** 10:00–17:00; **S:** 10:00–17:00. Large stock. PR: £1–100. Notes: *Hours are approximate. Sometimes closed on Thursday.*

Sterling Books, ■ 43a Locking Road, Weston–Super–Mare, BS23 3DG. Prop: David Nisbet. Tel: (01934) 625056. Web: www.abe.com. Est: 1966. Shop open: **T:** 10:00–17:30; **W:** 10:00–17:30; **Th:** 10:00–13:00; **F:** 10:00–17:30; **S:** 10:00–17:30. Very large stock. Spec: Academic/Scholarly; Advertising; Aeronautics; Antiquarian; Art; Bindings; Crafts; History - General. PR: £1–1,500. CC: AE; D; E; JCB; MC; V. Mem: ABA; PBFA; ILAB. Notes: *Also, bookbinding & restoration, picture-framing & a booksearch service.*

WILLITON

Michael Bishop, 10 Rylands Close, Williton, Taunton, TA4 4PE. Tel: (01984) 634542. Est: 2005. Private premises. Internet and Postal. Very small stock. Spec: Rural Life; Topography - Local; Travel - General. PR: £5–500. CC: via Abebooks. Mem: PBFA. Notes: *We trade at PBFA Book Fairs, and local fairs in the South West, by post with other PBFA members and some of our stock is listed on Abebooks.*

SOUTH YORKSHIRE

BALBY

Adams' Collectables, 55 Thomson Avenue, Balby, Doncaster, DN4 0NT. Prop: Michael Adams. Tel: 01302858371. Est: 2007. Private premises. Market Stall. Telephone First. Open: **T:** 09:00–17:30; **W:** 08:00–14:30; **Th:** 09:00–17:30; **F:** 09:00–17:30; **S:** 09:00–17:30; Closed for lunch: 13:00–14:00. Spec: Author - Blyton, Enid; Author - Dahl, Roald; Author - Potter, Beatrix; Music - Political Songs & Ballads; Music - Rock & Roll; Non-Fiction. Notes: *I specialise in children's books and annuals and biographies in comedy/entertainment, film, sport, military and history.*

DONCASTER

Adams Collectables, 55 Thomson Avenue, Balby, Doncaster, DN4 0NT. Prop: Michael Adams. Tel: 01302 858371. Est: 2006. Private premises. Internet and postal. Telephone First. Open: **M:** 09:00–17:30; **T:** 09:00–17:30; **W:** 09:00–17:30; **F:** 09:00–17:30; Closed for lunch: 13:00–14:00. Very small stock. Spec: Annuals; Antiques; Children's - General; Christmas; Irish Interest; Music - General; New Books; Sales & Marketing. PR: £1–100. CC: V. Notes: *Have a weekly market in Doncaster every Wednesday 08:00 to 14:00 Flea Market: secondhand sport memorabilia and Doncaster history.*

Hedgerow Books, 10 Whitbeck Close, Wadworth, Doncaster, DN11 9DZ. Prop: Peter & Elizabeth Hedge. Tel: (01302) 856311. Web: www.hedgerowbooks.com. Est: 1988. Private premises. Internet and Postal. Appointment necessary. Open: **M:** 09:00–21:00; **T:** 09:00–21:00; **W:** 09:00–21:00; **Th:** 09:00–21:00; **F:** 09:00–21:00; **S:** 09:00–12:30; Closed for lunch: 12:30–14:00. Small stock. Spec: Architecture; Ecclesiastical History & Architecture; History - Industrial; Sport - Boxing; Sport - Football (Soccer). PR: £1–500. CC: MC; V; Switch. Cata: Boxing. Mem: PBFA. VAT No: GB 657 8581 80.

Saxton Books Ltd, 18 Saxton Avenue, Doncaster, DN4 7AX. Tel: 01302 371600. Fax: 01302 371071. Web: www.saxtonbooks.com. Est: 1997. Private premises. Internet and Postal. Very small stock. Spec: Author - Austen, Jane; Author - Bates, H.E.; Author - Bramah, Ernest; Author - Flint, William Russell; Author - Rand, Ayn; Author - Shute, Neville; Economics; Engraving. PR: £10–1,000.

ECKINGTON

The Bibliophile, 42 Fern Close, Eckington, S21 4HE. Prop: (*) Michael P. Russell. Tel: (01246) 434025. Est: 1997. Private premises. Book fairs only. Spec: Freemasonry & Anti-Masonry; Medicine; Printing; Collectables; Ephemera. PR: £1–50.

ROTHERHAM

Anthony Singleton, 6 Birkwood Terrace, Braithwell, Rotherham, S66 7AE. Tel: (01709) 813396. Est: 1996. Private premises. Postal only. Small stock. Spec: History - General; Rural Life; Theology; Topography - General; Travel - General.

SHEFFIELD

Annie's Books, 28 Blackbrook Drive, Sheffield, S10 4LS. Prop: Chris Greaves. Tel: 0114 2306494. Web: www.anniesbooks.co.uk. Est: 1998. Mail order only; Internet and Postal. Appointment necessary. Open: **M:** 09:30–17:00; **T:** 09:30–17:00; **W:** 09:30–17:00; **Th:** 09:30–17:00; **F:** 09:30–17:00; Closed for lunch: 13:00–14:00. Spec: Adventure; Aeronautics; Aircraft; Alternative Medicine; Animals and Birds; Annuals; Antiques; Arms & Armour. CC: PayPal. Cata: animals, cats, childrens, thrillers, horror, fiction. Notes: *Subjects from adventure - witchcraft. Free, no obligation book search service.*

Baedekers & Murray Guides, 11 St. Quentin Drive, Sheffield, S17 4PN. Prop: Dr. R.H. Hickley. Tel: (0114) 236-6306. Web: www.roger_hickley@dsl.Pipex.com. Est: 1991. Private premises. Internet and Postal. Appointment necessary. Small stock. Spec: Guide Books; Travel - General. PR: £10–500. Cata: travel and topography. Corresp: French, German, Swedish, Finnish.

Biff Books and Records, ■ 11 Commonside, Sheffield, S10 1GA. Prop: Brian Andrews. Web: www.btinternet.com/~biffbooks/. Est: 1983. Shop. Appointment necessary. Spec: Archaeology; Cookery/Gastronomy; Crime (True); Gardening - General; History - General; Literary Criticism; Military; Music - General. PR: £1 – 150. Notes: *Small shop with erratic opening times, please email before visiting. More valuable stock stored elsewhere, viewable through my website. Please email first for stock over £4.00.*

Chantrey Books, 24 Cobnar Road, Sheffield, S8 8QB. Prop: Clare Brightman. Tel: 0114 2748958. Est: 1982. Private premises. Internet and Postal. Appointment necessary. Spec: Agriculture; Cookery/ Gastronomy; Farming & Livestock; Food & Drink; Gardening - General; Herbalism; Illustrated - 19th & 20th Century; Illustrators. CC: MC; V. Cata: Gardening, Rural Life, Cookery. Mem: PBFA. Notes: *Specialist in gardening, rural life, food and cookery. Bulk of stock is in these subject areas. Bookfairs attended regularly.*

Alan Hill Books, Unit 4, Meersbrook Works Valley Road, Sheffield, S8 9FT. Prop: Alan Hill. Tel: (01142) 556242. Est: 1980. Shop and/or showroom; Internet and Postal. Telephone First. Open: **M:** 10:30–13:30; **T:** 10:30–13:30; **W:** 10:30–13:30; **Th:** 10:30–13:30; **F:** 10:30–13:30. Large stock. Spec: Academic/Scholarly; Genealogy; Topography - Local. PR: £5–500. CC: MC; V. VAT No: GB 533 9950 19.

Howard Loftus Rail Books, 11 Collier Road, Kiverton Park, Sheffield, S26 6LR. Prop: Howard Loftus. Tel: 01909 771408. Private premises. Postal only. Open: **M:** 09:00–17:30; **T:** 09:00–17:30; **W:** 09:00–17:30; **Th:** 09:00–17:30; **F:** 09:00–17:30; **S:** 09:00–17:30; **Su:** 09:00–17:30; Closed for lunch: 13:00–14:00. Spec: Railways and Railroads. Notes: *Specialist in British Modern Traction Railway Books.*

The Porter Bookshop, ■ 227 Sharrowvale Road, Sheffield, S11 8ZE. Prop: Brian Tee. Tel: (0114) 266-7762. Est: 1988. Shop open but telephone first: **M:** 10:00–18:00; **T:** 10:00–18:00; **W:** 10:00–18:00; **Th:** 10:00–18:00; **F:** 10:00–18:00. Medium stock. Spec: Academic/Scholarly; Crime (True); Humanities; Literature.

Rare & Racy, ■ 164–166 Devonshire Street, Sheffield, S3 7SG. Prop: Allen Capes & Joseph Mhlongo. Tel: (0114) 270-1916. Web: www.rareandracy.co.uk. Est: 1969. Shop open: **M:** 10:00–18:00; **T:** 10:00–18:00; **W:** 10:00–18:00; **Th:** 10:00–18:00; **F:** 10:00–18:00; **S:** 10:00–18:00. Spec: Gardening - General; History - Local; Topography - Local. PR: £1–250. CC: MC; V; Solo, Maestro. Mem: PBFA. VAT No: GB 173 1507 80.

Tilleys Vintage Magazine Shop, ■ 281 Shoreham Street, Sheffield, S1 4SS. Prop: Antonius & Albertus Tilley. Tel: (0114) 275-2442. Web: www.tilleysmagazines.com. Est: 1978. Shop open: **T:** 10:00–16:30; **W:** 10:00–16:30; **Th:** 10:00–16:30; **F:** 10:00–16:30; **S:** 10:00–16:30. Very large stock. Spec: Comic Books & Annuals; Comics; Magazines & Periodicals - General; Spiritualism; Ephemera; Prints and Maps. PR: £1–200. CC: AE; MC; V. Notes: *Also at: 21 Derby Road, Chesterfield (q.v.)*

STAFFORDSHIRE

BURTON UPON TRENT

Ian J. Sherratt, Rhoslyn, Victoria St., Yoxall, Burton upon Trent, DE13 8NG. Est: 1989. Private premises. Postal only. Small stock. PR: £1–20. Notes: *Also attends book fairs.*

Mike Abrahams, 14 Meadowbrook Road, Lichfield, WS13 7RN. Tel: (01543) 256200. Est: 1979. Private premises. Appointment necessary. Spec: Antiques; Banking & Insurance; Canals/Inland Waterways; Children's; Collecting; Comic Books & Annuals; Cookery/Gastronomy; Crime (True). PR: £1–500.

Steve Brown (Books), 2 Curborough Cottages, Watery Lane, Lichfield, WS13 8ER. Prop: Steve Brown. Tel: (01543) 264498. Web: www.abebooks.com/servlet/StoreFrontDisplay?cid = 621. Est: 1992. Private premises. Internet and Postal. Appointment necessary. Small stock. Spec: Sport - Horse Racing (inc. Riding/Breeding/Equestrian). PR: £5–500. Cata: Horse Racing. Corresp: French. Notes: *Small general stock at Curborough Hall Antiques Centre, Watery Lane, Lichfield also at Brownhills Books, The Old Sorting Office, Main Street, Brownhills.*

David Clegg, 6 Longbridge Road, Lichfield, WS14 9EL. Prop: David Clegg. Tel: (01543) 252117. Est: 1984. Private premises. Postal only. Appointment necessary. Small stock. Spec: Author - Dickens, Charles; Occult; Religion - General; Travel - General. PR: £5–20.

Terry W. Coupland, 15 Harwood Road, Lichfield, WS13 7PP. Tel: (01543) 256599. Est: 1980. Private premises. Appointment necessary. Small stock. Spec: Bookbinding; Children's; Illustrated - General; Juvenile; Papermaking; Printing; Private Press; Publishing. PR: £5–1,500. Mem: PBFA. Notes: *Attends PBFA fairs, occasional catalogue specialising in the History of the Typographical Arts.*

Colin Shakespeare Books, 3 Chestnut Drive, Shenstone, Lichfield, WS14 OJH. Prop: Colin & Lilian Shakespeare. Tel: (01543) 480978. Est: 1991. Private premises. Postal only. Contactable. Open: **M:** 09:00–21:00; **T:** 09:00–21:00; **W:** 09:00–21:00; **Th:** 09:00–21:00; **F:** 09:00–21:00; **S:** 09:00–21:00; **Su:** 09:00–21:00. Small stock. Spec: Literature; Topography - General. PR: £3–1,500.

The Staffs Bookshop, 4 and 6 Dam Street, Lichfield, WS13 6AA. Prop: Miss Hawkins. Tel: (01543) 264093. Fax: (01543) 264093. Web: www.staffsbookshop.co.uk. Est: 1938. Shop and/or gallery; Internet and Postal. Shop open: **M:** 10:00–17:00; **T:** 10:00–17:00; **W:** 10:00–17:00; **Th:** 10:00–17:00; **F:** 10:00–17:00; **S:** 10:00–17:00. Very large stock. Spec: Author - Johnson, Samuel; Children's; Dolls & Dolls' Houses; General; History - General; Literature; Railways and Railroads; Theology. PR: £1–1,000. CC: MC; V; Maestro. VAT No: GB 784 5011 28. Notes: *Prints, Sheet Music, Ephemera.*

CANNOCK

Roger J. Knowles, 26 Church Road, Norton Canes, Cannock, Staffordshire, WS11 9PD. Tel: 01543 279313. Fax: 01543 458597. Est: 1981. Private premises. Book Fairs only. Small stock. PR: £5 – 500. GB VAT No. 421 0823 01. Notes: *Specialist in historical documents and manuscripts of all periods; printed ephemera of all kinds especially early newspapers. Learned society transactions from the 18th and early 19th C. Always interested in purchasing any of the above.*

MERE GREEN

St Giles Hospice Bookshop, ■ 284a Lichfield Road, Mere Green, Sutton Coldfield, B74 2UG. Tel: 01543 481042. Web: www.stgileshospice.com. Est: 1994. Shop open at: 6 Birchbrook Industrial Park, Lynn Lane, Shenstone, Lichfield WS14 0DJ. Open: **M:** 09:15–16:30; **T:** 09:15–16:30; **W:** 09:15–16:30; **Th:** 09:15–16:30; **F:** 09:15–16:30; **S:** 09:15–16:30. Spec: Collectables; Ephemera; Prints and Maps. CC: AE; D; E; JCB; MC; V. VAT No: GB 486 8830 86.

NEWCASTLE-UNDER-LYME

Keith Twigg Toy Books, 27 Lansdell Avenue, Porthill, Newcastle-under-Lyme, ST5 8ET. Tel: (01782) 642932. Est: 1970. Postal only. Spec: Dolls & Dolls' Houses; Toys. PR: £20–200.

STAFFORD

Ray Roberts (Booksellers), Whiston Hall Mews, Whiston Hall, Whiston, Nr. Penkridge, Stafford, ST19 5QH. Tel: (01785) 712232. Fax: (01785) 712232. Est: 1980. Private premises. Appointment necessary. Small stock. Spec: Motoring; Traction Engines; Travel - General; Vintage Cars; Collectables. PR: £1–500. CC: AE; MC; V. Notes: *Also: author and publisher – Bentley Specials & Special Bentleys.*

STOKE-ON-TRENT

Abacas Books & Cards, ■ 56–60 Millrise Road, Milton, Stoke-on-Trent, ST2 7BW. Prop: Dave & Margaret Mycock. Tel: (01782) 543005. Est: 1980. Shop open: **M:** 09:00–17:00; **T:** 09:00–17:00; **W:** 09:00–17:00; **Th:** 09:00–17:00; **F:** 09:00–17:00; **S:** 09:00–13:00. Medium stock. Spec: Art; Autobiography; Bindings; Biography; Ceramics; Cookery/Gastronomy; Fiction - General; Gardening - General. PR: £1–200. VAT No: GB 478 7684 71. Notes: *attends Buxton Book Fairs.*

Acumen Books, Rushton House, 167 Nantwich Road, Audley, Stoke-on-Trent, ST7 8DL. Prop: Managing Director: C.B. Pearson. Tel: (01782) 720753. Fax: (01782) 720798. Web: www.acumenbooks.co.uk. Est: 1978. Private premises. Internet and Postal. Appointment necessary. Open: **M:** 10:00–15:00; **Th:** 10:00–15:00. Spec: Railways and Railroads; Sport - Cricket. PR: £1–20. CC: MC; V. Mem: ACU&S MCIArb. VAT No: GB 319 3005 84. Notes: *We specialise in books for cricket umpires, scorers, coaches and other officials, both new and secondhand. Also players and spectators interested in Laws of Cricket - we also supply equipment.*

TAMWORTH

G. & J. Chesters, ■14 Market Street, Polesworth, Tamworth, B78 1HW. Prop: Geoff & Jean Chesters. Tel: (01827) 894743. Web: www.gandjchesters.com. Est: 1970. Shop open: **M:** 09:30–17:30; **T:** 09:30–17:30; **W:** 09:30–21:00; **Th:** 09:30–17:30; **F:** 09:30–17:30; **S:** 09:30–17:30. Very large stock. Spec: Academic/Scholarly; Anthropology; Criminology; Economics; Geography; Geology; History - General; Linguistics. PR: £1–1,000. CC: AE; MC; V; Maestro. VAT No: GB 112 6448 93. Notes: *Large stocks of academic subjects, enthusiasts' books, and original antique maps and prints. There are some 6 other bookshops within close range of Polesworth.*

UTTOXETER

J.O. Goodwin, Woodcrofts Farm, Highwood, Uttoxeter, ST14 8PS. Prop: J.O. Goodwin. Tel: (01889) 562792. Est: 1965. Private premises. Appointment necessary. Small stock. Spec: Prints and Maps. PR: £1–200. VAT No: GB 125 9041 83.

WOMBOURN

Rookery Bookery, 39 Rookery Road, Wombourn, WV5 0JH. Prop: Colin Hardwick. Tel: (01902) 895983. Est: 1987. Private premises. Appointment necessary. Small stock. PR: £1–250. Corresp: French.

YOXALL

Ray Sparkes (Books), The Hollies, Bond End, Yoxall, DE13 8NH. Tel: (01543) 472274. Est: 1987. Private premises. Appointment necessary. Small stock. Spec: Directories - General; Directories - British. PR: £2–3,000. Mem: PBFA. VAT No: GB 478 2190 24.

SUFFOLK

BECCLES

Besleys Books, ■ 4 Blyburgate, Beccles, NR34 9TA. Prop: Piers & Stephen Besley. Tel: (01502) 715762. Fax: {01502) 675649. Web: www.besleysbooks.demon.co.uk. Est: 1981. Shop open: **M:** 09:30–17:00; **T:** 09:30–17:00; **W:** 09:30–17:00; **Th:** 09:30–17:00; **F:** 09:30–17:00; **S:** 09:30–17:00. Large stock. Spec: Agriculture; Animals and Birds; Art; Art Reference; Author - Bell, Adrian; Books about Books; Botany; Colour-Plate. PR: £1–1,000. CC: JCB; MC; V. Cata: gardening; natural history; literature; private press. Mem: ABA; PBFA. Notes: *Traditional general antiquarian and secondhand bookshop.*

BOTESDALE

Unsworth's Antiquarian Booksellers, Crownleigh House, The Street, Botesdale, Suffolk. IP22 1BS. Prop: Charlie Unsworth. Tel: 07802 875 469. Fax: 01379 890 972. Web: www.unsworths.com. Est: 1986. Private premises. Internet and postal. Appointment necessary. Very small stock. Spec: Antiquarian; Bibliography; Books About Books; Byzantium; Classical Studies; Classics, The; Early Imprints; Fine and Rare. PR: £25 – 5,000. CC: AE, DC, EC, JCB, MC, V. Cata: occasionally. VAT No. GB 480 145 75.

BOXFORD

Dolphin Books, Old Coach House, Broad Street, Boxford, CO10 5DX. Prop: Mrs. Rita Watts. Tel: (01787) 211630. Web: www.ukbookworld.com/members/DOLPHINBOOKS. Est: 1988. Private premises. Internet and Postal. Telephone First. Small stock. Spec: Academic/Scholarly; Adventure; Agriculture; Animals and Birds; Anthologies; Art; Art - British; Art Deco. PR: £5–50. CC: PayPal. Notes: *Selected Stock also listed on Alibris.uk.com. Booksearch service.*

BUNGAY

Bardsley's Books, ■ 22 Upper Olland Street, Bungay, NR35 1BH. Prop: W.N.A. & D.H. Bardsley. Tel: (01986) 892077. Web: www.bardsleysbooks.co.uk. Est: 1998. Shop open: **M:** 10:00–17:30; **T:** 10:00–17:30; **Th:** 10:00–17:30; **F:** 10:00–17:30; **S:** 10:00–17:30. Very large stock. Spec: Antiquarian; Art; Bibles; Books about Books; Cinema/Film; Countries - Mexico; Countries - Poland; Ecclesiastical History & Architecture. PR: £1–250. CC: MC; V. Notes: *Also, cards, O.S. Maps, CDs & new books to order.*

Beaver Booksearch, 33 Hillside Road East, Bungay, NR35 1JU. Prop: Nicholas Watts. Tel: (01986) 896698. Web: www.beaverbooksearch.co.uk. Est: 1995. Private premises. Postal only. Small stock. Spec: Bridge; Booksearch. PR: £1–50. CC: AE; MC; V; SW. VAT No: GB 638 1296 25. Notes: *Professional Out-of-print Booksearch service. Office hours weekdays 9am-1pm.*

Scorpio Books, Autumn Cottage, Low Street, Ilketshall St Margaret, Bungay, NR35 1QZ. Prop: Lorna & Patrick Quorn. Tel: 01986 781721. Web: www.scorpiobooks.co.uk. Est: 1987. Private premises. Postal only. Appointment necessary. Spec: Aircraft; History - Women; Military History; Music - Jazz & Blues; Performing Arts; Women. CC: JCB; MC; V; paypal. Cata: Jazz, Military History, Aviation, Womens' Studies. Mem: PBFA.

BURES

Major Iain Grahame, Daws Hall, Lamarsh, Bures, CO8 5EX. Prop: Iain Grahame. Tel: (01787) 269213. Fax: (01787) 269634. Web: www.iaingrahamerarebooks.com. Est: 1979. Private premises. Internet and Postal. Appointment necessary. Medium stock. Spec: Africana; Fine & Rare; Natural History; Sport - Field Sports; Booksearch; Prints and Maps. PR: £5–50,000. CC: AE; MC; V. Corresp: French, Italian. Mem: ABA. VAT No: GB 341 7566 51. Notes: *Also, John Gould original lithographs.*

BURY ST. EDMUNDS

Bury Bookshop, ■ 28A Hatter Street, Bury St. Edmunds, IP33 1NE. Prop: Joe and Sheila Wakerley. Tel: (01284) 703107. Fax: 01284 755936. Est: 1980. Shop open: **M:** 09:00–17;00; **T:** 09:00–17:00; **W:** 09:00–17:00; **Th:** 09:00–1700; **F:** 09:00–17:00; **S:** 09:00–17:30. Spec: County - Local; History - Local; Topography - Local. CC: AE; E; MC; V. Notes: *Major stock of books on and about Suffolk.*

Janet Carters, 40 Church Lane, Barton Mills, Bury St. Edmunds, IP28 6AY. Prop: Janet Carters. Tel: (01638) 717619. Fax: (01638) 717619. Web: www.http://ukbookworld.com/members/janetcarters. Est: 1978. Private premises. Internet and Postal. Appointment necessary. Small stock. Spec: Sport - Horse Racing (inc. Riding/Breeding/Equestrian). PR: £2–500. Cata: Horseracing.

Churchgate Books, ■47 Churchgate Street, Bury St. Edmunds, IP33 1RG. Prop: Stephen Cook. Tel: 01284 704604. Est: 2006. Shop open: **M:** 09:30–17:00; **T:** 09:30–17:00; **W:** 09:30–17:00; **Th:** 09:30–17:00; **F:** 09:30–17:00; **S:** 09:30–17:00. Spec: Children's; County - Local; Military History. Corresp: French. VAT No: GB 884 3655 83. Notes: *Two roomed shop with general stock. Spec: East Anglia, Military History, Children's Collectables. Bookbinding and booksearch offered.*

Sally Smith Books, 13 Manor Garth, Pakenham, Bury St. Edmunds, IP31 2LB. Tel: (01359) 230431. Web: www.sallysmithbooks.co.uk. Est: 1989. Private premises. Internet only. Appointment necessary. Medium stock. Spec: Antiques; Art; Art Reference; Bibliography; Biography; Children's; Children's - Early Titles; Crafts. PR: £1–1,000. Corresp: French.

CLARE

Trinders' Fine Tools, ■ Malting Lane, Clare, Sudbury, CO10 8NW. Prop: Peter and Rosemary Trinder. Tel: (01787) 277130. Web: www.trindersfinetools.co.uk. Est: 1975. Shop open: **W:** 10:00–17:30; **Th:** 10:00–17:30; **F:** 10:00–17:30; **S:** 10:00–17:30; Closed for lunch: 13:00–14:00. Small stock. Spec: Antiques; Applied Art; Architecture; Art; Art Reference; Artists; Arts, The; Building & Construction. PR: £2–500. CC: AE; JCB; MC; V. Mem: PBFA. VAT No: GB 299 6575 77. Notes: *NB. Please phone before travelling lest we be closed! In addition to our books, we also trade from our Malting Lane shop as 20th Century Fashion', selling nearly new designer clothes and accessories.*

DEBENHAM

David Shacklock (Books), ■Cheese Hill House, 27 High St., Debenham, IP14 6QN. Prop: David Shacklock. Tel: (01728) 861286. Est: 1986. Shop open: **T:** 10:00–17:00; **F:** 14:00–20:00; **S:** 10:00–16:00. Medium stock. Spec: Annuals; Author - Baring-Gould, S.; Author - Conan Doyle, Sir Arthur; Author - Henty, G.A.; Author - Morton, H.V.; Author - Ruskin, John; Biography; Churchilliana. PR: £1–150. Notes: *Shop closed Tuesday 13:00–14:00. Stands at Halstead (Townsford Mill); Harwich (The Old Bank); Long Melford (Antiques Warehouse). Also at bookfairs (Cambridge/Missing; Dedham; Long Melford).*

EYE

Elizabeth Nelson, Owl Cottage, 153 The Street, Stoke Ash, Eye, IP23 7EW. Tel: (01379) 678481. Fax: (01379) 678481. Est: 1982. Private premises. Appointment necessary. Small stock. Spec: Antiques; Applied Art; Architecture; Art; Art History; Art Reference; Aviation; British Art & Design. PR: £5–1,500. CC: MC; V. Cata: Fine and Applied Arts, Antiques. Mem: PBFA. VAT No: GB 428 0755 47. Notes: *Visitors are welcome but please telephone beforehand.*

Thomas Rare Books, Valley Farm House, Yaxley, Eye, IP23 8BX. Prop: G.L. Thomas. Tel: (01379) 783288. Fax: (01379) 783288. Web: www.abebooks.com. VOIPpro: Skype. VOIPnum: 01379 783288. Est: 1978. Private premises. Postal only. Spec: Antiquarian; Marine Sciences; Maritime/Nautical; Maritime/Nautical - History; Maritime/Nautical - Log Books; Naval; Ship Modelling; Shipbuilding and Shipping. PR: £10–10,000. CC: MC; V. Cata: naval.

FELIXSTOWE

Books Only, 84 Garrison Lane, Felixstowe, IP11 7RQ. Prop: Colin E. Sharman. Tel: (01394) 285546. Web: www.booksonly.co.uk. Est: 1980. Private premises. Internet and Postal. Telephone First. Small stock. Spec: Aircraft; Antiquarian; Author - Bell, Adrian; Comedy; Cookery/Gastronomy; First Editions; General Stock; Humanism; Humour; Marxism. PR: £1–500. CC: PayPal.

Poor Richard's Books, ■ 17 Orwell Road, Felixstowe, IP11 7EP. Prop: Dick Moffat. Tel: 01394 283138. Web: www.poorrichards.co.uk. Est: 1997. Shop open: **M:** 09:30–17:00; **T:** 09:30–17:00; **W:** 09:30–17:00; **Th:** 09:30–17:00; **F:** 09:30–17:00; **S:** 09:30–17:00. Spec: Fiction - General; Fiction - Women; Literature; New Naturalist; Ornithology; Performing Arts; Poetry; Sport - Cricket. CC: MC; V; SO; SW. Corresp: French. Mem: PBFA. Notes: *Booksearch for all, but particularly our own customers; 2 floors of books, in several rooms. Car park nearby, and parking outside the shop when spaces available.*

Treasure Chest Books, ■ 61 Cobbold Road, Felixstowe, IP11 7BH. Prop: R. & R. Green. Tel: (01394) 270717. Web: www.abebooks.com. Est: 1982. Shop open: **M:** 09:30–17:30; **T:** 09:30–17:30; **W:** 09:30–17:30; **Th:** 09:30–17:30; **F:** 09:30–17:30; **S:** 09:30–17:30. Very large stock. Spec: Art; Aviation; Cinema/Film; Occult; Topography - Local; Transport; Collectables; Ephemera. CC: E; JCB; MC. Mem: PBFA. Notes: *None of our stock is on the Internet.*

FINNINGHAM

Abington Books, Primrose Cottage,Westhorpe Road, Finningham, IP.14-4.TW. Prop: Jack Haldane. Tel: 01449-78-0303. Fax: 01449-78-0202. Est: 1971. Private premises. Postal only. Contactable. Open: **M:** 09:00–17:30; **T:** 09:00–17:30; **W:** 09:00–17:30; **Th:** 09:00–17:30; **F:** 09:00–17:30; **S:** 09:00–17:30; **Su:** 09:00–17:30; Closed for lunch: 13:00–14:00. Verry small stock. Spec: Carpets - General; Carpets - Oriental; Tapestry. Corresp: French and German. VAT No: 213 3817 89. Notes: *We specialise in books of all periods and most languages on Oriental Carpets and Classical Tapistries, with a small number of interesting items on adjacent subjects.*

FRAMLINGHAM

Framlingham Bookshop, ■ 19 Market Hill, Framlingham, Nr. Woodbridge, IP13 9BB. Tel: (01728) 723046. Est: 1974. Shop open: **M:** 10:00–16:00; **T:** 10:00–16:00; **W:** 10:00–13:00; **Th:** 10:00–16:00; **F:** 10:00–16:00; **S:** 09:00–16:00. Medium stock. Spec: Fiction - Crime, Detective, Spy, Thrillers; Booksearch. PR: £2–200.

Mrs. A. Kent (Books), ■ 19 Market Hill, Framlingham, Nr. Woodbridge, IP13 9BB. Tel: (01728) 723046. Est: 1974. Shop open: **M:** 10:00–16:00; **T:** 10:00–16:00; **W:** 10:00–13:00; **Th:** 10:00–16:00; **F:** 10:00–16:00; **S:** 09:00–16:00; Closed for lunch: 13:00–14:00. Medium stock. Spec: Fiction - Crime, Detective, Spy, Thrillers; Booksearch. PR: £1–100.

HALESWORTH

Andrew Jones, 25 Rectory Street, Halesworth, IP19 8AE. Tel: (01986) 835944. Est: 1977. Private premises. Postal only. Small stock. Spec: Academic/Scholarly; Fine & Rare; History - General. PR: £5–1,000. Cata: History.

IPSWICH

Roy Arnold Books, 77 High Street, Needham Market, Ipswich, IP6 8AN. Prop: Roy Arnold. Tel: (01449) 720110. Fax: (01449) 722498. Web: www.royarnold.com. Est: 1976. Office and/or bookroom; Internet and Postal. Shop open: **M:** 10:00–17:30; **T:** 10:00–17:30; **W:** 10:00–17:30; **Th:** 10:00–17:30; **F:** 10:00–17:30; **S:** 10:00–17:30. Medium stock. Spec: Antiquarian; Antiques; Applied Art; Rural Life; Scientific Instruments; Windmills & Watermills; Woodwork; Booksearch. PR: £4–3,000. CC: JCB; MC; V. Mem: PBFA; TATHS, EAIA, MWTCA. VAT No: GB 334 0169 85. Notes: *Also, trade catalogues and new books on tools and trades & a booksearch service.*

The Art Book Company, 35 Belstead Road, Ipswich, IP2 8AU. Prop: Priscilla Pilkington. Tel: (01473) 602133. Fax: (01473) 602133. Est: 1974. Private premises. Postal only. Appointment necessary. Open: **M:** 09:30–18:30; **T:** 09:30–18:30; **W:** 09:30–18:30; **Th:** 09:30–18:30; **F:** 09:30–12:30; Closed for lunch: 13:30–16:30. Small stock. Spec: Annuals; Architecture; Art Deco; Art History; Art Nouveau; Art Reference; Artists; Arts, The. PR: £15–1,000. Cata: artists, design & graphics, architecture, textiles. VAT No: GB 728 7258 02.

Claude Cox Old & Rare Books, ■ College Gateway Bookshop, 3 & 5 Silent Street, Ipswich, IP1 1TF. Prop: Anthony Brian Cox. Tel: (01473) 254776. Fax: (01473) 254776. Web: www.claudecox.co.uk. Est: 1944. Shop open: **W:** 10:00–17:00; **Th:** 10:00–17:00; **F:** 10:00–17:00; **S:** 10:00–17:00. Medium stock. Spec: Antiquarian; Art Reference; Bibliography; Bibliophily; Bindings; Bookbinding; Books about Books; Children's - Early Titles. CC: E; JCB; MC; V; SW. Cata: General Antiquarian; Fine Printing; Suffolk. Corresp: French. Mem: ABA; PBFA; ILAB; PLA, PHS. VAT No: GB 304 7952 56. Notes: *We issue regular catalogues of General Antiquarian, Private Press & Typography, William Pickering Publications, Suffolk (NB Also stock speciality) & East Anglia, which may also be viewed at our website. Binding Repairs Suffolk Prints & Maps.*

Footrope Knots, 501 Wherstead Road, Ipswich, IP2 8LL. Prop: Des & Liz Pawson. Tel: (01473) 690090. Est: 1981. Private premises. Postal only. Appointment necessary. Small stock. Spec: Crafts; Manuals - Seamanship (see also under Seamanship); Maritime/Nautical; Ropemaking & Knots; Seamanship; Sport - Yachting (& Boating). PR: £1–100.

The Idler, ■ 37 High Street, Hadleigh, Ipswich, IP7 5AF. Prop: Bryan & Jane Haylock. Tel: (01473) 827752. Est: 1980. Shop open: **M:** 09:30–17:00; **T:** 09:30–17:00; **W:** 09:30–13:00; **Th:** 09:30–17:00; **F:** 09:30–17:00; **S:** 09:30–17:00. Medium stock. Spec: Art; New Books; Theatre; Booksearch. PR: £1–100. Mem: BA. VAT No: GB 410 6933 74. Notes: *Also, new books, publisher's remainders, art materials, greetings cards.*

LONG MELFORD

Lime Tree Books, ■ Hall Street, Long Melford, CO10 9JF. Prop: Bryan Marsh. Tel: (01787) 311532. Est: 1992. Shop open: **M:** 10:00–17:00; **T:** 10:00–17:00; **W:** 10:00–17:00; **Th:** 10:00–17:00; **F:** 10:00–17:00; **S:** 10:00–17:00; **Su:** 10:00–17:00. Medium stock. PR: £1–200. CC: MC; V. VAT No: GB 623 0516 79.

LOWESTOFT

A Book For All Reasons, Rockville House, 6 Pakefield Road, Lowestoft, NR33 0HS. Prop: G. A. Michael Sims. Tel: 01502 581011. Fax: 01502 574891. Web: www.abfar.co.uk. Est: 1984. Private premises. Internet and Postal. Appointment necessary. Open: **M:** 09:00–18:00; **T:** 09:00–18:00; **W:** 09:00–18:00; **Th:** 09:00–18:00; **F:** 09:00–18:00; **S:** 09:00–18:00; Closed for lunch: 13:00–16:00. Spec: Arms & Armour; Army, The; Author - Yates, Dornford; Fiction - General; Fiction - Historical; Fiction - Romantic; History - Local; Military. CC: JCB; MC; V; Switch, Maestro. Mem: PBFA; ibooknet. VAT No: GB 770 1056 57. Notes: *Also on www.ibooknet.com.*

R. W. Lamb, Talbot House, 158 Denmark Road, Lowestoft, NR32 2EL. Tel: (01502) 564306. Fax: (01502) 564306. Est: 1972. Private premises. Internet and Postal. Appointment necessary. Spec: Classical Studies.

NEWMARKET

Miles Apart, 5 Harraton House, Exning, Newmarket, CB8 7HF. Prop: Ian Mathieson. Tel: 01638 577627. Fax: 01638 577874. Web: www.sthelena.se. Est: 1994. Private premises. Appointment necessary. Open: **M:** 09:00–21:00; **T:** 09:00–21:00; **W:** 09:00–21:00; **Th:** 09:00–21:00; **F:** 09:00–21:00; **S:** 09:00–21:00; **Su:** 09:00–21:00. Spec: Countries - Falklands, The; Countries - South Atlantic Islands; Islands; Travel - General; Travel - Polar; War - Napoleonic. CC: MC; V. Cata: South Atlantic Islands, Antarctic and Travel. Mem: PBFA. Notes: *Specialising in islands of South Atlantic - St Helena, Ascension, Tristan, Falklands. Also the Antarctic and general travel.*

David Paramor, 25 St. Mary's Square, Newmarket, CB8 0HZ. Tel: (01638) 664416. Web: www.http:// ukbookworld.com/members/Paramor. Est: 1974. Private premises. Appointment necessary. Medium stock. Spec: Amusements; Cinema/Film; Dance; Drama; Entertainment - General; Music - General; Music - Folk & Irish Folk; Music - Gilbert & Sullivan. PR: £1–350. Notes: *I specialise in books & ephemera on all the performing arts, including musical theatre, Gilbert and Sullivan, original cast vinyl discs, The Spoken Word, picture postcards, & plays ancient & modern, etc. Also a good general stock.*

R.E. & G.B. Way, Brettons, Burrough Green, Newmarket, CB8 9NA. Prop: Greg Way. Tel: 01638 507217. Fax: 01638 508058. Web: www.way-books.co.uk. Est: 1958. Private premises. Telephone First. Open: **M:** 08:30–17:30; **T:** 08:30–17:30; **W:** 08:30–17:30; **Th:** 08:30–17:30; **F:** 08:30–17:30; **S:** 08:30–17:30. Spec: Animals and Birds; Natural History; Private Press; Sport - Big Game Hunting; Sport - Field Sports. CC: MC; V. Cata: Horses, Hunting and Field sports. Mem: PBFA. VAT No: GB 103 4378 02.

SAXMUNDHAM

Roger Ballantyne–Way, Kiln House, Benhall Low Street, Saxmundham, IP17 1JQ. Prop: Roger Ballantyne-Way. Tel: (01728) 604711. Est: 1979. Private premises. Internet and Postal. Appointment necessary. Medium stock. Spec: Architecture; Art; Art History; Art Reference; Artists; Arts, The; Author - Durrell, Lawrence; Countries - Greece. PR: £5–1,000. CC: MC; V; PayPal. Cata: Art. Mem: PBFA. Notes: *British Art, Illustrated, Private Press, Typography, Fine Printing, Design Domestic and Industrial, Architecture.*

Keith A. Savage, ■ 35 High Street, Saxmundham, IP17 1AJ. Prop: Keith Savage. Tel: 01728 604538. Fax: 01986 872231 (answerphone). Est: 1992. Shop open: **M:** 10:30–13:00; **T:** 10:30–17:00; **W:** 10:30–17:00; **F:** 10:30–17:00; **S:** 10:30–13:00. Small stock. Spec: Children's; Comic Books & Annuals; Comics; Ephemera; Prints and Maps. PR: £1–150.

Sax Books, ■ 4a High Street, Saxmundham, IP17 1DF. Prop: Richard W.L. Smith, MVO. Tel: (01728) 605775. Est: 2000. Shop open: **W:** 10:00–16:00; **Th:** 10:00–16:00; **F:** 10:00–16:00; **S:** 10:00–16:00. Medium stock. Spec: Animals and Birds; Antiques; Architecture; Army, The; Art History; Art Reference; Author - Churchill, Sir Winston; Autobiography. PR: £1–250. Notes: *Also open on Tuesdays 10-4 in Summer and near to Christmas, as well as on Bank Holiday Mondays.*

SOUTHWOLD

Richard Everett, ■Southwold Antiques Centre, Buckenham Mews, 83 High Street, Southwold, IP18 6DS. Tel: (01502) 723060. Shop open: **M:** 10:00–17:00; **T:** 10:00–17:00; **W:** 10:00–17:00; **Th:** 10:00–17:00; **F:** 10:00–17:00; **S:** 10:00–17:00; **Su:** 11:00–17:00. Small stock. Spec: Children's; Publishers - Warnes; Topography - Local. PR: £2–50. Mem: PBFA. Notes: *Richard Everett at Downham Market, Norfolk. Local topography includes Adrian Bell.*

SUDBURY

Beckham Books Ltd., Chilton Mount, Newton Road, Sudbury, CO10 2RS. Prop: Mr A.M. Beckham. Tel: (01787) 373683. Fax: (01787) 375441. Web: www.beckhambooks.com. Est: 1998. Office and/or bookroom; Internet and Postal. Telephone First. Open: **M:** 09:00–17:00; **T:** 09:00–17:00; **W:** 09:00–17:00; **Th:** 09:00–17:00; **F:** 09:00–17:00; **S:** 10:00–17:00; Closed for lunch: 12:00–13.00. Very large stock. Spec: Antiquarian; Bibles; Biblical Studies; Bindings; Children's; Cookery/Gastronomy; Countries - Great Britain; Countries - Holy Land, The. PR: £1–2,000. CC: AE; D; E; JCB; MC; V; Maestro. Cata: Antiquarian. Theology. Bibles. Prayer Books. Mem: PBFA. VAT No: GB 750 9305 36. Notes: *We specialize in theology and religious books including bibles and prayer books, but we also stock a wide range of other subjects. We now have over 17,000 books online, with thousands of additional books on our shelves.*

Parade Bookshop, ■ 10 North Street Parade, Sudbury, CO10 1GL. Prop: Mrs. G. Cawthorn. Tel: 01787 881626. Est: 1975. Shop open: **M:** 10:00–16:30; **T:** 10:00–16:30; **Th:** 10:00–16:30; **F:** 10:00–16:30; **S:** 10:00–16:30. CC: None.

Suffolk Rare Books, 7 New Street, Sudbury, CO10 1JB. Prop: T.M. Cawthorn. Tel: (01787) 372075. Web: www.abebooks.com. Est: 1975. Private premises. Telephone First. Open: **T:** 10:30–16:30; **Th:** 10:30–16:30; **F:** 10:30–16:30; **S:** 10:30–16:30. Medium stock. Spec: Aviation; History - Local; Maritime/Nautical; Military; Railways and Railroads; Topography - General; Topography - Local; Transport. PR: £1–40. CC: PayPal.

Derek Vanstone - Aviation Book, Tymperley Farm, Great Henny, Sudbury, CO10 7LX. Tel: (01787) 269291. Fax: (01787) 269291. Web: www.aircraftbooks.com. Est: 1996. Private premises. Internet and Postal. Contactable. Open: **M:** 09:00–18:00; **T:** 09:00–18:00; **W:** 09:00–18:00; **Th:** 09:00–18:00; **F:** 09:00–18:00; **S:** 09:00–13:00. Small stock. Spec: Aeronautics; Aircraft; Aviation; Maritime/Nautical; Military; Naval; War - World War II. PR: £1–200. CC: AE; MC; V. Cata: Aviation. Mem: PBFA. VAT No: GB 711 3364 72.

WESTLETON

Chapel Books, ■The Chapel, Westleton, Saxmundham, IP17 3AA. Prop: Robert Jackson. Tel: 01728 648616. Web: www.chapelbooks.com. Est: 1982. Shop open: **M:** 12:00–17:0; **T:** 12:00–17:0; **W:** 12:00–17:0; **Th:** 12:00–17:0; **F:** 12:00–17:0; **S:** 12:00–17:0; **Su:** 12:00–17:0; Closed for lunch: 12:00–13:00. CC: AE; MC; V; Maestro.

WOODBRIDGE

W.H. Collectables, 24 Ipswich Road, Woodbridge, IP12 4BU. Prop: Michael Wheeler. Tel: (01394) 385021. Fax: (01394) 385021. Est: 1981. Storeroom; Appointment necessary. Open: **M:** 09:00–20:00; **T:** 09:00–20:00; **W:** 09:00–20:00; **Th:** 09:00–20:00; **F:** 09:00–20:00. Large stock. Spec: Aeronautics; Alpinism/Mountaineering; Americana - General; Banking & Insurance; Children's; Colonial; Comics; Documents - General. PR: £10–500. CC: D; MC; V. Corresp: German. Mem: ES. Notes: *Stock also covers Australia, Canada and New Zealand.*

SURREY

ADDLESTONE

Corfe Books, ■ 163 Station Road, Addlestone, KT15 2BA. Prop: Mark Hayhoe. Tel: (01932) 850674. Fax: (01932) 850674. Est: 2001. Shop open: **W:** 10:00–15:00; **Th:** 10:00–15:00; **F:** 10:00–17:00; **S:** 10:00–17:00. Large stock. Spec: Aeronautics; Animals and Birds; Antiques; Archaeology; Architecture; Espionage; Fiction - General; History - General. PR: £1–300. Notes: *Nearly new stock from postal and airline lost property.*

ASHTEAD

Bagot Books, 2 Bagot Close, Ashtead, KT21 1NS. Prop: Nigel Smith. Tel: (01372) 430034. Web: www.bagotbooks.com. Est: 1999. Private premises. Internet and Postal. Medium stock. PR: £2–300. CC: PayPal. Mem: ibooknet.

BEDDINGTON

Mrs. Patricia Clear, 33 Cedars Road, Beddington, CR0 4PU. Prop: Mrs Patricia Clear. Tel: (020) 8681-0251. Web: www.patriciasbooks.co.uk. Est: 1990. Private premises. Postal only. Telephone First. Small stock. Spec: Children's. PR: £1–120. Cata: Childrens Books.

BYFLEET

Joppa Books Ltd., ■ 68 High Road, Byfleet, KT14 7QL. Prop: Nadeem M. Elissa. Tel: (01932) 336777. Fax: (01932) 348881. Web: www.joppabooks.co.uk. Est: 1989. Internet and Postal. Shop open: **M:** 10:30–16:00; **T:** 10:30–16:00; **W:** 10:30–16:00; **Th:** 10:30–16:00; **F:** 10:30–16:00; Closed for lunch: 12:00–14:00. Large stock. Spec: Antiquarian; Arabica; Archaeology; Asian Studies; Author - Bell, Gertrude; Author - Lawrence, T.E.; Byzantium; Countries - Afghanistan. PR: £5–5,000. CC: AE; MC; V; SW. Cata: Middle East and related areas. Corresp: Arabic, French. Mem: PBFA. VAT No: GB 493 7403 24. Notes: *Shop is usually staffed as stated, but please make an appointment to view stock.*

COBHAM

Nectar Books, P.O. Box 263, Cobham, KT11 2YZ. Prop: T.G. Kent. Tel: (01932) 868863. Est: 1976. Mail order only; Postal only. Contactable. Small stock. Spec: Broadcasting; Cinema/Film; Drama; Entertainment - General; Genealogy; Memorabilia; Music - General; Music - Popular. PR: £5–200. CC: Paypal. Notes: *Also a booksearch service.*

DORKING

A.J. Coombes, 24 Horsham Road, Dorking, RH4 2JA. Prop: John Coombes. Tel: (01306) 880736. Fax: (01306) 743641. Est: 1967. Private premises. Appointment necessary. Small stock. Spec: Architecture; History - General; History - British; History - Local; Topography - General; Topography - Local. Cata: British Topography & Local History. Corresp: German. Mem: ABA; ILAB. VAT No: GB 210 5273 14.

C.C. Kohler, The Gatehouse,Harrow Road West, Dorking, RH4 3BH. Prop: Chris and Michele Kohler. Tel: 01306 886407. Fax: 01306 741988. Est: 1963. Private premises. Appointment necessary. Medium stock. Spec: Special Collections. Corresp: German. Mem: ABA; ILAB. VAT No: GB 293 7862 08.

EAST EWELL

Ewell Books, 36 Arundel Avenue, East Ewell, Epsom, KT17 2RG. Prop: Stephen Fordham. Tel: 020 8393 6890. Web: www.ewellbooks.com. Est: 2003. Private premises. Internet and Postal. Telephone First. Small stock. Open: **M:** 09:00–17:30; **T:** 09:00–17:30; **W:** 09:00–17:30; **Th:** 09:00–17:30; **F:** 09:00–17:30; **S:** 09:00–17:30; **Su:** 09:00–17:30; Closed for lunch: 13:00–14:00. CC: PayPal. Notes: *Ewell Books formerly Ewell Bookshop, Surrey. We have a modest stock of rare books which can be viewed on our website.*

EAST HORSLEY

Emjay Books, Ashdene High Park Avenue, East Horsley, KT24 5DF. Prop: M. Gardner. Tel: (01483) 283373. Est: 1990. Private premises. Internet and Postal. Appointment necessary. Large stock. Spec: American Indians; Author - Bates, H.E.; Author - Byron, Lord; Author - Christie, Agatha; Author - Francis, Dick; Author - Tangye, D.; Motoring; Private Press. PR: £5–3,000. Notes: *Also, a booksearch service.*

Rowan House Books, Rowans, Norrels Ride, East Horsley, KT24 5EH. Prop: George Spranklins. Tel: (01483) 282482. Fax: (01483) 285924. Web: www.abebooks.com. Est: 1995. Private premises. Internet and Postal. Appointment necessary. Medium stock. Spec: Children's; First Editions; Illustrated - General. PR: £10–500. CC: MC; V.

EAST MOLESEY

Books Bought & Sold, ■ 68 Walton Road, East Molesey, KT8 0DL. Prop: P.J. Sheridan & W.J. Collyer. Tel: (020) 8224-3609. Fax: (020) 8224-3576. Web: www.booksinstore.co.uk. Est: 1985. Shop open: **T:** 10:00–17:00; **W:** 10:00–17:00; **Th:** 10:00–17:00; **F:** 10:00–17:00; **S:** 10:00–17:00. Medium stock. Spec: Aeronautics; Aviation; Children's; History - General; Illustrated - General; Military; Motoring; Railways and Railroads. PR: £1–900. CC: D; E; JCB; MC; V. VAT No: GB 644 1831 46. Notes: *Organisers of HD Book Fairs.*

Londinium Books, 10 Summer Avenue, East Molesey, KT8 9LU. Prop: Eric & Jean Mahoney. Tel: (020) 8398-7165. Web: www.abebooks.com. Market stand/stall; Shop open: **M:** 11:00–18:30; **S:** 11:00–18:30; **Su:** 11:00–18:30.

EGHAM

Blacklock's, ■8 Victoria Street, Englefield Green, Egham, TW20 0QY. Prop: Graham Dennis. Tel: (01784) 438025. Web: www.blacklockspoloart.com. Est: 1988. Shop open: **M:** 09:00–17:00; **W:** 09:00–17:00; **Th:** 09:00–17:00; **F:** 09:00–17:00; **S:** 09:00–13:00; Closed for lunch: 13:00–14:00. Small stock. Spec: Sport - Polo; Prints and Maps. PR: £2–250. CC: MC; V. Notes: *Prints and books on Venice. General bookshop and polo specialist.*

ELSTEAD

Brian P. Martin Antiquarian and Collectors' Books, ■ Honeypot Antiques, Milford Road, Elstead, GU8 5LB. Prop: Brian P. Martin. Tel: (01428) 682567, (01252) 703614, mobile 07773112101. Est: 1997. Shop at: 4 Upper Birtley, Haslemere Road, Brook, Godalming, Surrey GU8 5LB. Open: **M:** 10:00–17:00; **T:** 10:00–17:00; **W:** 10:00–17:00; **Th:** 10:00–17:00; **F:** 10:00–17:00; **S:** 10:00–17:00; **Su:** 11:00–17:00. Spec: Animals and Birds; Antiquarian; Antiques; Atlases; Author - Watkins-Pitchford, Denys ('B.B.'); Bindings; Botany; Children's. PR: £2–400. CC: MC; V. Notes: *Special interests: fishing, shooting, hunting, natural history, birds, Surrey, Sussex, Hampshire. Free book search. Easy doorstep parking at Honeypot Antiques, just 2m from A3 (M) at Milford, close to Godalming, Farnham, Guildford, Haslemere.*

Brian P. Martin (Books and Pictures), ■ Honeypot Antiques, Milford Road, Elstead, Nr. Godalming, GU8 6HP. Prop: Brian P. Martin. Tel: Shop (01252) 703614. Web: www.honeypotantiques.co.uk. Est: 2000. Shop open: **M:** 10:00–17:00; **T:** 10:00–17:00; **W:** 10:00–17:00; **Th:** 10:00–17:00; **F:** 10:00–17:00; **S:** 10:00–17:00; **Su:** 11:00–17:00. Spec: Agriculture; Animals and Birds; Antiques; Army, The; Arts, The; Bibles; Bindings; Botany. PR: £1–500. CC: AE; MC; V. Corresp: French, Spanish. Notes: *Home tel: (01428) 682567.*

ENGLEFIELD GREEN

Glasheen-Books, 57 Alexandra Road, Englefield Green, TW20 0RR. Prop: Patric Glasheen. Tel: 01784 479766. Est: 1996. Private premises. Internet and Postal. Contactable. Spec: Authors - British; Books about Books; Countries - General; County - Local; Fiction - General; Fiction - Science Fiction; Gardening - General; General. CC: MC; V. VAT No: GB 666 2692 03.

EPSOM

Vandeleur Antiquarian Books, 6 Seaforth Gardens, Stoneleigh, Epsom, KT19 0NR. Prop: E.H. Bryant. Tel: (020) 8393-7752. Fax: (020) 8393-7752. Est: 1971. Private premises. Appointment necessary. Small stock. Spec: Alpinism/Mountaineering; Antiquarian; Bindings; Sport - Big Game Hunting; Sport - Rowing; Travel - Africa; Travel - Americas; Travel - Asia. PR: £5–2,000. Cata: specific lists as requested. Mem: PBFA. Notes: *Exhibits at bookfairs. Also, rowing prints and Indian Mogul-style paintings. Maps.*

EWELL

J.W. McKenzie Ltd, ■ 12 Stoneleigh Park Road, Ewell, Epsom, KT19 0QT. Tel: (0208) 393 7700. Fax: (0208) 393 1694. Web: www.mckenzie-cricket.co.uk. Est: 1971. Internet and Postal. Shop open: **M:** 09:00–17:00; **T:** 09:00–17:00; **W:** 09:00–17:00; **Th:** 09:00–17:00; **F:** 09:00–17:00; **S:** 10:00–13:00; Closed for lunch: 13:00–14:00. Medium stock. Spec: Sport - Cricket. CC: E; JCB; MC; V. Cata: Cricket.

FARNHAM

Bodyline Books, The Oast House, Park Row, off Castle Street, Farnham, GU9 7JH. Prop: Giles Lyon and Mike Scott. Tel: 01252 727222. Web: www.bodylinebooks.co.uk. Est: 1996. Private premises. Internet and Postal. Appointment necessary. Open: **M:** 09:00–17:30; **T:** 09:00–17:30; **W:** 09:00–17:30; **Th:** 09:00–17:30; **F:** 09:00–17:30; **S:** 09:00–17:30; **Su:** 09:00–17:30; Closed for lunch: 13:00–14:00. Spec: Sport - General; Sport - American Football; Sport - Angling/Fishing; Sport - Archery; Sport - Athletics; Sport - Badminton; Sport - Ballooning; Sport - Baseball. CC: E; MC; V; Maestro, Solo. Cata: Football, Cricket, Rugby, Tennis, Golf, Boxing. Notes: *We hold the largest selection of Wisden's Cricketers Almanack in the world, with well over 1000 issues on our shelves at any one time.*

Derek Burden, 1 Boundstone Road, Wrecclesham, Farnham, GU10 4TH. Prop: Derek Burden. Tel: (01252) 793615. Fax: (01252) 794789. Est: 1967. Private premises. Internet and Postal. Appointment necessary. Large stock. Spec: Graphics; Illustrated - General; Prints and Maps. PR: £1–1,000.

Valentine Rare Books, Potters Hatch House, Crondall, Farnham, GU10 5PW. Prop: Anthony Surtees. Tel: (01252) 851495. Est: 1983. Private premises. Appointment necessary. Small stock. Spec: Fiction - General; Fiction - Historical; Fiction - Romantic; Fiction - Women; Literature; Literature in Translation; Travel - General; Travel - Middle East. PR: £20–10,000.

GODALMING

Crouch Rare Books, Syringa, Tuesley Lane, Godalming, GU7 1SB. Prop: A.S. Crouch. Tel: (01483) 420390. Fax: (01483) 421371. Web: www.crbooks.co.uk. Est: 1970. Storeroom; Internet and Postal. Appointment necessary. Medium stock. Spec: Academic/Scholarly; Antiquarian; Archaeology; Architecture; Classical Studies; Countries - Cyprus; Countries - Greece; Crafts. PR: £2–1,000. CC: AE; MC; V; Switch. Corresp: French, Greek, Latin, German, Italian, Spanish and Portuguese. VAT No: GB 417 6129 55. Notes: *Specialising mainly in Ancient Greek and Latin Texts and Literature.*

GUILDFORD

Apocalypse, 51 Woking Road, Guildford, GU1 1QD. Prop: Richard Grenville Clark. Tel: 01483 841550. Est: 1996. Mail order only; Internet and Postal. Appointment necessary. Spec: Academic/Scholarly; Adult; Aesthetic Movement; Aesthetics; Aircraft; Alchemy; Almanacs; Americana - General. CC: PayPal. Cata: Non-Fiction and Fiction of all kinds. Corresp: Some French. Notes: *Stock subjects include rare items from c. French Revolution. We also publish books on art, education, poetry and fiction [see: www.apocalypsepress.co.uk].*

Cecilia Marsden, 27 The Meadows, Guildford, GU2 4DT. Prop: Cecilia Marsden. Tel: 01483 567200. Fax: 01483 567200. Est: 1993. Private premises. Postal only. Appointment necessary. Open: **M:** 09:00–17:30; **T:** 09:00–17:30; **W:** 09:00–17:30; **Th:** 09:00–17:30; **F:** 09:00–17:30; **S:** 09:00–17:30; **Su:** 09:00–17:30; Closed for lunch: 13:00–14:00. Very small stock. Spec: Fiction - General; Fiction - Crime, Detective, Spy, Thrillers; Fiction - Science Fiction; Irish Interest; Literature - Irish.

HASLEMERE

Anglo-American Rare Books, Galleons Lap, P.O. Box 71, Haslemere, GU27 1YT. Prop: Jack Laurence. Tel: 01428 606462. Private premises. Postal only. Spec: Americana - General; Author - Eliot, T.S.; Author - Greene, Graham; Author - Hemingway, Ernest; Author - James, Henry; Author - Mailer, Norman; Author - Sassoon, Siegfried; Fiction - General. Mem: PBFA.

Bickford-Smith (G) (formerly Snowden Smith Books), Linden, Holdfast Lane, Haslemere, GU27 2EY. Prop: Gillian Bickford-Smith. Tel: 01428 641363. Fax: 01428 641363. Est: 1975. Private premises. Internet and Postal. Very small stock. Spec: Colonial; Countries - Africa; Countries - Arabian Peninsula; Countries - Asia; Countries - Balkans, The; Countries - Central Asia; Countries - China; Countries - Far East, The. Cata: on specialities listed.

HORLEY

Reigate Galleries, Cedar Cottage, Haroldslea Drive, Horley, RH6 9PH. Prop: K. & J. Morrish. Tel: (01293) 773426. Est: 1960. Private premises. Postal only. Appointment necessary. Small stock. PR: £5–300. CC: MC; V. Mem: PBFA.

LEATHERHEAD

Dandy Lion Editions, ■63 High Street, Leatherhead, KT22 8AQ. Prop: Angela McCarthy. Tel: (01372) 377785. Web: www.dandylioneditions.co.uk. Est: 1995. Shop open: **T:** 10:00–16:30; **W:** 10:00–16:30; **Th:** 10:00–16:30; **F:** 10:00–16:30; **S:** 09:00–16:30. Medium stock. Spec: Academic/Scholarly; Art; Aviation; Biography; Children's; Children's - Illustrated; Counties in England; County - Local. PR: £1–100. CC: AE; MC; V. Notes: *Retail shop plus internet & postal sales. General stock including Children's, Transport, History, Natural History, Local & topography & much more. Please visit our website www.dandylioneditions.co.uk.*

MITCHAM

J.G. Natural History Books, 149 Sherwood Park Road, Mitcham, CR4 1NJ. Prop: J. Greatwood. Tel: (020) 8764-4669. Fax: (020) 8764-4669. Web: www.reptilebooks.com. Est: 1969. Private premises. Internet and Postal. Appointment necessary. Spec: Gemmology; Herpetology; New Books. PR: £10–500. CC: MC; V; PayPal. Cata: herpetology; gemmology. Notes: *Also, new books.*

NEW MALDEN

Steve Baxter, 13 Westbury Road, New Malden, KT3 5BE. Tel: (020) 8942-4431. Web: www.baxterfinebooks.com. Private premises. Postal only. Small stock. Spec: Antiquarian; Author - Churchill, Sir Winston; Bindings; Churchilliana; Fine & Rare; First Editions; History - General; Literature. CC: AE; JCB; MC; V. Mem: ABA; PBFA; ILAB. VAT No: GB 711 1425 88.

OXTED

Postings, P.O. Box 1, Oxted, RH8 0FD. Prop: R.N. Haffner. Tel: (01883) 722646. Fax: (01883) 722646. Est: 1992. Private premises. Postal only. Small stock. Spec: Aviation; History - Postal; Philately; Railways and Railroads; Sport - Ballooning; Topography - Local; Transport; Ephemera. PR: £5–300. CC: E; JCB; MC; V. Mem: PTS. Notes: *Also, postcards.*

Secondhand Bookshop, ■ 27 Station Road West, Oxted, RH8 9HD. Prop: David Neal. Tel: (01883) 715755. Est: 1992. Shop open: **M:** 10:00–17:00; **T:** 10:00–17:00; **W:** 10:00–17:00; **Th:** 10:00–17:00; **F:** 10:00–17:00; **S:** 10:00–17:00. Medium stock. PR: £1–2,500. VAT No: GB 725 4573 27. Notes: *Out of hours please ring 01883 723131. Parking, turn into Morrisons directly off A25 - 2 hrs free at far end.*

REDHILL

Ivelet Books Ltd., 18 Fairlawn Drive, Redhill, RH11 6JP. Prop: Dr. S.A.Ahern. Tel: 01737 764520. Fax: 01737 760140. Web: http://ukbookworld.com/members/ivelet. Est: 1978. Private premises. Postal only. Spec: Architecture; Botany; Gardening; Natural history. PR: £2–3,000.

RICHMOND

W & A Houben, ■2, Church Court, Richmond, TW9 1JL. Prop: Chris Dunlop & Denise Dunlop. Tel: 020 8940 1055. Est: 1963. Shop open: **M:** 10:00–18:00; **T:** 10:00–18:00; **W:** 10:00–18:00; **Th:** 10:00–18:00; **F:** 10:00–18:00; **S:** 10:00–18:00. CC: MC; V. VAT No: GB 215 9473 53.

SURBITON

The Bookroom, ■ 146 Chiltern Drive, Surbiton, KT5 8LS. Prop: Keith Alexander. Tel: 020 8404 6644. Fax: 020 8404 6644. Web: www.abebooks.com/home/keithalexander. Est: 2002. Shop open: **W:** 11:00–18:00; **Th:** 11:00–18:00; **F:** 11:00–18:00; **S:** 10:00–18:00. Spec: Architecture; Architecture - Theatre; Art; Art - British; Art - Technique; Art - Theory; Art Deco; Art History. CC: JCB; MC; V; Solo, Maestro. Notes: *I accept PayPal.*

Caissa Books, 5 Pembroke Avenue, Berrylands, Surbiton, KT5 8HN. Prop: Mike Sheehan. Tel: (020) 8399 6591. Est: 1980. Private premises. Postal only. Contactable. Open: **M:** 14:00–17:00; **T:** 14:00–17:00; **W:** 14:00–17:00; **Th:** 14:00–17:00; **F:** 14:00–17:00. Small stock. Spec: Chess; Collectables; Ephemera; Prints and Maps. PR: £3–3,000. CC: MC; V. Cata: chess. Corresp: French and German. Notes: *Also deal in chess pictures, prints, ephemera, stamps, cancels, cigarette cards and postcards and collectables but not sets, only books on sets.*

Tony Hutchinson, 44 Raeburn Ave, Surbiton, KT5 9DP. Prop: Tony Hutchinson. Tel: 020 8399 8416. Web: www.flyingant.co.uk. Est: 1997. Private premises. Postal only. Appointment necessary. Spec: Aircraft; Magazines & Periodicals - General; Model Engineering; Model Railways; Science - General; Scientific Instruments; War - World War I; War - World War II. CC: PayPal. Notes: *Also trade out of Hampton Court Emporium, Surrey.*

SUTTON

Nonsuch Books, 176 Mulgrave Road, Cheam, Sutton, SM2 6JS. Prop: Robert and Lynette Gleeson. Tel: (020) 8770 7875. Est: 1990. Private premises. Postal only. Appointment necessary. Open: **M:** 09:00–17:00; **T:** 09:00–17:00; **W:** 09:00–17:00; **Th:** 09:00–17:00; **F:** 09:00–17:00; **S:** 09:00–17:00. Small stock. Spec: Archaeology; Architecture; Art; Art History; Art Reference; History - General; Illustrated - General; Literature. PR: £5–200.

WALLINGTON

RGS Books, 3 Dower Avenue, Wallington, SM6 0RG. Tel: (0208) 647 2003. Fax: (0208) 647 2003. Est: 1960. Private premises. Internet and Postal. Large stock. Spec: Art; Author - Wells, H.G.; Bibliography; Books about Books; Ex-Libris; Fiction - General; Heraldry; History - General. PR: £2–500. Mem: PLA; SB; RSA; CILIP. Notes: *Stocks titles on history of London.*

WALTON–ON–THAMES

Fred Lake, 104 Kings Road, Walton–on–Thames, KT12 2RE. Tel: (01932) 227824. Private premises. Postal only. Small stock. Spec: Sport - Archery. PR: £1–150.

WEYBRIDGE

Fun in Books, P.O. Box 608, Weybridge, KT13 3BL. Prop: Michael J. White. Tel: (01932) 852625. Est: 1994. Storeroom; Postal only. Spec: Freemasonry & Anti-Masonry; Glamour; Humour; Collectables; Ephemera. PR: £5–1,000. CC: MC; V.

Mrs. D.M. Green, 7 Tower Grove, Weybridge, KT13 9LX. Tel: (01932) 241105. Est: 1974. Private premises. Internet and Postal. Appointment necessary. Small stock. Spec: Atlases; Topography - General; Prints and Maps. PR: £1–3,500. Cata: lists on request. Notes: *British counties, British Topography and maps related to G.B. and counties.*

WINDLESHAM

Cold Tonnage Books, 22 Kings Lane, Windlesham, GU20 6JQ. Prop: Andy Richards. Tel: (01276) 475388. Est: 1989. Private premises. Internet and Postal. Appointment necessary. Medium stock. Spec: Fiction - Science Fiction. PR: £5–500. CC: MC; V. VAT No: GB 530 1816 81.

WOKING

Glenwood Books, Highlands, Cedar Road, Woking, GU22 0JJ. Prop: Lesleyanne Woolvett. Tel: 01483 725628. Fax: 01483 725628. Est: 1994. Private premises. Book fairs only. Contactable. Spec: Author - Austen, Jane; History - Local; Literature - 19th C. Cata: 19th Century Literature. Notes: *Small stock of local topography/history.*

Goldsworth Books & Prints Ltd, 16 Beacon Hill, Woking, GU21 7QR. Prop: Brian & Joyce Hartles. Tel: (01483) 767670. Fax: (01483) 767670. Web: www.goldsworthbooks.com. Est: 1986. Private premises. Internet and Postal. Appointment necessary. Very large stock. Spec: Booksearch; Prints and Maps. PR: £1–5,000. CC: JCB; MC; V. Mem: PBFA. VAT No: GB 641 2513 73.

Peter Kennedy, 2 Shirley Place, Knaphill, Woking, GU21 2PL. Tel: (01483) 797293. Web: www.peterkennedy.com. Est: 1972. Private premises. Internet and Postal. Appointment necessary. Open: **S:** 08:00–16:00. Medium stock. Spec: Antiques; Atlases; Botany; Illustrated - General; Natural History; Prints and Maps. PR: £15 – 5,000. CC: MC; V. Cat: occasionally. Mem: ABA; ILAB. Notes: *Also, antique prints. Callers welcome Mon-Friday by prior appointment only.*

World War II Books, P.O. Box 55, Woking, GU22 8HP. Prop: C.G. Palmer. Tel: (01483) 722880. Fax: (01483) 721548. Web: www.worldwarbooks.co.uk. Est: 1982. Postal only. Spec: Armed Forces - Australian Air Force; Armed Forces - Australian Army; Author - Rackham, Arthur; Military History; Naval; Navy, The; Shell County Guides (UK only); War - Australian. CC: V.

TYNE AND WEAR

NEWCASTLE UPON TYNE

Christopher Handley, 38 Beacon Drive, Wideopen, Newcastle Upon Tyne, NE13 7HB. Tel: (0191) 2367759. Web: www.DiarySearch.co.uk. Est: 1990. Private premises. Postal only. Appointment necessary. Small stock. Spec: Biography; Diaries; Journals. PR: £3–200. Cata: diaries and letters. Notes: *My website includes a bibliography of diaries printed in English.*

Frank Smith Maritime Aviation, ■ 92 Heaton Road, Newcastle upon Tyne, NE6 5HL. Prop: Alan Parker. Tel: (0191) 265-6333. Fax: (0191) 224-2620. Est: 1981. Internet and Postal. Shop open: **M:** 10:00–16:00; **T:** 10:00–16:00; **W:** 10:00–16:00; **Th:** 10:00–16:00; **F:** 10:00–16:00. Large stock. Spec: Aviation; Maritime/Nautical; Motoring; Shipbuilding and Shipping; Sport - Yachting (& Boating). PR: £4–1,000. CC: AE; E; JCB; MC; V. Cata: Maritime & Aviation. Corresp: German, French, Dutch. Mem: PBFA. VAT No: GB 297 9302 12.

Newcastle Books, 73 Titan House, Berry Close, Newcastle Upon Tyne, NE6 3DQ. Prop: Richard Cartwright. Tel: 0191 209 1720. Web: www.stores.ebay.co.uk/Newcastle-Books. Est: 2002. Private premises. Internet and Postal. Telephone First. Open: **M:** 09:00–20:00; **T:** 09:00–20:00; **W:** 09:00–20:00; **Th:** 09:00–20:00; **F:** 09:00–20:00; **S:** 09:00–22:00; **Su:** 09:00–22.00. Spec: Academic/Scholarly; Agriculture; Aircraft; Archaeology; Architecture; Autobiography; Bibliophily; Biography. CC: MC; V. Notes: *Specialise in obscure, out of print titles & wide selection of Ex-Reference library material. Local interest including Northumberland, Durham, art, indexes, london interest, reference, topography, British history & many other titles.*

NORTH SHIELDS

Keel Row Bookshop, ■ 11 Fenwick Terrace, North Shields, NE29 OLU. Prop: Anthony J Smithson. Tel: 01912960664. Web: www.keelrowbookshop.co.uk. Est: 1980. Shop. Open: **M:** 10:00–17:30; **T:** 10:00–17:30; **W:** 10:00–17:30; **Th:** 10:00–1730; **F:** 10:00–17:30; **S:** 10:00–17:30; **Su:** 10:00–17:30. Spec: Antiquarian; Art Reference; Aviation; Children's; Fiction - Historical; History - General; Industry; Maritime/Nautical - History. CC: MC; V. Cata: Antiquarian, Modern Firsts, Childrens. Mem: PBFA. Notes: *The shop is located a mile from the coast on the north bank of the tyne, a large eight-roomed Victorian townhouse with a well arranged good quality stock, in excess of 40,000 titles.*

WHITLEY BAY

The Rider Haggard Society, 27 Deneholm, Monkseaton, Whitley Bay, NE25 9AU. Prop: Roger Allen. Tel: (0191) 252-4516. Fax: (0191) 252-4516. Web: www.riderhaggardsociety.org.uk. Est: 1984. Private premises. Small stock. Spec: Author - Haggard, Sir Henry Rider; Author - Heyer, Georgette; Author - Stoker, B.; Booksearch. PR: £2–300. Cata: Haggard & general lists of fiction. Corresp: French, Spanish. Notes: *Also, Editor for the Rider Haggard Society.*

WARWICKSHIRE

ALCESTER

Home Farm Books, 44 Evesham Road, Cookhill, Alcester, B49 5LJ. Prop: Tony Read. Tel: (01789) 763115. Fax: (01789) 766086. Est: 1979. Private premises. Internet and Postal. Small stock. Spec: Cockfighting; Dogs; Firearms/Guns; Natural History; Rural Life; Sport - Angling/Fishing; Sport - Big Game Hunting; Sport - Falconry. PR: £2–400. CC: E; MC; V. Cata: dogs, fieldsports, natural history. Notes: *Also, a booksearch service.*

ATHERSTONE

Sit-a-While, 18-20 Church Street, Atherstone, CV9 1HA. Prop: Lisa Dundas. Tel: 01827 722593. Web: www.atherstonebooktown.com. Est: 2006. Private premises. Internet and Postal. Notes: *Trades on Abebooks and Amazon.*

Throckmorton's Bookshop, ■ 16 Market Place, Atherstone, CV9 1EX. Prop: Peter Playdon and Molly Rogers. Tel: 01827 717570. Web: www.atherstonebooktown.net. Est: 2005. Shop open: **T:** 10:00–17:00; **W:** 10:00–17:00; **Th:** 10:00–17:00; **F:** 10:00–17:00; **S:** 10:00–17:00; **Su:** 11:00–16:00. CC: MC; V. Corresp: French, Spanish.

BEDWORTH

Astley Book Farm, ■ Astley Lane, Bedworth, CV12 0NE. Prop: Vivienne Mills and Sarah Exley. Tel: 02476 490235. Web: www.astleybookfarm.com. Est: 2004. Shop open: **M:** 10:00–17:00; **T:** 10:00–17:00; **W:** 10:00–17:00; **Th:** 10:00–17:00; **F:** 10:00–17:00; **S:** 10:00–17:00; **Su:** 10:00–17:00. CC: AE; MC; V. VAT No: GB 831 8247 29. Notes: *Approximately 50,000 titles in stock.*

GREAT WALFORD

NV Books, 4 Carters Leaze, Great Walford, CV36 5NS. Prop: Tom Verrall. Tel: 0800 0830281. Est: 2005. Private premises. Internet only. Appointment necessary. Open: **M:** 09:00–18:00; **T:** 09:00–18:00; **W:** 09:00–18:00; **Th:** 09:00–18:00; **F:** 09:00–18:00; **S:** 09:00–18:00; **Su:** 09:00–18:00. Spec: Antiquarian; Author - Wodehouse, P.G.; Fine & Rare; First Editions; Limited Editions - General; Memoirs; Modern First Editions; Signed Editions. CC: MC; V; Solo, Maestro, Visa Electron. Cata: latest acquisitions by e-mail. VAT No: GB 783 9189 70. Notes: *Specialising in PG Wodehouse and Douglas Adams.*

HENLEY–IN–ARDEN

Arden Books & Cosmographia, 11 Pound Field, Wootton Wawen, Henley–in–Arden, B95 6AQ. Prop: David Daymond. Tel: (01564) 793476. Est: 1998. Private premises. Postal only. Small stock. Spec: Antiques; Art; Biography; Canals/Inland Waterways; Children's; Crafts; Food & Drink; Gardening - General. PR: £1–50. Corresp: French, German.

KENILWORTH

Frank & Stella Allinson, 25 Brooke Road, Kenilworth, CV8 2BD. Tel: (01926) 854662. Web: www.booksatpbfa.com. Est: 1989. Private premises. Internet and Postal. Appointment necessary. Spec: Academic/Scholarly; Aeronautics; Alpinism/Mountaineering; Archaeology - Industrial; Author - Ardizzone, Edward; Author - Brent-Dyer, Elinor M.; Author - Pratchett, Terry; Author - Searle, Ronald. PR: £3–40. CC: D; E; JCB; MC; V; Solo, Switch, Paypal. Mem: PBFA. VAT No: GB 776 6995 47. Notes: *We sell at book fairs and on the Internet, preferably would like orders through www.booksatpbfa.com to avoid ABE's exhorbitant charges. All orders through booksatpbfa over 10 will be post free in UK, reduced rates to the rest of the world.*

KINETON

Kineton Books, ■Bookshop, Southam Street, Kineton, CV35 0LP. Prop: J Neal. Tel: (01926) 640700. Web: www.kinetonbooks.co.uk. Est: 1998. Shop open: **W:** 10:00–17:00; **Th:** 10:00–17:00; **F:** 10:00–17:00; **S:** 10:00–16:00. Medium stock. Spec: Annuals; Author - Milligan, Spike; Children's; Children's - Illustrated; Expeditions; Exploration - Polar Regions; Famous People - Churchill, Sir Winston; First Editions. PR: £1–200. Cata: 8 a year.

LEAMINGTON SPA

Alexander's Books, 58 Greatheed Road, Leamington Spa, CV32 6ET. Prop: Andrew and Ros Parkes. Tel: (01926) 314508. Est: 1987. Private premises. Appointment necessary. Spec: Africana; Art; Australiana; Biography; Children's; Cookery/Gastronomy; Drama; History - General. PR: £2–500. Corresp: French, Italian.

STRATFORD-UPON-AVON

Chaucer Head Bookshop, ■ 21, Chapel Street, Stratford-upon-Avon, CV37 6EP. Prop: Richard and Vanessa James. Tel: 01789 415691. Web: www.chaucerhead.co.uk. Shop open: **M:** 10:00–17:30; **T:** 10:00–17:30; **W:** 10:00–17:30; **Th:** 10:00–17:30; **F:** 10:00–17:30; **S:** 10:00–17:30. Spec: Author - Shakespeare, William; Drama; Topography - Local. CC: MC; V; Switch, Visa Debit. Corresp: French, German.

Paul Meekins Books, Valentines, Long Marston, Stratford-upon-Avon, CV37 8RG. Prop: Paul Meekins. Tel: (01789) 722434. Fax: (01789) 722434. Web: www.paulmeekins.co.uk. Est: 1989. Private premises. Internet and Postal. Appointment necessary. Large stock. Spec: Arms & Armour; Aviation; Fashion & Costume; Firearms/Guns; History - General; History - Ancient; History - British; History - Middle Ages. PR: £2–200. CC: MC; V; Meastro.

The Stratford Bookshop, 43 Clopton Road, Stratford-upon-Avon, CV37 6SN. Prop: Sue and John Hill. Tel: 01789 298362. Web: www.thestratfordbookshop.co.uk. Private premises. Internet and Postal. Contactable. Spec: General. CC: Paypal. VAT No: GB 785 7543 76.

STUDLEY

Brewin Books Ltd., Doric House, 56 Alcester Road, Studley, B80 7NP. Prop: Director: K.A.F. Brewin. Tel: (01527) 854228. Fax: (01527) 852746. Web: www.brewinbooks.com. Est: 1973. Office and/or bookroom; Internet and Postal. Telephone First. Open: **M:** 09:00–17:00; **T:** 09:00–17:00; **W:** 09:00–17:00; **Th:** 09:00–17:00; **F:** 09:00–17:00; Closed for lunch: 13:00–13:30. Medium stock. Spec: Aviation; Genealogy; Local History; Military; Motoring; New Books; Railways and Railroads; Steam Engines. Mem: BA. VAT No: GB 705 0077 73. Notes: *Also, publishers of local history books and magazines.*

WARWICK

Duncan M. & V. Allsop, ■ 68 Smith Street, Warwick, CV34 4HU. Tel: (01926) 493266. Fax: (01926) 493266. Web: www./ukbookworld.com/members/allsop. Est: 1966. Book Fairs. Shop open: **M:** 11:00–16:30; **T:** 10:00–17:00; **W:** 10:00–17:00; **Th:** 10:00–17:00; **F:** 10:00–17:00; **S:** 10:00–17:00. Large stock. Spec: Antiquarian; Bindings; Counties in England; Fine & Rare. PR: £5–3,000. CC: MC; V; SW, SO. Mem: ABA; BA. Notes: *We stock a good selection of books in all subjects; including the county of Warwickshire. Also on abe.com.*

Eastgate Bookshop, ■ 11 Smith Street, Warwick, CV34 4JA. Prop: Robert Allsop. Tel: 01926 490607. Est: 1996. Shop open: **M:** 09:30–17:30; **T:** 09:30–17:30; **W:** 09:30–17:30; **Th:** 09:30–17:30; **F:** 09:30–17:30; **S:** 09:30–17:30. CC: AE; E; JCB; MC; V. Mem: PBFA. VAT No: GB 670 3384 38.

Phillip Robbins of Warwick, 3 Normandy Close, Hampton Magna, Warwick, CV35 8UB. Prop: Phillip John Robbins. Tel: (01926) 494368. Est: 1990. Private premises. Internet and Postal. Contactable. Small stock. Spec: Author - Moore, John; Conservation; Entomology; Magic & Conjuring; Manuals; Manuals - Seamanship (see also under Seamanship); Manuscripts; Marine Sciences. PR: £3–50. Mem: PBFA. Notes: *Secretary of the John Moore Society. Fair manager Birmingham Book Fair.*

WEST MIDLANDS

BILSTON

Christine M. Chalk (Old & Out of Print Books), Conway House, 17 Regent Street, Bilston, WV14 6AP. Prop: Mrs Christine Chalk. Tel: (01902) 403978. Est: 1996. Private premises. Postal only. Small stock. Spec: Art; Art Reference; Artists; Book Arts; Children's - Illustrated; Collectables; Collecting; Decorative Art. PR: £1–200. Cata: Art, Illustrated, Fiction, Biographies.

BIRMINGHAM

Afar Books International, 11 Church Place 135 Edward Road, Balsall Heath, Birmingham, B12 9JQ. Prop: Alf Richardson. Tel: (0121) 440-3918. Est: 1990. Private premises. Postal only. Medium stock. Spec: Anthropology; Black Studies; Colonial; Countries - Africa; Countries - Caribbean, The; Countries - Egypt; Egyptology; Voyages & Discovery. PR: £1–300. Notes: *only telephone evenings or Sunday.*

Albion Books, Beechcroft, 15 Woodlands Road, Saltley, Birmingham, B8 3AG. Prop: John Bentley. Tel: (0121) 328 2878. Est: 1984. Private premises. Postal only. Small stock. Spec: Military; Military History; War - General; War - World War I; Booksearch. PR: £1–150. Notes: *Also has stock on the 'origins of the Great war'.*

Birmingham Books, 202 Witton Lodge Road, Birmingham, B23 5BW. Prop: Mike Attree. Tel: (0121) 3845318. Est: 2004. Private premises. Internet and Postal. Appointment necessary. Spec: Alpinism/ Mountaineering; Author - Fleming, Ian; Author - Greene, Graham; Children's - Illustrated; Fiction - Crime, Detective, Spy, Thrillers; Fiction - Fantasy, Horror; Fiction - Science Fiction; Folio Society, The.

Elmfield Books, 24 Elmfield Crescent, Moseley, Birmingham, B13 9TN. Prop: Liz Palmer. Tel: (0121) 689-6246. Web: www.elmfieldbooks.co.uk. Est: 1999. Private premises. Internet and Postal. Appointment necessary. Small stock. Spec: Cookery/Gastronomy; Food & Drink; Illustrated - General; Natural History; Topography - General; Topography - Local. PR: £5–500. Notes: *Attends bookfairs and other events.*

Heritage, P.O. Box 3075, Edgbaston, Birmingham, B15 2EW. Prop: Gill & Jem Wilyman. Tel: 0121 455 0093. Est: 1985. Private premises. Postal only. Telephone First. Spec: Antiquarian; Atlases; Bindings; Cartography; Directories - General; Engraving; Ex-Libris; Fine & Rare. Cata: Ex-Libris, Heraldry, Maps, Private Press,. Mem: PBFA. Notes: *We also exhibit at PBFA Book Fairs. Our stock also includes maps, prints and ephemera, mainly relating to Midland Counties.*

Robin Doughty - Fine Books, 100a Frederick Road, Stechford, Birmingham, B33 8AE. Prop: Robin Doughty. Tel: 01210 783 7289. Est: 1994. Private premises. Postal only. Small stock. Spec: Antiquarian; Art; Art - British; Art Reference; Engraving; Illustrated - General; Illustrated - 19th & 20th Century; Literature. PR: £10–2,500. CC: PayPal. Cata: East Anglia, Art & Illustrated, Private Press,. Corresp: French. Mem: PBFA. Notes: *Deals from home and occasionally at Book Fairs.*

Readers World, ■ 137 Digbeth, Birmingham, B5 6DR. Prop: G.M. Eastwood. Tel: 0121 643 8664. Est: 1966. Shop. Open: **T:** 10:00–17:30; **W:** 10:00–17:30; **Th:** 10:00–17:30; **F:** 10:00–17:30; **S:** 10:00–17:30. Spec: Comic Books & Annuals; Military; Philosophy; Theatre; Vintage Paperbacks; Booksearch.

David Temperley, 19 Rotton Park Road, Edgbaston, Birmingham, B16 9JH. Prop: David Temperley. Tel: (0121) 454 0135. Fax: (0121) 454 1124. Est: 1969. Private premises. Appointment necessary. Medium stock. Spec: Atlases; Autolithography; Bindings; Colour-Plate; Decorative Art; Fine & Rare; Illustrated - General; Miniature Books.

Stephen Wycherley, ■508 Bristol Road, Selly Oak, Birmingham, B29 6BD. Prop: Stephen & Elizabeth Wycherley. Tel: (0121) 471-1006. Est: 1971. Shop open: **M:** 10:00–17:00; **T:** 10:00–17:00; **Th:** 10:00–17:00; **F:** 10:00–17:00; **S:** 10:00–17:00. Large stock. PR: £1–500. Corresp: French, Dutch. Mem: PBFA. Notes: *Summer (July-August) open on Thursdays, Fridays and Saturdays only.*

COVENTRY

Silver Trees Books, Silver Trees Farm, Balsall St., Balsall Common, Coventry, CV7 7AR. Prop: Brian and Elaine Hitchens. Tel: (01676) 533143. Fax: (01676) 533143. Web: www.abebooks.com. Est: 1999. Private premises. Postal only. Telephone First. Medium stock. Spec: Author - Crompton, Richmal; Ceramics; Children's; Gardening - General; General; Military; Modern First Editions. PR: £3–1,500. CC: AE; JCB; MC; V; Switch. Corresp: French.

Uncle Phil's Books, Wit's End 10, Mary Slessor Street, Coventry, CV3 3BY. Prop: Phil and Susie James. Tel: 02476 639989. Web: www.unclephilsbooks.co.uk. Est: 1962. Mail order only; Internet and Postal. Appointment necessary. Open: **M:** 09:00–17:30; **T:** 09:00–17:30; **W:** 09:00–17:30; **Th:** 09:00–17:30; **F:** 09:00–17:30; **S:** 09:00–17:30; **Su:** 09:00–17:30; Closed for lunch: 13:00–14:00. Spec: Antiques; Archaeology; Art; Art - Technique; Art - Theory; Art History; Artists; Arts, The. CC: MC; V; Switch, Maestro, Paypal. Cata: general stock. Mem: ibooknet. Notes: *We are an on-line or mail order business only.*

HALESOWEN

Anvil Books, ■ 52 Summer Hill, Halesowen, B63 3BU. Prop: J.K. Maddison and C.J.Murtagh. Tel: (0121) 550-0600. Est: 1997. Internet and Postal. Shop open: **Th:** 10:00–17:00; **S:** 10:00–17:00. Medium stock. Spec: Buses/Trams; Canals/Inland Waterways; History - Industrial; Industry; Maritime/ Nautical; Navigation; Railways and Railroads; Shipbuilding and Shipping. PR: £1–200.

Janus Books / Waverley Fairs, Newlands, 9 Hayley Park, Hayley Green, Halesowen, B63 1EJ. Prop: Royston Thomas Slim. Tel: (0121) 550-4123. Est: 1968. Private premises. Postal only. Small stock. Spec: Motoring; Topography - General; Topography - Local; War - General; Collectables; Ephemera; Prints and Maps. PR: £1–500. Notes: *(Incl: books on Black Country & Midland Local History) Also, book fair organiser – see prelims: Kinver (est 1981), Powick (Malvern) and Bromsgrove Antique Fairs.*

KINGSWINFORD

Wright Trace Books, 70 Ash Crescent, Kingswinford, DY6 8DH. Prop: Colin Micklewright and Pam Wright. Tel: (01384) 341211. Est: 2001. Private premises. Postal only. Small stock. Spec: Animals and Birds; Annuals; Dogs; Modern First Editions; Booksearch. PR: £5–1,000. CC: AE; D; E; JCB; MC; V; PayPal. Cata: Dogs, Specific interest Bull Breeds. Notes: *We can accept credit cards through our payment processor Paypal but you will need an internet access to allow this.*

OLDBURY

Anthony Dyson, 57 St John's Road, Oldbury, B68 9SA. Tel: (0121) 544-5386. Est: 1973. Private premises. Appointment necessary. Small stock. Spec: Fashion & Costume; Fiction - Crime, Detective, Spy, Thrillers; Literary Criticism; Literature. Notes: *8 catalogues a year.*

SOLIHULL

Court Hay Books, 1563 Warwick Road, Knowle, Solihull, B93 9LF. Prop: Howard and Gilian Walters. Tel: 01564 732 380. Web: www.courthaybooks.co.uk. Est: 1990. Private premises. Internet and Postal. Appointment necessary. Small stock. Spec: Botany; Flower Arranging; Forestry; Fungi; Gardening - General; Gardening - Organic; Horticulture. PR: £10–2,000. CC: AE; JCB; MC; V; Maestro. Cata: Yes. Notes: *Specialist Dealers in Books on The Garden, Garden History, Garden Design, Trees, Botany, Floras and Flower Arranging.*

Helion & Company Ltd, 26 Willow Road, Solihull, B91 1UE. Prop: D. Rogers. Tel: (0121) 705-3393. Fax: (0121) 711-4075. Web: www.helion.co.uk. Est: 1992. Private premises. Postal only. Very large stock. Spec: Academic/Scholarly; Arms & Armour; Aviation; Countries - Germany; Firearms/Guns; History - General; History - 19th Century; History - American. PR: £1–3,500. CC: AE; E; JCB; MC; V; Switch. Cata: on military history. Corresp: German, French, Spanish. Mem: IPG. VAT No: GB 797 4185 72. Notes: *Also, a free booksearch service.*

WALSALL

Brownhills Books, ■Old Sorting Office, 43c High Street, Brownhills, Walsall, W58 6SD. Prop: Jon Eadon. Tel: 01543 377660. Est: 2006. Shop open: **T:** 10:00–17:00; **W:** 10:00–17:00; **Th:** 10:00–17:00; **F:** 10:00–17:00; **S:** 10:00–17:00. Notes: *Fairs attended – Lichfield and Kinver.*

A.J. Mobbs, 65 Broadstone Avenue, Walsall, WS3 1JA. Tel: (01922) 477281. Web: www .mobbs.birdbooks.btinternet.co.uk. Est: 1982. Private premises. Internet and Postal. Appointment necessary. Small stock. Spec: Academic/Scholarly; Animals and Birds; Botany; Entomology; General Stock; Herpetology; Horticulture; Mammals. PR: £1–200. Notes: *Payment via PayPal accepted.*

SETI Books, 3C Kingswood Drive, Walsall, WS6 6NX. Prop: David J Ward. Tel: 01922 413277. Fax: 01922 413277. Web: www.ukbookworld.com/members/setibooks. Est: 2002. Private premises. Internet and Postal. Telephone First. Small stock. Spec: Autobiography; Biography; Conspiracy; Countries - England; Cryptozoology; Earth Mysteries; Esoteric; Famous People - Entertainers. PR: £1–175. Notes: *Paypal accepted.*

J. & M.A. Worrallo, 5 Allington Close Orchard Hills, Walsall, WS5 3DS. Prop: John & Mark Anthony Worrallo. Tel: (01922) 724519. Web: www.ukbookworld.com/members/worras. Est: 1980. Private premises. Postal only. Appointment necessary. Small stock. Spec: Booksearch. PR: £1–100. Notes: *Also, a booksearch service.*

WEST BROMWICH

Books at Star Dot Star, Flat 23 Salisbury House, Lily Street, West Bromwich, B71 1QD. Prop: Bruce Tober. Tel: (0121) 553-4284. Web: www.star-dot-star.net. Est: 2003. Private premises. Internet and Postal. Appointment necessary. Small stock. Spec: Antiquarian; British Books; Buses/Trams; Cookery - Professional; Cookery/Gastronomy; Fine & Rare; Food & Drink; History - General. PR: £5–1,000. CC: AE; JCB; MC; V; PayPal. Cata: various. Mem: IOBA.

WOLVERHAMPTON

Books & Bygones (Pam Taylor), ■19 Hollybush Lane, Penn, Wolverhampton, WV4 4JJ. Prop: Pam Taylor. Tel: (01902) 334020. Fax: (01902) 334747. Est: 1987. Shop open: **S:** 08:30–17:00; **Su:** 08:30–17:00. Medium stock. Spec: Authors - Women; Autographs; Dictionaries; Fiction - Science Fiction; History - General; History - Industrial; Magic & Conjuring; Performing Arts. PR: £1–10. Notes: *On Saturday and Sunday - telephone before travelling. Open other varied times or by appointment.*

R. & S. Crombie, 73 Griffiths Drive, Wednesfield, Wolverhampton, WV11 2JN. Tel: (01902) 733462. Est: 1995. Private premises. Book fairs only. Telephone First. PR: £1–100.

GS Cricket Books / The Old Book Shop, ■ 53 Bath Road, Chapel Ash, Wolverhampton, WV1 4EL. Prop: Gerry Stack. Tel: 01902 421055. Fax: 01902 569597. Est: 2005. Shop open: **T:** 10:00–16:30; **W:** 10:00–16:30; **Th:** 10:00–16:30; **F:** 09:00–16:30; **S:** 11:00–16:30. Spec: Sport - Cricket.

Mogul Diamonds, ■ 17 High Street, Albrighton, Wolverhampton, WV7 3JT. Prop: Gerald Leach. Tel: (01902) 372288. Web: www.ukbookworld.com/members/moguld. Est: 1999. Shop open: **M:** 09:00–17:30; **T:** 09:00–17:30; **W:** 09:30–17:30; **F:** 09:00–17:30; **S:** 09:00–13.00. Spec: Aircraft; Biography; Biology - General; History - Local; Music - General; Music - Classical; Music - Composers; Music - Musicians. PR: £1–200. CC: PayPal. Cata: sheet music. Corresp: French. Notes: *Specialises in books about Shropshire. Also sheet music - catalogues available printed, by e-mail or at website www.moguldiamonds.co.uk.*

The Old Bookshop, ■ 53 Bath Road, Wolverhampton, WV1 4EL. Prop: Jerry Stack. Tel: 01902 421055. Est: 1967. Shop open: **T:** 10:00–16:30; **W:** 10:00–16:30; **Th:** 10:00–16:30; **F:** 09:00–16:30; **S:** 10:00–16:30. Spec: Art; Embroidery; History - General; History - 19th Century; History - Local; History - Sports; Literature; Needlework. Cata: cricket.

WEST SUSSEX

ARUNDEL

Baynton–Williams Gallery, ■ 37a High Street, Arundel, BN18 9AG. Prop: Sarah & Roger Baynton–Williams. Tel: (01903) 883588. Fax: (01903) 883588. Web: www.baynton-williams.com. Est: 1946. Shop open: **M:** 10:00–18:00; **T:** 10:00–18:00; **W:** 10:00–18:00; **Th:** 10:00–18:00; **F:** 10:00–18:00; **S:** 10:00–18:00. Small stock. Spec: Antiquarian; Art Reference; Atlases; Maps & Mapmaking; Maritime/Nautical - History; Naval; Printing; Sport - Hunting. PR: £100–15,000. CC: MC; V. Cata: antiquarian maps and prints. Corresp: French. VAT No: GB 587-7418-83. Notes: *We undertake valuations for insurance and probate and are more than happy to advise on any aspect of collecting antiquarian maps and prints.*

Kim's Bookshop, ■ 10 High Street, Arundel, BN18 9AB. Prop: Mrs L Flowers. Tel: (01903) 882680. Est: 2003. Shop open: **M:** 10:00–17:00; **T:** 10:00–17:00; **W:** 10:00–17:00; **Th:** 10:00–17:00; **F:** 10:00–17:00; **S:** 09:30–17:30; **Su:** 10:30–17:00. Large stock. Spec: Antiquarian; Arts, The; Fiction - General; History - General; Music - General; Natural History; Topography - General; Topography - Local. CC: MC; V. Corresp: Spanish. Notes: *Also at 28 South Street, Chichester, West Sussex, PO19 1EL. Open on Bank Holidays 10:30–17:00.*

BILLINGSHURST

Bianco Library, Oaklands, West Chiltington Lane, Broadford Bridge, Billingshurst, RH13 9EA. Prop: Anthony Bianco. Tel: 01403 741038. Fax: 01403 741038. Web: www.biancolibrary.com. Est: 1999. Private premises. Internet only. Spec: Architecture; Art; Bibliography; Biography; Botany; Canals/Inland Waterways; Collecting; Colour-Plate. CC: PayPal. Notes: *Website has advanced search facility & multiple picture gallery. We have 70 book categories - see website.*

BOGNOR REGIS

Bookshelf – Aviation Books, 26 Westingway, Bognor Regis, PO21 2XX. Prop: Roger Billings. Tel: (01243) 866817. Est: 1996. Private premises. Internet and Postal. Telephone First. Spec: Aviation; Booksearch. PR: £1–300. CC: MC; V; PayPal. Cata: Aviation. Mem: PBFA. VAT No: GB 728 5963 88.

Mcbooks, 21 Upper Bognor Road, Bognor Regis, PO21 1JA. Prop: Emma Laing. Tel: 01243 868614. Web: www.meadowcroftbooks.demon.co.uk. Est: 1996. Private premises. Internet and Postal. Telephone First. Open: **M:** 09:00–17:30; **T:** 09:00–17:30; **W:** 09:00–17:30; **Th:** 09:00–17:30; **F:** 09:00–17:30; **S:** 09:00–17:30; **Su:** 09:00–17:30; Closed for lunch: 13:00–14:00. CC: MC; V; Maestro. VAT No: GB 699 0227 01. Notes: *Primarily booksearch.*

CHICHESTER

back2books.tv, Dorvic House, Quarry Lane, Chichester, PO19 8RR. Prop: David Combes. Tel: 01243 533536. Web: www.back2book.tv. Est: 2005. Mail order only; Internet and Postal. Contactable. Open: **M:** 09:00–17:30; **T:** 09:00–17:30; **W:** 09:00–17:30; **Th:** 09:00–17:30; **F:** 09:00–17:30; **S:** 09:00–17:30; **Su:** 09:00–17:30; Closed for lunch: 13:00–14:00. CC: AE; D; E; JCB; MC; V.

The Chichester Bookshop, ■ 39 Southgate, Chichester, PO19 1DP. Prop: Chris & Carol Lowndes. Tel: (01243) 785473. Web: www.chichesterbookshop.co.uk. Est: 1994. Shop open: **T:** 10:30–17:30; **W:** 10:30–17:30; **Th:** 10:30–17:30; **F:** 10:30–17:30; **S:** 10:30–17:30. Very large stock. Spec: Local studies - Sussex; Topography - Local. PR: £1–1,000. VAT No: GB 860 5568 09. Notes: *Five rooms on two floors full of books, sheet music, collectable postcards and all sorts of ephemera. If you can't see what you're looking for please ask, as we carry a large reserve stock on the premises.*

Peter Hancock Antiques, ■ 40–41 West Street, Chichester, PO19 1RP. Prop: Peter Hancock. Tel: (01243) 786173. Fax: (01243) 778865. Est: 1965. Shop. Appointment necessary. Open: **T:** 10:00–17:30; **W:** 10:00–17:30; **Th:** 10:00–17:30; **F:** 10:00–17:30; **S:** 10:30–17:30. Small stock. Spec: Aeronautics; Alpinism/Mountaineering; Americana - General; Antiquarian; Children's; Classics, The; Military; Mysticism. PR: £5–500. CC: AE; E; JCB; MC; V. VAT No: GB 192 8554 28. Notes: *And bookroom. Also, antiques.*

Kim's Bookshop, ■ 28 South Street, Chichester, PO19 1EL. Prop: Mrs L Flowers. Tel: (01243) 778477. Est: 2004. Shop open: **M:** 10:00–17:00; **T:** 10:00–17:00; **W:** 10:00–17:00; **Th:** 10:00–17:00; **F:** 10:00–17:00; **S:** 10:00–17:00. Large stock. Spec: Academic/Scholarly; Antiquarian; Art; Art - Technique; Arts, The; Fiction - General; History - General; Music - General. PR: £1–1,000. CC: MC; V. Corresp: Spanish. VAT No: GB 825 9120 31. Notes: *Also at 10 High Street, Arundel, West Sussex, BN18 9AB.*

EAST GRINSTEAD

The Bookshop, ■Tudor House, 22 High Street, East Grinstead, RH19 3AW. Prop: J. & H. Pye. Tel: (01342) 322669. Shop open: **M:** 09:00–17:30; **T:** 09:00–17:30; **W:** 09:00–17:30; **Th:** 09:00–17:30; **F:** 09:00–17:30; **S:** 09:00–17:30. Medium stock. Spec: History - General; Booksearch. CC: AE; MC; V. Mem: BA. VAT No: GB 472 9663 08.

GORING–BY–SEA

Barry Jones, Daymer Cottage, 28 Marine Crescent, Goring–by–Sea, BN12 4JF. Prop: Barry Jones. Tel: (01903) 244655. Fax: (01903) 244655. Est: 1990. Private premises. Appointment necessary. Medium stock. Spec: Railways and Railroads; Traction Engines; Transport; Ephemera. PR: £1–500. Notes: *Appointments only between 09:00 and 21:00. Railway Collectors Fairs Organiser.*

HASSOCKS

Post Mortem Books Ltd, 58 Stanford Ave, Hassocks, BN6 8JH. Prop: Ralph Spurrier. Tel: (01273) 843066. Fax: (0870) 161-7332. Web: www.postmortembooks.com. Est: 1979. Private premises. Internet and Postal. Appointment necessary. Open: **M:** 08:15–18:00; **T:** 08:15–18:00; **W:** 08:15–18:00; **Th:** 08:15–18:00; **F:** 10:00–18:00; **S:** 10:00–12:00. Medium stock. Spec: Fiction - Adventure; Fiction - Crime, Detective, Spy, Thrillers; Sherlockiana. PR: £5–1,000. CC: AE; MC; V; Maestro. Cata: crime fiction.

HORSHAM

Bookworms Paradise Ltd., PO Box 661, Horsham, RH13 5WR. Prop: Peter Miles. Tel: 044-(1)403-256530. Web: www.bookwormsparadise.com. Est: 1989. Mail order only; Internet and Postal. Contactable. Open: **M:** 09:00–19:30; **T:** 09:00–19:30; **W:** 09:00–19:30; **Th:** 09:00–19:30; **F:** 09:00–19:30; **S:** 09:00–19:30; **Su:** 09:00–16:00; Closed for lunch: 13:00–14:00. Spec: Antiques; Arms & Armour; Author - Asimov, Isaac; Author - Blyton, Enid; Author - Bradbury, Ray; Author - Charteris, Leslie; Author - Christie, Agatha; Author - Creasey, John. CC: MC; V; UK Issued Debit Cards. Cata: Science Fiction / Military / Cookery / Biography. VAT No: GB 810-8442-51. Notes: *Implementing an e-mail service for clients to sign up to that will notify them directly of any updates in subject area's they are interested in. Emails would be sent as soon as stock is listed.*

Horsham Rare Books, P.O. Box 770, Horsham, RH12 9BA. Tel: 01403 252187. Web: www. horshamrarebooks.com. Private premises. Internet and Postal. Contactable. Spec: Antiquarian; Art; Aviation; Bindings; Biography; History - General; History - Local; Topography - Local. CC: AE; MC; V; Maestro. Mem: PBFA.

Merlin Books, P.O. Box 153, Horsham, RH12 2YG. Prop: Mike Husband. Tel: (01403) 257626. Fax: (01403) 257626. Web: www.merlinbooks.com. Est: 1990. Private premises. Internet and Postal. Telephone First. Small stock. Spec: Motorbikes / motorcycles; Booksearch. PR: £2–60. CC: E; JCB; MC; V. Cata: Motorcycle. Notes: *New motorcycle books & manuals sold. Secondhand Motoring & Motorcycle books always wanted.*

Muttonchop Manuscripts, PO Box 815, Horsham, RH12 9EH. Prop: Roger Clarke. Tel: 01403-713050. Est: 1992. Private premises. Internet only. Appointment necessary. Medium stock. Spec: Agriculture; Antiquarian; Antiques; Bibliography; Bindings; Cities - City of London; Collectables; Dictionaries. PR: £5–5,000. Corresp: French. VAT No: GB 704 6864 26.

Michael Phelps, Felled Oaks, Brighton Road, Horsham, RH13 6ER. Prop: Michael Phelps. Tel: (01403) 754222. Est: 1974. Private premises. Appointment necessary. Spec: Acupuncture; Aeronautics; Alchemy; Anatomy; Anthropology; Antiquarian; Astronomy; Aviation. PR: £10–100. CC: E; MC; V. Cata: Science & Technol; Medicine, Nat His. Mem: ABA; ILAB. Notes: *Broad coverage of books the subjects stated above, but also associated ephemera engravings, etc. A surprisingly wide range. Buying on commission & valuations.*

LANCING

Paul Evans Rare Books, 13 Berriedale Drive, Sompting, Lancing, BN15 OLE. Prop: Paul Evans. Tel: (01903) 764655. Fax: (01903) 764655. Web: www.paulevansbooks.com. Est: 1991. Private premises. Postal only. Appointment necessary. Small stock. Spec: Academic/Scholarly; Antiquarian; Art; Art - Technique; Art History; Art Reference; Artists; Arts, The. PR: £5–30,000. CC: MC; V. Cata: Virginia Woolf, The Bloomsbury Group. Notes: *Books by/about Virginia Woolf, Vita Sackville-West, "Bloomsbury" and The Hogarth Press. Also Art, Ephemera, Manuscripts, Exotica by the above. V. Bell, R. Fry, Carrington, L. Strachey, Duncan Grant, other members of The Bloomsbury Group.*

LITTLEHAMPTON

Buckland Books, Holly Tree House, 18 Woodlands Road, Littlehampton, BN17 5PP. Prop: Mr. Chris Blanchett. Tel: (01903) 717648. Fax: (01903) 717648. Web: www.bucklandbooks.co.uk. Est: 1991. Private premises. Postal only. Appointment necessary. Small stock. Spec: Antique Stoves; Antiques; Archaeology; Architecture; Building & Construction; Ceramics; Collecting; Decorative Art. PR: £2–300. CC: MC; V; Maestro. Cata: Tiles, Mosaics, Brick/Terracotta, Marble/Stone. VAT No: GB 630 8660 43. Notes: *Also, new books on these subjects from around the world. Booksearch facility within our specailities also available.*

Chris Adam Smith Modern First Editions, 9 Western Road, Littlehampton, BN17 5NP. Prop: Chris Adam Smith. Tel: 01903 722392. Web: www.adamsmithbooks.com. Est: 1993. Mail order only; Internet only. Appointment necessary. Open: **T:** 09:00–17:30; **W:** 09:00–17:30; **Th:** 09:00–17:30; **F:** 09:00–17:30. Spec: Fiction - General; Fiction - Crime, Detective, Spy, Thrillers; Fiction - Historical; Fiction - Supernatural; Fiction - Young Adult Mystery & Adventure Series; Modern First Editions. CC: AE; D; MC; V; Paypal. Cata: Crime, Maritime, Children's, Science Fiction. Notes: *We cover most modern fiction in fine first edition and signed copies are a specialty.*

JB Books & Collectables, 14 Kingsmead, Thornlea Park, Lyminster, Littlehampton, BN17 7QS. Prop: Mrs J. Brittain. Tel: (01903) 725819. Web: www.jbbooks.co.uk. Est: 1997. Private premises. Internet and Postal. Telephone First. Open: **M:** 09:00–17:30; **T:** 09:00–17:30; **W:** 09:00–17:30; **Th:** 09:00–17:30; **F:** 09:00–17:30; **S:** 09:00–17:00; Closed for lunch: 13:00–14:00. Small stock. Spec: Antiquarian; Art - British; Art - Technique; Art History; Art Reference; Artists; Auction Catalogues; Children's. PR: £1–500. CC: Paypal. Mem: PBFA

South Downs Book Service, Garden Cottage, 39c Arundel Road, Littlehampton, BN17 7BY. Prop: Ms. J.A. Bristow. Tel: (01903) 723401. Fax: (01903) 726318. Est: 1994. Private premises. Appointment necessary. Open: **M:** 08:00–20:00; **T:** 08:00–20:00; **W:** 08:00–20:00; **Th:** 08:00–20:00; **F:** 08:00–20:00; **S:** 08:00–20:00; **Su:** 08:00–20:00. Small stock. Spec: Academic/Scholarly; Antiquarian; Ecclesiastical History & Architecture; Literature - Victorian; Social History; Ephemera; Prints and Maps. PR: £4–600. Notes: *accredited valuers and cataloguers to libraries to leading private libraries.*

MIDHURST

Canon Gate Books, 2 The Common off Carron Lane, Midhurst, GU29 9LF. Prop: Philip & Wendy Pegler. Tel: 01730 815962. Web: www.canongate-thoughtful-books.com. Est: 1980. Private premises. Internet and Postal. Appointment necessary. Small stock. Spec: Author - Thomas, Edward; Countries - Asia; Countries - India; Countries - Tibet; County - Local; Oriental; Religion - General; Religion - Buddhism. PR: £5–1,000. VAT No: GB 543 8777 05. Notes: *Our books are catalogued on Abebooks - we will undertake booksearch. Visits by appointment.*

Elmo Books, 13 Tufts Field, Midhurst, BN41 1WA. Prop: Elmo. Tel: 01730716351. Web: www.stores.ebay.co.uk/elmo-books. Est: 2003. Warehouse; Internet and Postal. Contactable. Spec: Automobilia/Automotive; Motorbikes / motorcycles; Sport - General; Sport - Football (Soccer); Sport - Motor Racing. CC: AE; D; E; JCB; MC; V. Notes: *Specialists in football & motoring/ motorsport books - plus other unusual rare books.*

Wheeler's Bookshop, ■ Red Lion Street, Midhurst, GU29 9PB. Tel: 01730 817666. Web: www.wheelersbookshop.co.uk. Shop open: **M:** 10:00–17:00; **T:** 10:00–17:00; **W:** 10:00–17:00; **Th:** 10:00–17:00; **F:** 10:00–17:00; **S:** 10:00–17:00. Spec: General Stock; New Books. CC: MC; V. Notes: *Thousands of secondhand books on many and varied subjects, plus a wide range of in-print titles. The shop has recently expanded upstairs, to accommodate even more books. Please call in if you are in the area.*

PETWORTH

Tim Boss, North Street, Petworth, GU28 0DD. Prop: Tim Boss. Tel: (01798) 343170. Est: 1993. Book fairs only. Small stock. Spec: Ephemera; Prints and Maps. PR: £1–350. Notes: *Also, 7,000 inexpensive prints and some maps.*

Petworth Antique Market (Bookroom), East Street, Petworth, GU28 0AB. Prop: Doris Rayment. Tel: (01798) 342073. Web: www.petworthantiquecentre.co.uk. Est: 1965. Shop and/or gallery; Shop open: **M:** 10:00–17:00; **T:** 10:00–17:00; **W:** 10:00–17:00; **Th:** 10:00–17:00; **F:** 10:00–17:00; **S:** 10:00–17:30. Spec: Antiques; Art; Bindings; Rural Life; Sport - Angling/Fishing; Sport - Field Sports. PR: £1–400. CC: MC; V; Maestro, Solo.

SHOREHAM–BY–SEA

Sansovino Books, 9 Mill Lane, Shoreham–By–Sea, BN43 5AG. Prop: Q. & R. Barry. Tel: (01273) 455753. Est: 1991. Storeroom; Appointment necessary. Medium stock. Spec: First Editions; Literature; Maritime/Nautical; Military; Private Press; Booksearch. PR: £5–200. Notes: *Also at: Sansovino, Stokelsy, Cleveland.*

STEYNING

dgbbooks, 15 Ingram Road, Steyning, BN44 3PF. Prop: Denise Bennett. Tel: (01903) 814895. Web: www.ukbookworld.com/members/dgbbooks. Est: 1999. Mail order only; Internet only. Contactable. Spec: Authors - Women; Biography; Fiction - General. PR: £5–50. Cata: Fiction, Biography Crafts. Notes: *Payment by Paypal, cheque or cash.*

WALDERTON

John Henly, 1 Brooklands, Walderton, Chichester, PO18 9EE. Tel: (023) 9263-1426. Fax: (023) 9263-1544. Est: 1986. Private premises. Postal only. Appointment necessary. Small stock. Spec: Geology; Mineralogy; Natural History; Palaeontology. CC: MC; V. Cata: Earth Sciences & Natural History. Mem: PBFA. VAT No: GB 582 5689 92.

WORTHING

Badgers Books, ■ 8–10 Gratwicke Road, Worthing, BN11 4BH. Prop: Ray Potter & Meriel Cocks. Tel: (01903) 211816. Est: 1982. Shop open: **M:** 09:00–17:30; **T:** 09:00–17:30; **W:** 09:00–17:30; **Th:** 09:00–17:30; **F:** 09:00–17:30; **S:** 09:00–18:00. Large stock. CC: E; JCB; MC; V; SW, EL, SO. VAT No: GB 587 5552 89.

Optimus Books, ■ 8 Ann Street, Worthing, BN11 1NX. Tel: (01903) 205895. Fax: (01903) 213438. Est: 1975. Internet and Postal. Contactable. Open: **M:** 09:30–16:30; **T:** 09:30–16:30; **W:** 09:30–16:30; **Th:** 09:30–16:30; **F:** 09:30–16:30; **S:** 10:00–12:00. Medium stock. Spec: Artists; Gardening - General; Native American. CC: MC; V. Mem: BA. VAT No: GB 921 4154 55.

WEST YORKSHIRE

ADDINGHAM

TP Children's Bookshop, ■ 71 Main Street, Addingham, Ilkley, LS29 0PS. Prop: Louise Harrison. Tel: 01943 830095. Est: 2005. Shop open: **F:** 10:00–16:00; **S:** 10:00–16:00. Spec: Annuals; Author - Brent-Dyer, Elinor M.; Author - Fairlie–Bruce, D.; Author - Hill, Lorna; Author - Johns, W.E.; Author - Oxenham, Elsie; Author - Saville, M.; Children's. CC: MC; V. Mem: PBFA. Notes: *Have traded for 5 years from private premises. Also, attends book fairs at least once a month. Note: Open at other times by appointment.*

BATLEY

Vintage Motorshop, ■ 749 Bradford Road, Batley, WF17 8HZ. Prop: R. & C. Hunt. Tel: (01924) 470773. Fax: (01924) 470773. Web: www.vintagemotorshop.co.uk. Est: 1976. Shop. Telephone First. Open: **Th:** 11:00–17:00; **F:** 11:00–17:00; **S:** 11:00–17:00. Medium stock. Spec: Buses/Trams; Motorbikes / motorcycles; Motoring; Sport - Motor Racing; Steam Engines; Traction Engines; Transport; Vintage Cars. PR: £1–30. CC: MC; V.

BRADFORD

Idle Booksellers (The), 5/7 Town Lane, Idle, Bradford, BD10 8PR. Prop: Ros Stinton & Michael Compton. Tel: (01274) 613737. Web: www.idlebooksellers.co.uk. Est: 1990. Private premises. Telephone First. Small stock. Spec: Author - Brontes, The; Author - Gissing, George; Genealogy; History - Local; Topography - Local; Yorkshire. PR: £1–600. CC: Paypal. Cata: George Gissing. Mem: PBFA.

Woodbine Books, 15 Stone Street, Bradford, BD15 9JR. Prop: Colin Neville. Tel: (01274) 824759. Web: www.abebooks.com/home/woodbine. Est: 1995. Private premises. Internet and Postal. Appointment necessary. Small stock. Spec: Art - British; Art Deco; Art History; Art Reference; Artists; Arts & Crafts Era; Author - Webb, Mary; Bindings. PR: £5–1,300. CC: via PayPal. Mem: PBFA; FPBA, PLA. Notes: *Specialising in fine press, limited editions, signed books, particularly artists/illustrators & books on Mary Webb.*

BRIGHOUSE

Northern Herald Books, 5 Close Lea, Rastrick, Brighouse, HD6 3AR. Prop: R.W. Jones. Tel: (01484) 721845. Est: 1985. Private premises. Postal only. Large stock. Spec: Academic/Scholarly; Communism; Economics; Free Thought; History - Anarchism; History - Economic Thought; History - Labour/ Radical Movements; History - Trotskyism. PR: £1–100. CC: AE; MC; V. Corresp: French, Spanish. Mem: PBFA.

CLECKHEATON

Sparrow Books, 10 Peaseland Close, Cleckheaton, BD19 3HA. Tel: (01274) 876995. Fax: (01274) 876995. Est: 1992. Private premises. Internet and Postal. Medium stock. Spec: Academic/Scholarly; Architecture; Geography; Geology; Politics; Topography - General; Topography - Local; Booksearch. PR: £1–80. Notes: *Mobile No: 07940 238441. Ebay shop: http://stores.ebay.co.uk/ Sparrow-Books ukbookworld site: http://ukbookworld.com/members/herault. Also sell books on Amazon.co.uk.*

GILVERSOME

Moorhead Books, Suffield Cottage, Gildersome Lane, Gildersome LS27 7BA. Prop: Frank Spicer. Tel: 0113 285 2264. Web: www.moorheadbooks.co.uk. Est: 1964. Private premises. Internet and Postal. Appointment necessary. Spec: Annuals; Art; Bibliography; Bindings; Children's; Colour-Plate; Cookery/Gastronomy; Miniature Books. Notes: *Also, attends Pudsey Book Fair.*

HALIFAX

M.R. Clark, 18 Balmoral Place, Halifax, HX1 2BG. Tel: (01422) 357475. Web: www.abebooks.com. Est: 1980. Private premises. Appointment necessary. Medium stock. Spec: Gardening - General; General; Natural History; Booksearch. Mem: PBFA. Notes: *Also, stock also on www.books@pbfa.co.uk and abebooks.com.*

HAWORTH

Hatchard & Daughters, ■ 91 Main Street, Haworth, BD22 8DA. Prop: Mary Hatchard. Tel: (01535) 648720. Est: 1989. Shop open: **F:** 12:00–17:00; **S:** 11:00–17:00; **Su:** 11:00–17:00. Spec: Author - Brontes, The; Illustrated - General; Railways and Railroads; Sport - General; Transport; West Yorkshire local history. PR: £5–200. CC: MC; V. Mem: PBFA.

Yorkshire Relics, ■ 11 Main Street, Haworth, BD21 8DA. Prop: Colin and Jacqueline Ruff. Tel: 01535 642218. Est: 1999. Shop open: **M:** 12:00–17:00; **T:** 12:00–17:00; **W:** 12:00–17:00; **Th:** 12:00–17:00; **F:** 12:00–17:00; **S:** 12:00–17:00; **Su:** 12:00–17:00. Spec: Annuals; Children's; Comic Books & Annuals; Comics; Magazines & Periodicals - General; Music - Popular; Music - Rock & Roll; Vintage Paperbacks.

HEBDEN BRIDGE

Christopher I. Browne, Hawdon Hall, Hebden Bridge, HX7 7AW. Prop: C.I. Browne. Tel: (01422) 844744. Fax: (01422) 844744. Web: www.gilbertandsullivanonline.com. Est: 1998. Private premises. Internet and Postal. Telephone First. Medium stock. Spec: Music - General; Music - Classical; Music - Composers; Music - Gilbert & Sullivan; Music - Gregorian Chants; Music - Illustrated Sheet Music; Music - Music Hall; Music - Musicians. CC: AE; MC; V. Mem: SASS/G&S Society. Notes: *also extensive Classical Music; online catalogue: books, sheet-music and long-playing vinyl records; fully searchable site: www.cbclassicalmusic.com. E-mail: sales@cbclassicalmusic.com.*

The Glass Key, Old Town Mill, Wadsworth, Hebden Bridge, HX7 8SW. Prop: James Fraser. Tel: 01422 842786. Web: www.theglasskey.co.uk. Est: 1990. Mail order only; Postal only. Contactable. Open: **Th:** 09:00–17:30; **F:** 09:00–17:30; **S:** 09:00–17:30; **Su:** 09:00–17:30; Closed for lunch: 13:00–14:00. Spec: Antiques; Author - 20th Century; Fiction - Crime, Detective, Spy, Thrillers; Fiction - Fantasy, Horror; Fiction - Science Fiction; Fiction - Supernatural; First Editions; Food & Drink. CC: AE; JCB; MC; V. Corresp: French. Mem: Ibooknet. Notes: *Currently trading via the internet only. Moving to Montmorillon in France in 2008 and opening retail premises there - Montmorillon is a mini Hay-on-Wye near Poitiers.*

HOLMFIRTH

Beardsell Books, ■ Toll House Bookshop, 32–34 Huddersfield Road, Holmfirth, HD9 2JS. Prop: Elaine V. Beardsell. Tel: (01484) 686541. Fax: (01484) 688406. Web: www.toll-house.co.uk. Est: 1977. Internet and Postal. Shop open: **M:** 09:00–17:00; **T:** 09:00–17:00; **W:** 09:00–17:00; **Th:** 09:00–17:00; **F:** 09:00–17:00; **S:** 09:00–17:30; **Su:** 13:00–16:30. Very large stock. Spec: Antiquarian; History - General; History - Local. PR: £1–1,000. CC: MC; V. Mem: ABA; PBFA; BA. VAT No: GB 333 4195 70.

Daisy Lane Books, ■ 15 Towngate, Holmfirth, HD9 1HA. Prop: J. & B. Townsend–Cardew. Tel: (01484) 688409. Est: 1990. Shop open: **M:** 09:30–17:00; **T:** 09:30–17:00; **W:** 09:30–17:00; **Th:** 09:30–17:00; **F:** 09:30–17:00; **S:** 09:30–17:00; **Su:** 09:30–17:00. Large stock.

Madalyn S. Jones, Horsegate Hill House, 3 Town End Road, Wooldale, Holmfirth, HD9 1AH. Prop: Madalyn S. Jones. Tel: (01484) 681580. Fax: (01484) 681580. Web: www.madalynjonesbooks.co.uk. Est: 1978. Private premises. Internet and Postal. Appointment necessary. Spec: Sculpture; Booksearch. Mem: PBFA. Notes: *General stock and a booksearch service. Specialising in books on sculpture and related arts.*

HORBURY

Rickaro Books, ■ 17 High Street, Horbury, Wakefield, WF4 5AB. Prop: Richard Knowles and Carole Heaton. Tel: 01924 278811. Fax: 01924 278811. Web: www.rickarobooks.co.uk. Est: 2001. Shop open: **M:** 08:30–17:30; **T:** 08:30–17:30; **W:** 08:30–17:30; **Th:** 08:30–17:30; **F:** 08:30–17:30; **S:** 08:30–17:30. Spec: Academic/Scholarly; Aircraft; Archaeology; Art; Art Reference; Artists; Author - Lawrence, T.E.; Author - Williamson, Henry. CC: E; MC; V. Cata: military, T.E. Lawrence, children's, local history. Mem: PBFA; BA. Notes: *We carry a wide range of stock both new books and antiquarian, we are open each weekday and Saturday and welcome visitors to browse. We will also travel to purchase good collections, single items or Valuations. Also exhibits at book fairs.*

HUDDERSFIELD

Aphra Books, See under 'Susan Taylor Books', Huddersfield, HD4 6XZ. Prop: Susan Taylor. Tel: 01484 662120. Open: **M:** 09:00–17:30; **T:** 09:00–17:30; **W:** 09:00–17:30; **Th:** 09:00–17:30; **F:** 09:00–17:30; **S:** 09:00–17:30; **Su:** 09:00–17:30; Closed for lunch: 13:00–14:00.

Children's Bookshop, ■37/39 Lidget Street, Lindley, Huddersfield, HD3 3JF. Prop: Sonia & Barry Benster. Tel: (01484) 658013. Fax: (01484) 460020. Est: 1975. Shop open: **M:** 09:00–17:00; **T:** 09:00–17:00; **W:** 09:00–17:00; **Th:** 09:00–17:00; **F:** 09:00–17:00; **S:** 09:00–17:00. Small stock. Spec: Author - Dickens, Charles; Author - Kipling, Rudyard; Author - Lawrence, D.H.; Autobiography; Bibliography; Biography; Children's; Christmas. CC: MC; V. Cata: Childrens. Mem: BA. VAT No: GB 185 0068 66. Notes: *Mainly new childrens books with a small antiquarian and second hand section.*

Elaine Lonsdale Books, 4 Scar Top, Golcar, Huddersfield, HD7 4DT. Prop: Elaine Lonsdale. Tel: 01484 644193. Fax: 01484 644193. Est: 1990. Private premises. Appointment necessary. Shop at: Books at: Hemswell Antique Centre (Building 2), Hemswell Cliff, Lincolnshire. Spec: Art - British; Author - 20th Century; Author - Alcotts, The; Authors - Women; Biography; Fiction - General; Fiction - Women; First Editions. PR: £1–100. CC: AE; MC; V. Mem: PBFA; Society of Bookbinders. Notes: *Also, bookbinder.*

Susan Taylor Books, 2 Top of the Hill, Thurstonland, Huddersfield, HD4 6XZ. Prop: Susan Taylor. Tel: 01484 662120. Est: 1987. Mail order only; Internet and Postal. Telephone First. Spec: Domesticity; Feminism; Fiction - Women; Housekeeping; Spiritual; Textiles; Women. Cata: Women; Spirituality, Textile Crafts; Domestic.

Nick Tozer Railway Books, ■ 159 Church Street, Paddock, Huddersfield, HD1 4UJ. Prop: Nick Tozer. Tel: (01484) 518159. Web: www.railwaybook.com. Est: 1997. Shop open: **T:** 14:00–20:00; **W:** 11:00–17:00; **Th:** 14:00–20:00; **S:** 11:00–17:00. Medium stock. Spec: Railways and Railroads; Booksearch. PR: £1–50. CC: MC; V; Maestro, Paypal. Notes: *Mail order- Internet etc, all reasonable hours. Retail premises open weekdays as shown with Saturdays being subject to show/fair commitments - please check on website or by phone.*

William H. Roberts, The Crease, 113 Hill Grove, Salendine Nook, Huddersfield, HD3 3TL. Tel: (01484) 654463. Fax: (01484) 654463. Web: www.williamroberts-cricket.com. Est: 1997. Private premises. Internet and Postal. Telephone First. Spec: Sport - Cricket. CC: V. Mem: PBFA.

ILKLEY

Fine Books at Ilkley, 41 Manley Road, Ilkley, LS29 8QP. Prop: Dr. F.P. Williams. Tel: (01943) 600168. Fax: (01943) 603828. Est: 1979. Private premises. Appointment necessary. Spec: Alpinism/Mountaineering; Antiquarian; Bindings; Children's - Illustrated; Natural History; Technical; Travel - Africa; Travel - Americas. PR: £10–1,000. Mem: ABA; PBFA; ILAB. VAT No: GB 427 7108 51.

Greenroom Books, 9 St. James Road, Ilkley, LS29 9PY. Prop: Geoff Oldham. Tel: (01943) 607662. Web: www.ukbookworld.com/members/greenroom. Est: 1991. Private premises. Internet and Postal. Appointment necessary. Open: **M:** 09:00–18:00; **T:** 09:00–18:00; **W:** 09:00–18:00; **Th:** 09:00–18:00; **F:** 09:00–18:00; **S:** 09:00–18:00. Small stock. Spec: Academic/Scholarly; Broadcasting; Cinema/Film; Comedy; Dance; Design; Drama; Entertainment - General. PR: £8–50. CC: PayPal. Corresp: French. Notes: *Specialises in the Performing Arts. Booksearch.*

Modern First Editions, 287 Leeds Road, Ilkley, LS29 8LL. Prop: Christian White. Tel: 01943 607366. Est: 2006. Private premises. Internet and Postal. Appointment necessary. Open: **M:** 09:00–17:30; **T:** 09:00–17:30; **W:** 09:00–17:30; **Th:** 09:00–17:30; **F:** 09:00–17:30; **S:** 09:00–17:30; **Su:** 09:00–17:30; Closed for lunch: 13:00–14:00. Spec: Architecture; Author - Beckett, S.; Author - Bloomsbury Group, The; Author - Brontes, The; Author - Christie, Agatha; Author - Eliot, G.; Author - Eliot, T.S.; Author - Fleming, Ian. Notes: *Specialisms include: Manuscripts, Literary and Historical Archives, Early Printed Books.*

Rupert Cavendish Books, 10 Elmete Grange, Main Street, Menston, Ilkley, LS29 6LA. Tel: 01943 884228. Est: 1994. Private premises. Postal Only. Small stock. Spec: Sport - General; Sport - Boxing; Sport - Cricket; Sport - Field Sports; Sport - Football (Soccer); Sport - Hunting; Sport - Racing; Sport - Rugby. PR: £5 – 800.

Skyrack Books, ■ 20 Skipton Road, Ilkley, LS29 9EJ. Prop: Steven Dyke. Tel: (01943) 601598. Fax: (01943) 601598. Est: 2000. Shop open: **T:** 10:00–17:00; **W:** 10:00–17:00; **Th:** 10:00–17:00; **F:** 10:00–17:00; **S:** 10:00–17:00; Closed for lunch: 13:00–14:00. Medium stock. Spec: Canals/Inland Waterways; History - Industrial; History - Local; New Books; Railways and Railroads; Topography - Local; Booksearch. PR: £1–100. Mem: BA. Notes: *And stocks on Yorkshire, new books, book tokens.*

Mark Sutcliffe Ltd, 14 St. John's Avenue, Addingham, Ilkley, LS29 0QB. Tel: (01943) 830117. Fax: (01943) 830117. Web: www.marksutcliffebooks.com. Est: 1996. Private premises. Internet and Postal. Appointment necessary. Small stock. Spec: Author - Blake, N.; Author - Carr, John Dickson; Author - Chandler, Raymond; Author - Crofts, Freeman Wills; Author - Fleming, Ian; Author - Hammett, Dashiell; Fiction - Crime, Detective, Spy, Thrillers; First Editions. PR: £5–3,000. CC: E; JCB; MC; V. Cata: Detective Fiction, Modern Firsts, Children's. Mem: PBFA. Notes: *Specializing in Detective Fiction, especially, Dashiell Hammett, Raymond Chandler, The Crime Club and the Golden Age 1920-1943.*

KIRKSTALL

The Bookshop, Kirkstall, ■ 10 Commercial Road, Kirkstall, Leeds, LS5 3AQ. Prop: R.A. & P.P. Brook. Tel: (0113) 278-0937. Fax: (0113) 278-0937. Est: 1982. Shop open: **M:** 10:15–16:30; **T:** 10:15–16:30; **W:** 10:15–16:30; **Th:** 10:15–16:30; **F:** 10:15–16:30; **S:** 10:15–16:30. Large stock. Spec: Antiquarian. PR: £1–2,000. CC: MC; V. Corresp: Spanish.

LEEDS

Bates & Hindmarch, 2 Cumberland Road, Headingley, Leeds, LS6 2EF. Prop: Jeffery Bates. Tel: (0113) 278-3306. Fax: (0113) 2783306. Web: www.abebooks.com. Est: 1987. Private premises. Appointment necessary. Small stock. Spec: Almanacs; Antiquarian; Bindings; Countries - Afghanistan; Countries - Asia; Countries - Central Asia; Countries - India; Countries - Iran. PR: £20–1,000. CC: AE; JCB; MC; V; Maestro, Delta, Switch. VAT No: GB 417 9947 06. Notes: *Very specialist stock. India and the East India Company, books on India published before 1948, Delhi Durbars, Royal Tours, Princely India, the British in India. Folding maps and city plans outside UK.*

Best Buy Books & Records, Christopher Court, 4 Christopher Road, Leeds, LS6 2JX. Prop: M D Burr. Tel: (0113) 2286112. Web: www.bestb.uy.com. Est: 1996. Warehouse; Internet and Postal. Contactable. Spec: Academic/Scholarly; Accountancy; Adult; Aeronautics; Africana; Anatomy; Anthropology; Antiquarian. PR: £5–5,000. CC: AE; D; E; JCB; MC; V. Notes: *We have over 100,000 unique book and 300,000 unique music items. Rare, unusual and general. All in stock and for sale on our fully searchable website www.bestb.uy.com.*

John Blanchfield, 5 Stanmore Place, Leeds, LS4 2RR. Prop: John Blanchfield. Tel: (0113) 274-2406. Est: 1984. Private premises. Internet and Postal. Appointment necessary. Medium stock. Spec: Academic/Scholarly; History - Industrial; Industry. PR: £5–500. CC: JCB; V. Mem: PBFA. VAT No: GB 405 5743 61. Notes: *and PBFA book fairs.*

The Bookshop, Kirkstall, ■ 10 Commercial Road, Leeds, LS5 3AQ. Prop: Roy and Pippa Brook. Tel: 0113 2780937. Web: www.abebooks.com/home/kirkstall. Shop open: **M:** 10:15–16:30; **T:** 10:15–16:30; **W:** 10:15–16:30; **Th:** 10:15–16:30; **F:** 10:15–16:30; **S:** 10:15–16:30. Spec: Booksearch. CC: E; MC; V.

Draca Books, 22 Templenewsam Road, Leeds, LS15 0DX. Prop: Dr. & Mrs Michael Dickenson. Tel: 0113 294 7188. Web: www.dracabooks.co.uk. Est: 2004. Private premises. Internet and Postal. Appointment necessary. Spec: Author - Ahlberg, Janet & Allan; Author - Ardizzone, Edward; Author - Blyton, Enid; Author - Buckeridge, A.; Author - Dahl, Roald; Author - Lewis, C.S.; Author - Milne, A.A.; Author - Ransome, Arthur. CC: PayPal. Corresp: French, German. Notes: *Entry also appears on www.yorkbooksellers.co.uk.*

Find That Book, 74 Oxford Avenue, Guiseley, Leeds, LS20 9BX. Prop: David Herries. Tel: (01943) 872699. Web: www.findthatbook.demon.co.uk. Est: 1991. Private premises. Internet and Postal. Spec: Booksearch.

Leeds Bookseller, 3 Wedgewood Drive, Roundhay, Leeds, LS8 1EF. Prop: J.B. Wilkinson. Tel: (0113) 266-7183. Est: 1980. Private premises. Postal only. Contactable. Small stock. Spec: Academic/Scholarly; Palaeography. PR: £1–8.

Peregrine Books (Leeds), 27 Hunger Hills Avenue, Horsforth, Leeds, LS18 5JS. Prop: J. & M.A. Whitaker. Tel: (0113) 258-5495. Est: 1986. Private premises. Appointment necessary. Small stock. Spec: Natural History; Travel - General. PR: £5–3,000. Notes: *Also publishers of books on natural history.*

David Spenceley Books, 75 Harley Drive, Leeds, LS13 4QY. Prop: David Spenceley. Tel: (0113) 257-0715 (24h). Web: www.abebooks.com/home/davidspenceleybooks. Est: 1990. Private premises. Internet and Postal. Contactable. Open: **M:** 09:00–21:00; **T:** 09:00–21:00; **W:** 09:00–21:00; **Th:** 09:00–21:00; **F:** 09:00–21:00; **S:** 09:00–17:00; **Su:** 09:00–19:00; Closed for lunch: 12:00–14:00. Medium stock. Spec: Academic/Scholarly; Antiquarian; Archives; Arms & Armour; Author - Chaucer, Geoffrey; Author - Peters, Ellis; Biography; Calligraphy. PR: £1–200. CC: PayPal. Notes: *Contactable at all reasonable hours. We also sell new books direct from the publisher and offer a book search within our own field of British history.*

Graham Sykes, 81 Gledhow Park Grove, Leeds, LS7 4JW. Tel: (0113) 262-1547. Est: 1985. Private premises. Postal only. Small stock. Spec: Fine Art; First Editions; History - General; Natural History; Palaeontology; Photography; Topography - General; Travel - General. Mem: PBFA.

Woodlands Books, 65 Gledhow Wood Road, Leeds, LS8 4DG. Prop: Bill & Valerie Astbury. Tel: (0113) 266-7834. Est: 1986. Private premises. Postal only. Small stock. Spec: Music - General; Music - Musicians. PR: £2–150.

LIVERSEDGE

Heckmondwike Book Shop, ■ 66 Union Road, Liversedge, WF15 7JF. Prop: David Sheard. Tel: (01924) 505666. Web: www.heckmondwike-book-shop.com/. Est: 1984. Internet and Postal. Telephone First. Open: S: 10:00–16:00. Large stock. Spec: Author - Charteris, Leslie; Author - Christie, Agatha; Author - Creasey, John; Author - Wheatley, Dennis; Fiction - General; Fiction - Crime, Detective, Spy, Thrillers; Fiction - Science Fiction; Publishers - Batsford. PR: £1–500. VAT No: GB 427 5900 45. Notes: *Will open shop at other times by arrangement or email requirements for listing on eBay. Major stocks of paperbacks 1940 - 1972.*

MIRFIELD

D. & M. Books, 5a Knowl Road, Mirfield, WF14 8DQ. Prop: Daniel J. Hanson. Tel: (01924) 495768. Fax: (01924) 491267. Web: www.dandmbooks.com. Est: 1989. Warehouse; Internet and Postal. Telephone First. Small stock. Spec: Annuals; Author - Blake, Sexton; Author - Blyton, Enid; Author - Brent-Dyer, Elinor M.; Author - Crompton, Richmal; Author - Johns, W.E.; Author - Oxenham, Elsie; Author - Richards, Frank. PR: £10–1,000. CC: JCB; MC; V. Cata: Children's books, annuals, comics. Mem: PBFA. VAT No: GB 686 8348 71. Notes: *Also suppliers and manufacturers of book jacket covers and mailing supplies. We are the official UK distributor for Brodart. Catalogue available upon request.*

NORMANTON

Andrew Warrender, 4 West Street, Normanton, WF6 2AP. Tel: (01924) 892117. Fax: (01924) 215327. Web: www.warrender.demon.co.uk. Est: 1995. Private premises. Postal only. Small stock. Spec: Author - Fleming, Ian; Modern First Editions. PR: £1–150.

OTLEY

Books Upstairs, ■ 9 New Market [Street], Otley, LS21 3AE. Prop: John Hepworth. Est: 2002. Shop open: **T:** 11:00–16:00; **F:** 11:00–16:00; **S:** 11:00–16:00.

Chevin Books, 19 Manor Square, Otley, LS21 3AP. Prop: Simon Michael. Tel: (01943) 466599. Est: 1996. Private premises. Shop open: **Th:** 10:00–17:00; **F:** 10:00–17:00; **S:** 10:00–17:00. Medium stock. Spec: Architecture; Art History; Aviation; Folio Society, The; Literature; Military; Military History; Motoring. PR: £1–1,000. CC: MC; V.

TODMORDEN

Border Bookshop, ■ 61a & 63 Halifax Road, Todmorden, OL14 5BB. Prop: Victor H. Collinge. Tel: (01706) 814721. Web: www.borderbookshop.co.uk. Est: 1980. Shop open: **M:** 10:00–17:00; **W:** 10:00–17:00; **Th:** 10:00–17:00; **F:** 10:00–17:00; **S:** 10:00–17:00; Closed for lunch: 13:00–14:00. Large stock. Spec: Children's; Comic Books & Annuals; Comics; Magazines & Periodicals - General; Nostalgia; Sport - Cricket; Sport - Football (Soccer); Ephemera. CC: AE; E; JCB; MC; V. Cata: british comics & storypapers. Corresp: French. Mem: BA. Notes: *Also, new books, book tokens & book ordering service.*

John Eggeling Books, Claremont South, 56 Burnley Road, Todmorden, OL14 5LH. Prop: John Eggeling. Tel: (01706) 816487. Fax: (01706) 816487. Web: www.abebooks.com/home/TODBOOKS/. Est: 1972. Private premises. Internet and Postal. Appointment necessary. Medium stock. Spec: Adult; Adventure; Africana; Anthologies; Australiana; Author - General; Author - 20th Century; Author - Benson, A.C. PR: £2–10,000. CC: MC; V; Switch. Cata: Fiction by Minor Authors. Notes: *Stock covers all fiction genres plus pre-1950 fiction magazines and paperbacks. Emphasis on Colonial, Regional, Science Fiction, Fantasy, Supernatural, Detective, and fiction of social relevance. With emphasis in Victorian and Edwardian.*

Judith Mansfield, Claremont South, 56 Burnley Road, Todmorden, OL14 5LH. Prop: Judith Mansfield. Tel: (01706) 816487. Fax: (01706) 816487. Web: www.abebooks.com/home/TODBOOKS/. Est: 1983. Private premises. Internet and Postal. Appointment necessary. Spec: Applied Art; Carpets - General; Crafts; Crochet; Decorative Art; Dyes; Embroidery; Hairdressing. CC: MC; V; PayPal. Cata: Needlework, textiles, costume and fashion. Mem: PBFA; Textile Society.

Magpie Books, Mellor Barn Farm, Peel Cottage Road, Walsden, Todmorden, OL14 7QJ. Prop: Graeme Roberts. Tel: (01706) 815005. Web: www.magpie-books.co.uk. Private premises. Internet and Postal. Appointment necessary. Medium stock. PR: £5–2,000. CC: AE; JCB; MC; V. Mem: Ibooknet. Notes: *Large general stock.*

WAKEFIELD

Westgate End Bookshop and Gallery, ■ 166 Westgate, Wakefield, WF2 9SR. Prop: Tim Burton. Tel: 01924 377509. Est: 1998. Shop. Open: **T:** 09:30–16:30; **W:** 09:30–16:30; **Th:** 09:30–16:30; **F:** 09:30–16:30; **S:** 09:30–16:30.

WETHERBY

Steve Schofield Golf Books, 29 Nichols Way, Wetherby, LS22 6AD. Tel: (01937) 581276. Fax: (01937) 581276. Est: 1993. Private premises. Postal only. Contactable. Open: **M:** 09:00–17:00; **T:** 09:00–17:00; **W:** 09:00–17:00; **Th:** 09:00–17:00; **F:** 09:00–17:00. Small stock. Spec: Sport - Golf. PR: £10–1,500. CC: MC; V.

WILTSHIRE

BRADFORD ON AVON

Ex Libris, ■ 1 The Shambles, Bradford on Avon, BA15 1JS. Prop: Jim Wolland & Carole Stone. Tel: (01225) 863595. Fax: (01225) 863595. Est: 1980. Internet and Postal. Shop open: **M:** 09:00–17:30; **T:** 09:00–17:30; **W:** 09:00–17:30; **Th:** 09:00–17:30; **F:** 09:00–17:30; **S:** 09:00–17:30. PR: £1–10. CC: AE; JCB; MC. Mem: BA. Notes: *Also new books.*

CALNE

Clive Farahar & Sophie Dupre, Horsebrook House, XV The Green, Calne, SN11 8DQ. Tel: (01249) 821121. Fax: (01249) 821202. Web: www.farahardupre.co.uk. Est: 1978. Private premises. Internet and Postal. Appointment necessary. Open: **M:** 09:00–17:00; **T:** 09:00–17:00; **W:** 09:00–17:00; **Th:** 09:00–17:00; **F:** 09:00–17:00; **S:** 10:00–13:00; Closed for lunch: 13:00–14:00. Large stock. Spec: Antiquarian; Autographs; Documents - General; Letters; Literature; Manuscripts; Photography; Royalty - General. PR: £10–10,000. CC: AE; JCB; MC; V; Delta, Maestro, Connect, Debit. Corresp: French. Mem: ABA; ILAB; PADA, Manuscript Society. VAT No: GB 341 0770 87.

Michael Rogers, 1 Derry Hill Farm, Old Derry Hill, Calne, SN11 9PJ. Prop: Michael Rogers. Tel: 01249 650050. Est: 1996. Private premises. Postal only. Spec: Author - Shelley, Percy B; Author - Wilson, Colin; Beat Writers; Counterculture. Corresp: German.

CHIPPENHAM

Vernon Askew Books, Preston East Farm, Nr. Lyneham, Chippenham, SN15 4DX. Prop: Vernon Askew. Tel: (01249) 892177 and 890846. Fax: (01249) 892177. Est: 1997. Storeroom; Appointment necessary. Very large stock. Spec: Alpinism/Mountaineering; Aviation; Bibliography; Biography; Bull Fighting; Byzantium; Churchilliana; Countries - Cyprus. PR: £3–75. Corresp: Swedish. Notes: *Contactable all week but by appointment.*

Ben Bass, Greyne House Marshfield, Chippenham, SN14 8LU. Tel: (01225) 891279. Est: 1989. Storeroom; Internet and Postal. Telephone First. Open: **M:** 08:00–20:00; **T:** 08:00–20:00; **W:** 08:00–20:00; **Th:** 08:00–20:00; **F:** 08:00–20:00. Large stock. Spec: Author - Bates, H.E.; Author - Chesterton, G.K.; Author - Cunningham-Grahame, R.B.; Author - Durrell, Gerald; Author - Machen, Arthur; Author - Morris, William; Author - Simenon, Georges; Author - Tangye, D. PR: £2–20. CC: PayPal. Corresp: French, German, Italian, Spanish. Notes: *Street car parking is still reasonably easy.*

Granny's Attic, ■The Old Citadel, Attic Rooms, Bath Road, Chippenham, SN15 2AA. Tel: 01249 715327. Est: 2005. Shop open: **M:** 09:45–16:00; **T:** 09:45–16:00; **W:** 09:45–16:00; **Th:** 09:45–16:00; **F:** 09:45–16:00; **S:** 09:45–16:00. Notes: *General stock.*

Tony Pollastrone Railway Books, 4, Wells Close, Chippenham, SN14 0QD. Prop: Tony Pollastrone. Tel: 01249 444298. Web: www.tp-railbooks.co.uk. Est: 2000. Private premises. Internet and Postal. Appointment necessary. Open: **M:** 09:00–17:30; **T:** 09:00–17:30; **W:** 09:00–17:30; **Th:** 09:00–17:30; **F:** 09:00–17:30; **S:** 09:00–17:30; **Su:** 09:00–17:30; Closed for lunch: 13:00–14:00. Spec: Canals/Inland Waterways; History - Industrial; Public Transport; Railways and Railroads. CC: MC; V; Switch/ Maestro. Cata: Railways, Canals, and General Interest. VAT No: GB 840 9362 23.

COLERNE

Chris Phillips, 28 Roundbarrow Close, Colerne, Chippenham, SN14 8EF. Prop: Chris Phillips. Tel: (01225) 742755. Fax: 0870 8312098. Est: 1997. Private premises. Small stock. Spec: Antiquarian; Antiques; Archaeology - Industrial; Architecture; Art; Children's - Illustrated; Illustrated - General; Literature. PR: £1–500. CC: JCB; MC; V; most Major Cards. Corresp: French. Mem: PBFA. Notes: *Booksearch, Valuations for Insurance or Probate. Books purchased.*

CORSHAM

Ashwell Books, Lower Leaze House, Bath Road, Box, Corsham, SN13 8DU. Prop: J. De Normann. Tel: (01225) 742786. Est: 1960. Private premises. Postal only. Appointment necessary. Spec: Botany; Gardening - General. PR: £5–100. Corresp: French, Italian, Spanish.

DEVIZES

D'Arcy Books, ■The Chequers, High Street, Devizes, SN10 1AT. Prop: Colin & Jenifer MacGregor. Tel: Shop (01380) 726922. Est: 1974. Shop open: **M:** 10:00–17:00; **T:** 10:00–17:00; **W:** 10:00–17:00; **Th:** 10:00–17:00; **F:** 10:00–17:00; **S:** 10:00–17:00. Large stock. Spec: Archaeology; Architecture; Arts, The; Aviation; Children's; Cookery/Gastronomy; Fiction - General; Gardening - General. VAT No: GB 196 1414 55. Notes: *Also, a booksearch, bookbinding & repair service.*

Enigma Books, 3 Carriage Court, Station Road, Devizes, SN10 1AB. Prop: A.E.R.M. Stevens. Tel: (01380) 738414. Est: 1976. Private premises. Postal only. Appointment necessary. Small stock. Spec: Fiction - Crime, Detective, Spy, Thrillers; Fiction - Fantasy, Horror; Fiction - Supernatural; First Editions; Ghosts; Literature - Victorian; Occult; Supernatural. PR: £5–1,000. Cata: Victorian & Edwardian Fiction.

MALMESBURY

Earth Science Books, Old Swan House, Swan Barton, Sherston, Malmesbury, SN16 0LJ. Prop: Geoff Carss. Tel: (01666) 840995. Web: www.earthsciencebooks.com. Est: 2002. Private premises. Internet and Postal. Contactable. Small stock. Spec: Academic/Scholarly; Animals and Birds; Antiquarian; Archaeology; Coastal Defence; Conchology (see also Malacology); Conservation; Evolution. PR: £3–10,000. Notes: *Specialist in Geology, Palaeontology, Mineralogy books - regional memoirs and pre-1850 geological related material.*

MARLBOROUGH

Anthony Spranger, 67 London Road, Marlborough, SN8 2AJ. Prop: Anthony Spranger. Tel: 01672 516338. Private premises. Book fairs only. Telephone First. Spec: Alpinism/Mountaineering; Army, The; Art - British; Art Reference; Autobiography; Biography; Broadcasting; Churchilliana. CC: AE; JCB; MC; V; Switch. Corresp: French. Mem: PBFA. VAT No: GB 639 6193 04.

John Bevan Catholic Bookseller, Romans Halt, Mildenhall, Marlborough, SN8 2LX. Prop: John Bevan. Tel: (01672) 519817. Web: www.catholic-books.co.uk. Est: 1978. Storeroom; Internet and Postal. Telephone First. Medium stock. Spec: Religion - Catholic; Religion - Christian; Theology. PR: £1–500. CC: AE; MC; V. Cata: Roman Catholic Literature. Corresp: French, German. Mem: PBFA.

Katharine House Gallery, ■Katharine House, The Parade, Marlborough, SN8 1NE. Prop: Christopher Gange. Tel: (01672) 514040. Web: www.katharinehousegallery.co.uk. Est: 1983. Shop open: **T:** 10:00–17:30; **W:** 10:00–17:30; **Th:** 10:00–17:30; **F:** 10:00–17:30; **S:** 10:00–17:30. Medium stock. Spec: Antiquarian; Art; Illustrated - General; Modern First Editions. PR: £3–300. CC: MC; V. Notes: *Also, 20thC British art and antiques.*

Military Parade Bookshop, The Parade, Marlborough, SN8 1NE. Prop: Graham & Peter Kent. Tel: (01672) 515470. Fax: (01980) 630150. Web: www.militaryparadebooks.com. Est: 1988. Spec: Aviation; Maritime/Nautical; Military History. PR: £2–150.

Nevis Railway Bookshops, ■Katharine House Gallery, The Parade, Marlborough, SN8 1NE. Prop: N.J. Bridger. Tel: Shop (01672) 514040. Web: www.nevis-railway-bookshops.co.uk. Est: 1988. Shop open: **T:** 10:00–17:30; **W:** 10:00–17:30; **Th:** 10:00–17:30; **F:** 10:00–17:30; **S:** 10:00–17:30; Closed for lunch: 13:00–14:15. Medium stock. Spec: Archaeology; Canals/Inland Waterways; Railways and Railroads. PR: £1–75. Notes: *Alt. tel no: 01635 200507. Stock includes 50,000 photos. Railway Book and Magazine Search, Newbury, Berks (q.v.) Nevis Railway Bookshop, Goring-on-Thames, Oxon (q.v.) Mainly industrial archeology.*

POTTERNE

M Godding Ltd, 22 Highlands, Potterne, SN10 5NS. Prop: Mark Godding. Tel: 01380 727872. Fax: 01380 726531. Web: www.mgodding,com. Est: 2006. Office and/or bookroom; Internet only. Telephone First. Open: **M:** 09:00–17:30; **T:** 09:00–17:30; **W:** 09:00–17:30; **Th:** 09:00–17:30; **F:** 09:00–17:30; **S:** 09:00–17:30; **Su:** 09:00–17:30; Closed for lunch: 13:00–14:00. Spec: General Stock. CC: AE; MC; V; PayPal. Notes: *Please feel free to contact us about book enquiries. We sell and buy used books.*

RAMSBURY

Heraldry Today, ■ Parliament Piece, Ramsbury, Nr. Marlborough, SN8 2QH. Prop: Rosemary Pinches. Tel: (01672) 520617. Fax: (01672) 520183. Web: www.heraldrytoday.co.uk. Est: 1954. Shop open: **M:** 10:00–16:00; **T:** 10:00–16:00; **W:** 10:00–16:00; **Th:** 10:00–16:00; **F:** 10:00–13:00. Large stock. Spec: Biography; Ex-Libris; Genealogy; Heraldry; History - General; Royalty - General; School Registers/ Rolls of Honour; Booksearch. PR: £1–5,000. CC: E; MC; V; Maestro. Cata: heraldry, genealogy and peerage. Corresp: French. Mem: ABA; ILAB. VAT No: GB 238 8244 41. Notes: *Also, back-numbers of journals, new books, periodicals & a booksearch service.*

SALISBURY

Badger, Boxwood, Broad Chalke, Salisbury, SP5 5EP. Prop: Peter Bletsoe. Tel: (01722) 326033. Est: 1987. Market stand/stall; Shop open: **M:** 10:00–17:00; **T:** 10:00–17:00; **W:** 10:00–17:00; **Th:** 10:00–17:00; **F:** 10:00–17:00; **S:** 10:00–17:00. Small stock. Spec: Prints and Maps. PR: £5–200. CC: AE; D; E; JCB; MC; V.

Ellwood Books, ■ 38 Winchester Street, Salisbury, SP1 1HG. Prop: Mark Harrison. Tel: (01722) 322975. Web: www.ellwoodbooks.com. Est: 2001. Shop open: **M:** 10:00–17:00; **T:** 10:00–17:00; **W:** 10:00–17:00; **Th:** 10:00–17:00; **F:** 10:00–17:00; **S:** 10:00–17:00. Medium stock. Spec: Alternative Medicine; Antiquarian; Archaeology; Art - British; Celtica; Fiction - General; Fine & Rare; Folio Society, The. PR: £1–50. CC: AE; D; E; JCB; MC; V; switch/Solo. Mem: PBFA. VAT No: GB 832 0693 40. Notes: *Also attends London HD bookfairs, PBFA fairs & Internet trading.*

John & Judith Head, ■The Barn Book Supply, 88 Crane Street, Salisbury, SP1 2QD. Prop: John and Judith Head. Tel: (01722) 327767. Fax: (01722) 339888. Web: www.johnandjudithhead.co.uk. Est: 1958. Appointment necessary. Shop open: **M:** 10:00–17:00; **T:** 10:00–17:00; **W:** 10:00–17:00; **Th:** 10:00–17:00; **F:** 10:00–17:00; Closed for lunch: 13.00–14.00. Medium stock. Spec: Author - Edwards, Lionel; Dogs; Fisheries; Fishes; Sport - Angling/Fishing; Sport - Archery; Sport - Big Game Hunting; Sport - Coursing. PR: £1–18,000. CC: AE; D; E; JCB; MC; V; Mae, So. Cata: angling and field sports. Mem: ABA; ILAB. VAT No: GB 188 9664 84. Notes: *Open on Saturday by appointment.*

Rosemary Pugh Books, 59b Old Sarum Airfield, Salisbury, SP4 6DZ. Prop: Mrs. R M Pugh, Mr J M Pugh, Mr A.E. Pugh. Tel: 01722 330132. Fax: 01722 330132. Web: www.rosemarypughbooks.co.uk. Est: 1990. Storeroom; Internet and Postal. Telephone First. Open: **M:** 08:00–16:00; **T:** 08:00–16:00; **W:** 08:00–16:00; **Th:** 08:00–16:00. Spec: Bibles; Ecclesiastical History & Architecture; Ecology; Feminism; Gnostics / Gnosticism; Holocaust; Hymnology; Iconography. CC: JCB; MC; V; Delta, Maestro, Solo, Fortoak. Cata: Areas within Theology. Mem: PBFA; FSB. VAT No: GB 699 1250 01.

SWINDON

Peter Barnes, 138 Ermin Street, Stratton St Margaret, Swindon, SN3 4NQ. Prop: Peter Barnes. Tel: (01793) 821327. Est: 2001. Private premises. Postal only. Small stock. Spec: Aviation; History - General; Magazines & Periodicals - General; Military; Military History; Naval; Topography - General; Topography - Local. PR: £1–50. Notes: *Exhibits at book fairs.*

Bookmark (Children's Books), Fortnight, Wick Down, Broad Hinton, Swindon, SN4 9NR. Prop: Anne & Leonora Excell. Tel: (01793) 731693. Fax: (01793) 731782. Est: 1973. Private premises. Internet and Postal. Appointment necessary. Open: **M:** 09:00–18:00; **T:** 09:00–18:00; **W:** 09:00–18:00; **Th:** 09:00–18:00; **F:** 09:00–18:00; **S:** 10:00–18:00. Medium stock. Spec: Annuals; Antiquarian; Author - Aesop; Author - Ahlberg, Janet & Allan; Author - Aldin, Cecil; Author - Ardizzone, Edward; Author - Ballantyne, Robert M.; Author - Barker, Cecily M. PR: £5–2,000. CC: E; JCB; MC; V; Maestro Delta. Cata: Childrens Books and related juvenilia. Mem: PBFA. Notes: *Main PBFA bookfairs. Also, a specialist booksearch service leonora-excell@btconnect.com.*

Collectors Corner, ■ 227 Kingshill, Swindon, SN1 4NG. Prop: Fred Stevens. Tel: (01793) 521545. Est: 1986. Postal and shop, open: **M:** 10:30–16:30; **T:** 10:30–16:30; **Th:** 10:30–16:30; **F:** 10:30–16:30; **S:** 10:30–16:30; Closed for lunch: 12:00–12:30. Small stock. Spec: Collecting; Military; Railways and Railroads; Topography - Local; Transport; Collectables; Ephemera; Prints and Maps. PR: £1–100. Notes: *Stock includes: postcards, cigarette cards, coins, medals, badges, toys, and ephemera.*

Ice House Books, Hard Crag, Foxhill, Swindon, SN4 0DR. Prop: Mr Simon Miles. Tel: 01793 791975. Web: www.icehousebooks.co.uk. Est: 2000. Warehouse; Internet and Postal. Appointment necessary. Shop at: Unit A Pigeon House Lane, Stratton St. Margaret, Swindon, SN3 4QH. Open: **M:** 09:00–18:00; **T:** 09:00–18:00; **W:** 09:00–18:00; **Th:** 09:00–18:00; **F:** 09:00–18:00; **S:** 09:00–18:00; **Su:** 09:00–18:00; Closed for lunch: 13:00–14:00. Spec: Academic/Scholarly; Arts, The; Author - Francis, Dick; Author - Pratchett, Terry; Evolution; History - General; Natural History; Philology. CC: MC; V; SW. Cata: website updates. Notes: *Spec. Academic and professional non-fiction; sciences; arts; social sciences; equestrian; classics; politics; humanities. Relocated under new ownership from Leicester.*

WARMINSTER

Sturford Books, Landfall, 35 Corton, Warminster, BA12 0SY. Prop: Robert Mayall. Tel: (01985) 850478/85058. Est: 1993. Private premises. Postal only. Appointment necessary. Small stock. Spec: Archaeology - Industrial; Art; Autobiography; Biography; Fiction - General; Fiction - Historical; Foreign Texts; History - General. PR: £5–800. CC: JCB; MC; V. Cata: History, Literature and Travel.

WESTBURY

Aardvark Books, 50 Bratton Road, Westbury, BA13 3EP. Prop: Clive & Caroline Williams. Tel: (01225) 867723. Fax: (01225) 867723. Web: www.aardvarkmilitarybooks.com. Est: 1998. Private premises. Internet and Postal. Telephone First. Open: **M:** 09:00–19:00; **T:** 09:00–19:00; **W:** 09:00–19:00; **Th:** 09:00–19:00; **F:** 09:00–19:00; **S:** 09:00–19:00; **Su:** 09:00–19:00. Large stock. Spec: Aircraft; Armed Forces - Australian Air Force; Armed Forces - Australian Army; Armed Forces - Australian Navy; Arms & Armour; Army, The; Company History; Heraldry. PR: £5–250. CC: MC; V; SWITCH. Notes: *We are a family run, military history dealership. We have a wide range of stock but specialise in WWI and WWII.*

Zardoz Books, 20 Whitecroft, Dilton Marsh, Westbury, BA13 4DJ. Prop: M Flanagan. Tel: (01373) 865371. Web: www.zardozbooks.co.uk. Est: 1990. Warehouse; Internet and Postal. Appointment necessary. Very large stock. Spec: Author - Lovecraft, H.P.; Author - Rohmer, Sax; Author - Wallace, Edgar; Beat Writers; Books about Books; Cinema/Film; Crime (True); Erotica. PR: £2–100. CC: MC; V. Notes: *50000 plus paperback and hardcover mainly fiction plus collectors books and magazines. Areas SF, Horror, Crime, Western, Adventure etc.*

WOOTTON BASSETT

G. Jackson, 10 Dryden Place, Wootton Bassett, SN4 8JP. Prop: Geoffrey Jackson. Tel: (01793) 849660. Fax: (01793) 849660. Est: 2001. Private premises. Appointment necessary. Open: **M:** 09:30–17:30; **T:** 09:30–17:30; **W:** 09:30–17:30; **Th:** 09:30–17:30; **F:** 09:30–17:30. Small stock. Spec: Antiquarian; Antiques; Art Reference; Author - Graves, Robert; Bibliography; Children's; Children's - Illustrated; Countries - India. PR: £25–9,000. CC: MC; V; PayPal.

WORCESTERSHIRE

BESFORD

Louise Ross Books, 28 Besford Court, Besford, Nr. Worcester, WR8 9LZ. Tel: (01368) 550461. Est: 1977. Private premises. Postal only. Contactable. Small stock. Spec: Children's; Illustrated - General; Literature. PR: £25–5,000.

BEWDLEY

Clent Books of Bewdley, Rose Cottage, Habberley Road, Bewdley, DY12 1JA. Prop: Ivor Simpson. Tel: (01299) 401090. Web: www.clentbooks.co.uk. Est: 1977. Private premises. Internet and Postal. Medium stock. Spec: Antiquarian; Author - Read, Miss; Author - Young, Francis Brett; Autobiography; Biography; Fiction - General; General; History - General. PR: £20–200.

DROITWICH

Grant Books, The Coach House, New Road, Cutnall Green, Droitwich, WR9 0PQ. Prop: Bob & Shirley Grant. Tel: (01299) 851588. Fax: (01299) 851446. Web: www.grantbooks-memorabilia.com. Est: 1972. Office and/or bookroom; Internet and Postal. Shop open: **M:** 09:00–17:00; **T:** 09:00–17:00; **W:** 09:00–17:00; **Th:** 09:00–17:00; **F:** 09:00–17:00. Small stock. Spec: Antiquarian; Sport - Golf. PR: £10–2,500. CC: AE; D; MC; V; US dollars. Cata: Golf and related books and ephemera. Mem: PBFA; BGCS; GCS(USA). VAT No: GB 275 8638 10. Notes: *Golf Books small stock around 300 listed on our website. Publishing Golf books.*

DROITWICH SPA

M. & D. Books, ■ 16 High Street, Droitwich Spa, WR9 8EW. Prop: Mike Hebden. Tel: (01905) 775814. Est: 1996. Internet and Postal. Shop open: **T:** 10:00–17:00; **W:** 10:00–17:00; **Th:** 10:00–17:00; **F:** 10:00–17:00; **S:** 09:30–17:00. Medium stock. Spec: Topography - Local. PR: £1–250. CC: JCB; MC; V; Maestro, Solo.

GREAT MALVERN

The Malvern Bookshop, ■ 7 Abbey Road, Great Malvern, WR14 3ES. Prop: Howard and Julie Hudson. Tel: (01684) 575915. Fax: (01684) 575915. Est: 1955. Shop open: **M:** 10:00–17:00; **T:** 10:00–17:00; **W:** 10:00–17:00; **F:** 10:00–17:00; **S:** 10:00–17:00. Large stock. Spec: Antiques; Architecture; Art; Aviation; Bindings; Biography; Books about Books; Children's. PR: £1–1,000. Notes: *Also, a booksearch service.*

Wildside Books, Rectory House, 26 Priory Road, Great Malvern, WR14 3DR. Prop: Chris & Christine Johnson. Tel: (01684) 562818. Fax: (01684) 566491. Web: www.wildsidebooks.co.uk. Est: 1982. Private premises. Internet and Postal. Appointment necessary. Small stock. Spec: Art; Natural History; New Naturalist; Ornithology; Zoology. PR: £20–20,000. CC: MC; V; SW, Mae. Cata: Ornithology; Natural History; Naturalists' Travel. Notes: *We are biased toward ornithology where we aim to source the best available copies for the collector. We sell many books to clients via their 'wants' list, and recommend you lodge your list with us. The New Naturalists is another speciality.*

KIDDERMINSTER

M. & M. Baldwin, ■ 24 High St, Cleobury Mortimer, Kidderminster, DY14 8BY. Prop: Mark & Myfanwy Baldwin. Tel: (01299) 270110. Web: www.enigmatixuk.com. Est: 1978. Shop open: **W:** 14:00–18:00; **S:** 10:00–18:00; Closed for lunch: 13:00–14:00. Medium stock. Spec: Author - Rolt, L.T.C.; Aviation; Canals/Inland Waterways; Crafts; Cryptography; Espionage; History - Industrial; Maritime/Nautical. PR: £1–500. CC: MC; V. Corresp: French. Mem: Fedn of Small Businesses. VAT No: GB 547 6638 05. Notes: *We also publish books on, and give presentations and demonstrations on, WW2 Codebreaking (Enigma, Bletchley Park, etc).*

Lion Books, ■ 52 Blackwell St, Kidderminster, DY10 2EE. Prop: Colin Raxter. Tel: (0156) 745060. Web: www.lionbooks.co.uk. Est: 1987. Shop open: **T:** 10:30–17:00; **Th:** 10:30–17:00; **F:** 10:30–17:00; **S:** 10:30–14:00; Closed for lunch: 13:00–14:00. Medium stock. Spec: Counties in England; Sport - Angling/Fishing; Sport - Cricket; Sport - Football (Soccer); Sport - Motor Racing; Sport - Rugby. PR: £1–1,000. CC: E; JCB; MC; V; Paypal. Mem: PBFA. Notes: *Telephone advisable, due to book fair/ buying commitments and not all stock available in shop.*

Salsus Books, Elderfield Gardens, 42 Coventry Street, Kidderminster, DY10 2BT. Prop: Dr. D.T. Salt. Tel: (01562) 742081. Fax: (01562) 824583. Est: 1991. Private premises. Internet and Postal. Appointment necessary. Medium stock. Spec: Academic/Scholarly; Anthropology; Ecclesiastical History & Architecture; Religion - General; Religion - Catholic; Religion - Christian; Religion - Christianity, Syrian Orthodox; Theology. PR: £1–250. CC: JCB; MC; V; SW. Cata: theology religion. Mem: PBFA. Notes: *books bought and sold in specialist areas: 'irvingites' catholic apostolic church, syriaca, eastern churches, academic theology, religion, anthropology.*

MALVERN

Jonathan Gibbs Books, The Lakes Cottages, Drake Street, Welland, Malvern, WR13 6LN. Prop: Jonathan and Angela Gibbs. Tel: (01684) 593169. Web: www.jgibbsbooks.co.uk. Est: 2001. Private premises. Internet and Postal. Appointment necessary. Small stock. Spec: Academic/Scholarly; Antiquarian; Literature; Music - General; Music - Classical; Music - Illustrated Sheet Music; Music - Printed, Sheet Music & Scores; Performing Arts. PR: £10–1,000. CC: AE; MC; V. Cata: music. Mem: PBFA.

Golden Age Books, PO Box 45, Malvern, WR14 1XT. Prop: Tony Byatt, Adrian and Gillian Ainge. Tel: (01684) 578419. Web: www.ukbookworld.com/members/goldenage. Est: 1981. Private premises. Internet and Postal. Appointment necessary. Small stock. Spec: Academic/Scholarly; Archaeology; Bibles; Biblical Studies; History - Ancient; Judaica; Religion - General; Religion - Christian. PR: £1–500. CC: E; JCB; MC; V; Maestro, Switch. Cata: English Bibles, translations and texts, & related. Notes: *We also sell new Bibles and books on the Bible, and Bible study aids including study of Hebrew and Greek. 3 printed catalogues a year, plus online/email catalogues available on request.*

Worcester Rare Books, 73 Spring Lane, Malvern, WR14 1AJ. Prop: D.I. Lloyd. Tel: 01684 892155. Est: 1972. Private premises. Internet and Postal. Appointment necessary. Very small stock. Spec: Academic/Scholarly; Antiquarian; Architecture; Medicine; Philosophy; Religion - General; Science - General; Science - History of. PR: £10–200. CC: MC; V. Cata: occasionally. Corresp: French, German. Mem: PBFA.

MALVERN WELLS

Valerie Merritt, Pear Tree House, 17 King Edwards Road, Malvern Wells, WR14 4AJ. Tel: 01684 566777. Fax: 01684 566777. Est: 1975. Private premises. Postal only. Appointment necessary. Spec: Gardening - General; Horticulture; Parks and gardens; Plant Hunting; Pomology. Cata: Gardens, Garden Design, Plant Hunting, etc.

PERSHORE

Coach House Books, ■ 17a Bridge Street, Pershore, WR10 1AJ. Prop: Michael & Sue Ellingworth. Tel: (01386) 554633. Fax: (01386) 554633. Est: 1982. Telephone First. Shop open: **W:** 09:00–17:00. Medium stock. Spec: Architecture; Art; Art Reference; Author - Lawrence, T.E.; Biography; Counties in England; Folio Society, The; Horticulture. PR: £5–2,000. CC: AE; D; MC; V. Corresp: French. Mem: BA. VAT No: GB 396 2460 27.

Ian K. Pugh Books, ■ 40 Bridge Street, Pershore, WR10 1AT. Tel: (01386) 552681. Mob: 07968429112. Est: 1974. Shop open: **M:** 10:30–15:30; **T:** 10:30–15:30; **W:** 10:30–15:30; **Th:** 10:30–15:30; **F:** 10:30–15:30; **S:** 09:30–17:00. Medium stock. Spec: Fine Art; Horticulture; Illustrated - General; Collectables. PR: £1–7,000. Notes: *My opening times are dictated to a large extent by school picking up times so in the school holidays I try to open longer till 5pm if possible. Ringing first before a special trip is advisable.*

Sedgeberrow Books, ■ 25 High Street, Pershore, WR10 1AA. Prop: Mrs. Jayne Winter. Tel: (01386) 751830. Web: www.sedgeberrowbooks.co.uk. Est: 1985. Shop open: **M:** 9:00–17:00; **T:** 9:00–17:00; **W:** 09:00–17:00; **Th:** 09:00–17:00; **F:** 09:00–17:00; **S:** 09:00–17:00. Very Large stock. Spec: Author - Moore, John; Author - Young, Francis Brett; Aviation; History - Local; Military; Mind, Body & Spirit; Railways and Railroads; Steam Engines; Topography - General. PR: £1–300. CC: MC; V; Switch. Cata: occasionally.

STOURPORT

P. and P. Books, Dairy Cottage, Yarhampton, Stourport, DY13 0UY. Prop: J.S. Pizey. Tel: (01299) 896996. Fax: (01299) 896996. Est: 1982. Private premises. Telephone First. Small stock. Spec: Archaeology; Countries - Arabia; Countries - Arabian Peninsula; Countries - Egypt; Countries - Holy Land, The; Countries - Middle East, The; Countries - Sudan; Egyptology. PR: £5–2,000. CC: None. Cata: Egyptology and archaeology of the Middle East. Corresp: French. Mem: ABA. VAT No: GB 441 7426 59. Notes: *Early (19-18th C.) travel in Egypt and the Middle East. Egyptology.*

WORCESTER

Ann & Mike Conry, 14 St George's Square, Worcester, WR1 1HX. Tel: 01905 25330. Web: www.abe.com. Est: 1998. Private premises. Internet and Postal. Spec: History - Irish; Irish Interest; Literary Criticism; Literary Travel; Literature; Literature - Irish; Modern First Editions; Politics. Notes: *For sale through Abe but direct contact available. Specialists in football, Irish interest and modern firsts.*

Bookworms of Evesham, ■81 Port Street, Evesham, Worcester, WR11 3LF. Prop: T.J. Sims. Tel: (01386) 45509. Est: 1971. Shop open: **T:** 10:00–17:00; **W:** 10:00–17:00; **Th:** 10:00–17:00; **F:** 10:00–17:00; **S:** 10:00–17:00. Medium stock. Spec: Art; History - General; Literature; Military; Topography - Local; Transport; Travel - General. Mem: PBFA. Notes: *Fairs attended: Cheltenham, Bath, Cirencester; and Churchdown Book Fair (organiser).*

Restormel Books, 1 East Comer, St. John's, Worcester, WR2 6BE. Prop: Roy Slade. Tel: (01905) 422290. Est: 1978. Display/stand; Shop open: **M:** 10:00–17:00; **T:** 10:00–17:00; **W:** 10:00–17:00; **Th:** 10:00–17:00; **F:** 10:00–17:00; **S:** 10:00–17:00. Small stock. Spec: Collecting; Topography - Local; Collectables. PR: £1–50. Corresp: French, Spanish.

CHANNEL ISLANDS

JERSEY

ST. HELIER

Books and Things Limited, ■ First Tower, St. Helier, Jersey, JE2 3LN. Prop: Sarah Burrow. Tel: 01534 759949. Fax: n/a. Web: www.newnats.com. Est: 1998. Shop open: **M:** 10:00–16:00; **T:** 10:00–16:00; **W:** 10:00–16:00; **Th:** 10:00–16:00; **F:** 10:00–16:00; **S:** 10:00–16:00; **Su:** 10:00–16:00. Medium stock. Spec: Countries - Channel Islands, The; Natural History; New Naturalist. PR: £1–5,000. Corresp: English.

GUERNSEY

ST PETER PORT

Early Times, Suite 5, Manor House, Les Vardes, St. Peter Port, Guernsey GY1 1BG. Prop: David Godfrey. Tel: 01481 725168. Fax: 01481 725168. Web: www.earlytimes.gg. Est: 1972 Mail order only, Internet and postal. Very large stock. PR: £10 – 30,000. CC: MC, V. Corresp: Spanish. Mem: Ephemera Socciety. Notes: We specialise in mainly single issues of antique newspapers, from 1665-1945.

VALE

Channel Islands Galleries Limited, ■ Les Clospains Rue de L'Ecole, Vale, Guernsey, GY3 5LL. Prop: Geoffrey P. & Christine M. Gavey. Tel: Shop (01481) 247337. Fax: (01481) 243538. Est: 1967. Shop. and post. Shop open: **M:** 10:00–17:00; **T:** 10:00–17:00; **W:** 10:00–17:00; **Th:** 10:00–13:00; **F:** 10:00–17:00; **S:** 10:00–13:00. Small stock. Spec: Antiquarian; Atlases; History - General; Natural History; Topography - General; Topography - Local; Prints and Maps. PR: £5–4,000. CC: E; MC; V. Corresp: French, German. Notes: *Also, antique maps, prints, watercolours and paintings - featuring The Channel Islands, coins & CI bank notes.*

ISLE OF MAN

Garretts Antiquarian Books, 4 Summerhill, Douglas, IM2 4PJ. Prop: Mr. Jonathon Hall. Tel: (01624) 675065. Est: 1987. Private premises. Internet and Postal. Telephone First. Small stock. Spec: Countries - Isle of Man; History - Local; Topography - Local. PR: £1–1,000. Mem: PBFA.

PORT ERIN

Bridge Bookshop Ltd, Shore Road, Port Erin, IM9 6HL. Tel: 01624 833376. Fax: 01624 835381.

NORTHERN IRELAND

CO. ANTRIM

BELFAST

The Bookstore, ■ 21 North Street, Belfast, BT1 1NA. Prop: W. Burlingham. Tel: . Shop open: **M:** 11:00–17:00; **T:** 11:00–17:00; **W:** 11:00–17:00; **Th:** 11:00–17:00; **F:** 11:00–17:00; **S:** 11:00–17:00. Notes: *General stock.*

Evangelical Bookshop, ■ 15 College Square East, Belfast, Co. Antrim, BT1 6DD. Tel: (028) 9032-0529. Fax: (028) 9043-8330. Est: 1926. Shop open: **M:** 09:00–17:30; **T:** 09:00–17:30; **W:** 09:00–17:30; **Th:** 09:00–17:30; **F:** 09:00–17:30; **S:** 09:00–17:30. Spec: Religion - Christian; Theology. PR: £1–150. CC: MC; V. Mem: BA. Notes: *Also, Christian booksellers.*

P. & B. Rowan, Carleton House, 92 Malone Road, Belfast, BT9 5HP. Prop: Peter & Briad Rowan. Tel: (028) 9066-6448. Fax: (028) 9066-3725. Est: 1973. Private premises. Appointment necessary. Large stock. Spec: Academic/Scholarly; Antiquarian; Archives; Countries - Ireland; Economics; Fine & Rare; History - Irish; Irish History & Literature. PR: £2–25. CC: MC; V. Cata: Irish History, Literature, & Antiquarian. Corresp: French. Mem: PBFA; IADA.

LISBURN

JIRI Books, 11 Mill Road, Lisburn, BT27 5TT. Prop: Jim and Rita Swindall. Tel: 028 90826443. Fax: 028 90826443. Est: 1978. Private premises. Internet and Postal. Appointment necessary. Spec: Author - Heaney, Seamus; Countries - Ireland; History - Irish; Irish Interest. CC: MC; V. Cata: Irish interest. Notes: *Long established secondhand and antiquarian booksellers specialising in books of Irish interest. Founders and organisers of the annual Belfast Book Fair, which takes place on the second Saturday in November in the Wellington Park Hotel.*

CO. ARMAGH

ARMAGH

Craobh Rua Books, 12 Woodford Gardens, Armagh, BT60 2AZ. Prop: James Vallely. Tel: (028) 3752-6938. Est: 1990. Private premises. Internet and Postal. Appointment necessary. Medium stock. Spec: Antiquarian; Author - James, Henry; Author - Machen, Arthur; Author - Tourtel, M; Author - Yeats, W.B.; Bull Fighting; Churchilliana; Countries - Antarctic, The. PR: £1–400. CC: MC; V. Cata: Irish Related. Corresp: French. Notes: *Also, a booksearch service.*

CO. DERRY

LONDONDERRY

Foyle Books, ■ 12 Magazine Street, Londonderry, BT48 6HH. Prop: Ken Thatcher and Art Byrne. Tel: 02871372530. Est: 1980. Shop open: **M:** 11:00–17:00; **T:** 11:00–17:00; **W:** 11:00–17:00; **Th:** 11:00–17:00; **F:** 11:00–17:00; **S:** 10:00–17:00. Spec: Countries - Ireland; History - Irish; Literature - Irish. Cata: Irish History, Literature, Theology.

George Harris, 163 Legavallon Road Dungiven, Londonderry, BT47 4QN. Prop: George Harris. Tel: (02877) 740012. Est: 1976. Private premises. Appointment necessary. Medium stock. Spec: Aeronautics; Arms & Armour; Aviation; Irish Interest; Military; Military History; Naval; War - General. PR: £5–500. Corresp: French. Mem: PBFA. Notes: *Attends PBFA fairs.*

CO. DOWN

BALLYGOWAN

Saintfield Antiques & Fine Books, Vestry Hall, 49 Vestry Road, Ballygowan, BT23 6HQ. Prop: (*) Joseph Leckey. Tel: (028) 97528428. Web: www.antiquesireland.com. Est: 1988. Private premises. Internet and Postal. Appointment necessary. Medium stock. Spec: Academic/Scholarly; Aircraft; Art; Broadcasting; Children's; Cinema/Film; Company History; Exploration. PR: £1–500. CC: MC; V. Notes: *Our preferred method of payment is by PayPal, although we accept Sterling cheques and money orders. On www.antiquesireland.com, under how to order and pay, there is a Buy Now icon. This is a direct link to PayPal.*

BALLYNAHINCH

Davidson Books, 34 Broomhill Road, Ballynahinch, BT24 8QD. Prop: Arthur Davidson. Tel: (028) 9756-2502. Fax: (028) 9756-2502. Est: 1958. Private premises. Postal only. Appointment necessary. Medium stock. Spec: History - National; Irish Interest; Literature; Topography - Local; Ephemera; Prints and Maps.

BANGOR

Books Ulster, 12 Bayview Road, Bangor, BT19 6AL. Prop: D.A. Rowlinson. Tel: (028) 914-70310. Web: www.booksulster.com. Est: 1995. Private premises. Postal only. Large stock. Spec: Irish Interest. PR: £1–500. CC: JCB; MC; V.

DONAGHADEE

Prospect House Books, Prospect House, 4 Millisle Road, Donaghadee, BT21 0HY. Web: www.antiquarianbooksellers.co.uk. Est: 1983. Private premises. Internet and Postal. Appointment necessary. Spec: Africana; Agriculture; Animals and Birds; Archaeology; Architecture; Art; Asian Studies; Banking & Insurance. CC: MC; V. Cata: Irish related, ornithology, medicine, religion,. Notes: *Smaller subjects: philosophy, philology, Scotland, Travel.*

HOLYWOOD

The Old Abbey Bookshop, ■ Audley Court, 118 High Street, Holywood, BT18 9HW. Prop: Harold Mitchell. Tel: 028 9042 5472. Est: 1996. Shop open: **T:** 09:00–13:00; **Th:** 09:00–13:00; **S:** 09:00–17:00. Spec: Antiquarian; Children's; Irish Interest; Natural History; Poetry.

CO. FERMANAGH

ENNISKILLEN

John Gowan Books, ■ Drumaraw, Springfield, Enniskillen, Co. Fermanagh, BT74 8AS. Tel: (02866) 341239. Fax: (02866) 341844. Web: www.gowanbooks.com. Est: 1991. Shop open: **M:** 09:00–19:00; **T:** 09:00–19:00; **W:** 09:00–19:00; **Th:** 09:00–19:00; **F:** 09:00–19:00; **S:** 09:00–19:00. Spec: Antiquarian; Irish Interest; Theology. PR: £1–500. CC: MC; V.

LACK

Barnacle Books, Largy, Lack, Enniskillen, County Fermanagh BT93 0DF. Prop: Ken Harron. Tel: 078 166 10875. Web: www.barnaclebooks.com. Est: 2002. Private premises. Internet and postal. Medium stock. Spec: Countries - Ireland; Fine & Rare; First Editions; Irish History & Literature; Irish Interest; Poetry; Sport - Angling/Fishing; Topography - Local. PR: £5-500. Cata: bi-annual on Books related to Ireland.

REPUBLIC OF IRELAND

CO. CAVAN

COOTEHILL

Sillan Books, Richelieu, Drumgreen, Cootehill. Prop: Patricia H. Smyth. Tel: 0044 49 5552343. Fax: 00444 49 5552343. Web: www.abebooks.com. Est: 1990. Mail order only; Postal only. Telephone First. Spec: Antiquarian; Children's; History - General; History - Library; History - Local; Illustrated - General; Irish Interest; Literature - 19th C. CC: MC; V. Cata: Irish/Childrens/Religion/History/ Biography/General. Notes: *Books of Irish Interest-History, local and general, literature, topography, Childrens, Religion, General. Maps and prints.*

CO. CLARE

DOOLIN

Doolin Dinghy Books, ■ Fisher Street, Doolin. Prop: Cynthia Sinnott Griffin. Tel: (065) 70 74449 / 7075980. Est: 1982. Shop open: **M:** 10:00–20:00; **T:** 10:00–20:00; **W:** 10:00–20:00; **Th:** 10:00–20:00; **F:** 10:00–20:00; **S:** 10:00–20:00; **Su:** 12:00–15:00. Small stock. Spec: Adventure; Alternative Medicine; American Indians; Americana - General; Art; Author - 19th Century; Author - Cather, Willa; Author - Cooper, James F. PR: £1–150. Cata: Irish interest/ American Lit/ general. Corresp: French. Mem: ASBI. Notes: *Between November to February, short hours or by appointment. Stock includes Irish, British and American fiction. Alternate tel. No. 065 7075980.*

ENNIS

Orchid Book Distributors, Unit 2 Fitzpatrick Centre, Tulla Road, Ennis. Tel: 00 353 65 6842 862. Fax: 00 353 65 6842 862. Web: www.orchidbooks.org. Est: 2002. Shop and/or showroom; Internet and Postal. Shop open: **T:** 10:00–18:00; **W:** 10:00–18:00; **Th:** 10:00–18:00; **F:** 10:00–18:00; **S:** 10:00–18:00. Closed for lunch: 13:00–14:00. Spec: Acupuncture; Alternative Medicine; American Indians; Anatomy; Art - Theory; Arts & Crafts Era; Biology - General; Botany. CC: MC; V. Corresp: Dutch, French, German. VAT No: IE 5333275R.

CO. CORK

BALLYDEHOB

Barbara and Jack O'Connell (t/a Schull Books), ■ The Bookshop Main Street, Ballydehob. Prop: Barbara & Jack O'Connell. Tel: (+353) [0]28 37317. Fax: (+353) [0]28 37317. Web: www.schullbooks.net. Est: 1981. Shop open in summer: **M:** 11:00–17:00; **T:** 11:00–17:00; **W:** 11:00–17:00; **Th:** 11:00–17:00; **F:** 11:00–17:00; **S:** 11:00–17:00. Medium stock. Spec: Antiquarian; Countries - Ireland; General Stock; History - Irish; Irish History & Literature; Irish Interest; Literature - Irish; Military. PR: £10–500. CC: E; MC; V. Cata: Irish interest, military history, general stock. Corresp: French, German, Irish. Notes: *These details are for our summer shop in Ballydehob village, June - Sept. We also do regular book fairs throughout Ireland and issue catalogues. Please contact us for further information.*

BANTRY

Karen Millward, Coorycommane Coomhola, Bantry. Prop: Karen Millward. Tel: 00353-27-53898. Web: www.ukbookworld.com/members/irishmaid. Est: 2001. Private premises. Internet and Postal. Telephone First. Open: **M:** 09:00–17:30; **T:** 09:00–17:30; **W:** 09:00–17:30; **Th:** 09:00–17:30; **F:** 09:00–17:30; **S:** 09:00–17:30; **Su:** 09:00–12:00; Closed for lunch: 13:00–14:00. Spec: Animals and Birds; Author - Frost, Robert; Author - Joyce, James; Author - Russell, W; Author - Thomas, Edward; Author - Wilde, Oscar; Autobiography; Biography. CC: MC; V; Sterling or Euro Cheques/PayPal. Mem: The Independent Book Sellers' Network Limited. Notes: *Irish Books a speciality. I also carry a large comprehensive general stock of quality books.*

Michael J Carroll, Sunville House, Wolfe Tone Square, Bantry. Prop: Michael J Carroll. Tel: +353 (0) 27 50064. Fax: + 353 (0) 27 52042. Web: www.abebooks.com. Private premises. Internet and Postal. Appointment necessary. Spec: Antiquarian; Biography; Celtica; Countries - Ireland; Ecclesiastical History & Architecture; Folklore; Guide Books; History - General. CC: None. Corresp: Spanish. Notes: *Specialising in Irish History.*

DUNMANWAY

Darkwood Books, Darkwood, Dunmanway. Prop: Annette Sheehan. Tel: (023) 55470. Fax: (023) 55224. Web: www.darkwoodbooks.com. Est: 2000. Private premises. Internet and Postal. Medium stock. Spec: Architecture; Art; Art History; Art Reference; Artists; Arts, The; Author - Somerville & Ross; Author - Walsh, M. PR: £1–500. CC: MC; V. Cata: Irish Interest.

ROSSCARBERY

C.P. Hyland, 4, Closheen Lane, Rosscarbery, n/a. Prop: Cal & Joan Hyland. Tel: (023) 8848063. Web: www.cphyland.com. Est: 1966. Private premises. Internet and Postal. Telephone First. Open: **M:** 10:00–22:00; **T:** 10:00–22:00; **W:** 10:00–22:00; **Th:** 10:00–22:00; **F:** 10:00–22:00; **S:** 10:00–22:00; **Su:** 12:00–22:00. Large stock. Spec: Celtica; Countries - Ireland; Irish Interest; Languages - National. PR: £1–10,000. Cata: Relating to Ireland. Corresp: Gaelic. VAT No: IE 9/T/09940R.

CO. DONEGAL

CARNDONAGH

The Bookshop, ■ Court Place, Carndonagh. Prop: Michael Herron. Tel: 07493 74389. Fax: 07493 74935. Est: 1989. Shop open at: Churchtown, Carndonagh, Co Donegal. Open: **M:** 14:00–18:00; **T:** 14:00–18:00; **Th:** 14:00–18:00; **F:** 14:00–18:00; **S:** 14:00–18:00; **Su:** 14:00–18:00. Very large stock. Spec: Antiquarian; First Editions; History - Local; Irish Interest; Medicine; Philosophy; Religion - Christian; Science - General. PR: £1–100. Notes: *Also, half price sales in August, December and Easter.*

CO. DUBLIN

BALLINTEER

Taney Books, 13 The Close, Woodpark, Ballinteer, . Prop: Morrough Lacy. Tel: 2157880. Est: 1982. Private premises. Market Stall. Telephone First. Open: **S:** 11:00–18:00; **Su:** 11:00–18:00. Spec: Antiquarian; Cartography; Countries - Ireland; Geography; Prints and Maps. Cata: Irish Interest. Notes: *Attends Temple Bar Book Market, Temple Bar Square, Dublin 2. Phone 186 1902892 11:00–18:00 Saturday and Sunday. My online stock is on abebooks.com.*

BLACKROCK

Carraig Books Ltd., ■ 73 Main Street, Blackrock. Prop: Sean L. Day. Tel: (01) 2882575. Fax: (01) 2834209. Est: 1968. Shop open: **M:** 09:30–17:00; **T:** 09:30–17:00; **W:** 09:30–17:00; **Th:** 09:30–17:00; **F:** 09:30–17:00; **S:** 10:00–17:00; Closed for lunch: 13:00–14:00. Spec: Architecture; Art; Art History; Author - 19th Century; Author - 20th Century; Author - Belloc, Hilaire; Author - Benson, R.H.; Author - Chesterton, G.K. PR: £2–100. CC: AE; MC; V. Cata: Irish, General Interests & Catholic. Notes: *We issue catalogues to anywhere in the world, feel free to contact us with your details if you wish to receive one. Be sure to let us know what subjects you are interested in.*

Samovar Books, 63 Ardagh Park, Blackrock. Prop: Louis Hemmings. Tel: 00-353-1-2104990. Web: www.samovarbooks.com. Est: 1993. Private premises. Internet only. Contactable. Open: **M:** 09:00–17:30; **T:** 09:00–17:30; **W:** 09:00–17:30; **Th:** 09:00–17:30; **F:** 09:00–17:30; **S:** 09:00–17:30; **Su:** 09:00–17:30; Closed for lunch: 13:00–14:00. Spec: Africana; Archaeology; Architecture; Author - Inklings, The; Autobiography; Bibles; Biblical Studies; Biography. CC: MC; V. Cata: theology, topography, politics, history, Irish. Mem: Librarians Christian Fellowship. Notes: *Ireland's ONLY online used theology book dealer.*

CLONTARF

Read Ireland, 392 Clontarf Road, Clontarf 3. Prop: Gregory Carr. Tel: 35318532063. Fax: 35318532063. Web: www.readireland.ie. Est: 1995. Private premises. Internet only. Appointment necessary. Open: **M:** 09:00–17:30; **T:** 09:00–17:30; **W:** 09:00–17:30; **Th:** 09:00–17:30; **F:** 09:00–17:30; **S:** 09:00–17:30; **Su:** 09:00–17:30; Closed for lunch: 13:00–14:00. Spec: Author - Beckett, S.; Author - Heaney, Seamus; Author - Yeats, W.B.; Countries - Ireland; History - Irish; Irish Interest. CC: MC; V. Cata: Irish Interest only. VAT No: IE5093937G. Notes: *Ireland's Irish Interest Specialist Internet Booksellers.*

DUBLIN

Cathach Books Ltd, ■ 10 Duke Street, Dublin, 2. Prop: David Cunningham. Tel: +353 16718676. Fax: +353 1675120. Web: www.rarebooks.ie. Est: 1988. Shop open: **M:** 09:30–17:45; **T:** 09:30–17:45; **W:** 09:30–17:45; **Th:** 09:30–17:45; **F:** 09:30–17:45; **S:** 09:30–17:45. CC: AE; JCB; V; Laser. Cata: Literature, History (mostly Irish interest). Mem: ABA; BA; ILAB. Notes: *Together with our general stock, we offer an excellent selection of rare and first edition books by Oscar Wilde, James Joyce and William Butler Yeats. In addition, we stock a wide variety of Books on Irish History.*

Chapters Bookstore, ■ Ivy Exchange Parnell Street, Dublin 1. Prop: William Kinsella. Manager John Gannon. Tel: 00 353 1 8723297. Fax: 00 353 1 8723044. Web: www.chapters.ie. Est: 1982. Shop open: **M:** 09:30–18:30; **T:** 09:30–18:30; **W:** 09:30–18:30; **Th:** 09:30–20:00; **F:** 09:30–18:30; **S:** 09:30–18:30; **Su:** 12:00–18:30. Very large stock. Spec: Booksearch. PR: £1–1,000. CC: AE; MC; V. Mem: BA. VAT No: IE 643 9260 D. Notes: *(Alternate Tel: (01) 872-0773, 872-3024).*

De Burca Rare Books, 'Cloonagashel' 27 Priory Drive, Blackrock, Dublin. Prop: Eamonn & Vivien de Burca. Tel: (01) 288-2159. Fax: (01) 283-4080. Web: www.deburcararebooks.com. Est: 1979. Private premises. Internet and Postal. Telephone First. Large stock. Spec: Bindings; Countries - Ireland; Culture - National; Genealogy; History - National; Incunabula; Irish Interest; Literature. PR: £5–30,000. CC: JCB; MC. Corresp: French, German, Italian. Mem: ABA; PBFA; ILAB. VAT No: IE 16193333M. Notes: *Also, manuscripts of Irish interest, a worldwide mail order service & publishers of fine historical books.*

Glenbower Books, 46 Howth Road Clontarf, Dublin 3. Prop: Martin Walsh. Tel: (01) 833-5305. Web: www.abebooks.com/home/GLENBOWERBOOKS. Private premises. Postal only. Medium stock. Spec: Academic/Scholarly; Antiquarian; Bridge; Chemistry; Chess; Children's - Early Titles; Economics; Fiction - General. PR: £3–340. CC: Paypal.

Greene's Bookshop Ltd, ■ Unit 7, 78 Furze Road, Sandyford Industrial Estate, Dublin 18. Tel: 00-353-1-6762554. Fax: 00-353-1-6789091. Web: www.greenesbookshop.com. Est: 1843. Internet and Postal. Shop open: **M:** 09:00–16:30; **T:** 09:00–16:30; **W:** 09:00–16:30; **Th:** 09:09–16:30; **F:** 09:00–16:30; **S:** 09:00–16:30. Medium stock. Spec: Countries - Ireland; Irish Interest. CC: AE; D; MC; V. VAT No: IE 4810086O. Notes: *Not a walk in shop - see website for details.*

Obscurebooks, 17 St. Peters Crescent, Walkinstown, Dublin. Prop: Tom Murray. Tel: +353-1-4567830. Web: www.obscurebooks.co.uk. Est: 2005. Mail order only; Internet only. Appointment necessary. Open: **M:** 09:00–17:30; **T:** 09:00–17:30; **W:** 09:00–17:30; **Th:** 09:00–17:30; **F:** 09:00–17:30; **S:** 09:00–17:30; **Su:** 09:00–17:30; Closed for lunch: 13:00–14:00. CC: PayPal.

Phelan Books, 7 May Street, Drumcondra, Dublin 3. Prop: Brian J. Phelan. Tel: (01) 874-7316. Est: 1995. Spec: Antiques; Architecture; Decorative Art; Fine Art; Booksearch. PR: £5–200.

Stokes Books, ■19 Market Arcade, South Great George's Street, Dublin 2. Prop: Stephen Stokes. Tel: (01) 671-3584. Fax: (01) 671-3181. Web: www.usedbooksirleand.ie. Est: 1982. Shop open: **M:** 11:00–18:00; **T:** 11:00–18:00; **W:** 11:00–18:00; **Th:** 11:00–18:00; **F:** 11:00–18:00; **S:** 11:00–18:00. Spec: Architecture - Theatre; Countries - Ireland; Culture - National; History - Irish; Irish Interest; Languages - Foreign; Literature; Literature - Irish. PR: £5–50. CC: AE; MC; V. Cata: Irish History and Literature. Corresp: German.

DUN LAOGHAIRE

James Fenning, Antiquarian Books, 12 Glenview, Rochestown Avenue, Dun Laoghaire. Prop: Jim & Chris Fenning. Tel: (01) 2857855. Fax: (01) 2857919. Est: 1969. Private premises. Internet and Postal. Appointment necessary. Open: **M:** 08:00–16:00; **T:** 08:00–16:00; **W:** 08:00–16:00; **F:** 08:00–16:00. Small stock. Spec: Antiquarian. PR: £20–15,000. CC: MC; V. Mem: ABA; ILAB. VAT No: IE 9T568850.

Naughton Booksellers, ■ 8 Marine Terrace, Dun Laoghaire. Prop: Susan Naughton. Tel: +353 1 280 4392. Web: www.naughtonsbooks.com. Est: 1976. Shop open: **M:** 10:00–17:00; **T:** 10:00–17:00; **W:** 10:00–17:00; **Th:** 10:00–17:00; **F:** 10:00–17:00; **S:** 10:00–17:00. Spec: Academic/Scholarly; Anthologies; Antiquarian; Art History; Arts, The; Author - General; Author - 20th Century; Biography. CC: AE; MC; V. VAT No: IE 8495489V.

NEWCASTLE

Lyonshill Books, Peamount Road, Newcastle, Co. Dublin. Prop: Eddie and Kay Murphy. Tel: 00 353 1 4589237. Web: www.dublincitybookfair.com. Est: 1998. Private premises. Book fairs only. Small Stock. Spec: Academic/Scholarly; Arts, The; Associations - Gaelic Athletic; Author - Heaney, Seamus; Joyce, James; Countries - Ireland; History - Irish; Irish Interest. PR: 20 Euros upwards. Cata: bi-annually on Ireland, History and Literature. Corresp: Irish and French. Notes: *We sell mainly books of Irish and Scholarly interest, history and literature, art and some general stock. Catalogues are free and can be hardcopy or softcopy.*

STILLORGAN

Dublin Bookbrowsers, 12 Weirview Drive, Stillorgan. Prop: Dave Downes. Tel: (00353) 872636347. Fax: (00353) 1210300. Web: www.abebooks.com. Est: 1996. Private premises. Appointment necessary. Large stock. Spec: Antiquarian; Irish Interest; Sport - General; Sport - Boxing; Sport - Golf. PR: £1–20,000. CC: MC; V. Cata: Ireland, Irish literature, Irish sport, general. Corresp: some French. Mem: PBFA.

CO. GALWAY

GALWAY

Charlie Byrne's Bookshop, ■ The Cornstore Middle Street, Galway. Prop: Charlie Byrne. Tel: (0035) 391 561766. Fax: (0035) 391 561766. Web: www.charliebyrne.com. Internet and Postal. Shop open: **M:** 09:00–18:00; **T:** 09:00–18:00; **W:** 09:00–18:00; **Th:** 09:00–18:00; **F:** 09:00–20:00; **S:** 09:00–18:00; **Su:** 12:00–18:00. Spec: Archaeology; Architecture; Art; Children's; Classical Studies; Classics, The; Cookery/Gastronomy; Fiction - General. CC: AE; MC; V. Notes: *Our warehouse also contains an extra 40,000 books.*

Kenny's Bookshop & Art Galleries Ltd., Liosban Business Park, Tuam Road, Galway. Prop: Conor Kenny. Tel: (091) 709350. Fax: (091) 709351. Web: www.kennys.ie. Est: 1940. Office and/or bookroom; Internet and Postal. Shop open: **M:** 09:00–17:00; **T:** 09:00–17:00; **W:** 09:00–17:00; **Th:** 09:00–17:00; **F:** 09:00–17:00. Very large stock. PR: £2–16,000. CC: AE; D; JCB; MC; V. Mem: ABA; PBFA; ILAB. VAT No: IE 6328356V.

MOYARD

The House of Figgis Ltd, Ross House, Moyard. Prop: Neville Figgis. Tel: (095) 41092. Fax: (095) 41261. Est: 1974. Private premises. Postal only. Appointment necessary. Small stock. Spec: Antiquarian; Early Imprints; History - Irish; Irish Interest; Literature; Literature - Irish; Modern First Editions. CC: MC; V. Cata: Ireland - General antiquarian. VAT No: IE9 N 543 41S.

CO. LAOIS

VICARSTOWN

Courtwood Books, Vicarstown, Stradbally, Vicarstown. Prop: PJ Tynan. Tel: (057) 8626384. Web: www.biblio.com. Est: 1984. Private premises. Internet and Postal. Appointment necessary. Medium stock. Spec: Author - Beckett, S.; Author - Joyce, James; Author - Wilde, Oscar; Author - Yeats, W.B.; Countries - Ireland; Engineering; History - Local; Illustrated - 19th & 20th Century. PR: £1–500. Cata: Mostly Irish interest.

CO. LEITRIM

CARRICK–ON–SHANNON

Trinity Rare Books, ■ Bridge Street, Carrick–on–Shannon. Prop: Nick Kaszuk. Tel: 00353 71 9622144. Web: www.trinityrarebooks.com. Est: 1999. Shop open: **M:** 09:30–18:00; **T:** 09:30–18:00; **W:** 09:30–18:00; **Th:** 09:30–18:00; **F:** 09:30–18:00; **S:** 09:30–18:00; **Su:** 13:00–17:00. Large stock. Spec: Agriculture; American Indians; Animals and Birds; Antiquarian; Antiquities; Archaeology; Architecture; Art. PR: £3–150. Cata: irish books. Corresp: French, German.

CO. LIMERICK

ADARE

George Stacpoole, ■ Main Street, Adare. Prop: George Stacpoole. Tel: (061) 396409. Fax: (061) 396733. Web: www.georgestacpooleantiques.com. Shop open: **M:** 10:00–17:30; **T:** 10:00–17:30; **W:** 10:00–17:30; **Th:** 10:00–17:30; **F:** 10:00–17:30; **S:** 10:00–17:30. Spec: History - Local; Sport - Field Sports; Booksearch; Prints and Maps. PR: £5–2,000. CC: AE; E; JCB; MC; V. Mem: IADA. Notes: *Also, a booksearch service.*

LIMERICK

The Celtic Bookshop, ■ 2 Rutland Street, Limerick. Prop: Caroline O'Brien. Tel: (061) 401155. Est: 1982. Internet and Postal. Telephone First. Open: **M:** 10:00–17:00; **T:** 10:00–17:00; **W:** 10:00–17:00; **Th:** 10:00–17:00; **F:** 10:00–17:00; **S:** 10:00–17:00. Medium stock. Spec: Academic/Scholarly; Antiquarian; Countries - Ireland; Fiction - General; History - General; History - Irish; Literature - Irish. PR: £3–1,000. CC: MC; V. Cata: Ireland. Corresp: Irish. VAT No: IE3229665i.

John O'Brien Books, 26 High Street, Limerick. Prop: John O'Brien. Tel: (061) 412833. Est: 1988. Private premises. Internet and Postal. Appointment necessary. Shop at: Mount Arley, Drumline, Newmarket on Fergus, Co. Clare. Ireland. Medium stock. Spec: Art; Art History; Biography; Cinema/Film; Fiction - General; Folio Society, The; History - General; Irish Interest. PR: £1–400. CC: MC; V. Cata: Irish Interest. VAT No: 192 620 9a.

CO. TIPPERARY

ROSCREA

Roscrea Bookshop & Newsagents, ■ Rosemary Square, Roscrea. Prop: Tom and Pauline Deegan. Tel: 00-353-505-22894. Fax: 00-353-504-28092. Web: www.roscreabookshop.com. Est: 1997. Shop. Telephone First. Open: **M:** 07:30–19:00; **T:** 07:30–19:00; **W:** 07:30–20:00; **Th:** 07:30–19:00; **F:** 07:30–19:00; **S:** 07:30–20:00; **Su:** 07:30–14:00. Large stock. Spec: Academic/Scholarly; Africana; Agriculture; American Indians; Bibles; Children's; Children's - Illustrated; Christmas. PR: £3–50. CC: MC; V. Corresp: French and Irish. Mem: BA; LAI. VAT No: IE 327613 4P.

CO. WEXFORD

BUNCLODY

Fuchsia Books, Ballypreacus, Bunclody. Prop: Mary Mackey. Tel: 054 75577. Est: 1988. Private premises. Internet and Postal. Contactable. Small stock. Spec: History - National; Irish Interest; Booksearch; Prints and Maps. PR: £10–500.

NEW ROSS

Britons Catholic Library, Riverview Arthurstown, New Ross. Prop: Mr. N. M. Gwynne. Tel: (51) 389111. Est: 1976. Private premises. Appointment necessary. Small stock. Spec: Religion - Catholic. PR: £2–100. Notes: *Stock majors on traditional Catholic titles.*

SCOTLAND

Including the Unitary Authorities of Aberdeenshire, Angus, Argyll & Bute, Borders, Clackmannan, Dumfries & Galloway, Dumbarton & Clydebank, Dundee, East Ayrshire, East Dunbartonshire, East Lothian, East Renfrewshire, Edinburgh, Falkirk, Fife, Glasgow, Highland, Inverclyde, Mid Lothian, Moray, North Ayrshire, North Lanarkshire, Orkney Islands, Perthshire & Kinross, Renfrewshire, Shetland Islands, South Ayrshire, South Lanarkshire, Stirling, Western Isles and West Lothian

BORDERS

INNERLEITHEN

Spike Hughes Rare Books, Willow Bank, Damside, Innerleithen, EH44 6HR. Tel: (01896) 830019. Fax: (01896) 831499. Est: 1981. Private premises. Internet and Postal. Appointment necessary. Small stock. Spec: Countries - Scotland; Fine & Rare; History - General; History - Local; History - National; Literature; Philosophy; Social History. PR: £10–5,000. CC: MC; V. Mem: ABA. VAT No: GB 345 4470 55.

Last Century Books, ■ 34 High Street, Innerleithen, EH44 6HF. Prop: Keith & Gillian Miller. Tel: 01896 831759. Web: www.lastcenturybooks.com. Est: 1998. Shop open: **M:** 11:00–17:00; **T:** 11:00–17:00; **W:** 11:00–17:00; **Th:** 11:00–17:00; **F:** 11:00–17:00; **S:** 11:00–17:00. Spec: Art; Countries - Scotland; Fiction - General; Military; Religion - General. CC: E; JCB; MC; V; Maestro.

JEDBURGH

G. & R. Stone, Hap House, 5 Allerton Court, Jedburgh, Roxburghshire, TD8 6RT. Prop: Gillian & Ralph Stone. Tel: (01835) 864147. Fax: (01835) 864147. Est: 1972. Private premises. Appointment necessary. Spec: Agriculture; Antiquarian; Natural History; Poetry; Women. PR: £5–100. CC: MC; V. Mem: PBFA.

MELROSE

The Bookroom, ■ 1 Dingleton Road, Melrose, TD6 9QS. Tel: 01896 823 337. Est: 2004. Shop open: **M:** 09:00–17:30; **T:** 09:00–17:30; **W:** 09:00–17:30; **Th:** 09:00–17:30; **F:** 09:00–17:30; **S:** 09:00–17:30; **Su:** 09:00–17:30; Closed for lunch: 13:00–14:00.

Stroma Books, Charlesfield, St. Boswells, Melrose, TD6 0HH. Prop: Kenneth Roberts. Tel: (01835) 824169. Web: www.biblio.com/bookstores/stroma.html. Est: 2000. Private premises. Internet and Postal. Appointment necessary. Medium stock. Spec: Academic/Scholarly; Art; Biography; Children's; Children's - Illustrated; Cinema/Film; Cookery/Gastronomy; Countries - Scotland. PR: £1–500. CC: AE; JCB; MC; V; M, SW, SO.

SELKIRK

Wheen O'Books, Glyndwr, Mill Street, Selkirk, TD7 5AE. Prop: Margaret Tierney. Tel: (01750) 721009. Web: www.wheenobooks.com. Est: 1997. Private premises. Internet only. Telephone First. Large stock. Spec: Adventure; Animals and Birds; Annuals; Army, The; Art; Author - General; Autobiography; Aviation. PR: £2–1,500. CC: PayPal. Cata: General, Scottish, Military, Children, Crime,. Notes: *General stock. You can browse our books at http://www.wheenobooks.com for hard to find, out of print, used, and rare books at decent prices with first-class personal service.*

WEST LINTON

Linton Books, ■ Deanfoot Road, West Linton, EH46 7DY. Prop: Derek Watson. Tel: (01968) 660339. Fax: (01968) 661701. Est: 1994. Shop open: **M:** 10:30–17:30; **T:** 10:30–17:30; **W:** 10:30–17:30; **Th:** 10:30–17:30; **F:** 10:30–17:30; **S:** 10:30–17:30; **Su:** 12:00–17:00. Small stock. Spec: Mythology; Scottish Interest. PR: £1–150. CC: E; MC; V. Mem: BA. Notes: *Winter opening: Closed Thursdays and Sunday morning.*

CENTRAL

BY DUNBLANE

Sheriffmuir Books, Glentye Sheriffmuir, by Dunblane, FK15 0LN. Tel: 01786 822269. Private premises. Postal only. Open in Summer.

CALLANDER

HP Bookfinders, Mosslaird Brig O'Turk, Callander, FK17 8HT. Tel: (01877) 376377. Fax: (01877) 376377. Web: www.hp-bookfinders.co.uk. Est: 1986. Private premises. Internet and Postal. Contactable. Small stock. Spec: Booksearch. CC: E; JCB; MC; V; Switch.

Kings Bookshop Callander, ■ 91–93 Main Street, Callander, Trossachs, FK17 8BQ. Prop: Ian King & Sally Evans. Tel: (01877) 339 449. Est: 1987. Shop open: **M:** 09:00–19:00; **T:** 09:00–19:00; **W:** 09:00–19:00; **Th:** 09:00–19:00; **F:** 09:00–19:00; **S:** 09:00–19:00; **Su:** 09:00–19:00. Spec: Bindings; Classical Studies; Poetry; Scottish Interest. PR: £1–1,000. CC: cheques or cash only. Cata: Scottish, poetry, bindings, classics. Notes: *Shop open Monday through to Sunday. NB When sending e-mails - add 'bookshop' to subject field. Good bookbindings for sale.*

DOLLAR

Volume Three, 4, The Glebe, Dollar, Clackmannanshire, FK14 7AN. Prop: Helen Prior. Tel: 01259 742168. Web: www.ukbookworld.com/members/volumethree. Est: 2002. Mail order only; Internet and Postal. Contactable. Spec: out-of-print.

LARBERT

Dave Simpson, Lorne Villa, 161 Main Street, Larbert, Stirlingshire, FK5 4AL. Tel: (01324) 558628. Fax: (01324) 558628. Est: 2000. Private premises. Internet and Postal. Contactable. Small stock. Spec: Author - General; Author - 19th Century; Author - 20th Century; Author - Asimov, Isaac; Author - Barker, Cecily M.; Author - Barrie, J.M.; Author - Bates, H.E.; Author - Belloc, Hilaire. PR: £10–300. CC: E; JCB; MC; V; Switch. Notes: *Sells through Abebooks.com, Amazon.co.uk, The Book and Magazine Collector and long standing contacts.*

DUMFRIES & GALLOWAY

CASTLE DOUGLAS

Benny Gillies Books Ltd, ■ 33 Victoria Street, Kirkpatrick Durham, Castle Douglas, DG7 3HQ. Prop: Benny Gillies. Tel: 01556 650412. Web: www.bennygillies.co.uk. Est: 1979. Shop. Telephone First. Open: **M:** 10:00–17:00; **T:** 10:00–17:00; **W:** 10:00–17:00; **Th:** 10:00–17:00; **F:** 10:00–17:00; **S:** 10:00–17:00. Small stock. Spec: Countries - Scotland; County - Local; Scottish Interest; Topography - Local; Prints and Maps. PR: £5-1,500. CC: AE; MC; V. Cata: Scotland. Corresp: French. Mem: PBFA. VAT No: GB 499 0638 93. Notes: *Specialist dealer in Scottish material only (Books maps and prints) Kirkpatrick Durham is situated 6 miles from Castle Douglas. Hours are irregular so please telephone before making a special journey especially in winter.*

Douglas Books, ■ 207 King Street, Castle Douglas, Kirkcudbrightshire, DG7 1DT. Prop: Martin Close. Tel: (01556) 504006. Est: 1995. Shop open: **M:** 11:00–17:00; **T:** 11:00–17:00; **W:** 11:00–17:00; **Th:** 11:00–17:00; **F:** 11:00–17:00; **S:** 11:00–17:00. PR: £1–100. CC: MC; V.

DALBEATTIE

Dalbeattie Books, ■ 65 High Street, Dalbeattie, DG5 4HA. Prop: Pauline Warner. Tel: 01556 610228. Fax: 01556 612239. Web: www.dalbeattiebooks.com. Est: 2002. Shop open: **M:** 10:00–16:00; **T:** 10:00–16:00; **Th:** 10:00–16:00; **F:** 10:00–16:00; **S:** 10:00–17.30; Closed for lunch: 13:00–14:00. Spec: Art History; Autobiography; Cats; Children's; Crafts; Military; New Age; New Books. Notes: *Also sell on internet - see web page.*

DUMFRIES

Anwoth Books, ■ Mill on the Fleet, Gatehouse of Fleet, Dumfries, DG7 2HS. Prop: R. Munro. Tel: 01557814774. Est: 1992. Shop. Open in Summer. Open: **M:** 10:30–17:00; **T:** 10:30–17:00; **W:** 10:30–17:00; **Th:** 10:30–17:00; **F:** 10:30–17:00; **S:** 10:30–17:00; **Su:** 10:30–17:00; Closed for lunch: 13:00–14:00. Spec: Children's; Ethnology; Ornithology; Poetry; Rural Life; Scottish Interest. CC: JCB; MC; V. Corresp: German. Notes: *Full hours from April to October. Open Friday and Saturday during November, December, February and March.*

KIRKCUDBRIGHT

Solway Books, ■ 14 St. Cuthbert's Street, Kirkcudbright, DG6 4HZ. Prop: Mrs Beverley Chadband. Tel: 01557 330635. Web: www.solwaybooks.co.uk. Est: 2003. Shop open: **M:** 10:00–17:00; **T:** 10:00–17:00; **W:** 10:00–17:00; **Th:** 10:00–17:00; **F:** 10:00–17:00; **S:** 10:00–17:00. Spec: Ephemera; Prints and Maps. PR: £1–300. CC: AE; JCB; MC; V; Sw. Mem: BA. VAT No: GB 843 0978 11.

Vailima Books, ■ 61 High Street, Kirkcudbright, DG6 4JZ. Prop: Elizabeth Kirby. Tel: (01557) 330583. Est: 1988. Shop open: **M:** 10:00–17:00; **T:** 10:00–17:00; **Th:** 10:00–17:00; **F:** 10:00–17:00; **S:** 10:00–17:00. Small stock. Spec: Railways and Railroads; Transport. PR: £1–20. Notes: *Large stock of railways and other transport.*

MOFFAT

Moffat Book Exchange, ■ 5 Well Street, Moffat, DF10 9DP. Prop: Andy Armstrong. Tel: (01683) 220059. Est: 1998. Shop open: **M:** 10:00–16:30; **W:** 10:00–16:30; **Th:** 10:00–16:30; **F:** 10:00–16:30; **S:** 10:00–17:00; **Su:** 13:00–16:00; Closed for lunch: 13:00–14:00. Spec: Fiction - General. PR: £1–25. Notes: *stock includes large selection of paperback fiction, and large selection of general non-fiction.*

THORNHILL

Mr. Mac, Stenhouse Cottage, Tynron, Thornhill, DG3 4LD. Prop: Ranald McDonald. Tel: 01848 200469. Web: www.mrmacbooks.co.uk. Est: 1995. Private premises. Internet and Postal. Appointment necessary. Spec: Animals and Birds; Countries - Scotland; Food & Drink; Scottish Interest; Wine. PR: £2–100. CC: AE; D; E; JCB; MC; V; PAYPAL. Cata: Scottish Interest. Mem: PBFA. Notes: *We specialise in books related to Scotland, but we also stock a wide range of general and academic books.*

WHITHORN

Pend Books, ■ 55 George Street, Whithorn, Newton Stewart, DG8 8NU. Prop: Julia M. Watt. Tel: 01988 500469. Fax: 01988 500469. Est: 2000. Internet and Postal. Appointment necessary. Open: **M:** 09:00–17:30; **T:** 09:00–17:30; **W:** 09:00–17:30; **Th:** 09:00–17:30; **F:** 09:00–17:30; **S:** 09:00–17:30; **Su:** 09:00–17:30; Closed for lunch: 13:00–14:00. CC: AE; JCB; MC; V. Corresp: French, German. VAT No: GB 817 1312 57.

WIGTOWN

AA1 Books at Windy Hill, ■ Unit 3 Duncan Park, Wigtown, DG8 9JD. Prop: Robin Richmond. Tel: (01988) 40324. Est: 2001. Shop open: **M:** 10:00–17:00; **T:** 10:00–17:00; **W:** 10:00–17:00; **Th:** 10:00–17:00; **F:** 10:00–17:00; **S:** 08:00–17:00. Very large stock. Spec: Children's; Espionage; Fiction - Crime, Detective, Spy, Thrillers; Fiction - Fantasy, Horror; Fiction - Science Fiction; Fiction - Westerns; Ghosts; History - General. PR: £1–150. CC: AE; MC; V. Corresp: French, German. Notes: *Also, new books. In association with Ming Books. Hours quoted are summer hours.*

A.P. & R. Baker Limited, The Laigh House, Church Lane, Wigtown, DG8 9HT. Prop: Anthony P. & Rosemary Baker. Tel: (01988) 403348. Fax: (01988) 403443. Web: www.apandrbaker.co.uk. Est: 1974. Private premises. Postal only. Telephone First. Spec: Anthropology; Archaeology; Archaeology - Industrial; Arthurian; History - General; History - Middle Ages; History - Modern; History - Napoleonic. PR: £2–500. CC: JCB; MC; V; Delta, Solo Electron Train (SW & U). Cata: Archaeology & History. Mem: Wigtown Chamber of Commerce.

The BookShop, ■17 North Main Street, Wigtown, DG8 9HL. Prop: Shaun Bythell. Tel: 01988 402499. Web: www.the-bookshop.com. Est: 1984. Shop open: **M:** 09:00–17:00; **T:** 09:00–17:00; **W:** 09:00–17:00; **Th:** 09:00–17:00; **F:** 09:00–17:00; **S:** 09:00–17:00. Spec: Aircraft; Antiquarian; Antiques; Art - British; Aviation; Canals/Inland Waterways; Churchilliana; Cinema/Film. CC: MC; V. Notes: *Scotland's largest second-hand book shop, 9 large rooms with books on all subjects. Take advantage of our free coffee, or relax in one of the armchairs in front of the woodburning stove.*

Byre Books, ■ 24 South Main St., Wigtown, DG8 9EH. Prop: Laura Mustian and Shani Mustian. Tel: (01988) 402133. Web: www.byrebooks.co.uk. Est: 2000. Internet and Postal. Shop open: **M:** 10:00–17:30; **T:** 10:00–17:30; **W:** 10:00–17.30; **Th:** 10:00–17:30; **F:** 10:00–17:30; **S:** 10:00–17:30; **Su:** 11:00–16:30. Small stock. Spec: Aboriginal; American Indians; Anthropology; Anthroposophy; Arthurian; Arthurian (King Arthur); Author - Aesop; Author - Shakespeare, William. PR: £3–100. CC: E; JCB; MC; V; Switch, Delta. Corresp: French, Spanish. Mem: Wigtown Book Trades Ass. VAT No: GB 789 1742 76. Notes: *During the winter we are usually closed on a Wednesday, and our opening hours are 10:00-16:00. Please call before visiting for exact times during your stay.*

G. C. Books Ltd., Unit 10, Book Warehouse, Bladnoch Bridge Estate, Wigtown, DG8 9AB. Prop: Beverley and Keith Chadband. Tel: 01988 402 688. Fax: 01988 402 688. Est: 2005. Warehouse; Internet and Postal. Shop open: **M:** 10:00–17:00; **T:** 10:00–17:00; **W:** 10:00–17:00; **Th:** 10:00–17:00; **F:** 10:00–17:00; **S:** 10:00–17:00. Spec: Academic/Scholarly; Africana; Aircraft; Antiquarian; Archaeology; Architecture; Atlases; Autobiography. CC: MC; V; PayPal. Cata: as required. Mem: FSB. Notes: *Visitors, Trade Overseas Enquiries Welcome - Free Booksearch Service - International Shipping.*

M.E. McCarty, Bookseller, ■ 13 North Main St., Wigtown, DG8 9HL. Tel: (01988) 402062. VOIPnum: orkbooks. Est: 1980. Shop open: **M:** 10:00–17:00; **T:** 10:00–17:00; **W:** 10:00–17:00; **Th:** 10:00–17:00; **F:** 10:00–17:00; **S:** 10:00–17:00; **Su:** 10:00–17:00. Spec: Literature; Maritime/Nautical; Travel - General. PR: £1–100. CC: AE; JCB; MC; V; Maestro, Solo. Corresp: French, German, Norwegian. Notes: *Also at: 54 Junction Road, Kirkwall Orkney. 01856 870860.*

Ming Books, Beechwood House, Acre Place, Wigtown, DG8 9DU. Prop: Marion Richmond. Tel: (01988) 403241. Web: www.alibris.com/bookstore/GALLOWAY. Est: 1982. Office and/or bookroom; Internet and Postal. Appointment necessary. Open: **M:** 10:00–18:00; **T:** 10:00–18:00; **W:** 10:00–18:00; **Th:** 10:00–18:00; **F:** 10:00–18:00; **S:** 10:00–18:00; Closed for lunch: 12:00–13:00. Very large stock. Spec: Author - Bellaires, George; Author - Conan Doyle, Sir Arthur; Author - Cornwell, Bernard; Author - Creasey, John; Author - Crofts, Freeman Wills; Author - Sayers, Dorothy; Author - Simenon, Georges; Cats. PR: £4–1,000. CC: AE; MC; V; Paypal;. Cata: crime fiction; Penguins. Corresp: German and French. Mem: IOBA. VAT No: GB 432 9993 15. Notes: *AA1 BOOKS AT WINDY HILL Unit 3 Duncan Park Wigtown is the retail outlet. Open Monday to Saturday in Summer 11-4 winter Monday 11-3 otherwise by appointment or chance.*

Reading Lasses, ■17 South Main Street, Wigtown, DG8 9EH. Prop: Angela Everitt. Tel: 00 (44) 1988 403266. Web: www.reading-lasses.com. Est: 1997. Shop open: **M:** 10:00–17:00; **T:** 10:00–17:00; **W:** 10:00–17:00; **Th:** 10:00–17:00; **F:** 10:00–17:00; **S:** 10:00–17:00; **Su:** 12:00–17:00. Spec: Academic/Scholarly; Adult; African-American Studies; Africana; Alternative Medicine; Anthropology; Art; Asian Studies. CC: MC; V. Mem: PBFA. Notes: *The bookshop hosts an award-winning cafe specialising in home-made and local produce.*

Transformer, ■ 26 Bladnoch, Wigtown, DG8 9AB. Prop: C.A. Weaver. Tel: 0044 (0) 1988-403455. Web: www.abebooks.com/home/TRANSFORMER/home.htm. Est: 1998. Internet and Postal. Open in Summer. Very large stock. Spec: Academic/Scholarly; Astronomy; Biology - General; Chemistry; Children's; Countries - China; Countries - Japan; Countries - Korea. PR: £1–400. Corresp: French. Notes: *Open by appointment or chance. Can accept payments by Paypal.*

FIFE

ANSTRUTHER

Rising Tide Books, 51 John Street, Cellardyke, Anstruther, KY10 3BA. Prop: Stephen Checkland. Tel: (01333) 310948. Fax: (01333) 310948. Est: 1997. Private premises. Book fairs only. Appointment necessary. Small stock. Spec: Illustrated - General; Modern First Editions; Scottish Interest. PR: £5–500. Mem: PBFA.

DUNFERMLINE

Larry Hutchison (Books), 27 Albany Street, Dunfermline, KY12 OQZ. Tel: (01383) 725566. Fax: (01383) 620394. Web: www.larryhutchisobooks.com. Est: 1987. Private premises. Appointment necessary. Medium stock. Spec: Antiquarian; Countries - Scotland; Fine & Rare; Folklore; Genealogy; History - General; History - Industrial; Literature. PR: £5–5,000. CC: AE; MC; V. Cata: Scottish. Corresp: most major European. Mem: PBFA. VAT No: GB 716 9500 30. Notes: *Also, a booksearch service.*

Gary Walker, Swallowdrum Cottage, Milesmark, Dunfermline, KY12 9BB. Prop: Gary Walker. Tel: (01383) 737977. Private premises. Open. Small stock. PR: £2–500. Notes: *Open daily.*

KIRKCALDY

R. Campbell Hewson Books, 6 West Albert Road, Kirkcaldy, KY1 1DL. Tel: (01592) 262051. Est: 1996. Private premises. Appointment necessary. Small stock. Spec: Author - Burton, R.F.; Ethnography; Rural Life; Sport - Big Game Hunting; Travel - Africa; Voyages & Discovery. PR: £10–3,500.

Kelpie's Books, 18 Denburn Place, Kirkcaldy, KY2 5BL. Prop: Ann-Marie Lawson. Tel: 077612344677. Web: www.stores.ebay.co.uk/Kelpies-Books-Too. Est: 2003. Mail order only; Internet and Postal. Contactable. Open: **M:** 09:00–22:00; **T:** 09:00–22:00; **W:** 09:00–22:00; **Th:** 09:00–22:00; **F:** 09:00–22:00; **S:** 12:00–22:00; **Su:** 12:00–22:00. Spec: Agriculture; Animals and Birds; Aquatics; Author - Blyton, Enid; Author - Potter, Beatrix; Author - Tangye, D.; Cats; Children's. Notes: *Specialists in children's vintage books.*

Midnight Oil Books, ■ 120 Commercial Street, Kirkcaldy KY1 2NX. Prop: David McHutchon. Tel: (10592) 260618. Web: www.midoil.co.uk. Est: 2005. Shop, open M: 09:30–17:30; **T:** 09:30–17:30; **W:** 09:30–17:30; **Th:** 09:30–17:30; **F:** 09:30–17:30; **S:** 09:30–17:30. Large stock. Spec: Foreign Texts; General stock; Linguistics; Philology; Scottish Interest. PR: 10p – £8,000. CC: JCB; MC; V; Meastro; Pin Train; Solo; Electron, Visa. Cata: occasionally on Linguistics, Philogy; Foreign Languages. CorresP: French, German, Polish, Russian. VAT: GB 934 0656 26. Notes: *Home of the Ravenscraig Press. Telephone orders welcome. Booksearch conducted. Stamps fpr sale, Client List, Book Clubs, Philosophy circle. Late opening by appointment.*

NEWPORT ON TAY

Gordon Bettridge, 4 Myrtle Terrace, Newport on Tay, DD6 8DN. Tel: (01382) 542377. Est: 1984. Private premises. Postal only. Spec: Advertising; Bibliography; Books about Books; Calligraphy; Illustrated - General; Journals; Papermaking; Printing. PR: £1–75.

Mair Wilkes Books, 3 St. Mary's Lane, Newport on Tay, DD6 8AH. Tel: (01382) 542260. Est: 1969. Storeroom; Shop open: **T:** 10:00–16:30; **W:** 10:00–16:30; **Th:** 10:00–16:30; **F:** 10:00–16:30; **S:** 10:00–16:30; Closed for lunch: 12:30–14:00. Spec: Academic/Scholarly; Bindings; Fine & Rare; History of Ideas; Medicine - History of; Modern First Editions; Neurology; Psychology/Psychiatry. PR: £2–1,000. CC: AE; MC; V; PayPal. Cata: on Scottish Interests. Mem: PBFA. VAT No: GB 397 9923 69. Notes: *Scottish Antiques Ctre, Abernyte, Inchture, Perthshire.*

ST. ANDREWS

The Bouquiniste Bookshop, ■ 31 Market Street, St. Andrews, KY16 9NS. Prop: E Anne Anderson. Tel: 01334 467724. Est: 1982. Shop open: **M:** 11:00–17:00; **T:** 11:00–17:00; **W:** 11:00–17:00; **Th:** 11:00–17:00; **F:** 11:00–17:00; **S:** 10:00–17:00. Spec: Scottish Interest. Corresp: French.

GRAMPIAN

ABERDEEN

Aberdeen Antique and Art Centre, 24 South College Street, Aberdeen. Tel: 01224 575075. Shop and/or gallery; Shop open: **M:** 10:00–17:00; **T:** 10:00–17:00; **W:** 10:00–17:00; **Th:** 10:00–17:00; **F:** 10:00–17:00; **S:** 10:00–17:00; **Su:** 12:00–16:00.

To find the latest information on dealers

Search www.sheppardsworld.co.uk

Books and Beans, ◼ 22 Belmont Street, Aberdeen, AB10 1JH. Prop: Craig Willox. Tel: 01224 646438. Fax: 01224 646483. Web: www.booksandbeans.co.uk. Est: 2003. Shop open: **M:** 09:30–16:30; **T:** 09:30–16:30; **W:** 09:30–16:30; **Th:** 09:30–16:30; **F:** 09:30–16:30; **S:** 09:00–16:15; **Su:** 10:30–15:30. Spec: Fiction - General; Fiction - Crime, Detective, Spy, Thrillers; Fiction - Fantasy, Horror; Fiction - Science Fiction; General Stock. CC: AE; E; JCB; MC; V; Switch. VAT No: GB 827 2519 23. Notes: *Books and Beans opened in 2003. Situated in the heart of Aberdeen, Scotland on Belmont Street just off the main thoroughfare of Union Street. Offering Fair Trade Coffee/Tea, Great Food, Internet Access & a wide selection of 2nd Hand Books.*

Clifford Milne Books, 16, Airyhall Avenue, Aberdeen, AB15 7QU. Tel: 01224 324128. Est: 1994. Private premises. Postal only. Spec: Art; Countries - Scotland; Modern First Editions; Sport - General. Mem: PBFA.

Elizabeth Ferguson, 34 Woodburn Avenue, Aberdeen, AB15 8JQ. Tel: (01224) 315949. Fax: (01224) 315949. Est: 2000. Private premises. Postal only. Contactable. Small stock. Spec: Art History; Children's; Children's - Early Titles; Children's - Illustrated; Countries - Scotland; History - Scottish; Illustrated - General; Juvenile. PR: £5–500. Cata: children's; natural history; Scottish interest. Corresp: French, German. Notes: *Small stock children's, illustrated and Scottish books; postcards; sheet music at Aberdeen Antique and Art Centre, 24 South College Street. Opening hours 10am-5pm daily. Telephone 01224 575075 (q.v.) Booksearch service from Home address.*

Kevin S. Ogilvie Modern First, 559 King Street, Aberdeen, AB24 5SU. Tel: 07841 289308. Est: 1991. Private premises. Postal only. Spec: Children's; Fiction - Crime, Detective, Spy, Thrillers; First Editions; Modern First Editions; Signed Editions. PR: £7–100.

Old Aberdeen Bookshop, ◼ 140 Spital, Aberdeen, AB24 3TU. Tel: 01224 658355. Est: 1996. Shop open: **M:** 11:30–17:00; **T:** 11:30–17:00; **W:** 11:30–17:00; **Th:** 11:30–17:00; **F:** 11:30–17:00; **S:** 11:30–17:00. Medium stock. Spec: Academic/Scholarly; Art; Esoteric; Literature; Military; Theology. PR: £1–20. CC: D; MC; V.

BALLATER

McEwan Fine Books, Glengarden, Ballater, AB35 5UB. Prop: Dr. Peter McEwan. Tel: (01339) 755429. Fax: (01339) 755995. Est: 1968. Private premises. Postal only. Appointment necessary. Medium stock. Spec: Animals and Birds; Art - British; Art History; Art Reference; Artists; Author - Watkins-Pitchford, Denys ('B.B.'); Canadiana; Ceramics. PR: £5–5,000. CC: E; MC; V; LAPADA. Cata: Scottish (non-fiction); family histories; polar. Corresp: German. Mem: LAPADA. Notes: *Rhod McEwan Golf Books (q.v.) Also, works of art.*

Rhod McEwan Golf Books, Glengarden, Ballater, AB35 5UB. Tel: (013397) 55429. Fax: (013397) 55995. Web: www.rhodmcewan.com. Est: 1985. Private premises. Appointment necessary. Medium stock. Spec: Sport - Golf. PR: £3–5,000. CC: E; MC; V; PayPal, Debit. Corresp: German, Hungarian, Russian. Mem: ABA; PBFA; ILAB. VAT No: GB 605 2115 89. Notes: *At same premises: McEwan Fine Books. (q.v.) Also, golf posters, paintings and memorabilia.*

Deeside Books, ◼ 18-20 Bridge Street, Ballater, Aberdeenshire, AB35 5QP. Prop: Bryn Wayte. Tel: 01339 754080. Fax: 01339 754080. Est: 1998. Shop open: **M:** 10:00–17:00; **T:** 10:00–17:00; **W:** 10:00–17:00; **Th:** 10:00–17:00; **F:** 10:00–17:00; **S:** 10:00–17:00; **Su:** 12:00–17:00. Spec: Arms & Armour; Army, The; Cookery/Gastronomy; Countries - Africa; Countries - Arctic, The; First Editions; History - General; Maritime/Nautical - History. CC: AE; JCB; MC; V. Mem: PBFA. VAT No: GB 716 9705 12. Notes: *Large varied stock with an emphasis on Scottish, Travel, Polar and Climbing, Transport, Military and Field Sports.*

BANCHORY

Elizabeth Ferguson, Books at Banchory Gallery, 75 High Street, Banchory, Kincardineshire, AB34. Prop: Elizabeth Ferguson. Tel: 01330 824142. Est: 2000. Shop and/or gallery; Open. Shop at: 34 Woodburn Avenue, Aberdeen AB15 8JQ. Open: **M:** 10:00–17:00; **T:** 10:00–17:00; **W:** 10:00–17:00; **Th:** 10:00–17:00; **F:** 10:00–17:00; **S:** 10:00–17:00. Spec: Botany; Children's; Children's - Early Titles; Children's - Illustrated; Comic Books & Annuals; Countries - Scotland; Dolls & Dolls' Houses; Folklore. CC: MC; V. Cata: children's, illustrated, natural history, Scottish. Corresp: French and German. Notes: *Small interesting stock of secondhand and antiquarian books, postcards and sheet music within Gallery selling contemporary art and objects, prints and maps. Good general stock booksearch undertaken.*

DINNET

Jane Jones Books, ■ The Old Shop, Dinnet, Nr Aboyne, AB34 5JY. Prop: Jane Jones. Tel: 013398 85662. Web: www.ukbookworld.com/members/jonesbooks. Est: 2001. Shop open: **M:** 11:00–18:00; **T:** 11:00–18:00; **Th:** 11:00–18:00; **F:** 11:00–18:00; **S:** 11:00–18:00; **Su:** 11:00–18:00. Spec: Agriculture; Animals and Birds; Children's; Dogs; Farming & Livestock; History - General; Literature - Scottish; Natural History. Mem: PBFA. Notes: *Attends Scottish Fairs and occasionally in Northern England.*

ELLON

Grampian Books, South Ardo Methlick, Ellon, Aberdeenshire, AB41 7HP. Prop: David Fleming. Tel: 01651 806165. Est: 1990. Private premises. Internet and Postal. Appointment necessary. Spec: Countries - Scotland; County - Local; Folklore; Genealogy; History - Scottish; Literature - Scottish; Medieval; Parish Registers. CC: MC; V. Cata: Scottish. Corresp: French, Spanish. Mem: PBFA. VAT No: GB 553 1059 63. Notes: *Specialist seller of Scottish books. Free catalogues available on request. We are keen to purchase good-quality Scottish, and other books, from single items to collections and libraries. Customers 'Wants' lists welcomed.*

FOCHABERS

Alba Books, Maxwell Street, Fochabers, IV32 7DE. Prop: Mike Seton. Tel: (01343) 820575. Fax: (01343) 820780. Web: www.albabooks.com. Est: 1997. Warehouse; Internet and Postal. Appointment necessary. Very large stock. Spec: Alternative Medicine; Art; Biology - General; Countries - Scotland; Education & School; Gynaecology; Literature; Maritime/Nautical. PR: £2–200. CC: AE; E; MC; V; Switch. Corresp: French, German,. Mem: IBooknet. VAT No: GB 751 3324 56.

FORRES

Logie Steading Bookshop, ■ Dunphail, Forres, Morayshire, IV36 2QN. Prop: Helen Trussell. Tel: 01309 611373. Est: 2005. Shop. Open: **M:** 11:00–17:00; **T:** 11:00–17:00; **W:** 11:00–17:00; **Th:** 11:00–17:00; **F:** 11:00–17:00; **S:** 11:00–17:00; **Su:** 11:00–17:00. Spec: Author - Walsh, M.; Scottish Interest; Scottish Maps and Prints. CC: MC; V. VAT No: GB 890 4385 01. Notes: *Secondhand bookshop in converted 1926 Model Farm buildings. In delightful rural setting 6 miles S. of Forres. Cafe, gallery, farm/garden shop, antique country furniture, textiles, dressmaker, trompe l'oeil, museum. Phone 1st to view anytime.*

HUNTLY

Orb's Bookshop, ■ 33a Deveron Street, Huntly, AB54 8BY. Prop: Anne Lamb. Tel: (01466) 793765. Est: 2001. Shop open: **M:** 09:15–17:00; **T:** 09:15–17:00; **W:** 09:15–17:00; **Th:** 09:15–17:00; **F:** 09:15–17:00; **S:** 09:15–16:00; Closed for lunch: 13:00–14:00. Spec: Animals and Birds; Author - Barrie, J.M.; Author - Borrow, George; Author - Buchan, John; Author - Burns, Robert; Author - Francis, Dick; Author - Heyer, Georgette; Author - Kipling, Rudyard. CC: MC; V; Maestro. Corresp: French. Mem: BA; FSB. Notes: *Also, new books. Open Saturdays 9:15 to 16:00 (no lunch break).*

HIGHLAND

CULBOKIE

Tom Coleman, 2 Schoolcroft, Culbokie, IV7 8LB. Prop: Tom Coleman. Tel: (01349) 877502. Est: 1998. Private premises. Postal only. Appointment necessary. Medium stock. Spec: General Stock; Scottish Interest. PR: £10–1,000. CC: PayPal.

DURNESS

Loch Croispol Bookshop & Restaurant, ■ 2, Balnakeil, Durness, IV27 4PT. Prop: Kevin Crowe. Tel: 01971-511777. Web: www.scottish-books.net. Est: 1999. Shop open: **M:** 10:00–17:00; **T:** 10:00–17:00; **W:** 10:00–17:00; **Th:** 10:00–17:00; **F:** 10:00–17:00; **S:** 10:00–17:00; **Su:** 10:00–16:00. Spec: Countries - Scotland; History - Scottish; Literature - Scottish; Poetry; Scottish Enlightenment; Scottish Interest; Seafaring & Shipping. CC: MC; V; Maestro, Paypal. VAT No: GB 734 9262 18. Notes: *We specialise in Scottish titles. We also have a large stock of poetry. We also stock general adult and children's titles. Members of the international cooperative of independent booksellers: www.worldbookmarket.com.*

FORT WILLIAM

Creaking Shelves, Arkaig Cottage, Achintore Road, Fort William, Inverness-shire, PH33 6RN. Prop: Chris Robinson. Tel: (01397) 702886. Web: www.abebooks.com. Est: 1998. Private premises. Postal only. Appointment necessary. Small stock. Spec: Alpinism/Mountaineering; Countries - Scotland; History - Scottish; Mountains; Natural History; New Naturalist; Scottish Interest; Topography - Local. PR: £5–500.

INVERNESS

Leakey's Bookshop Ltd, ■ Church Street, Inverness, IV1 1EY. Prop: Charles Leakey. Tel: (01463) 239947. Est: 1979. Shop open: **M:** 10:00–17:30; **T:** 10:00–17:30; **W:** 10:00–17:30; **Th:** 10:00–17:30; **F:** 10:00–17:30; **S:** 10:00–17:30. Very large stock. Spec: Countries - Scotland; Culture - National; Scottish Enlightenment; Scottish Interest; Topography - Local; Prints and Maps. CC: E; JCB; MC; V. Notes: *Stock level - 80,000.*

LOCHCARRON

Blythswood Charity Shop, ■ Main Street, Lochcarron, IV54 8YD. Prop: Blythswood Trading Ltd. Tel: (01520) 722337. Fax: (01520) 722264. Web: www.blythswood.org. Est: 1984. Internet and Postal. Shop open: **Th:** 10:00–16:00; **F:** 10:00–16:00; **S:** 10:00–16:00. Medium stock. Spec: Biography; First Editions; Religion - General; Religion - Christian; Theology; Booksearch; Collectables. PR: £2–200. CC: MC; V. Mem: BA. VAT No: GB 742 9279 06. Notes: *Also at: Portree, Isle of Skye. Dingwell, Ross-shire. Stornoway, Isle of Lewis, and Cromer, Norfolk. Also, new books.*

MUIR OF ORD

Mercat Books, 33 Tarradale Gardens, Muir of Ord, IV6 7SJ. Tel: 01463 870072. Fax: 01463 870072. Web: www.mercatbooks.com. Est: 1994. Private premises. Internet and Postal. Contactable. Spec: Aircraft; Alpinism/Mountaineering; Animals and Birds; Archaeology; Art; Art Reference; Author - Blyton, Enid; Author - Brent-Dyer, Elinor M. Notes: *Mercat Books has now closed its shop premises but still trades via the internet and by direct postal trade. Please note the new contact details. Payment only by cheque. Please feel free to contact me by phone or e-mail for titles or subject.*

THURSO

Tall Tales Bookshop, ■ 1 Princes Street, Thurso, Caithness, KW14 7HF. Prop: Stan Morrison. Tel: 07900 284488. Est: 1955. Shop open: **M:** 09:15–17:15; **T:** 09:15–17:15; **W:** 09:15–17:15; **Th:** 09:15–17:15; **F:** 09:15–17:15; **S:** 09:15–17:15.

ISLES OF SCOTLAND

ISLE OF ARRAN

Barnhill Books, Old Schoolhouse, Kilmory, Isle of Arran, KA27 8PQ. Prop: John Rhead. Tel: (01770) 870368. Est: 1985. Private premises. Postal only. Spec: Alpinism/Mountaineering; Gardening - General; Natural History; Ornithology; Plant Hunting; Sport - Big Game Hunting; Sport - Falconry; Sport - Field Sports. PR: £5–2,000. Cata: ornithology, fieldsports, natural history, big game.

Audrey McCrone, Windyridge, Whiting Bay, Isle of Arran, North Ayrshire, KA27 8QT. Tel: (01770) 700564. Web: www.ukbookworld.com/members/finora. Est: 1980. Private premises. Internet and Postal. Telephone First. Small stock. Spec: Aircraft; Alpinism/Mountaineering; Animals and Birds; Anthologies; Antiquarian; Antiquities; Archaeology; Architecture. PR: £5–200. Cata: Scottish. War, Biography, Poetry, Mysteries.

Johnston's Marine Stores, Old Pier, Lamlash, Isle of Arran, KA27 8JN. Prop: Donald Johnston. Tel: (01770) 600333. Est: 1990. Spec: Marine/Nautical. PR: GBP £1–100.

ISLE OF COLONSAY

Georgina Hobhouse, ■ The Bookshop, Port Mor, Isle of Colonsay, Argyll PA61 7YW. Prop: Georgina Hobhouse. Tel: 01951 200375. Est: 1990. Shop. Open in summer. M: 14:00–17:00; **T:** 14:00–17:00; **W:** 12:00–17:00; **Th:** 14:00–17:00; **F:** 14:00–17:00; **S:** 12:00–17:00. Very small stock. Spec: Islands; Natural History; Scottish Interest; Seafaring & Shipping; Whaling. PR: £1 – 150. CC: MC; V. Corresp: Gailic, French.

Colonsay Bookshop, ■ Isle of Colonsay, Argyll, PA61 7YR. Prop: Kevin & Christa Byrne. Tel: (01951) 200232. Fax: (01951) 200232. Web: www.colonsay.org.uk. Est: 1988. Shop. Open in Summer: **M:** 14.00–17:00; **T:** 14:00–17:00; **W:** 12:00–17:00; **Th:** 14:00–17:00; **F:** 14:00–17:00; **S:** 12:00–17:00. Small stock. Spec: Archaeology; Authors - Local; Celtica; Conservation; Countries - Scotland; History - Irish; History - Local; History - Scottish. PR: £1–300. CC: MC; V; Switch. Notes: *Also, new books & publisher. Specialising in West Highland and other Scottish history. New relevant books in natural history etc and maps and guide books.*

ISLE OF IONA

The Iona Bookshop, ■ The Old Printing Press Building, Isle of Iona, Argyll, PA76 6SL. Prop: Angus L. & Alison Johnston. Tel: (01681) 700699. Est: 1978. Shop open: **M:** 10:30–16:30; **T:** 10:30–16:30; **W:** 10:30–16:30; **Th:** 10:30–16:30; **F:** 10:30–16:30; **S:** 10:30–16:30; **Su:** 10:30–16:30. Small stock. Spec: Countries - Scotland; History - Local; Topography - Local. PR: £1–500. Notes: *Winter: open by appointment only. Also, Celtic tapestry kits.*

ORKNEY ISLANDS

Bygone Books, Chuccaby Farm, Longhope, Orkney, KW16 3PQ. Prop: Isaac Lipkowitz. Tel: (01856) 701443. Est: 1987. Private premises. Postal only. Appointment necessary. Small stock. Spec: Illustrated - General; Kabbala/Cabbala/Cabala; Magick; Mysticism; Occult; Paganism. PR: £1–200.

WESTERN ISLES

M.E. McCarty, Bookseller, ■ 54 Junction Road, Kirkwall, KW15 1AG. Prop: Moi McCarty. Tel: 01856 870860. Est: 1986. Shop open: **M:** 10:30–17:00; **T:** 10:30–17:00; **W:** 10:30–17:00; **Th:** 10:30–17:00; **F:** 10:30–17:00; **S:** 10:00–17:00; Closed for lunch: 13:00–14:00. Medium stock. Spec: Literature; Maritime/Nautical; Travel - General. PR: £1–100. CC: AE; JCB; MC; V; Maestro, Solo. Notes: *13 North Main Street, Wigtown, Scotland (q.v.).*

LOTHIAN

EDINBURGH

Archways Sports Books, P.O. Box 13018, Edinburgh, EH14 2YA. Prop: Iain C. Murray. Web: www.archwaysbooks.com. Est: 1992. Mail order only; Internet and Postal. Appointment necessary. Spec: Sport - General; Sport - American Football; Sport - Athletics; Sport - Badminton; Sport - Baseball; Sport - Basketball; Sport - Billiards/Snooker/Pool; Sport - Bowls. CC: AE; D; E; JCB; MC; V. Cata: Sports.

Armchair Books, ■ 72-74 West Port, Edinburgh, EH1 2LE. Prop: David Govan. Tel: (0131) 229-5927. Web: www.armchairbooks.co.uk. Est: 1989. Shop open: **M:** 10:00–19:00; **T:** 10:00–19:00; **W:** 10:00–19:00; **Th:** 10:00–19:00; **F:** 10:00–18:00; **S:** 10:00–18:00; **Su:** 10:00–18:00. Large stock. Spec: Africana; Annuals; Art; Author - Belloc, Hilaire; Author - Buchan, John; Author - Chesterton, G.K.; Author - Conan Doyle, Sir Arthur; Author - Kipling, Rudyard. PR: £1–1,000. CC: MC; V.

Aurora Books Ltd, ■ 6, Tanfield, Edinburgh, EH3 5DA. Prop: Tom and Annabel Chambers. Tel: 00 44 (0)131 557 8466. Fax: 00 44 (0)131 557 8466. Web: www.aurorabooks.co.uk. Est: 2003. Shop open: **T:** 10:00–18:00; **W:** 10:00–18:00; **Th:** 10:00–18:00; **F:** 10:00–18:00; **S:** 10:00–18:00. Large stock. Spec: Art; Artists; Arts, The; Author - General; Author - 20th Century; Biography; Children's; Countries - General. PR: £2–2,000. CC: AE; JCB; MC; V; Maestro, Solo, Visa Electron. VAT No: GB 808 8104 30.

Peter Bell, ■ 68 West Port, Edinburgh, EH1 2LD. Tel: (0131) 229-0562/556-2198. Fax: (0131) 229-0562. Web: www.peterbell.net. Est: 1980. Shop open: **T:** 14:00–17:00; **Th:** 14:00–17:00; **F:** 14:00–17:00; **S:** 11:00–17:00. Medium stock. Spec: Academic/Scholarly; Autobiography; Biography; Company History; Countries - England; Countries - Scotland; Ecclesiastical History & Architecture; Ecclesiology. PR: £1–500. CC: MC; V. Cata: miscellanies of new stock. Mem: PBFA; ILAB. VAT No: GB 416 0959 50. Notes: *Most stock on the internet. Shop open by appointment or chance in addition to the above (and daily in the Festival). Please ring if travelling.*

Blacket Books, 1 Leadervale Terrace, Edinburgh, EH16 6NX. Prop: Elizabeth and Ian Laing. Tel: 0131-666-1542. Web: www.blacketbooks.co.uk. Est: 1985. Private premises. Internet and Postal. Telephone First. Small stock. Spec: Children's; Military; Scottish Interest. PR: £10–1,500. CC: JCB; MC; V. Mem: PBFA. Notes: *We are general book dealers but with some emphasis on Scottish, military and children's books. We sell at book fairs and on the internet but visitors are welcome by appointment.*

The Bookworm, ■ 210 Dalkeith Road, Edinburgh, EH16 5DT. Prop: Peter Ritchie. Tel: 0131 662 4357. Web: www.scottishbookworm.com. Est: 1986. Shop open: **M:** 09:30–17:30; **T:** 09:30–17:30; **W:** 09:30–17:30; **Th:** 09:30–17:30; **F:** 09:30–17:30; **S:** 09:30–17:00. Spec: Aircraft; Arms & Armour; Army, The; Art Reference; Fiction - General; Fiction - Crime, Detective, Spy, Thrillers; Fiction - Fantasy, Horror; Fiction - Science Fiction. CC: AE; D; JCB; MC; V.

D Robertson (Booksellers & Booksearch Services), 48 Caiystane Avenue, Edinburgh, EH10 6SH. Prop: D Robertson. Tel: 0131 445 1221. Web: www.ukbookworld.com/members/david1955. Est: 2006. Mail order only; Internet and Postal. Shop open: **M:** 09:00–17:30; **T:** 09:00–17:30; **W:** 09:00–17:30; **Th:** 09:00–17:30; **F:** 09:00–17:30; **S:** 09:00–17:30; **Su:** 09:00–17:30; Closed for lunch: 13:00–14:00. Spec: Booksearch. CC: Cash, Cheque, Postal Order, PayPal.

Duncan & Reid, ■ 5 Tanfield, Edinburgh, EH3 5DA. Prop: Maraget Duncan. Tel: 0131 556 4591. Est: 1978. Shop open: **T:** 11:00–17:00; **W:** 11:00–17:00; **Th:** 11:00–17:00; **F:** 11:00–17:00; **S:** 11:00–17:00. Spec: Antiquarian; Antiques; Art; Fashion & Costume; Literature; Scottish Interest. CC: MC; V. Corresp: French and German.

Grant, 14 Winton Drive, Edinburgh, EH10 7ES. Tel: 0131 477 0922. Private premises. Internet and Postal. Open: **S:** 09:00–17:30; **Su:** 09:00–17:30. Spec: Aviation; Military History. Cata: Military, Aviation, 2nd World War. Mem: PBFA.

Grant & Shaw Ltd., 10/5 Leslie Place, Edinburgh, EH4 1NH. Prop: A.S. Grant. Tel: (0131) 332 8088. Fax: (0131) 332 9080. Est: 1989. Private premises. Appointment necessary. Spec: Antiquarian. PR: £20–10,000. CC: MC; V. Mem: ABA.

Jay Books, Rowll House, 1A Roull Grove, Edinburgh, EH12 7JP. Prop: David Brayford. Tel: 0131 467 0309. Est: 1977. Private premises. Telephone First. Open: **M:** 09:00–21:00; **T:** 09:00–21:00; **W:** 09:00–21:00; **Th:** 09:00–21:00; **F:** 09:00–21:00; **S:** 09:00–21:00; **Su:** 09:00–21:00. Spec: Animals and Birds; Antiquarian; Earth Sciences; Flora & Fauna; Natural History; New Naturalist; Ornithology; Science - General. CC: MC; V. Corresp: Spanish German French. Mem: ABA; PBFA; ILAB. Notes: *Valuations for probate and insurance.*

Main Point Books, ■ 8 Lauriston Street, Edinburgh, EH3 9DJ. Prop: Richard Browne. Tel: (0131) 228 4837. Fax: (0131) 228 4837. Est: 2001. Shop open: **T:** 11:00–17:00; **W:** 11:00–17:00; **Th:** 11:00–17:00; **F:** 11:00–17:00; **S:** 11:00–17:00. Medium stock. Spec: Alpinism/Mountaineering; Esoteric; Fiction - General; Literature; Poetry; Scottish Interest; Sport - Climbing & Trekking; Theology.

McNaughtan's Bookshop, ■3a and 4a Haddington Place, Leith Walk, Edinburgh, EH7 4AE. Prop: Elizabeth A. Strong. Tel: (0131) 556-5897. Fax: (0131) 556 8220. Web: www.mcnaughtansbookshop.com. Est: 1957. Shop open: **W:** 11:00–17:00; **Th:** 11:00–17:00; **F:** 11:00–17:00; **S:** 11:00–17:00. Very large stock. Spec: Antiquarian; Applied Art; Architecture; Art; Children's; Cookery/Gastronomy; Countries - Scotland; History - General. PR: £1–3,500. CC: JCB; MC; V; Maestro. Mem: ABA; ILAB. VAT No: GB 327 3505 69.

The Old Town Bookshop, ■ 8 Victoria Street, Edinburgh, EH1 2HG. Prop: Ronald Wilson. Tel: (0131) 225-9237. Fax: (0131) 229-1503. Web: www.oldtownbookshop.co.uk. Est: 1992. Shop open: **M:** 10:30–17:45; **T:** 10:30–17:45; **W:** 10:30–17:45; **Th:** 10:30–17:45; **F:** 10:30–17:45; **S:** 10:00–17:45. Medium stock. Spec: Architecture; Art; Art Reference; Bindings; Botany; Catalogues Raisonnes; Children's; Country Houses. PR: £1–3,000. CC: MC; V; SW. Mem: PBFA. Notes: *Exhibits at 18 book fairs around the country.*

David Page, 47 Spottiswoode Road, Edinburgh, EH9 1DA. Tel: (0131) 447-4553. Fax: (0131) 447-4553. Private premises. Postal only. Telephone First. Small stock. Spec: Alpinism/Mountaineering; Mountains; Natural History; Plant Hunting; Travel - General; Travel - Africa; Travel - Asia; Travel - Asia, South East. Cata: Mountaineering, Travel. Corresp: French, German.

Pinnacle Books, 13 Westgarth Avenue, Edinburgh, EH13 0BB. Tel: 0131 441 3870. Web: www.pinnaclebooks.net. Private premises. Internet and Postal. Appointment necessary. Spec: Alpinism/Mountaineering; Exploration; Mountain Men; Mountains; Scottish Interest; Sport - Skiing; Travel - Americas; Travel - Asia. Cata: Mountaineering. Mem: PBFA. Notes: *Pinnacle Books is a specialist antiquarian bookshop with a large selection of rare and interesting secondhand books in the following areas - Mountaineering, Central Asia, Polar Exploration, Skiing, Scottish Topography and Travel.*

Andrew Pringle Booksellers, ■ 62 West Port, Edinburgh, EH1 2LD. Tel: (0131) 228-8880. Fax: Same. Web: www.pringlebooks.co.uk. Est: 1988. Shop open: **M:** 11:00–17:30; **T:** 11:00–17:30; **W:** 11:00–17:30; **Th:** 11:00–17:30; **F:** 11:00–17:30; **S:** 11:00–17:30. Medium stock. Spec: Antiquarian; Art; Author - Buchan, John; Biography; History - General; History - National; Literature; Maritime/ Nautical. PR: £3–500. CC: JCB; MC; V; Switch. Corresp: French. Mem: ABA; PBFA; ILAB.

Robertson Books, 60 Craigcrook Road, Edinburgh, EH4 3PJ. Prop: Vanessa Robertson. Tel: 0131 343 3118. Web: www.robertsonbooks.co.uk. Est: 2003. Private premises. Internet and Postal. Spec: Children's. CC: cheque. Cata: children's books. Mem: Ibooknet. Notes: *Specialists in children's literature.*

Second Edition, ■ 9 Howard Street, Edinburgh, EH3 5JP. Prop: Mrs. Maureen E. Tel: (0131) 556-9403. Web: www.secondeditionbookshop.co.uk. Est: 1978. Shop. Market Stall. Shop open: **M:** 12:00–17:00; **T:** 12:00–17:00; **W:** 12:00–17:00; **Th:** 12:00–17:00; **F:** 12:00–17:00; **S:** 12:00–17:00. Large stock. Spec: Countries - Scotland; History - Scottish; Literature - Scottish; Scottish Interest. PR: £10–2,000. Cata: occasionally on Scottish subjects. Corresp: Slovenian.

The Old Children's Bookshelf, ■ 175 Canongate, Edinburgh, EH8 8BN. Prop: Shirley Neilson. Tel: 0131 558 3411. Est: 1998. Shop open: **M:** 10:30–17:00; **T:** 10:30–17:00; **W:** 10:30–17:00; **Th:** 10:30–17:00; **F:** 10:30–17:00; **S:** 10:30–17:00; **Su:** 11:00–16:30. Spec: Annuals; Children's; Children's - Illustrated; Comic Books & Annuals; Comics; Education & School; Juvenile; Pop-Up, Movable & Cut Out. CC: AE; MC; V. Cata: on children's books only. Mem: PBFA. Notes: *Exhibits at PBFA fairs.*

Till's Bookshop, ■ 1 Hope Park Crescent (Buccleugh Street), Edinburgh, EH8 9NA. Tel: (0131) 667-0895. Web: www.tillsbookshop.co.uk. Est: 1986. Internet and Postal. Shop open: **M:** 12:00–19:30; **T:** 12:00–19:30; **W:** 12:00–19:30; **Th:** 12:00–19:30; **F:** 12:00–19:30; **S:** 11:00–18:00; **Su:** 12:00–17:30. Large stock. Spec: Alternative Medicine; Annuals; Arts, The; Children's; Cinema/Film; Classics, The; Comic Books & Annuals; Drama. PR: £2–100. CC: AE; D; E; JCB; MC; V; De, SW, SO. Notes: *We also sell cinema posters, LP's, comics etc. A wide range of subjects, not solely books.*

John Updike Rare Books, 7 St. Bernard's Row, Edinburgh, EH4 1HW. Prop: John S. Watson & Edward G. Nairn. Tel: (0131) 332-1650. Fax: (0131) 332-1347. Est: 1965. Private premises. Appointment necessary. Medium stock. Spec: Books about Books; Children's; Churchilliana; Drama; Fine & Rare; Fine Printing; First Editions; Illustrated - General. Mem: ABA.

HADDINGTON

Yeoman Books, 37 Hope Park Crescent, Haddington, East Lothian, EH41 3AN. Prop: D.A. Hyslop. Tel: (01620) 822307. Est: 1924. Private premises. Appointment necessary. Small stock. Spec: Aviation; Military; Military History; Motorbikes / motorcycles; Motoring; War - General. PR: £5–150. Mem: PBFA. Notes: *Also attends PBFA book fairs.*

NORTH BERWICK

The Penny Farthing, ■ 23 Quality Street, North Berwick, East Lothian, EH39. Prop: Stuart Tait. Tel: 01620 89 0114. Est: 1983. Shop open: **M:** 10:00–18:00; **T:** 10:00–18:00; **W:** 10:00–18:00; **Th:** 10:00–18:00; **F:** 10:00–18:00; **S:** 10:00–18:00; **Su:** 14:00–18:00; Closed for lunch: 13:00–14:00. Spec: Animals and Birds; Annuals; Archaeology; Children's; Children's - Early Titles; Children's - Illustrated; Countries - Africa; Countries - Asia. Notes: *Attends Scotfair, Edinburgh.*

STRATHCLYDE

AIRDRIE

Brown-Studies, Woodside Cottage, Longriggend, Airdrie, ML6 7RU. Prop: (*) Mr. M.G. & Mrs. B.J. Brown. Tel: (01236) 843826. Fax: (01236) 842545. Web: www.brown-studies-books.co.uk. Est: 1990. Private premises. Internet and Postal. Appointment necessary. Open: **M:** 09:00–20:00; **T:** 09:00–20:00; **W:** 09:00–20:00; **Th:** 09:00–20:00; **F:** 09:00–20:00; **S:** 09:00–20:00; **Su:** 09:00–20:00. Very large stock. Spec: Artists; Author - Read, Miss; Building & Construction; Cookery/Gastronomy; D.I.Y. (Do It Yourself); Ecology; Gardening - General; Herbalism. PR: £3–300. CC: E; JCB; MC; V; Switch/ PAYPAL. VAT No: GB 556 6923 05. Notes: *Illustrators - J S Goodall.*

AYR

Ainslie Books, ■ 1 Glendoune St., Girvan, Ayr, KA26 0AA. Prop: Gordon Clark. Tel: (01465) 715453. Fax: (01465) 715453. Web: www.ainsliebooks.co.uk. Internet and Postal. Shop open: **T:** 10:00–17:00; **W:** 10:00–17:00; **Th:** 10:00–17:00; **F:** 10:00–17:00; **S:** 10:00–17:00. Large stock. Spec: Academic/ Scholarly; Shorthand; Booksearch. PR: £1–200. CC: MC; V. Notes: *Free booksearch.*

CAMPBELTOWN

The Old Bookshelf, ■ 8 Cross Street, Campbeltown, PA28 6HU. Prop: Cynthia Byrne. Tel: (01586) 551114. Web: www.theoldbookshelf.co.uk. Est: 2001. Internet and Postal. Shop open: **M:** 10:00– 17:00; **T:** 10:00–17:00; **W:** 10:00–17:00; **Th:** 10:00–17:00; **F:** 10:00–17:00; **S:** 10:00–15:00. Large stock. Spec: History - Local; Scottish Interest; Topography - Local. PR: £2–3,000. CC: AE; E; JCB; MC; V; Maestro. Corresp: Spanish. Mem: ibooknet. VAT No: GB 808 8668 81. Notes: *Books about and on Kintyre.*

GLASGOW

Alba Secondhand Music, ■ 55 Otago Street, Glasgow, G12 8PQ. Prop: Robert Lay. Tel: (0141) 357 1795. Web: www.albamusick.co.uk. Est: 1994. Shop open: **M:** 11:00–17:30; **T:** 11:00–17:30; **W:** 11:00–17:30; **Th:** 11:00–17:30; **F:** 11:00–17:30; **S:** 11:00–17:30. Large stock. Spec: Music - General; Music - Classical; Music - Composers; Music - Folk & Irish Folk; Music - Gilbert & Sullivan; Music - Gregorian Chants; Music - Illustrated Sheet Music; Music - Musicians. PR: £1–100. CC: MC; V. Notes: *Shop located behind Otago cafe & open at other times by appointment.*

Jack Baldwin, 34 Hamilton Park Avenue, Glasgow, G12 8DT. Prop: Jack Baldwin. Tel: (0141) 334-8684. Fax: (0141) 334-8684. Web: www.jackbaldwin.dial.pipex.com. Est: 1985. Private premises. Internet and Postal. Appointment necessary. Small stock. Spec: Antiquarian; Countries - Baltic States; Countries - Latin America; Countries - Mexico; Countries - Portugal; Countries - Russia; Countries - South America; Countries - Spain. PR: £5–1,000. CC: JCB; MC; V. Corresp: French, German, Italian, Spanish, Portuguese.

Books At The Barras, London Road Market, London Road, Glasgow, G4 0TS. Prop: Barry Thurston. Tel: 07986 118480. Est: 11988. Market stall. Open: **S:** 09:00–16:00; **Su:** 10:00–16:00. Medium stock. Spec: Children's, Scottish Interest. PR: 50p –£200. Notes: *A medium sized general stock with an accent on Scottish, children's and collectable books.*

Caledonia Books, ■ 483 Great Western Road, Kelvinbridge, Glasgow, G12 8HL. Prop: Maureen Smillie & Charles McBride. Tel: (0141) 334-9663. Fax: (0141) 334-9663. Web: www.caledoniabooks.co.uk. Est: 1984. Shop open: **M:** 10:30–18:00; **T:** 10:30–18:00; **W:** 10:30–18:00; **Th:** 10:30–18:00; **F:** 10:30– 18:00; **S:** 10:30–18:00. Spec: Art; Art History; Bibliography; Biography; Cinema/Film; Drama; Fiction - General; History - General. PR: £2–200. CC: MC; V.

Cooper Hay Rare Books, ■ 185 Bath Street, Glasgow, G2 4HG. Prop: Cooper Hay and Marianne Hay. Tel: (0141) 333-1992. Fax: (0141) 333-1992. Web: www.cooperhay.com. Est: 1985. Shop open: **M:** 10:00–17:30; **T:** 10:00–17:30; **W:** 10:00–17:30; **Th:** 10:00–17:30; **F:** 10:00–17:30; **S:** 10:00–13:00; Closed for lunch: 13:00–14:15. Medium stock. Spec: Antiquarian; Art; Art - British; Art Reference; Bibliography; Bindings; Books about Books; Children's - Illustrated. PR: £5–5,000. CC: MC; V. Cata: Scottish. Mem: ABA; ILAB. VAT No: GB 402 9241 83. Notes: *Attends ABA fairs in Edinburgh and Chelsea.*

The Studio, ■ De Courcy's Arcade, 5-21 Cresswell Lane, Glasgow, G12 8AA. Prop: Liz McKelvie. Tel: (0141) 334 8211. Web: www.glasgowwestend.co.uk/shopping/antiques/studio. Est: 1997. Shop open: **T:** 10:00–17:30; **W:** 10:00–17:30; **Th:** 10:00–17:30; **F:** 10:00–17:30; **S:** 10:00–17:30; **Su:** 12:00–17:00. Small stock. Spec: Bindings; Children's - Illustrated; Decorative Art; History - Local; Publishers - Blackie. PR: £5–1,000. CC: D; E; JCB; MC; V; SW, MAE. Notes: *Also, books about Glasgow and Glasgow style antques, furnishings, metalware, textiles, ceramics - circa 1900.*

Thistle Books, 61 Otago Street, Glasgow, G12 8PQ. Prop: Robert Dibble. Tel: (0141) 334 8777. Est: 1997. Open: **M:** 11:00–17:30; **T:** 11:00–17:30; **W:** 11:00–17:30; **Th:** 11:00–17:30; **F:** 11:00–17:30; **S:** 11:00– 17:30. Large stock. Spec: Fiction - General; History - General; History - National; History - Scottish; Literature - Scottish; Modern First Editions; Scottish Interest. PR: £1–100.

HELENSBURGH

McLaren Books Ltd, 22 John street, Helensburgh, Argyll & Bute, G84 8BA. Prop: George Newlands. Tel: 01436 676453. Web: www.mclarenbooks.co.uk. Est: 1976. Office and/or bookroom; Contactable. Open: **F:** 10:00–17:00; **S:** 10:00–17:00. Spec: Deep Sea Diving; Fisheries; Maritime/Nautical; Maritime/Nautical - History; Maritime/Nautical - Log Books; Naval; Navigation; Navy, The. CC: MC; V. Cata: All Aspects of Maritime History. Mem: ABA; PBFA; ILAB. Notes: *Friday and Saturday are the official 'open' days. We are often open on other days, but best to phone first. Specialist Maritime Stock with small quality general selection.*

IRVINE

D. Webster, 43 West Road, Irvine, KA12 8RE. Tel: (01294) 272257. Fax: (01294) 276322. Est: 1958. Private premises. Appointment necessary. Small stock. Spec: Circus; Physical Culture; Sport - Highland Games; Sport - Weightlifting/Bodybuilding; Sport - Wrestling; Booksearch; Collectables; Ephemera. PR: £5–40. Notes: *Also, booksearch. davidpwebster@hotmail.com.*

KILMARNOCK

Roberts Books, 8, Main Road, Waterside, Kilmarnock, Ayrshire, KA3 6JB. Prop: Richard Roberts. Tel: (01560) 600349. Fax: (01560) 600349. Web: www.ukbookworld.com/members/roberts. Est: 1976. Private premises. Internet and Postal. Appointment necessary. Small stock. Spec: Academic/Scholarly; Architecture; British Books; Building & Construction; Countries - England; Countries - Japan; Countries - Scotland; Earth Sciences. PR: £5–450. Corresp: French, German.

TAYSIDE

ABERFELDY

Freader's Books, ■ 8 Dunkeld Street, Aberfeldy, PH15 2DA. Prop: Christopher Rowley. Tel: (01887) 829519. Fax: (01887) 829519. Est: 1991. Shop open: **M:** 10:00–16:00; **T:** 10:00–16:00; **Th:** 10:00–16:00; **F:** 10:00–16:00; **S:** 10:00–16:00; Closed for lunch: 13:00–14:00. Small stock. Spec: Countries - Scotland; General; Natural History; Physics; Scottish Interest; Topography - General; Topography - Local. PR: £4–200. Mem: BA.

ARBROATH

A Jolly Good Read, 94 Brechin Road, Arbroath, DD11 1SX. Tel: (01241) 877552. Web: www.ajollygoodread.co.uk. Est: 2004. Private premises. Internet and Postal. Contactable. Small stock. Spec: Children's. PR: £5–500. CC: PayPal. Cata: Childrens Books.

BLAIRGOWRIE

Blairgowrie Books, ■ 3 Meadow Place, Blairgowrie, PH10 6NG. Prop: Marlene Hill. Tel: 01250 875855. Est: 1981. Shop open: **M:** 09:00–17:30; **T:** 09:00–17:30; **W:** 09:00–17:30; **Th:** 09:00–17:30; **F:** 09:00–17:30; **S:** 09:00–17:30; **Su:** 09:00–17:30; Closed for lunch: 13:00–14:00. Spec: Ephemera; Prints and Maps.

DUNDEE

Big Bairn Books, ■ 17 Exchange Street, Dundee, DD1 3DJ. Prop: Douglas Hill. Tel: 01382 220225. Est: 1998. Shop open: **M:** 10:30–17:00; **T:** 10:30–17:00; **W:** 10:30–17:00; **Th:** 10:30–17:00; **F:** 10:30–17:00; **S:** 10:30–17:00. Spec: Annuals; Art; Military; Poetry; Scottish Interest; Sport - Angling/Fishing; Sport - Football (Soccer); Sport - Golf. Notes: *Also, postcards and greetings cards.*

DUNKELD

Dunkheld Antiques, ■ Tay Terrace, Dunkeld, Perthshire, PH8 0DX. Prop: David Dytch. Tel: 01350 728832. Fax: 01350 727008. Web: www.dunkeldantiques.co.uk. Est: 1986. Shop open: **M:** 11:00–17:30; **T:** 11:00–17:30; **W:** 11:00–17:30; **Th:** 11:00–17:30; **F:** 11:00–17:30; **S:** 10:00–17:30; **Su:** 12:00–17:30. Spec: Alpinism/Mountaineering; Animals and Birds; Art; Literature - Scottish; Natural History; Ornithology; Topography - General; Transport. CC: MC; V. Notes: *Variation in hours: from November to Easter Friday 11:00-17:00, Saturday 10:00- 17:00.*

FORFAR

Hilary Farquharson, Deuchar Farm, Fern, Forfar, DD8 3QZ. Prop: H. Farquharson. Tel: (01356) 650278. Fax: (01356) 650417. Est: 1992. Private premises. Book fairs only. Appointment necessary. Open: **M:** 09:00–21:00; **T:** 09:00–21:00; **W:** 09:00–21:00; **Th:** 09:00–21:00; **F:** 09:00–21:00; **S:** 09:00–21:00; **Su:** 09:00–21:00. Medium stock. Spec: Agriculture; Antiquarian; Architecture; Authors - Local; Countries - Scotland; Farming & Livestock; Fine & Rare; Genealogy. PR: £5–1,000. CC: JCB; MC; V. Mem: PBFA.

KILLIECRANKIE

Atholl Fine Books, Clunemore, Killiecrankie, Pitlochry, PH16 5LS. Prop: Nancy Foy Cameron. Tel: 01796 473470. Est: 1988. Private premises. Internet and Postal. Appointment necessary. Open: **M:** 09:00–17:30; **T:** 09:00–17:30; **W:** 09:00–17:30; **F:** 09:00–17:30; **S:** 09:00–17:30; **Su:** 09:00–17:30; Closed for lunch: 13:00–14:00. Spec: Antiquarian; Author - Pennant, Thomas; Authors - Local; Bindings; Countries - Scotland; Fine & Rare; Fine leather bindings (see also Fine & Rare); Fishes. CC: none, Abe if needed. Corresp: French. Notes: *Very happy to deal over the phone, 01796 473 470.*

PERTH

Bookseeker, P O Box 7535, Perth, PH2 1AF. Prop: Paul Thompson. Tel: (01738) 620688. Web: www. bookseeker.myby.co.uk. Private premises. Postal only. Spec: Quakers, The; Religion - Quakers; Booksearch. Notes: *Booksearch only. Specialise in Quakerism, but will look for anything.*

PITLOCHRY

Glacier Books, Ard-Darach Strathview Terrace, Pitlochry, PH16 5AT. Prop: Chris Bartle. Tel: (01796) 470056. Fax: (01796) 470056. Web: www.glacierbooks.com. Est: 1999. Private premises. Internet and Postal. Telephone First. Open: **M:** 10:00–15:00; **W:** 10:00–15:00; **F:** 10:00–15:00. Medium stock. Spec: Alpinism/Mountaineering; Arctic - Antarctica; Countries - Alaska; Countries - Americas, The; Countries - Antarctic, The; Countries - Arctic, The; Countries - Asia; Countries - Bhutan. PR: £1–3,000. CC: MC; V. Cata: Mountaineering, Polar. Notes: *Scotland's largest stock of Mountaineering and Polar Travel Books.*

STRATHTAY

Strathtay Antiquarian - Secondhand Books, Upper Derculich, Pitlochry, Strathtay, PH9 0LR. Prop: Alistair and Pamela Robinson. Tel: 01887 840373. Fax: 01887 840777. Est: 2006. Private premises. Internet and Postal. Open: **M:** 09:00–17:30; **T:** 09:00–17:30; **W:** 09:00–17:30; **Th:** 09:00–17:30; **F:** 09:00–17:30; **S:** 09:00–17:30; **Su:** 09:00–17:30; Closed for lunch: 13:00–14:00. Spec: Antiques; Biography; Children's; Fiction - General; Modern First Editions; Scottish Interest; Sport - Field Sports; Sport - Golf.

WALES

The Unitary Authorities of Caerphilly, Cardiff, Carmarthenshire, Ceredigion, Conwy, Denbighshire, Dyfed, Flintshire, Gwynedd, Monmouthshire, Neath Port Talbot, Newport, Powys, Rhondda Cynon Taff, Swansea and Wrexham.

CAERPHILLY

NEW TREDEGAR

Tom Saunders, 9 Woodland Terrace, New Tredegar, NP24 6LL. Tel: (01443) 836946. Web: www. ukbookworld.com/members/BUDDYBOY. Est: 1989. Private premises. Postal only. Telephone First. Small stock. Spec: Academic/Scholarly; Biography; Chess; Children's; Education & School; Politics; Religion - General; Sport - American Football. PR: £3–50.

CARDIFF

CARDIFF

Bear Island Books, ■ Cardiff Central Market, St. Mary Street, Cardiff, CF10 1AU. Tel: (029) 2038 8631. Shop open: **M:** 10:00–17:00; **T:** 10:00–17:00; **W:** 10:00–17:00; **Th:** 10:00–17:00; **F:** 10:00–17:00; **S:** 10:00–17:00. Spec: History - Local; Topography - Local; Welsh Interest. CC: PayPal.

Capital Bookshop, ■ 27 Morgan Arcade, Cardiff, CF10 1AF. Prop: A.G. Mitchell. Tel: (029) 2038-8423. Est: 1981. Shop open: **M:** 10:00–17:30; **T:** 10:00–17:30; **W:** 10:00–17:30; **Th:** 10:00–17:30; **F:** 10:00–17:30; **S:** 10:00–17:30. Large stock. Spec: Antiquarian; Countries - Wales; Booksearch; Prints and Maps. PR: £1–500. CC: E; MC; V; Mae, So. Mem: PBFA.

Len Foulkes, 28 St. Augustine Road, Heath, Cardiff, CF14 4BE. Tel: (029) 2062-7703. Est: 1971. Private premises. Postal only. Very large stock. PR: £5–100. Notes: *Now semi-retired.*

Whitchurch Books Ltd., ■ 67 Merthyr Road, Whitchurch, Cardiff, CF14 1DD. Prop: Dr. G.L. Canvin. Tel: (029) 20521956. Est: 1994. Shop open: **T:** 10:00–17:30; **W:** 10:00–17:30; **Th:** 10:00–17:30; **F:** 10:00–17:30; **S:** 10:00–17:30. Very large stock. Spec: Anthropology; Antiquarian; Antiquities; Archaeology; Archaeology - Industrial; Art History; Arthurian; Arthurian (King Arthur). PR: £1–100. CC: AE; D; E; JCB; MC; V; SW; S; EL. Cata: History & Archaeology. Mem: WBA. VAT No: GB 648 3263 23. Notes: *Also, a booksearch service.*

Nicholas Willmott Bookseller, 97 Romilly Road, Canton, Cardiff, CF5 1FN. Prop: Nicholas Willmott & Judith Wayne. Tel: (029) 2037-7268. Fax: (029) 2037-7268. Web: www.members.lycos.co.uk/nicholaswillmott/id17.htm. Est: 1982. Private premises. Postal only. Contactable. Large stock. Spec: Authors - Women; Autobiography; Biography; Drama; Feminism; Fiction - General; History - General; Humour. PR: £2–500. Corresp: French. VAT No: GB 368 3564 19. Notes: *Freelance tenor.*

CARMARTHENSHIRE

AMMANFORD

Discovery Bookshop, 52 Cwmamman Road, Garnant, Ammanford, SA18 1LT. Prop: George & Kate Stent. Tel: 01269 823839. Web: www.discoverybookshop.co.uk. Est: 2002. Shop and/or showroom; Shop open: **M:** 10:00–17:00; **T:** 10:00–17:00; **W:** 10:00–17:00; **Th:** 10:00–17:00; **F:** 10:00–17:00. Spec: Aircraft; Americana - General; Art; Autobiography; Biblical Studies; Biography; Cookery/Gastronomy; Crafts. CC: PayPal. Notes: *Retail/trade sales through the shop premises. Direct sales over the phone and internet sales through three internet sites.*

Stobart Davies Limited, Stobart House, Pontyclerc, Penybanc Road, Ammanford, SA18 3HP. Tel: (01269) 593100. Fax: (01269) 596116. Web: www.stobartdavies.com. Est: 1989. Office and/or bookroom; Internet and Postal. Shop open: **M:** 09:00–17:00; **T:** 09:00–17:00; **W:** 09:00–17:00; **Th:** 09:00–17:00; **F:** 09:00–17:00. Very large stock. Spec: Building & Construction; Crafts; D.I.Y. (Do It Yourself); Design; Forestry; Furniture; Woodland Crafts; Woodwork. PR: £3–60. CC: AE; D; MC; V. Cata: Woodworking. Mem: BA. Notes: *Stobart Davies is a specialist, independent British publisher and distributor of books on wood and woodworking skills appealing to both professional and amateur craftsmen.*

CARMARTHEN

Sue Lloyd-Davies, 94 St. Catherine Street, Carmarthen, SA31 1RF. Prop: Sue Lloyd-Davies. Tel: (01267) 235462. Fax: (01267) 235462. Est: 1979. Private premises. Internet and Postal. Telephone First. Open: **M:** 10:00–20:00; **T:** 10:00–20:00; **W:** 10:00–20:00; **Th:** 10:00–20:00; **F:** 10:00–20:00; **S:** 10:00–20:00; **Su:** 11:00–20:00; Closed for lunch: odd–times. Medium stock. Spec: Annuals; Architecture; Art; Children's; Children's - Illustrated; First Editions; General Stock; Illustrated - General. PR: £5–2,000. CC: E; JCB; MC; V; Switch etc. Corresp: French, Japanese, Welsh, Mandarin Chinese. Mem: PBFA; WBA. Notes: *Traded for 28 years, to date, now mainly selling online and exhibiting at Major London Bookfairs only. View by Appointment. Happy to see customers but they must be able to squeeze through the book aisles/piles! Regret no wheelchair access.*

CEREDIGION

ABERYSTWYTH

Aber Books and Collectables, ■ 17 Northgate Street, Aberystwyth, SY23 2JS. Prop: Caroline Walters and Nigel Davies. Tel: 01970 630333. Est: 2005. Shop open: **M:** 10:00–17:30; **T:** 10:00–17:30; **W:** 12:00–17:30; **Th:** 10:00–17:30; **F:** 10:00–17:30; **S:** 11:00–17:00. CC: AE; JCB; MC; V; Solo, Switch, Electron.

Colin Hancock, Ty'n Y Llechwedd Hall, Llandre, Aberystwyth, SY24 5BX. Prop: Colin Hancock. Tel: 01970 828709. Fax: 01970 828709. Est: 1998. Private premises. Appointment necessary. Spec: Antiquarian; Archaeology; Celtica; Countries - Wales; County - Local; Culture - National; Dictionaries; Fine & Rare. Corresp: French, Welsh. Mem: Welsh Booksellers Association.

Ystwyth Books, ■ 7 Princess Street, Aberystwyth, SY23 1DX. Prop: Martin Ashby. Tel: (01970) 639479. Est: 1976. Shop open: **M:** 09:30–17:30; **T:** 09:30–17:30; **W:** 09:30–17:30; **Th:** 09:30–17:30; **F:** 09:30–17:30; **S:** 09:30–17:30. Medium stock. Spec: Art; Countries - Wales; History - Industrial; Poetry; Theatre; Topography - Local. PR: £2–100. CC: E; MC; V; PayPal. Corresp: French, Welsh. Mem: BA. VAT No: GB 915 0257 48. Notes: *Over 90,000 books in stock which includes books on Nature Conservation and Wildlife.*

CARDIGAN

Books in Cardigan, ■ 2, Pwllhai, Cardigan, SA43 1BZ. Prop: Mary Sinclair. Tel: (012 39) 682517. Web: www.http://cardiganbooks.hypermart.net/. Est: 1986. Internet and Postal. Shop open: **M:** 09:00–17:00; **T:** 09:00–17:00; **W:** 09:00–17:00; **Th:** 09:00–17:00; **F:** 09:00–17:00; **S:** 09:00–17:00. Large stock. Spec: Travel - General; Welsh Interest. Corresp: French, Spanish, Portuguese. Notes: *Cardigan Market Stall open 6 days a week.*

LAMPETER

Barry Thomas Poultry Books, The Vicarage, Felinfach, Lampeter, SA48 8AE. Tel: (01570) 470944. Fax: (01570) 471557. Est: 1976. Private premises. Internet and Postal. Contactable. Open: **M:** 09:00–21:00; **T:** 09:00–21:00; **W:** 09:00–21:00; **Th:** 09:00–21:00; **F:** 09:00–21:00. Small stock. Spec: Cockfighting; Poultry; Ephemera; Prints and Maps. PR: £1–1,000. Corresp: French, German, Welsh.

TREGARON

Nigel Bird (Books), Bryn Hir Llwynygroes, Tregaron, SY25 6PY. Prop: Nigel & Sue Bird. Tel: (01974) 821281. Web: www.nigelbirdbooks.co.uk. Est: 1985. Private premises. Internet and Postal. Telephone First. Open: **M:** 10:00–18:00; **T:** 10:00–18:00; **W:** 10:00–18:00; **Th:** 10:00–18:00; **F:** 10:00–18:00; Closed for lunch: 13:00–14:00. Medium stock. Spec: Author - Rolt, L.T.C.; Canals/Inland Waterways; Railways and Railroads; Traction Engines; Transport. PR: £1–200. CC: E; JCB; MC; V. Cata: Railways. VAT No: GB 549 6927 83. Notes: *I offer a booksearch service for railway titles only. Answer machine when closed.*

CONWY

COLWYN BAY

Bay Bookshop, ■ 14 Seaview Road, Colwyn Bay, LL29 8DG. Prop: A.P. Morley. Tel: (01492) 531642. Web: www.baybookshop.co.uk. Est: 1973. Shop open: **M:** 09:00–17:00; **T:** 09:00–17:00; **W:** 09:00–17:00; **Th:** 09:00–17:00; **F:** 09:00–17:00; **S:** 09:00–17:00. Spec: Collectables; Ephemera; Prints and Maps. PR: £1–500. CC: E; MC; V.

Colwyn Books, ■ 66 Abergele Road, Colwyn Bay, LL29 7PP. Prop: John & Linda Beagan. Tel: (01492) 530683. Web: www.colwynbooks.co.uk. Est: 1989. Shop open: **T:** 09:30–17:00; **Th:** 09:30–17:00; **F:** 09:30–17:00; **S:** 09:30–17:00; Closed for lunch: 13:00–13:30. Medium stock. Spec: Author - General; Countries - Wales; Fiction - General; General Stock; History - General; New Books; Publishers - Haynes Publishing; Religion - General. PR: £1–15. Cata: Religion and theology, French. Corresp: Welsh. Mem: Welsh Booksellers Assoc. Notes: *Also selling new books published by Gwasg Carreg Gwalch, and hand-made bookmarks and greetings cards. Books in French.*

D. Gathern, 42a Seaview Road, Colwyn Bay, LL29 8DG. Prop: David Gathern. Tel: 01492 532569. Private premises. Appointment necessary. Open: **M:** 09:30–17:30; **T:** 09:30–17:30; **W:** 09:30–17:30; **Th:** 09:30–17:30; **F:** 09:30–17:30; **S:** 09:30–17:30; **Su:** 10:00–17:30. Medium stock. Spec: Sport - General; Sport - Athletics; Sport - Baseball; Sport - Boxing; Sport - Cricket; Sport - Football (Soccer); Sport - Golf; Sport - Horse Racing (inc. Riding/Breeding/Equestrian). CC: PayPal.

owenbooks65, 13 Wynn Drive, Old Colwyn, Colwyn Bay, LL29 9DE. Prop: Jack Owen. Tel: (01492) 516600. Est: 1989. Private premises. Internet only. Appointment necessary. Small stock. Spec: Countries - Europe; Countries - France; Foreign Texts; Languages - African; Languages - Foreign; Languages - National. CC: Paypal. Cata: Foreign languages. Corresp: French, Italian, German, Spanish. Mem: WBA. Notes: *Amazon, Biblio, Alibris.*

Rhos Point Books, ■ 85 The Promenade, Rhos–on–Sea, Colwyn Bay, LL28 4PR. Prop: Gwyn & Beryl Morris. Tel: (01492) 545236. Fax: (01492) 540862. Web: www.ukbookworld.com/members/brynglas. Est: 1986. Internet and Postal. Shop open: **T:** 10:00–17:30; **W:** 10:00–17:30; **Th:** 10:00–17:30; **F:** 10:00–17:30; **S:** 10:00–17:30; **Su:** 11:00–17:30. Medium stock. Spec: Antiquarian; Welsh Interest. PR: £1–300. CC: MC; V. Corresp: Welsh.

Yesterday's News, 43 Dundonald Road, Colwyn Bay, LL29 7RE. Prop: Elfed Jones. Tel: (01492) 531195. Web: www.giftnewspapers.co.uk/. Est: 1967. Private premises. Shop open: **M:** 09:00–21:00; **T:** 09:00–21:00; **W:** 09:00–21:00; **Th:** 09:00–21:00; **F:** 09:00–21:00; **S:** 09:00–21:00. Very large stock. Spec: Broadcasting; Canadiana; Churchilliana; Cinema/Film; Comic Books & Annuals; Comics; Crime (True); Entertainment - General. PR: £5–50. Corresp: German, Welsh. Notes: *Majors in newspapers, periodicals and paper ephemera.*

LLANRWST

Prospect Books, 10 Trem Arfon, Llanrwst, LL26 0BP. Prop: M. R. Dingle. Tel: 01492 640111. Web: www.gunbooks.co.uk. Est: 1982. Private premises. Appointment necessary. Open: **M:** 09:00–17:30; **T:** 09:00–17:30; **W:** 09:00–17:30; **Th:** 09:00–17:30; **F:** 09:00–17:30. Spec: Arms & Armour; Firearms/Guns; Weapons. CC: JCB; MC; V; Maestro/Switch. Cata: weapons. Notes: *Specialist books on weaponry.*

TREFRIW

Roz Hulse, Llanrwst Road, Trefriw, LL27 0JR. Prop: Roz Hulse. Tel: (01492) 640963. Web: www.rozhulse.com. Est: 2004. Private premises. Internet and Postal. Appointment necessary. Small stock. Spec: Academic/Scholarly; Alpinism/Mountaineering; American Northwest; Animals and Birds; Antiquarian; Arctic - Antarctica; Atlases; Author - Barrie, J.M. PR: £40–5,000. CC: MC; V. Cata: Illustrated, Private Press, Travel, Nat. History. Notes: *Excellent, proven international Customer Support offered. Response to all contact within 8 hours. Beautiful Books and Maps.*

LLANDUDNO

Madoc Books, ■ 5 Madoc Street, Llandudno LL30 2YL. Prop: Patrick and Sarah Elliot. Tel: (01492) 871590. Web: www.madocbooks.co. Est: 1994. Shop. Open: **W:** 10:00–14:00; **Th:** 10:00–14:00; **F:** 10:00–14:00; **S:** 10:00–16:00. Small stock. Spec: Antiquarian; Bibliography; Bindings:; Books about Books; Botany; Celtica; Colour Plate. PR: £50–500. CC: MC; V. Mem: PBFA, WBA. Notes: *Madoc Books specialises in rare antiquarian books with a Welsh interest. Including topography, literature, poetry, mountaineering, travel, and history. We also have a fine collection of private press, fine and custom bindings.*

LLANGOLLEN

Books, ■ 17 Castle Street, Llangollen, LL20 8NY. Prop: Mr. Thor Sever. Tel: (01978) 860334. Web: www.llangollen.org.uk/pages/books.htm. Est: 1983. Shop open: **M:** 10:00–17:00; **T:** 10:00–17:00; **W:** 10:00–17:00; **Th:** 10:00–17:00; **F:** 10:00–17:00; **S:** 10:00–17:00; **Su:** 10:00–17:00. Spec: Alpinism/ Mountaineering; American Indians; Art; Astrology; Cinema/Film; Countries - Melanesia; Folklore; Gardening - General. PR: £3–50. CC: JCB; MC; V.

OLD COLWYN

J V Owen, 13 Wynn Drive, Old Colwyn, LL29 9DE. Tel: (01492) 516600. Fax: (01492) 516600. Est: 2002. Private premises. Postal only. Appointment necessary. Small stock. Spec: Countries - France; Foreign Texts; Languages - Foreign. PR: £1–100. CC: PayPal. Cata: Foreign languages. Corresp: French, German, Italian,Spanish. Mem: WBA. Notes: *My books are listed on Amazon, Biblio and Alibris. The listings are so arranged that there are books on each list that are not on the others; but there a number that are common to two or three of the lists.*

E. Wyn Thomas, Old Quarry 9 Miners Lane, Old Colwyn, LL29 9HG. Prop: E. Wyn Thomas. Tel: (01492) 515336. Est: 1947. Private premises. Postal only. Appointment necessary. Small stock. Spec: Countries - Wales; Fiction - General; History - General; Natural History; Topography - Local; Prints and Maps. PR: £1–1,000. Corresp: Welsh.

RHYL

Siop y Morfa, ■ 109 Stryd Fawr, Rhyl, Sir Ddinbych, LL18 1TR. Prop: Dafydd Timothy. Tel: (01745) 339197. Web: www.siopymorfa.com. VOIPpro: skype. Est: 1980. Internet and Postal. Shop open: **M:** 09:30–17:30; **T:** 09:30–17:30; **W:** 09:30–17:30; **Th:** 09:30–17:30; **F:** 09:30–17:30; **S:** 09:30–17:30; Closed for lunch: 13:00–14:00. Medium stock. Spec: History - National; Literature; Welsh Interest. PR: £5–200. CC: AE; JCB; MC; V; Solo. Corresp: French, Cymraeg/Welsh. Mem: PBFA. VAT No: GB 771 0696 20.

FLINTSHIRE

MOLD

BOOKS4U, 7 The Firs, Mold, CH7 1JX. Prop: Norman MacDonald. Tel: (01352) 751121. Web: www.http://ukbookworld.com/members/bks4u. Est: 1997. Private premises. Internet and Postal. Appointment necessary. Medium stock. Spec: Academic/Scholarly; Aeronautics; Agriculture; Aircraft; Animals and Birds; Annuals; Antiquarian; Antiquities. PR: £1–1,500. CC: PayPal.

GLAMORGAN

FERNDALE

Norman F. Hight, 149 North Road, Ferndale, CF43 4RA. Tel: (01443 756552. Est: 1998. Private premises. Internet and Postal. Appointment necessary. Open: **M:** 10:00–19:00; **T:** 10:00–18:00; **W:** 10:00–19:00; **Th:** 10:00–19:00; **F:** 10:00–18:00; **S:** 10:00–14:00. Small stock. Spec: Fiction - Crime, Detective, Spy, Thrillers; Fiction - Fantasy, Horror; Fiction - Science Fiction; Modern First Editions. PR: £1–200. CC: PayPal.

NEATH

www.rugbyrelics.com, 61 Leonard Street, Neath, SA11 3HW. Prop: Dai Richards. Tel: (01639) 729000. Fax: (01639) 729000. Web: www.rugbyrelics.com. Est: 1991. Private premises. Postal only. Appointment necessary. Small stock. Spec: Sport - Athletics; Sport - Boxing; Sport - Cricket; Sport - Cycling; Sport - Football (Soccer); Sport - Golf; Sport - Olympic Games, The; Sport - Rugby. PR: £2–2,000. CC: MC; V.

GWENT

CHEPSTOW

Glance Back Books, 17 Upper Church Street, Chepstow, NP6 5EX. Prop: Greg Lance–Watkins. Tel: (01291) 626562. Fax: (01291) 626562. Web: www.glanceback.co.uk. Est: 1981. Private premises. Internet and Postal. PR: £1–2,000. CC: paypal. Notes: *Large general stock.*

GWYNEDD

BANGOR

The Muse Bookshop, ■ 43 Holyhead Road, Bangor, LL57 2EU. Prop: Huw Jones. Tel: (01248) 362072. Fax: (01248) 362072. Est: 1992. Shop open: **M:** 09:00–17:30; **T:** 09:00–17:30; **W:** 09:00–17:30; **Th:** 09:00–18:30; **F:** 09:00–17:30; **S:** 10:00–16:30. Medium stock. Spec: Aboriginal; Academic/Scholarly; Accountancy; Adirondack Mountains, The; Adult; Alpinism/Mountaineering; Natural History; New Naturalist. PR: £0–500. CC: MC; V. Mem: BA. Notes: *Also, new books.*

BETHESDA

A.E. Morris, ■ 40 High Street, Bethesda, LL57 3AN. Prop: A. E. Morris. Tel: (01248) 602533. Est: 1987. Shop open: **M:** 10:00–16:30; **T:** 10:00–16:30; **W:** 10:00–16:30; **Th:** 10:00–16:30; **F:** 10:00–16:30; **S:** 10:00–16:30. Spec: Prints and Maps. PR: £1–100.

BLAENAU FFESTINIOG

P. & D. Doorbar, Min-y-ffordd Bethania, Blaenau Ffestiniog, LL41 3LZ. Prop: Mr. K.P. & Mr. D.L. Doorbar. Tel: (01766) 831995. Fax: (01766) 831995. Web: www.doorbar.co.uk/books/. Est: 1991. Shop and/or showroom; Internet and Postal. Contactable. Shop at: Llyfrau Llanbedr Books, Wenallt, Llanbedr Gwynedd, LL45 2LD. Open: **T:** 13:30–17:00; **Th:** 13:30–17:00; **S:** 10:30–17:00. Small stock. Spec: Art; Art - Technique; Art History; Art Reference; Children's; Children's - Illustrated; Dogs; Gypsies. PR: £5–500. Mem: PBFA. Also at: Llyfrau Llanbedr Books, Wenallt, Llanbedr Gwynedd, LL45 2LD.

Siop Lyfrau'r Hen Bost, ■ 45 High Street, Blaenau Ffestiniog, LL41 3AA. Prop: Elin Angharad Jones. Tel: (01766) 831802. Est: 1988. Shop open: **M:** 10:00–16:30; **T:** 10:00–16:30; **W:** 10:00–16:30; **Th:** 10:00–16:30; **F:** 10:00–16:30; **S:** 10:00–15:30. Medium stock. Spec: Countries - Wales; History - Local; Journals; Literature; New Books; Welsh Interest; Ephemera. PR: £1–200. Corresp: Welsh. Mem: BA; WBA. Notes: *Large stock of out of print Welsh books.*

CRICCIETH

Capel Mawr Collectors Centre, ■ 21 High Street, Criccieth, LL52 0BS. Prop: Alun & Dee Turner. Tel: (01766) 523600. Est: 1998. Shop. Open: **M:** 11:00–17:00; **T:** 11:00–17:00; **W:** 11:00–17:00; **Th:** 11:00–17:00; **F:** 11:00–17:00; **S:** 11:00–17:00; **Su:** 11:00–16:00. Very large stock. Spec: Cinema/Film; Comics; Cookery/Gastronomy; Counterculture; Fiction - General; Food & Drink; Sport - General; Theology. PR: £1–100. CC: AE; E; JCB; MC; V. Notes: *Winter opening Thursday, Friday, Saturday 10:00–17:00. Also, collactables & ephemera.*

DOLGELLAU

Cader Idris Bookshop, ■2 Maldwyn House, Finsbury Square, Dolgellau, LL40 1TR. Prop: Barbara Beeby & Son. Tel: 07743378300. Web: www.dyfivalleybookshop.com. Shop. Telephone First. Mem: WBA. Notes: *Sister shop to The Dyfi Valley Bookshop. Machynlleth.*

MONMOUTHSHIRE

ABERGAVENNY

Ms. Sonia A. Hughes, 'Avondale' 13 Lansdown Drive, Abergavenny, NP7 6AW. Prop: Ms. Sonia A. Hughes. Tel: (01873) 853967. Est: 1999. Private premises. Postal only. Small stock. Spec: Biography; Humour; Illustrated - General; Booksearch. PR: £2–50.

Skirrid Books, 58 Poplars Road, Mardy, Abergavenny, NP7 6LX. Prop: Mrs. G.M. Parry. Tel: (01873) 857004. Est: 1995. Private premises. Postal only. Very small stock. Spec: Fiction - Supernatural; History - General. PR: £5–250. CC: PayPal. Cata: occasionally on Supernatural Fiction.

LLANVAPLEY

Monmouth House Books, Monmouth House, Llanvapley, Abergavenny, NP7 8SN. Prop: Richard Sidwell. Tel: (01600) 780236. Fax: (01600) 780532. Web: www.monmouthhousebooks.co.uk. Est: 1985. Private premises. Postal only. Contactable. Small stock. Spec: Architecture; Booksearch. PR: £5–1,000. Cata: Architecture & related subjects. VAT No: GB 615 8003 63. Notes: *Also, booksearch & stock lists on architecture only. Publishes facsimile reprints of early architectural books.*

TINTERN

Stella Books, ■ Monmouth Road, Tintern, NP16 6SE. Prop: Chris Tomaszewski. Tel: (01291) 689755. Fax: (01291) 689998. Web: www.stellabooks.com. Est: 1990. Shop open: **M:** 09:30–17:30; **T:** 09:30–17:30; **W:** 09:30–17:30; **Th:** 09:30–17:30; **F:** 09:30–17:30; **S:** 09:30–17:30; **Su:** 09:30–17:30. Very large stock. Spec: Antiquarian; Author - Blyton, Enid; Author - Johns, W.E.; Cats; Children's; Countries - Wales; Dogs; History - General. PR: £5-25,000. CC: AE; JCB; MC; V. Cata: quarterly all. Corresp: French. Mem: PBFA; Ibooknet.co.uk. VAT No: GB 667 0422 36. Notes: *Wants matching. Let us know your interests and books you are seeking. Over 4,000 different catalogues issued quarterly by email and post. Partner shop: Rose's Books, 14 Broad Street, Hay-On-Wye, HR3 5DB.*

PEMBROKESHIRE

NEWPORT

Carningli Centre, ■ East St, Newport, SA42 0SY. Prop: Ann Gent. Tel: 01239 820724. Web: www.carningli.co.uk. Est: 1982. Shop open: **M:** 10:00–17:30; **T:** 10:00–17:30; **W:** 10:00–17:30; **Th:** 10:00–17:30; **F:** 10:00–17:30; **S:** 10:00–17:30. Spec: Agriculture; Animals and Birds; Anthologies; Antiques; Art; Cookery/Gastronomy; Countries - Wales; D.I.Y. (Do It Yourself). CC: AE; MC; V; Maestro. VAT No: GB 491 0134 72. Notes: *Book search now available.*

TENBY

Cofion Books and Postcards, ■ Bridge Street, Tenby, SA70 7BU. Prop: Albie Smosarski. Tel: (01834) 845741. Fax: (01834) 843864. Web: www.cofion.com. Est: 1994. Shop open: **M:** 10:30–17:30; **T:** 10:30–17:30; **W:** 10:30–17:30; **Th:** 10:30–17:30; **F:** 10:30–17:30; **S:** 10:30–17:30; **Su:** 11:30–17:30. Very large stock. Spec: Academic/Scholarly; Aeronautics; Aircraft; Alpinism/Mountaineering; American Indians; American Revolution, The; Animals and Birds; Annuals. PR: £1–500. CC: Cash and cheques only. Notes: *Wide general book choice. Vast Edwardian to modern picture postcards plus other varied collectables. Good general stock, booksearch undertaken.*

POWYS

BEULAH

Myra Dean Illustated Books, Crossways, Beulah, LD5 4UB. Prop: Myra Dean. Tel: 01591 620647. Web: www.myradean-illustratedbooks.co.uk. Est: 1984. Private premises. Internet and Postal. Appointment necessary. Open: **M:** 09:00–17:30; **T:** 09:00–17:30; **W:** 09:00–17:30; **Th:** 09:00–17:30; **F:** 09:00–17:30; **S:** 09:00–17:30; **Su:** 09:00–17:30; Closed for lunch: 13:00–14:00. Spec: Art; Art - British; Artists; Author - Ardizzone, Edward; Author - Cook, Beryl; Author - Dulac, Edmund; Author - Flint, William Russell; Author - Gill, Eric. CC: MC; V. Cata: Illustrated, private press, art, limited editions.

BRECON

Andrew Morton Books, ■ 11 Lion Yard, Brecon, LD3 7BA. Tel: (01874) 620086. Est: 1999. Shop open: **M:** 09:30–17:30; **T:** 09:30–17:30; **W:** 09:30–17:30; **Th:** 09:30–17:30; **F:** 09:30–17:30; **S:** 09:30–17:30. Very large stock. Spec: Art; Children's; Crafts; History - General; Literature; Military. PR: £2–30. CC: MC; V; SW, SO. Notes: *Also, open on Sundays in season.*

C J Renwick Books, 95 The Struet, Brecon, LD3 7LS. Prop: Kit Renwick. Tel: 01874 622479. Est: 1995. Private premises. Internet and Postal. Telephone First. Open: **M:** 09:00–17:30; **T:** 09:00–17:30; **W:** 09:00–17:30; **Th:** 09:00–17:30; **F:** 09:00–17:30; **S:** 09:00–17:30; **Su:** 09:00–17:30; Closed for lunch: 13:00–14:00. Spec: Africana; Antiquarian; Applied Art; Architecture; Art; Art - British; Art - Theory; Art History. CC: MC; V. Corresp: French, Italian. Mem: PBFA.

BUILTH WELLS

Louise Boer, Arthurian Books, The Rectory, Rhosgoch, Builth Wells, LD2 3JU. Prop: Louise Boer. Tel: (01497) 851260. Fax: (01497) 851260. Est: 1996. Private premises. Internet and Postal. Contactable. Medium stock. Spec: Academic/Scholarly; Arthurian; Business Studies; Literary Criticism. PR: £2–150. CC: MC; V. Corresp: Dutch.

HAY ON WYE

The Addyman Annexe, ■ 27 Castle Street, Hay–on–Wye, HR3 5DF. Prop: Derek Addyman and Anne Brichto. Tel: 01497 821600. Web: www.hay-on-wyebooks.com. Shop open: **M:** 10:00–17:30; **T:** 10:00–17:30; **W:** 10:00–17:30; **Th:** 10:00–17:30; **F:** 10:00–17:30; **S:** 10:00–17:30; **Su:** 10:00–17:30. Spec: Bindings; Literature; Military; Modern First Editions. CC: MC; V; Mae.

Addyman Books, ■ 39 Lion Street, Hay–on–Wye, HR3 5AA. Prop: Derek Addyman & Anne Brichto. Tel: (01497) 821136. Fax: (01497) 821732. Web: www.hay-on-wyebooks.com. Est: 1987. Internet and Postal. Shop open: **M:** 10:00–17:30; **T:** 10:00–17:30; **W:** 10:00–17:30; **Th:** 10:00–17:30; **F:** 10:00–17:30; **S:** 10:00–17:30; **Su:** 10:30–17:30. Large stock. Spec: Adult; Aeronautics; Africana; Agriculture; Aircraft; Americana - General; Anthologies; Antiquarian. PR: £1–20,000. CC: MC; V; De, SW, Maestro, Solo. Notes: *Murder & Mayhem, 5 Lion St., Hay-on-Wye (q.v) The Addyman Annexe, 27 Castle St., Hay-on-Wye, (q.v.) NB: add 'via Hereford' after Hay-on-Wye when sending by post.*

C. Arden, Bookseller, ■ 'Radnor House', Church Street, Hay–on–Wye, HR3 5DQ. Prop: Chris & Catherine Arden: Darren & Claire Bloodworth. Tel: (01497) 820471. Fax: (01497) 820498. Web: www.ardenbooks.co.uk. Est: 1993. Internet and Postal. Shop open: **M:** 10:30–17:30; **T:** 10:30–17:30; **W:** 10:30–17:30; **Th:** 10:30–17:30; **F:** 10:30–17:30; **S:** 10:30–17:30; **Su:** 11:00–16:00. Medium stock. Spec: Antiquarian; Apiculture; Biology - General; Botany; Conservation; Ecology; Entomology; Evolution. PR: £3–10,000. CC: JCB; MC; V. Cata: Natural History, Gardening, Zoology, Botany, Bee. Mem: PBFA. Notes: *Shop open March to December 7 days a week. Closed in January. During February, open Friday, Saturday, Sunday & Monday.*

Boz Books, ■ 13a Castle Street, Hay–on–Wye, HR3 5DF. Prop: Peter Harries. Tel: (01497) 821277. Fax: (01497) 821277. Web: www.bozbooks.co.uk. Est: 1987. Internet and Postal. Shop open: **M:** 10:00–17:00; **T:** 10:00–17:00; **W:** 10:00–17:00; **Th:** 10:00–17:00; **F:** 10:00–17:00; **S:** 10:00–17:00; Closed for lunch: 13:00–14:00. Medium stock. Spec: Author - Austen, Jane; Author - Ballantyne, Robert M.; Author - Braddon, Mary Elizabeth; Author - Brontes, The; Author - Dickens, Charles; Author - Peake, Mervyn; Author - Thomas, Dylan; Fiction - General. PR: £5–10,000. CC: JCB; MC; V. Mem: ABA. VAT No: GB 489 1240 27. Notes: *Opening times vary in winter.*

Hancock & Monks Music Emporium, ■ 6 Broad Street, Hay–on–Wye, HR3 5DB. Prop: Eric Hancock & Jerry Monks. Tel: (01591) 610555. Fax: (01591) 610555. Web: www.hancockandmonks.co.uk. Est: 1974. Shop open: **M:** 10:00–17:00; **T:** 10:00–17:00; **W:** 10:00–17:00; **Th:** 10:00–17:00; **F:** 10:00–17:00; **S:** 10:00–17:00; **Su:** 10:00–17:00. Medium stock. Spec: Cinema/Film; Music - General; Music - Classical; Music - Composers; Music - Gilbert & Sullivan; Music - Gregorian Chants; Music - Illustrated Sheet Music; Music - Jazz & Blues. PR: £1–250. CC: MC; V; Maestro. Cata: CDs, Scores & Books on Music. VAT No: GB 139 8108 51. Notes: *Long established classical music retailer selling CDs, DVDs, Sheet Music, Scores and Books on Music. Worldwide mail order. Extensive on-line catalogue.*

Books at Hay Castle, ■ Hay Castle, Oxford Road, Hay–on–Wye, HR3 5DQ. Prop: Hope Booth (Hay-On-Wye Bookbuyers). Tel: (01497) 820503. Web: www.boothbooks.co.uk. Est: 1987. Shop open: **M:** 10:00–17:30; **T:** 10:00–17:30; **W:** 10:00–17:30; **Th:** 10:00–17:30; **F:** 10:00–17:30; **S:** 10:00–17:30; **Su:** 10:00–17:30. Very large stock. Spec: Aircraft; American Indians; Architecture; Art; Art - British; Art - Theory; Authors - Local; Automobilia/Automotive. PR: £1–2,500. CC: AE; D; MC; V. Corresp: French. Mem: WBA. Notes: *Also, photographic images from 1850s onwards and prints. Also wholesale orders from our warehouse, orders put together for interior decorators etc. Independent Kingdom of Hay (1977) and home of International Book Town Movement.*

Francis Edwards in Hay–on–Wye, ■ The Old Cinema, Castle Street, Hay–on–Wye, via Hereford, HR3 5DF. Prop: Hay Cinema Bookshop Ltd. Tel: (01497) 820071. Fax: (01497) 821900. Web: www.francisedwards.co.uk. Est: 1855. Shop open: **M:** 09:00–19:00; **T:** 09:00–19:00; **W:** 09:00–19:00; **Th:** 09:00–19:00; **F:** 09:00–19:00; **S:** 09:00–19:00; **Su:** 11:30–17:30. Medium stock. Spec: Architecture; Art; Economics; Folklore; History - General; Law - General; Literature; Medicine. PR: £20–10,000. CC: AE; D; E; JCB; MC; V; Switch. Cata: Voyages, Naval, Military, Art, Literature, Science. Mem: ABA; PBFA; ILAB. VAT No: GB 594 2720 23.

Hay Cinema Bookshop Ltd., ■ Castle Street, Hay–on–Wye, HR3 5DF. Tel: (01497) 820071. Fax: (01497) 821900. Web: www.haycinemabookshop.co.uk. Est: 1982. Shop open: **M:** 09:00–19:00; **T:** 09:00–19:00; **W:** 09:00–19:00; **Th:** 09:00–19:00; **F:** 09:00–19:00; **S:** 09:00–19:00; **Su:** 11:30–17:30. Very large stock. Spec: Academic/Scholarly; Aeronautics; Applied Art; Art; Calligraphy; Cinema/Film; Cookery/Gastronomy; Economics. PR: £1–25. CC: AE; D; JCB; MC; V. VAT No: GB 594 2720 23. Notes: *Quinto, 48a Charing Cross Road, London WC2H 0BB (q.v.) Quinto, 63 Great Russell Street, London WC1B 3BF. Fine and Antiquarian books in all subjects via our sister business Francis Edwards.*

HCB Wholesale, Unit 2, Forest Road Enterprise Park, Hay–on–Wye, HR3 5DS. Prop: (A Division of Hay Cinema Bookshop Ltd.). Tel: (01497) 820333. Fax: (01497) 821192. Web: www.hcbwholesale.co.uk. Est: 2002. Warehouse; Shop open: **M:** 09:00–18:00; **T:** 09:00–18:00; **W:** 09:00–18:00; **Th:** 09:00–18:00; **F:** 09:00–18:00. Very large stock. Spec: Art; Children's; Cinema/Film; Cookery/Gastronomy; Crime (True); Fiction - Crime, Detective, Spy, Thrillers; Fiction - Fantasy, Horror; Gardening - General. Notes: *Main stock: publishers' returns, academic overstocks, and remainders. NB: add 'via Hereford' after Hay-on-Wye when sending by post.*

Kestrel Books, 6 De Breos Court, Hay–on–Wye, HR3 5DL. Prop: David Rees. Tel: 01497 822890. Fax: 01497 822891. Web: www.hay-kestrel.com. Est: 2005. Private premises. Appointment necessary. Open: **M:** 09:00–17:30; **T:** 09:00–17:30; **W:** 09:00–17:30; **Th:** 09:00–17:30; **F:** 09:00–17:30; **S:** 09:00–17:30; **Su:** 09:00–17:30; Closed for lunch: 13:00–14:00. Very small stock. Spec: Modern First Editions. PR: £25 – 2,000. CC: MC; V. Cata: quarterly. VAT No: GB 863 5090 18. Notes: *Specialist in Modern First Editions.*

Marijana Dworski Books, ■ Backfold, Hay–on–Wye, HR3 5EQ. Prop: Marijana Dworski. Tel: (01497) 820200. Web: www.dworskibooks.com. Est: 1991. Shop open: **M:** 10:30–17:00; **T:** 10:30–17:00; **W:** 10:30–17:00; **Th:** 10:30–17:00; **F:** 10:30–17:00; **S:** 10:30–17:30; Closed for lunch: 13:00–14:00. Spec: Art; Countries - Balkans, The; History - General; History - Imperial Russia; History - Russian Imperial; Languages - African; Languages - Ancient; Languages - Foreign. CC: D; JCB; MC; V; debit. Cata: Balkans, Russian, Central/Eastern Europe. Corresp: French, German, Croatian. VAT No: GB 794 1222 28. Notes: *U.K's premier specialists in language books: Dictionaries and Grammars in 350 languages from Akkadian to Zulu. Also a large selection of books on the Balkans, Central and Southeastern Europe, Russia & Central Asia.*

Murder & Mayhem, ■ 5 Lion Street, Hay–on–Wye, HR3 5AA. Prop: Derek Addyman & Anne Brichto. Tel: (01497) 821613. Fax: (01497) 821732. Web: www.hay-on-wyebooks.com. Est: 1997. Shop open: **M:** 10:30–17:30; **T:** 10:30–17:30; **W:** 10:30–17:30; **Th:** 10:30–17:30; **F:** 10:30–17:30; **S:** 10:30–17:30. Medium stock. Spec: Crime (True); Criminology; Fiction - Crime, Detective, Spy, Thrillers; Fiction - Fantasy, Horror; Sherlockiana. PR: £1–1,000. CC: MC; V; switch, maestro, solo. Notes: *Addyman Books, 39 Lion Street, Hay-on-Wye (q.v.).*

O'Donoghue Books, PO Box 162, Hay–on–Wye, HR3 5WZ. Prop: Sean O'Donoghue. Tel: 01497 822831. Web: www.intertextuality.com. Est: 1994. Private premises. Internet only. Large stock. Spec: Academic/Scholarly; Biography; Philosophy; Politics; Psychology/Psychiatry; Social Sciences; Sociology. PR: £10–50. CC: MC; V; Switch Maestro. Mem: Ibooknet. VAT No: GB 751 8509 19.

Oxford House Books, ■ Montpelier, 21 Broad Street, Hay–on–Wye, HR3 5DB. Prop: Paul Harris. Tel: (01497) 820191. Web: www.oxfordhousebooks.com. Est: 2003. Shop open: **M:** 10:30–17:30; **T:** 10:30–17:30; **W:** 10:30–17:30; **Th:** 10:30–17:30; **F:** 10:30–17:30; **S:** 10:30–17:30; **Su:** 10:30–17:30. CC: MC; V; Electron, Maestro, Solo, Delta, Switch. Notes: *Shop hours are for Spring/Summer/Autumn. Some variations possible during Winter. A call ahead is advised. We are always keen to purchase good collections of Philosophy, Theology, History, Art, and related subjects. Will travel if necessary.*

The Poetry Bookshop, ■ Ice House, Brook Street, Hay–on–Wye, HR3 5BQ. Prop: Christopher & Melanie Prince. Tel: (01497) 821812. Fax: n/a. Web: www.poetrybookshop.co.uk. Est: 1998. Shop open: **M:** 10:00–18:00; **T:** 10:00–18:00; **W:** 10:00–18:00; **Th:** 10:00–18:00; **F:** 10:00–18:00; **S:** 10:00–18:00; **Su:** 11:00–17:00. Large stock. Spec: Academic/Scholarly; Anthologies; Antiquarian; Autobiography; Beat Writers; Bindings; Biography; Counterculture. PR: £1–10,000. CC: MC; V; Maestro/Visa Debit. VAT No: GB 831 777 901. Notes: *All subjects that relate to poets and poetry inc criticism, biography, readers guides, work in translation and anthologies.*

Rose's Books, ■ 14 Broad Street, Hay–on–Wye, HR3 5DB. Tel: (01497) 820013. Fax: (01497) 820031. Web: www.rosesbooks.com. Est: 1982. Internet and Postal. Shop open: **M:** 09:30–17:30; **T:** 09:30–17:30; **W:** 09:30–17:30; **Th:** 09:30–17:30; **F:** 09:30–17:30; **S:** 09:30–17:30; **Su:** 09:30–17:30. Large stock. Spec: Children's; Children's - Illustrated; Illustrated - General; Publishers - Ladybird Books. PR: £1–2,000. CC: AE; JCB; MC; V; SW. Cata: childrens. Mem: PBFA; www.ibooknet.co.uk. VAT No: GB 667 0422 36. Notes: *bookmatch service - we can let you know when a book comes into stock.*

Mark Westwood Books, High Town, Hay–on–Wye, HR3 5AE. Tel: (01497) 820068. Fax: (01497) 821641. Est: 1987. Storeroom; Postal only. Very large stock. Spec: Folio Society, The; History - General; Mathematics; Medicine; Medicine - History of; New Naturalist; Philosophy; Psychology/Psychiatry. PR: £5–1,000. CC: E; JCB; MC; V. Corresp: French. Mem: ABA; PBFA. VAT No: GB 315 3343 88. Notes: *See entry Westwood Books in Sedberg.*

LLANDRINDOD WELLS

Udo K.H. Polczynski, Rose & Crown, Llanbadarn Fynydd, Llandrindod Wells, LD1 6YH. Prop: Udo K.H. Polczynski. Tel: 01597 840569. Fax: 01597 840569. Est: 1984. Private premises. Internet and Postal. Appointment necessary. Medium stock. Spec: Anthropology; Archaeology; History - Science; Philology; Philosophy. PR: £10–5,000. Cata: on special collections. Corresp: French, German, Malay, Polish, Russian, Spanish.

LLANIDLOES

The Great Oak Bookshop, ■ Great Oak Street, Llanidloes, SY18 6BW. Prop: B. Boswell. Tel: (01686) 412959. Web: www.midwales.com/gob. Est: 1988. Internet and Postal. Shop open: **M:** 09:30–17:30; **T:** 09:30–17:30; **W:** 09:30–17:30; **Th:** 09:30–17:30; **F:** 09:30–17:30; **S:** 09:30–16:30. Very large stock. Spec: Autobiography; Biography; Countries - Wales; Welsh Interest. PR: £1–50. CC: AE; E; JCB; MC; V. Corresp: German, French. Mem: BA; WBA. Notes: *Also, new books, greetings cards & a resident parrot.*

Trade Priced Old Books, Neuadd Ddu Llangurig, Llanidloes, SY18 6RX. Prop: Sally Winston-Smith. Tel: (01686) 440730 m077 477 88 429. Web: www.DeadMensMinds.co.uk. Est: 2000. Private premises. Internet and Postal. Small stock. Spec: Antiquarian; Arts, The; Philosophy; Taxidermy; Theology; Collectables. PR: £10–2,000. CC: PayPal/cheques. Cata: Art, Philosophy, Theology, all pre 1830. Notes: *All our books are 16th-19th Century and many are not previously listed. Mostly leatherbound and part of treasured stock, a number of our odd volumes have helped happy searchers worldwide to complete their collections since the Millennium!*

LLANWRTYD WELLS

Andrew Dally, Berthllwyd Beulah, Llanwrtyd Wells, Powys, LD5 4UN. Prop: Andrew Dally. Tel: (01591) 610892. Est: 2001. Private premises. Internet and Postal. Contactable. Small stock. Spec: History - Photography; Memorabilia; Military; Military History; Photography; Royalty - General; War - General; War - World War I. PR: £1–200.

MACHYNLLETH

Coch-y-Bonddu Books Ltd., ■ Papyrus Pentrerhedyn Street, Machynlleth, SY20 8DJ. Prop: Paul Morgan. Tel: (01654) 702837. Fax: (01654) 702857. Web: www.anglebooks.com. Est: 1982. Internet and Postal. Shop open: **M:** 09:00–17:00; **T:** 09:00–17:00; **W:** 09:00–17:00; **Th:** 09:00–17:00; **F:** 09:00–17:00; **S:** 09:00–17:00. Large stock. Spec: Africana; Agriculture; Animals and Birds; Antiquarian; Author - Buchan, John; Author - Dinesen, Isak; Author - Jefferies, R.; Author - Seymour, John. PR: £1–2,000. CC: D; E; MC; V. Cata: Quarterley, Fishing & Field Sports. Corresp: French, German, Spanish, Portuguese, Welsh. Mem: PBFA; BA. Notes: *We stock new books in our fields, as well as remainders, s/hand and antiquarian.*

Dyfi Valley Bookshop, ■ 6 Doll Street, Machynlleth, SY20 8BQ. Prop: Barbara Beeby & Son. Tel: (01654) 703849. Web: www.dyfivalleybookshop.com. Est: 1988. Shop open: **M:** 09:30–17:00; **T:** 09:30–17:00; **W:** 09:30–17:00; **Th:** 09:30–17:00; **F:** 09:30–17:00; **S:** 09:30–17:00; Closed for lunch: 12:00–12:30. Medium stock. Spec: Arms & Armour; Firearms/Guns; Military; Sport - Archery; Sport - Field Sports; Welsh Interest. PR: £1–500. CC: AE; JCB; MC; V. Cata: Archery. Corresp: French. Mem: WBA.

Martin's Books, Zion Chapel, Llanwrin, Machynlleth, SY20 8QH. Prop: Martin Ashby. Tel: (01650) 511595. Est: 2000. Storeroom; Internet and Postal. Appointment necessary. Spec: Animals and Birds; Biography; Botany; Fiction - General; First Editions; Natural History; Ornithology; Poetry. PR: £6–500. Mem: PBFA.

MONTGOMERY

Castle Bookshop, The Old Rectory, Llandyssil, Montgomery, SY15 6LQ. Prop: C.N., E.J. & S.J. Moore. Tel: (01686) 668484. Fax: (01686) 668842. Web: www.archaeologybooks.co.uk. Est: 1987. Office and/or bookroom; Telephone first. Large stock. Spec: Archaeology; Archaeology - Industrial; Architecture; Countries - Wales; Welsh Interest. PR: £5–1,000. CC: JCB; MC; V; Switch/Maestro. Cata: Archaeology, Architecture, Wales, Celtic Studies. Corresp: French, German, Welsh. Mem: ABA; PBFA; ILAB. VAT No: GB 482 4054 51.

NEW MILLS

DustyBooks, Fronoleu Ty Hir, New Mills, SY16 3NW. Prop: Bernard Conwell. Tel: (01686) 651115. Fax: (01442) 270808. Web: www.dustybooks.co.uk. Est: 1993. Office and/or bookroom; Internet and Postal. Open: **M:** 09:30–17:30; **T:** 09:30–17:30; **W:** 09:30–17:30; **Th:** 09:30–17:30; **F:** 09:30–17:30. Spec: Author - Farnol, Jeffery; Author - Forester, C.S.; Author - Heyer, Georgette; Author - Sabatini, R.; Author - Shute, Neville; Cookery/Gastronomy; Crafts; Food & Drink. PR: £5–250. CC: AE; JCB; MC; V. VAT No: GB 682 4165 26.

NEWTOWN

David Archer, The Pentre, Kerry, Newtown, SY16 4PD. Prop: David Archer & Alison Brown. Tel: (01686) 670382. Web: www.david-archer-maps.co.uk. Est: 1985. Private premises. Internet and Postal. Telephone First. Open: **M:** 08:30–20:00; **T:** 08:30–20:00; **W:** 08:30–20:00; **Th:** 08:30–20:00; **F:** 08:30–20:00; **S:** 09:00–13:00. Very large stock. Spec: Cartography; Geography; Geology; Transport; Prints and Maps. PR: £1–150. Mem: Welsh Booksellers Assoc. Notes: *We buy and sell Ordnance Survey maps from 1801 to the present, plus a few related maps.*

D.M. Newband, Drefor Cottage,Kerry, Newtown, SY16 4PQ. Prop: D.M. Newband. Tel: (01686) 670205. Fax: please ask. Web: www.davidnewbandbooks.co.uk. Est: 1983. Office and/or bookroom; Internet and Postal. Appointment necessary. Open: **M:** 09:00–19:00; **T:** 09:00–19:00; **W:** 09:00–19:00; **Th:** 09:00–19:00; **F:** 09:00–19:00; **S:** 09:00–19:00; **Su:** 10:00–18:00. Small stock. Spec: Railways and Railroads; Steam Engines; Transport; Booksearch. PR: £1–200. CC: Paypal. Notes: *Also, a booksearch service; valuation service railways only.*

Tant Yn Ellen Books, Draenllwynellen Sarn, Newtown, SY16 4ET. Prop: Jim and June Crundwell. Tel: 01686 668475. Est: 2002. Private premises. Market Stall. Appointment necessary. Open: **M:** 09:00–17:30; **T:** 09:00–17:30; **W:** 09:00–17:30; **Th:** 09:00–17:30; **F:** 09:00–17:30; **S:** 09:00–17:30; **Su:** 09:00–17:30; Closed for lunch: 13:00–14:00. Spec: Botany; Children's; Children's - Illustrated; Cookery/Gastronomy; Entomology; Gardening - General; Natural History; Poetry. Notes: *Exhibits at local book fairs. Much Wenlock and Church Stretton.*

PRESTEIGNE

Antique & Book Shop, ■ 2 Hereford Street, Presteigne, LD8 2AW. Prop: A. L. Bird. Tel: (01544) 260316. Est: 1988. Shop open: **M:** 10:00–17:00; **T:** 10:00–17:00; **W:** 10:00–17:00; **Th:** 10:00–17:00; **F:** 10:00–17:00; **S:** 10:00–17:00. Large stock. Spec: Topography - Local. PR: £1–200. Notes: *Open on Sundays by appointment.*

Tony Bird, 2 Hereford Street, Presteigne, LD8 2AW. Tel: (01544) 260316. Private premises. Spec: Topography - Local.

Kingshead Books, ■ 45 High St., Presteigne. Prop: Ivan Monckton. Tel: (01547) 560100. Est: 1983. Shop open: **M:** 09:00–17:00; **T:** 09:00–17:00; **W:** 09:00–17:00; **Th:** 09:00–17:00; **F:** 09:00–17:00; **S:** 09:00–17:00. Medium stock. Spec: Natural History; Welsh Interest; Collectables; Ephemera. PR: £1–250. Notes: *Also postcards.*

TALGARTH

The Strand Bookshop, ■ Regent Street, Talgarth, LD3 0DB. Prop: Ms Kate Cardwell. Tel: (01874) 711195. Shop open: **M:** 10:00–15:30; **Th:** 10:00–15:30; **F:** 10:00–15:30; **S:** 10:00–17:00; **Su:** 09:00–17:00. Medium stock. PR: £1–50.

WELSHPOOL

D. & J. Young, Fairview Cottage, Groes Llwyd, Welshpool, SY21 9BZ. Prop: David & Joy Young. Tel: (01938) 553149. Web: www.abebooks.com. Est: 25 years. Private premises. Postal only. Appointment necessary. Small stock. Spec: Calligraphy; Crafts; Crochet; Embroidery; Fashion & Costume; Knitting; Lace; Railways and Railroads. PR: £1–300. CC: use Paypal, or cheques.

YSTRAD MEURIG

Garfi Books, ■ Bron y Graig, Pontrhydygroes, Ystrad Meurig, SY25 6DN. Prop: Barbara & Salvatore Garfi. Tel: 01974 282684. Est: 2000. Shop at: The Book Unit, Brecon Antiques Centre, 22a High St., Brecon, Powys LD3 7LA. Open: **M:** 10:00–17:00; **T:** 10:00–17:00; **W:** 10:00–17:00; **Th:** 10:00–17:00; **F:** 10:00–17:00; **S:** 10:00–17:00. Medium stock. Spec: Alpinism/Mountaineering; Anthropology; Archaeology; Art; Art History; Author - Aldin, Cecil; Author - Armour, G. D.; Author - Churchill, Sir Winston. PR: £1 – 300. CC: MC; V; Maestro & Switch. Notes: *Open Sundays from Easter to Christmas 11:00-16:00.*

SWANSEA

PONTARDAWE

Mollie's Loft Books, 31 Cilmaengwyn, Pontardawe, SA8 4QL. Prop: M.J.P. Evans. Tel: (01792) 863556. Web: www.Molliesloft.com. Est: 1998. Private premises. Internet and Postal. Appointment necessary. Small stock. Spec: Science - General; Technology; Welsh Interest. PR: £5–150. CC: MC; V; Switch. Corresp: French.

SWANSEA

Dylans Bookstore, ■Salubrious House, 23 King Edward Road, Swansea, SA1 4LL. Prop: Jeff and Elizabeth Towns. Tel: 01792 655255. Fax: 01792 655255. Web: www.dylans.com. Est: 1970. Internet and Postal. Telephone First. Open: **T:** 12:00–16:00; **W:** 12:00–16:00; **Th:** 12:00–16:00; **F:** 12:00–16:00. Spec: Academic/Scholarly; African-American Studies; Antiquarian; Arthurian; Author - Steadman, Ralph; Author - Thomas, Dylan; Author - Thomas, Edward; Author - Watkins, Vernon. CC: JCB; MC; V. Cata: Dylan Thomas, Wales, women. Corresp: French. Mem: ABA; BA; ILAB; Welsh Booksellers Association. Notes: *We have two open shops in Swansea - the other is in the Dylan Thomas Centre. We exhibit at bookfairs and sell on the Internet.*

WEST CROSS

J.M. Farringdon, Ariel Cottage, 8 Hadland Terrace, West Cross, SA3 5TT. Prop: M.G. Farringdon. Tel: (01792) 405267. Fax: (01792) 405267. Est: 1970. Private premises. Internet and Postal. Appointment necessary. Very small stock. Spec: Antiquarian; Author - Masefield, John; Author - Ransome, Arthur; Bell-Ringing (Campanology); Booksearch. PR: £20–1,000. Cata: occasionally on Bells and Bell-Ringing. VAT No: GB 558 2330 40. Notes: *Also publishing as 'Ariel House Publications'.*

TORFAEN

Blaenavon Books, ■ 71 Broad Street, Blaenavon, NP4 9NH. Prop: James Hanna. Tel: (01495) 793093. Est: 2003. Shop open: **M:** 10:00–17:00; **T:** 10:00–17:00; **W:** 10:00–17:00; **Th:** 10:00–17:00; **F:** 10:00–17:00; **S:** 09:00–17:00; **Su:** 10:00–17:00. Medium stock. Spec: Art; Design; Photography. PR: £1–100. CC: MC; V; SW, SO. Notes: *Only open Sundays in summer. Large general stock.*

Broadleaf Books, ■ 12 Broad Street, Blaenavon, NP4 9ND. Prop: Joanna Chambers. Tel: (01495) 792852. Est: 2003. Shop open: **T:** 10:00–17:00; **W:** 10:00–17:00; **Th:** 10:00–17:00; **F:** 10:00–17:00; **S:** 10:00–17:00. Medium stock. Spec: Children's; Design; Natural History; Photography. PR: £1–50. CC: V. Notes: *Good collection of photography and natural history with broad range of other subjects.*

Browning Books, ■ 33 Broad Street, Blaenavon, NP4 9NF. Prop: Stephanie and Andrew Nummelin. Tel: (01495) 790089. Web: www.browningbooks.co.uk. Est: 2001. Internet and Postal. Shop open: **T:** 10:00–17:00; **W:** 10:00–17:00; **Th:** 10:00–17:00; **F:** 10:00–17:00; **S:** 10:00–17:00. Medium stock. Spec: Children's; Children's - Illustrated; Countries - Wales; History - Local; Languages - National; Mining; New Books; Railways and Railroads. PR: £1–150. CC: AE; E; JCB; MC; V; MAE, ELEC. Mem: BA.

Queen Victoria PH, Prince Street, Blaenavon, NP4 9BD. Prop: Kim Winstone. Tel: 01495 791652. Web: www.webster.uk.net/queenvictoriainn. Est: 2003. Storeroom; Shop open: **M:** 11:00–23:00; **T:** 11:00–23:00; **W:** 11:00–23:00; **Th:** 11:00–23:00; **F:** 11:00–23:00; **S:** 11:00–23:00; **Su:** 12:00–20:30. Spec: Cookery/Gastronomy; Gardening - General; Military; Military History. Notes: *Accommodation available. In Good Beer Guide.*

The Railway Shop, ■ 13a Broad Street, Blaenavon, NP4 9ND. Prop: Peter Hunt. Tel: (01495) 792263. Web: www.railwaymodelshop.co.uk. Est: 1998. Shop open: **M:** 11:00–17:30; **T:** 11:00–17:30; **W:** 11:00–17:30; **Th:** 11:00–17:30; **F:** 11:00–17:30; **S:** 11:00–16:00. Large stock. Spec: Railways and Railroads; Shipbuilding and Shipping; Transport. PR: £1–20. CC: MC; V.

WREXHAM

Berwyn Books, Bryn-y-Grog Hall, Marchwiel, Wreham LL13 7BG. Prop: Mr. J.R.S. Hall. Tel: (01978) 266606. Showroom. Postal only. Medium stock. PR: £5–300. CC: AE; MC; V.

ALPHABETICAL INDEX BY NAME OF BUSINESS

(Business name followed by county, some of which have been abbreviated)

2 Ravens, Cumbria 78
32 Seconds, East Sussex 104
A Holmes Books, Nottinghamshire................ 203
A. & H. Peasgood, Cambs........................... 66
A. & R. Booksearch, Cornwall..................... 73
Ænigma Designs (Books), Devon.................. 86
AA1 Books, Dumfries & Galloway................ 269
Aardvark Books, Wiltshire.......................... 254
Aardvark Books, Lincolnshire...................... 150
Abacus Books, Gr Manchester 118
Abacus Gallery, Staffordshire....................... 224
Abbey Books, Cornwall 73
Aber Books and Collectables, Ceredigion......... 282
Aberdeen Antique and Art Centre, Grampian... 271
Abington Books, Suffolk 227
Abrahams (Mike), Staffordshire.................... 223
Acanthophyllum Books, Wirral 184
Acumen Books, Staffordshire........................ 224
Addyman Annexe (The), Powys..................... 287
Addyman Books, Powys.............................. 287
Adrem Books, Herts 130
Adrian Greenwood, Oxfordshire 207
Adrian Walker, Bedfordshire........................ 53
Afar Books International, West Midlands........ 238
African Studies, Dorset 91
ahbooks, Merseyside 184
Ainslie Books, Strathclyde........................... 278
Aitchison (Lesley), Bristol 58
Al Saqi Books, London W........................... 171
Alan Redmond Books, Lincolnshire............... 148
Alastor Rare Books, Hampshire 124
Alauda Books, Cumbria.............................. 76
Alba Books, Grampian 273
Alba Secondhand Music, Strathclyde.............. 278
Albion Books, West Midlands....................... 238
Albion Bookshop, Kent 135
Alec–Smith Books (Alex), East Yorkshire........ 107
Alexander's Books, Warwickshire................... 237
Alister & Garon Books, Cambs...................... 63
All Books, Essex 111
Allhalland Books, Devon............................. 84
Allinson (Frank & Stella), Warwickshire 236
Allsop (Duncan M.), Warwickshire................ 237
Allsworth Rare Books Ltd., London SW......... 166
ALLTHINGSBOOKS, Durham 97
Alpha Books, London N............................. 156
Altea Antique Maps & Books, London W....... 171
Alton Secondhand Books, Hampshire............. 121
Altshuler (Jean), Cumbria 78
Ambra Books, Bristol 58
Americanabooksuk, Cumbria....................... 76
Amnesty International UK, Berkshire.............. 56
Amos (Denis W.), Herts............................. 130
Ampersand Books, Norfolk......................... 189
Amwell Book Company, London EC............. 155
Anchor Books, Lincolnshire........................ 149
Ancient Art Books, London SW................... 166
Andrew Hunter Rare Books, London SW 166
Andrew Morton (Books), Powys................... 287

Andrews Books & Collectables, Cheshire......... 69
Andron (G.W.), London N 156
Anglo-American Rare Books, Surrey.............. 232
Ann & Mike Conry, Worcestershire............... 257
Anne Harris Books & Bags Booksearch, Devon 88
Annie's Books, S Yorkshire......................... 221
Anthony Neville, Kent............................... 138
Anthony Sillem, East Sussex........................ 102
Anthony Spranger, Wiltshire........................ 252
Anthony Vickers Books, N Yorkshire............. 195
Anthony W. Laywood, Nottinghamshire 203
Anthony Whittaker, Kent............................ 135
Anthroposophical Books, Glos 116
Antiquary Ltd., (Bar Bookstore), N Yorkshire .. 194
Antique & Book Shop, Powys...................... 291
Antique City Bookshop, London E 154
Antique Map and Bookshop (The), Dorset 94
Antique Prints of the World, London N.......... 156
Antiques on High, Oxfordshire..................... 207
Anvil Books, West Midlands 239
Anwoth Books Ltd, Dumfries & Galloway 269
Any Amount of Books, London WC 176
Any Old Books, Hampshire 121
Aphra Books, West Yorkshire....................... 246
Apocalypse, Surrey 232
Applin (Malcolm), Berkshire....................... 55
Arboretum Bookshop, Lincolnshire 150
Arcadia, Oxfordshire 207
Archer (David), Powys.............................. 290
Archer (Steve), London Outer 180
Archivist (The), Devon.............................. 90
Archways Sports Books, Lothian 275
Arden Books & Cosmographia, Warwickshire... 236
Arden, Bookseller (C.), Powys..................... 287
Ardis Books, Hampshire 126
Argent (Alan), Isle of Wight 134
Armchair Auctions, Hampshire 121
Armchair Books, Lothian 275
Armitage (Booksearch), (Kate), Devon 84
Armstrong's Books & Collectables, Leics......... 145
Arnold (Roy), Suffolk............................... 227
Ars Artis, Oxfordshire 207
Arslan Books Etc., East Sussex..................... 99
Art Book Company, (The), Suffolk................ 227
Art Reference Books, Hampshire 124
Artco, Nottinghamshire............................. 204
Arthur Hook, Bristol................................ 58
Arts & Antiques Centre (The), Cheshire.......... 69
Ash Rare Books, London SW....................... 166
Ashwell Books, Wiltshire........................... 252
Askew Books (Vernon), Wiltshire.................. 251
Astley Book Farm, Warwickshire................... 236
Atholl Fine Books, Tayside 280
Atlantis Bookshop, London WC................... 176
Atlas, London N..................................... 156
Aucott and Thomas, Leics 145
Aurelian Books, London NW 160
Aurora Books Ltd, Lothian......................... 275
Austen (Phillip), Lincolnshire...................... 151

Austwick Hall Books, N Yorkshire 192
authorshome, Cambs 66
Autolycus, Shropshire 212
Autumn Leaves, Lincolnshire 150
Avedikian Rare Books, Somerset 216
Avery (Alan), N Yorkshire 194
Aviabooks, Glos 114
Avon Books, Bristol 58
Avonworld Books, Somerset 216
Axe Rare & Out of Print Books (Richard), N
    Yorkshire 193
Ayre (Peter J.), Somerset 219

B D McManmon, Lancashire 144
babelog.books, Herefordshire 127
back2books.tv, West Sussex 241
Backfold Books, Herefordshire 127
baconboooks, London WC 176
Badger, Wiltshire 253
Badger Books, Somerset 219
Badgers Books, West Sussex 244
Baedekers & Murray Guides, S Yorkshire 221
Baggins Book Bazaar, Kent 139
Baker - Books for the Collector (Colin), Devon . 89
Baker (Gerald), Bristol 60
Baker Limited (A.P. & R.),
    Dumfries & Galloway 269
Baldwin (Jack), Strathclyde 278
Baldwin (M. & M.), Worcestershire 255
Baldwin's Scientific Books, Essex 111
Ballantyne–Way (Roger), Suffolk 228
Bancroft (David G.), Isle of Wight 133
Bannatyne Books, London N 156
Barbican Bookshop, N Yorkshire 196
Barcombe Services, Essex 108
Bardsley's Books, Suffolk 225
Barely Read Books, Kent 141
Barlow (Vincent G.), Hampshire 125
Barlow Moor Books, Gr Manchester 118
Barmby (C. & A.J.), Kent 140
Barn Books, Shropshire 214
Barn Books, Buckinghamshire 61
Barnacle Books, County Fermanagh 261
Barnes - Books (Lyndon), Shropshire 212
Barnes (Peter), Wiltshire 253
Barnhill Books, Isle of Arran 274
Baron - Scientific Book Sales (P.J.), Somerset ... 216
Baron (Christopher), Cheshire 68
Baron (H.), London NW 160
Barron (Robert M.), Kent 139
Barry McKay Rare Books, Cumbria 76
Barter Books, Northumberland 201
Bass (Ben), Wiltshire 251
Bates & Hindmarch, West Yorkshire 248
Bates Books, London Outer 180
Bath Book Exchange, Somerset 215
Bath Old Books, Somerset 215
Batterham (David), London W 171
Baxter - Books (Eddie), Somerset 220
Baxter (Steve), Surrey 233
Bay Bookshop, Conwy 283
Baynton–Williams Gallery, West Sussex 241
Bayntun (George), Somerset 215
BC Books, Cheshire 69
Bear Island Books, Cardiff 281

Beardsell Books, West Yorkshire 246
Beardsley (A.E.), Nottinghamshire 204
Beaton (Richard), East Sussex 103
Beaumont Travel Books, London SE 163
Beaver Booksearch, Suffolk 225
Beck (John), East Sussex 103
Beckham Books Ltd., Suffolk 229
Beckside Books, Cumbria 78
Beighton (Brian), Norfolk 186
Belfry Books, Nottinghamshire 203
Bell (Peter), Lothian 275
Ben–Nathan (Jack), London Outer 180
Bennett & Kerr Books, Oxfordshire 205
Benny Gillies Books Ltd, Dumfries & Galloway 268
Bermondsey Basement Bookstore, London SE .. 163
Bernard Dixon and Kath Adams, London Outer 182
Bernstein (Nicholas), London W 171
Bertram Rota Ltd., London WC 176
Berwick Books, Lincolnshire 150
Berwyn Books, Wales 292
Besleys Books, Suffolk 225
Bettridge (Gordon), Fife 271
Bevan (John), Wiltshire 252
Beverley Old Bookshop, East Yorkshire 106
Beware of the Leopard, Bristol 58
Bianco Library, West Sussex 241
Bibliophile (The), S Yorkshire 221
Bibliophile Books, London E 154
Bibliopola, London NW 160
Biblipola, London NW 160
Bickford-Smith (G.) (formerly Snowden Smith
    Books), Surrey 232
Biff Books and Records, S Yorkshire 221
Big Bairn Books, Tayside 279
Bilski (Gill), Buckinghamshire 61
Birchden Books, London E 154
Bird (Tony), Powys 291
Bird Books (Nigel), Ceredigion 283
Birdnet Optics Ltd., Derbyshire 82
Birmingham Books, West Midlands 238
Bishopston Books, Bristol 58
Black Cat Books, Norfolk 187
Black Cat Bookshop, Leics 147
Black Five Books, Shropshire 214
Black Gull Books, London N 156
Black Voices, Merseyside 184
Blacket Books, Lothian 276
Blacklock's, Surrey 231
Blackman Books, Cheshire 71
Blackpool Book Warehouse, Lancashire 142
Blackwell's Music Shop, Oxfordshire 208
Blackwell's Rare Books, Oxfordshire 208
Blaenavon Books, Torfaen 292
Blairgowrie Books, Tayside 279
Blanchfield (John), West Yorkshire 248
Blest (Peter), Kent 138
Bloomsbury Bookshop, London Outer 181
Blore's Bookshop (Geoffrey), Nottinghamshire .. 204
Bluntisham Books, Cambs 63
Blythswood Bookshop, Highland 274
Bob Mallory (Books), Derbyshire 83
Bodders Books, Shropshire 212
Bodyline Books, Surrey 232
Boer (Louise), Arthurian Books, Powys 287
Boer War Books, N Yorkshire 197

Bolland Books, Bedfordshire......................... 53
Bolton Books, Hampshire........................... 121
Bonham (J. & S.L.), London W 171
Bonython Bookshop, Cornwall.................... 75
Book Aid, Durham.............................. 97
Book Annex (The), Essex 109
Book Business (The), London W 171
Book Castle, (The), Bedfordshire................... 53
Book Depot (The), London NW................... 160
Book Emporium, N Yorkshire 194
Book End, Essex.................................... 108
Book For All Reasons (A.), Suffolk 228
Book Gallery (The), Cornwall 74
Book House (The), Cumbria....................... 76
Book Jungle (The), East Sussex 105
Book Mad, Lancashire............................. 142
Book Mongers, London SW........................ 166
Book Palace (The), London SE 163
Bookbarrow, Cambs 63
Bookbox, Glos 115
Bookcase, Cumbria................................. 76
Bookcupboard, Devon.............................. 88
Bookends, Norfolk 188
Bookends, Hampshire.............................. 122
Bookends of Fowey, Cornwall 72
Bookfare, Cumbria 80
Booklore, Leics.................................... 146
BookLovers.co.uk, Somerset 218
Bookmark (Children's Books), Wiltshire.......... 253
Booknotes, Essex 110
Bookpassage (The), Shropshire.................... 212
Bookroom (The), Surrey........................... 233
Bookroom, The, Borders 267
Bookroom (The), Isle of Wight.................... 134
Bookroom at Brown & White, The, Glos 117
Bookroom at Heritage Antiques Centre, Herts .. 129
Books, Oxfordshire................................. 205
Books, Kent 137
Books, Denbighshire............................... 284
Books & Bygones, Berkshire....................... 57
Books & Bygones (Pam Taylor), West Midlands 240
Books & Collectables Ltd., Cambs 63
Books & Ink, Oxfordshire.......................... 205
Books & Things, London W........................ 171
Books Afloat, Dorset............................... 96
Books and Beans, Grampian 272
Books and Things, Channel Islands 258
Books Antiques & Collectables, Devon 90
Books at Star Dot Star, West Midlands 240
Books At The Barras, Lanarkshire 278
Books at the Warehouse, N Yorkshire............ 193
Books B.C., London Outer 180
Books Bought & Sold, Surrey 231
Books for Amnesty, Bristol 58
Books for Content, Herefordshire................. 127
Books in Cardigan, Ceredigion 282
Books on Spain, London Outer 182
Books Only, Suffolk................................ 226
Books Ulster, Co. Down 261
Books Upstairs, West Yorkshire 249
Books With Care, Bedfordshire 53
books2books, Devon................................ 88
BOOKS4U, Flintshire.............................. 284
Bookseeker, Tayside............................... 280
Bookseller (The), Cumbria 79

Booksets.com Ltd, Shropshire 214
Bookshelf – Aviation Books, West Sussex........ 241
Bookshelf (The),, N Yorkshire 195
Bookshop (The), Norfolk 191
Bookshop (The), West Sussex 242
Bookshop (The), Co. Donegal..................... 263
Bookshop (The), G Manchester 118
Bookshop at the Plain, Lincolnshire............... 149
Bookshop on the Heath, The, London SE 163
Bookshop, Kirkstall (The), West Yorkshire 248
BookShop, The, Dumfries & Galloway........... 270
Booksmart, Northamptonshire 199
Bookstand, Dorset.................................. 94
Bookstore, The, Co. Antrim 260
Booktrace International, Devon.................... 86
Bookworld, Shropshire............................. 213
Bookworm (The), Lothian 276
Bookworm Alley, Devon 89
Bookworms, Norfolk............................... 186
Bookworms of Evesham, Worcestershire 257
Bookworms Paradise Ltd., West Sussex 242
Bookzone, Berkshire 55
Booth (Booksearch Service), (Geoff), Cheshire... 68
Booth Books, Herefordshire 127
Boox-Box (The), Shropshire 212
Border Bookshop, West Yorkshire 249
Boris Books, Somerset 216
Bosco Books, Cornwall 72
Bosorne Books, Cornwall 75
Boss (Tim), West Sussex........................... 243
Bott, (Bookdealers) Ltd., (Martin),
    G Manchester 118
Botting & Berry, East Sussex 103
Boulevard Books, East Sussex 102
Bouquiniste Bookshop, Fife........................ 271
Bow Windows Book Shop, East Sussex 103
Bowers Chess Suppliers (Francis), Cambs 67
Bowie Books & Collectables, East Yorkshire 107
Bowland Bookfinders, Lancashire.................. 143
Boxwood Books & Prints, Somerset............... 219
Boz Books, Powys.................................. 287
Bracton Books, Cambs 63
Brad Books, Essex................................. 110
Brazenhead Ltd., Norfolk 188
Brewin Books Ltd., Warwickshire 237
Bridge Books, Cumbria 81
Bridge Bookshop Ltd, Isle of Man 259
Bridport Old Books, Dorset 92
Bright (P.G.), Cambs............................... 65
Brighton Books, East Sussex....................... 99
Brimstones, East Sussex 104
Brinded (Scott), Kent 138
Bristol Books, Bristol 60
Bristow & Garland, Hampshire 123
Britons Catholic Library, Co. Wexford 266
Broadhurst of Southport Ltd., Merseyside 185
Broadleaf Books, Torfaen.......................... 292
Broadwater Books, Hampshire 125
Brock Books, N Yorkshire......................... 192
Brown (Books) (P.R.), Durham 98
Brown (Books) (Steve), Staffordshire 223
Brown (K.C.), Berkshire........................... 55
Brown and Rivans Ltd, Devon..................... 90
Browne (Christopher I.), West Yorkshire......... 246
Brownhills Books, West Midlands 239

Browning Books, Torfaen 292
Brown-Studies, Strathclyde 277
Browse Books, Lancashire 143
Browsers Bookshop, Cornwall 72
Browzers, G Manchester 118
Bruce Holdsworth Books, East Sussex 105
Buckland Books, West Sussex 243
Buckley (Sybil), N Yorkshire 194
Bufo Books, Hampshire 125
Bunyan Books, Bedfordshire 53
Burak (Steve), London WC 176
Burden (Derek), Surrey 232
Burden Ltd., (Clive A.), Herts 131
Burebank Books, Norfolk 186
Burmester (James), Bristol 58
Burroughs (Andrew), Lincolnshire 152
Burton–Garbett (A.), London Outer 182
Bury Bookshop, Suffolk 225
Butcher (Pablo), Oxfordshire 206
Butler Rare Books, Buckinghamshire 61
Butterworth (Robert F.), Lancashire 144
Butts Books (Mary), Berkshire 56
Byblos Antiquarian & Rare Book, Hampshire .. 122
Bygone Books, Isles of Scotland 275
Byre Books, Dumfries & Galloway 270
Byrom Textile Bookroom (Richard), Lancashire 142

C J Renwick Books, Powys 287
Cader Idris Books, Powys 290
Cader Idris Bookshop, Gwynedd 286
Caduceus Books, Leics 145
Caissa Books, Surrey 233
Caledonia Books, Strathclyde 278
Caliver Books, Essex 109
Calluna Books, Dorset 95
Camden Books, Somerset 215
Cameron (Mrs Janet), Kent 140
Cameron House Books, Isle of Wight 133
Camilla's Bookshop, East Sussex 101
Camden Lock Books, London EC 155
Campbell (Fiona), London SE 163
Campbell Art Books (Marcus), London SE 163
Campbell Hewson Books (R.), Fife 271
Candle Lane Books, Shropshire 213
Canon Gate Books, West Sussex 243
Canterbury Bookshop (The), Kent 136
Capel Mawr Collectors Centre, Gwynedd 285
Capital Bookshop, Cardiff 281
Carlton Books, Norfolk 189
Carnforth Bookshop (The), Lancashire 142
Carningli Centre, Pembrokeshire 286
Carraig Books Ltd., Co. Dublin 263
Carter, (Brian), Oxfordshire 210
Carters (Janet), Suffolk 225
Cassidy (Bookseller) (P.), Lincolnshire 151
Castle Bookshop, Powys 290
Castle Bookshop, Essex 108
Castle Hill Books, Herefordshire 128
Cat Lit, Somerset 218
Catalyst Booksearch Services, Devon 87
Cathach Books Ltd, Co. Dublin 264
Cavendish Books (Rupert), West Yorkshire 247
Cavendish Rare Books, London N 156
Cavern Books, Cheshire 70
Cecilia Marsden, Surrey 232

Celtic Bookshop (The), Co. Limerick 266
Chalk (Old & Out of Print Books)
  (Christine M.), West Midlands 238
Chalmers Hallam (E.), Hampshire 125
Chandos Books, Devon 85
Channel Islands Galleries Limited, C.I. 258
Chantrey Books, S Yorkshire 222
Chapel Books, Suffolk 229
Chapman (Neville), Lancashire 144
Chapter & Verse, Lincolnshire 150
Chapter House Books, Dorset 94
Chapter Two, London SE 163
Chapters Bookstore, Co. Dublin 264
Charles Bossom, Cambs 65
Charlie Byrne's Bookshop, Co. Galway 265
Chas J. Sawyer, Kent 140
Chaters Motoring Booksellers, London Outer ... 181
Chaucer Bookshop, Kent 136
Chaucer Head Bookshop, Warwickshire 237
Chelifer Books, Cumbria 80
Cheshire Book Centre, Cheshire 69
Chesters (G. & J.), Staffordshire 224
Chevin Books, West Yorkshire 249
Chichester Bookshop (The), Herefordshire 241
Childrens Bookshop, West Yorkshire 247
Children's Bookshop (The), Herefordshire 127
Chris Adam Smith Modern First Editions,
  West Sussex 243
Chris Phillips, Wiltshire 252
Chris Porter Books, Norfolk 186
Christine's Book Cabin, Leics 147
Christopher Saunders (Orchard Books), Glos 115
Chthonios Books, East Sussex 102
Church Green Books, Oxfordshire 210
Church Street Books, Norfolk 186
Church Street Bookshop, London N 156
Churchgate Books, Suffolk 226
Cirencester Arcade, Glos 114
Clapham (M. & B.), Hampshire 124
Claras Books, East Sussex 101
Clarendon Books, Leics 145
Clark (M.R.), West Yorkshire 245
Clark (Nigel A.), London SE 163
Clarke (Janet), Somerset 215
Clarke Books (David), Somerset 218
Classic Bindings Ltd, London SW 166
Classic Crime Collections, G Manchester 119
Classics Bookshop (The), Oxfordshire 205
Clear (Mrs. Patricia), Surrey 230
Clegg (David), Staffordshire 223
Clements (R.W.), London Outer 181
Clent Books, Worcestershire 255
Clevedon Books, Somerset 217
Clewlow Books of Whitby, N Yorkshire 196
Clifford Elmer Books Ltd., Cheshire 68
Clifford Milne Books, Grampian 272
Clifton Books, Essex 111
Coach House Books, Worcestershire 256
Cobbles Books, Somerset 217
Cobnar Books, Kent 141
Cobweb Books, N Yorkshire 194
Coch-y-Bonddu Books, Powys 290
Cocks (Brian), Cambs 67
Cofion Books, Pembrokeshire 286
Cold Tonnage Books, Surrey 234

Coleman (Tom), Highland 273
Colin Hancock, Ceredigion 282
Colin Page Books, East Sussex 99
Collards Bookshop, Devon 90
Collectable Books, London SE 163
Collectables (W.H.), Suffolk 229
Collectors Carbooks, Northamptonshire......... 199
Collectors Corner, Wiltshire........................ 253
Collinge & Clark, London WC..................... 176
Colonsay Bookshop, Isle of Colonsay............ 275
Colwyn Books, Conwy 283
Combat Arts Archive, Durham 97
Compass Books, Devon 85
Cooking = The Books, Glos........................ 115
Cooks Books, East Sussex 99
Coombes (A.J.), Surrey.............................. 230
Cooper Hay Rare Books, Strathclyde............. 278
Coopercollectablebooks, Hampshire............... 123
Copnal Books, Cheshire............................. 69
Copperplate Antique Maps and Prints, Herts.... 132
Corder (Mark W.), Kent 139
Corfe Books, Surrey.................................. 230
Cornell Books, Glos.................................. 117
Cornerstone Books, Devon 88
Cornucopia Books, Lincolnshire 151
Corvus Books, Buckinghamshire................... 61
Cotswold Internet Books, Glos..................... 113
Cottage Books, Leics 145
Cottage Bookshop (The), Buckinghamshire 62
Coulthurst (Richard), G Manchester 120
Country Books, Derbyshire.......................... 82
Countrymans Gallery (The), Leics 145
Countryside Books, Hampshire 121
Coupland (Terry W.), Staffordshire................ 223
Court Hay Books, West Midlands.................. 239
Courtenay Bookroom, Oxfordshire................ 205
Courtney & Hoff, N Yorkshire..................... 197
Courtwood Books, Co. Laois....................... 265
Courtyard Books, Glos 113
Cover to Cover, Merseyside......................... 185
Cowley, Auto–in–Print (John), Essex.............. 108
Cowley, Bookdealer (K.W.), Somerset 217
Cox (Geoff), Devon 90
Cox Music (Lisa), Devon............................ 86
Cox Old & Rare Books (Claude), Suffolk 227
Cox Rare Books (Charles), Cornwall.............. 73
Cox, Andrew, Shropshire............................ 214
Crabtree (Mrs. C.), G Manchester 120
Cranhurst Books, London NW 160
Craobh Rua Books, Co. Armagh................... 260
Crawford (Elizabeth), London EC 155
Creaking Shelves, Highland 274
Crimes Ink, London E............................... 154
Criterion Books, London Outer 181
Crombie (R. & S.), West Midlands 240
Crosby (Simon), East Sussex....................... 102
Crosby Nethercott Books, London Outer 180
Cross (Ian), Berkshire............................... 55
Crouch Rare Books, Surrey......................... 232
Croydon Bookshop, London Outer 180
Ctesiphon Books, G Manchester 120
Cumming Limited (A. & Y.), East Sussex........ 104
Curlews, Durham..................................... 97
Curtle Mead Books, Isle of Wight 133
Cygnet Books, East Yorkshire...................... 107

Cymric Books, Berkshire............................ 56
D Robertson (Booksellers & Booksearch
   Services), Lothian................................. 276
D. & M. Books, West Yorkshire................... 249
D.C. Books, Lincolnshire............................ 149
Dadd, Stephen, Kent................................ 135
Daeron's Books, Buckinghamshire................. 62
Daisy Lane Books, West Yorkshire 246
Daisyroots Book Centre (Daisyroots
   Books Ltd), Cumbria 77
Dalbeattie Books, Dumfries & Galloway 269
Dalby (Richard), N Yorkshire...................... 195
Dales & Lakes Book Centre, Cumbria............ 79
Dally (Andrew), Powys.............................. 289
Dance Books Ltd, Hampshire...................... 121
Dancing Goat Bookshop (The), Norfolk 187
Dandy Lion Editions, Surrey....................... 233
D'Arcy Books, Wiltshire............................ 252
Darkwood Books, Co. Cork........................ 263
Dartmoor Book Gallery, Devon 87
Dartmoor Bookshop (The), Devon................ 84
DaSilva Puppet Books, Dorset 93
Dave Jelfs, Devon 85
David (G.), Cambs 63
David Flint, Hampshire 124
David Houston - Bookseller, London E 154
David Summerfield Books, East Sussex........... 99
David Warnes Books, Herefordshire 128
davidleesbooks.com, Herefordshire 127
Davids Ltd., (Roy), Oxfordshire 208
Davidson Books, Co. Down 261
Davis, Antiquarian Books (Guy), Notts 204
Dawlish Books, Devon 86
DBS Childrens Collectable Books, Hampshire... 123
de Beaumont (Robin), London SW 166
De Burca Rare Books, Co. Dublin 264
de Visser Books, Cambs 63
Dean Byass, Bristol.................................. 60
Dearman Rare Books (Rebecca), Leics 145
Debbage (John), Norfolk 189
Decorum Books, London N 156
Deeside Books, Grampian........................... 272
Delectus Books, London WC....................... 176
Delph Books, G Manchester........................ 120
Demar Books (Grant), Kent 140
Demetzy Books, Oxfordshire 206
Dene Barn Books & Prints, Somerset 219
Dennys Sanders & Greene Ltd, East Sussex 100
Derek Stirling Bookseller, Kent 141
Design Gallery 1850-1950 (The), Kent 141
Deverell Books, Bristol.............................. 59
Dew (Roderick), East Sussex 101
dgbbooks, West Sussex 244
Dinnages Transport Publishing, East Sussex 103
Discovery Bookshop, Carmarthenshire............ 281
Dobson (Bob), Lancashire 142
Dodsworth (Ian), Cumbria.......................... 77
Dolphin Books, Suffolk.............................. 225
Don Kelly Books, London W 172
Donovan Military Books (Tom), East Sussex..... 99
Doodles Bookshop, N Yorkshire 195
Dooley (Rosemary), Cumbria....................... 77
Doolin Dinghy Books, Co. Clare 262
Doorbar (P. & D.), Gwynedd 285
Dorchester Bookshop (The), Dorset.............. 92

Dormouse Bookshop (The), Norfolk 189
Dorset Bookshop (The), Dorset 91
Dorset Rare Books, Dorset 94
Double - B - Books Ltd, Somerset................ 59
Douglas Books, Dumfries & Galloway 268
Douglas Saville Numismatic Books, Berkshire... 55
DPE Books, Devon 87
Draca Books, West Yorkshire 248
Draycott Books, Glos................................ 114
Driffield Bookshop (The), East Yorkshire 106
Drummond Pleasures of Past Times (David),
    London WC 176
Drury Rare Books (John), Essex................... 110
Du Ry Medieval Manuscripts (Marc–Antoine),
    London W 172
Dublin Bookbrowsers, Co. Dublin................ 265
Duck (William), Hampshire......................... 124
Duncan & Reid, Lothian............................ 276
Dunkheld Antiques, Tayside........................ 279
Dunn Antiques & Books (Hamish),
    Northumberland 202
Dunstan Books, Dorset............................. 91
Dusty Books, Powys 290
Dylans Bookstore, Swansea........................ 291
Dyson (Anthony), West Midlands 239

Eagle Bookshop (The), Bedfordshire 53
Earlsfield Bookshop, London SW.................. 166
Early Times, Guernsey, Channel Islands.......... 258
Earth Science Books, Wiltshire 252
East Riding Books, East Yorkshire................ 107
Eastcote Bookshop (The), London Outer......... 180
Eastern Books of London, London SW 166
Eastern Traveller (The), Somerset 219
Eastgate Bookshop, Warwickshire 237
Eastgate Bookshop, East Yorkshire 106
Eastleach Books, Berkshire......................... 56
Eastwood Books (David), Cornwall 72
Eclectica, London SE 164
ECR Books, Dorset 92
Edmund Pollinger Rare Books, London SW..... 166
Edrich (I.D.), London E............................ 154
Edwards (Alan & Margaret), Kent 141
Edwards (Christopher), Oxfordshire............... 209
Edwards (London) Limited (Francis),
    London WC 176
Edwards in Hay–on–Wye (Francis), Powys 288
Edwards, Fiona, Nottinghamshire 203
Eggeling Books (John), West Yorkshire 249
Eggle (Mavis), Herts 130
Elaine Lonsdale Books, West Yorkshire 247
Elgar (Raymond), East Sussex..................... 99
Elizabeth Ferguson, Grampian 272
Ellis (J.R. & R.K.), Norfolk 189
Ellis, Bookseller (Peter), London WC 177
Ellwood Editions, Wiltshire 253
Elmfield Books, West Midlands.................... 238
Elmo Books, West Sussex.......................... 243
Elstree Books, Herts................................ 130
Elton Engineering Books, London W 172
Ely Books, Cambs.................................. 65
Embleton (Paul), Essex 111
Emjay Books, Surrey............................... 231
Empire Books, N Yorkshire 197
Endeavour Books, N Yorkshire.................... 196

Engaging Gear Ltd., Essex 108
English (Toby), Oxfordshire........................ 209
Enigma Books, Wiltshire 252
Enscot Books, London SE 164
Erian Books, London N............................ 156
Esoteric Dreams Bookshop, Cumbria 77
Esplin (David), Hampshire 124
Eton Antique Bookshop, Berkshire................ 57
Evangelical Bookshop, Co. Antrim 260
Evans (Mark), Lincolnshire 151
Evans Books (Paul), West Sussex 243
Everett (Richard), Norfolk 187
Everett (Richard, at the Southwold Antiques
    Centre), Suffolk 229
Evergreen Livres, Glos............................. 116
Ewell Books, Surrey................................ 230
Ex Libris, Wiltshire................................ 251
Exeter Rare Books, Devon......................... 86
Exeter's Antiques Centre on the Quay, Devon... 86

Facet Books, Dorset................................ 91
Fair Hare Books, Hampshire 125
Falconwood Transport & Military Bookshop,
    London Outer.................................... 183
Falmouth Bookshop, Cornwall..................... 72
Family-Favourites, East Yorkshire................. 106
Fantastic Literature, Essex 110
Fantasy Centre, London N 156
Farahar & Dupre (Clive & Sophie), Wiltshire ... 251
Farnborough Gallery, Hampshire................... 122
Farquharson, (Hilary), Tayside..................... 280
Farringdon (J.M.), Swansea........................ 291
Faversham Books, Kent............................ 137
Fawkes (Keith), London NW 160
Fenning (James), Co. Dublin 265
Ferdinando (Steven), Somerset 218
Ferguson (Elizabeth), Grampian 272
Fiction First, Cheshire 69
Fielden, Co. Durham 97
Fifteenth Century Bookshop (The), East Sussex. 104
Finch Rare Books Ltd. (Simon), London W..... 172
Find That Book, West Yorkshire 248
Fine Art Catalogues, Cumbria 80
Fine Books at Ilkley, West Yorkshire 247
Fine Books Oriental, London W14................ 172
Fireside Bookshop, Cumbria....................... 81
First Edition, The, Essex 109
First State Books, London W 172
firstpagebooks, Norfolk............................ 189
Firsts in Print, Somerset 219
Fishburn Books, London NW...................... 160
Fisher & Sperr, London N......................... 157
Fisher Nautical, East Sussex 99
Fitzsimons (Anne), Cumbria 76
Fletcher (H.M.), Herts 131
Fogg Rare Books & Manuscripts (Sam),
    London W 172
Folios Limited, London SW 167
Footballana, Berkshire.............................. 56
Footrope Knots, Suffolk........................... 227
Forbury Fine Books, Berkshire..................... 56
Ford (Richard), London W......................... 172
Ford Books (David), Herts 130
Forder (R.W.), Hampshire 121
ForensicSearch, Herts 131

Forest Books, Nottinghamshire 204
Forest Books, Rutland............................... 211
Forest Books of Manchester, Cheshire........... 70
Formby Antiques (Jeffrey), Glos 115
Fortune Green Books, London NW............... 160
Fossgate Books, N Yorkshire...................... 197
Foster (Stephen), London NW 160
Foster Bookshop (Paul), London SW............ 167
Fosters Bookshop, London W 172
Fotheringham (Alex), Northumberland 201
Foulkes (Len), Cardiff 281
Fox Books (J. & J.), Kent........................... 139
Foyle Books, Co. Derry 260
Framlingham Bookshop, Suffolk.................. 227
Francis, S. L., Sussex............................... 103
Franks Booksellers, G Manchester 119
Freader's Books, Tayside........................... 279
Freeman's Corner Shop, Norfolk 189
Frew Limited (Robert), London SW 167
Freya Books & Antiques, Norfolk................ 189
Frost (Richard), Herts 129
Fuchsia Books, Co. Wexford 266
Fuller D'Arch Smith, London W 172
Fullerton's Booksearch, Norfolk 188
Fun in Books, Surrey 234
Furneaux Books (Lee), Devon..................... 89
Fylde Books, Lancashire 144

G Collins Bookdealers, Herts...................... 130
G&S Books, Kent 138
G. C. Books Ltd., Dumfries & Galloway........ 270
Gage Postal Books, Essex 111
Gallimaufry Books, Herts 131
Galloway & Porter Limited, Cambs.............. 64
Game Advice, Oxfordshire......................... 208
Gander, (Jacques), Glos 114
Garbett Antiquarian Books (Michael), Glos 115
Gardener & Cook, London SW.................... 167
Garfi Books, Powys 291
Garretts Antiquarian Books, Isle of Man........ 259
Garwood & Voigt, Kent............................ 139
Gaskell Rare Books (Roger), Cambs............. 66
Gathern (D.), Conwy 283
Gay's The Word, London WC 177
Gekoski (R.A.), London WC....................... 177
Gemini–Books, Shropshire 214
Geneva Books, London SW 167
Geophysical Books, Kent........................... 139
George Gregory, Somerset 215
George St. Books, Derbyshire 83
Georgina Hobhouse, Argyll........................ 274
Gerald Lee Maritime Books, East Sussex........ 105
GfB: the Colchester Bookshop, Essex 108
Gibbard (A. & T.), East Sussex 101
Gibberd (Jane), London SE........................ 164
Gibbs Books, (Jonathan), Worcestershire......... 256
Gibbs Bookshop Ltd., G Manchester 119
Gilbert (R.A.), Somerset........................... 219
Gilbert and Son (H.M.), Hampshire.............. 126
Gildas Books, Cheshire 68
Gillmark Gallery, Herts............................. 130
Glacier Books, Tayside.............................. 280
Gladstone Books, Lincolnshire 150
Glance Back Books, Gwent......................... 285
Glasheen-Books, Surrey 231

Glenbower Books, Co. Dublin 264
Glenwood Books, Surrey............................ 234
Glyn's Books, Shropshire........................... 212
Golden Age Books, Worcestershire................ 256
Golden Books Group, Devon 85
Golden Goose Books, Lincolnshire................ 150
Goldman (Paul), Dorset 94
Goldsworth Books, Surrey 234
Golfiana, London W 172
Good Book Shop, The, Devon..................... 90
Good Books, Shropshire 213
Good for Books, Lincolnshire 149
Goodden (Peter), Somerset......................... 215
Goodwin (J.O.), Staffordshire..................... 224
Goodyer (Nicholas), London N 157
Goodyer, Natural History Books (Eric), Leics... 146
Gowan Books (John), Co. Fermanagh............ 261
Graham (John), Dorset 96
Grahame (Major Iain), Suffolk 225
Grahame Thornton, Bookseller, Dorset........... 93
Grampian Books, Grampian........................ 273
Granny's Attic, Wiltshire 251
Grant, Lothian 276
Grant & Shaw Ltd., Lothian 276
Grant Books, Worcestershire 255
Gravity Books, Lincolnshire 149
Grayling (David A.H.), Cumbria 78
Grays of Westminster, London SW 167
Great Grandfather's, Lancashire 143
Great Hall Bookshop, Buckinghamshire.......... 61
Great Oak Bookshop (The), Powys 289
Green (Mrs. D.M.), Surrey......................... 234
Green (Paul), Cambs 67
Green Ltd. (G.L.), Herts 131
Green Man Books, East Sussex 101
Green Meadow Books, Cornwall 74
Greene's Bookshop Ltd, Co. Dublin 264
Greenroom Books, West Yorkshire 247
Greensleeves, Oxfordshire 206
Greer (Robin), London SW........................ 167
Gresham Books, Somerset 217
Greta Books, Durham 97
Grove Bookshop (The), N Yorkshire 195
GS Cricket Books / The Old Book Shop, West
    Midlands 240
Guildmaster Books, Cheshire 70
Guisborough Bookshop (The), N Yorkshire 192

Hab Books, London W............................. 172
Hadfield (G.K.), Cumbria 79
Halewood & Sons, Lancashire..................... 144
Hall, (Anthony C.) Antiquarian Bookseller,
    London Outer 183
Hall's Bookshop, Kent.............................. 140
Halson Books, Cheshire 71
Hambleton Books, N Yorkshire 196
Hames (Peter), Devon.............................. 84
Hamish Riley-Smith, Norfolk...................... 191
Hanborough Books, Oxfordshire................... 208
Hancock & Monks Music Emporium, Powys ... 288
Hancock (Peter), West Sussex 241
Handley (Christopher), Tyne and Wear........... 235
Handsworth Books, Essex.......................... 112
Hanshan Tang Books, London SW 167
Harlequin, Devon................................... 90

Harlequin Books, Bristol 59
Harlequin Gallery, Lincolnshire 150
Harrington (Adrian), London W 173
Harrington Antiquarian Bookseller (Peter),
   London SW 167
Harris (George J.), Co. Derry 260
Harrowden Books of Finedon, Northants 200
Hart (John), Norfolk 186
Harvest Books, Lancashire 144
Harwich Old Books, Essex 109
Haskell (R.H. & P.), Dorset 94
Hatchard & Daughters, West Yorkshire 246
Haunted Bookshop (The), Cambs 64
Hava Books, London SE 164
Hawes Books, Norfolk 190
Hawkes (James), London 164
Hawkridge Books, Derbyshire 82
Hawley (C.L.), N Yorkshire 195
Hay Castle, Powys 288
Hay Cinema Bookshop Ltd., Powys 288
HCB Wholesale, Powys 288
Head (John & Judith), Wiltshire 253
Heartland Old Books, Devon 89
Heath (A.R.), Bristol 59
Heckmondwike Book Shop, West Yorkshire 249
Hedgerow Books, S Yorkshire 221
Helion & Company, West Midlands 239
Hellenic Bookservices, London NW 161
Helmsley Antiquarian & Secondhand Books,
   N Yorkshire 193
Hemswell Antique Centre, Lincolnshire 149
Hencotes Books & Prints, Northumberland 201
Heneage Art Books (Thomas), London SW 168
Henly (John), West Sussex 244
Hennessey Bookseller (Ray), East Sussex 100
Heppa (Christopher), Essex 108
Heraldry Today, Wiltshire 253
Herb Tandree Philosophy Books, Glos 116
Hereford Booksearch (John Trevitt),
   Herefordshire 128
Hereward Books, Cambs 66
Heritage, West Midlands 238
Heritage Books, Isle of Wight 133
Herne Bay Books, Kent 138
Hesketh & Ward Ltd., London SW 168
Heywood Hill Limited (G.), London W 173
Hicks (Ronald C.), Cornwall 73
High Street Book Shop, East Sussex 102
High Street Books, Devon 86
Higher Octave Books, Bristol 59
Hight (Norman F.), Glamorgan 285
Hill (John S.), Devon 86
Hill (Peter), Hampshire 122
Hill Books (Alan), S Yorkshire 222
Hill House Books, Devon 88
Hilton (Books) (P.J.), London W 173
Hindsight Books, Herts 131
Hine (Anne), Somerset 217
Hobgoblin Books, Hampshire 125
Hodgkins and Company Limited (Ian), Glos 116
Hodgson (Books) (Richard J.),
   N Yorkshire 196
Hodgson (Judith), London W 173
Hogan (F. & J.), London N 157
Holdenhurst Books, Dorset 91

Hollett and Son (R.F.G.), Cumbria 79
Hollingshead (Chris), London Outer 182
Holmes Books (Harry), East Yorkshire 107
Holtom (Christopher), Glos 115
Home Farm Books, Warwickshire 236
Hoovey's Books, East Sussex 102
Hornsey's, N Yorkshire 194
Horsham Rare Books, West Sussex 242
House of Figgis Ltd (The), Co. Galway 265
Howard Loftus Rail Books, S Yorkshire 222
Howes Bookshop, East Sussex 102
HP Bookfinders, Central 268
Hünersdorff Rare Books, London SW 168
Hughes (Ms. Sonia A.), Monmouthshire 286
Hughes Rare Books (Spike), Borders 267
hullbooks.com, East Yorkshire 106
Humanist Book Services, Cornwall 72
Humber Books, Lincolnshire 148
Hummingbird Books, Herefordshire 128
Hungerford Antiques Centre, Berkshire 55
Hunter and Krageloh, Derbyshire 83
Hurst (Jenny), Kent 137
Hutchison (Books) (Larry), Fife 271
Hyland (C.P.), Co. Cork 263
Hylton Booksearch, Merseyside 184
Ian Briddon, Derbyshire 82
Ian Marr Rare Books, Cornwall 73
Ian McKelvie Bookseller, London N 157
Ice House Books, Wiltshire 254
IDEA, London EC 155
Idle Booksellers (The), West Yorkshire 245
Idle Genius Books, London N 157
Idler (The), Suffolk 227
Inch's Books, Kent 137
Indoislamica, London SW 168
Inner Bookshop (The), Oxfordshire 208
Innes Books, Shropshire 212
Inprint, Glos 116
Intech Books, Northumberland 201
InterCol London, London N 157
Interesting Books, Wirral, Merseyside 184
Internet Bookshop UK Ltd., Glos 113
Interstellar Master Traders, Lancashire 143
Invicta Booksearch, Kent 140
Invicta Bookshop, Berkshire 56
Invisible Books, East Sussex 100
Iona Bookshop (The), Isle of Iona 275
Island Books, Devon 85
Ivelet Books Ltd., Surrey 233

J & J Burgess Booksellers, Cambs 64
J and J Books, Lincolnshire 149
J.A. Heacock, Cheshire 69
J.B. Books, Berkshire 57
J.C. Books, Norfolk 191
J.C. Books, Devon 87
J.C. Deyong Books (Previously of Snowden
   Smith Books), London SW 168
J.E. Burns Booksellers, Merseyside 185
J.G. Natural History Books, Surrey 233
J.H. Day, Hampshire 124
J.L. Book Exchange, East Yorkshire 106
Jabberwock Books, Lincolnshire 149
Jackdaw Books, Norfolk 188
Jackson (M.W.), Wiltshire 254

Jackson (W.E.), Hampshire 125
Jade Mountain Bookshop, Hampshire 125
James Fergusson Books & Manuscripts,
  London W 173
James M Pickhard (Rare Books), Leics 145
Jane & John Kinnaird, Cumbria 78
Jane Badger Books, Northamptonshire 199
Jane Jones Books, Grampian 273
Janus Books, West Midlands 239
Jarndyce Antiquarian Booksellers, London WC. 177
Jarvis Books, Derbyshire 83
Jay Books, Lothian 276
JB Books & Collectables, West Sussex 243
Jean Hedger, Berkshire 55
Jenny Hurst, Kent 138
Jermy & Westerman, Nottinghamshire 204
Jill Howell, East Sussex 102
JIRI Books, Co. Antrim 260
Jobson (N.W.), Oxfordshire 206
Joel Segal Books, Devon 86
John Barton, Hampshire 126
John Clifford, Dorset 92
John Gorton Booksearch, East Sussex 105
John L Capes (Books Maps & Prints), N Yorks 196
John Read Antiques, Shropshire 213
John Underwood Antiquarian Books, Norfolk .. 189
Johnson Rare Book Collections (C.R.),
  London NW 161
Johnston's Marine Stores, Scotland 274
Jolly Good Read (A.), Tayside 279
Jones (Andrew), Suffolk 227
Jones (Barry), West Sussex 242
Jonkers Rare Books, Oxfordshire 207
Joppa Books Ltd., Surrey 230
Judd Books, London WC 177
Judith Mansfield, West Yorkshire 249
Junk & Spread Eagle, London SE 164
Just Books, Cornwall 75

K Books, Cheshire 70
K.S.C. Books, Cheshire 70
Kabristan Archives, Shropshire 214
Kalligraphia (formerly Charmouth Bounty
  Books), Isle of Wight 133
Karen Millward, Co. Cork 263
Karen Thomson, Oxfordshire 209
Katesbooks, Devon 85
Katharine House Gallery, Wiltshire 252
Katnap Arts, Norfolk 190
Kay Books, London W 173
Keeble Antiques, Somerset 218
Keegan's Bookshop, Berkshire 57
Keel Row Bookshop, Tyne and Wear 235
Keith Langford, London E 154
Kellow Books, Oxfordshire 206
Kelly Books Ltd, Devon 89
Kelpie's Books, Fife 271
Kelsall (George), G Manchester 118
Kemp Bookseller, Michael S, G Manchester 118
Kendall–Carpenter (Tim), G Manchester 119
Kennedy & Farley, East Sussex 104
Kennedy (Peter), Surrey 234
Kenneth Ball, East Sussex 100
Kenny's Bookshop & Art Galleries Ltd.,
  Co. Galway 265

Ken's Paper Collectables, Buckinghamshire 62
Kent (Books) (Mrs. A.), Suffolk 227
Kent T. G., Surrey 230
Kentish (B. & N.), Oxfordshire 205
Kenya Books, East Sussex 100
Keogh's Books, Glos 115
Kernaghans, Merseyside 185
Kerr (Norman), Cumbria 77
Kestrel Books, Powys 288
Keswick Bookshop, Cumbria 78
Kevin S. Ogilvie Modern First Editions,
  Grampian 272
Key Books (Sarah), Cambs 64
Kilgarriff (Raymond), East Sussex 105
Kilgour (Sporting Books) (Ian), Leics 147
Killeen (John), N Yorkshire 193
Kim's Bookshop, West Sussex 241
Kim's Bookshop, West Sussex 242
Kineton Nooks, Warwickshire 236
Kingfisher Book Service, Nottinghamshire 204
Kings Bookshop Callander, Central 268
Kingsgate Books & Prints, Hampshire 126
Kingshead Books, Powys 291
Kingsmere Books, Bedfordshire 53
Kingswood Books, Dorset 94
Kirkcudbright Books, Dumfries & Galloway 269
Kirkdale Bookshop, London SE 164
Kirkland Books, Cumbria 78
Kirkman Ltd., (Robert), Bedfordshire 54
Kirkpatrick (Robert J.), London W 173
Kitley (A.J.), Bristol 59
Knapton Bookbarn, N Yorkshire 197
Knowles - Antiquary (Roger J.), Staffordshire... 223
Knowles (John), Norfolk 187
Kohler (C.C.), Surrey 230
Korn (M. Eric), London N 157
Kunkler Books (Paul), Cambs 64
Kyrios Books, Nottinghamshire 203

L.M.S. Books, Herts 131
Lake (David), Norfolk 190
Lake (Fred), Surrey 234
Lamb (R.W.), Suffolk 228
Lamb's Tales Books, Devon 87
Lane Books (Shirley), Isle of Wight 134
Langford Press, Lincolnshire 151
Lankester Antiques and Books, Essex 110
Larkham Books (Patricia), Glos 117
Last Century Books, Borders 267
Lawrence Books, Nottinghamshire 203
Lawson & Company (E.M.), Oxfordshire 206
Leabeck Books, Oxfordshire 208
Leaf Ends, Northumberland 202
Leakey's Bookshop, Highland 274
Leapman Ltd. (G. & R.), Herts 130
Lee Rare Books (Rachel), Bristol 59
Leeds Bookseller, West Yorkshire 248
Leeper (Romilly), London SW 168
Left on The Shelf, Cumbria 78
Leigh Gallery Books, Essex 110
Lenton (Alfred), Leics 145
Leo Cadogan, London N 157
Letterbox Books, Nottinghamshire 203
Lewis (J.T. & P.), Cornwall 73
Lewis First Editions, Kent 136

Libris (Weston) Books, Somerset 216
Liddle (Steve), Bristol 58
Lighthouse Books (The), Dorset 92
Lime Tree Books, Suffolk 228
Lincolnshire Heritage Ltd, Lincolnshire........... 150
Linton Books, Borders............................... 267
Lion Books, Worcestershire........................ 255
Little Bookshop (The), Cumbria 80
Little Bookshop (The), G Manchester............. 119
Little Stour Books, Kent 136
Lloyd-Davies (Sue), Carmarthenshire 282
Loch Croispol Bookshop & Restaurant,
   Highland 273
Loft Bookshop, Cornwall 73
Logie Steading Bookshop, Grampian 273
Londinium Books, Surrey 231
London & Sussex Antiquarian Book &
   Print Services, East Sussex 101
Longden (George), Cheshire 70
Loretta Lay Books, London NW 161
Lost Books, Northamptonshire..................... 200
Lowe (John), Norfolk................................ 188
Lucas (Richard), London NW...................... 161
Lucius Books, N Yorkshire 197
Lymelight Books & Prints, Dorset................. 93
Lyng Heath Books, Norfolk 190
Lyngheath Books, Norfolk.......................... 188
Lyonshill Books, Co. Dublin 265

M Godding Ltd, Wiltshire 253
M. & D. Books, Worcestershire.................... 255
M. and A.C. Thompson, Norfolk.................. 191
Macbuiks, N Yorkshire.............................. 193
Macfarlane (Mr. H.), Essex 111
Mactaggart (Caroline), Dorset...................... 92
Madalyn S. Jones, West Yorkshire 246
Madoc Books, Conwy 284
Maggs Brothers Limited, London W.............. 173
Maggy Browne, Lincolnshire 148
Maghreb Bookshop (The), London WC.......... 177
Magis Books, Leics.................................. 146
Magpie Books, West Yorkshire 250
Main Point Books, Lothian......................... 276
Mainly Fiction, Cheshire 68
Main–Smith & Co. Ltd. (Bruce), Leics............ 146
Mair Wilkes Books, Fife 271
Malvern Bookshop (The), Worcestershire 255
Mandalay Bookshop, London SW 168
Manna Bookshop, Somerset 220
Mannwaring (M.G.), Bristol 59
Marathon Books, Lancashire....................... 142
Marble Hill Books, Outer London................. 182
Marcan, Bookseller (Peter), London SE 164
Marcet Books, London SE.......................... 164
March House Books, Somerset..................... 217
Marchpane, London WC............................ 177
Marco Polo Travel & Adventure Books, Dorset   92
Marijana Dworski Books, Powys 288
Marine & Cannon Books, Cheshire 71
Marine and Cannon Books, Cheshire 69
Marine Workshop Bookshop, Dorset 93
Marjon Books, Essex................................ 111
Market Place Books, Cumbria 77
Marks Limited (Barrie), London N................ 157
Marlborough Rare Books Ltd., London W...... 173

Marshall Rare Books (Bruce), Glos 113
Martin - Bookseller (Colin), East Yorkshire 107
Martin (Books and Pictures), (Brian P.), Surrey . 231
Martin (Brian), Surrey 231
Martin Bookshop & Gallery (Richard), Hants... 123
Martin Music Books (Philip), N Yorkshire 197
Martin's Books, Powys 290
Mason (Mary), Oxfordshire......................... 205
Mayfly Ephemera, London W...................... 173
Mayhew (Veronica), Berkshire...................... 57
Maynard & Bradley, Leics 146
Mcbooks, West Sussex 241
McCarty, Bookseller (M.E.),
   Dumfries & Galloway............................. 270
McCarty, Bookseller (M.E.), Western Isles....... 275
McCaughtrie (K.A.), N Yorkshire................. 192
McConnell Fine Books, Kent....................... 137
McCrone (Audrey), Isle of Arran 274
McEwan Fine Books, Grampian.................... 272
McEwan Golf Books (Rhod), Grampian......... 272
McGee (Terence J.), London Outer 180
McGlynn (John), Lancashire........................ 142
McInnes (P.F. & J.R.), Dorset 91
McKenzie (J.W.), Surrey 232
McLaren Books Ltd, Strathclyde 279
McNaughtan's Bookshop, Lothian 276
medievalbookshop, Herts............................ 132
Meekins Books (Paul), Warwickshire.............. 237
Mellon's Books, East Sussex 101
Melvin Tenner, London W.......................... 173
Mercat Books, Highland 274
Mereside Books, Cheshire........................... 70
Merlin Books, West Sussex 242
Mermaid Books (Burlingham), Norfolk........... 191
Merseyside Books, Merseyside...................... 185
Michael Bishop PBFA, Somerset 220
Michael D. Raftery (Books), Leics................. 147
Michael Graves-Johnston, London SW 168
Michael J Carroll, Co. Cork 263
Michael Rogers, Wiltshire 251
michaelsbookshop.com, Kent........................ 139
Midnight Oil Books, Fife 271
Miles Apart, Suffolk................................. 228
Milestone Books, Devon 89
Milestone Publications Goss & Crested China,
   Hampshire 123
Military Bookworm, London SE.................... 164
Military Parade Bookshop, Wiltshire.............. 252
MilitaryHistoryBooks.com, Kent................... 137
Millard (R.W.), Somerset........................... 216
Miller (Stephen), London Outer.................... 183
Mills Rare Books (Adam), Cambs................. 64
Ming Books, Dumfries & Galloway............... 270
Minster Gate Bookshop, N Yorkshire 197
Missing Books, Essex 109
MK Book Services, Cambs 66
Mobbs (A.J.), West Midlands 239
Modern First Editions, London Outer 181
Modern First Editions, West Yorkshire........... 247
Modern Firsts Etc, Lancashire 142
Modern Welsh Publications Ltd., Merseyside.... 184
Modlock (Lilian), Dorset............................ 93
Moffat Book Exchange,
   Dumfries & Galloway............................. 269
Mogul Diamonds, West Midlands................. 240

Mollie's Loft, Swansea 291
Monmouth House Books, Monmouthshire 286
Moon's Bookshop (Michael), Cumbria 80
Moore (C.R.), Shropshire 213
Moore (Eric T.), Herts 130
Moore (Peter), Cambs 64
Moore (Sue), Cornwall 73
Moorhead Books, West Yorkshire 245
Moorside Books, Lancashire 143
Morgan (H.J.), Bedfordshire 54
Morley Case, Hampshire 125
Morris (A.E.), Gwynedd 285
Morris Secondhand & Antiquarian Books
   (Chris), Oxfordshire 208
Morten (Booksellers) (E.J.), G Manchester 119
Moss Books, Glos 113
Moss End Bookshop, Berkshire 57
Mostly Mysteries Bookstore, Lincolnshire 150
Mothergoose Bookshop, Isle of Wight 133
Mountaineering Books, London N 157
Mount's Bay Books, Cornwall 74
Mr Books Bookshop, Kent 140
Mr. Mac, Dumfries & Galloway 269
Mr. Pickwick of Towcester, Northamptonshire .. 199
MSR Books, Kent 138
Much Ado Books, East Sussex 99
Much Binding, Norfolk 186
Mulyan (Don), Merseyside 185
Mundy (David), Herts 129
Mundy (David), Buckinghamshire 61
Murch Booksend, (Herbert), London SE 165
Murder & Mayhem, Powys 288
Murphy (C.J.), Norfolk 189
Muse Bookshop (The), Gwynedd 285
Music By The Score, Cornwall 72
Musicalania, Norfolk 188
Muttonchop Manuscripts, West Sussex 242
My Back Pages, London SW 168
Myra Dean Illustated Books, Powys 287

N V Books, Warwickshire 236
N1 Books, East Sussex 105
Nakota Curios, East Sussex 102
National Trust Second Hand Bookshop,
   Norfolk 190
Nautical Antique Centre (The), Dorset 96
Needham Books, (Russell), Somerset 219
Neil Summersgill, Lancashire 142
Neil's Books, London NW 161
Nelson (Elizabeth), Suffolk 226
Nevis Railway Books, Oxfordshire 207
Nevis Railway Bookshops (The Antique &
   Book Collector), Wiltshire 252
Nevitsky (Philip), G Manchester 119
New Strand, The, Herefordshire 127
Newband (D.M.), Powys 290
Newcastle Bookshop At Haltwhistle,
   Northumberland 201
Newgate Books and Translations,
   Northumberland 201
Newlyn Books, Cornwall 74
Newport Book Shop, Shropshire 213
Nibris Books, London SW 169
Nicholson of Chester (Richard), Cheshire 68
Nicolas - Antiquarian Bookseller, London N 157

Niner (Marcus), Isle of Wight 133
Nineteenth Century Books, Oxfordshire 209
Nonsuch Books, Surrey 234
Northern Herald Books, West Yorkshire 245
Norton Books, N Yorkshire 192
Nostalgia Publications Ltd., N Yorkshire 197
Nostalgia Unlimited, Merseyside 184
Not Just Books, Dorset 94

Oak Tree Press, Oxfordshire 207
Oakwood Books, Glos 115
Oasis Booksearch, Cambs 67
Oast Books, Kent 136
O'Brien Books & Photo Gallery, Co. Limerick .. 266
Obscurebooks, Co. Dublin 264
Occultique, Northamptonshire 199
O'Connor Fine Books, Lancashire 144
Octagon Books, Cambs 66
O'Donoghue Books, Powys 289
Offa's Dyke Books, Shropshire 213
O'Flynn Books, N Yorkshire 197
O'Flynn Books, N Yorkshire 197
Old Aberdeen Bookshop, Grampian 272
Old Book Company, (The), West Yorkshire 248
Old Bookshelf (The), Strathclyde 278
Old Bookshop (The), West Midlands 240
Old Celtic Bookshop (The), Devon 87
Old Hall Bookshop (The), Northamptonshire ... 199
Old Station Pottery & Bookshop (The), Norfolk 191
Old Town Bookshop (The), Lothian 276
Olynthiacs, Shropshire 213
Oopalba Books, Cheshire 71
Optimus Books Ltd, West Sussex 244
Orange Skies Books, Cumbria 80
Orangeberry Books, Oxfordshire 207
Orbis Books (London) Ltd., London W 173
Orb's Bookshop, Grampian 273
Orchid Book Distributors, Co. Clare 262
O'Reilly - Mountain Books (John), Derbyshire .. 83
Orlando Booksellers, Lincolnshire 150
Orssich (Paul), London SW 169
Osterley Bookshop, London Outer 182
Othello's Bookshop, Essex 110
Ouse Valley Books, Bedfordshire 54
Outcast Books, Herefordshire 127
Over-Sands Books, Cumbria 77
Owen (J.V.), Conwy 284
owenbooks65, Conwy 283
Oxford House Books, Powys 289
Oxley (Laurence), Hampshire 121

P. and P. Books, Worcestershire 256
P.H. Whetman, London N 159
Pagan Limited (Hugh), Hampshire 122
Page (David), Lothian 276
Pages of Ages, Cumbria 76
Palladour Books, Hampshire 125
Pamona Books, Lancashire 144
Pandion Books, N Yorkshire 194
Pantiles Bookshop, Kent 140
Paper Moon Books, Glos 116
Paper Pleasures, Somerset 218
Paperbacks Plus, Bristol 59
Parade Bookshop, Suffolk 229
Paragon Books, Somerset 217

Paramor (C.D.), Suffolk 228
Parikian, Rare Books (Diana), London W 174
Park (Mike), London Outer.......................... 182
Park Gallery & Bookshop (The),
  Northamptonshire 200
Parker Books (Mike), Cambs...................... 64
Parkinsons Books, Merseyside...................... 185
Parlour Bookshop (The), Oxfordshire............. 206
Parrott (Jeremy), London E.......................... 154
Parrott Books, Oxfordshire 209
Past & Present Books, Glos......................... 114
Past Sentence, Kent 137
Pastmasters, Derbyshire............................. 83
Paul Hoare, Cornwall................................ 74
Pauline Harries Books, Hampshire 123
Peake (Robin), Lincolnshire........................ 152
Pedlar's Pack Books, Devon 84
Peel (Valerie), Berkshire 56
Pemberley Books, Buckinghamshire 62
Pend Books, Dumfries & Galloway 269
Pendleburys Bookshop, London N 158
Pendleside Books, Lancashire...................... 143
Penny Farthing, The, Lothian 277
Pennymead Books, N Yorkshire 193
Peregrine Books (Leeds), West Yorkshire........ 248
Period & Classical Collections, East Sussex 103
Periplus Books, Buckinghamshire.................. 62
Periwinkle Press, Kent 136
Peter Clay, Cornwall 73
Peter Lyons Books, Glos 113
Peter M Daly, Hampshire 126
Peter Pan Bookshop, Norfolk 190
Peter White, Hampshire 121
Peter's Bookshop, Norfolk 190
Petersfield Bookshop (The), Hampshire........... 124
Peterson (Tony), Essex.............................. 111
Petworth Antique Market (Bookroom),
  West Sussex.. 244
Phelan Books, Co. Dublin 264
Phelps (Michael), West Sussex...................... 242
Phenotype Books, Cumbria.......................... 79
Philip Hopper, Essex................................ 110
Phillip Robbins of Warwick, Warwickshire 237
Phillips (Nigel), Hampshire......................... 122
Phillips of Hitchin (Antiques) Ltd., Herts......... 131
Photo Books International, London WC......... 177
Phototitles.com, Lincolnshire 151
Piccadilly Rare Books, East Sussex 105
Pickering & Chatto, London W..................... 174
Pickering Bookshop, N Yorkshire 196
Pimpernel Booksearch, London SW 169
Pinnacle Books, Lothian............................ 276
Pittville Books, Glos................................. 113
Plurabelle Books, Cambs 65
Pocket Bookshop (The), Devon 87
Poetry Bookshop (The), Powys..................... 289
Polczynski (Udo K.H.), Powys...................... 289
Pollak (P.M.), Devon................................ 88
Polmorla Books, Cornwall 75
Pooks Motor Books, Leics........................... 146
Poole (William), London W 174
Poor Richard's Books, Suffolk 226
Popeley (Frank T.), Cambs 67
Porcupine Books, London Outer................... 181
Pordes Books Ltd., (Henry), London WC........ 177

Porter Bookshop (The), S Yorkshire 222
Portobello Books, London W 174
Portus Books, Hampshire 122
Post Mortem Books, West Sussex 242
Post–Horn Books, N Yorkshire.................... 192
Postings, Surrey 233
Potterton Books, N Yorkshire...................... 196
Pratt (B.A. & C.W.M.), Herefordshire 128
Preston Book Company, Lancashire 144
Price (John), London N 158
Price (R.D.M. & I.M.) (Books), G Manchester.. 120
Price (R.W.), Nottinghamshire 203
Priestpopple Books, Northumberland 201
Primrose Hill Books, London NW 161
Pringle Booksellers (Andrew), Lothian............ 277
Print Matters, London SE........................... 165
Prior (Michael), Lincolnshire 152
Probsthain (Arthur), London WC 178
Prospect Books, Conwy 283
Prospect House Books, Co. Down................. 261
PsychoBabel Books & Journals, Oxfordshire.... 205
Pugh Books (Ian K.), Worcestershire............. 256
Pyecroft (Ruth), Glos 116

Quadrille at Delehar, London W................... 174
Quaritch Ltd., (Bernard), London W.............. 174
Queen Victoria PH, Torfaen 292
Quentin Books Ltd, Essex........................... 108
Quest Books, East Yorkshire 107
Quest Booksearch, Cambs.......................... 65
Quinto of Charing Cross Road, London WC ... 178

R M Books, Herts.................................... 132
R & B Graham Trading, Cornwall................. 73
R. & A. Books, East Sussex 101
R. S. & P. A. Scowen, London Outer............. 181
R.E. & G.B. Way, Suffolk 228
Raftery Books (Michael D.), Leics................. 147
Railway Book and Magazine Search, Berks...... 56
Railway Shop (The), Torfaen 292
Rainbow Books, East Sussex 100
Rainford (Sheila), Herts 129
Ramrod Antiques, N Yorkshire..................... 195
Randall (Tom), Somerset............................ 218
Rare & Racy, S Yorkshire 222
Rare Books & Berry, Somerset..................... 218
Rassam (Paul), London NW 161
Ray Rare and Out of Print Books (Janette),
  N Yorkshire 198
Rayner (Hugh Ashley), Somerset 215
Read - Gorleston Books, (C.&J.), Norfolk 187
Read Ireland, Co. Dublin 264
Readers Rest, Lincolnshire.......................... 150
Readers World, West Midlands 238
Reading Lasses, Dumfries & Galloway 270
Reads, Dorset 95
Reaveley Books, Devon 87
Rebecca Rare Books, London W 171
Recollectionsbookshop.co.uk, Cornwall........... 74
Red Rose Books, G Manchester 118
Red Star Books, Herts.............................. 129
Rees & O'Neill Rare Books, London WC........ 178
Reeves Technical Books, N Yorkshire 195
Reference Works Ltd., Dorset....................... 95
Regent Furniture, Oxfordshire...................... 209

Reid of Liverpool, Merseyside...................... 184
Reigate Galleries, Surrey............................. 232
Restormel Books, Worcestershire 257
Resurgam Books, East Yorkshire.................. 106
RGS Books, Surrey 234
Rhodes, Bookseller (Peter), Hampshire 125
Rhos Point Books, Conwy.......................... 283
Richard Axe Rare & Out of Print Books, N
    Yorkshire.. 192
Richard Connole, Devon............................ 85
Richard Thornton Books, London N 158
Richmond Books, N Yorkshire 194
Rickaro Books, West Yorkshire.................... 246
Riddell (Peter), East Yorkshire.................... 106
Rider Haggard Society (The), Tyne and Wear... 235
Riderless Horse Books, Norfolk.................... 186
Riley, Bookdealers (Alan and Joy),
    Northamptonshire 199
Ripping Yarns, London N 158
Rising Tide Books, Fife............................. 270
River Reads Bookshop, Devon..................... 90
Riverside Books, Kent 135
Riviera Books, Norfolk............................. 188
Roadmaster Books, Kent............................ 136
Robert (Leslie), London W 174
Robert G Sawers Ltd, London NW.............. 161
Robert Humm & Co, Lincolnshire 152
Robert Temple, London N.......................... 158
Roberts (Booksellers), (Ray), Staffordshire 224
Roberts Books, Strathclyde 279
Roberts Fine Books (Julian), Lincolnshire........ 151
Robert's Shop, East Sussex 102
Roberts Wine Books (John), Bristol.............. 59
Robertshaw (John), Cambs 66
Robertson Books, Lothian 277
Robin Doughty - Fine Books, West Midlands... 238
Rochdale Book Company, G Manchester........ 120
Rods Books, Devon................................. 88
Roger Collicott Books, Cornwall 74
Roger Lucas Booksellers, Lincolnshire 149
Roger Treglown, Cheshire 70
Rogers Turner Books, London SE................. 165
Roland Books, Kent 138
Rolfe (John), London SE............................ 165
Rolling Stock Books, G Manchester 120
Rookery Bookery, Staffordshire..................... 224
Roosterbooks, Northamptonshire.................. 199
Rosanda Books, Leics 146
Roscrea Bookshop & Newsagents,
    Co. Tipperary 266
Rose Books, G Manchester......................... 119
Rosemary Pugh Books, Wiltshire 253
Rose's Books, Powys................................ 289
Rosley Books, Cumbria 81
Ross & Company Ltd., (Louise), Worcestershire 255
Ross Old Books & Prints, Herefordshire 128
Rothwell & Dunworth, Somerset 217
Roundstone Books, Lancashire..................... 143
Roundwood Books, Shropshire 214
Rowan (H. & S.J.), Dorset.......................... 91
Rowan (P. & B.), Co. Antrim 260
Rowan House Books, Surrey 231
Roz Hulse, Conwy.................................. 284
Ruebotham (Kirk), Cheshire........................ 71
Rugby Relics, Glamorgan........................... 285

Ruskin Books, Kent................................. 135
Russell (Charles), London SW..................... 169
Rutland Bookshop (The), Rutland 211
Ryde Bookshop (The), Isle of Wight............. 133
Rye Old Books, East Sussex 104
Ryeland Books, Northamptonshire................ 199

S.P.C.K., Bristol 59
S.P.C.K., Hampshire................................ 126
SaBeRo Books, London SW........................ 169
Sabin (Printed Works) (P.R. & V.), Kent......... 135
St Ann's Books, Worcestershire 255
St Mary's Books & Prints, Lincolnshire 152
St Paul's Street Bookshop, Lincolnshire 152
St Philip's Books, Oxfordshire..................... 208
St Swithin's Illustrated & Children's Books,
    London W 174
Saintfield Antiques & Fine Books, Co. Down ... 261
Salsus Books, Worcestershire 256
Salway Books, Essex 112
Samovar Books, Co. Dublin........................ 264
Sandpiper Books Ltd., London SW 169
Sandstone Books, Kent.............................. 136
Sansovino Books, West Sussex 244
Saracen Books, Derbyshire.......................... 83
Saunders (Tom), Caerphilly 281
Savage (Keith A.), Suffolk 228
Savery Books, East Sussex 100
Savona Books, Lincolnshire......................... 151
Sax Books, Suffolk 228
Scarthin Books, Derbyshire 82
Schofield Golf Books (Steve), West Yorkshire... 250
Schull Books, Co. Cork 262
Schutte (David), Hampshire......................... 124
Sclanders (Beatbooks), (Andrew), London EC... 155
Scorpio Books, Suffolk 225
Scott (Peter), East Sussex........................... 104
Scrivener's Books & Bookbinding, Derbyshire... 82
Sea Chest Nautical Bookshop (The), Devon 88
Seabreeze Books, Lancashire........................ 144
Secondhand Bookshop, Surrey 233
Secondhand Bookshop, The, Kent................. 140
Sedgeberrow Books, Worcestershire 256
Seeber (Liz), East Sussex 102
Sen Books, Hampshire.............................. 126
Sensawunda Books, Cheshire 68
Sephton (A.F.), London W 174
Sesemann (Julia), Kent.............................. 135
SETI Books, Staffordshire.......................... 239
Seydi Rare Books (Sevin), London NW 161
Shacklock Books (David), Suffolk 226
Shakeshaft (Dr. B.), Cheshire 71
Shakespeare Books (Colin), Staffordshire........ 223
Shapero Rare Books (Bernard J.), London W... 175
Sharpe (Mary), Somerset 219
Shearwater Books, Northumberland............... 201
Sheet Music Warehouse (The), Devon 88
Shelley (E. & J.), Buckinghamshire 61
Sheriffmuir Books, Central......................... 268
Sherlaw-Johnson (Austin), Oxfordshire 209
Sherratt (Ian J.), Staffordshire 223
Sillan Books, Co. Cavan........................... 262
Silver Trees Books, West Midlands................ 238
Silverman (Michael), London SE 165
Simmonds (Anthony J.), London SE.............. 165

Simon Finch Rare Books, Norfolk 188
Simon Hunter Antique Maps, East Sussex 103
Simon Lewis Transport Books, Glos 114
Simon's Books, Somerset 219
Simply Read Books, East Sussex 100
Simpson (Dave), Central 268
Sims (Sue), Dorset 91
Sims Reed Limited, London SW 169
Singleton (Anthony), S Yorkshire 221
Siop Lyfrau'r Hen Bost, Gwynedd 285
Siop y Morfa, Denbighshire 284
Sit-a-While, Warwickshire 236
Skelton (Tony), Kent 140
Skipton Antiques Centre, N Yorkshire 195
Skoob Books, London WC 178
Skyrack Books, West Yorkshire 247
Sleepy Elephant Books & Artefacts, Cumbria ... 80
Slightly Foxed on Gloucester Road, London SW. 167
Smith (Clive), Essex 109
Smith (David & Lynn), London Outer 181
Smith (Ray), Herts 129
Smith Books (Keith), Herefordshire 128
Smith Books (Nigel), Surrey 230
Smith Books, (Sally), Suffolk 226
Smith Maritime Aviation Books (Frank),
    Tyne and Wear 235
Soccor Books Limited, Lincolnshire 148
Sol Books, Devon 84
Solaris Books, East Yorkshire 106
Soldridge Books Ltd, Hampshire 124
Solitaire Books, Somerset 216
Sotheran Limited (Henry), London W 175
South Downs Book Service, West Sussex 243
Sparkes (Books) (Ray), Staffordshire 224
Sparrow Books, West Yorkshire 245
Spearman Books, East Sussex 104
Spelman (Ken), N Yorkshire 198
Spenceley Books (David), West Yorkshire 248
Spike's Books, N Yorkshire 192
Spink, London WC 178
Spooner & Co, Somerset 219
Spooner (John E.), Dorset 91
Spurrier (Nick), Kent 137
Squirrel Antiques, Hampshire 122
St Giles Hospice Bookshop, Staffordshire 223
Stacpoole (George), Co. Limerick 266
Staffs Bookshop (The), Staffordshire 223
Stained Glass Books, Kent 139
Stalagluft Books, Tyne and Wear 235
Staniland (Booksellers), Lincolnshire 152
Stansbury (Rosemary), Devon 88
Star Lord Books, G Manchester 119
Stella Books, Monmouthshire 286
Stepping Stones Bookshop, N Yorkshire 193
Sterling Books, Somerset 220
Stern Antiquarian Bookseller (Jeffrey),
    N Yorkshire 198
Steven Simpson Books, Norfolk 190
Stevens (Joan), Cambs 65
Stinton (Judith), Dorset 92
Stobart Davies Limited, Carmarthenshire 282
Stokes Books, Co. Dublin 264
Stone Trough Books, N Yorkshire 198
Stone, (G.& R.), Borders 267
Stothert Old Books, Cheshire 68

Stour Bookshop, Dorset 95
Strand Bookshop (The), Powys 291
Strathtay Antiquarian - Secondhand Books,
    Tayside 280
Stroh (M.A.), London E 154
Stroma Books, Borders 267
Studio (The), Strathclyde 278
Studio Bookshop, East Sussex 100
Sturford Books, Wiltshire 254
Sub Aqua Prints and Books, Hampshire 123
Sue Lowell Natural History Books, London W . 175
Suffolk Rare Books, Suffolk 229
Sugen & Co., N Yorkshire 193
Summerfield Books Ltd, Cumbria 79
Surprise Books, Glos 113
Susan Taylor Books, West Yorkshire 247
Susanne Schulz-Falster Rare Books, London N . 158
Sutcliffe (Mark), West Yorkshire 248
Sutcliffe (Victor), Norfolk 187
Sykes (Graham), West Yorkshire 249
Symes Books (Naomi), Cheshire 71

T V Coles Books, Cambs 67
Talisman Books, Cheshire 70
Tall Tales Bookshop, Highland 274
Taney Books, Co. Dublin 263
Tant Yn Ellen Books, Powys 290
Tarka Books, Devon 84
Tasburgh Books, Norfolk 190
Taylor & Son (Peter), Herts 132
Taylor Rare Books (Michael), Norfolk 187
Temperley (David), West Midlands 238
Tennis Collectables, Cheshire 68
Terence Kaye - Bookseller, London NW 161
Tetbury Old Books, Glos 117
Thanatos Books, G Manchester 119
The Bookshop, Kirkstall, West Yorkshire 248
The End Bookshop, Devon 88
The Glass Key, West Yorkshire 246
The Meads Book Service, East Sussex 101
The Old Abbey Bookshop, Co. Down 261
The Old Children's Bookshelf, Lothian 277
The Old Music Master, Bristol 60
The Sanctuary Bookshop, Dorset 94
The Stratford Bookshop, Warwickshire 237
Theatreshire Books, N Yorkshire 192
Thin Read Line, Merseyside 184
Thistle Books, Strathclyde 278
Thomas (Barry), Ceredigion 282
Thomas (E. Wyn), Conwy 284
Thomas Rare Books, Suffolk 226
Thornber (Peter M.), N Yorkshire 195
Thorne (John), Essex 109
Thorntons of Oxford Ltd., Oxfordshire 206
Throckmorten's Bookshop, Warwickshire 236
Tiffin (Tony and Gill), Durham 97
Tiger Books, Kent 136
Tilleys Vintage Magazine Shop, Derbyshire 82
Tilleys Vintage Magazine Shop, S Yorkshire 222
Till's Bookshop, Lothian 277
Tilston (Stephen E.), London SE 165
Tim Bryers Ltd, London WC 178
Tin Drum Books, Leics 146
Tindley & Chapman, London WC 178
Titford (John), Derbyshire 82

Tombland Bookshop, Norfolk 190
Tony Hutchinson, Surrey............................. 233
Tony Pollastrone Railway Books, Wiltshire 251
Tooley, Adams & Co, Oxfordshire 209
Torc Books, Norfolk 188
Towers (Mark), Lancashire 143
Townsend (John), Berks 57
Towpath Bookshop, G Manchester................. 119
Tozer Railway Books (Nick), West Yorkshire ... 247
TP Children's Bookshop, West Yorkshire 245
Trade Priced Old Books, Powys.................... 289
Transformer, Dumfries & Galloway 270
Travel Bookshop (The), London W 175
Traveller's Bookshelf (The), Somerset 218
Travis & Emery Music Bookshop, London WC 178
Treadwell's Books, London WC 178
Treasure Chest Books, Suffolk 226
Treasure Island (The), G Manchester 119
Treasure Trove Books, Leics........................ 146
Tregenna Place Second Hand Books, Cornwall . 74
Trevorrow (Edwin), Herts 129
Trigon Books, Dorset 95
Trinders' Fine Tools, Suffolk 226
Trinity Rare Books, Co. Leitrim 266
Trotman (Ken), Cambs 66
Trotter Books (John), London N 158
Tsbbooks, London SW 169
Tucker (Alan & Joan), Glos 116
Tuft (Patrick), London Outer...................... 181
Turret House, Norfolk 191
Turton (John), Durham 98
Twigg (Keith), Staffordshire........................ 224
Twiggers Booksearch, Bedfordshire............... 53
Tyger Press, London N 158

ULoveBooks, Devon.................................. 90
Uncle Phil's Books, West Midlands 239
Undercover Books, Lincolnshire 152
Underwater Books, East Sussex 102
Unsworths Booksellers, London WC.............. 178
Unsworth's Booksellers, Suffolk.................... 225
Updike Rare Books (John), Lothian 277
Upper–Room Books, Somerset..................... 217

Vailima Books, Dumfries & Galloway 269
Valentine Rare Books, London W.................. 175
Valerie Merritt, Worcestershire 256
Vandeleur Antiquarian Books, Surrey............. 231
Vanstone - Aviation Books, (Derek), Suffolk 229
Venables (Morris & Juliet), Bristol................. 59
Ventnor Rare Books, Isle of Wight................ 134
Verandah Books, Dorset 95
Victoria Bookshop (The), Devon................... 84
Victorian Gallery (The), Shropshire............... 214
Village Books, Norfolk 186
Vinovium Books, Durham 97
Vintage Motorshop, West Yorkshire 245
Vokes (Jeremiah), Durham.......................... 97
Vokes Books Ltd., N Yorkshire.................... 194
Volume Three, Central............................... 268
Volumes of Motoring, Glos......................... 113
W & A Houben, Surrey 233
Wadard Books, Kent 137
Wakeman Books (Frances),
    Nottinghamshire 204

Walden Books, London NW 161
Walker (Gary), Fife 271
Walker Fine Books (Steve), Dorset................ 92
War & Peace Books, Hampshire................... 122
Ward (R.F. & C.), Norfolk 187
Warnes (Felicity J.), London Outer............... 180
Warrender (Andrew), West Yorkshire............. 249
Warrington Book Loft (The), Cheshire 71
Warsash Nautical Bookshop, Hampshire......... 126
Warwick Leadley Gallery, London SE............ 165
Waterfield's, Oxfordshire 209
Waterstone's, London WC.......................... 179
Watkins (R.G.), Somerset 215
Watkins Books Ltd., London WC.................. 179
Waxfactor, East Sussex 100
Way's Bookshop, Oxfordshire 207
Wayside Books and Cards, Oxfordshire 206
Wealden Books, Kent................................ 138
Webb Books (John), S Yorkshire 221
Webster (D.), Strathclyde............................ 279
Weiner (Graham), London N 158
Weininger Antiquarian Books (Eva M.),
    London NW....................................... 161
Wells (Mary), London SW.......................... 169
Wembdon Books, Somerset 216
Wenlock Books, Shropshire 213
Wensum Books, Norfolk 190
Weobley Bookshop, Herefordshire................. 128
Westcountry Oldbooks, Devon 90
Westfield Books, N Yorkshire 198
Westgate Bookshop, Lincolnshire.................. 151
Westgate End Bookshop and Gallery, West
    Yorkshire.. 250
Westons, Herts 132
Westwood Books (Mark), Powys 289
Westwood Books Ltd, Cumbria.................... 80
Wetherell (Frances), Cambs........................ 65
Wheeler's Bookshop, West Sussex 243
Wheen O'Books, Borders............................ 267
Whelan (P. & F.), Kent.............................. 140
Whig Books Ltd., Leics.............................. 147
Whistler (R.A.), East Sussex 99
Whistler's Books, London SW 169
Whitchurch Books Ltd., Cardiff.................... 281
White (C.R.), London W 175
White (David), Cambs............................... 65
White (Mrs. Teresa), London W 175
White Eagle Books, London NW 162
Whitehall Books, East Sussex....................... 103
Whitfield (Ken), Essex 110
Whittle, Bookseller (Avril), Cumbria 80
Wiend Books, Lancashire 143
Wilbraham (J. & S.), London NW 162
Wildy & Sons Ltd, London WC 179
William H. Roberts, West Yorkshire.............. 247
Williams (Bookdealer), (Richard),
    North Lincolnshire 153
Williams Rare Books (Nigel), London WC 179
Willmott Bookseller (Nicholas), Cardiff.......... 281
Wilson (David), Buckinghamshire 61
Wilson (James), Herts............................... 129
Wilson (Manuscripts) Ltd., (John), Glos.......... 114
Winchester Bookshop (The), Hampshire......... 126
Winghale Books, Lincolnshire 152
Wise (Derek), East Sussex.......................... 104

Witmeha Productions, Leics 147
Wizard Books, Cambs 67
Woburn Books, London N 159
Wood (Peter), Cambs 65
Wood Cricket Books (Martin), Kent 139
Woodbine Books, West Yorkshire 245
Woodland Books, Devon............................ 84
Woodlands Books, West Yorkshire 249
Woodside Books, Kent 135
Woolcott Books, Dorset 92
Worcester Rare Books, Worcestershire 256
Words Etcetera Bookshop, Dorset 93
World War Books, Kent 141
World War II Books, Surrey 234
Worlds End Bookshop, London SW 169
Worrallo (J. & M.A.), West Midlands 240
Wright (Norman), Dorset 95
Wright Trace Books, West Midlands 239
www.AntiqueWatchStore.com, Herts.............. 129
Wycherley (Stephen), West Midlands.............. 238
Wychwood Books, Glos 116
Wykeham Books, London SW 170
Wyseby House Books, Berks 55

Xanadu Books, Durham 98
Ximenes Rare Books Inc., Glos.................... 115

Yarborough House Bookshop, Shropshire 212
Yarwood Rare Books (Edward), G Manchester. 118
Yates Antiquarian Books (Tony), Leics........... 146
Yeoman Books, Lothian 277
Yesterday Tackle & Books, Dorset 92
Yesterday's Books, Dorset 92
Yesterday's News, Conwy 283
Yesteryear Railwayana, Kent 139
Yewtree Books, Cumbria............................ 78
York (Graham), Devon.............................. 86
York Modern Books, N Yorkshire 196
Yorkshire Relics, West Yorkshire.................. 246
Young (D. & J.), Powys............................. 291
Ystwyth Books, Ceredigion 282

Zardoz Books, Wiltshire............................ 254

ALPHABETICAL INDEX BY NAME OF PROPRIETOR

Adams (N.T.) = G. David 63
Adams (V.) = Upper–Room Books 217
Addyman (D.) = Addyman Books 287
Addyman (D.) = Murder & Mayhem 288
Ainge (G.) = Golden Age Books.................... 256
Aitman (T.) = Black Voices.......................... 184
Allcoat (K.) = Tarka Books 84
Allen (P.J.) = Robert Temple....................... 158
Allen (R.) = Bufo Books 125
Allinson (J. & M.) = Facet Books 91
Allsop (D.) = Duncan M. Allsop 237
Almond (G.) = Westgate Bookshop............... 151
Altshuler (J.) = Jean Altshuler...................... 78
Ameringen (B.) = Porcupine Books 181
Anderson (S.) = The Travel Bookshop Ltd. 175
Andrews (Mrs. J.) = Alton Secondhand Books... 121
Ansorge (E. & W.) = Barn Books 61
Applin (M.) = Malcolm Applin 55
Aptaker (N.) = Neil's Books........................ 161
Archer (D.) = David Archer 290
Ardley (C.M.) = Faversham Books................ 137
Aris (J.) = ECR Books 92
Armishaw (K.& S.) = River Reads Bookshop 90
Armstrong (A.) = Moffat Book Exchange 269
Arthur (E.J.L.) = Fantasy Centre 156
Arthy (J. and S.) = Yewtree Books................ 78
Ashby (M.) = Martin's Books....................... 290
Ashcroft (R.E.) = The Inner Bookshop............ 208
Ashworth (R.H.) = Whistler's Books.............. 169
Askew Books (V.) = Vernon Askew Books 251
Asplin (D.C.) = G. David........................... 63
Astbury (B. & V.) = Woodlands Books 249
Attree (M.) = Birmgham Books..................... 238
Austen (P.) = Phillip Austen 151

Bacon (J) = Bookzone 55
Baggott (L. & H.) = Wychwood Books 116
Bainbridge (S.R.) = Offa's Dyke Books........... 213
Baine (Mr & Mrs) = The Rutland Bookshop..... 211
Baker (J.A.) = J.B. Books 57
Baldwin (D. & J.) = Rosanda Books............... 146
Ball (B.W.) = Harlequin Books 59
Ball (C.F. & J.A.) = J.C. Books.................... 191
Ball (E.W.) = Fantasy Centre 156
Bamping (A.) = Tyger Press 158
Bangor (Viscount) = Hesketh & Ward Ltd........ 168
Barfield (I.&K.) = hullbooks.com 106
Barker (J.) = Nostalgia Publications Ltd........... 197
Barnes (R. & M.) = Church Green Books 210
Baron (Dr. P.J.) = P.J. Baron - Scientific
  Book Sales 216
Barrett (J. & P.) = Hobgoblin Books 125
Barry (Q. & R.) = Sansovino Books 244
Bartle (C.) = Glacier Books 280
Bartley (M.) = Howes Bookshop 102
Bastians(M) = Eton Antique Bookshop 57
Bates (G. & J.) = Bates Books 180
Bates (J.) = Bates & Hindmarch 248
Batten (P.) = Whitehall Books 103

Bayliss (Dr G.M) = War & Peace Books.......... 122
Bayntun-Coward (C.) = George Gregory.......... 215
Bayntun–Coward (G.) = George Bayntun......... 215
Beard (P.) = Hill House Books...................... 88
Beardsell (E.V.) = Beardsell Books 246
Beattie (A.) = Americanabooksuk 76
Beckham (J.E.) = Beckham Books Ltd............. 229
Beeby (B. & Son) = Cader Idris Books 290
Beer (D.W.) = Crosby Nethercott Books.......... 180
Bell (J.) = Fortune Green Books.................... 160
Bell (S.) = Green Meadow Books.................. 74
Bennett (D.) = dgbbooks............................ 244
Benster (S. & B.) = Childrens Bookshop 247
Bentley (J.) = Albion Books 238
Beresiner (Y.) = InterCol London 157
Bertsein (N.) = Nicholas Bernstein................. 171
Berry (D.) = Botting & Berry....................... 103
Berry (M.) = Rare Books & Berry.................. 218
Besley (P.& G.) = Besleys Books 225
Biro (T. & S.) = Collectable Books................ 163
Blackman (M. & R.) = Blackman Books.......... 71
Blakemore (I.) = Rosley Books 81
Blanchett (C.) = Buckland Books 243
Blessett (J.) = St. Paul's Street Bookshop......... 152
Blessett (S.) = Wizard Books 67
Bletsoe (P.) = Badger 253
Blore (G.T.) = Jermy & Westerman................ 204
Boehm (H.) = Artco 204
Bond (R.) = Marathon Books 142
Boon (H.) = Fullerton's Booksearch 188
Borthwick (T.) = The Old Station Pottery &
  Bookshop 191
Boss (T.) = Tim Boss 243
Boswell (B.) = The Great Oak Bookshop 289
Botting (J.) = Botting & Berry 103
Bowe (T.B.) = Browse Books....................... 143
Bowie (J.) = Bowie Books & Collectables 107
Boyd–Cropley (J.M.) = Cottage Books 145
Boyns (R.and G.) = The Sea Chest Nautical
  Bookshop 88
Brachotte (P.) = Chapter Two...................... 163
Bradbury (A.) = Brad Books, ... 110
Bradley (S.) = Maynard & Bradley................. 146
Brewin (K.A.F.) = Brewin Books Ltd.............. 237
Brichto (A.) = Murder & Mayhem 288
Brichto (A.) = Addyman Books..................... 287
Bridger (N.J.) = Nevis Railway Books 207
Bridger (N.J.) = Nevis Railway Bookshops 252
Bridger (N.J.) = Railway Book and Magazine
  Search 56
Bristow (J.A.) = South Downs Book Service 243
Brittain (J.) = JB Books & Collectables 243
Broad (S.) = Camilla's Bookshop................... 101
Brook (R.A. & P.P.) = The Bookshop, Kirkstall. 248
Brooman (J. & J.) = Spearman Books 104
Brotchie (A.) = Atlas................................ 156
Brown (A.) = David Archer 290
Brown (M.G. & B.J.) = Brown-Studies 277
Brown (P.) = Bookbox 115

Brown (R. & R.) = Ken Trotman 66
Browne (M.) = Maggy Browne 148
Browne (R.) = Main Point Books 276
Bryant (E.H.) = Vandeleur Antiquarian Books... 231
Bryers (T.) = Tim Bryers Ltd........................ 178
Buck (J.) = Polmorla Books 75
Buckler (R. & S.) = Cobweb Books 194
Budek (P.M. & M.M.) = The Eagle Bookshop... 53
Burca (E.) = De Burca Rare Books 264
Burca (V.) = De Burca Rare Books 264
Burden (C.) = Clive A. Burden Ltd................. 131
Burden (D.) = Derek Burden 232
Burgin (A.) = Woburn Books 159
Burkett (D.) = Musicalania 188
Burley (J.) = Camden Lock Books 155
Burmester (J.R.) = James Burmester 58
Burridge (Dr. Peter) = Quest Books 107
Burrow (b.) = Books and Things 258
Burrows (N. & H.) = Modern First Editions 181
Burton (R.F.) = The Parlour Bookshop 206
Burwood (N.) = Any Amount of Books........... 176
Bush (F.) = Othello's Bookshop 110
Butler (T.) = Stour Bookshop 95
Button (C.) = Little Stour Books 136
Byatt (T.) = Golden Age Books 256
Byrne (C.) = The Old Bookshelf 278
Byrne (C.) = Charlie Byrne's Bookshop 265
Byrne (K. & C.) = Colonsay Bookshop 275
Byrom (J.) = Towpath Bookshop.................... 119
Byrom (R.) = Richard Byrom Textile Bookroom 142

Cahn (M.) = Plurabelle Books 65
Canvin (G.L.) = Whitchurch Books Ltd........... 281
Carlile (G.) = East Riding Books 107
Carmody (P.) = Brighton Books 99
Carpenter (R.D.) = Bonython Bookshop 75
Carruthers (Dr. G.B.) = London & Sussex
   Ant. Books & Print Sevices 101
Carss (G.) = Earth Science Books 252
Cartwright (S.) = babelog.books 127
Case (D.) = Morley Case 125
Casey (K.F.) = Sub Aqua Prints and Books...... 123
Casson (C.) = Norton Books 192
Cauwood (R.) = The Treasure Island 119
Cawthorn (T.M.) = Suffolk Rare Books 229
Chadband (Mrs. B.) = Solway Books 269
Chaddock (M.) = Antiquary Ltd.
   (Bar Bookstore) 194
Chambers (J.) = Broadleaf Books.................... 292
Chapman (C.) = Paragon Books 217
Chapman (R.) = Tindley & Chapman 178
Chatten (D.) = Riviera Books 188
Checkland (S.) = Rising Tide Books 270
Checkley (A.) = Stothert Old Books 68
Cheke (A.S.) = The Inner Bookshop 208
Child (M.) = michaelsbookshop.com............... 139
Christian Literature Stalls = Barbican Bookshop. 196
Churcher (P.R.) = The Victoria Bookshop 84
Churchill–Evans (D.) = Marine and Cannon
   Books... 69
Churchill-Evans (Mrs D.) = Marine & Cannon
   Books... 71
Clark (A. & G.) = Ainslie Books 278
Clarke (J.) = Janet Clarke........................... 215
Clarke (R.) = Muttonchop Manuscripts 242

Clarke (V.) = The Little Bookshop................. 119
Clegg (D.) = David Clegg............................ 223
Clement (C.) = Brighton Books 99
Cockram (A.) = Golden Goose Books............. 150
Cocks (M.) = Badgers Books......................... 244
Collard (B.) = Collards Bookshop 90
Collett (D.W.) = Military Bookworm 164
Collie (R.) = Sandpiper Books Ltd. 169
Collinge (V.H.) = The Border Bookshop 249
Collins (A.) = Pedlar's Pack Books 84
Collyer (W.J.) = Books Bought & Sold 231
Combellack (P. & J.) = Kellow Books 206
Compton (M.) = The Idle Booksellers 245
Connolly (T.) = Booknotes 110
Conwell (B.) = Dusty Books.......................... 290
Cook (M.) = Internet Bookshop UK Ltd. 113
Cook (K. & D.) = Dorset Bookshop, The 91
Cooper (R.J.) = Marjon Books 111
Cope (D.) = Left on The Shelf...................... 78
Corbett (C.) = Corvus Books........................ 61
Corbett (R.) = Booklore.............................. 146
Corbett (S.) = Booklore 146
Cork (A.) = Roundwood Books 214
Cornell (G.) = Cornell Books........................ 117
Cornish (I.) = Ambra Books 58
Corrall (L.) = The Pocket Bookshop.............. 87
Corrigan (B.) = BC Books............................ 69
Coupe (M.) = Eclectica 164
Court (Mr. & Mrs.) = Bannatyne Books 156
Court (R. & A.) = Mountaineering Books 157
Cox (G.A.) = Kirkdale Bookshop 164
Cox (A.B.) = Claude Cox Old & Rare Books 227
Cox (L.) = Lisa Cox Music 86
Cox (P.) = Peter Pan Bookshop...................... 190
Cox (P.) = Peter's Bookshop 190
Cozens (N.) = Lymelight Books & Prints 93
Cranwell (J.) = Bookworld........................... 213
Cree (R.) = R & R Books 116
Cresswell (P.M.) = Humber Books 148
Crimmings (T.) = Criterion Books.................. 181
Crook (C.) = Bath Old Books........................ 215
Cross (J.) = Books & Collectables Ltd. 63
Crouch (A.S.) = Crouch Rare Books 232
Culme-Seymour (M.A.) = Marco Polo Travel &
   Adventure Books,................................... 92
Cundy (D.) = Dene Barn Books & Prints 219

Dakin (B.) = Letterbox Books 203
Daly (K.) = Rainbow Books 100
Dancy (J.E. & A.B.) = Broadwater Books 125
Danks (N.) = ForensicSearch........................ 131
D'Arch Smith (T.) = Fuller D'Arch Smith 172
Davies (G.&R.) = Gemini–Books.................... 214
Davies (J. & L.) = Stepping Stones Bookshop.... 193
Daymond (D.) = Arden Books & Cosmographia 236
de Visser (E.) = de Visser Books.................... 63
Deegan (T.&P.) = Roscrea Bookshop &
   Newsagents 266
Degnan (P.) = Kay Books 173
Della–Ragione (G.) = Henry Pordes Books Ltd.. 177
Demar (G.) = Grant Demar Books 140
De Martini (M.) = Altea Antique Maps & Books 171
Dennis (G.) = Blacklock's............................. 231
Dennys (N.) = Slightly Foxed on Gloucester
   Road... 167

Devlin (Mrs P.) = The Warrington Book Loft ... 71
Dibble (R.) = Thistle Books 278
Dinnage (Mr G. & C.) = Dinnages Transport/
Picture Publishing................................. 103
Dixon (C.) = Earlsfield Bookshop 166
Dobbyn (D. & A.) = Yesterday Tackle and Books 92
Dodson (T.) = Undercover Books 152
Dollery (A.) = Kingswood Books.................... 94
Donaldson (A.) = Judd Books 177
Donoghue (A.) = Bookcupboard 88
Doran (A.) = Falconwood Transport & Military
Bookshop 183
Douthwaite (G. & W.) = Clevedon Books 217
Downes (D.) = Dublin Bookbrowsers.............. 265
Doyle (A.) = Books & Collectables Ltd........... 63
Dreda (A.) = Wenlock Books 213
Dreyer (M. & E.) = Philip Martin Music Books . 197
Driver (M.) = Waxfactor............................. 100
Druett (D.) = Pennymead Books 193
Duckworth (A.) = Sen Books 126
Duerdoth (S.) = Eric Goodyer, Natural History
Books 146
Dunbar (D.) = Aurelian Books 160
Dunn (C.R.) = Anchor Books....................... 149
Dwyer (D.&J.) = Newgate Books and
Translations.. 201
Dyke (S.) = Skyrack Books.......................... 247

Eastman (P.V.) = Eastern Books of London...... 166
Edmonds (M.J.) = The Dorchester Bookshop 92
Edmunds (D.R.D.) = John Drury Rare Books... 110
Edwards (C.) = Christopher Edwards.............. 209
Elgar (R.) = Raymond Elgar 99
Elissa (N.M.) = Joppa Books Ltd.................. 230
Elithorn (A.) = Game Advice 208
Ellingworth (M. & S.) = Coach House Books.... 256
Elliston (P.) = Firsts in Print,...................... 219
Erskine (M.) = Christopher Edwards.............. 209
Evans (M.) = Mark Evans 151
Evans (M.) = Mollie's Loft 291
Evans (S.) = Kings Bookshop Callander 268
Excell (A. & L.F.) = Bookmark (Children's
Books)... 253

Fairrington (P.) = Manna Bookshop 220
Farley (F.) = Kennedy & Farley 104
Farnsworth (B.) = Ouse Valley Books 54
Fenning (J. & C.) = James Fenning, Antiquarian
Books 265
Fernee (B.) = Caduceus Books 145
Figgis (N.) = The House of Figgis Ltd 265
Finch (M.) = Wadard Books 137
Fines (R.) = Chapter & Verse 150
Finlay (Dr. R. & Dr L.A.) = Barlow Moor
Books 118
Fishburn (J.) = Fishburn Books..................... 160
Fisher (B.) = March House Books.................. 217
Fisher (C.) = Bookbox............................... 115
Fisher (S. & J.) = Fisher Nautical 99
Flanagan (M. & L.) = Zardoz Books 254
Flint (P.) = Birdnet Optics Ltd. 82
Flowers (L.) = Kim's Bookshop 242
Flowers (L.) = Kim's Bookshop 241
Ford (G.) = Books With Care....................... 53
Ford (J.) = Books Antiques & Collectables 90

Fordyce (D.) = Lewis First Editions............... 136
Forster (C.A.) = C.R. Johnson Rare Book
Collections 161
Foster (J.A.) = The Park Gallery & Bookshop... 200
Foster (P.) = Paul Foster Bookshop............... 167
Foster (W.A.&M.A.) = Fosters Bookshop 172
Fothergill (T.) = Ken Spelman 198
Fowkes (M.) = Kingsgate Books & Prints 126
Francombe (C.) = Camilla's Bookshop 101
French (S.) = Dawlish Books....................... 86
Fruin (C.) = L.M.S. Books 131

Gange (C.) = Katharine House Gallery........... 252
Gardner (A.) = Daeron's Books 62
Gardner (J. & M.) = The Children's Bookshop .. 127
Gardner (M.) = Emjay Books....................... 231
Gardner (S.) = Forbury Fine Books............... 56
Garwood (N.) = Garwood & Voigt 139
Gavey (G.P.& C.M.) = Channel Islands
Galleries Ltd... 258
Gentil (P.) = Aviabooks 114
Gestetner (J.) = Marlborough Rare Books Ltd... 173
Gibbs (J.) = Hummingbird Books 128
Gibson (J.A.B. & J.L.) = Wayside Books
& Cards 206
Gilbert (R.A.) = R.A. Gilbert 219
Giles (D. G.) = Ancient Art Books................. 166
Gipps (A.) = Woodside Books 135
Gleeson (L.) = Nonsuch Books 234
Gleeson (R.) = Nonsuch Books 234
Glover (S.) = Handsworth Books................... 112
Goddard (J.) = Solaris Books 106
Goddard (M.) = Rose's Books 289
Golden (I. and A.) = Golden Books Group 85
Goodenough (M.) = Inprint 116
Goodfellow (A.P.) = Carlton Books............... 189
Goodwin (J.O.) = J.O. Goodwin................... 224
Goodyer (E.) = Eric Goodyer, Natural
History Books 146
Gorman (N.) = medievalbookshop 132
Gorton (J.) = John Gorton Booksearch 105
Gosden (S.G.) = Fantastic Literature 110
Goss (M.) = The Dancing Goat Bookshop 187
Goss (M.R.) = Delectus Books..................... 176
Goulding (J.) = Optimus Books Ltd 244
Govan (D.) = Armchair Books...................... 275
Gowen (M.) = The Book Jungle 105
Graham (K. & J.) = Ken's Paper Collectables.... 62
Grant (B.& S.) = Grant Books 255
Grant (F.) = The Little Bookshop 80
Greatbatch (P.) = Richard Booth's Bookshop.... 127
Greatwood (J.) = J.G. (Natural History Books).. 233
Green (J.R.) = Castle Bookshop 108
Green (R.&R.) = Treasure Chest Books........... 226
Green (W., M. & O.D.) = Ampersand Books 189
Greenwood (N.) = Right Now Books (Burma)... 168
Gretton (B.) = Leigh Gallery Books............... 110
Greysmith (B.) = Pedlar's Pack Books............. 84
Grogan (P.) = R.A. Gekoski 177
Gwynne (Mr. N.M.) = Britons Catholic Library. 266

Habraszewski (T.) = Hab Books 172
Hadfield (G.K. & J.V.) = G.K. Hadfield 79
Hadfield–Tilly (N.R.) = G.K. Hadfield 79
Hadley (P.J.) = Harwich Old Books................ 109

Haffner (R.N.) = Postings............................. 233
Halewood (M.) = Preston Book Company........ 144
Hall (D.) = Hanborough Books..................... 208
Hall (J.) = Garretts Antiquarian Books........... 259
Hall (S.&T.) = Invicta Bookshop 56
Hallgate (J.) = Lucius Books 197
Hamburger (R.B.) = Riderless Horse Books...... 186
Hancock (E.) = Hancock & Monks 288
Hanna (J.) = Blaenavon Books...................... 292
Hanson (D. & M.) = D. & M. Books 249
Hardman (L.R.) = Broadhurst of Southport Ltd. 185
Hardwick (C.) = Rookery Bookery................. 224
Harlow (Dr. B.J. & S.) = Tiger Books 136
Harper (T.) = World War Books 141
Harries (P.) = Boz Books 287
Harris (K.) = Books on Spain....................... 182
Harrison (S.J.) = Bracton Books................... 63
Hartles (D.B. & J.) = Goldsworth Books.......... 234
Haslam (J.) = Brock Books........................... 192
Haslem (J.) = Oakwood Books...................... 115
Havercroft (J.) = Hava Books....................... 164
Hawes (S. & J.) = Bosco Books..................... 72
Hawkin (S.) = The Staffs Bookshop............... 223
Hay Cinema Bookshop Ltd = Francis
  Edwards in Hay–on–Wye 288
Haycox (E.) = Richard Booth's Bookshop 127
Hayhoe (M.) = Corfe Books......................... 230
Haylock (B. & J.) = The Idler...................... 227
Hearn (K.) = Newlyn Books 74
Heatley (Mr. & Mrs. P.R.) = The Dartmoor
  Bookshop 84
Hebden (M.) = M. & D. Books..................... 255
Hedge (P. & E.) = Hedgerow Books 221
Herbert (W.) = Photo Books International....... 177
Herries (D.) = Find That Book 248
Herron (M.) = The Bookshop....................... 263
Hessey (A.) = Reads 95
Hewson (E.) = Kabristan Archives 214
Hickley (Dr. R.H.) = Baedekers & Murray
  Guides 221
Hill (A.) = Alan Hill Books.......................... 222
Hill (K.R.) = Stained Glass Books 139
Hill (S.J.) = Stained Glass Books 139
Hinchcliffe (C.) = Empire Books................... 197
Hinchliffe (Mrs. A.) = Whig Books Ltd........... 147
Hinde (H.M.) = Ystwyth Books 282
Hine (J.) = Gresham Books.......................... 217
Hiscock (L.) = E. Chalmers Hallam................ 125
Hitchens (B. & E.) = Silver Trees Books 238
HMV Media Group = Waterstone's 179
Hodgkins (J.R.) = Clifton Books 111
Holman (P.) = Invisible Books 100
Holtom (C.) = Christopher Holtom 115
Hooper–Bargery (E.) = Music By The Score 72
Hornseys' (B.,S., &D.) = Hornseys' of Rippon ... 194
Horsnell (B.) = Footballana 56
Hougham (M.) = Verandah Books.................. 95
Howard (D.) = Outcast Books 127
Howard (J.) = Photo Books International......... 177
Howell (N.) = Rolling Stock Books 120
Hoy (I.) = Ian Hodgkins and Company Limited. 116
Hubbard (P.) = Bufo Books 125
Hudson (H.G.) = The Malvern Bookshop 255
Hughes (A.R.) = Roland Books 138
Hughes (P.D.) = Deverell Books.................... 59

Hulse (R.) = Roz Hulse 284
Hunt (P.) = The Railway Shop 292
Hunt (R. & C.) = Vintage Motorshop............. 245
Hunter (J.A.) = Hunter and Krageloh 83
Husband (M.) = Merlin Books....................... 242
Hutchison (C. & R.) = Chapter House Books.... 94
Hyslop (D.A.) = Yeoman Books..................... 277

Inch (P.&E.) = Inch's Books......................... 137
Innes (P.) = Innes Books............................ 212
Ions (B. & G.) = Richmond Books................. 194
Irvine (J.A.M.) = R.A. Gekoski..................... 177
Irwin (C. & M.) = The Book House 76
Israel (N.) = Nibris Books 169
Ives (B.) = Simon's Books 219
Izzard (S.) = Hall's Bookshop 140

Jackson–Harris (V.) = Quadrille 174
James (J.A.R.) = Village Books 186
Jameson (C.) = Potterton Books 196
Jeffers (D.) = My Back Pages 168
Johnson (C.R.) = C.R. Johnson Rare Book
  Collections 161
Johnson (I.A.) = Pembury Books................... 62
Johnson (J.) = Reaveley Books...................... 87
Johnson (M.L.) = Seabreeze Books 144
Johnson (P.) = The Bookshop....................... 118
Johnston (A.L. & A.) = The Iona Bookshop 275
Johnston (I. & H.) = Winghale Books 152
Jones (B.) = Pastmasters............................. 83
Jones (B.) = Barry Jones 242
Jones (E.) = Yesterday's News 283
Jones (E.A.) = Siop Lyfrau'r Hen Bost 285
Jones (H.M.) = Books for Content 127
Jones (N.) = Musebookshop......................... 285
Jones (R.) = Ex Libris 251
Jones (R.W.) = Northern Herald Books........... 245

Karlou (P.G.) = Crouch Rare Books 232
Kaszuk (N.) = Trinity Rare Books 266
Kay (J. & J.) = K Books 70
Keegan (J.&J.) = Keegan's Bookshop.............. 57
Kelly (P.) = Book Mongers 166
Kemp (N.) = Judd Books............................. 177
Kennedy (H.) = Kennedy & Farley 104
Kent (G. & P.) = Military Parade Bookshop 252
Kenyon (H.S.) = Brazenhead Ltd................... 188
Kernaghan (A.&B.) = Kernaghans 185
Key (S.) = Sarah Key Books 64
Kaindra Associates Ltd = Valerie Peel............. 56
Kinderman (G.) = Brimstones....................... 104
King (A. & C.A.) = Wealden Books 138
King (I. W.) = Kings Bookshop Callander........ 268
King (M.R.) = MK Book Services 66
Kinnaird (J. & J.) = Keswick Bookshop........... 78
Kinsella (W.) = Chapters Bookstore 264
Kirby (E.) = Vailima Books 269
Kitley (A.J.) = A.J. Kitley........................... 59
Knapman (C.) = Collectors Carbooks 199
Koh (J.) = Bernard Quaritch Ltd. 174
Kousah (M.G.) = Ely Books 65
Kowalski (S.) = Mereside Books 70
Kunkler (P.) = Paul Kunkler Books................ 64

Laing (E.) = Blacket Books.......................... 276

Laithwaite (S.) = Mereside Books 70
Lake (B.) = Jarndyce Antiquarian Booksellers.... 177
Lamb (B.) = Reference Works Ltd. 95
Lamb (J.) = Tasburgh Books........................ 190
Lamb (J. & E.) = Lamb's Tales 87
Lamont (D.) = The Bookpassage 212
Lawson (T.&J.) = Second Nature at Knapton
   Bookbarn 197
Lankester (P.) = Lankester Antiques and Books . 110
Larkham (P.) = Dive In Books 117
Lawrence (A.) = Lawrence Books 203
Lay (R.) = Alba Secondhand Music............... 278
Laywood (W.) = Forest Books...................... 204
Layzell (M.) = Othello's Bookshop 110
Leach (G.) = Mogul Diamonds 240
Leckey (J.) = Saintfield Antiques and Fine Books 261
Ledraw (J.) = J.L. Book Exchange 106
Lee (R.) = Rachel Lee Rare Books................ 59
Leek (R.J.) = Modern Firsts Etc. 142
Leeper (R.) = Romilly Leeper 168
Leeson (J.) = Eric T. Moore Books 130
Levete (G.) = The Book Business 171
Levett (G.) = Grays of Westminster............... 167
Lewsey (C.) = Freya Books & Antiques 189
Liddell (S. & E.) = Bookworms 186
Liddle (S.) = Steve Liddle 58
Lidgett (D.J. & C.) = D.C. Books 149
Lidyard (F.W.) = Ruskin Books 135
Lipson (P.) = Antiques on High 207
Lloyd (D.I.) = Worcester Rare Books 256
Lovett (M. J.) = Occultique......................... 199
Lowndes (C.) = The Chichester Bookshop 241
Lucas (R.) = Richard Lucas 161
Lunt (J.) = Books at the Warehouse 193

McBride (C.) = Caledonia Books 278
McCarthy (A.) = Dandy Lion Ediitons............ 233
McClement (R.H. & J.M.) = Draycott Books 114
McConnell (N.) = McConnell Fine Books 137
McCrory (M.) = Books B.C. 180
MacDonald (N.) = BOOKS4U 284
MacGregor (C. & J.) = D'Arcy Books............. 252
MacGregor (N.) = Olynthiacs 213
McKee (C.) = Orlando Booksellers................. 150
Mackey (M.) = Fuchsia Books...................... 266
McKirdy (T.) = Cooks Books 99
MacTaggart (C.) = Bridport Old Books 92
Madani (M.B.) = The Maghreb Bookshop........ 177
Madden (H.) = Cavern Books 70
Maddison (J.K.) = Anvil Books..................... 239
Maddock (T.) = Alpha Books 156
Maggs (E.) = Maggs Brothers Limited............ 173
Mair (J.) = Mair Wilkes Books 271
Manning (R.) = R. & A. Books 101
Marcan (P.) = Peter Marcan........................ 164
Marsh (B.) = Lime Tree Books 228
Marshall (A.) = Warsash Nautical Bookshop..... 126
Marten (W.) = Bookstand 94
Martin (R. & E.) = Richard Martin Bookshop
   & Gallery... 123
Mather (H.S.G) = Wykeham Books 170
Matthews (J.) = Eddie Baxter - Books............ 220
Mattley (J.E.) = Phenotype Books 79
May (E. & D.) = The Eastcote Bookshop......... 180
Mayall (M. & R.) = Sturford Books 254

Mayes (W.) = Mr. Pickwick of Towcester......... 199
Maynard (D.) = Maynard & Bradley 146
McGivney (J.) = Kenya Books...................... 100
McKelvie (L.) = The Studio 278
Meeuws (W.A.) = Thorntons of Oxford Ltd..... 206
Menelaou (M.) = Antique Prints of the World ... 156
Michael (S.) = Chevin Books 249
Micklewright (C.) = Wright Trace Books 239
Miles (D.) = The Canterbury Bookshop.......... 136
Millard (A.) = R. & A. Books 101
Millard (R.) = Wembdon Books.................... 216
Miller (G.) = Resurgam Books 106
Miller (P.) = Ken Spelman.......................... 198
Minet (P.P.B.) = Piccadilly Rare Books 105
Missing (C.) = Missing Books...................... 109
Mitchell (A.G.) = Capital Bookshop 281
Mitchell (C.) = Ripping Yarns 158
Mitchell (D.R. & M.E.) = Bruce Main–Smith
   & Co. Ltd. 146
Mitchell (Dr. D.J.) = Scarthin Books 82
Monckton (I.) = Kingshead Books 291
Monks (J.) = Hancock & Monks.................... 288
Moore (C.N., E.J. & S.J.) = Castle Bookshop.... 290
Moore (R.) = R M Books 132
Morgan (Dr. D.H. & R.A.) = Turret House...... 191
Morgan (P.) = Coch-y-Bonddu Books 290
Morgan–Hughes (A.) = Black Cat Books 187
Morley (A.P.) = Bay Bookshop 283
Morris (G. & B.) = Rhos Point Books............. 283
Morrish (K. & J.) = Reigate Galleries 232
Morton (A.) = Andrew Morton Books 287
Moy (R.F.) = Spread Eagle Bookshop............. 164
Mucci (R. M.) = Robert's Shop..................... 102
Mullen (P. & M.) = Yesteryear Railwayana 139
Mullett (G.&A.) = The Eastern Traveller.......... 219
Mundy (D.) = David Mundy at Heritage
   Antiques.. 129
Mundy (D.) = David Mundy at Nooks
   and Crannies 61
Murdoch (G.) = Armchair Auctions 121
Murphy (R.P.) = Rods Books....................... 88
Murtagh (C.J.) = Anvil Books 239
Mustin (L. and S.) = Byre Books................... 270
Mycock (D. & M.) = Abacus Books and Cards . 224

Nairn (E.G.) = John Updike Rare Books 277
Nash (M. & V.) = Marine and Cannon Books... 69
Nassau (J.) = Jarndyce Antiquarian Booksellers . 177
Naylor (Dr. A.C.I.) = Bookfare..................... 80
Neal (D.) = The Secondhand Bookshop.......... 140
Neal (D.) = Secondhand Bookshop 233
Neal (j.) = Kineton Books 236
Nearn (Rev. D.H.) = Heritage Books 133
Neil (D.) = Westcountry Oldbooks................. 90
Neville (C.) = Woodbine Books..................... 245
Newbold (R.) = Booktrace International 86
Newland (J.& C.) = Cotswold Internet Books.... 113
Newman (P.) = Castle Hill Books 128
Newton (D.) = Tasburgh Books..................... 190
Nicholls (P. & C.) = Boxwood Books & Prints... 219
Nicholls (T.) = Paperbacks Plus 59
Nisbet (D.) = Sterling Books 220
Noble (C. & M.) = Christine's Book Cabin....... 147
Nummelin (S.&A.) = Browning Books 292

O'Brien (C.) = The Celtic Bookshop 266
Obeney (P.) = Idle Genius Books 157
O'Connell (B. & J.) = Schull Books 262
O'Connor (J.&E.) = O'Connor Fine Books 144
O'Donnell (G.) = Bristol Books 60
Ogden (P.) = Galloway & Porter Limited 64
O'Keeffe (N.S.) = Evergreen Livres 116
Oldham (G.) = Greenroom Books 247
Oldham (Dr. T.) = Wyseby House Books 55
Ollerhead (P.E.) = Copnal Books 69
O'Neill (A.) = Rees & O'Neill Rare Books 178
Overton Fuller (J.) = Fuller D'Arch Smith 172
Owen (J.) = owenbooks65 283
Owen (J.V.) = Colwyn Books 283

Painell (C.) = The Design Gallery 1850-1950 141
Palmer (E.) = Elmfield Books, ... 238
Park (M.) = Mike Park 182
Parker (A.) = Frank Smith Maritime Aviation ... 235
Parker (M.) = Mike Parker Books 64
Parr (K.) = Kyrios Books 203
Parry (R.C.) = Exeter Rare Books 86
Partington (F. & J.) = Tennis Collectables 68
Paterson = Quentin Books Ltd 108
Pattenden (C.) = Red Star Books 129
Patterson (J.B.) = Priestpopple Books 201
Pawson (D. & L.) = Footrope Knots 227
Pearce (P.) = Hencotes Books & Prints 201
Prearson (C.B.) = Acumen Books 224
Peers (C.J.) = Mainly Fiction 68
Peggs (K.) = All Books 111
Pegler (P. & W.) = Canon Gate Bookshop 243
Penney (B.) = Invisible Books 100
Perry (I.) = The Strand Bookshop 291
Perry (M.) = Barn Books 214
Petrie (I.R.) = Bookworms 186
Phil (M.) = Rosanda Books 146
Phillips (C.) = Chris Phillips 252
Phillips (C.) = Bath Old Books 215
Phillips (J.) = Phillips of Hitchin 131
Phillips (J.) = Periplus Books 62
Lipkowitz (I.) = Bygone Books 275
Piercy (N.S.) = Crimes Ink 154
Pilkington (P.) = The Art Book Company 227
Pinches (R.) = Heraldry Today 253
Pine (L.) = Milestone Publications Goss
& Crested China 123
Pinto (P.) = Interstellar Master Traders 143
Pipe (M.) = Enscot Books 164
Pizey (J.S.) = P. and P. Books 256
Platt (R.) = Bookshop on the Heath, The 163
Pogmore (Mrs. E.M.) = Books 205
Poklewski–Koziell (S.) = Classic Bindings 166
Pollock (Dr. J.) = Whig Books Ltd 147
Pook (B.&J.) = ... 146
Potter (R.) = Badgers Books 244
Powell (J. & A.) = Palladour Books 125
Pratt (R.J.) = Hereward Books 66
Pretlove (M.) = Gillmark Gallery 130
Prince (C.) = The Poetry Bookshop 289
Proctor (C.D. & H.M.) = The Antique Map &
Bookshop 94
Purkis (H.H. & P.A.) = Harry Holmes Books 107
Pye (J. & H.) = The Bookshop 242
Pyecroft (R.) = R & R Books 116

Quigley (A.) = Bibliophile Books 154

Ralph (A.) = Art Reference Books 124
Ramsden (G.) = Stone Trough Books 198
Raxter (C.) = Lion Books 255
Read (C. & J.) = C. & J. Read - Gorleston
Books 187
Read (T.) = Home Farm Books 236
Reading (B. & J.) = Oast Books 136
Reding (Mrs. P.F.) = Croydon Bookshop 180
Rees (Prof. D.B.) = Modern Welsh
Publications Ltd. 184
Reese (R.W.) = Holdenhurst Books 91
Reeve (A.) = Cover to Cover 185
Rhead (J.) = Barnhill Books 274
Richards (A.) = Cold Tonnage Books 234
Richards (D.) = Rugby Relics 285
Richardson (A.) = Afar Books International 238
Richmond (M.) = Ming Books 270
Richmond (M.) = AA1 Books 269
Ridler (Dr. A.M.) = Nineteenth Century Books .. 209
Riley (A. & J.) = Ryeland Books, ... 199
Ritchie (J.) = Books Afloat 96
Robbins (P.J.) = Phillip Robbins of Warwick 237
Roberts (G.) = Magpie Books 250
Robinson (C.) = Creaking Shelves 274
Robinson (T.F.) = J.C. Books 191
Robinson–Brown (P.) = P.R. Brown (Books) 98
Rockall (J.) = Kingswood Books 94
Rogers (D.) = Helion & Company 239
Rogers (M.) = Michael Rogers 251
Rogers (P.J.) = Croydon Bookshop 180
Rogers (P.J.) = Rogers Turner Books 165
Rowan (H.) = H. & S.J. Rowan 91
Ronald (A.) = A. & R. Booksearch 73
Ronald (R.) = A. & R. Booksearch 73
Ronan (S.) = Chthonios Books 102
Roper (B.) = Eastgate Bookshop 106
Ross (M.C.) = Avonworld Books 216
Rothschild (R.) = Twiggers Booksearch 53
Routh (S.A.) = Gage Postal Books 111
Rowley (F.) = Freader's Books 279
Rowlinson (D.A.) = Books Ulster 261
Russell (M.P.) = The Bibliophile 221

St. Aubyn (H.M. & J.R.) = Woolcott Books 92
Salin (P.) = Sarah Key Books 64
Salt (D.T.) = Salsus Books 256
Sames (M.D.) = The Ryde Bookshop 133
Sancto (R.G.) = Bunyan Books 53
Saunders (P. & E.) = Post–Horn Books 192
Savage (K.) = Keith Savage 228
Scott (T.) = Mount's Bay Books 74
Sedgwick (D.) = Moorside Books 143
Seers (P.R. & C.) = Greensleeves 206
Sephton (A.F.) = A.F Sephton 174
Sesemann (J.) = Luia Sesemann 135
Seton (M.) = Alba Books 273
Sever (T.P.) = Books 284
Seward (P.& G.) = The Carnforth Bookshop 142
Seydi (S.) = Sevin Seydi Rare Books 161
Shakeshaft (B.L.) = Dr. B. Shakeshaft 71
Shakespeare (C. & L.) = Colin Shakespeare 223
Sharman (L.) = Treasure Trove Books 146
Sharpe (A.&J.) = Grove Rare Books 195

Sheard (D.) = Heckmondwike Book Shop 249
Sheehan (A.) = Darkwood Books 263
Sheehan (M.) = Caissa Books 233
Sheffield (R.) = Roosterbooks 199
Shelley (A. & J.) = Bow Windows Book Shop ... 103
Shelly (E.& J.) = E.J. Shelly 61
Sheppard (R.D.) = Fireside Bookshop 81
Sheridan (P.J.) = Books Bought & Sold 231
Shire (C.) = Theatreshire Books 192
Siddons (D.) = Forest Books 211
Sidwell (R.) = Monmouth House Books 286
Simpson (I.) = Clent Books 255
Simpson (K.M.L.) = Black Five Books 214
Simpson O'Gara (J.P.) = Allhalland Books 84
Sims (T.J.) = Bookworms of Evesham 257
Sinclair (M.) = Books in Cardigan 282
Slade (R.) = Restormel Books 257
Slim (R.T.) = Janus Books & Antiques 239
Sloggett (T.) = Leabeck Books 208
Smillie (M.) = Caledonia Books 278
Smith (A.) = Orlando Booksellers 150
Smith (E.) = Bookstand 94
Smith (G.D.) = Great Grandfather's 143
Smith (G.E. & M.K.) = Book End 108
Smith (J.) = Clarendon Books 145
Smith (K.) = Keith Smith Books 128
Smith (M.) = Enscot Books........................... 164
Smith (M.) = Chelifer Books 80
Smith (N.) = Nigel Smith Books 230
Smith (R.W.L.) = Sax Books 228
Smosarki (A.) = Cofion Books 286
Sparkes (J.) = Combat Arts Archive 97
Spooner (B.J.) = Spooner & Co 219
Spranklins (G.) = Rowan House Books 231
Sproates (S.) = ForensicSearch 131
Spurrier (R.) = Post Mortem Books 242
Steadman (J.) = The Traveller's Bookshelf 218
Steenson (M.M.) = Books & Things 171
Stevens (A.E.R.M.) = Enigma Books 252
Stevens (E.) = Fortune Green Books 160
Stevens (F.) = Collectors Corner 253
Stevens (G.R.) = The Driffield Bookshop 106
Stevens (J.) = Joan Stevens 65
Stevenson (K.) = Game Advice 208
Stinton (R.) = The Idle Booksellers 245
Stoddart (A.) = Hellenic Bookservices 161
Stone (A.) = Squirrel Antiques 122
Stones (L. A.) = The Bookshelf 195
Strong (E.A.) = McNaughtan's Bookshop 276
Stroud (F.P.A.) = Chaters Motoring Booksellers. 181
Stuart (E.) = First State Books 172
Suchar (V. & E.) = Camden Books 215
Sutcliffe (E.) = Pendleside Books 143
Sutherland (S.) = Allhalland Books 84
Suttie (D.S.) = Bowland Bookfinders.............. 143
Sutton (M.) = The Old Celtic Bookshop 87

Tall (J. & N.) = Badger Books 219
Tandree (H. & A.) = Anthroposophical Books... 116
Tatam (J.) = Cat Lit 218
Tatman (C.) = Beverley Old Bookshop 106
Taylor (P. & S.) = Greyfriars Books 108
Taylor (P.H.) = Farnborough Bookshop &
   Gallery.. 122
Taylor (P.) = Books & Bygones..................... 240

Tebay (K.M.) = Red Rose Books 118
Tee (B.) = The Porter Bookshop.................... 222
Thompson (M. & A.C.) = The Bookshop......... 191
Thompson (P.) = Bookseeker......................... 280
Thomson (G.) = Greta Books........................ 97
Thornhill (J. & M.) = Candle Lane Books........ 213
Thredder (P.) = Ross Old Books & Prints 128
Tierney (Dr. J. & Mrs. I.) = Hawkridge Books .. 82
Tierney (M.) = Wheen O'Books,.................... 267
Tilley (A. & A.) = Tilleys Vintage Magazine Shop 82
Timothy (D.) = Siop y Morfa 284
Timson (L.) = Humanist Book Services 72
Tindley (J.) = Tindley & Chapman 178
To (W.) = Mike Park 182
Tober (B.) = Bruce Tober............................. 240
Tomaszewski (C.) = Stella Books 286
Tootell (J.) = Pimpernel Booksearch 169
Townsend (J. & J.) = The Old Hall Bookshop ... 199
Townsend–Cardew (J. & B.) = Daisy Lane Books 246
Tozer (N.) = Roscrea Bookshop..................... 247
Tranter (P.) = Orangeberry Books.................. 207
Travis (R., B., and S.) = SaBeRo Books 169
Traylen (N. & T.) = Ventnor Rare Books......... 134
Treece (M.) = Cornerstone Books 88
Trevitt (J.) = Hereford Booksearch 128
Trinder (R.) = Trinders' Fine Tools 226
Tuft (P.) = Patrick Tuft 181
Turnbull (P.M.) = The Countryman's Gallery.... 145
Turner (A. & D.) = Capel Mawr Collectors
   Centre... 285
Turner (A.J.) = Rogers Turner Books 165
Turner (L.M.) = Bath Book Exchange............. 215
Twitchett (D.E.) = Engaging Gear Ltd............. 108
Tyers (N.A.M., M.G.D. & P.A.) = St. Mary's
   Books & Prints 152
Tynan (P.) = Courtwood Books 265
Tyson (L.) = Paper Pleasures 218
Tyson (S.R.) = Over-Sands Books 77

Unsworth (C.) = Unsworth's Booksellers.......... 178
Unwin (D.) = Eastleach Books...................... 56

Valentine Ketchum (V.A. & B.J.) = Staniland
   (Booksellers).. 152
Vallely (J.) = Craobh Rua Books 260
Vaupres (J.) = The Lighthouse Books.............. 92
Vetterlein (M.) = Birchden Books 154
Voigt (R.G.) = Garwood & Voigt 139

Wagstaff (A.) = Booksmart 199
Wakeman (P. & F.) = Frances Wakeman Books 204
Waldron (C.) = Bookends............................ 122
Walker (D.) = Chelifer Books 80
Walker (G.) = Gary Walker 271
Wallace (N.) = Minster Gate Bookshop 197
Wallbaum (C.) = H. Baron 160
Walsh (M.) = Glenbower Books 264
Walters (H. & G.) = Court Hay Books............ 239
Walters (M.) = Kingfisher Book Service 204
Ward (D.J.) = SETI Books 229
Warwick (D.C.) = The Nautical Antique Centre . 96
Warwick (N.) = Readers Rest 150
Watson (D.) = Linton Books 267
Watson (J.S.) = John Updike Rare Books 277
Watts (M.D.) = Bookshop at the Plain 149

Watts (N.) = Beaver Booksearch.................... 225
Watts (R.) = Dolphin Books 225
Wayne (J.) = Nicholas Willmott Bookseller 281
Weaver (C.A.) = Transformer 270
Weir (D. & J.L.) = Yesterday's Books 92
Weissman (S.) = Ximenes Rare Books Inc. 115
Welford (R.G.M.& M.E.) = Oasis Booksearch ... 67
Wells (M.) = Mary Wells............................ 169
Wesley (P.) = Harlequin 90
Weston (J.) = Westons Booksellers Ltd 132
West–Skinn (R.) = Golden Goose Books.......... 150
West–Skinn (R.) = Harlequin Gallery.............. 150
Westwood (F.) = The Petersfield Bookshop....... 124
Wheeler (M.A.) = W.H. Collectables............... 229
Whitaker (J. & M.A.) = Peregrine Books (Leeds) 248
Whitby (M.) = Sevin Seydi Rare Books 161
White (M.J.) = Fun in Books 234
Whitehorn (J.) = Heartland Old Books............ 89
Wiberg (C.) = The Book Depot..................... 160
Wicks (J.) = Just Books 75
Wilkes (A.) = Mair Wilkes Books 271
Wilkinson (D. & T.) = The Book Gallery 74
Wilkinson (D.&J.) = Autolycus 212
Wilkinson (D.J.) = Intech Books.................... 201
Wilkinson (J.B.) = Leeds Bookseller................ 248
Williams (C. & C.) = Aardvark Books............. 254
Williams (J.) = Bookworm Alley.................... 89
Williams (J. & J.) = Octagon Books............... 66
Williams (M.) = Hellenic Bookservices............. 161
Williams (Dr. S.M.) = Barcombe Services 108
Willmott (N.) = Nicholas Willmott Bookseller ... 281
Wills (T.) = Volumes of Motoring.................. 113
Wilson (H.G.E.) = Dales and Lakes Book
  Centre... 79
Wilson (J. & G.) = John Wilson (Manuscripts)
  Ltd. 114
Wilson (L.) = Halson Books......................... 71
Wilson (R.) = Classic Crime Collections........... 119
Wilson (R.) = The Old Town Bookshop 276
Winston–Smith (M. & S.) = Trade Priced Old
  Books... 289
Winter (Mrs.J.) = Sedgeberrow Books 256
Wise (C.) = Atlantis Bookshop...................... 176
Woodhouse (G.) = Gillmark Gallery............... 130
Woolley (P. & K.) = Black Cat Bookshop 147
Worms (L.) = Ash Rare Books 166
Worthy (J.S. & S.) = Rochdale Book Company . 120
Wright (C.) = Yarborough House Bookshop 212
Wright (M. & S.) = Roadmaster Books 136
Wright (P.) = Wright Trace Books 239
Wynne (N.) = Grays of Westminster............... 167

Yablon (G.A.) = Ian Hodgkins and Company
  Limited 116
Young (I. & S.) = Autumn Leaves 150
Young (R.) = Bridport Old Books 92
Young (S.) = Antiques on High..................... 207

Zealley (C.J.) = St. Philip's Books 208

SPECIALITY INDEX
Index of dealers by stock speciality followed by county

ABORIGINAL

Byre Books, Dumfries & Galloway 270
Inner Bookshop (The), Oxfordshire 208
J.C. Deyong Books (Previously
of Snowden Smith Books), London SW 168
Michael Graves-Johnston, London SW 168
Muse Bookshop (The), Gwynedd 285
R. & A. Books, East Sussex 101
Watkins Books Ltd., London WC 179

ACADEMIC/SCHOLARLY

Adrem Books, Herts 130
Ainslie Books, Strathclyde 278
Al Saqi Books, London W 171
Alec–Smith Books (Alex), East Yorkshire 107
All Books, Essex 111
Allinson (Frank & Stella), Warwickshire 236
Alpha Books, London N 156
Antiquary Ltd., (Bar Bookstore), N Yorkshire .. 194
Any Amount of Books, London WC 176
Apocalypse, Surrey 232
Austwick Hall Books, North Yorkshire 192
B D McManmon, Lancashire 144
Barcombe Services, Essex 108
Baron - Scientific Book Sales (P.J.), Somerset ... 216
Bell (Peter), Lothian 275
Bennett & Kerr Books, Oxfordshire 205
Berwick Books, Lincolnshire 150
Blanchfield (John), West Yorkshire 248
Bloomsbury Bookshop, London O 181
Bodders Books, Shropshire 212
Boer (Louise), Arthurian Books, Powys 287
Book Business (The), London W 171
BOOKS4U, Flintshire 284
Bookshop (The), Greater Manchester 118
Bookshop at the Plain, Lincolnshire 149
Bowland Bookfinders, Lancashire 143
Bracton Books, Cambridgeshire 63
Brighton Books, East Sussex 99
Burak (Steve), London WC 176
Camden Books, Somerset 215
Celtic Bookshop (The), Co. Limerick 266
Chapman (Neville), Lancashire 144
Charles Bossom, Cambridgeshire 65
Chesters (G. & J.), Staffordshire 224
Church Street Bookshop, London N 156
Clarendon Books, Leicestershire 145
Clevedon Books, Somerset 217
Clifton Books, Essex 111
Cobnar Books, Kent 141
Cofion Books, Pembrokeshire 286
Corder (Mark W.), Kent 139
Cornucopia Books, Lincolnshire 151
Country Books, Derbyshire 82
Courtenay Bookroom, Oxfordshire 205
Crouch Rare Books, Surrey 232
Dales & Lakes Book Centre, Cumbria 79
Dandy Lion Editions, Surrey 233
David (G.), Cambridgeshire 63

de Visser Books, Cambridgeshire 63
Delectus Books, London WC 176
Derek Stirling Bookseller, Kent 141
Dolphin Books, Suffolk 225
Dooley (Rosemary), Cumbria 77
Dylans Bookstore, Swansea 291
Eagle Bookshop (The), Bedfordshire 53
Earth Science Books, Wiltshire 252
Eastern Books of London, London SW 166
Eastleach Books, Berks 56
Ellis, Bookseller (Peter), London WC 177
Empire Books, North Yorkshire 197
English (Toby), Oxfordshire 209
Evans Books (Paul), West Sussex 243
Facet Books, Dorset 91
Farnborough Gallery, Hampshire 122
Fireside Bookshop, Cumbria 81
Fortune Green Books, London NW 160
Fossgate Books, North Yorkshire 197
G. C. Books Ltd., Dumfries & Galloway 270
Galloway & Porter Limited, Cambridgeshire 64
Game Advice, Oxfordshire 208
GfB: the Colchester Bookshop, Essex 108
Gibbs Books, (Jonathan), Worcestershire 256
Gildas Books, Cheshire 68
Gladstone Books, Lincolnshire 150
Glenbower Books, Co. Dublin 264
Golden Age Books, Worcestershire 256
Goldman (Paul), Dorset 94
Greenroom Books, West Yorkshire 247
Handsworth Books, Essex 112
Harwich Old Books, Essex 109
Hawkes (James), London 164
Hawley (C.L.), North Yorkshire 195
Hay Cinema Bookshop Ltd., Powys 288
Helion & Company, West Midlands 239
Hellenic Bookservices, London NW 161
Herb Tandree Philosophy Books, Glos 116
Hill Books (Alan), South Yorkshire 222
hullbooks.com, East Yorkshire 106
Hurst (Jenny), Kent 137
Ice House Books, Wiltshire 254
Inner Bookshop (The), Oxfordshire 208
Innes Books, Shropshire 212
Internet Bookshop UK Ltd., Gloucestershire 113
Invisible Books, East Sussex 100
Island Books, Devon 85
Jackdaw Books, Norfolk 188
Joel Segal Books, Devon 86
Jones (Andrew), Suffolk 227
K.S.C. Books, Cheshire 70
Kenya Books, East Sussex 100
Kim's Bookshop, West Sussex 242
Kingswood Books, Dorset 94
Lee Rare Books (Rachel), Bristol 59
Leeds Bookseller, West Yorkshire 248
Lowe (John), Norfolk 188
Lyonshill Books, Co. Dublin 265
Maghreb Bookshop (The), London WC 177

Mair Wilkes Books, Fife 271
Marine & Cannon Books, Cheshire 71
Marine and Cannon Books, Cheshire 69
medievalbookshop, Herts........................... 132
Mellon's Books, East Sussex 101
Michael Graves-Johnston, London SW 168
Mobbs (A.J.), West Midlands 239
Morgan (H.J.), Bedfordshire 54
Murphy (C.J.), Norfolk 189
Muse Bookshop (The), Gwynedd 285
My Back Pages, London SW 168
Needham Books, (Russell), Somerset.............. 219
Northern Herald Books, West Yorkshire........ 245
O'Donoghue Books, Powys.......................... 289
Offa's Dyke Books, Shropshire 213
O'Flynn Books, North Yorkshire................... 197
Old Aberdeen Bookshop, Grampian 272
Old Book Company, (The), West Yorkshire 248
Oopalba Books, Cheshire............................ 71
Outcast Books, Herefordshire....................... 127
Period & Classical Collections, East Sussex 103
Pittville Books, Gloucestershire..................... 113
Plurabelle Books, Cambridgeshire.................. 65
Poetry Bookshop (The), Powys...................... 289
Pollak (P.M.), Devon 88
Poole (William), London W 174
Pordes Books Ltd., (Henry), London WC....... 177
Porter Bookshop (The), South Yorkshire......... 222
Portus Books, Hampshire 122
Priestpopple Books, Northumberland 201
PsychoBabel Books & Journals, Oxfordshire..... 205
Quest Books, East Yorkshire 107
R. & A. Books, East Sussex 101
Reading Lasses, Dumfries & Galloway 270
Red Star Books, Herts 129
Reeves Technical Books, North Yorkshire 195
Reid of Liverpool, Merseyside...................... 184
Rickaro Books, West Yorkshire.................... 246
Robert Temple, London N.......................... 158
Roberts Books, Strathclyde 279
Roscrea Bookshop & Newsagents,
   Co. Tipperary 266
Rosley Books, Cumbria 81
Rowan (P. & B.), Co. Antrim 260
Roz Hulse, Conwy 284
St Mary's Books & Prints, Lincolnshire 152
St Philip's Books, Oxfordshire...................... 208
Saintfield Antiques & Fine Books, Co. Down ... 261
Salsus Books, Worcestershire 256
Sandpiper Books Ltd., London SW 169
Saunders (Tom), Caerphilly 281
Scarthin Books, Derbyshire 82
Scott (Peter), East Sussex 104
South Downs Book Service, West Sussex........ 243
Sparrow Books, West Yorkshire 245
Spelman (Ken), North Yorkshire 198
Spenceley Books (David),
   West Yorkshire..................................... 248
Spurrier (Nick), Kent 137
Stalagluft Books, Tyne and Wear.................. 235
Staniland (Booksellers), Lincolnshire 152
Sterling Books, Somerset............................. 220
Stern Antiquarian Bookseller (Jeffrey), N Yorks . 198
Stevens (Joan), Cambridgeshire..................... 65
Stroma Books, Borders 267

Studio Bookshop, East Sussex....................... 100
Sue Lowell Natural History Books, London W . 175
Symes Books (Naomi), Cheshire 71
The Sanctuary Bookshop, Dorset.................. 94
Thorntons of Oxford Ltd., Oxfordshire.......... 206
Tiffin (Tony and Gill), Durham 97
Tiger Books, Kent 136
Tombland Bookshop, Norfolk 190
Transformer, Dumfries & Galloway 270
Venables (Morris & Juliet), Bristol................ 59
Ventnor Rare Books, Isle of Wight................ 134
Victoria Bookshop (The), Devon.................. 84
Vinovium Books, Durham 97
Walden Books, London NW 161
Warrington Book Loft (The), Cheshire 71
Warsash Nautical Bookshop, Hampshire......... 126
Waterfield's, Oxfordshire 209
Waterstone's, London WC........................... 179
Watkins Books Ltd., London WC.................. 179
Weiner (Graham), London N 158
Westwood Books Ltd, Cumbria 80
Williams (Bookdealer), (Richard),
   North Lincolnshire 153
Winchester Bookshop (The), Hampshire.......... 126
Winghale Books, Lincolnshire 152
Wizard Books, Cambridgeshire...................... 67
Woburn Books, London N 159
Worcester Rare Books, Worcestershire 256
Yates Antiquarian Books (Tony), Leicestershire. 146

ACCOUNTANCY
Jade Mountain Bookshop, Hampshire............ 125
Muse Bookshop (The), Gwynedd 285
Old Book Company, (The), West Yorkshire 248
Quaritch Ltd., (Bernard), London W............. 174
Susanne Schulz-Falster Rare Books, London N. 158

ACUPUNCTURE
Chthonios Books, East Sussex....................... 102
Inner Bookshop (The), Oxfordshire................ 208
Joel Segal Books, Devon 86
Occultique, Northamptonshire....................... 199
Orchid Book Distributors, Co. Clare.............. 262
Phelps (Michael), West Sussex....................... 242
Watkins Books Ltd., London WC................... 179

ADIRONDACK MOUNTAINS, THE
Muse Bookshop (The), Gwynedd 285

ADULT
Addyman Books, Powys............................... 287
Adrem Books, Herts 130
Apocalypse, Surrey 232
Delectus Books, London WC........................ 176
Eggeling Books (John), West Yorkshire 249
Muse Bookshop (The), Gwynedd 285
N1 Books, East Sussex 105
Old Book Company, (The), West Yorkshire 248
R. & A. Books, East Sussex 101
Reading Lasses, Dumfries & Galloway 270
Spike's Books, North Yorkshire.................... 192
Tsbbooks, London SW 169
Woodland Books, Devon.............................. 84

ADVENTURE

Annie's Books, South Yorkshire 221
Blackpool Book Warehouse, Lancashire.......... 142
Bodders Books, Shropshire.......................... 212
Booth (Booksearch Service), (Geoff), Cheshire... 68
Cox (Geoff), Devon 90
Dolphin Books, Suffolk............................. 225
Doolin Dinghy Books, Co. Clare 262
Eastern Traveller (The), Somerset................. 219
Edmund Pollinger Rare Books, London SW..... 166
Eggeling Books (John), West Yorkshire 249
Joel Segal Books, Devon 86
Keith Langford, London E 154
Mulyan (Don), Merseyside.......................... 185
Parker Books (Mike), Cambridgeshire 64
R. & A. Books, East Sussex 101
Rods Books, Devon.................................. 88
Wheen O'Books, Borders............................ 267

ADVERTISING

All Books, Essex 111
Barry McKay Rare Books, Cumbria.............. 76
Batterham (David), London W...................... 171
Bettridge (Gordon), Fife............................ 271
Books & Things, London W......................... 171
Bowland Bookfinders, Lancashire.................. 143
Chapman (Neville), Lancashire..................... 144
Cornucopia Books, Lincolnshire 151
Debbage (John), Norfolk 189
Derek Stirling Bookseller, Kent 141
Embleton (Paul), Essex 111
Facet Books, Dorset.................................. 91
Franks Booksellers, Greater Manchester.......... 119
Hill House Books, Devon 88
Ian Marr Rare Books, Cornwall 73
IDEA, London EC.................................... 155
Joel Segal Books, Devon 86
Junk & Spread Eagle, London SE 164
Lowe (John), Norfolk................................ 188
Mulyan (Don), Merseyside.......................... 185
Pordes Books Ltd., (Henry), London WC........ 177
Prior (Michael), Lincolnshire 152
Pyecroft (Ruth), Gloucestershire 116
R. & A. Books, East Sussex 101
Roland Books, Kent 138
Saint Swithin's Illustrated & Children's Books,
   London W 174
Sterling Books, Somerset 220

AERONAUTICS

Addyman Books, Powys.............................. 287
Adrem Books, Herts 130
All Books, Essex 111
Allinson (Frank & Stella), Warwickshire 236
Anchor Books, Lincolnshire 149
Annie's Books, South Yorkshire 221
Anthony Vickers Books, North Yorkshire 195
Aviabooks, Gloucestershire 114
Barbican Bookshop, North Yorkshire.............. 196
Books Bought & Sold, Surrey 231
BOOKS4U, Flintshire................................ 284
Camilla's Bookshop, East Sussex 101
Cheshire Book Centre, Cheshire.................... 69
Clarke Books (David), Somerset 218
Clevedon Books, Somerset 217

Cocks (Brian), Cambridgeshire 67
Cofion Books, Pembrokeshire 286
Collectables (W.H.), Suffolk 229
Corfe Books, Surrey.................................. 230
Cornucopia Books, Lincolnshire 151
Cox (Geoff), Devon 90
Facet Books, Dorset.................................. 91
Fireside Bookshop, Cumbria........................ 81
Hancock (Peter), West Sussex 241
Harrington Antiquarian Bookseller (Peter),
   London SW 167
Harris (George J.), Co. Derry 260
Hay Cinema Bookshop Ltd., Powys.............. 288
Holdenhurst Books, Dorset 91
Island Books, Devon................................. 85
Lost Books, Northamptonshire...................... 200
Lowe (John), Norfolk................................ 188
Milestone Books, Devon 89
MilitaryHistoryBooks.com, Kent................... 137
N1 Books, East Sussex 105
Old Book Company, (The), West Yorkshire 248
Phelps (Michael), West Sussex 242
Pollak (P.M.), Devon 88
Pordes Books Ltd., (Henry), London WC........ 177
R. & A. Books, East Sussex 101
Read - Gorleston Books, (C.&J.), Norfolk 187
Robert Humm & Co, Lincolnshire 152
Salway Books, Essex 112
Sterling Books, Somerset 220
Stroh (M.A.), London E 154
T V Coles Books, Cambridgeshire 67
Thin Read Line, Merseyside 184
Vanstone - Aviation Books, (Derek), Suffolk 229
Weiner (Graham), London N 158
Westons, Herts 132

AESTHETIC MOVEMENT

Apocalypse, Surrey 232
Books & Things, London W......................... 171
Cox Rare Books (Charles), Cornwall.............. 73
Delectus Books, London WC........................ 176
Design Gallery 1850-1950 (The), Kent 141
Harrington (Adrian), London W.................... 173
R. & A. Books, East Sussex 101

AESTHETICS

Apocalypse, Surrey 232
Joel Segal Books, Devon 86
Parkinsons Books, Merseyside...................... 185
Pittville Books, Gloucestershire.................... 113
R. & A. Books, East Sussex 101
Susanne Schulz-Falster Rare Books, London N. 158

AFRICANA

Addyman Books, Powys.............................. 287
African Studies, Dorset 91
Alexander's Books, Warwickshire.................. 237
All Books, Essex 111
Allsworth Rare Books Ltd., London SW......... 166
Armchair Books, Lothian 275
Ayre (Peter J.), Somerset 219
Barn Books, Buckinghamshire 61
Beaumont Travel Books, London SE 163
Black Voices, Merseyside............................ 184
Bloomsbury Bookshop, London O 181

Bonham (J. & S.L.), London W 171
C J Renwick Books, Powys 287
Chalmers Hallam (E.), Hampshire 125
Chas J. Sawyer, Kent 140
Coch-y-Bonddu Books, Powys 290
Delectus Books, London WC 176
Edmund Pollinger Rare Books, London SW 166
Eggeling Books (John), West Yorkshire 249
Empire Books, North Yorkshire 197
G. C. Books Ltd., Dumfries & Galloway 270
Grahame (Major Iain), Suffolk 225
Grayling (David A.H.), Cumbria 78
Hennessey Bookseller (Ray), East Sussex 100
J & J Burgess Booksellers, Cambridgeshire 64
Joel Segal Books, Devon 86
Kennedy & Farley, East Sussex 104
Kenya Books, East Sussex 100
Marcet Books, London SE 164
Michael Graves-Johnston, London SW 168
MK Book Services, Cambridgeshire 66
Old Book Company, (The), West Yorkshire 248
Peter M Daly, Hampshire 126
Pordes Books Ltd., (Henry), London WC 177
Preston Book Company, Lancashire 144
Prospect House Books, Co. Down 261
Quaritch Ltd., (Bernard), London W 174
R. & A. Books, East Sussex 101
Reading Lasses, Dumfries & Galloway 270
Roscrea Bookshop & Newsagents,
    Co. Tipperary 266
SaBeRo Books, London SW 169
Samovar Books, Co. Dublin 264
Smith (Ray), Herts 129
Thin Read Line, Merseyside 184
Thorntons of Oxford Ltd., Oxfordshire 206
White (C.R.), London W 175
Wiend Books, Lancashire 143
Woburn Books, London N 159
Yesterday's Books, Dorset 92
York (Graham), Devon 86

AFRICAN-AMERICAN STUDIES

Black Voices, Merseyside 184
Dylans Bookstore, Swansea 291
Michael Graves-Johnston, London SW 168
Reading Lasses, Dumfries & Galloway 270
Watkins Books Ltd., London WC 179
Woburn Books, London N 159
Yesterday's Books, Dorset 92

AGRICULTURE

Addyman Books, Powys 287
Alec–Smith Books (Alex), East Yorkshire 107
Barn Books, Shropshire 214
Besleys Books, Suffolk 225
Blest (Peter), Kent 138
Books for Content, Herefordshire 127
BOOKS4U, Flintshire 284
Burmester (James), Bristol 58
Carningli Centre, Pembrokeshire 286
Cassidy (Bookseller) (P.), Lincolnshire 151
Castle Hill Books, Herefordshire 128
Chantrey Books, South Yorkshire 222
Cheshire Book Centre, Cheshire 69
Clarke Books (David), Somerset 218

Clifton Books, Essex 111
Cobnar Books, Kent 141
Coch-y-Bonddu Books, Powys 290
Cottage Books, Leicestershire 145
Country Books, Derbyshire 82
Dales & Lakes Book Centre, Cumbria 9
Debbage (John), Norfolk 189
Dolphin Books, Suffolk 225
Drury Rare Books (John), Essex 110
Farquharson, (Hilary), Tayside 280
Ferdinando (Steven), Somerset 218
Gladstone Books, Lincolnshire 150
Greta Books, Durham 97
Guildmaster Books, Cheshire 70
Hodgson (Books) (Richard J.), North Yorkshire 196
Hollingshead (Chris), London O 182
Island Books, Devon 85
Jade Mountain Bookshop, Hampshire 125
Jane Jones Books, Grampian 273
Joel Segal Books, Devon 86
Kelpie's Books, Fife 271
Martin (Books and Pictures), (Brian P.), Surrey . 231
Muttonchop Manuscripts, West Sussex 242
New Strand, The, Herefordshire 127
Park (Mike), London O 182
Parkinsons Books, Merseyside 185
Peter M Daly, Hampshire 126
Phenotype Books, Cumbria 79
Prospect House Books, Co. Down 261
Quaritch Ltd., (Bernard), London W 174
R. & A. Books, East Sussex 101
Randall (Tom), Somerset 218
Roscrea Bookshop & Newsagents,
    Co. Tipperary 266
Savona Books, Lincolnshire 151
Stalagluft Books, Tyne and Wear 235
Stone, (G.& R.), Borders 267
Thin Read Line, Merseyside 184
Thornber (Peter M.), North Yorkshire 195
Trinity Rare Books, Co. Leitrim 266
Westons, Herts 132

AIDS CRISIS, THE

Cox Music (Lisa), Devon 86
R. & A. Books, East Sussex 101
Westons, Herts 132

AIRCRAFT

Aardvark Books, Wiltshire 254
Addyman Books, Powys 287
Adrem Books, Herts 130
Anchor Books, Lincolnshire 149
Annie's Books, South Yorkshire 221
Apocalypse, Surrey 232
Beware of the Leopard, Bristol 58
Blackpool Book Warehouse, Lancashire 142
Books Only, Suffolk 226
BOOKS4U, Flintshire 284
BookShop, The, Dumfries & Galloway 270
Bookworm (The), Lothian 276
Booth (Booksearch Service), (Geoff), Cheshire... 68
Brad Books, Essex 110
Broadhurst of Southport Ltd., Merseyside 185
Clarke Books (David), Somerset 218
Cocks (Brian), Cambridgeshire 67

Cofion Books, Pembrokeshire 286
Cornucopia Books, Lincolnshire 151
Cox (Geoff), Devon 90
Discovery Bookshop, Carmarthenshire........... 281
Eastgate Bookshop, East Yorkshire 106
Farnborough Gallery, Hampshire.................. 122
G. C. Books Ltd., Dumfries & Galloway......... 270
Gallimaufry Books, Herts 131
Hay Castle, Powys.................................... 288
Island Books, Devon 85
J & J Burgess Booksellers, Cambridgeshire....... 64
J.B. Books, Berks..................................... 57
Jade Mountain Bookshop, Hampshire 125
Joel Segal Books, Devon 86
Kingfisher Book Service, Nottinghamshire 204
Lost Books, Northamptonshire..................... 200
Marcet Books, London SE........................... 164
Marine & Cannon Books, Cheshire 71
Marine and Cannon Books, Cheshire 69
McCrone (Audrey), Isle of Arran 274
Mercat Books, Highland 274
MilitaryHistoryBooks.com, Kent................... 137
Mogul Diamonds, West Midlands 240
Not Just Books, Dorset.............................. 94
Park Gallery & Bookshop (The), Northants 200
Parrott Books, Oxfordshire 209
R. & A. Books, East Sussex 101
Rickaro Books, West Yorkshire..................... 246
Robert Humm & Co, Lincolnshire 152
Roosterbooks, Northamptonshire.................. 199
Rothwell & Dunworth, Somerset 217
Saintfield Antiques & Fine Books, Co. Down ... 261
Salway Books, Essex 112
Scorpio Books, Suffolk 225
Stalagluft Books, Tyne and Wear 235
Stroh (M.A.), London E 154
Tarka Books, Devon................................. 84
Thin Read Line, Merseyside 184
Tony Hutchinson, Surrey............................ 233
Vanstone - Aviation Books, (Derek), Suffolk 229
Weiner (Graham), London N 158
Woodland Books, Devon............................ 84

ALCHEMY

Alpha Books, London N 156
Apocalypse, Surrey 232
Atlantis Bookshop, London WC.................... 176
Caduceus Books, Leicestershire.................... 145
Chthonios Books, East Sussex 102
Gilbert (R.A.), Somerset 219
Inner Bookshop (The), Oxfordshire................ 208
Joel Segal Books, Devon 86
Magis Books, Leicestershire......................... 146
Needham Books, (Russell), Somerset.............. 219
Occultique, Northamptonshire...................... 199
Parkinsons Books, Merseyside...................... 185
Phelps (Michael), West Sussex 242
Pollak (P.M.), Devon 88
Quaritch Ltd., (Bernard), London W.............. 174
Susanne Schulz-Falster Rare Books, London N. 158
Victoria Bookshop (The), Devon.................... 84
Watkins Books Ltd., London WC.................. 179
Weiner (Graham), London N 158

ALCOHOLICS ANONYMOUS

Delectus Books, London WC........................ 176

ALMANACS

Apocalypse, Surrey 232
Bates & Hindmarch, West Yorkshire.............. 248
Beighton (Brian), Norfolk 186
Derek Stirling Bookseller, Kent 141
R. & A. Books, East Sussex 101
Watkins Books Ltd., London WC.................. 179
Weiner (Graham), London N 158
Yates Antiquarian Books (Tony), Leicestershire. 146

ALPINISM/MOUNTAINEERING

Allinson (Frank & Stella), Warwickshire 236
Anthony Spranger, Wiltshire........................ 252
Anthony Vickers Books, North Yorkshire 195
Askew Books (Vernon), Wiltshire.................. 251
Bannatyne Books, London N........................ 156
Barnhill Books, Isle of Arran 274
Beaumont Travel Books, London SE 163
Birmingham Books, West Midlands 238
Bonham (J. & S.L.), London W 171
Books, Denbighshire 284
Booth (Booksearch Service), (Geoff), Cheshire... 68
Bosco Books, Cornwall.............................. 72
Carnforth Bookshop (The), Lancashire 142
Cavendish Rare Books, London N 156
Cheshire Book Centre, Cheshire.................... 69
Church Street Books, Norfolk...................... 186
Cofion Books, Pembrokeshire 286
Collectables (W.H.), Suffolk 229
Creaking Shelves, Highland 274
Daisyroots Book Centre (Daisyroots
   Books Ltd), Cumbria 77
Dales & Lakes Book Centre, Cumbria............ 9
Dartmoor Bookshop (The), Devon................. 84
David Warnes Books, Herefordshire 128
Dunkheld Antiques, Tayside........................ 279
Eastcote Bookshop (The), London O 180
Eastleach Books, Berks 56
Fine Books at Ilkley, West Yorkshire 247
Fireside Bookshop, Cumbria........................ 81
Garfi Books, Powys 291
George St. Books, Derbyshire 83
Gildas Books, Cheshire.............................. 68
Glacier Books, Tayside 280
Hancock (Peter), West Sussex 241
Hill (Peter), Hampshire............................. 122
Hollett and Son (R.F.G.), Cumbria 79
Holmes Books (Harry), East Yorkshire........... 107
Hunter and Krageloh, Derbyshire 83
Internet Bookshop UK Ltd., Gloucestershire 113
Jane & John Kinnaird, Cumbria 78
Jarvis Books, Derbyshire 83
Joel Segal Books, Devon 86
Kirkland Books, Cumbria........................... 78
Letterbox Books, Nottinghamshire 203
Little Bookshop (The), Cumbria 80
Main Point Books, Lothian.......................... 276
McCrone (Audrey), Isle of Arran 274
Mercat Books, Highland 274
Mountaineering Books, London N 157
Muse Bookshop (The), Gwynedd 285
O'Reilly - Mountain Books (John), Derbyshire.. 83

Page (David), Lothian 276
Parrott Books, Oxfordshire 209
Peter M Daly, Hampshire 126
Pinnacle Books, Lothian............................ 276
Portus Books, Hampshire 122
Post–Horn Books, North Yorkshire............... 192
Quaritch Ltd., (Bernard), London W............. 174
R. & A. Books, East Sussex 101
Riddell (Peter), East Yorkshire 106
Rods Books, Devon................................... 88
Roz Hulse, Conwy 284
Scarthin Books, Derbyshire 82
Vandeleur Antiquarian Books, Surrey............ 231
Yewtree Books, Cumbria............................ 78

ALTERNATIVE MEDICINE
Alba Books, Grampian 273
Annie's Books, South Yorkshire 221
Cornucopia Books, Lincolnshire 151
Dales & Lakes Book Centre, Cumbria........... 79
Doolin Dinghy Books, Co. Clare 262
Ellwood Editions, Wiltshire 253
Esoteric Dreams Bookshop, Cumbria 77
Game Advice, Oxfordshire 208
Greensleeves, Oxfordshire 206
Hurst (Jenny), Kent 137
Inner Bookshop (The), Oxfordshire............... 208
Joel Segal Books, Devon 86
London & Sussex Antiquarian Book &
   Print Services, East Sussex 101
Lowe (John), Norfolk............................... 188
Needham Books, (Russell), Somerset............. 219
Occultique, Northamptonshire...................... 199
Old Celtic Bookshop (The), Devon 87
Oopalba Books, Cheshire............................ 71
Orchid Book Distributors, Co. Clare 262
Outcast Books, Herefordshire....................... 127
R. & A. Books, East Sussex 101
Reading Lasses, Dumfries & Galloway 270
Rebecca Hardie Rare Books, London W 171
Roundstone Books, Lancashire...................... 143
Till's Bookshop, Lothian............................ 277
Watkins Books Ltd., London WC.................. 179
Westwood Books Ltd, Cumbria.................... 80

AMATEUR RADIO [HAM RADIO]
Bookbarrow, Cambridgeshire........................ 63
R. & A. Books, East Sussex 101
Woodland Books, Devon............................. 84

AMERICAN INDIANS
Americanabooksuk, Cumbria........................ 76
Bookbarrow, Cambridgeshire........................ 63
Books, Denbighshire 284
Byre Books, Dumfries & Galloway................ 270
Chelifer Books, Cumbria 80
Clifford Elmer Books Ltd., Cheshire 68
Cofion Books, Pembrokeshire 286
Cornucopia Books, Lincolnshire 151
Dancing Goat Bookshop (The), Norfolk 187
Doolin Dinghy Books, Co. Clare 262
Eastcote Bookshop (The), London O 180
Emjay Books, Surrey................................. 231
Fireside Bookshop, Cumbria........................ 81
Hay Castle, Powys................................... 288

Inner Bookshop (The), Oxfordshire................ 208
Intech Books, Northumberland 201
Joel Segal Books, Devon 86
Marble Hill Books, Outer London................. 182
Michael Graves-Johnston, London SW 168
Needham Books, (Russell), Somerset.............. 219
Occultique, Northamptonshire...................... 199
Orchid Book Distributors, Co. Clare.............. 262
R. & A. Books, East Sussex 101
Roscrea Bookshop & Newsagents,
   Co. Tipperary 266
Scarthin Books, Derbyshire 82
Trinity Rare Books, Co. Leitrim 266
Watkins Books Ltd., London WC................. 179

AMERICAN NORTHWEST
Americanabooksuk, Cumbria........................ 76
Joel Segal Books, Devon 86
Michael Graves-Johnston, London SW 168
Roz Hulse, Conwy 284

AMERICAN REVOLUTION, THE
Adrem Books, Herts 130
Cofion Books, Pembrokeshire 286
J & J Burgess Booksellers, Cambridgeshire....... 64
Joel Segal Books, Devon 86
R. & A. Books, East Sussex 101

AMERICANA
- GENERAL
Addyman Books, Powys.............................. 287
Americanabooksuk, Cumbria........................ 76
Anglo-American Rare Books, Surrey............... 232
Apocalypse, Surrey.................................. 232
Booksets.com Ltd, Shropshire 214
Brad Books, Essex.................................. 110
Cavern Books, Cheshire 70
Clifford Elmer Books Ltd., Cheshire 68
Collectables (W.H.), Suffolk 229
Dancing Goat Bookshop (The), Norfolk 187
Discovery Bookshop, Carmarthenshire............ 281
Doolin Dinghy Books, Co. Clare 262
Ely Books, Cambridgeshire 65
Fireside Bookshop, Cumbria........................ 81
Hancock (Peter), West Sussex 241
Joel Segal Books, Devon 86
Knowles - Antiquary (Roger J.), Staffordshire... 223
Preston Book Company, Lancashire 144
Quaritch Ltd., (Bernard), London W............. 174
Shakeshaft (Dr. B.), Cheshire...................... 71
Winghale Books, Lincolnshire 152

- SOUTHWEST
Americanabooksuk, Cumbria........................ 76
Joel Segal Books, Devon 86

AMISH
Apocalypse, Surrey.................................. 232
Chapter Two, London SE........................... 163
Joel Segal Books, Devon 86

AMUSEMENTS
Jean Hedger, Berks 55
Joel Segal Books, Devon 86
Paramor (C.D.), Suffolk 228

R. & A. Books, East Sussex 101

ANATOMY

J & J Burgess Booksellers, Cambridgeshire....... 64
Joel Segal Books, Devon 86
Old Book Company, (The), West Yorkshire 248
Orchid Book Distributors, Co. Clare.............. 262
Phelps (Michael), West Sussex..................... 242
Pollak (P.M.), Devon 88
Quaritch Ltd., (Bernard), London W.............. 174
R M Books, Herts.................................. 132
R. & A. Books, East Sussex 101
Rebecca Hardie Rare Books, London W 171
Savona Books, Lincolnshire....................... 151
Watkins Books Ltd., London WC.................. 179
Weiner (Graham), London N 158

ANIMALS AND BIRDS

Adrem Books, Herts 130
Alauda Books, Cumbria............................. 76
Annie's Books, South Yorkshire 221
Apocalypse, Surrey 232
Backfold Books, Herefordshire..................... 127
Belfry Books, Nottinghamshire.................... 203
Besleys Books, Suffolk 225
Blest (Peter), Kent 138
BOOKS4U, Flintshire.............................. 284
Brock Books, North Yorkshire..................... 192
Calluna Books, Dorset.............................. 95
Camilla's Bookshop, East Sussex 101
Carningli Centre, Pembrokeshire................... 286
Chandos Books, Devon.............................. 85
Cheshire Book Centre, Cheshire.................... 69
Coch-y-Bonddu Books, Powys 290
Cofion Books, Pembrokeshire 286
Corfe Books, Surrey............................... 230
Cornucopia Books, Lincolnshire 151
Countryside Books, Hampshire 121
Dales & Lakes Book Centre, Cumbria............ 79
Delectus Books, London WC....................... 176
Demar Books (Grant), Kent....................... 140
Dolphin Books, Suffolk............................ 225
Dunkheld Antiques, Tayside....................... 279
Earth Science Books, Wiltshire.................... 252
Edmund Pollinger Rare Books, London SW..... 166
Esoteric Dreams Bookshop, Cumbria............. 77
Ford Books (David), Herts 130
Good for Books, Lincolnshire...................... 149
Goodyer (Nicholas), London N.................... 157
Grahame Thornton, Bookseller, Dorset.......... 93
Grayling (David A.H.), Cumbria 78
Greta Books, Durham 97
Inner Bookshop (The), Oxfordshire............... 208
Island Books, Devon............................... 85
J & J Burgess Booksellers, Cambridgeshire....... 64
Jack and Molly's Trading Co...................... 90
Jade Mountain Bookshop, Hampshire 125
Jane Jones Books, Grampian 273
Jay Books, Lothian................................ 276
Jenny Hurst, Kent................................. 138
Joel Segal Books, Devon 86
Junk & Spread Eagle, London SE 164
Karen Millward, Co. Cork......................... 263
Kelpie's Books, Fife 271
Kingfisher Book Service, Nottinghamshire 204

Mandalay Bookshop, London SW 168
Martin (Books and Pictures), (Brian P.)., Surrey. 231
Martin (Brian), Surrey 231
Martin's Books, Powys 290
Mayhew (Veronica), Berks 57
McCrone (Audrey), Isle of Arran.................. 274
McEwan Fine Books, Grampian.................... 272
Mercat Books, Highland 274
Mobbs (A.J.), West Midlands 239
Mr. Mac, Dumfries & Galloway 269
New Strand, The, Herefordshire 127
O'Flynn Books, North Yorkshire................... 197
Orb's Bookshop, Grampian........................ 273
Park Gallery & Bookshop (The), Northants 200
Parkinsons Books, Merseyside..................... 185
Parrott Books, Oxfordshire 209
Penny Farthing, The, Lothian 277
Peter M Daly, Hampshire.......................... 126
Phenotype Books, Cumbria 79
Popeley (Frank T.), Cambridgeshire............... 67
Prospect House Books, Co. Down................. 261
R. & A. Books, East Sussex 101
R.E. & G.B. Way, Suffolk 228
Richard Thornton Books, London N 158
Roland Books, Kent 138
Roz Hulse, Conwy 284
Saintfield Antiques & Fine Books, Co. Down ... 261
Sax Books, Suffolk 228
Scarthin Books, Derbyshire 82
Shakeshaft (Dr. B.), Cheshire..................... 71
Shearwater Books, Northumberland............... 201
Sue Lowell Natural History Books, London W . 175
Tarka Books, Devon............................... 84
Thin Read Line, Merseyside 184
Treasure Island (The), Greater Manchester....... 119
Trinity Rare Books, Co. Leitrim 266
Wheen O'Books, Borders.......................... 267
Wright Trace Books, West Midlands.............. 239

ANNUALS

Aardvark Books, Lincolnshire..................... 150
Annie's Books, South Yorkshire 221
Armchair Books, Lothian 275
Armstrong's Books & Collectables, Leicestershire 145
Art Book Company, (The), Suffolk................ 227
Big Bairn Books, Tayside 279
Book Palace (The), London SE 163
Bookmark (Children's Books), Wiltshire.......... 253
books2books, Devon............................... 88
BOOKS4U, Flintshire.............................. 284
Booth (Booksearch Service), (Geoff), Cheshire... 68
Brock Books, North Yorkshire..................... 192
Camilla's Bookshop, East Sussex 101
Catalyst Booksearch Services, Devon.............. 87
Cavern Books, Cheshire 70
Cheshire Book Centre, Cheshire.................... 69
Cofion Books, Pembrokeshire 286
D. & M. Books, West Glamorgan 249
Dales & Lakes Book Centre, Cumbria............ 79
Dawlish Books, Devon 86
Eastcote Bookshop (The), London O 180
Esoteric Dreams Bookshop, Cumbria............. 77
Fifteenth Century Bookshop (The), East Sussex. 104
firstpagebooks, Norfolk 189
Green Meadow Books, Cornwall 74

Hab Books, London W................................ 172
Hambleton Books, North Yorkshire 196
Ian Briddon, Derbyshire............................. 82
Intech Books, Northumberland 201
Jack and Molly's Trading Co....................... 90
Joel Segal Books, Devon 86
K Books, Cheshire.................................... 70
Katnap Arts, Norfolk................................ 190
Key Books (Sarah), Cambridgeshire.............. 64
Kineton Nooks, Warwickshire...................... 236
Lloyd-Davies (Sue), Carmarthenshire 282
March House Books, Somerset...................... 217
Moorhead Books, West Yorkshire.................. 245
Murphy (C.J.), Norfolk.............................. 189
Old Celtic Bookshop (The), Devon................ 87
Old Station Pottery & Bookshop (The), Norfolk 191
Park Gallery & Bookshop (The), Northants 200
Parker Books (Mike), Cambridgeshire 64
Penny Farthing, The, Lothian 277
Pickering Bookshop, North Yorkshire 196
R. & A. Books, East Sussex 101
Reeves Technical Books, North Yorkshire 195
Roland Books, Kent 138
Scrivener's Books & Bookbinding, Derbyshire... 82
Shacklock Books (David), Suffolk 226
Shakeshaft (Dr. B.), Cheshire...................... 71
Surprise Books, Gloucestershire 113
Tarka Books, Devon 84
The Old Children's Bookshelf, Lothian 277
Tiger Books, Kent 136
Till's Bookshop, Lothian 277
TP Children's Bookshop, West Yorkshire 245
Treasure Trove Books, Leicestershire.............. 146
Wheen O'Books, Borders............................ 267
Wiend Books, Lancashire 143
Williams (Bookdealer), (Richard),
  North Lincolnshire 153
Wright Trace Books, West Midlands.............. 239
Xanadu Books, Durham 98
Yorkshire Relics, West Yorkshire.................. 246

ANTHOLOGIES

Addyman Books, Powys.............................. 287
Carningli Centre, Pembrokeshire................... 286
Cornucopia Books, Lincolnshire 151
Cowley, Bookdealer (K.W.), Somerset 217
Dales & Lakes Book Centre, Cumbria............ 79
Dolphin Books, Suffolk............................. 225
Eggeling Books (John), West Yorkshire 249
Jackdaw Books, Norfolk 188
Kennedy & Farley, East Sussex 104
McCrone (Audrey), Isle of Arran 274
Poetry Bookshop (The), Powys..................... 289
R. & A. Books, East Sussex 101
Robert Temple, London N........................... 158

ANTHROPOLOGY

Afar Books International, West Midlands........ 238
Apocalypse, Surrey 232
Baker Limited (A.P. & R.),
  Dumfries & Galloway.......................... 269
Beaumont Travel Books, London SE 163
Bracton Books, Cambridgeshire.................... 63
Byre Books, Dumfries & Galloway................ 270
Chalmers Hallam (E.), Hampshire................. 125

Chesters (G. & J.), Staffordshire 224
David Warnes Books, Herefordshire 128
Delectus Books, London WC....................... 176
Dennys Sanders & Greene Ltd, East Sussex 100
Fireside Bookshop, Cumbria........................ 81
Game Advice, Oxfordshire 208
Garfi Books, Powys 291
J.C. Deyong Books (Previously of
  Snowden Smith Books), London SW 168
Joel Segal Books, Devon 86
Kenya Books, East Sussex 100
Kingswood Books, Dorset 94
Maghreb Bookshop (The), London WC.......... 177
Mandalay Bookshop, London SW 168
Michael Graves-Johnston, London SW 168
Old Book Company, (The), West Yorkshire 248
Peter M Daly, Hampshire........................... 126
Phelps (Michael), West Sussex..................... 242
Polczynski (Udo K.H.), Powys..................... 289
Pollak (P.M.), Devon 88
Portobello Books, London W....................... 174
Preston Book Company, Lancashire 144
R. & A. Books, East Sussex 101
Reading Lasses, Dumfries & Galloway 270
Rhodes, Bookseller (Peter), Hampshire 125
Salsus Books, Worcestershire 256
Stern Antiquarian Bookseller (Jeffrey), North
  Yorkshire.. 198
Watkins Books Ltd., London WC................... 179
Whitchurch Books Ltd., Cardiff.................... 281
Woburn Books, London N 159
Yesterday's Books, Dorset 92

ANTHROPOSOPHY

Anthroposophical Books, Gloucestershire 116
Byre Books, Dumfries & Galloway................ 270
Greensleeves, Oxfordshire 206
Inner Bookshop (The), Oxfordshire................ 208
Joel Segal Books, Devon 86
Reads, Dorset 95
Star Lord Books, Greater Manchester 119
Watkins Books Ltd., London WC................... 179

ANTIQUARIAN

Addyman Books, Powys.............................. 287
Adrem Books, Herts 130
Al Saqi Books, London W........................... 171
Alastor Rare Books, Hampshire.................... 124
Alec–Smith Books (Alex), East Yorkshire 107
Allsop (Duncan M.), Warwickshire................ 237
Altea Antique Maps & Books, London W....... 171
Anthony W. Laywood, Nottinghamshire 203
Antiquary Ltd., (Bar Bookstore), N Yorks...... 194
Antique Map and Bookshop (The), Dorset 94
Any Amount of Books, London WC 176
Apocalypse, Surrey 232
Arden, Bookseller (C.), Powys..................... 287
Ardis Books, Hampshire 126
Arnold (Roy), Suffolk............................... 227
Art Reference Books, Hampshire 124
Atholl Fine Books, Tayside 280
Austwick Hall Books, North Yorkshire.......... 192
Autolycus, Shropshire............................... 212
Axe Rare & Out of Print Books (Richard),
  N Yorkshire 193

Baldwin (Jack), Strathclyde 278
Baldwin's Scientific Books, Essex 111
Bardsley's Books, Suffolk.............................. 225
Barmby (C. & A.J.), Kent............................. 140
Bates & Hindmarch, West Yorkshire.............. 248
Bath Old Books, Somerset 215
Baxter (Steve), Surrey 233
Baynton–Williams Gallery, West Sussex 241
Beardsell Books, West Yorkshire.................. 246
Beaton (Richard), East Sussex...................... 103
Beckham Books Ltd., Suffolk 229
Bernstein (Nicholas), London W.................. 171
Bertram Rota Ltd., London WC 176
Bibliopola, London NW.............................. 160
Biblipola, London NW............................... 160
Blackwell's Rare Books, Oxfordshire.............. 208
Book Business (The), London W 171
Bookcase, Cumbria.................................... 76
Booklore, Leicestershire.............................. 146
Bookmark (Children's Books), Wiltshire.......... 253
Books at Star Dot Star, West Midlands 240
Books on Spain, London O.......................... 182
Books Only, Suffolk.................................. 226
BOOKS4U, Flintshire................................. 284
Booksets.com Ltd, Shropshire...................... 214
Bookshop (The), Co. Donegal....................... 263
Bookshop, Kirkstall (The), West Yorkshire 248
BookShop, The, Dumfries & Galloway 270
Bookstand, Dorset..................................... 94
Booth (Booksearch Service), (Geoff), Cheshire... 68
Bow Windows Book Shop, East Sussex 103
Bowie Books & Collectables, East Yorkshire 107
Brad Books, Essex..................................... 110
Brinded (Scott), Kent 138
Brock Books, North Yorkshire..................... 192
Bunyan Books, Bedfordshire........................ 53
Burak (Steve), London WC......................... 176
Butler Rare Books, Buckinghamshire 61
Byblos Antiquarian & Rare Book, Hampshire .. 122
C J Renwick Books, Powys.......................... 287
Camden Books, Somerset 215
Capital Bookshop, Cardiff........................... 281
Castle Hill Books, Herefordshire................... 128
Celtic Bookshop (The), Co. Limerick 266
Chandos Books, Devon............................... 85
Channel Islands Galleries Limited,
    Channel Islands 258
Chapter & Verse, Lincolnshire...................... 150
Chelifer Books, Cumbria 80
Cheshire Book Centre, Cheshire................... 69
Chris Phillips, Wiltshire............................. 252
Clent Books, Worcestershire........................ 255
Clifford Elmer Books Ltd., Cheshire 68
Cobnar Books, Kent 141
Cobweb Books, North Yorkshire 194
Coch-y-Bonddu Books, Powys 290
Cofion Books, Pembrokeshire 286
Colin Hancock, Ceredigion 282
Collectable Books, London SE...................... 163
Cooper Hay Rare Books, Strathclyde 278
Courtenay Bookroom, Oxfordshire................. 205
Courtney & Hoff, North Yorkshire................. 197
Cox Old & Rare Books (Claude), Suffolk 227
Cox Rare Books (Charles), Cornwall.............. 73
Cox, Andrew, Shropshire............................ 214

Craobh Rua Books, Co. Armagh................... 260
Crouch Rare Books, Surrey.......................... 232
Daeron's Books, Buckinghamshire................. 62
Dales & Lakes Book Centre, Cumbria........... 79
Dartmoor Book Gallery, Devon 87
Dartmoor Bookshop (The), Devon............... 84
Dave Jelfs, Devon 85
David (G.), Cambridgeshire......................... 63
davidleesbooks.com, Herefordshire 127
Dean Byass, Bristol.................................. 60
Debbage (John), Norfolk............................ 189
Delph Books, Greater Manchester................. 120
Dennys Sanders & Greene Ltd, East Sussex 100
Derek Stirling Bookseller, Kent 141
Drury Rare Books (John), Essex................... 110
Dublin Bookbrowsers, Co. Dublin................. 265
Duncan & Reid, Lothian............................. 276
Dylans Bookstore, Swansea 291
Eagle Bookshop (The), Bedfordshire 53
Early Times, Guernsey, Channel Islands......... 258
Earth Science Books, Wiltshire.................... 252
Eastleach Books, Berks 56
Eastwood Books (David), Cornwall 72
Eclectica, London SE 164
Eggle (Mavis), Herts 130
Ellwood Editions, Wiltshire 253
Ely Books, Cambridgeshire 65
Eton Antique Bookshop, Berks 57
Evans Books (Paul), West Sussex 243
Farahar & Dupre (Clive & Sophie), Wiltshire ... 251
Farquharson, (Hilary), Tayside..................... 280
Farringdon (J.M.), Swansea......................... 291
Fenning (James), Co. Dublin 265
Finch Rare Books Ltd. (Simon), London W..... 172
Fine Books at Ilkley, West Yorkshire 247
Fireside Bookshop, Cumbria........................ 81
Fletcher (H.M.), Herts 131
Forest Books, Nottinghamshire 204
Foster (Stephen), London NW 160
Foster Bookshop (Paul), London SW 167
Fosters Bookshop, London W 172
Fotheringham (Alex), Northumberland 201
Fox Books (J. & J.), Kent........................... 139
Freeman's Corner Shop, Norfolk 189
Frew Limited (Robert), London SW 167
G. C. Books Ltd., Dumfries & Galloway......... 270
Gardener & Cook, London SW..................... 167
Gibbs Books, (Jonathan), Worcestershire......... 256
Gilbert and Son (H.M.), Hampshire............... 126
Gillmark Gallery, Herts.............................. 130
Glenbower Books, Co. Dublin 264
Golden Books Group, Devon 85
Good for Books, Lincolnshire 149
Goodyer, Natural History Books (Eric), Leics... 146
Gowan Books (John), Co. Fermanagh............. 261
Grahame Thornton, Bookseller, Dorset........... 93
Grant & Shaw Ltd., Lothian 276
Grant Books, Worcestershire 255
Green Man Books, East Sussex 101
Gresham Books, Somerset 217
Greta Books, Durham 97
Grove Bookshop (The), North Yorkshire 195
Guildmaster Books, Cheshire....................... 70
Hamish Riley-Smith, Norfolk....................... 191
Hanborough Books, Oxfordshire................... 208

Hancock (Peter), West Sussex 241
Hanshan Tang Books, London SW 167
Harrington (Adrian), London W.................. 173
Harrington Antiquarian Bookseller (Peter),
   London SW.. 167
Hava Books, London SE........................... 164
Hawkes (James), London............................ 164
Hennessey Bookseller (Ray), East Sussex 100
Heritage, West Midlands 238
Hilton (Books) (P.J.), London W 173
Hodgson (Judith), London W 173
Hollett and Son (R.F.G.), Cumbria 79
Holtom (Christopher), Gloucestershire............ 115
Horsham Rare Books, West Sussex 242
House of Figgis Ltd (The), Co. Galway 265
Howes Bookshop, East Sussex 102
Humber Books, Lincolnshire 148
Hutchison (Books) (Larry), Fife................... 271
Ian Briddon, Derbyshire............................. 82
Ian Marr Rare Books, Cornwall 73
Island Books, Devon................................. 85
Jackson (M.W.), Wiltshire.......................... 254
Jade Mountain Bookshop, Hampshire 125
Jarndyce Antiquarian Booksellers, London WC. 177
Jay Books, Lothian.................................... 276
JB Books & Collectables, West Sussex 243
Joel Segal Books, Devon 86
John Underwood Antiquarian Books, Norfolk.. 189
Joppa Books Ltd., Surrey 230
Junk & Spread Eagle, London SE................. 164
Just Books, Cornwall 75
Karen Thomson, Oxfordshire...................... 209
Kay Books, London W............................... 173
Keel Row Bookshop, Tyne and Wear 235
Kemp Bookseller, Michael S, G Manchester..... 118
Kerr (Norman), Cumbria 77
Kilgarriff (Raymond), East Sussex 105
Kim's Bookshop, West Sussex...................... 241
Kim's Bookshop, West Sussex...................... 242
Kingswood Books, Dorset 94
Kirkman Ltd., (Robert), Bedfordshire............ 54
Knowles - Antiquary (Roger J.), Staffordshire... 223
Korn (M. Eric), London N 157
Lake (David), Norfolk............................... 190
Lawson & Company (E.M.), Oxfordshire 206
Leo Cadogan, London N 157
Liddle (Steve), Bristol 58
Lymelight Books & Prints, Dorset 93
Madoc Books, Conwy 284
Mandalay Bookshop, London SW 168
Marble Hill Books, Outer London................. 182
Marine & Cannon Books, Cheshire 71
Marine and Cannon Books, Cheshire 69
Martin (Brian), Surrey 231
Martin Bookshop & Gallery (Richard), Hants... 123
McConnell Fine Books, Kent....................... 137
McCrone (Audrey), Isle of Arran 274
McNaughtan's Bookshop, Lothian 276
Mermaid Books (Burlingham), Norfolk.......... 191
Michael Graves-Johnston, London SW 168
Michael J Carroll, Co. Cork 263
Miller (Stephen), London O 183
Minster Gate Bookshop, North Yorkshire 197
Moore (C.R.), Shropshire 213
Moorside Books, Lancashire....................... 143

Much Binding, Norfolk.............................. 186
Murphy (C.J.), Norfolk.............................. 189
Muttonchop Manuscripts, West Sussex 242
N V Books, Warwickshire........................... 236
N1 Books, East Sussex 105
Neil Summersgill, Lancashire....................... 142
Nibris Books, London SW........................... 169
Norton Books, North Yorkshire................... 192
Offa's Dyke Books, Shropshire 213
O'Flynn Books, North Yorkshire................. 197
Old Book Company, (The), West Yorkshire 248
Pagan Limited (Hugh), Hants 122
Park Gallery & Bookshop (The), Northants 200
Parker Books (Mike), Cambridgeshire 64
Parkinsons Books, Merseyside...................... 185
Paul Hoare, Cornwall 74
Pemberley Books, Buckinghamshire.............. 62
Period & Classical Collections, East Sussex 103
Peter M Daly, Hants................................. 126
Phelps (Michael), West Sussex..................... 242
Phillips (Nigel), Hants............................... 122
Poetry Bookshop (The), Powys..................... 289
Potterton Books, North Yorkshire................. 196
Preston Book Company, Lancashire 144
Price (John), London N 158
Pringle Booksellers (Andrew), Lothian 277
PsychoBabel Books & Journals, Oxfordshire..... 205
Quaritch Ltd., (Bernard), London W.............. 174
R. & A. Books, East Sussex 101
Rayner (Hugh Ashley), Somerset 215
Red Star Books, Herts............................... 129
Rhos Point Books, Conwy 283
Richard Thornton Books, London N 158
Robert Temple, London N........................... 158
Roberts Fine Books (Julian), Lincolnshire........ 151
Robertshaw (John), Cambridgeshire.............. 66
Robin Doughty - Fine Books, West Midlands... 238
Rochdale Book Company, Greater Manchester . 120
Roger Collicott Books, Cornwall 74
Roger Treglown, Cheshire 70
Rosley Books, Cumbria 81
Rothwell & Dunworth, Somerset 217
Rowan (H. & S.J.), Dorset 91
Rowan (P. & B.), Co. Antrim 260
Roz Hulse, Conwy 284
Rye Old Books, East Sussex 104
St Philip's Books, Oxfordshire..................... 208
Scarthin Books, Derbyshire 82
Schull Books, Co. Cork 262
Scrivener's Books & Bookbinding, Derbyshire... 82
Seabreeze Books, Lancashire....................... 144
Seydi Rare Books (Sevin), London NW 161
Sillan Books, Co. Cavan............................ 262
Sims Reed Limited, London SW................... 169
Smith (Clive), Essex 109
South Downs Book Service, West Sussex......... 243
Spelman (Ken), North Yorkshire 198
Spenceley Books (David), West Yorkshire........ 248
Spooner & Co, Somerset 219
Staniland (Booksellers), Lincolnshire 152
Stella Books, Monmouthshire 286
Sterling Books, Somerset 220
Stern Antiquarian Bookseller (Jeffrey), North
   Yorkshire... 198
Stone, (G.& R.), Borders 267

Stothert Old Books, Cheshire........................ 68
Susanne Schulz-Falster Rare Books, London N. 158
Taney Books, Co. Dublin 263
Taylor & Son (Peter), Herts........................ 132
The Old Abbey Bookshop, Co. Down 261
Thomas Rare Books, Suffolk 226
Thornber (Peter M.), North Yorkshire............ 195
Thorntons of Oxford Ltd., Oxfordshire........... 206
Tiger Books, Kent..................................... 136
Tim Bryers Ltd, London WC 178
Tombland Bookshop, Norfolk 190
Tooley, Adams & Co, Oxfordshire 209
Trade Priced Old Books, Powys................... 289
Trinity Rare Books, Co. Leitrim 266
Turton (John), Durham 98
ULoveBooks, Devon.................................. 90
Unsworth's Booksellers, Suffolk.................... 225
Vandeleur Antiquarian Books, Surrey............. 231
Venables (Morris & Juliet), Bristol................ 59
Ventnor Rare Books, Isle of Wight............... 134
Vinovium Books, Durham 97
Wadard Books, Kent 137
Waterfield's, Oxfordshire 209
Watkins Books Ltd., London WC 179
Weiner (Graham), London N 158
Wembdon Books, Somerset 216
Westcountry Oldbooks, Devon...................... 90
Westfield Books, North Yorkshire................. 198
Westwood Books Ltd, Cumbria.................... 80
Whitchurch Books Ltd., Cardiff.................... 281
Wilbraham (J. & S.), London NW 162
Winchester Bookshop (The), Hants............... 126
Woburn Books, London N 159
Worcester Rare Books, Worcestershire............ 256
Words Etcetera Bookshop, Dorset................. 93
Worlds End Bookshop, London SW 169
Ximenes Rare Books Inc., Gloucestershire 115
Yates Antiquarian Books (Tony), Leics........... 146
Yesterday's Books, Dorset 92
York (Graham), Devon.............................. 86

ANTIQUE PAPER

Antique Prints of the World, London N.......... 156
Chas J. Sawyer, Kent 140
Early Times, Guernsey, Channel Islands.......... 258
Embleton (Paul), Essex 111
Hava Books, London SE............................. 164
Period & Classical Collections, East Sussex 103

ANTIQUE STOVES

Buckland Books, West Sussex 243
Randall (Tom), Somerset........................... 218
Stroh (M.A.), London E 154

ANTIQUES

Abacus Books, Greater Manchester 118
Abrahams (Mike), Staffordshire.................... 223
Addyman Books, Powys.............................. 287
Ancient Art Books, London SW 166
Annie's Books, South Yorkshire 221
Anthony Vickers Books, North Yorkshire 195
Antiques on High, Oxfordshire..................... 207
Apocalypse, Surrey 232
Arden Books & Cosmographia, Warwickshire... 236
Arnold (Roy), Suffolk............................... 227

Art Reference Books, Hants 124
Autumn Leaves, Lincolnshire....................... 150
Aviabooks, Gloucestershire 114
Axe Rare & Out of Print Books (Richard),
    North Yorkshire 193
baconboooks, London WC 176
Barmby (C. & A.J.), Kent.......................... 140
Bookcase, Cumbria 76
Books & Collectables Ltd., Cambridgeshire 63
BookShop, The, Dumfries & Galloway........... 270
Bookworms Paradise Ltd., West Sussex 242
Browse Books, Lancashire 143
Browzers, Greater Manchester...................... 118
Buckland Books, West Sussex 243
Carningli Centre, Pembrokeshire................... 286
Chaucer Bookshop, Kent............................ 136
Cheshire Book Centre, Cheshire.................... 69
Chichester Bookshop (The), Herefordshire 241
Chris Phillips, Wiltshire............................. 252
Clark (Nigel A.), London SE....................... 163
Cobbles Books, Somerset............................ 217
Cofion Books, Pembrokeshire 286
Corfe Books, Surrey................................. 230
Cornucopia Books, Lincolnshire.................... 151
Crabtree (Mrs. C.), Greater Manchester 120
Delectus Books, London WC....................... 176
Don Kelly Books, London W 172
Duncan & Reid, Lothian............................ 276
Early Times, Guernsey, Channel Islands.......... 258
Eastcote Bookshop (The), London O 180
Eastgate Bookshop, East Yorkshire 106
Eton Antique Bookshop, Berks 57
Exeter's Antiques Centre on the Quay, Devon... 86
Foster (Stephen), London NW 160
Golden Goose Books, Lincolnshire................. 150
Gresham Books, Somerset 217
Hadfield (G.K.), Cumbria........................... 79
Hanshan Tang Books, London SW 167
Heneage Art Books (Thomas), London SW 168
Hennessey Bookseller (Ray), East Sussex 100
Hollett and Son (R.F.G.), Cumbria 79
Hornsey's, North Yorkshire......................... 194
Jackson (M.W.), Wiltshire.......................... 254
Jade Mountain Bookshop, Hants 125
Jane & John Kinnaird, Cumbria.................... 78
Joel Segal Books, Devon 86
Katharine House Gallery, Wiltshire 252
Keeble Antiques, Somerset.......................... 218
Kennedy (Peter), Surrey 234
Keswick Bookshop, Cumbria........................ 78
Kingfisher Book Service, Nottinghamshire 204
Leabeck Books, Oxfordshire........................ 208
Malvern Bookshop (The), Worcestershire 255
Martin (Books and Pictures), (Brian P.), Surrey. 231
Martin (Brian), Surrey 231
Milestone Publications Goss & Crested
    China, Hants 123
Moss End Bookshop, Berks 57
Muttonchop Manuscripts, West Sussex 242
Nelson (Elizabeth), Suffolk......................... 226
New Strand, The, Herefordshire 127
Nibris Books, London SW.......................... 169
Offa's Dyke Books, Shropshire..................... 213
O'Flynn Books, North Yorkshire................... 197
Old Book Company, (The), West Yorkshire 248

Park Gallery & Bookshop (The), Northants 200
Pauline Harries Books, Hants 123
Peter M Daly, Hants................................ 126
Petworth Antique Market (Bookroom),
  West Sussex... 244
Phelan Books, Co. Dublin 264
Phillips of Hitchin (Antiques) Ltd., Herts........ 131
Pordes Books Ltd., (Henry), London WC........ 177
Potterton Books, North Yorkshire................ 196
Quadrille at Delehar, London W.................. 174
R. & A. Books, East Sussex 101
Rees & O'Neill Rare Books, London WC........ 178
Reference Works Ltd., Dorset 95
Roland Books, Kent 138
Rowan (H. & S.J.), Dorset.......................... 91
Saintfield Antiques & Fine Books, Co. Down ... 261
Sax Books, Suffolk 228
Smith Books, (Sally), Suffolk 226
Stothert Old Books, Cheshire...................... 68
Strathtay Antiquarian - Secondhand Books,
  Tayside 280
Studio Bookshop, East Sussex 100
Tarka Books, Devon 84
The Glass Key, West Yorkshire.................... 246
Thin Read Line, Merseyside 184
Treasure Island (The), Greater Manchester....... 119
Trinders' Fine Tools, Suffolk 226
Uncle Phil's Books, West Midlands 239
Ventnor Rare Books, Isle of Wight................ 134
Whittle, Bookseller (Avril), Cumbria 80
Worlds End Bookshop, London SW 169
www.AntiqueWatchStore.com, Herts.............. 129
Wychwood Books, Gloucestershire 116

ANTIQUITIES
Apocalypse, Surrey 232
BOOKS4U, Flintshire.............................. 284
Cofion Books, Pembrokeshire 286
Don Kelly Books, London W 172
Eastern Traveller (The), Somerset................. 219
Hanshan Tang Books, London SW 167
Hava Books, London SE............................ 164
Joel Segal Books, Devon 86
Keith Langford, London E 154
McCrone (Audrey), Isle of Arran 274
Michael Graves-Johnston, London SW 168
N1 Books, East Sussex 105
O'Flynn Books, North Yorkshire 197
Parkinsons Books, Merseyside...................... 185
Price (John), London N 158
R. & A. Books, East Sussex 101
Seydi Rare Books (Sevin), London NW 161
Thorntons of Oxford Ltd., Oxfordshire........... 206
Trinity Rare Books, Co. Leitrim 266
Whitchurch Books Ltd., Cardiff.................... 281
Wychwood Books, Gloucestershire 116

ANTI-SEMITISM
Joel Segal Books, Devon 86

APICULTURE
Arden, Bookseller (C.), Powys...................... 287
Bunyan Books, Bedfordshire........................ 53
Edmund Pollinger Rare Books, London SW..... 166
Joel Segal Books, Devon 86

Mayhew (Veronica), Berks 57

APPLIED ART
Amwell Book Company, London EC.............. 155
Ancient Art Books, London SW.................. 166
Anthony Whittaker, Kent 135
Arnold (Roy), Suffolk.............................. 227
Ars Artis, Oxfordshire 207
Art Reference Books, Hants 124
Artco, Nottinghamshire............................ 204
Aviabooks, Gloucestershire 114
Barmby (C. & A.J.), Kent.......................... 140
Batterham (David), London W..................... 171
Books & Things, London W........................ 171
Bruce Holdsworth Books, East Sussex 105
Butts Books (Mary), Berks.......................... 56
C J Renwick Books, Powys........................ 287
Cheshire Book Centre, Cheshire.................... 69
Cornucopia Books, Lincolnshire 151
Cover to Cover, Merseyside......................... 185
Decorum Books, London N 156
Dew (Roderick), East Sussex 101
Eastleach Books, Berks.............................. 56
Fosters Bookshop, London W 172
Handsworth Books, Essex 112
Hay Cinema Bookshop Ltd., Powys.............. 288
Heneage Art Books (Thomas), London SW 168
Hennessey Bookseller (Ray), East Sussex 100
High Street Books, Devon 86
Hodgkins and Company Limited (Ian),
  Gloucestershire 116
IDEA, London EC.................................. 155
Island Books, Devon................................ 85
Jane & John Kinnaird, Cumbria 78
Joel Segal Books, Devon 86
Judith Mansfield, West Yorkshire 249
Keith Langford, London E 154
Keswick Bookshop, Cumbria........................ 78
Mannwaring (M.G.), Bristol 59
Martin - Bookseller (Colin), East Yorkshire 107
McNaughtan's Bookshop, Lothian 276
N1 Books, East Sussex 105
Nelson (Elizabeth), Suffolk 226
Oopalba Books, Cheshire............................ 71
Pagan Limited (Hugh), Hants 122
Peter M Daly, Hants................................ 126
Phillips of Hitchin (Antiques) Ltd., Herts........ 131
Potterton Books, North Yorkshire................ 196
R. & A. Books, East Sussex 101
Ray Rare and Out of Print Books (Janette),
  North Yorkshire 198
Reads, Dorset 95
Rees & O'Neill Rare Books, London WC........ 178
Scrivener's Books & Bookbinding, Derbyshire... 82
Sleepy Elephant Books & Artefacts, Cumbria ... 80
Spelman (Ken), North Yorkshire 198
Staniland (Booksellers), Lincolnshire 152
Tasburgh Books, Norfolk 190
Trinders' Fine Tools, Suffolk 226
Wyseby House Books, Berks 55

APPRAISALS & VALUATIONS
Book Business (The), London W 171
Chapter Two, London SE............................ 163
Church Street Books, Norfolk...................... 186

Liddle (Steve), Bristol 58
Martin (Books and Pictures), (Brian P.), Surrey . 231
Sax Books, Suffolk 228
Slightly Foxed on Gloucester Road, London SW 167
Thornber (Peter M.), North Yorkshire............ 195
Watkins (R.G.), Somerset 215

AQUATICS
Kelpie's Books, Fife.................................. 271
Parkinsons Books, Merseyside...................... 185
R. & A. Books, East Sussex 101
Steven Simpson Books, Norfolk 190

ARABICA
Al Saqi Books, London W 171
Apocalypse, Surrey 232
Bonham (J. & S.L.), London W 171
Delectus Books, London WC...................... 176
Hamish Riley-Smith, Norfolk...................... 191
Joppa Books Ltd., Surrey 230
Marcet Books, London SE.......................... 164
Needham Books, (Russell), Somerset.............. 219
Quaritch Ltd., (Bernard), London W............. 174
R. & A. Books, East Sussex 101
Thorntons of Oxford Ltd., Oxfordshire........... 206
Watkins Books Ltd., London WC................. 179

ARACHNOLOGY
Antique Map and Bookshop (The), Dorset 94
Lymelight Books & Prints, Dorset................. 93
Parkinsons Books, Merseyside...................... 185
Savona Books, Lincolnshire......................... 151

ARCHAEOLOGY
Addyman Books, Powys............................. 287
Alauda Books, Cumbria 76
Ancient Art Books, London SW 166
Antiquary Ltd., (Bar Bookstore), N Yorkshire .. 194
Apocalypse, Surrey 232
Atlantis Bookshop, London WC................... 176
B D McManmon, Lancashire 144
Baker Limited (A.P. & R.), Dumfries
  & Galloway....................................... 269
Baldwin's Scientific Books, Essex 111
Barmby (C. & A.J.), Kent........................... 140
Barn Books, Buckinghamshire....................... 61
Beaumont Travel Books, London SE 163
Biff Books and Records, South Yorkshire........ 221
Bonython Bookshop, Cornwall..................... 75
Books B.C., London O 180
Bosco Books, Cornwall............................... 72
Bosorne Books, Cornwall 75
Bracton Books, Cambridgeshire.................... 63
Brad Books, Essex 110
Brock Books, North Yorkshire..................... 192
Buckland Books, West Sussex 243
Burebank Books, Norfolk............................ 186
Castle Bookshop, Essex.............................. 108
Castle Bookshop, Powys............................. 290
Castle Hill Books, Herefordshire................... 128
Charlie Byrne's Bookshop, Co. Galway........... 265
Cheshire Book Centre, Cheshire.................... 69
Classics Bookshop (The), Oxfordshire............. 205
Clements (R.W.), London O........................ 181
Colin Hancock, Ceredigion 282

Colonsay Bookshop, Isle of Colonsay............. 275
Corfe Books, Surrey.................................. 230
Cornucopia Books, Lincolnshire 151
Crouch Rare Books, Surrey......................... 232
D'Arcy Books, Wiltshire............................. 252
Earth Science Books, Wiltshire 252
Eastgate Bookshop, East Yorkshire 106
Ellwood Editions, Wiltshire 253
Ford Books (David), Herts 130
Freeman's Corner Shop, Norfolk 189
G. C. Books Ltd., Dumfries & Galloway......... 270
Garfi Books, Powys 291
GfB: the Colchester Bookshop, Essex 108
Gildas Books, Cheshire 68
Gladstone Books, Lincolnshire 150
Golden Age Books, Worcestershire................ 256
Green Man Books, East Sussex 101
Hall's Bookshop, Kent............................... 140
Hanshan Tang Books, London SW 167
Hava Books, London SE............................. 164
Ian Marr Rare Books, Cornwall 73
Idle Genius Books, London N 157
Island Books, Devon 85
J & J Burgess Booksellers, Cambridgeshire....... 64
Jackdaw Books, Norfolk............................. 188
Jade Mountain Bookshop, Hants 125
Joel Segal Books, Devon 86
John Barton, Hants 126
Joppa Books Ltd., Surrey 230
Just Books, Cornwall 75
Kingswood Books, Dorset 94
Larkham Books (Patricia), Gloucestershire....... 117
Lowe (John), Norfolk................................ 188
Maghreb Bookshop (The), London WC.......... 177
Mannwaring (M.G.), Bristol 59
McCrone (Audrey), Isle of Arran.................. 274
medievalbookshop, Herts............................ 132
Mercat Books, Highland 274
Michael Graves-Johnston, London SW 168
Minster Gate Bookshop, North Yorkshire 197
Mulyan (Don), Merseyside........................... 185
N1 Books, East Sussex 105
Nevis Railway Bookshops (The Antique &
  Book Collector), Wiltshire......................... 252
Nonsuch Books, Surrey.............................. 234
Not Just Books, Dorset............................... 94
Old Station Pottery & Bookshop (The), Norfolk 191
P. and P. Books, Worcestershire 256
Parkinsons Books, Merseyside...................... 185
Parrott Books, Oxfordshire 209
Penny Farthing, The, Lothian 277
Peter M Daly, Hants................................. 126
Polczynski (Udo K.H.), Powys 289
Pordes Books Ltd., (Henry), London WC........ 177
Prospect House Books, Co. Down................. 261
Quaritch Ltd., (Bernard), London W............. 174
Quest Books, East Yorkshire 107
R. & A. Books, East Sussex 101
Reads, Dorset 95
Rickaro Books, West Yorkshire..................... 246
Roland Books, Kent 138
St Mary's Books & Prints, Lincolnshire 152
Samovar Books, Co. Dublin 264
Scott (Peter), East Sussex........................... 104
Scrivener's Books & Bookbinding, Derbyshire... 82

Spooner & Co, Somerset 219
Stalagluft Books, Tyne and Wear 235
Staniland (Booksellers), Lincolnshire 152
Taylor & Son (Peter), Herts......................... 132
Thorntons of Oxford Ltd., Oxfordshire 206
Tombland Bookshop, Norfolk 190
Trinity Rare Books, Co. Leitrim 266
Uncle Phil's Books, West Midlands 239
Westwood Books Ltd, Cumbria.................... 80
Whitchurch Books Ltd., Cardiff.................... 281
Winchester Bookshop (The), Hants................ 126
Winghale Books, Lincolnshire 152

ARCHAEOLOGY - INDUSTRIAL

Allinson (Frank & Stella), Warwickshire 236
Anthony Vickers Books, North Yorkshire 195
Baker Limited (A.P. & R.), Dumfries &
    Galloway.. 269
Bott, (Bookdealers) Ltd., (Martin), Greater
    Manchester 118
Browsers Bookshop, Cornwall...................... 72
Castle Bookshop, Powys............................. 290
Chris Phillips, Wiltshire............................. 252
Cornucopia Books, Lincolnshire 151
Cox (Geoff), Devon 90
Dales and Lakes Book Centre, Cumbria.......... 79
Debbage (John), Norfolk............................ 189
Joel Segal Books, Devon 86
Kingswood Books, Dorset 94
Liddle (Steve), Bristol 58
Randall (Tom), Somerset 218
Robert Humm & Co, Lincolnshire 152
Salway Books, Essex 112
Sturford Books, Wiltshire 254
Whitchurch Books Ltd., Cardiff.................... 281
Wiend Books, Lancashire 143

ARCHITECTURE

A. & H. Peasgood, Cambridgeshire 66
Abacus Books, Greater Manchester 118
Acanthophyllum Books, Wirral 184
Addyman Books, Powys.............................. 287
Al Saqi Books, London W........................... 171
Amwell Book Company, London EC.............. 155
Anne Harris Books & Bags Booksearch, Devon 88
Anthony Vickers Books, North Yorkshire 195
Antiquary Ltd., (Bar Bookstore), N Yorkshire .. 194
Antique Map and Bookshop (The), Dorset 94
Antiques on High, Oxfordshire..................... 207
Apocalypse, Surrey 232
Ars Artis, Oxfordshire 207
Art Book Company, (The), Suffolk................ 227
Art Reference Books, Hants 124
Aviabooks, Gloucestershire 114
Ballantyne–Way (Roger), Suffolk 228
Barmby (C. & A.J.), Kent........................... 140
Batterham (David), London W...................... 171
Bennett & Kerr Books, Oxfordshire 205
Bermondsey Basement Bookstore, London SE .. 163
Bianco Library, West Sussex....................... 241
Birchden Books, London E 154
Book Business (The), London W 171
Bookroom (The), Surrey............................. 233
Books, Kent 137
Booth (Booksearch Service), (Geoff), Cheshire... 68
Bosco Books, Cornwall.............................. 72
Brad Books, Essex.................................... 110
Brazenhead Ltd., Norfolk 188
Brighton Books, East Sussex........................ 99
Broadhurst of Southport Ltd., Merseyside 185
Buckland Books, West Sussex 243
Butts Books (Mary), Berks.......................... 56
C J Renwick Books, Powys......................... 287
Camden Books, Somerset 215
Carraig Books Ltd., Co. Dublin 263
Castle Bookshop, Powys............................. 290
Chandos Books, Devon............................... 85
Chapter & Verse, Lincolnshire...................... 150
Charlie Byrne's Bookshop, Co. Galway........... 265
Chevin Books, West Yorkshire...................... 249
Chris Phillips, Wiltshire............................. 252
Classic Bindings Ltd, London SW 166
Clevedon Books, Somerset 217
Coach House Books, Worcestershire 256
Collectable Books, London SE 163
Coombes (A.J.), Surrey.............................. 230
Corfe Books, Surrey.................................. 230
Cornucopia Books, Lincolnshire 151
Cottage Books, Leics................................. 145
Country Books, Derbyshire 82
Courtney & Hoff, North Yorkshire................ 197
Cover to Cover, Merseyside......................... 185
Crouch Rare Books, Surrey.......................... 232
D'Arcy Books, Wiltshire............................. 252
Darkwood Books, Co. Cork......................... 263
Dartmoor Bookshop (The), Devon 84
Debbage (John), Norfolk............................ 189
Decorum Books, London N 156
Dew (Roderick), East Sussex 101
Duck (William), Hants............................... 124
Edwards (London) Limited (Francis),
    London WC.. 176
Edwards in Hay–on–Wye (Francis), Powys 288
Elton Engineering Books, London W 172
Empire Books, North Yorkshire 197
English (Toby), Oxfordshire......................... 209
Farquharson, (Hilary), Tayside...................... 280
Forest Books of Manchester, Cheshire............ 70
Foster (Stephen), London NW 160
Fosters Bookshop, London W 172
Fotheringham (Alex), Northumberland 201
Freeman's Corner Shop, Norfolk................... 189
G. C. Books Ltd., Dumfries & Galloway......... 270
George St. Books, Derbyshire 83
GfB: the Colchester Bookshop, Essex 108
Gladstone Books, Lincolnshire 150
Good for Books, Lincolnshire 149
Goodyer (Nicholas), London N 157
Gravity Books, Lincolnshire 149
Gresham Books, Somerset 217
Greta Books, Durham 97
Grove Bookshop (The), North Yorkshire 195
Hall's Bookshop, Kent............................... 140
Hanshan Tang Books, London SW 167
Harrington Antiquarian Bookseller (Peter),
    London SW.. 167
Harwich Old Books, Essex.......................... 109
Haskell (R.H. & P.), Dorset 94
Hay Castle, Powys.................................... 288
Hedgerow Books, South Yorkshire................ 221

Helmsley Antiquarian & Secondhand Books,
North Yorkshire 193
Heywood Hill Limited (G.), London W 173
Hicks (Ronald C.), Cornwall 73
Hornsey's, North Yorkshire......................... 194
Hünersdorff Rare Books, London SW 168
Hurst (Jenny), Kent 137
IDEA, London EC.................................... 155
Inch's Books, Kent 137
Island Books, Devon 85
Ivelet Books Ltd., Surrey 233
Jackdaw Books, Norfolk 188
Jade Mountain Bookshop, Hants 125
Jane & John Kinnaird, Cumbria 78
Jenny Hurst, Kent 138
Joel Segal Books, Devon 86
Judd Books, London WC 177
Katnap Arts, Norfolk................................ 190
Kelsall (George), Greater Manchester 118
Keswick Bookshop, Cumbria........................ 78
Kingswood Books, Dorset 94
Liddle (Steve), Bristol 58
Lighthouse Books (The), Dorset 92
Lloyd-Davies (Sue), Carmarthenshire 282
Lymelight Books & Prints, Dorset 93
Maghreb Bookshop (The), London WC.......... 177
Malvern Bookshop (The), Worcestershire 255
Mandalay Bookshop, London SW 168
Mannwaring (M.G.), Bristol 59
Marble Hill Books, Outer London................. 182
Marlborough Rare Books Ltd., London W 173
Martin - Bookseller (Colin), East Yorkshire 107
McCrone (Audrey), Isle of Arran 274
McNaughtan's Bookshop, Lothian 276
Missing Books, Essex 109
Modern First Editions, West Yorkshire.......... 247
Monmouth House Books, Monmouthshire 286
Mulyan (Don), Merseyside 185
My Back Pages, London SW 168
Nelson (Elizabeth), Suffolk 226
Newcastle Bookshop At Haltwhistle,
Northumberland 201
Nonsuch Books, Surrey.............................. 234
Octagon Books, Cambridgeshire 66
Old Town Bookshop (The), Lothian 276
Oopalba Books, Cheshire............................ 71
Pagan Limited (Hugh), Hants 122
Parkinsons Books, Merseyside...................... 185
Parrott Books, Oxfordshire 209
Pauline Harries Books, Hampshire 123
Period & Classical Collections, East Sussex 103
Peter M Daly, Hampshire........................... 126
Phelan Books, Co. Dublin 264
Phillips of Hitchin (Antiques) Ltd., Herts......... 131
Pordes Books Ltd., (Henry), London WC........ 177
Portobello Books, London W 174
Potterton Books, North Yorkshire................. 196
Prospect House Books, Co. Down.................. 261
PsychoBabel Books & Journals, Oxfordshire..... 205
Quaritch Ltd., (Bernard), London W.............. 174
R. & A. Books, East Sussex 101
Ray Rare and Out of Print Books (Janette),
North Yorkshire 198
Read - Gorleston Books, (C.&J.), Norfolk 187
Reads, Dorset 95

Rees & O'Neill Rare Books, London WC........ 178
Reeves Technical Books, North Yorkshire 195
Roberts Books, Strathclyde 279
Rochdale Book Company, Greater Manchester . 120
Roland Books, Kent 138
Rothwell & Dunworth, Somerset 217
Ryeland Books, Northants........................... 199
St Mary's Books & Prints, Lincolnshire 152
Saintfield Antiques & Fine Books, Co. Down ... 261
Samovar Books, Co. Dublin........................ 264
Sax Books, Suffolk 228
Scarthin Books, Derbyshire 82
Scrivener's Books & Bookbinding, Derbyshire... 82
Seydi Rare Books (Sevin), London NW 161
Slightly Foxed on Gloucester Road,
London SW.. 167
Sotheran Limited (Henry), London W 175
Sparrow Books, West Yorkshire 245
Spelman (Ken), North Yorkshire 198
Spooner & Co, Somerset 219
Stalagluft Books, Tyne and Wear.................. 235
Staniland (Booksellers), Lincolnshire 152
Stern Antiquarian Bookseller (Jeffrey), North
Yorkshire.. 198
Tasburgh Books, Norfolk............................ 190
Theatreshire Books, North Yorkshire 192
Tilston (Stephen E.), London SE................... 165
Tombland Bookshop, Norfolk 190
Trinders' Fine Tools, Suffolk 226
Trinity Rare Books, Co. Leitrim 266
Walden Books, London NW 161
Westons, Herts 132
Westwood Books Ltd, Cumbria..................... 80
Wiend Books, Lancashire 143
Winchester Bookshop (The), Hampshire.......... 126
Woburn Books, London N 159
Worcester Rare Books, Worcestershire............ 256
Worlds End Bookshop, London SW 169
Wychwood Books, Gloucestershire 116
Wyseby House Books, Berks 55

ARCHITECTURE - THEATRE

Apocalypse, Surrey 232
Bookroom (The), Surrey............................. 233
Collectable Books, London SE 163
Cover to Cover, Merseyside......................... 185
Decorum Books, London N 156
Gravity Books, Lincolnshire 149
Hünersdorff Rare Books, London SW 168
Jackdaw Books, Norfolk 188
Minster Gate Bookshop, North Yorkshire 197
Not Just Books, Dorset.............................. 94
Pagan Limited (Hugh), Hampshire 122
Quaritch Ltd., (Bernard), London W.............. 174
R. & A. Books, East Sussex 101
Seydi Rare Books (Sevin), London NW 161
Stokes Books, Co. Dublin........................... 264
Terence Kaye - Bookseller, London NW 161
Thorntons of Oxford Ltd., Oxfordshire........... 206
Tilston (Stephen E.), London SE................... 165

ARCHIVES

Book Gallery (The), Cornwall 74
Early Times, Guernsey, Channel Islands.......... 258
Joel Segal Books, Devon 86

Kenny's Bookshop & Art Galleries Ltd.,
Co. Galway 265
Knowles - Antiquary (Roger J.), Staffordshire... 223
Quaritch Ltd., (Bernard), London W.............. 174
R. & A. Books, East Sussex 101
Rowan (P. & B.), Co. Antrim 260
Spenceley Books (David), West Yorkshire........ 248
Stroh (M.A.), London E 154
Thornber (Peter M.), North Yorkshire............ 195

ARCTIC - ANTARCTICA
Adrem Books, Herts 130
Antique Map and Bookshop (The), Dorset 94
Bluntisham Books, Cambridgeshire................. 63
Bunyan Books, Bedfordshire......................... 53
Glacier Books, Tayside 280
Michael Graves-Johnston, London SW 168
Peter M Daly, Hampshire............................ 126
Roz Hulse, Conwy 284

ARMED FORCES AUSTRALIAN
- AIR FORCE
Aardvark Books, Wiltshire........................... 254
Marine and Cannon Books, Cheshire 69
R. & A. Books, East Sussex 101
World War II Books, Surrey 234

- ARMY
Aardvark Books, Wiltshire........................... 254
Burroughs (Andrew), Lincolnshire................. 152
Marine & Cannon Books, Cheshire 71
Marine and Cannon Books, Cheshire 69
MilitaryHistoryBooks.com, Kent................... 137
World War II Books, Surrey 234

- NAVY
Aardvark Books, Wiltshire........................... 254
Burroughs (Andrew), Lincolnshire................. 152
Marine & Cannon Books, Cheshire 71
Marine and Cannon Books, Cheshire 69
R. & A. Books, East Sussex 101

ARMENIAN
Antique Prints of the World, London N.......... 156

ARMS & ARMOUR
Aardvark Books, Wiltshire........................... 254
Annie's Books, South Yorkshire 221
Book For All Reasons (A.), Suffolk 228
Bookworm (The), Lothian 276
Bookworms Paradise Ltd., West Sussex 242
Burroughs (Andrew), Lincolnshire................. 152
Cader Idris Books, Powys........................... 290
Caliver Books, Essex 109
Chalmers Hallam (E.), Hampshire................. 125
Chelifer Books, Cumbria 80
Deeside Books, Grampian........................... 272
Duck (William), Hampshire......................... 124
Harris (George J.), Co. Derry 260
Helion & Company, West Midlands 239
Heneage Art Books (Thomas), London SW 168
J & J Burgess Booksellers, Cambridgeshire....... 64
Kingfisher Book Service, Nottinghamshire 204
Lost Books, Northants............................... 200
Meekins Books (Paul), Warwickshire.............. 237

MilitaryHistoryBooks.com, Kent................... 137
N1 Books, East Sussex 105
Old Book Company, (The), West Yorkshire 248
Prospect Books, Conwy 283
PsychoBabel Books & Journals, Oxfordshire..... 205
R. & A. Books, East Sussex 101
Ramrod Antiques, North Yorkshire................ 195
Rods Books, Devon 88
Spenceley Books (David), West Yorkshire........ 248
Stroh (M.A.), London E 154
Thin Read Line, Merseyside 184
Wizard Books, Cambridgeshire..................... 67

ARMY, THE
Aardvark Books, Wiltshire........................... 254
Addyman Books, Powys.............................. 287
Anthony Spranger, Wiltshire........................ 252
Apocalypse, Surrey 232
Black Five Books, Shropshire 214
Book For All Reasons (A.), Suffolk 228
Bookworm (The), Lothian 276
Brad Books, Essex.................................. 110
Cornucopia Books, Lincolnshire 151
Deeside Books, Grampian 272
Eastgate Bookshop, East Yorkshire 106
Farnborough Gallery, Hampshire 122
Gallimaufry Books, Herts 131
Island Books, Devon................................ 85
Jade Mountain Bookshop, Hampshire 125
Joel Segal Books, Devon 86
Kingfisher Book Service, Nottinghamshire 204
Lost Books, Northants............................... 200
Mandalay Bookshop, London SW 168
Marine & Cannon Books, Cheshire 71
Marine and Cannon Books, Cheshire 69
Martin (Books and Pictures), (Brian P.), Surrey . 231
MilitaryHistoryBooks.com, Kent................... 137
N1 Books, East Sussex 105
Not Just Books, Dorset............................. 94
R. & A. Books, East Sussex 101
Rods Books, Devon 88
Rothwell & Dunworth, Somerset 217
Sax Books, Suffolk 228
Thin Read Line, Merseyside 184
War & Peace Books, Hampshire................... 122
Wheen O'Books, Borders............................ 267
Winchester Bookshop (The), Hampshire.......... 126

ART
A. & H. Peasgood, Cambridgeshire 66
Abacus Books, Greater Manchester 118
Abacus Gallery, Staffordshire....................... 224
Addyman Books, Powys.............................. 287
Al Saqi Books, London W 171
Alba Books, Grampian 273
Alexander's Books, Warwickshire................... 237
Alister & Garon Books, Cambridgeshire.......... 63
Americanabooksuk, Cumbria 76
Amwell Book Company, London EC.............. 155
Andrew Morton (Books), Powys................... 287
Anne Harris Books & Bags Booksearch, Devon 88
Anthony Neville, Kent............................... 138
Antiquary Ltd., (Bar Bookstore), N Yorkshire .. 194
Antiques on High, Oxfordshire..................... 207
Apocalypse, Surrey 232

Arden Books & Cosmographia, Warwickshire... 236
Armchair Books, Lothian 275
Art Reference Books, Hampshire 124
Artco, Nottinghamshire.............................. 204
Aurora Books Ltd, Lothian......................... 275
Autumn Leaves, Lincolnshire....................... 150
Aviabooks, Gloucestershire 114
Avonworld Books, Somerset........................ 216
Ballantyne–Way (Roger), Suffolk 228
Bardsley's Books, Suffolk............................ 225
Barmby (C. & A.J.), Kent........................... 140
Barn Books, Buckinghamshire...................... 61
Bath Old Books, Somerset 215
Besleys Books, Suffolk 225
Bianco Library, West Sussex........................ 241
Big Bairn Books, Tayside 279
Blaenavon Books, Torfaen 292
Book Annex (The), Essex 109
Book Gallery (The), Cornwall 74
Book Palace (The), London SE 163
Bookbarrow, Cambridgeshire....................... 63
Bookcase, Cumbria 76
Bookroom (The), Surrey............................. 233
Books, Denbighshire 284
Books, Kent 137
Books & Collectables Ltd., Cambridgeshire...... 63
Books Antiques & Collectables, Devon 90
BOOKS4U, Flintshire................................ 284
Bookshop on the Heath, The, London SE 163
Bookworms, Norfolk.................................. 186
Bookworms of Evesham, Worcestershire 257
Booth (Booksearch Service), (Geoff), Cheshire... 68
Bosco Books, Cornwall 72
Bosorne Books, Cornwall 75
Brad Books, Essex.................................... 110
Brazenhead Ltd., Norfolk 188
Brighton Books, East Sussex........................ 99
Bristol Books, Bristol 60
Broadhurst of Southport Ltd., Merseyside 185
Brock Books, North Yorkshire...................... 192
Browsers Bookshop, Cornwall....................... 72
Bruce Holdsworth Books, East Sussex 105
Butcher (Pablo), Oxfordshire 206
Butts Books (Mary), Berks 56
C J Renwick Books, Powys.......................... 287
Caledonia Books, Strathclyde....................... 278
Cameron House Books, Isle of Wight............. 133
Campbell Art Books (Marcus), London SE....... 163
Carnforth Bookshop (The), Lancashire 142
Carningli Centre, Pembrokeshire 286
Carraig Books Ltd., Co. Dublin 263
Cassidy (Bookseller) (P.), Lincolnshire 151
Catalyst Booksearch Services, Devon............... 87
Cavern Books, Cheshire 70
Chalk (Old & Out of Print Books)
    (Christine M.), West Midlands 238
Chandos Books, Devon............................... 85
Charlie Byrne's Bookshop, Co. Galway........... 265
Chaucer Bookshop, Kent............................ 136
Cheshire Book Centre, Cheshire.................... 69
Chichester Bookshop (The), Herefordshire 241
Chris Phillips, Wiltshire.............................. 252
Classic Bindings Ltd, London SW 166
Clements (R.W.), London O......................... 181
Clifford Milne Books, Grampian.................... 272

Coach House Books, Worcestershire 256
Cobbles Books, Somerset............................ 217
Cobweb Books, North Yorkshire.................... 194
Cofion Books, Pembrokeshire....................... 286
Cooper Hay Rare Books, Strathclyde.............. 278
Cover to Cover, Merseyside......................... 185
Crabtree (Mrs. C.), Greater Manchester 120
Cross (Ian), Berks 55
Cumming Limited (A. & Y.), East Sussex........ 104
Dales & Lakes Book Centre, Cumbria 79
Dandy Lion Editions, Surrey 233
Darkwood Books, Co. Cork......................... 263
Dartmoor Book Gallery, Devon 87
Dartmoor Bookshop (The), Devon................. 84
David (G.), Cambridgeshire.......................... 63
David Flint, Hampshire 124
de Beaumont (Robin), London SW 166
Decorum Books, London N 156
Discovery Bookshop, Carmarthenshire............. 281
Dolphin Books, Suffolk.............................. 225
Doolin Dinghy Books, Co. Clare 262
Doorbar (P. & D.), Gwynedd....................... 285
Duncan & Reid, Lothian............................. 276
Dunkheld Antiques, Tayside......................... 279
Eastcote Bookshop (The), London O 180
Eastgate Bookshop, East Yorkshire 106
Eastleach Books, Berks 56
Edwards (London) Limited (Francis),
    London WC....................................... 176
Edwards in Hay–on–Wye (Francis), Powys 288
Edwards, Fiona, Nottinghamshire 203
Ellis, Bookseller (Peter), London WC 177
Ely Books, Cambridgeshire 65
English (Toby), Oxfordshire.......................... 209
Evans Books (Paul), West Sussex 243
Farnborough Gallery, Hampshire.................... 122
Finch Rare Books Ltd. (Simon),
    London W 172
Fine Art Catalogues, Cumbria 80
Fireside Bookshop, Cumbria......................... 81
Fisher & Sperr, London N........................... 157
Ford Books (David), Herts 130
Fortune Green Books, London NW................. 160
Foster Bookshop (Paul), London SW.............. 167
Fosters Bookshop, London W 172
Fotheringham (Alex), Northumberland 201
Francis, S. L., Sussex................................. 103
Freeman's Corner Shop, Norfolk 189
Furneaux Books (Lee), Devon....................... 89
Garfi Books, Powys 291
George St. Books, Derbyshire 83
GfB: the Colchester Bookshop, Essex 108
Gladstone Books, Lincolnshire 150
Golden Goose Books, Lincolnshire................. 150
Goldman (Paul), Dorset 94
Good for Books, Lincolnshire....................... 149
Goodyer (Nicholas), London N..................... 157
Gravity Books, Lincolnshire 149
Hall's Bookshop, Kent............................... 140
Hanshan Tang Books, London SW 167
Harlequin Gallery, Lincolnshire..................... 150
Harrington (Adrian), London W..................... 173
Hay Castle, Powys.................................... 288
Hay Cinema Bookshop Ltd., Powys................ 288
HCB Wholesale, Powys.............................. 288

Helmsley Antiquarian & Secondhand Books,
    North Yorkshire 193
Heneage Art Books (Thomas), London SW 168
Hennessey Bookseller (Ray), East Sussex 100
Hicks (Ronald C.), Cornwall 73
High Street Books, Devon 86
Hill House Books, Devon 88
Hodgkins and Company Limited (Ian),
    Gloucestershire 116
Horsham Rare Books, West Sussex 242
Idler (The), Suffolk 227
Internet Bookshop UK Ltd., Gloucestershire 113
Jackdaw Books, Norfolk 188
Jade Mountain Bookshop, Hampshire 125
Jane & John Kinnaird, Cumbria 78
Jean Hedger, Berks 55
Joel Segal Books, Devon 86
Judd Books, London WC 177
Just Books, Cornwall 75
Katharine House Gallery, Wiltshire 252
Katnap Arts, Norfolk 190
Keeble Antiques, Somerset 218
Kennedy & Farley, East Sussex 104
Kenny's Bookshop & Art Galleries Ltd.,
    Co. Galway 265
Keogh's Books, Gloucestershire 115
Keswick Bookshop, Cumbria 78
Kim's Bookshop, West Sussex 242
Last Century Books, Borders 267
Leabeck Books, Oxfordshire 208
Leigh Gallery Books, Essex 110
Lenton (Alfred), Leics 145
Liddle (Steve), Bristol 58
Lloyd-Davies (Sue), Carmarthenshire 282
Lymelight Books & Prints, Dorset 93
Malvern Bookshop (The), Worcestershire 255
Mandalay Bookshop, London SW 168
Mannwaring (M.G.), Bristol 59
Marijana Dworski Books, Powys 288
Martin - Bookseller (Colin), East Yorkshire 107
Mason (Mary), Oxfordshire 205
McNaughtan's Bookshop, Lothian 276
Mercat Books, Highland 274
Minster Gate Bookshop, North Yorkshire 197
Moorhead Books, West Yorkshire 245
Morley Case, Hampshire 125
Mulyan (Don), Merseyside 185
Mundy (David), Herts 129
My Back Pages, London SW 168
Myra Dean Illustated Books, Powys 287
N1 Books, East Sussex 105
Nelson (Elizabeth), Suffolk 226
New Strand, The, Herefordshire 127
Newcastle Bookshop At Haltwhistle,
    Northumberland 201
Newlyn Books, Cornwall 74
Niner (Marcus), Isle of Wight 133
Nonsuch Books, Surrey.............................. 234
O'Brien Books & Photo Gallery, Co. Limerick .. 266
Octagon Books, Cambridgeshire 66
Offa's Dyke Books, Shropshire 213
Old Aberdeen Bookshop, Grampian 272
Old Bookshop (The), West Midlands 240
Old Station Pottery & Bookshop (The), Norfolk 191
Old Town Bookshop (The), Lothian 276

Oopalba Books, Cheshire............................ 71
Paper Pleasures, Somerset 218
Paul Hoare, Cornwall............................... 74
Pauline Harries Books, Hampshire 123
Period & Classical Collections, East Sussex 103
Peter Lyons Books, Gloucestershire 113
Peter M Daly, Hampshire........................... 126
Petworth Antique Market (Bookroom),
    West Sussex 244
Pordes Books Ltd., (Henry), London WC....... 177
Pringle Booksellers (Andrew), Lothian 277
Print Matters, London SE........................... 165
Prospect House Books, Co. Down 261
PsychoBabel Books & Journals, Oxfordshire..... 205
Quaritch Ltd., (Bernard), London W 174
Quinto of Charing Cross Road, London WC ... 178
R. & A. Books, East Sussex 101
Ray Rare and Out of Print Books (Janette),
    North Yorkshire 198
Reading Lasses, Dumfries & Galloway 270
Reads, Dorset 95
Rees & O'Neill Rare Books, London WC........ 178
RGS Books, Surrey 234
Richard Thornton Books, London N 158
Richmond Books, North Yorkshire 194
Rickaro Books, West Yorkshire 246
River Reads Bookshop, Devon...................... 90
Robin Doughty - Fine Books, West Midlands... 238
Roland Books, Kent 138
Rowan (H. & S.J.), Dorset 91
St Ann's Books, Worcestershire 255
Saintfield Antiques & Fine Books, Co. Down ... 261
Sclanders (Beatbooks), (Andrew), London EC... 155
Scott (Peter), East Sussex........................... 104
Scrivener's Books & Bookbinding, Derbyshire... 82
Seabreeze Books, Lancashire........................ 144
Silverman (Michael), London SE................... 165
Sims Reed Limited, London SW 169
Slightly Foxed on Gloucester Road, London SW 167
Smith Books, (Sally), Suffolk 226
Sotheran Limited (Henry), London W 175
Spelman (Ken), North Yorkshire 198
Staniland (Booksellers), Lincolnshire 152
Sterling Books, Somerset 220
Stern Antiquarian Bookseller (Jeffrey), North
    Yorkshire.. 198
Stone Trough Books, North Yorkshire 198
Stothert Old Books, Cheshire....................... 68
Stroma Books, Borders 267
Studio Bookshop, East Sussex...................... 100
Sturford Books, Wiltshire 254
Tarka Books, Devon 84
Tasburgh Books, Norfolk 190
Tilston (Stephen E.), London SE................... 165
Tombland Bookshop, Norfolk 190
Treasure Chest Books, Suffolk 226
Treasure Island (The), Greater Manchester...... 119
Trinders' Fine Tools, Suffolk 226
Trinity Rare Books, Co. Leitrim 266
Uncle Phil's Books, West Midlands 239
Upper-Room Books, Somerset...................... 217
Venables (Morris & Juliet), Bristol................. 59
Village Books, Norfolk 186
Wadard Books, Kent 137
Walden Books, London NW 161

Watkins Books Ltd., London WC 179
Waxfactor, East Sussex 100
Westwood Books Ltd, Cumbria.................... 80
Wetherell (Frances), Cambridgeshire 65
Wheen O'Books, Borders........................... 267
Whig Books Ltd., Leics............................. 147
Whitehall Books, East Sussex...................... 103
Whitfield (Ken), Essex 110
Wiend Books, Lancashire 143
Winchester Bookshop (The), Hampshire.......... 126
Woburn Books, London N 159
Wood (Peter), Cambridgeshire..................... 65
Words Etcetera Bookshop, Dorset................ 93
Worlds End Bookshop, London SW 169
Wychwood Books, Gloucestershire 116
Wyseby House Books, Berks 55
Xanadu Books, Durham 98
Ystwyth Books, Ceredigion 282

- AFRO-AMERICAN

Apocalypse, Surrey 232
Campbell Art Books (Marcus), London SE...... 163
Decorum Books, London N 156
Michael Graves-Johnston, London SW 168
R. & A. Books, East Sussex 101
Stevens (Joan), Cambridgeshire.................... 65
Watkins Books Ltd., London WC 179

- BRITISH

Addyman Books, Powys............................. 287
Anthony Sillem, East Sussex....................... 102
Anthony Spranger, Wiltshire....................... 252
Bermondsey Basement Bookstore, London SE .. 163
Book Gallery (The), Cornwall 74
Book Palace (The), London SE 163
Bookroom (The), Surrey............................ 233
Books & Things, London W........................ 171
BookShop, The, Dumfries & Galloway 270
Brock Books, North Yorkshire..................... 192
Butts Books (Mary), Berks......................... 56
C J Renwick Books, Powys......................... 287
Campbell Art Books (Marcus), London SE...... 163
Cooper Hay Rare Books, Strathclyde 278
Decorum Books, London N 156
Dolphin Books, Suffolk............................. 225
Elaine Lonsdale Books, West Yorkshire 247
Ellwood Editions, Wiltshire 253
Farnborough Gallery, Hampshire.................. 122
Hay Castle, Powys.................................. 288
Hennessey Bookseller (Ray), East Sussex 100
Hornsey's, North Yorkshire........................ 194
IDEA, London EC................................... 155
JB Books & Collectables, West Sussex 243
Jean Hedger, Berks 55
Joel Segal Books, Devon 86
Just Books, Cornwall 75
Liddle (Steve), Bristol 58
McEwan Fine Books, Grampian.................... 272
My Back Pages, London SW 168
Myra Dean Illustated Books, Powys 287
Newcastle Bookshop At Haltwhistle,
    Northumberland 201
R. & A. Books, East Sussex 101
Robin Doughty - Fine Books, West Midlands... 238
Tasburgh Books, Norfolk 190

Thorntons of Oxford Ltd., Oxfordshire........... 206
Treasure Island (The), Greater Manchester....... 119
Woburn Books, London N 159
Woodbine Books, West Yorkshire................. 245

- ENCAUSTIC

Cover to Cover, Merseyside........................ 185

- TECHNIQUE

Addyman Books, Powys............................. 287
Apocalypse, Surrey 232
Aviabooks, Gloucestershire 114
Book Annex (The), Essex 109
Bookroom (The), Surrey............................ 233
Bruce Holdsworth Books, East Sussex 105
Campbell Art Books (Marcus), London SE...... 163
Cheshire Book Centre, Cheshire................... 69
Cornucopia Books, Lincolnshire 151
Cover to Cover, Merseyside........................ 185
Crabtree (Mrs. C.), Greater Manchester 120
Decorum Books, London N 156
Doorbar (P. & D.), Gwynedd 285
DPE Books, Devon 87
Evans Books (Paul), West Sussex 243
Farnborough Gallery, Hampshire.................. 122
Hennessey Bookseller (Ray), East Sussex 100
Jade Mountain Bookshop, Hampshire 125
JB Books & Collectables, West Sussex 243
Joel Segal Books, Devon 86
Just Books, Cornwall 75
Kim's Bookshop, West Sussex...................... 242
McCrone (Audrey), Isle of Arran 274
N1 Books, East Sussex 105
Oopalba Books, Cheshire........................... 71
Peter Lyons Books, Gloucestershire 113
Portobello Books, London W 174
Print Matters, London SE.......................... 165
R. & A. Books, East Sussex 101
Scrivener's Books & Bookbinding,
    Derbyshire 82
Sleepy Elephant Books & Artefacts, Cumbria ... 80
Uncle Phil's Books, West Midlands 239
Walden Books, London NW 161
Whittle, Bookseller (Avril), Cumbria 80

- THEORY

Addyman Books, Powys............................. 287
Amwell Book Company, London EC.............. 155
Apocalypse, Surrey 232
Book Annex (The), Essex 109
Book Palace (The), London SE 163
Bookroom (The), Surrey............................ 233
Bruce Holdsworth Books, East Sussex 105
C J Renwick Books, Powys......................... 287
Campbell Art Books (Marcus),
    London SE....................................... 163
Cheshire Book Centre, Cheshire................... 69
Cover to Cover, Merseyside........................ 185
Decorum Books, London N 156
Farnborough Gallery, Hampshire.................. 122
Hay Castle, Powys.................................. 288
IDEA, London EC................................... 155
Jade Mountain Bookshop, Hampshire 125
Joel Segal Books, Devon 86
Just Books, Cornwall 75

Newcastle Bookshop At Haltwhistle,
　Northumberland 201
Orchid Book Distributors, Co. Clare 262
Peter Lyons Books, Gloucestershire 113
Price (John), London N 158
R. & A. Books, East Sussex 101
Savery Books, East Sussex 100
Scrivener's Books & Bookbinding, Derbyshire... 82
Stevens (Joan), Cambridgeshire.................... 65
Uncle Phil's Books, West Midlands 239
Walden Books, London NW 161
Whittle, Bookseller (Avril), Cumbria 80
Woburn Books, London N 159

ART DECO
Art Book Company, (The), Suffolk................ 227
Batterham (David), London W..................... 171
Bookroom (The), Surrey............................ 233
Cheshire Book Centre, Cheshire................... 69
Cornucopia Books, Lincolnshire 151
Cover to Cover, Merseyside......................... 185
Decorum Books, London N 156
Design Gallery 1850-1950 (The), Kent 141
Dolphin Books, Suffolk............................ 225
Don Kelly Books, London W 172
Hennessey Bookseller (Ray), East Sussex 100
Joel Segal Books, Devon 86
Lymelight Books & Prints, Dorset................. 93
N1 Books, East Sussex 105
Print Matters, London SE........................... 165
R. & A. Books, East Sussex 101
Scrivener's Books & Bookbinding, Derbyshire... 82
Woodbine Books, West Yorkshire................. 245

ART HISTORY
Addyman Books, Powys............................. 287
Amwell Book Company, London EC.............. 155
Antiques on High, Oxfordshire.................... 207
Apocalypse, Surrey 232
Ars Artis, Oxfordshire 207
Art Book Company, (The), Suffolk................ 227
Art Reference Books, Hampshire 124
Aviabooks, Gloucestershire 114
Axe Rare & Out of Print Books (Richard),
　North Yorkshire 193
Ballantyne–Way (Roger), Suffolk 228
Belfry Books, Nottinghamshire.................... 203
Bennett & Kerr Books, Oxfordshire 205
Book Annex (The), Essex 109
Book Gallery (The), Cornwall 74
Book Palace (The), London SE 163
Bookroom (The), Surrey............................ 233
books2books, Devon................................ 88
Booth (Booksearch Service), (Geoff), Cheshire... 68
Bosco Books, Cornwall............................. 72
Brock Books, North Yorkshire..................... 192
Browsers Bookshop, Cornwall...................... 72
Bruce Holdsworth Books, East Sussex 105
Butts Books (Mary), Berks......................... 56
C J Renwick Books, Powys......................... 287
Caledonia Books, Strathclyde...................... 278
Camden Books, Somerset 215
Campbell Art Books (Marcus), London SE...... 163
Carnforth Bookshop (The), Lancashire 142
Carraig Books Ltd., Co. Dublin 263

Chaucer Bookshop, Kent............................ 136
Cheshire Book Centre, Cheshire................... 69
Chevin Books, West Yorkshire 249
Clark (Nigel A.), London SE 163
Clevedon Books, Somerset 217
Cornucopia Books, Lincolnshire 151
Dalbeattie Books, Dumfries & Galloway 269
Darkwood Books, Co. Cork........................ 263
Dartmoor Bookshop (The), Devon................ 84
Dave Jelfs, Devon 85
Decorum Books, London N 156
Delectus Books, London WC....................... 176
Dolphin Books, Suffolk............................ 225
Don Kelly Books, London W 172
Doorbar (P. & D.), Gwynedd 285
DPE Books, Devon 87
Ellis, Bookseller (Peter), London WC 177
Esoteric Dreams Bookshop, Cumbria 77
Evans Books (Paul), West Sussex 243
Ferguson (Elizabeth), Grampian 272
Fisher & Sperr, London N.......................... 157
Ford Books (David), Herts 130
Forest Books of Manchester, Cheshire............ 70
Foster (Stephen), London NW 160
Garfi Books, Powys 291
Goldman (Paul), Dorset 94
Gravity Books, Lincolnshire 149
Hall's Bookshop, Kent.............................. 140
Hanshan Tang Books, London SW 167
Heneage Art Books (Thomas), London SW 168
Hill House Books, Devon 88
Jane & John Kinnaird, Cumbria 78
JB Books & Collectables, West Sussex 243
Joel Segal Books, Devon 86
Just Books, Cornwall 75
Katnap Arts, Norfolk 190
Kelsall (George), Greater Manchester 118
Keogh's Books, Gloucestershire.................... 115
Kingsgate Books & Prints, Hampshire 126
Kingswood Books, Dorset 94
Kunkler Books (Paul), Cambridgeshire 64
Marcet Books, London SE.......................... 164
Martin - Bookseller (Colin), East Yorkshire 107
McCrone (Audrey), Isle of Arran 274
McEwan Fine Books, Grampian.................... 272
Nelson (Elizabeth), Suffolk........................ 226
Newcastle Bookshop At Haltwhistle,
　Northumberland 201
Newlyn Books, Cornwall........................... 74
Nonsuch Books, Surrey............................. 234
O'Brien Books & Photo Gallery, Co. Limerick.. 266
Old Book Company, (The), West Yorkshire 248
Pagan Limited (Hugh), Hampshire 122
Period & Classical Collections, East Sussex 103
Peter Lyons Books, Gloucestershire 113
Pordes Books Ltd., (Henry), London WC........ 177
Portobello Books, London W 174
PsychoBabel Books & Journals, Oxfordshire..... 205
Quaritch Ltd., (Bernard), London W.............. 174
R. & A. Books, East Sussex 101
Ray Rare and Out of Print Books (Janette),
　N Yorkshire 198
Rothwell & Dunworth, Somerset 217
Ryeland Books, Northants 199
St Philip's Books, Oxfordshire..................... 208

Savery Books, East Sussex 100
Sax Books, Suffolk 228
Scrivener's Books & Bookbinding, Derbyshire... 82
Seydi Rare Books (Sevin), London NW 161
Sleepy Elephant Books & Artefacts, Cumbria ... 80
Staniland (Booksellers), Lincolnshire 152
Tasburgh Books, Norfolk 190
Taylor & Son (Peter), Herts........................ 132
The Sanctuary Bookshop, Dorset.................... 94
Thorntons of Oxford Ltd., Oxfordshire........... 206
Uncle Phil's Books, West Midlands 239
Walden Books, London NW 161
Westwood Books Ltd, Cumbria..................... 80
Wetherell (Frances), Cambridgeshire 65
Whitchurch Books Ltd., Cardiff..................... 281
Whittle, Bookseller (Avril), Cumbria 80
Woburn Books, London N 159
Woodbine Books, West Yorkshire................. 245
Words Etcetera Bookshop, Dorset................. 93
Wyseby House Books, Berks 55

ART NOUVEAU

Apocalypse, Surrey 232
Art Book Company, (The), Suffolk................ 227
Batterham (David), London W..................... 171
Bookroom (The), Surrey............................ 233
Books & Things, London W 171
Cornucopia Books, Lincolnshire 151
Cover to Cover, Merseyside........................ 185
Decorum Books, London N 156
Design Gallery 1850-1950 (The), Kent 141
Don Kelly Books, London W 172
Joel Segal Books, Devon 86
Lymelight Books & Prints, Dorset................. 93
N1 Books, East Sussex 105
Print Matters, London SE........................... 165
R. & A. Books, East Sussex 101

ART REFERENCE

Abbey Books, Cornwall 73
Amwell Book Company, London EC.............. 155
Anthony Spranger, Wiltshire....................... 252
Any Amount of Books, London WC............... 176
Ars Artis, Oxfordshire 207
Art Book Company, (The), Suffolk................ 227
Art Reference Books, Hampshire 124
Artco, Nottinghamshire............................. 204
Atlas, London N..................................... 156
Aviabooks, Gloucestershire 114
Ballantyne–Way (Roger), Suffolk 228
Barlow (Vincent G.), Hampshire 125
Barmby (C. & A.J.), Kent........................... 140
Baynton–Williams Gallery, West Sussex 241
Besleys Books, Suffolk 225
Beware of the Leopard, Bristol 58
Birchden Books, London E 154
Blackpool Book Warehouse, Lancashire.......... 142
Book Gallery (The), Cornwall 74
Book Palace (The), London SE 163
Bookroom (The), Surrey............................ 233
Books & Things, London W 171
books2books, Devon................................ 88
Bookworm (The), Lothian 276
Bosco Books, Cornwall 72
Boxwood Books & Prints, Somerset............... 219
Brock Books, North Yorkshire..................... 192
Bruce Holdsworth Books, East Sussex 105
Butts Books (Mary), Berks.......................... 56
Campbell Art Books (Marcus), London SE...... 163
Chalk (Old & Out of Print Books)
    (Christine M.), West Midlands 238
Cheshire Book Centre, Cheshire.................... 69
Clark (Nigel A.), London SE 163
Coach House Books, Worcestershire 256
Cofion Books, Pembrokeshire 286
Cooper Hay Rare Books, Strathclyde.............. 278
Cover to Cover, Merseyside......................... 185
Cox Old & Rare Books (Claude), Suffolk 227
Criterion Books, London O.......................... 181
Darkwood Books, Co. Cork 263
Dartmoor Bookshop (The), Devon................. 84
Dave Jelfs, Devon 85
Decorum Books, London N 156
Delectus Books, London WC....................... 176
Don Kelly Books, London W 172
Doorbar (P. & D.), Gwynedd 285
English (Toby), Oxfordshire........................ 209
Evans Books (Paul), West Sussex 243
Farnborough Gallery, Hampshire................... 122
Foster (Stephen), London NW 160
GfB: the Colchester Bookshop, Essex 108
Goldman (Paul), Dorset 94
Hanshan Tang Books, London SW 167
Harwich Old Books, Essex.......................... 109
Hennessey Bookseller (Ray), East Sussex 100
Hodgkins and Company Limited (Ian),
    Gloucestershire 116
Hornsey's, North Yorkshire......................... 194
IDEA, London EC 155
Jackdaw Books, Norfolk 188
Jackson (M.W.), Wiltshire.......................... 254
Jane & John Kinnaird, Cumbria.................... 78
JB Books & Collectables, West Sussex 243
Joel Segal Books, Devon 86
John Gorton Booksearch, East Sussex 105
Just Books, Cornwall 75
Katnap Arts, Norfolk................................ 190
Keel Row Bookshop, Tyne and Wear 235
Kelsall (George), Greater Manchester.............. 118
Keogh's Books, Gloucestershire 115
Kingsgate Books & Prints, Hampshire 126
Mannwaring (M.G.), Bristol 59
Martin - Bookseller (Colin), East Yorkshire 107
McEwan Fine Books, Grampian..................... 272
Mercat Books, Highland 274
Murphy (C.J.), Norfolk.............................. 189
My Back Pages, London SW 168
N1 Books, East Sussex 105
Nelson (Elizabeth), Suffolk 226
Newcastle Bookshop At Haltwhistle,
    Northumberland 201
Newlyn Books, Cornwall 74
Nonsuch Books, Surrey.............................. 234
O'Flynn Books, North Yorkshire................... 197
Old Town Bookshop (The), Lothian 276
Pagan Limited (Hugh), Hampshire 122
Parrott Books, Oxfordshire 209
Peter Lyons Books, Gloucestershire 113
Potterton Books, North Yorkshire.................. 196
Priestpopple Books, Northumberland 201

Print Matters, London SE............................ 165
R. & A. Books, East Sussex 101
Rickaro Books, West Yorkshire.................... 246
Robin Doughty - Fine Books, West Midlands... 238
Savery Books, East Sussex 100
Sax Books, Suffolk 228
Scrivener's Books & Bookbinding, Derbyshire... 82
Seydi Rare Books (Sevin), London NW 161
Smith Books, (Sally), Suffolk 226
Staniland (Booksellers), Lincolnshire 152
Stevens (Joan), Cambridgeshire..................... 65
Studio Bookshop, East Sussex...................... 100
Sue Lowell Natural History Books, London W . 175
Tasburgh Books, Norfolk 190
The Sanctuary Bookshop, Dorset.................. 94
Trigon Books, Dorset................................. 95
Trinders' Fine Tools, Suffolk 226
Ventnor Rare Books, Isle of Wight............... 134
Watkins (R.G.), Somerset 215
Westwood Books Ltd, Cumbria..................... 80
Wetherell (Frances), Cambridgeshire 65
Woodbine Books, West Yorkshire................. 245
Worlds End Bookshop, London SW 169
Wyseby House Books, Berks 55
York (Graham), Devon............................... 86

ARTHURIAN (KING ARTHUR)

Addyman Books, Powys.............................. 287
Annie's Books, South Yorkshire 221
Antique Map and Bookshop (The), Dorset 94
Apocalypse, Surrey 232
Backfield Books, Herefordshire.................... 127
Baker Limited (A.P. & R.), Dumfries &
   Galloway.. 269
Bennett & Kerr Books, Oxfordshire 205
Boer (Louise), Arthurian Books, Powys 287
Bonython Bookshop, Cornwall..................... 75
Byre Books, Dumfries & Galloway................ 270
Cheshire Book Centre, Cheshire.................... 69
Cofion Books, Pembrokeshire 286
Daeron's Books, Buckinghamshire................. 62
Dolphin Books, Suffolk 225
Dylans Bookstore, Swansea......................... 291
Fifteenth Century Bookshop (The), East Sussex. 104
Green Man Books, East Sussex 101
Greer (Robin), London SW.......................... 167
Inner Bookshop (The), Oxfordshire................ 208
Joel Segal Books, Devon 86
Jonkers Rare Books, Oxfordshire 207
Minster Gate Bookshop, North Yorkshire 197
PsychoBabel Books & Journals, Oxfordshire..... 205
R. & A. Books, East Sussex 101
Randall (Tom), Somerset............................. 218
Whitchurch Books Ltd., Cardiff.................... 281
Wiend Books, Lancashire 143
Wizard Books, Cambridgeshire..................... 67

ARTISTS

Addyman Books, Powys.............................. 287
Amwell Book Company, London EC.............. 155
Apocalypse, Surrey 232
Ars Artis, Oxfordshire 207
Art Book Company, (The), Suffolk................ 227
Art Reference Books, Hampshire 124
Artco, Nottinghamshire.............................. 204

Aurora Books Ltd, Lothian.......................... 275
Aviabooks, Gloucestershire 114
baconboooks, London WC 176
Ballantyne–Way (Roger), Suffolk 228
Book Palace (The), London SE 163
Bookroom (The), Surrey............................. 233
Books, Kent 137
Booth (Booksearch Service), (Geoff), Cheshire... 68
Bow Windows Book Shop, East Sussex 103
Brock Books, North Yorkshire..................... 192
Brown-Studies, Strathclyde......................... 277
Bruce Holdsworth Books, East Sussex 105
Butts Books (Mary), Berks.......................... 56
C J Renwick Books, Powys......................... 287
Cameron House Books, Isle of Wight............. 133
Campbell Art Books (Marcus), London SE...... 163
Chalk (Old & Out of Print Books)
   (Christine M.), West Midlands 238
Cheshire Book Centre, Cheshire.................... 69
Clark (Nigel A.), London SE 163
Cofion Books, Pembrokeshire 286
Cornucopia Books, Lincolnshire 151
Darkwood Books, Co. Cork......................... 263
Dartmoor Bookshop (The), Devon 84
David Flint, Hampshire 124
Decorum Books, London N 156
Ellis, Bookseller (Peter), London WC 177
Embleton (Paul), Essex 111
Evans Books (Paul), West Sussex 243
Fine Art Catalogues, Cumbria 80
Foster (Stephen), London NW 160
Harwich Old Books, Essex.......................... 109
Hodgkins and Company Limited (Ian),
   Gloucestershire.................................... 116
IDEA, London EC.................................... 155
Jack and Molly's Trading Co....................... 90
Jade Mountain Bookshop, Hampshire 125
Jane & John Kinnaird, Cumbria 78
JB Books & Collectables, West Sussex 243
Jean Hedger, Berks 55
Joel Segal Books, Devon 86
Just Books, Cornwall 75
Kenny's Bookshop & Art Galleries Ltd.,
   Co. Galway 265
Keogh's Books, Gloucestershire.................... 115
Langford Press, Lincolnshire........................ 151
Martin - Bookseller (Colin), East Yorkshire 107
McEwan Fine Books, Grampian..................... 272
Myra Dean Illustated Books, Powys 287
Newcastle Bookshop At Haltwhistle,
   Northumberland 201
Not Just Books, Dorset.............................. 94
Optimus Books Ltd, West Sussex 244
Peter Lyons Books, Gloucestershire 113
Print Matters, London SE........................... 165
R. & A. Books, East Sussex 101
Ray Rare and Out of Print Books (Janette),
   North Yorkshire 198
Read - Gorleston Books, (C.&J.), Norfolk 187
Rickaro Books, West Yorkshire.................... 246
Saint Swithin's Illustrated & Children's Books,
   London W 174
Sephton (A.F.), London W 174
Sims Reed Limited, London SW 169
Stevens (Joan), Cambridgeshire..................... 65

Studio Bookshop, East Sussex 100
Sue Lowell Natural History Books, London W . 175
Trinders' Fine Tools, Suffolk 226
Uncle Phil's Books, West Midlands 239
Upper–Room Books, Somerset...................... 217
Westwood Books Ltd, Cumbria................... 80
Woburn Books, London N 159
Woodbine Books, West Yorkshire................. 245
Wyseby House Books, Berks 55

ARTISTS - CHICAGO
Decorum Books, London N 156
R. & A. Books, East Sussex 101

ARTS & CRAFTS ERA
Addyman Books, Powys............................. 287
Annie's Books, South Yorkshire 221
Books & Things, London W........................ 171
Bruce Holdsworth Books, East Sussex 105
Decorum Books, London N 156
Design Gallery 1850-1950 (The), Kent 141
Dolphin Books, Suffolk.............................. 225
Hornsey's, North Yorkshire......................... 194
Jade Mountain Bookshop, Hampshire 125
Joel Segal Books, Devon 86
Orchid Book Distributors, Co. Clare.............. 262
Pagan Limited (Hugh), Hampshire 122
R. & A. Books, East Sussex 101
Reeves Technical Books, North Yorkshire 195
Woodbine Books, West Yorkshire................. 245

ARTS, THE
Addyman Books, Powys............................. 287
All Books, Essex 111
Amwell Book Company, London EC............. 155
Apocalypse, Surrey 232
Art Book Company, (The), Suffolk................ 227
Artco, Nottinghamshire.............................. 204
Aurora Books Ltd, Lothian......................... 275
Ballantyne–Way (Roger), Suffolk 228
Batterham (David), London W..................... 171
Beware of the Leopard, Bristol..................... 58
Book Annex (The), Essex 109
Book Business (The), London W 171
Book Palace (The), London SE 163
Bookbox, Gloucestershire 115
Brock Books, North Yorkshire..................... 192
Bruce Holdsworth Books, East Sussex 105
C J Renwick Books, Powys......................... 287
Camilla's Bookshop, East Sussex 101
Chaucer Bookshop, Kent............................ 136
Cofion Books, Pembrokeshire 286
Collectable Books, London SE 163
Cornucopia Books, Lincolnshire 151
Cover to Cover, Merseyside......................... 185
D'Arcy Books, Wiltshire............................ 252
Darkwood Books, Co. Cork 263
Decorum Books, London N 156
Dennys Sanders & Greene Ltd, East Sussex 100
Dolphin Books, Suffolk.............................. 225
Don Kelly Books, London W 172
Ellis, Bookseller (Peter), London WC 177
Evans Books (Paul), West Sussex 243
Farnborough Gallery, Hampshire................... 122
Fossgate Books, North Yorkshire 197

Foster (Stephen), London NW 160
Harwich Old Books, Essex.......................... 109
Hawley (C.L.), North Yorkshire 195
Hornsey's, North Yorkshire......................... 194
Ice House Books, Wiltshire 254
IDEA, London EC.................................... 155
Jane & John Kinnaird, Cumbria................... 78
Joel Segal Books, Devon 86
Junk & Spread Eagle, London SE................. 164
Just Books, Cornwall 75
Kim's Bookshop, West Sussex............... 241, 242
Lenton (Alfred), Leics............................... 145
Little Bookshop (The),
  Greater Manchester 119
Lyonshill Books, Co. Dublin 265
Martin - Bookseller (Colin), East Yorkshire 107
Martin (Books and Pictures), (Brian P)., Surrey . 231
Murch Booksend, (Herbert), London SE......... 165
N1 Books, East Sussex 105
Newcastle Bookshop At Haltwhistle,
  Northumberland 201
Newlyn Books, Cornwall............................ 74
Peter Lyons Books, Gloucestershire 113
Pordes Books Ltd., (Henry), London WC........ 177
Print Matters, London SE........................... 165
R. & A. Books, East Sussex 101
Ray Rare and Out of Print Books (Janette),
  North Yorkshire 198
Read - Gorleston Books, (C.&J.), Norfolk 187
Richard Thornton Books, London N 158
Susanne Schulz-Falster Rare Books, London N. 158
Till's Bookshop, Lothian............................ 277
Trade Priced Old Books, Powys.................... 289
Trinders' Fine Tools, Suffolk 226
Trinity Rare Books, Co. Leitrim 266
Tucker (Alan & Joan), Gloucestershire 116
Uncle Phil's Books, West Midlands 239
Waterfield's, Oxfordshire 209
Wizard Books, Cambridgeshire..................... 67
Woburn Books, London N 159
Wyseby House Books, Berks 55

ASIAN STUDIES
Cavendish Rare Books, London N 156
Eastern Traveller (The), Somerset.................. 219
Hanshan Tang Books, London SW 167
Joel Segal Books, Devon 86
Joppa Books Ltd., Surrey 230
Mandalay Bookshop, London SW 168
Prospect House Books, Co. Down................. 261
PsychoBabel Books & Journals, Oxfordshire..... 205
R. & A. Books, East Sussex 101
Rayner (Hugh Ashley), Somerset 215
Reading Lasses, Dumfries & Galloway 270
Thorntons of Oxford Ltd., Oxfordshire........... 206

ASIAN-AMERICAN STUDIES
R. & A. Books, East Sussex 101
Watkins Books Ltd., London WC................. 179

ASSASSINATIONS
Clifford Elmer Books Ltd., Cheshire 68
Crimes Ink, London E................................ 154
R. & A. Books, East Sussex 101

ASSOCIATIONS - GAELIC ATHLETIC
Lyonshill Books, Co. Dublin 265

ASTROLOGY
Alpha Books, London N 156
Bookbarrow, Cambridgeshire........................ 63
Books, Denbighshire 284
Caduceus Books, Leics............................. 145
Cheshire Book Centre, Cheshire.................... 69
Cofion Books, Pembrokeshire 286
Delectus Books, London WC........................ 176
Glyn's Books, Shropshire.......................... 212
Green Man Books, East Sussex 101
Greensleeves, Oxfordshire 206
Inner Bookshop (The), Oxfordshire................ 208
Jade Mountain Bookshop, Hampshire 125
Joel Segal Books, Devon 86
Occultique, Northants............................. 199
Old Book Company, (The), West Yorkshire 248
R. & A. Books, East Sussex 101
Star Lord Books, Greater Manchester 119
Watkins Books Ltd., London WC.................. 179
Waxfactor, East Sussex 100

ASTRONAUTICS
Duck (William), Hampshire........................ 124
K Books, Cheshire................................. 70
R. & A. Books, East Sussex 101
Stroh (M.A.), London E 154
Westons, Herts 132
Westwood Books Ltd, Cumbria.................... 80

ASTRONOMY
Addyman Books, Powys............................ 287
Altea Antique Maps & Books, London W....... 171
Apocalypse, Surrey 232
Aviabooks, Gloucestershire 114
Baldwin's Scientific Books, Essex 111
Bookshop on the Heath, The, London SE 163
Cheshire Book Centre, Cheshire.................... 69
Cofion Books, Pembrokeshire 286
Esplin (David), Hampshire......................... 124
Hadfield (G.K.), Cumbria.......................... 79
Jade Mountain Bookshop, Hampshire 125
Just Books, Cornwall 75
Macfarlane (Mr. H.), Essex 111
Moorside Books, Lancashire....................... 143
N1 Books, East Sussex 105
Phelps (Michael), West Sussex 242
Portobello Books, London W 174
Quaritch Ltd., (Bernard), London W.............. 174
R. & A. Books, East Sussex 101
Rebecca Hardie Rare Books, London W.......... 171
Stroh (M.A.), London E 154
Transformer, Dumfries & Galloway............... 270
Turret House, Norfolk............................. 191
Wayside Books and Cards, Oxfordshire 206
Westons, Herts 132
Westwood Books Ltd, Cumbria.................... 80
Wiend Books, Lancashire 143

ATLASES
Adrem Books, Herts 130
Altea Antique Maps & Books, London W....... 171
Apocalypse, Surrey 232

Arthur Hook, Bristol.............................. 58
Barron (Robert M.), Kent.......................... 139
Baynton–Williams Gallery, West Sussex 241
Burden Ltd., (Clive A.), Herts..................... 131
Channel Islands Galleries Limited,
  Channel Islands 258
Cheshire Book Centre, Cheshire.................... 69
Clevedon Books, Somerset 217
Copperplate Antique Maps and Prints, Herts.... 132
Corvus Books, Buckinghamshire................... 61
Cumming Limited (A. & Y.), East Sussex........ 104
Frew Limited (Robert), London SW 167
G. C. Books Ltd., Dumfries & Galloway......... 270
Garwood & Voigt, Kent............................ 139
Gillmark Gallery, Herts............................ 130
Green (Mrs. D.M.), Surrey......................... 234
Harrington Antiquarian Bookseller (Peter),
  London SW..................................... 167
Hava Books, London SE........................... 164
Heritage, West Midlands 238
Hogan (F. & J.), London N 157
Kennedy (Peter), Surrey 234
Kentish (B. & N.), Oxfordshire.................... 205
Lymelight Books & Prints, Dorset................. 93
Marshall Rare Books (Bruce), Gloucestershire... 113
Martin (Brian), Surrey 231
Michael Graves-Johnston, London SW 168
Murphy (C.J.), Norfolk............................ 189
Neil Summersgill, Lancashire 142
Nicholson of Chester (Richard), Cheshire 68
O'Flynn Books, North Yorkshire 197
Old Book Company, (The), West Yorkshire 248
Preston Book Company, Lancashire 144
R. & A. Books, East Sussex 101
Roz Hulse, Conwy 284
Russell (Charles), London SW..................... 169
Shapero Rare Books (Bernard J.), London W ... 175
Temperley (David), West Midlands 238
Tim Bryers Ltd, London WC 178
Yates Antiquarian Books (Tony), Leics........... 146

ATOMIC
Wayside Books and Cards, Oxfordshire 206

AUCTION CATALOGUES
Aitchison (Lesley), Bristol 58
Apocalypse, Surrey 232
Bookshop on the Heath, The, London SE 163
Campbell Art Books (Marcus), London SE...... 163
Clark (Nigel A.), London SE....................... 163
Fossgate Books, North Yorkshire 197
JB Books & Collectables, West Sussex 243
Not Just Books, Dorset............................ 94
Period & Classical Collections, East Sussex 103
R. & A. Books, East Sussex 101
Stroh (M.A.), London E 154
Studio Bookshop, East Sussex...................... 100
Susanne Schulz-Falster Rare Books, London N. 158
Thornber (Peter M.), North Yorkshire........... 195
Watkins (R.G.), Somerset 215

AUDIO/SOUND/ACOUSTICS
Kelly Books Ltd, Devon............................ 89
Maggy Browne, Lincolnshire 148
Watkins Books Ltd., London WC................. 179

AUSTRALIANA

Alexander's Books, Warwickshire 237
Antique Prints of the World, London N 156
Bonham (J. & S.L.), London W 171
Eggeling Books (John), West Yorkshire 249
Ely Books, Cambridgeshire 65
Empire Books, North Yorkshire 197
Joel Segal Books, Devon 86
Michael Graves-Johnston, London SW 168
MK Book Services, Cambridgeshire 66
Moore (Peter), Cambridgeshire 64
Preston Book Company, Lancashire 144
Quaritch Ltd., (Bernard), London W 174
Watkins Books Ltd., London WC 179

AUTHOR
- GENERAL

Aurora Books Ltd, Lothian 275
Bookpassage (The), Shropshire 212
books2books, Devon 88
Broadwater Books, Hampshire 125
Colwyn Books, Conwy 283
Cornucopia Books, Lincolnshire 151
Eggeling Books (John), West Yorkshire 249
Ely Books, Cambridgeshire 65
Harrington (Adrian), London W 173
Hylton Booksearch, Merseyside 184
J & J Burgess Booksellers, Cambridgeshire 64
Jackdaw Books, Norfolk 188
Jade Mountain Bookshop, Hampshire 125
Joel Segal Books, Devon 86
Kingfisher Book Service, Nottinghamshire 204
Murphy (C.J.), Norfolk 189
Oak Tree Press, Oxfordshire 207
Priestpopple Books, Northumberland 201
R. & A. Books, East Sussex 101
Reading Lasses, Dumfries & Galloway 270
Simpson (Dave), Central 268
Star Lord Books, Greater Manchester 119
Watkins Books Ltd., London WC 179
Wheen O'Books, Borders 267

- 19TH CENTURY

Ash Rare Books, London SW 166
Beaton (Richard), East Sussex 103
Bookroom (The), Surrey 233
Carraig Books Ltd., Co. Dublin 263
Derek Stirling Bookseller, Kent 141
Dolphin Books, Suffolk 225
Doolin Dinghy Books, Co. Clare 262
Fifteenth Century Bookshop (The), East Sussex. 104
Foster Bookshop (Paul), London SW 167
Jack and Molly's Trading Co 90
John L Capes (Books Maps & Prints), North
    Yorkshire 196
Jonkers Rare Books, Oxfordshire 207
Park Gallery & Bookshop (The), Northants 200
Quaritch Ltd., (Bernard), London W 174
Robert Temple, London N 158
Simpson (Dave), Central 268
Stevens (Joan), Cambridgeshire 65
Tiger Books, Kent 136

- 20TH CENTURY

Apocalypse, Surrey 232

Ash Rare Books, London SW 166
Aurora Books Ltd, Lothian 275
Barmby (C. & A.J.), Kent 140
Beaton (Richard), East Sussex 103
Bookpassage (The), Shropshire 212
Bookroom (The), Surrey 233
books2books, Devon 88
Carraig Books Ltd., Co. Dublin 263
Cornucopia Books, Lincolnshire 151
Dolphin Books, Suffolk 225
Eggeling Books (John), West Yorkshire 249
Elaine Lonsdale Books, West Yorkshire 247
Fifteenth Century Bookshop (The), East Sussex. 104
Foster Bookshop (Paul), London SW 167
Good for Books, Lincolnshire 149
Island Books, Devon 85
Jack and Molly's Trading Co 90
Joel Segal Books, Devon 86
Jonkers Rare Books, Oxfordshire 207
Mannwaring (M.G.), Bristol 59
Marble Hill Books, Outer London 182
Mellon's Books, East Sussex 101
Oak Tree Press, Oxfordshire 207
Park Gallery & Bookshop (The), Northants 200
R. & A. Books, East Sussex 101
Rhodes, Bookseller (Peter), Hampshire 125
Robert Temple, London N 158
SaBeRo Books, London SW 169
Simpson (Dave), Central 268
The Glass Key, West Yorkshire 246

- ABBEY, EDWIN
Trinity Rare Books, Co. Leitrim 266

- AESOP
Bookmark (Children's Books), Wiltshire 253
Byre Books, Dumfries & Galloway 270
Fifteenth Century Bookshop (The), East Sussex. 104
Jean Hedger, Berks 55
R. & A. Books, East Sussex 101

- AHLBERG, JANET & ALLAN
Bookmark (Children's Books), Wiltshire 253
Cranhurst Books, London NW 160
Draca Books, West Yorkshire 248
Fifteenth Century Bookshop (The), East Sussex. 104
Intech Books, Northumberland 201
Jean Hedger, Berks 55

- AICKMAN, R.
Harrington (Adrian), London W 173
R. & A. Books, East Sussex 101
Trinity Rare Books, Co. Leitrim 266

- ALCOTTS, THE
Bilski (Gill), Buckinghamshire 61
Elaine Lonsdale Books, West Yorkshire 247
Jean Hedger, Berks 55

- ALDIN, CECIL
Bookmark (Children's Books), Wiltshire 253
Booth (Booksearch Service), (Geoff), Cheshire... 68
Children's Bookshop (The), Herefordshire 127
Cranhurst Books, London NW 160
Fifteenth Century Bookshop (The), East Sussex. 104

Garfi Books, Powys 291
Jean Hedger, Berks.................................... 55
Jonkers Rare Books, Oxfordshire 207
Lucius Books, North Yorkshire.................... 197
R. & A. Books, East Sussex 101
Rothwell & Dunworth, Somerset 217
St Mary's Books & Prints, Lincolnshire 152

- AMICIS, EDMONDO DE
Trinity Rare Books, Co. Leitrim 266

- ANNA KAVAN
Riderless Horse Books, Norfolk.................... 186

- ARDIZZONE, EDWARD
Allinson (Frank & Stella), Warwickshire 236
Bookmark (Children's Books), Wiltshire.......... 253
Booth (Booksearch Service), (Geoff), Cheshire... 68
Cameron House Books, Isle of Wight 133
Children's Bookshop (The), Herefordshire....... 127
Cranhurst Books, London NW 160
Criterion Books, London O........................ 181
Draca Books, West Yorkshire...................... 248
Fifteenth Century Bookshop (The), East Sussex. 104
Jean Hedger, Berks.................................. 55
Key Books (Sarah), Cambridgeshire.............. 64
Mason (Mary), Oxfordshire......................... 205
Myra Dean Illustated Books, Powys 287
Old Station Pottery & Bookshop (The), Norfolk 191
Periwinkle Press, Kent 136
R. & A. Books, East Sussex 101

- ARMOUR, G. D.
Garfi Books, Powys 291
Jean Hedger, Berks.................................. 55
Trinity Rare Books, Co. Leitrim 266

- ARNOLD, MATTHEW
Jarndyce Antiquarian Booksellers, London WC. 177
Tiger Books, Kent 136

- ASIMOV, ISAAC
Adrem Books, Herts 130
Annie's Books, South Yorkshire 221
Apocalypse, Surrey 232
Bookworms Paradise Ltd., West Sussex 242
Booth (Booksearch Service), (Geoff), Cheshire... 68
Cranhurst Books, London NW 160
Esoteric Dreams Bookshop, Cumbria 77
Simpson (Dave), Central 268
Wayside Books and Cards, Oxfordshire 206

- AUSTEN, JANE
Apocalypse, Surrey 232
Booth (Booksearch Service), (Geoff), Cheshire... 68
Boris Books, Somerset 216
Boz Books, Powys 287
Burmester (James), Bristol.......................... 58
Cofion Books, Pembrokeshire 286
Cox, Andrew, Shropshire............................ 214
Dolphin Books, Suffolk............................. 225
Foster Bookshop (Paul), London SW 167
Glenwood Books, Surrey 234
Hodgkins and Company Limited (Ian),
   Gloucestershire..................................... 116

Island Books, Devon.................................. 85
Jarndyce Antiquarian Booksellers, London WC. 177
Liddle (Steve), Bristol 58
R. & A. Books, East Sussex 101
Rye Old Books, East Sussex 104
Sharpe (Mary), Somerset 219
Tiger Books, Kent 136
Trinity Rare Books, Co. Leitrim 266
Valentine Rare Books, London W................. 175
Webb Books (John), South Yorkshire............. 221

- BADEN-POWELL, LORD ROBERT
Chalmers Hallam (E.), Hampshire................. 125
Greta Books, Durham 97
R. & A. Books, East Sussex 101
White (C.R.), London W............................ 175

- BAEDEKER, KARL TRAVEL: ANTIQUARIAN
Adrem Books, Herts 130
Hodgson (Books) (Richard J.), North Yorkshire 196
Shapero Rare Books (Bernard J.), London W ... 175

- BAINBRIDGE, BERYL
Annie's Books, South Yorkshire 221
Apocalypse, Surrey 232
Booth (Booksearch Service), (Geoff), Cheshire... 68
Cranhurst Books, London NW 160
Dolphin Books, Suffolk............................. 225
Intech Books, Northumberland 201
R. & A. Books, East Sussex 101
Surprise Books, Gloucestershire 113
Trinity Rare Books, Co. Leitrim 266

- BAKER, DENYS V.
Island Books, Devon................................. 85
Mount's Bay Books, Cornwall 74
Portus Books, Hampshire 122

- BALDWIN, JAMES
Black Voices, Merseyside............................ 184

- BALLANTYNE, ROBERT M.
Beaton (Richard), East Sussex...................... 103
Bookmark (Children's Books), Wiltshire.......... 253
Booth (Booksearch Service), (Geoff), Cheshire... 68
Boz Books, Powys 287
Dolphin Books, Suffolk............................. 225
Fifteenth Century Bookshop (The), East Sussex. 104
Oasis Booksearch, Cambridgeshire................. 67
R. & A. Books, East Sussex 101
Tiger Books, Kent 136
Trinity Rare Books, Co. Leitrim 266

- BARING-GOULD, S.
Beaton (Richard), East Sussex...................... 103
Chapter Two, London SE............................ 163
Country Books, Derbyshire 82
Ely Books, Cambridgeshire 65
Island Books, Devon................................. 85
Randall (Tom), Somerset............................ 218
Shacklock Books (David), Suffolk 226
Tiger Books, Kent 136

- BARKER, CECILY M.

Bookmark (Children's Books), Wiltshire.......... 253
Dolphin Books, Suffolk............................. 225
Fifteenth Century Bookshop (The), East Sussex. 104
First Edition, The, Essex 109
Intech Books, Northumberland 201
Jean Hedger, Berks.................................. 55
Key Books (Sarah), Cambridgeshire............... 64
Lucius Books, North Yorkshire.................... 197
Simpson (Dave), Central 268

- BARKER, CLIVE

Annie's Books, South Yorkshire 221
Apocalypse, Surrey 232

- BARNES, DJUNA

Norton Books, North Yorkshire 192

- BARNES, WILLIAM

Antique Map and Bookshop (The), Dorset 94
Country Books, Derbyshire......................... 82
Tiger Books, Kent................................... 136

- BARRIE, J.M.

Adrem Books, Herts 130
Bookmark (Children's Books), Wiltshire.......... 253
Cranhurst Books, London NW 160
Criterion Books, London O......................... 181
Fifteenth Century Bookshop (The), East Sussex. 104
First Edition, The, Essex 109
Green Meadow Books, Cornwall 74
Greta Books, Durham 97
Jean Hedger, Berks.................................. 55
Orb's Bookshop, Grampian......................... 273
R. & A. Books, East Sussex 101
Roz Hulse, Conwy 284
Simpson (Dave), Central 268
Tiger Books, Kent................................... 136

- BATES, H.E.

Apocalypse, Surrey 232
Bass (Ben), Wiltshire 251
Bookshop on the Heath, The, London SE 163
Country Books, Derbyshire 82
Emjay Books, Surrey................................ 231
Heppa (Christopher), Essex 108
Intech Books, Northumberland 201
Island Books, Devon................................ 85
Park Gallery & Bookshop (The), Northants 200
R. & A. Books, East Sussex 101
Simpson (Dave), Central 268
Webb Books (John), South Yorkshire............. 221

- BAUM, FRANK

Bookmark (Children's Books), Wiltshire.......... 253
R. & A. Books, East Sussex 101

- BEARDSLEY, AUBREY

Apocalypse, Surrey 232
Books & Things, London W......................... 171
Booth (Booksearch Service), (Geoff), Cheshire... 68
Intech Books, Northumberland 201
Jean Hedger, Berks.................................. 55
R. & A. Books, East Sussex 101
Roz Hulse, Conwy 284

- BEATON, CECIL

Apocalypse, Surrey 232
Books & Things, London W......................... 171
R. & A. Books, East Sussex 101

- BECKETT, S.

Apocalypse, Surrey 232
Courtwood Books, Co. Laois....................... 265
Modern First Editions, West Yorkshire........... 247
Norton Books, North Yorkshire 192
Parrott (Jeremy), London E......................... 154
R. & A. Books, East Sussex 101
Read Ireland, Co. Dublin 264
Trinity Rare Books, Co. Leitrim 266

- BELL, ADRIAN

Besleys Books, Suffolk 225
Books Only, Suffolk................................. 226
Country Books, Derbyshire 82
Debbage (John), Norfolk........................... 189
Dolphin Books, Suffolk............................. 225

- BELL, GERTRUDE

Joppa Books Ltd., Surrey 230

- BELLAIRES, GEORGE

James M Pickhard (Rare Books), Leics........... 145
Ming Books, Dumfries & Galloway 270
Treasure Trove Books, Leics....................... 146

- BELLOC, HILAIRE

Armchair Books, Lothian 275
Bookmark (Children's Books), Wiltshire.......... 253
Carraig Books Ltd., Co. Dublin 263
Country Books, Derbyshire 82
Dolphin Books, Suffolk............................. 225
Fifteenth Century Bookshop (The), East Sussex. 104
Intech Books, Northumberland 201
Island Books, Devon................................ 85
R. & A. Books, East Sussex 101
Rosley Books, Cumbria 81
St Philip's Books, Oxfordshire 208
Simpson (Dave), Central 268
Tiger Books, Kent................................... 136

- BENNETT, (ENOCH) ARNOL

Ash Rare Books, London SW....................... 166
Bookshop on the Heath, The, London SE 163
Boris Books, Somerset 216
Tiger Books, Kent................................... 136

- BENNETT, J.G.

Needham Books, (Russell), Somerset.............. 219
R. & A. Books, East Sussex 101
Watkins Books Ltd., London WC.................. 179

- BENSON, A.C.

Booth (Booksearch Service), (Geoff), Cheshire... 68
Eggeling Books (John), West Yorkshire 249
Island Books, Devon................................ 85
Tiger Books, Kent................................... 136

- BENSON, E.F.

Beaton (Richard), East Sussex..................... 103
Booth (Booksearch Service), (Geoff), Cheshire... 68

Boris Books, Somerset 216
Eggeling Books (John), West Yorkshire 249
Parrott (Jeremy), London E........................ 154
The Meads Book Service, East Sussex 101
Tiger Books, Kent.................................. 136
Tsbbooks, London SW 169

- BENSON, R.H.

Beaton (Richard), East Sussex..................... 103
Carraig Books Ltd., Co. Dublin 263
Eggeling Books (John), West Yorkshire 249
Jackdaw Books, Norfolk 188
St Philip's Books, Oxfordshire..................... 208

- BETJEMAN, SIR JOHN

Baker - Books for the Collector (Colin), Devon . 89
Booth (Booksearch Service), (Geoff), Cheshire... 68
Boris Books, Somerset 216
Ellis, Bookseller (Peter), London WC 177
Fifteenth Century Bookshop (The), East Sussex. 104
Intech Books, Northumberland 201
Island Books, Devon............................... 85
Jonkers Rare Books, Oxfordshire 207
McGee (Terence J.), London O 180

- BLACKSTONE, SIR WILLIAM

Jackdaw Books, Norfolk 188

- BLACKWOOD, A.

Delectus Books, London WC....................... 176
Eggeling Books (John), West Yorkshire 249
Fantastic Literature, Essex 110

- BLAKE, N.

Sutcliffe (Mark), West Yorkshire.................. 248

- BLAKE, SEXTON

D. & M. Books, West Yorkshire.................. 249
Wright (Norman), Dorset 95

- BLOOMSBURY GROUP, THE

Bow Windows Book Shop, East Sussex 103
Bruce Holdsworth Books, East Sussex 105
Criterion Books, London O........................ 181
Evans Books (Paul), West Sussex 243
Fifteenth Century Bookshop (The), East Sussex. 104
Island Books, Devon............................... 85
Modern First Editions, West Yorkshire.......... 247
Much Ado Books, East Sussex.................... 99
R. & A. Books, East Sussex 101
Tiger Books, Kent 136

- BLYTON, ENID

Adrem Books, Herts 130
Annie's Books, South Yorkshire 221
Apocalypse, Surrey 232
Beck (John), East Sussex 103
Bookmark (Children's Books), Wiltshire.......... 253
Bookshop on the Heath, The, London SE 163
Bookworms Paradise Ltd., West Sussex 242
Boris Books, Somerset 216
Chapter Two, London SE.......................... 163
Cofion Books, Pembrokeshire 286
Cygnet Books, East Yorkshire..................... 107
D. & M. Books, West Yorkshire.................. 249

Draca Books, West Yorkshire...................... 248
Facet Books, Dorset............................... 91
Fifteenth Century Bookshop (The), East Sussex. 104
Green Meadow Books, Cornwall 74
Heppa (Christopher), Essex 108
James M Pickhard (Rare Books), Leics........... 145
Jonkers Rare Books, Oxfordshire 207
K Books, Cheshire................................. 70
Kelpie's Books, Fife............................... 271
Key Books (Sarah), Cambridgeshire............... 64
Kingfisher Book Service, Nottinghamshire 204
Lake (David), Norfolk............................. 190
Little Stour Books, Kent 136
Lucius Books, North Yorkshire.................... 197
Mercat Books, Highland 274
Oasis Booksearch, Cambridgeshire................ 67
Old Celtic Bookshop (The), Devon 87
Park Gallery & Bookshop (The), Northants 200
R. & A. Books, East Sussex 101
Schutte (David), Hampshire....................... 124
Sesemann (Julia), Kent............................ 135
Simpson (Dave), Central 268
Stella Books, Monmouthshire 286
Surprise Books, Gloucestershire 113
Talisman Books, Cheshire......................... 70
Treasure Trove Books, Leics...................... 146
Wright (Norman), Dorset 95

- BORGES, J.L.

Adrem Books, Herts 130

- BORROW, GEORGE

Adrem Books, Herts 130
Country Books, Derbyshire........................ 82
Debbage (John), Norfolk 189
Nineteenth Century Books, Oxfordshire 209
Orb's Bookshop, Grampian........................ 273
Tiger Books, Kent................................. 136
York (Graham), Devon............................ 86

- BOSWELL, JAMES

Evans Books (Paul), West Sussex 243
Island Books, Devon............................... 85

- BOWEN, M.

Dolphin Books, Suffolk 225
Eggeling Books (John), West Yorkshire 249

- BOWLES, PAUL

Adrem Books, Herts 130
Criterion Books, London O........................ 181
Riderless Horse Books, Norfolk................... 186
Trinity Rare Books, Co. Leitrim 266

- BRADBURY, RAY

Annie's Books, South Yorkshire 221
Bookworms Paradise Ltd., West Sussex 242

- BRADDON, MARY ELIZABETH

Beaton (Richard), East Sussex..................... 103
Boz Books, Powys................................. 287
Tiger Books, Kent................................. 136

- BRAMAH, ERNEST

Dolphin Books, Suffolk............................ 225

Lucius Books, North Yorkshire 197
Webb Books (John), South Yorkshire............. 221

- BRENT-DYER, ELINOR M.
Allinson (Frank & Stella), Warwickshire 236
Annie's Books, South Yorkshire 221
Badger Books, Somerset............................ 219
Bilski (Gill), Buckinghamshire 61
Bookmark (Children's Books), Wiltshire.......... 253
Boris Books, Somerset 216
Children's Bookshop (The), Herefordshire....... 127
D. & M. Books, West Yorkshire.................... 249
Fifteenth Century Bookshop (The), East Sussex. 104
Green Meadow Books, Cornwall 74
Intech Books, Northumberland 201
Key Books (Sarah), Cambridgeshire.............. 64
Little Stour Books, Kent 136
Lucius Books, North Yorkshire 197
Mercat Books, Highland 274
Sims (Sue), Dorset 91
TP Children's Bookshop, West Yorkshire....... 245
Treasure Trove Books, Leics...................... 146

- BROMFIELD, LOUIS
Dolphin Books, Suffolk............................ 225

- BRONTES, THE
Boris Books, Somerset 216
Boz Books, Powys.................................. 287
Dolphin Books, Suffolk............................ 225
Grove Bookshop (The), North Yorkshire 195
Hatchard & Daughters, West Yorkshire.......... 246
Hodgkins and Company Limited (Ian),
    Gloucestershire 116
Idle Booksellers (The), West Yorkshire 245
Jonkers Rare Books, Oxfordshire.................. 207
Modern First Editions, West Yorkshire........... 247
Period & Classical Collections, East Sussex 103
R. & A. Books, East Sussex 101
Sharpe (Mary), Somerset 219
Tiger Books, Kent 136

- BROOKE, RUPERT
Annie's Books, South Yorkshire 221
Apocalypse, Surrey 232
Ellis, Bookseller (Peter), London WC 177
R. & A. Books, East Sussex 101
Simpson (Dave), Central 268
Smith Books (Keith), Herefordshire 128

- BROWNING, ROBERT
Cox Rare Books (Charles), Cornwall.............. 73
R. & A. Books, East Sussex 101
Rosley Books, Cumbria 81
Tiger Books, Kent 136

- BRUCE, MARY GRANT
Bilski (Gill), Buckinghamshire 61
Fifteenth Century Bookshop (The), East Sussex. 104

- BUCHAN, JOHN
Armchair Books, Lothian 275
Avonworld Books, Somerset....................... 216
Bannatyne Books, London N....................... 156
Booth (Booksearch Service), (Geoff), Cheshire... 68

Coch-y-Bonddu Books, Powys 290
Ellis, Bookseller (Peter), London WC 177
Greta Books, Durham 97
Heppa (Christopher), Essex 108
Orb's Bookshop, Grampian......................... 273
Pringle Booksellers (Andrew), Lothian 277
Simpson (Dave), Central 268
Tiger Books, Kent 136

- BUCKERIDGE, A.
Adrem Books, Herts 130
Baker - Books for the Collector (Colin), Devon. 89
Beck (John), East Sussex 103
Bookmark (Children's Books), Wiltshire.......... 253
Booth (Booksearch Service), (Geoff), Cheshire... 68
Children's Bookshop (The), Herefordshire....... 127
Draca Books, West Yorkshire...................... 248
Fifteenth Century Bookshop (The), East Sussex. 104
Key Books (Sarah), Cambridgeshire.............. 64
Little Stour Books, Kent 136
R. & A. Books, East Sussex 101
Schutte (David), Hampshire........................ 124
Treasure Trove Books, Leics...................... 146

- BUKOWSKI, CHARLES
Apocalypse, Surrey 232
Sclanders (Beatbooks), (Andrew), London EC... 155

- BUNYAN, JOHN
Bunyan Books, Bedfordshire....................... 53
Chapter Two, London SE........................... 163
Kirkman Ltd., (Robert), Bedfordshire............. 54
Oasis Booksearch, Cambridgeshire................. 67
Rosley Books, Cumbria 81

- BURGESS, A.
Adrem Books, Herts 130
Cranhurst Books, London NW 160
Ellis, Bookseller (Peter), London WC 177
Olynthiacs, Shropshire 213
Simpson (Dave), Central 268

- BURNEY, FANNY
Dolphin Books, Suffolk............................ 225
Island Books, Devon 85
Sharpe (Mary), Somerset 219
Tiger Books, Kent 136

- BURNS, ROBERT
Adrem Books, Herts 130
Mercat Books, Highland 274
Orb's Bookshop, Grampian......................... 273
Tiger Books, Kent 136

- BURROUGHS, EDGAR R.
Adrem Books, Herts 130
Book Palace (The), London SE 163
Eggeling Books (John), West Yorkshire 249

- BURROUGHS, WILLIAM
Apocalypse, Surrey 232
Lucius Books, North Yorkshire 197
Sclanders (Beatbooks), (Andrew), London EC... 155
Watkins Books Ltd., London WC................. 179

- BURTON, R.F.
Campbell Hewson Books (R.), Fife................ 271
Chas J. Sawyer, Kent 140

- BURTON, SIR RICHARD F.
Bonham (J. & S.L.), London W 171

- BYRON, LORD
Adrem Books, Herts 130
Alec–Smith Books (Alex), East Yorkshire 107
Cox Rare Books (Charles), Cornwall.............. 73
Emjay Books, Surrey.................................. 231
Jarndyce Antiquarian Booksellers, London WC. 177
R. & A. Books, East Sussex 101
Roz Hulse, Conwy 284
Wise (Derek), East Sussex........................... 104

- CALDICOTT, R.
Bookmark (Children's Books), Wiltshire.......... 253
Booth (Booksearch Service), (Geoff), Cheshire... 68
Children's Bookshop (The), Herefordshire........ 127
Fifteenth Century Bookshop (The), East Sussex. 104
First Edition, The, Essex 109
Jean Hedger, Berks 55
R. & A. Books, East Sussex 101
Simpson (Dave), Central 268

- CAMERON, JULIA MARGARET
Cameron House Books, Isle of Wight............. 133
Dolphin Books, Suffolk.............................. 225

- CARLYLE, THOMAS
Priestpopple Books, Northumberland 201
Tiger Books, Kent..................................... 136

- CARR, JOHN DICKSON
Annie's Books, South Yorkshire 221
Booth (Booksearch Service), (Geoff), Cheshire... 68
James M Pickhard (Rare Books), Leics........... 145
Lucius Books, North Yorkshire.................... 197
Sutcliffe (Mark), West Yorkshire.................. 248

- CARROLL, LEWIS
Apocalypse, Surrey 232
Bookmark (Children's Books), Wiltshire.......... 253
Chas J. Sawyer, Kent 140
Cranhurst Books, London NW 160
Fifteenth Century Bookshop (The), East Sussex. 104
First Edition, The, Essex 109
Foster Bookshop (Paul), London SW 167
Jean Hedger, Berks.................................... 55
Key Books (Sarah), Cambridgeshire............... 64
Little Stour Books, Kent 136
Marchpane, London WC.............................. 177
R. & A. Books, East Sussex 101
Tiger Books, Kent..................................... 136

- CARTER, FREDERICK
Apocalypse, Surrey 232

- CARY, JOYCE
Booth (Booksearch Service), (Geoff), Cheshire... 68
Simpson (Dave), Central 268

- CATHER, WILLA
Doolin Dinghy Books, Co. Clare 262
Tiger Books, Kent..................................... 136

- CECIL, H.
Booth (Booksearch Service), (Geoff), Cheshire... 68
Wayside Books and Cards, Oxfordshire 206

- CERVANTES SAAVEDRA, MIGUEL DE
Apocalypse, Surrey 232
Booth (Booksearch Service), (Geoff), Cheshire... 68
Orssich (Paul), London SW......................... 169

- CHANDLER, RAYMOND
Cranhurst Books, London NW 160
Dolphin Books, Suffolk.............................. 225
James M Pickhard (Rare Books), Leics........... 145
Lucius Books, North Yorkshire.................... 197
R. & A. Books, East Sussex 101
Simpson (Dave), Central 268
Sutcliffe (Mark), West Yorkshire.................. 248

- CHAPMAN, ABEL
Chalmers Hallam (E.), Hampshire................. 125
Chas J. Sawyer, Kent 140

- CHARTERIS, LESLIE
Bookworms Paradise Ltd., West Sussex 242
Cranhurst Books, London NW 160
Heckmondwike Book Shop, West Yorkshire 249
James M Pickhard (Rare Books), Leics........... 145
K Books, Cheshire.................................... 70
Lucius Books, North Yorkshire.................... 197
Simpson (Dave), Central 268
Surprise Books, Gloucestershire 113

- CHAUCER, GEOFFREY
Bennett & Kerr Books, Oxfordshire............... 205
Booth (Booksearch Service), (Geoff), Cheshire... 68
medievalbookshop, Herts............................. 132
Spenceley Books (David), West Yorkshire........ 248
Tiger Books, Kent..................................... 136

- CHESTERTON, G.K.
Annie's Books, South Yorkshire 221
Armchair Books, Lothian 275
Bass (Ben), Wiltshire 251
Booth (Booksearch Service), (Geoff), Cheshire... 68
Carraig Books Ltd., Co. Dublin 263
Daeron's Books, Buckinghamshire................. 62
Dolphin Books, Suffolk.............................. 225
Fifteenth Century Bookshop (The), East Sussex. 104
Greta Books, Durham................................. 97
R. & A. Books, East Sussex 101
Rosley Books, Cumbria 81
St Philip's Books, Oxfordshire..................... 208
Tiger Books, Kent..................................... 136

- CHRISTIE, AGATHA
Adrem Books, Herts 130
Annie's Books, South Yorkshire 221
Apocalypse, Surrey 232
Bookworms Paradise Ltd., West Sussex 242
Classic Crime Collections, Greater Manchester .. 119
Cranhurst Books, London NW 160

Emjay Books, Surrey 231
First Edition, The, Essex 109
Heckmondwike Book Shop, West Yorkshire 249
Idle Genius Books, London N 157
Intech Books, Northumberland 201
Island Books, Devon 85
James M Pickhard (Rare Books), Leics 145
Jonkers Rare Books, Oxfordshire 207
Lucius Books, North Yorkshire 197
McGee (Terence J.), London O 180
Modern First Editions, West Yorkshire 247
R. & A. Books, East Sussex 101
Simpson (Dave), Central 268
Treasure Trove Books, Leics 146
Wayside Books and Cards, Oxfordshire 206
Williams Rare Books (Nigel), London WC 179

- CHURCHILL, SIR WINSTON
Adrem Books, Herts 130
Annie's Books, South Yorkshire 221
Apocalypse, Surrey 232
Baxter (Steve), Surrey 233
Bookshop on the Heath, The, London SE 163
Booth (Booksearch Service), (Geoff), Cheshire... 68
Chas J. Sawyer, Kent 140
Derek Stirling Bookseller, Kent 141
Dolphin Books, Suffolk 225
Fifteenth Century Bookshop (The), East Sussex. 104
First Edition, The, Essex 109
Foster Bookshop (Paul), London SW 167
Frew Limited (Robert), London SW 167
Garfi Books, Powys 291
Harrington (Adrian), London W 173
Island Books, Devon 85
Junk & Spread Eagle, London SE 164
Kirkman Ltd., (Robert), Bedfordshire 54
Lost Books, Northamptonshire 200
Portus Books, Hampshire 122
Prior (Michael), Lincolnshire 152
R. & A. Books, East Sussex 101
Sax Books, Suffolk 228
Simpson (Dave), Central 268
White (C.R.), London W 175

- CLARE, JOHN
Country Books, Derbyshire 82
Park Gallery & Bookshop (The), Northants 200
R. & A. Books, East Sussex 101
Rye Old Books, East Sussex 104
Tiger Books, Kent 136

- CLARKE, ARTHUR C.
Annie's Books, South Yorkshire 221
Apocalypse, Surrey 232
Cameron House Books, Isle of Wight 133
Cranhurst Books, London NW 160
Simpson (Dave), Central 268
Wayside Books and Cards, Oxfordshire 206

- COBBETT, WILLIAM
Country Books, Derbyshire 82
Debbage (John), Norfolk 189
Greta Books, Durham 97
Island Books, Devon 85
Tiger Books, Kent 136

- COCTEAU, JEAN
Norton Books, North Yorkshire 192
R. & A. Books, East Sussex 101

- COETZEE, J.M.
Apocalypse, Surrey 232
Criterion Books, London O 181
Dolphin Books, Suffolk 225
Modern First Editions, London O 181
Oak Tree Press, Oxfordshire 207

- COLERIDGE, SAMUEL T.
Alec–Smith Books (Alex), East Yorkshire 107
Island Books, Devon 85
Jane & John Kinnaird, Cumbria 78
Jarndyce Antiquarian Booksellers, London WC. 177
R. & A. Books, East Sussex 101
Roz Hulse, Conwy 284
Tiger Books, Kent 136

- CONAN DOYLE, SIR ARTHUR
Adrem Books, Herts 130
Antique Map and Bookshop (The), Dorset 94
Apocalypse, Surrey 232
Armchair Books, Lothian 275
Black Cat Bookshop, Leics 147
Eggeling Books (John), West Yorkshire 249
Fantastic Literature, Essex 110
Fifteenth Century Bookshop (The), East Sussex. 104
First Edition, The, Essex 109
Harrington (Adrian), London W 173
Island Books, Devon 85
Lucius Books, North Yorkshire 197
McGee (Terence J.), London O 180
Ming Books, Dumfries & Galloway 270
Preston Book Company, Lancashire 144
R. & A. Books, East Sussex 101
Shacklock Books (David), Suffolk 226
Simpson (Dave), Central 268
Tiger Books, Kent 136

- CONRAD, JOSEPH
Adrem Books, Herts 130
Booth (Booksearch Service), (Geoff), Cheshire... 68
Greta Books, Durham 97
Parrott (Jeremy), London E. 154
Tiger Books, Kent 136

- COOK, BERYL
Apocalypse, Surrey 232
Baker - Books for the Collector (Colin), Devon. 89
Facet Books, Dorset 91
Intech Books, Northumberland 201
Jean Hedger, Berks 55
Myra Dean Illustated Books, Powys 287
R. & A. Books, East Sussex 101
Surprise Books, Gloucestershire 113

- COOPER, JAMES F.
Doolin Dinghy Books, Co. Clare 262

- CORELLI, MARIE
Adrem Books, Herts 130
Beaton (Richard), East Sussex 103
Eggeling Books (John), West Yorkshire 249

Inner Bookshop (The), Oxfordshire............... 208
Tiger Books, Kent................................... 136

- CORNWELL, BERNARD

Annie's Books, South Yorkshire 221
Apocalypse, Surrey 232
Booth (Booksearch Service), (Geoff), Cheshire... 68
Dolphin Books, Suffolk............................. 225
Harrington (Adrian), London W................... 173
Heppa (Christopher), Essex 108
Intech Books, Northumberland 201
James M Pickhard (Rare Books), Leics........... 145
Ming Books, Dumfries & Galloway 270
Simpson (Dave), Central 268
Surprise Books, Gloucestershire 113
Wayside Books and Cards, Oxfordshire 206

- COWARD, NOEL

Adrem Books, Herts 130
Avonworld Books, Somerset........................ 216
First Edition, The, Essex 109
R. & A. Books, East Sussex 101

- CRANE, WALTER

Adrem Books, Herts 130
Bookmark (Children's Books), Wiltshire.......... 253
Fifteenth Century Bookshop (The), East Sussex. 104
Hodgkins and Company Limited (Ian),
  Gloucestershire 116
Jean Hedger, Berks.................................. 55
Simpson (Dave), Central 268

- CREASEY, JOHN

Adrem Books, Herts 130
Annie's Books, South Yorkshire 221
Bookworms Paradise Ltd., West Sussex 242
Classic Crime Collections, Greater Manchester.. 119
Heckmondwike Book Shop, West Yorkshire 249
Ming Books, Dumfries & Galloway 270

- CRICHTON, MICHAEL

Annie's Books, South Yorkshire 221
Booth (Booksearch Service), (Geoff), Cheshire... 68
Dolphin Books, Suffolk............................. 225
Fantastic Literature, Essex 110
R. & A. Books, East Sussex 101
Simpson (Dave), Central 268

- CROFTS, FREEMAN WILLS

Ellis, Bookseller (Peter), London WC 177
Heppa (Christopher), Essex 108
James M Pickhard (Rare Books), Leics........... 145
Lucius Books, North Yorkshire 197
Ming Books, Dumfries & Galloway 270
Sutcliffe (Mark), West Yorkshire.................. 248
Tiger Books, Kent................................... 136

- CROMPTON, RICHMAL

Adrem Books, Herts 130
Annie's Books, South Yorkshire 221
Beck (John), East Sussex 103
Bilski (Gill), Buckinghamshire 61
Black Cat Bookshop, Leics 147
Bookmark (Children's Books), Wiltshire.......... 253
Boris Books, Somerset 216

Children's Bookshop (The), Herefordshire........ 127
D. & M. Books, West Yorkshire................... 249
Facet Books, Dorset................................. 91
Fifteenth Century Bookshop (The), East Sussex. 104
First Edition, The, Essex 109
Green Meadow Books, Cornwall 74
Intech Books, Northumberland 201
Key Books (Sarah), Cambridgeshire.............. 64
Lake (David), Norfolk.............................. 190
Little Stour Books, Kent 136
Lucius Books, North Yorkshire 197
Oasis Booksearch, Cambridgeshire................ 67
R. & A. Books, East Sussex 101
Richard Thornton Books, London N 158
Schutte (David), Hampshire........................ 124
Silver Trees Books, West Midlands................ 238
Surprise Books, Gloucestershire 113

- CROSBY, HARRY & CARESSE

Norton Books, North Yorkshire 192

- CROWLEY, ALEISTER

Atlantis Bookshop, London WC................... 176
Bookworms Paradise Ltd., West Sussex 242
Caduceus Books, Leics.............................. 145
Chthonios Books, East Sussex 102
Delectus Books, London WC....................... 176
Inner Bookshop (The), Oxfordshire............... 208
Lucius Books, North Yorkshire 197
Occultique, Northamptonshire..................... 199
PsychoBabel Books & Journals, Oxfordshire..... 205

- CRUICKSHANK, G.

Bookmark (Children's Books), Wiltshire.......... 253
Jean Hedger, Berks.................................. 55
R. & A. Books, East Sussex 101
Tiger Books, Kent................................... 136

- CUNARD, NANCY

Norton Books, North Yorkshire 192

- CUNNINGHAM-GRAHAME, R.B.

Bass (Ben), Wiltshire 251

- DAHL, ROALD

Adrem Books, Herts 130
Annie's Books, South Yorkshire 221
Bookmark (Children's Books), Wiltshire.......... 253
Boris Books, Somerset 216
Children's Bookshop (The), Herefordshire........ 127
Deverell Books, Bristol 59
Draca Books, West Yorkshire...................... 248
Fifteenth Century Bookshop (The), East Sussex. 104
Green Meadow Books, Cornwall 74
Intech Books, Northumberland 201
Jean Hedger, Berks................................. 55
Jonkers Rare Books, Oxfordshire 207
Key Books (Sarah), Cambridgeshire.............. 64
Lucius Books, North 'Yorkshire 197
R. & A. Books, East Sussex 101
Simpson (Dave), Central 268
Surprise Books, Gloucestershire 113

- DARWIN, CHARLES

Adrem Books, Herts 130

Cameron House Books, Isle of Wight............. 133
Hodgson (Books) (Richard J.), North Yorkshire 196
Island Books, Devon................................. 85
Korn (M. Eric), London N 157
Lymelight Books & Prints, Dorset................. 93
Pollak (P.M.), Devon 88
R. & A. Books, East Sussex 101

- DAVID, ELIZABETH
Clarke (Janet), Somerset........................... 215
Seeber (Liz), East Sussex 102
Talisman Books, Cheshire.......................... 70

- DE SADE, MARQUIS
Apocalypse, Surrey 232
Booth (Booksearch Service), (Geoff), Cheshire... 68
Watkins Books Ltd., London WC................. 179

- DERELTH, AUGUST
Adrem Books, Herts 130

- DICK, PHILIP K
Adrem Books, Herts 130
Bookworms Paradise Ltd., West Sussex 242
Booth (Booksearch Service), (Geoff), Cheshire... 68
James M Pickhard (Rare Books), Leics............ 145
Surprise Books, Gloucestershire 113

- DICKENS, CHARLES
Adrem Books, Herts 130
Apocalypse, Surrey 232
Ash Rare Books, London SW....................... 166
Boris Books, Somerset.............................. 216
Boz Books, Powys.................................. 287
Cameron House Books, Isle of Wight............. 133
Charles Bossom, Cambridgeshire.................. 65
Childrens Bookshop, West Yorkshire 247
Clegg (David), Staffordshire........................ 223
Derek Stirling Bookseller, Kent 141
Fifteenth Century Bookshop (The), East Sussex. 104
First Edition, The, Essex 109
Foster Bookshop (Paul), London SW............. 167
Golden Books Group, Devon 85
Harrington (Adrian), London W.................. 173
Hava Books, London SE............................ 164
Island Books, Devon................................ 85
Jarndyce Antiquarian Booksellers, London WC. 177
Minster Gate Bookshop, North Yorkshire 197
Mr. Pickwick of Towcester, Northants............ 199
Park Gallery & Bookshop (The), Northants 200
Preston Book Company, Lancashire 144
R. & A. Books, East Sussex 101
Simpson (Dave), Central 268
Tiger Books, Kent.................................. 136
Trinity Rare Books, Co. Leitrim 266
Valentine Rare Books, London W................ 175

- DINESEN, ISAK
Booth (Booksearch Service), (Geoff), Cheshire... 68
Chalmers Hallam (E.), Hampshire................. 125
Coch-y-Bonddu Books, Powys 290
Esoteric Dreams Bookshop, Cumbria 77
White (C.R.), London W........................... 175

- DR. SEUSS
Children's Bookshop (The), Herefordshire........ 127
Jean Hedger, Berks................................. 55

- DU MAURIER, DAPHNE
Annie's Books, South Yorkshire 221
Apocalypse, Surrey 232
Baker - Books for the Collector (Colin), Devon. 89
Bonython Bookshop, Cornwall..................... 75
Bookends of Fowey, Cornwall 72
Booth (Booksearch Service), (Geoff), Cheshire... 68
Chapman (Neville), Lancashire..................... 144
Dolphin Books, Suffolk............................. 225
Fifteenth Century Bookshop (The), East Sussex. 104
Island Books, Devon................................ 85
Simpson (Dave), Central 268

- DULAC, EDMUND
Bookmark (Children's Books), Wiltshire.......... 253
Children's Bookshop (The), Herefordshire........ 127
Cranhurst Books, London NW 160
Fifteenth Century Bookshop (The), East Sussex. 104
First Edition, The, Essex 109
Jean Hedger, Berks................................. 55
Lucius Books, North Yorkshire 197
Minster Gate Bookshop, North Yorkshire 197
Myra Dean Illustated Books, Powys 287
R. & A. Books, East Sussex 101
Rye Old Books, East Sussex 104
Trinity Rare Books, Co. Leitrim 266

- DUMAS, ALEXANDRE
Annie's Books, South Yorkshire 221
Beaton (Richard), East Sussex...................... 103
Eggeling Books (John), West Yorkshire 249
R. & A. Books, East Sussex 101
Tiger Books, Kent.................................. 136

- DUNSANY, LORD
Books & Things, London W........................ 171
Eggeling Books (John), West Yorkshire 249
Roz Hulse, Conwy 284

- DURRELL, GERALD
Adrem Books, Herts 130
Annie's Books, South Yorkshire 221
Apocalypse, Surrey 232
Bass (Ben), Wiltshire 251
Bookmark (Children's Books), Wiltshire.......... 253
Booth (Booksearch Service), (Geoff), Cheshire... 68
Dolphin Books, Suffolk............................. 225
Fifteenth Century Bookshop (The), East Sussex. 104
Green Meadow Books, Cornwall 74
Island Books, Devon................................ 85
R. & A. Books, East Sussex 101
Simpson (Dave), Central 268

- DURRELL, LAWRENCE
Adrem Books, Herts 130
Apocalypse, Surrey 232
Avonworld Books, Somerset........................ 216
Ballantyne–Way (Roger), Suffolk 228
Barmby (C. & A.J.), Kent........................... 140
Booth (Booksearch Service), (Geoff), Cheshire... 68
Cameron House Books, Isle of Wight............. 133

Carraig Books Ltd., Co. Dublin 263
Criterion Books, London O......................... 181
Fifteenth Century Bookshop (The), East Sussex. 104
Island Books, Devon................................. 85
Norton Books, North Yorkshire 192
R. & A. Books, East Sussex 101

- DYMOCK POETS, THE
Ellis, Bookseller (Peter), London WC 177
Smith Books (Keith), Herefordshire 128

- EDWARDS, LIONEL
Booth (Booksearch Service), (Geoff), Cheshire... 68
Head (John & Judith), Wiltshire 253
Island Books, Devon................................. 85
Jean Hedger, Berks................................... 55
Surprise Books, Gloucestershire 113

- ELIOT, G.
Annie's Books, South Yorkshire 221
Booth (Booksearch Service), (Geoff), Cheshire... 68
Dolphin Books, Suffolk.............................. 225
Jarndyce Antiquarian Booksellers, London WC. 177
Modern First Editions, West Yorkshire........... 247
Rye Old Books, East Sussex 104
Sharpe (Mary), Somerset 219
Tiger Books, Kent 136

- ELIOT, T.S.
Anglo-American Rare Books, Surrey.............. 232
Apocalypse, Surrey 232
Booth (Booksearch Service), (Geoff), Cheshire... 68
Ellis, Bookseller (Peter), London WC 177
Evans Books (Paul), West Sussex 243
Jonkers Rare Books, Oxfordshire 207
Lucius Books, North Yorkshire 197
Modern First Editions, West Yorkshire........... 247
R. & A. Books, East Sussex 101
Rosley Books, Cumbria 81
Simpson (Dave), Central 268
Tiger Books, Kent 136

- EMERSON, RALPH WALDO
Tiger Books, Kent 136

- FAIRLIE–BRUCE, D.
Bilski (Gill), Buckinghamshire 61
Bookmark (Children's Books), Wiltshire.......... 253
Boris Books, Somerset 216
Children's Bookshop (The), Herefordshire........ 127
Fifteenth Century Bookshop (The), East Sussex. 104
Green Meadow Books, Cornwall 74
Intech Books, Northumberland 201
Key Books (Sarah), Cambridgeshire............... 64
Sims (Sue), Dorset................................... 91
TP Children's Bookshop, West Yorkshire........ 245

- FARNOL, JEFFERY
Adrem Books, Herts 130
Boris Books, Somerset 216
Doolin Dinghy Books, Co. Clare 262
Dusty Books, Powys 290
Fifteenth Century Bookshop (The), East Sussex. 104
Heppa (Christopher), Essex 108
Tiger Books, Kent 136

- FARRELL, JAMES T.
Fifteenth Century Bookshop (The), East Sussex. 104

- FAULKNER, WILLIAM
Booth (Booksearch Service), (Geoff), Cheshire... 68
Ellis, Bookseller (Peter), London WC 177
R. & A. Books, East Sussex 101
Tiger Books, Kent 136

- FIELDING, HENRY
R. & A. Books, East Sussex 101
Tiger Books, Kent 136

- FITZGERALD, F.S.
Annie's Books, South Yorkshire 221
R. & A. Books, East Sussex 101

- FLEMING, IAN
Annie's Books, South Yorkshire 221
Apocalypse, Surrey 232
Birmingham Books, West Midlands 238
Black Cat Bookshop, Leics 147
Books, Oxfordshire.................................. 205
Bookshop on the Heath, The, London SE 163
Bookworms Paradise Ltd., West Sussex 242
Booth (Booksearch Service), (Geoff), Cheshire... 68
Classic Crime Collections, Greater Manchester .. 119
Cranhurst Books, London NW 160
Ellis, Bookseller (Peter), London WC 177
First Edition, The, Essex 109
Foster Bookshop (Paul), London SW 167
Harrington (Adrian), London W................... 173
Intech Books, Northumberland 201
James M Pickhard (Rare Books), Leics........... 145
Jonkers Rare Books, Oxfordshire 207
Lucius Books, North Yorkshire 197
Mainly Fiction, Cheshire 68
Modern First Editions, West Yorkshire........... 247
R. & A. Books, East Sussex 101
Saint Mary's Books & Prints, Lincolnshire....... 152
Simpson (Dave), Central 268
Sutcliffe (Mark), West Yorkshire.................. 248
Warrender (Andrew), West Yorkshire............. 249
Williams Rare Books (Nigel), London WC 179

- FLINT, WILLIAM RUSSELL
Booth (Booksearch Service), (Geoff), Cheshire... 68
Island Books, Devon................................. 85
Myra Dean Illustated Books, Powys 287
R. & A. Books, East Sussex 101
Webb Books (John), South Yorkshire............. 221

- FOREST, A.
Adrem Books, Herts 130
Badger Books, Somerset............................. 219
Bilski (Gill), Buckinghamshire 61
Children's Bookshop (The), Herefordshire........ 127
Fifteenth Century Bookshop (The), East Sussex. 104
Key Books (Sarah), Cambridgeshire............... 64
Sims (Sue), Dorset................................... 91

- FORESTER, C.S.
Adrem Books, Herts 130
Booth (Booksearch Service), (Geoff), Cheshire... 68
Criterion Books, London O......................... 181

Dusty Books, Powys 290
Fifteenth Century Bookshop (The), East Sussex. 104
Greta Books, Durham 97
Heppa (Christopher), Essex 108
Prior (Michael), Lincolnshire 152
R. & A. Books, East Sussex 101
Simpson (Dave), Central 268
Surprise Books, Gloucestershire 113

- FOWLES, JOHN
Adrem Books, Herts 130
Apocalypse, Surrey 232
Barmby (C. & A.J.), Kent.......................... 140
Booth (Booksearch Service), (Geoff), Cheshire... 68
Dolphin Books, Suffolk............................. 225
Lymelight Books & Prints, Dorset 93
Simpson (Dave), Central 268
The Sanctuary Bookshop, Dorset 94
Trinity Rare Books, Co. Leitrim 266

- FRANCIS, DICK
Adrem Books, Herts 130
Annie's Books, South Yorkshire 221
Apocalypse, Surrey 232
Booth (Booksearch Service), (Geoff), Cheshire... 68
Emjay Books, Surrey................................ 231
firstpagebooks, Norfolk............................ 189
Greta Books, Durham 97
Ice House Books, Wiltshire 254
Intech Books, Northumberland 201
James M Pickhard (Rare Books), Leics........... 145
Kennedy & Farley, East Sussex 104
Lucius Books, North Yorkshire 197
Orb's Bookshop, Grampian......................... 273
Park Gallery & Bookshop (The), Northants 200
R. & A. Books, East Sussex 101
Simpson (Dave), Central 268

- FREEMAN, R. AUSTIN
Lucius Books, North Yorkshire 197
Tiger Books, Kent................................... 136

- FREUD, SIGMUND
Apocalypse, Surrey 232
Delectus Books, London WC...................... 176
PsychoBabel Books & Journals, Oxfordshire..... 205
Trinity Rare Books, Co. Leitrim 266
Watkins Books Ltd., London WC................. 179

- FROST, ROBERT
Karen Millward, Co. Cork 263
Smith Books (Keith), Herefordshire 128

- GARDNER, EARLE STANLEY
Adrem Books, Herts 130
Annie's Books, South Yorkshire 221
Bookworms Paradise Ltd., West Sussex 242

- GASKELL, E.
Adrem Books, Herts 130
Dolphin Books, Suffolk............................. 225
Fifteenth Century Bookshop (The), East Sussex. 104
Hodgkins and Company Limited (Ian),
  Gloucestershire 116
Sharpe (Mary), Somerset 219

Tiger Books, Kent................................... 136

- GILBERT, MICHAEL
Adrem Books, Herts 130
James M Pickhard (Rare Books), Leics........... 145
Lucius Books, North Yorkshire.................... 197
R. & A. Books, East Sussex 101

- GILL, ERIC
Booth (Booksearch Service), (Geoff), Cheshire... 68
Collinge & Clark, London WC..................... 176
Myra Dean Illustated Books, Powys 287

- GISSING, GEORGE
Beaton (Richard), East Sussex 103
Dolphin Books, Suffolk............................. 225
Idle Booksellers (The), West Yorkshire 245
Jarndyce Antiquarian Booksellers, London WC. 177
Tiger Books, Kent................................... 136

- GOREY, EDWARD
Cranhurst Books, London NW 160
Jean Hedger, Berks................................. 55
Myra Dean Illustated Books, Powys 287

- GOSS, W.H.
Milestone Publications Goss & Crested China,
  Hampshire 123
R. & A. Books, East Sussex 101

- GOUDGE, ELIZABETH
Adrem Books, Herts 130
Baker - Books for the Collector (Colin), Devon. 89
Bilski (Gill), Buckinghamshire 61
Bookmark (Children's Books), Wiltshire.......... 253
Booth (Booksearch Service), (Geoff), Cheshire... 68
Boris Books, Somerset 216
Children's Bookshop (The), Herefordshire....... 127
Fifteenth Century Bookshop (The), East Sussex. 104
Island Books, Devon................................ 85
Oasis Booksearch, Cambridgeshire................ 67
R. & A. Books, East Sussex 101

- GRAVES, ROBERT
Apocalypse, Surrey 232
Avonworld Books, Somerset....................... 216
Barmby (C. & A.J.), Kent.......................... 140
Berwick Books, Lincolnshire 150
Fifteenth Century Bookshop (The), East Sussex. 104
Island Books, Devon................................ 85
Jackson (M.W.), Wiltshire.......................... 254
R. & A. Books, East Sussex 101

- GREENE, GRAHAM
Adrem Books, Herts 130
Anglo-American Rare Books, Surrey.............. 232
Apocalypse, Surrey 232
Birmingham Books, West Midlands............... 238
Booth (Booksearch Service), (Geoff), Cheshire... 68
Cranhurst Books, London NW 160
Dennys Sanders & Greene Ltd, East Sussex 100
Dolphin Books, Suffolk............................. 225
Ellis, Bookseller (Peter), London WC 177
Fifteenth Century Bookshop (The), East Sussex. 104
firstpagebooks, Norfolk............................ 189

Frost (Richard), Herts 129
Harrington (Adrian), London W................... 173
Intech Books, Northumberland 201
Jonkers Rare Books, Oxfordshire 207
Lucius Books, North Yorkshire 197
R. & A. Books, East Sussex 101
Simpson (Dave), Central 268
Trinity Rare Books, Co. Leitrim 266
Wayside Books and Cards, Oxfordshire 206
Williams Rare Books (Nigel), London WC 179

- GREY, ZANE
Adrem Books, Herts 130
Annie's Books, South Yorkshire 221

- GURDJIEFF, W.I.
Inner Bookshop (The), Oxfordshire............... 208
Needham Books, (Russell), Somerset............. 219
Riderless Horse Books, Norfolk................... 186
Watkins Books Ltd., London WC 179
Yarwood Rare Books (Edward), G Manchester. 118

- HAGGARD, SIR HENRY RIDER
Debbage (John), Norfolk............................ 189
Fifteenth Century Bookshop (The), East Sussex. 104
John L Capes (Books Maps & Prints), North
  Yorkshire... 196
Lucius Books, North Yorkshire.................... 197
Rider Haggard Society (The), Tyne and Wear... 235
Tiger Books, Kent.................................. 136
Trinity Rare Books, Co. Leitrim 266

- HALL S.C.
Milestone Publications Goss & Crested China,
  Hampshire 123
Tiger Books, Kent.................................. 136

- HAMMETT, DASHIELL
Booth (Booksearch Service), (Geoff), Cheshire... 68
Lucius Books, North Yorkshire.................... 197
Sutcliffe (Mark), West Yorkshire.................. 248
Trinity Rare Books, Co. Leitrim 266

- HANFF, HELENE
Booth (Booksearch Service), (Geoff), Cheshire... 68

- HARDY, THOMAS
Annie's Books, South Yorkshire 221
Antique Map and Bookshop (The), Dorset 94
Apocalypse, Surrey 232
Books Afloat, Dorset............................... 96
Booth (Booksearch Service), (Geoff), Cheshire... 68
Boris Books, Somerset............................. 216
Country Books, Derbyshire........................ 82
Cox Rare Books (Charles), Cornwall.............. 73
Derek Stirling Bookseller, Kent 141
Dolphin Books, Suffolk............................ 225
Ferdinando (Steven), Somerset 218
Fifteenth Century Bookshop (The), East Sussex. 104
Island Books, Devon............................... 85
John Clifford, Dorset............................... 92
Lymelight Books & Prints, Dorset................. 93
Myra Dean Illustated Books, Powys 287
Period & Classical Collections, East Sussex 103
Sharpe (Mary), Somerset 219

Stinton (Judith), Dorset............................ 92
Tiger Books, Kent.................................. 136
Valentine Rare Books, London W................. 175
Walker Fine Books (Steve), Dorset 92
Words Etcetera Bookshop, Dorset................. 93

- HAWTHORNE, NATHANIAL
Tiger Books, Kent.................................. 136

- HEANEY, SEAMUS
Apocalypse, Surrey 232
JIRI Books, Co. Antrim............................ 260
Lyonshill Books, Co. Dublin 265
Modern First Editions, London O................. 181
Read Ireland, Co. Dublin 264
Skelton (Tony), Kent............................... 140
Trinity Rare Books, Co. Leitrim 266
Words Etcetera Bookshop, Dorset................. 93

- HEARN, LAFCADIO
Tiger Books, Kent.................................. 136

- HEATH, AMBROSE
Clarke (Janet), Somerset........................... 215

- HEINE, HEINRICH
Apocalypse, Surrey 232

- HEINLEIN, ROBERT A.
Adrem Books, Herts 130
Annie's Books, South Yorkshire 221
Bookworms Paradise Ltd., West Sussex 242
Booth (Booksearch Service), (Geoff), Cheshire... 68
Cranhurst Books, London NW 160
James M Pickhard (Rare Books), Leics........... 145
Trinity Rare Books, Co. Leitrim 266

- HEMINGWAY, ERNEST
Adrem Books, Herts 130
Anglo-American Rare Books, Surrey.............. 232
Apocalypse, Surrey 232
Cranhurst Books, London NW 160
Dolphin Books, Suffolk............................ 225
First Edition, The, Essex 109
Foster Bookshop (Paul), London SW 167
Norton Books, North Yorkshire................... 192
R. & A. Books, East Sussex 101
Simpson (Dave), Central 268

- HENTY, G.A.
Adrem Books, Herts 130
Antique Map and Bookshop (The), Dorset 94
Bookmark (Children's Books), Wiltshire......... 253
Booth (Booksearch Service), (Geoff), Cheshire... 68
Boris Books, Somerset............................. 216
Charles Bossom, Cambridgeshire.................. 65
Doolin Dinghy Books, Co. Clare 262
Eclectica, London SE 164
Facet Books, Dorset................................ 91
Fifteenth Century Bookshop (The), East Sussex. 104
Greta Books, Durham 97
Little Stour Books, Kent 136
R. & A. Books, East Sussex 101
Shacklock Books (David), Suffolk 226
Tiger Books, Kent.................................. 136

- HERBERT, JAMES
Adrem Books, Herts 130
Annie's Books, South Yorkshire 221
Booth (Booksearch Service), (Geoff), Cheshire... 68
Old Celtic Bookshop (The), Devon 87
R. & A. Books, East Sussex 101
Surprise Books, Gloucestershire 113

- HERRIOT, JAMES
Annie's Books, South Yorkshire 221
Annie's Books, South Yorkshire 221
Booth (Booksearch Service), (Geoff), Cheshire... 68
Hambleton Books, North Yorkshire 196
Island Books, Devon 85
Island Books, Devon 85

- HESSE, HERMANN
Adrem Books, Herts 130
Apocalypse, Surrey 232

- HEYER, GEORGETTE
Annie's Books, South Yorkshire 221
Apocalypse, Surrey 232
Baker - Books for the Collector (Colin), Devon. 89
Bookworms Paradise Ltd., West Sussex 242
Booth (Booksearch Service), (Geoff), Cheshire... 68
Boris Books, Somerset 216
Dusty Books, Powys 290
Fifteenth Century Bookshop (The), East Sussex. 104
Intech Books, Northumberland 201
Orb's Bookshop, Grampian......................... 273
R. & A. Books, East Sussex 101
Rider Haggard Society (The), Tyne and Wear... 235

- HILL, LORNA
Badger Books, Somerset............................. 219
Bilski (Gill), Buckinghamshire 61
Bookmark (Children's Books), Wiltshire.......... 253
Boris Books, Somerset 216
Fifteenth Century Bookshop (The), East Sussex. 104
Green Meadow Books, Cornwall 74
Intech Books, Northumberland 201
TP Children's Bookshop, West Yorkshire 245

- HODGSON, W.H.
Booth (Booksearch Service), (Geoff), Cheshire... 68
Eggeling Books (John), West Yorkshire 249
R. & A. Books, East Sussex 101
Trinity Rare Books, Co. Leitrim 266

- HOOD, THOMAS
R. & A. Books, East Sussex 101
Tiger Books, Kent 136

- HORNUNG, E.W.
Eggeling Books (John), West Yorkshire 249
Tiger Books, Kent 136

- HOUSMAN, A.E.
Adrem Books, Herts 130
Antiquary Ltd., (Bar Bookstore),
   North Yorkshire 194
Cox Rare Books (Charles), Cornwall............. 73
Dolphin Books, Suffolk............................. 225
Island Books, Devon 85

R. & A. Books, East Sussex 101

- HUBBARD, L. RON
Annie's Books, South Yorkshire 221
PsychoBabel Books & Journals, Oxfordshire..... 205
Watkins Books Ltd., London WC................. 179

- HUDSON, W.H.
Country Books, Derbyshire......................... 82
Dolphin Books, Suffolk............................. 225

- HUNTER, ALAN
Hylton Booksearch, Merseyside 184

- HUXLEY, ALDOUS
Adrem Books, Herts 130
Booth (Booksearch Service), (Geoff), Cheshire... 68
Cranhurst Books, London NW 160
Dolphin Books, Suffolk............................. 225
Island Books, Devon 85
Kennedy & Farley, East Sussex 104
R. & A. Books, East Sussex 101
Trinity Rare Books, Co. Leitrim 266
Watkins Books Ltd., London WC................. 179

- HUYSMANS, J.K.
Delectus Books, London WC....................... 176
Eggeling Books (John), West Yorkshire 249
Trinity Rare Books, Co. Leitrim 266

- INKLINGS, THE
Daeron's Books, Buckinghamshire................. 62
English (Toby), Oxfordshire......................... 209
Island Books, Devon 85
Rosley Books, Cumbria 81
Saint Philip's Books, Oxfordshire 208
Samovar Books, Co. Dublin 264

- INNES, HAMMOND
Annie's Books, South Yorkshire 221
Booth (Booksearch Service), (Geoff), Cheshire... 68
Dolphin Books, Suffolk............................. 225
Eggeling Books (John), West Yorkshire 249
Fifteenth Century Bookshop (The), East Sussex. 104
R. & A. Books, East Sussex 101
Simpson (Dave), Central 268

- ISHERWOOD, CHRISTOPHER
Adrem Books, Herts 130
Booth (Booksearch Service), (Geoff), Cheshire... 68
Criterion Books, London O......................... 181
R. & A. Books, East Sussex 101
Simpson (Dave), Central 268
Tsbbooks, London SW 169

- JACOB, VOILET
Jean Hedger, Berks................................. 55

- JAMES, HENRY
Anglo-American Rare Books, Surrey.............. 232
Anthony Neville, Kent.............................. 138
Craobh Rua Books, Co. Armagh.................. 260
R. & A. Books, East Sussex 101
Tiger Books, Kent 136
Valentine Rare Books, London W................. 175

- JAMES, M.R.
Adrem Books, Herts 130
Apocalypse, Surrey 232
Bennett & Kerr Books, Oxfordshire 205
Island Books, Devon 85
Trinity Rare Books, Co. Leitrim 266

- JEFFERIES, R.
Adrem Books, Herts 130
Chalmers Hallam (E.), Hampshire 125
Coch-y-Bonddu Books, Powys 290
Country Books, Derbyshire 82
Dolphin Books, Suffolk 225
Fifteenth Century Bookshop (The), East Sussex. 104
Island Books, Devon 85
John L Capes (Books Maps & Prints), North
    Yorkshire 196
Myra Dean Illustated Books, Powys 287
Tiger Books, Kent 136

- JEWETT, S.O.
Milestone Publications Goss & Crested China,
    Hampshire 123

- JOHNS, W.E.
Adrem Books, Herts 130
Annie's Books, South Yorkshire 221
Ardis Books, Hampshire 126
Barely Read Books, Kent 141
Bilski (Gill), Buckinghamshire 61
Black Cat Bookshop, Leics 147
books2books, Devon 88
Bookshop on the Heath, The, London SE 163
Bookworms Paradise Ltd., West Sussex 242
Chapter Two, London SE 163
Cotswold Internet Books, Gloucestershire 113
Cranhurst Books, London NW 160
D. & M. Books, West Yorkshire 249
Facet Books, Dorset 91
Fifteenth Century Bookshop (The), East Sussex. 104
First Edition, The, Essex 109
Harrington (Adrian), London W 173
Intech Books, Northumberland 201
Key Books (Sarah), Cambridgeshire 64
Lake (David), Norfolk 190
Little Stour Books, Kent 136
Lucius Books, North Yorkshire 197
Schutte (David), Hampshire 124
Simpson (Dave), Central 268
Stella Books, Monmouthshire 286
TP Children's Bookshop, West Yorkshire 245
Treasure Trove Books, Leics 146
Wright (Norman), Dorset 95

- JOHNSON, SAMUEL
Adrem Books, Herts 130
Apocalypse, Surrey 232
Evans Books (Paul), West Sussex 243
Foster Bookshop (Paul), London SW 167
Jarndyce Antiquarian Booksellers, London WC. 177
R. & A. Books, East Sussex 101
Staffs Bookshop (The), Staffordshire 223
Tiger Books, Kent 136
Walker Fine Books (Steve), Dorset 92

- JOYCE, JAMES
Annie's Books, South Yorkshire 221
Apocalypse, Surrey 232
Booth (Booksearch Service), (Geoff), Cheshire... 68
Courtwood Books, Co. Laois 265
Cranhurst Books, London NW 160
Ellis, Bookseller (Peter), London WC 177
Foster Bookshop (Paul), London SW 167
Intech Books, Northumberland 201
Jonkers Rare Books, Oxfordshire 207
Karen Millward, Co. Cork 263
Lyonshill Books, Co. Dublin 265
Modern First Editions, West Yorkshire 247
Norton Books, North Yorkshire 192
R. & A. Books, East Sussex 101
Simpson (Dave), Central 268
Trinity Rare Books, Co. Leitrim 266
Williams Rare Books (Nigel), London WC 179

- KEATS, JOHN
Adrem Books, Herts 130
Alec–Smith Books (Alex), East Yorkshire 107
Island Books, Devon 85
Jarndyce Antiquarian Booksellers, London WC. 177
Myra Dean Illustated Books, Powys 287
Tiger Books, Kent 136

- KEEPING, CHARLES
Bookmark (Children's Books), Wiltshire 253
Cameron House Books, Isle of Wight 133
Children's Bookshop (The), Herefordshire 127
Cranhurst Books, London NW 160
Fifteenth Century Bookshop (The), East Sussex. 104
Jean Hedger, Berks 55
Key Books (Sarah), Cambridgeshire 64
Myra Dean Illustated Books, Powys 287

- KENT, ALEXANDER
Adrem Books, Herts 130
Annie's Books, South Yorkshire 221
Bookworms Paradise Ltd., West Sussex 242
Boris Books, Somerset 216
K Books, Cheshire 70
Simpson (Dave), Central 268

- KEROUAC, JACK
Roz Hulse, Conwy 284
Sclanders (Beatbooks), (Andrew), London EC... 155
Trinity Rare Books, Co. Leitrim 266

- KERSH, GERALD
Adrem Books, Herts 130
Eggeling Books (John), West Yorkshire 249
James M Pickhard (Rare Books), Leics 145
R. & A. Books, East Sussex 101

- KING, C. DALY
Eggeling Books (John), West Yorkshire 249
Trinity Rare Books, Co. Leitrim 266

- KING, STEPHEN
Adrem Books, Herts 130
Annie's Books, South Yorkshire 221
Apocalypse, Surrey 232
Booth (Booksearch Service), (Geoff), Cheshire... 68

Cranhurst Books, London NW 160
Fantastic Literature, Essex 110
Old Celtic Bookshop (The), Devon............... 87
R. & A. Books, East Sussex 101
Simpson (Dave), Central 268
Talisman Books, Cheshire.......................... 70

- KIPLING, RUDYARD
Adrem Books, Herts 130
Annie's Books, South Yorkshire 221
Apocalypse, Surrey 232
Armchair Books, Lothian 275
Avonworld Books, Somerset....................... 216
Bookshop on the Heath, The, London SE 163
Booth (Booksearch Service), (Geoff), Cheshire... 68
Childrens Bookshop, West Yorkshire 247
Country Books, Derbyshire 82
Cranhurst Books, London NW 160
Criterion Books, London O......................... 181
Daeron's Books, Buckinghamshire................. 62
Debbage (John), Norfolk............................ 189
Faversham Books, Kent 137
Fifteenth Century Bookshop (The), East Sussex. 104
First Edition, The, Essex 109
Foster Bookshop (Paul), London SW 167
Greta Books, Durham 97
Harrington (Adrian), London W................... 173
Jarndyce Antiquarian Booksellers, London WC. 177
Jean Hedger, Berks................................. 55
Macbuiks, North Yorkshire......................... 193
Orb's Bookshop, Grampian......................... 273
R. & A. Books, East Sussex 101
Simpson (Dave), Central 268
Tiger Books, Kent 136
Verandah Books, Dorset 95
Wykeham Books, London SW 170

- KOONTZ, DEAN
Annie's Books, South Yorkshire 221
Apocalypse, Surrey 232
Bookworms Paradise Ltd., West Sussex 242
Cranhurst Books, London NW 160
Old Celtic Bookshop (The), Devon............... 87
R. & A. Books, East Sussex 101
Simpson (Dave), Central 268
Talisman Books, Cheshire.......................... 70

- LAITHWAITE, ERIC
K.S.C. Books, Cheshire............................. 70

- LANG, ANDREW
Bookmark (Children's Books), Wiltshire.......... 253
Booth (Booksearch Service), (Geoff), Cheshire... 68
Cranhurst Books, London NW 160
Eclectica, London SE 164
Fifteenth Century Bookshop (The), East Sussex. 104
First Edition, The, Essex 109
Greer (Robin), London SW......................... 167
Greta Books, Durham 97
Hodgkins and Company Limited (Ian),
    Gloucestershire.................................... 116
Jean Hedger, Berks................................. 55
R. & A. Books, East Sussex 101
Randall (Tom), Somerset............................ 218
Simpson (Dave), Central 268

- LAWRENCE, D.H.
Adrem Books, Herts 130
Apocalypse, Surrey 232
Armchair Books, Lothian 275
Booth (Booksearch Service), (Geoff), Cheshire... 68
Childrens Bookshop, West Yorkshire 247
Modern First Editions, West Yorkshire........... 247
Norton Books, North Yorkshire 192
R. & A. Books, East Sussex 101
Simpson (Dave), Central 268
Tilston (Stephen E.), London SE.................. 165
Trinity Rare Books, Co. Leitrim 266

- LAWRENCE, T.E.
Adrem Books, Herts 130
Antique Map and Bookshop (The), Dorset 94
Apocalypse, Surrey 232
Avedikian Rare Books, Somerset 216
Bookshop on the Heath, The, London SE 163
Booth (Booksearch Service), (Geoff), Cheshire... 68
Coach House Books, Worcestershire 256
Dolphin Books, Suffolk 225
Fifteenth Century Bookshop (The), East Sussex. 104
Island Books, Devon................................. 85
Jonkers Rare Books, Oxfordshire.................. 207
Joppa Books Ltd., Surrey 230
Lymelight Books & Prints, Dorset................. 93
Moorside Books, Lancashire........................ 143
R. & A. Books, East Sussex 101
Rickaro Books, West Yorkshire.................... 246
Trinity Rare Books, Co. Leitrim 266
Watkins (R.G.), Somerset 215
Words Etcetera Bookshop, Dorset................. 93

- LE CARRE, JOHN
Annie's Books, South Yorkshire 221
Apocalypse, Surrey 232
Bookshop on the Heath, The, London SE 163
Booth (Booksearch Service), (Geoff), Cheshire... 68
Cranhurst Books, London NW 160
Island Books, Devon................................. 85
James M Pickhard (Rare Books), Leics........... 145
Modern First Editions, West Yorkshire........... 247
Oak Tree Press, Oxfordshire....................... 207
Park Gallery & Bookshop (The), Northants 200
R. & A. Books, East Sussex 101
Simpson (Dave), Central 268
Surprise Books, Gloucestershire 113
Trinity Rare Books, Co. Leitrim 266
Wayside Books and Cards, Oxfordshire 206

- LEAR, EDWARD
Adrem Books, Herts 130
Bookmark (Children's Books), Wiltshire.......... 253
Fifteenth Century Bookshop (The), East Sussex. 104
Jean Hedger, Berks................................. 55
Myra Dean Illustated Books, Powys 287
R. & A. Books, East Sussex 101

- LEFANU, J.S.
Beaton (Richard), East Sussex...................... 103
Doolin Dinghy Books, Co. Clare 262
Eggeling Books (John), West Yorkshire 249
Tiger Books, Kent................................... 136

- LEHMANN, J.
Adrem Books, Herts 130
Evans Books (Paul), West Sussex 243

- LEWIS, C.S.
Adrem Books, Herts 130
Annie's Books, South Yorkshire 221
Apocalypse, Surrey 232
Armchair Books, Lothian 275
Booth (Booksearch Service), (Geoff), Cheshire... 68
Boris Books, Somerset 216
Chapter Two, London SE............................ 163
Children's Bookshop (The), Herefordshire........ 127
Cranhurst Books, London NW 160
Daeron's Books, Buckinghamshire................. 62
Draca Books, West Yorkshire...................... 248
First Edition, The, Essex 109
Inner Bookshop (The), Oxfordshire................ 208
Jonkers Rare Books, Oxfordshire 207
Key Books (Sarah), Cambridgeshire............... 64
Lewis First Editions, Kent 136
Lucius Books, North Yorkshire 197
Oasis Booksearch, Cambridgeshire................. 67
R. & A. Books, East Sussex 101
Rosley Books, Cumbria 81
St Philip's Books, Oxfordshire...................... 208
Trinity Rare Books, Co. Leitrim 266

- LEWIS, SINCLAIR
Booth (Booksearch Service), (Geoff), Cheshire... 68

- LEWIS, WYNDHAM
Adrem Books, Herts 130
Booth (Booksearch Service), (Geoff), Cheshire... 68
Dolphin Books, Suffolk............................. 225
Myra Dean Illustated Books, Powys 287
Norton Books, North Yorkshire................... 192
Trinity Rare Books, Co. Leitrim 266

- LINDSAY, NORMAN
Norton Books, North Yorkshire.................. 192

- LONDON, JACK
Adrem Books, Herts 130
Booth (Booksearch Service), (Geoff), Cheshire... 68
Doolin Dinghy Books, Co. Clare 262
Eggeling Books (John), West Yorkshire 249
R. & A. Books, East Sussex 101
Trinity Rare Books, Co. Leitrim 266

- LORCA, GARCIA
Orssich (Paul), London SW........................ 169
Trinity Rare Books, Co. Leitrim 266

- LOTI, PIERRE
Trinity Rare Books, Co. Leitrim 266

- LOVECRAFT, H.P.
Adrem Books, Herts 130
Eggeling Books (John), West Yorkshire 249
Trinity Rare Books, Co. Leitrim 266
Watkins Books Ltd., London WC................. 179
Zardoz Books, Wiltshire............................ 254

- LOWRY, MALCOLM
Apocalypse, Surrey.................................. 232
Fifteenth Century Bookshop (The), East Sussex. 104
Trinity Rare Books, Co. Leitrim 266

- LUCAS, E.V.
Brock Books, North Yorkshire.................... 192
Eggeling Books (John), West Yorkshire 249

- MACDONALD, BETTY
Booth (Booksearch Service), (Geoff), Cheshire... 68

- MACDONALD, GEORGE
Adrem Books, Herts 130
Beaton (Richard), East Sussex..................... 103
Bookmark (Children's Books), Wiltshire.......... 253
Booth (Booksearch Service), (Geoff), Cheshire... 68
Daeron's Books, Buckinghamshire................. 62
Eclectica, London SE 164
Eggeling Books (John), West Yorkshire 249
Fifteenth Century Bookshop (The), East Sussex. 104
Jarndyce Antiquarian Booksellers, London WC. 177
Jean Hedger, Berks................................. 55
Orb's Bookshop, Grampian......................... 273
Rosley Books, Cumbria 81
Simpson (Dave), Central 268
Tiger Books, Kent 136
Wayside Books and Cards, Oxfordshire 206

- MACHEN, ARTHUR
Apocalypse, Surrey 232
Bass (Ben), Wiltshire................................ 251
Craobh Rua Books, Co. Armagh.................. 260
Delectus Books, London WC....................... 176
Eggeling Books (John), West Yorkshire 249
Trinity Rare Books, Co. Leitrim 266

- MACLEAN, ALISTAIR
Adrem Books, Herts 130
Annie's Books, South Yorkshire 221
Booth (Booksearch Service), (Geoff), Cheshire... 68
R. & A. Books, East Sussex 101
Simpson (Dave), Central 268
Trinity Rare Books, Co. Leitrim 266

- MADOX FORD, FORD
Norton Books, North Yorkshire.................. 192
R. & A. Books, East Sussex 101
Tiger Books, Kent................................... 136
Trinity Rare Books, Co. Leitrim 266

- MAILER, NORMAN
Adrem Books, Herts 130
Anglo-American Rare Books, Surrey.............. 232
Apocalypse, Surrey 232
Booth (Booksearch Service), (Geoff), Cheshire... 68
Trinity Rare Books, Co. Leitrim 266

- MANNIN, ETHEL
Booth (Booksearch Service), (Geoff), Cheshire... 68
Carraig Books Ltd., Co. Dublin 263
Dolphin Books, Suffolk............................. 225
Doolin Dinghy Books, Co. Clare 262
Eggeling Books (John), West Yorkshire 249
Trinity Rare Books, Co. Leitrim 266

- MARVELL, ANDREW
Alec–Smith Books (Alex), East Yorkshire 107
Derek Stirling Bookseller, Kent 141

- MASEFIELD, JOHN
Adrem Books, Herts 130
Apocalypse, Surrey 232
Criterion Books, London O........................ 181
Farringdon (J.M.), Swansea........................ 291
Fifteenth Century Bookshop (The), East Sussex. 104
Prior (Michael), Lincolnshire 152
R. & A. Books, East Sussex 101
Smith Books (Keith), Herefordshire 128
Trinity Rare Books, Co. Leitrim 266

- MASTERS, JOHN
Adrem Books, Herts 130
Avonworld Books, Somerset........................ 216
Booth (Booksearch Service), (Geoff), Cheshire... 68
Dolphin Books, Suffolk.............................. 225
Eggeling Books (John), West Yorkshire 249
Fifteenth Century Bookshop (The), East Sussex. 104
Orb's Bookshop, Grampian......................... 273
Trinity Rare Books, Co. Leitrim 266

- MAUGHAM, SOMERSET
Adrem Books, Herts 130
Booth (Booksearch Service), (Geoff), Cheshire... 68
Boris Books, Somerset 216
Doolin Dinghy Books, Co. Clare 262
Greta Books, Durham 97
Orb's Bookshop, Grampian......................... 273
R. & A. Books, East Sussex 101
Roz Hulse, Conwy 284
Trinity Rare Books, Co. Leitrim 266
Wayside Books and Cards, Oxfordshire 206

- MELVILLE, HERMAN
Adrem Books, Herts 130
Tiger Books, Kent................................... 136
Trinity Rare Books, Co. Leitrim 266

- MENCKEN, H.L.
Trinity Rare Books, Co. Leitrim 266

- MICHAUX, FRANCOIS
Trinity Rare Books, Co. Leitrim 266

- MICHENER, JAMES
Adrem Books, Herts 130
Avonworld Books, Somerset........................ 216
Booth (Booksearch Service), (Geoff), Cheshire... 68
Trinity Rare Books, Co. Leitrim 266

- MILLER, HENRY
Adrem Books, Herts 130
Apocalypse, Surrey 232
Booth (Booksearch Service), (Geoff), Cheshire... 68
Delectus Books, London WC........................ 176
Norton Books, North Yorkshire 192
R. & A. Books, East Sussex 101
Trinity Rare Books, Co. Leitrim 266

- MILLIGAN, SPIKE
Adrem Books, Herts 130

Bookmark (Children's Books), Wiltshire.......... 253
Bookworms Paradise Ltd., West Sussex 242
Cranhurst Books, London NW 160
Fifteenth Century Bookshop (The), East Sussex. 104
James M Pickhard (Rare Books), Leics........... 145
Kineton Nooks, Warwickshire...................... 236
R. & A. Books, East Sussex 101
Simpson (Dave), Central 268
Trinity Rare Books, Co. Leitrim 266
Wayside Books and Cards, Oxfordshire 206

- MILNE, A.A.
Annie's Books, South Yorkshire 221
Antique Map and Bookshop (The), Dorset 94
Bookmark (Children's Books), Wiltshire.......... 253
Bookstand, Dorset................................... 94
Booth (Booksearch Service), (Geoff), Cheshire... 68
Boris Books, Somerset 216
Children's Bookshop (The), Herefordshire........ 127
Cranhurst Books, London NW 160
Dolphin Books, Suffolk.............................. 225
Draca Books, West Yorkshire...................... 248
Fifteenth Century Bookshop (The), East Sussex. 104
First Edition, The, Essex 109
Foster Bookshop (Paul), London SW............. 167
Harrington (Adrian), London W................... 173
Jean Hedger, Berks 55
Jonkers Rare Books, Oxfordshire 207
R. & A. Books, East Sussex 101
Simpson (Dave), Central 268
Surprise Books, Gloucestershire 113
Trinity Rare Books, Co. Leitrim 266

- MILTON J.
Apocalypse, Surrey 232
R. & A. Books, East Sussex 101
Trinity Rare Books, Co. Leitrim 266

- MOORE, JOHN
Adrem Books, Herts 130
Cornell Books, Gloucestershire..................... 117
Country Books, Derbyshire 82
Dolphin Books, Suffolk.............................. 225
Engaging Gear Ltd., Essex.......................... 108
Island Books, Devon................................. 85
Phillip Robbins of Warwick, Warwickshire 237
Sedgeberrow Books, Worcestershire 256
Surprise Books, Gloucestershire 113

- MORGAN, CHARLES
Adrem Books, Herts 130
Avonworld Books, Somerset........................ 216
Booth (Booksearch Service), (Geoff),
    Cheshire 68
Dolphin Books, Suffolk.............................. 225
Trinity Rare Books, Co. Leitrim 266

- MORRIS, JAN
Trinity Rare Books, Co. Leitrim 266

- MORRIS, WILLIAM
Adrem Books, Herts 130
Bass (Ben), Wiltshire 251
Bruce Holdsworth Books, East Sussex 105
Collinge & Clark, London WC..................... 176

Hodgkins and Company Limited (Ian),
  Gloucestershire.. 116
R. & A. Books, East Sussex 101
Upper–Room Books, Somerset..................... 217

- MORTON, H.V.
Adrem Books, Herts 130
Apocalypse, Surrey 232
Booth (Booksearch Service), (Geoff), Cheshire... 68
Boris Books, Somerset 216
Dolphin Books, Suffolk............................. 225
Fifteenth Century Bookshop (The), East Sussex. 104
Island Books, Devon.................................. 85
Oasis Booksearch, Cambridgeshire................. 67
Orb's Bookshop, Grampian......................... 273
Shacklock Books (David), Suffolk 226

- MURDOCH, I.
Adrem Books, Herts 130
Annie's Books, South Yorkshire 221
Apocalypse, Surrey 232
Booth (Booksearch Service), (Geoff), Cheshire... 68
Boris Books, Somerset 216
Cranhurst Books, London NW 160
Dolphin Books, Suffolk............................. 225
Doolin Dinghy Books, Co. Clare 262
Ellis, Bookseller (Peter), London WC 177
R. & A. Books, East Sussex 101
Reaveley Books, Devon 87
Simpson (Dave), Central 268
Trinity Rare Books, Co. Leitrim 266

- NEEDHAM, V.
Bilski (Gill), Buckinghamshire...................... 61
Bookmark (Children's Books), Wiltshire.......... 253
Boris Books, Somerset 216
Children's Bookshop (The), Herefordshire........ 127
Fifteenth Century Bookshop (The), East Sussex. 104
Key Books (Sarah), Cambridgeshire............... 64

- NEWMAN, CARDINAL
Cox Rare Books (Charles), Cornwall.............. 73
Oasis Booksearch, Cambridgeshire................. 67
St Philip's Books, Oxfordshire...................... 208

- NIALL, IAN
Chalmers Hallam (E.), Hampshire................. 125
Fifteenth Century Bookshop (The), East Sussex. 104
Island Books, Devon.................................. 85

- NICOLL, MAURICE
Needham Books, (Russell), Somerset.............. 219

- NIN, ANAIS
Apocalypse, Surrey 232
Lucius Books, North Yorkshire.................... 197
Norton Books, North Yorkshire 192
Trinity Rare Books, Co. Leitrim 266

- NORTON, MARY
Adrem Books, Herts 130
Annie's Books, South Yorkshire 221
Bookmark (Children's Books), Wiltshire.......... 253
Fifteenth Century Bookshop (The), East Sussex. 104
John Underwood Antiquarian Books, Norfolk.. 189

- O'BRIAN, PATRICK
Bookworms Paradise Ltd., West Sussex 242
Boris Books, Somerset 216
Fifteenth Century Bookshop (The), East Sussex. 104
Harrington (Adrian), London W................... 173
Intech Books, Northumberland 201
James M Pickhard (Rare Books), Leics.......... 145
Lucius Books, North Yorkshire.................... 197
Orb's Bookshop, Grampian......................... 273
Simpson (Dave), Central 268
Surprise Books, Gloucestershire 113
Trinity Rare Books, Co. Leitrim 266

- OPPENHEIM, E. PHILLIPS
Adrem Books, Herts 130
Book For All Reasons (A.), Suffolk............... 228
First Edition, The, Essex 109
Trinity Rare Books, Co. Leitrim 266

- ORAGE, A.R.
Needham Books, (Russell), Somerset.............. 219

- ORCZY, BARONESS
Children's Bookshop (The), Herefordshire........ 127
Fifteenth Century Bookshop (The), East Sussex. 104
Lucius Books, North Yorkshire.................... 197
Parrott (Jeremy), London E......................... 154
Simpson (Dave), Central 268
Tiger Books, Kent.................................... 136

- ORWELL, GEORGE
Adrem Books, Herts 130
Apocalypse, Surrey 232
Booth (Booksearch Service), (Geoff), Cheshire... 68
Cranhurst Books, London NW 160
Criterion Books, London O......................... 181
Fifteenth Century Bookshop (The), East Sussex. 104
First Edition, The, Essex 109
Heppa (Christopher), Essex 108
Island Books, Devon.................................. 85
James M Pickhard (Rare Books), Leics.......... 145
Lucius Books, North Yorkshire.................... 197
Mandalay Bookshop, London SW 168
Modern First Editions, West Yorkshire.......... 247
R. & A. Books, East Sussex 101
Trinity Rare Books, Co. Leitrim 266

- OSBORNE, JOHN
Apocalypse, Surrey 232
R. & A. Books, East Sussex 101

- OUSPENSKY, P.D.
Needham Books, (Russell), Somerset.............. 219

- OWL, GREY
Adrem Books, Herts 130
Bookmark (Children's Books), Wiltshire.......... 253
Booth (Booksearch Service), (Geoff), Cheshire... 68
Fifteenth Century Bookshop (The), East Sussex. 104
Greta Books, Durham 97
Trinity Rare Books, Co. Leitrim 266

- OXENHAM, ELSIE
Adrem Books, Herts 130
Badger Books, Somerset 219

Bilski (Gill), Buckinghamshire 61
Bookmark (Children's Books), Wiltshire.......... 253
Boris Books, Somerset 216
Children's Bookshop (The), Herefordshire........ 127
Cranhurst Books, London NW 160
D. & M. Books, West Yorkshire................... 249
Fifteenth Century Bookshop (The), East Sussex. 104
Green Meadow Books, Cornwall 74
Intech Books, Northumberland 201
Key Books (Sarah), Cambridgeshire............... 64
Little Stour Books, Kent 136
Lucius Books, North Yorkshire................... 197
Mercat Books, Highland 274
R. & A. Books, East Sussex 101
Sims (Sue), Dorset.................................. 91
TP Children's Bookshop, West Yorkshire........ 245
Trinity Rare Books, Co. Leitrim 266

- PALIN, MICHAEL
Apocalypse, Surrey 232
Booth (Booksearch Service), (Geoff), Cheshire... 68
R. & A. Books, East Sussex 101

- PARGETER, EDITH
Annie's Books, South Yorkshire 221
Baker - Books for the Collector (Colin), Devon. 89
Boris Books, Somerset 216
Simpson (Dave), Central 268

- PASTERNAK, BORIS
Adrem Books, Herts 130
Dolphin Books, Suffolk............................. 225
Park Gallery & Bookshop (The), Northants 200

- PAUL BOWLES
Adrem Books, Herts 130
Riderless Horse Books, Norfolk................... 186
Trinity Rare Books, Co. Leitrim 266
Tsbbooks, London SW 169

- PEAKE, MERVYN
Boz Books, Powys.................................. 287
Cameron House Books, Isle of Wight............. 133
Criterion Books, London O........................ 181
Fifteenth Century Bookshop (The), East Sussex. 104
Kemp Bookseller, Michael S, Greater Manchester...
118
Lucius Books, North Yorkshire................... 197
Simpson (Dave), Central 268
Trinity Rare Books, Co. Leitrim 266

- PENNANT, THOMAS
Atholl Fine Books, Tayside 280

- PEPYS, SAMUEL
Fifteenth Century Bookshop (The), East Sussex. 104
Island Books, Devon................................ 85
R. & A. Books, East Sussex 101

- PETER CAREY
R. & A. Books, East Sussex 101
Trinity Rare Books, Co. Leitrim 266

- PETERS, ELLIS
Adrem Books, Herts 130

Annie's Books, South Yorkshire 221
Baker - Books for the Collector (Colin), Devon. 89
Booth (Booksearch Service), (Geoff), Cheshire... 68
Cranhurst Books, London NW 160
Dolphin Books, Suffolk............................. 225
Fifteenth Century Bookshop (The), East Sussex. 104
James M Pickhard (Rare Books), Leics........... 145
Simpson (Dave), Central 268
Spenceley Books (David), West Yorkshire....... 248
Surprise Books, Gloucestershire 113
Trinity Rare Books, Co. Leitrim 266

- PICASSO, PABLO
Adrem Books, Herts 130
Apocalypse, Surrey 232
Brock Books, North Yorkshire.................... 192
R. & A. Books, East Sussex 101
Trinity Rare Books, Co. Leitrim 266

- PINTER, HAROLD
Adrem Books, Herts 130
R. & A. Books, East Sussex 101
Trinity Rare Books, Co. Leitrim 266

- POE, EDGAR ALLAN
First Edition, The, Essex 109
R. & A. Books, East Sussex 101

- POPE, A
Derek Stirling Bookseller, Kent 141
R. & A. Books, East Sussex 101
Trinity Rare Books, Co. Leitrim 266

- POTTER, BEATRIX
Adrem Books, Herts 130
Annie's Books, South Yorkshire 221
Bookmark (Children's Books), Wiltshire.......... 253
Bookstand, Dorset.................................. 94
Booth (Booksearch Service), (Geoff), Cheshire... 68
Boris Books, Somerset 216
Children's Bookshop (The), Herefordshire........ 127
Cranhurst Books, London NW 160
Dolphin Books, Suffolk............................. 225
Fifteenth Century Bookshop (The), East Sussex. 104
Hodgkins and Company Limited (Ian),
  Gloucestershire 116
Jean Hedger, Berks................................. 55
Jonkers Rare Books, Oxfordshire 207
Kelpie's Books, Fife............................... 271
Key Books (Sarah), Cambridgeshire............... 64
R. & A. Books, East Sussex 101
Simpson (Dave), Central 268
Treasure Trove Books, Leics....................... 146

- POWELL, ANTHONY
Apocalypse, Surrey 232
Criterion Books, London O........................ 181
Fifteenth Century Bookshop (The), East Sussex. 104
R. & A. Books, East Sussex 101
Trinity Rare Books, Co. Leitrim 266

- POWYS FAMILY, THE
Adrem Books, Herts 130
Antique Map and Bookshop (The), Dorset 94
Berwick Books, Lincolnshire....................... 150

Books Afloat, Dorset.................................. 96
Boris Books, Somerset 216
Criterion Books, London O......................... 181
Dolphin Books, Suffolk............................. 225
Ferdinando (Steven), Somerset 218
Fifteenth Century Bookshop (The), East Sussex. 104
Green Man Books, East Sussex 101
Island Books, Devon................................ 85
Trigon Books, Dorset............................... 95
Words Etcetera Bookshop, Dorset.................. 93

- PRATCHETT, TERRY
Adrem Books, Herts 130
Allinson (Frank & Stella), Warwickshire 236
Annie's Books, South Yorkshire 221
Bookworms Paradise Ltd., West Sussex 242
Cranhurst Books, London NW 160
Daeron's Books, Buckinghamshire................. 62
Fantastic Literature, Essex 110
Fiction First, Cheshire 69
Fifteenth Century Bookshop (The), East Sussex. 104
Green Meadow Books, Cornwall 74
Ice House Books, Wiltshire 254
Intech Books, Northumberland 201
L.M.S. Books, Herts 131
R. & A. Books, East Sussex 101
SaBeRo Books, London SW........................ 169
Simpson (Dave), Central 268
Surprise Books, Gloucestershire 113
Talisman Books, Cheshire.......................... 70
Trinity Rare Books, Co. Leitrim 266

- PRIESTLEY, J.B.
Apocalypse, Surrey 232
Booth (Booksearch Service), (Geoff), Cheshire... 68
Cameron House Books, Isle of Wight............. 133
Criterion Books, London O......................... 181
Fifteenth Century Bookshop (The), East Sussex. 104
Greta Books, Durham 97
Orb's Bookshop, Grampian......................... 273
Simpson (Dave), Central 268

- PRONZINI, BILL
Eggeling Books (John), West Yorkshire 249

- QUENEAU, RAYMOND
Delectus Books, London WC....................... 176
Trinity Rare Books, Co. Leitrim 266

- QUILLER-COUCH, SIR A.T.
Beaton (Richard), East Sussex...................... 103
Bookends of Fowey, Cornwall 72
Booth (Booksearch Service), (Geoff), Cheshire... 68
Eggeling Books (John), West Yorkshire 249
Fifteenth Century Bookshop (The), East Sussex. 104
First Edition, The, Essex 109
Island Books, Devon................................ 85
R & B Graham Trading, Cornwall 73
Tiger Books, Kent 136

- RACKHAM, ARTHUR
Adrem Books, Herts 130
Apocalypse, Surrey 232
Bookmark (Children's Books), Wiltshire.......... 253
Bow Windows Book Shop, East Sussex 103

Chalmers Hallam (E.), Hampshire................. 125
Charles Bossom, Cambridgeshire.................. 65
Children's Bookshop (The), Herefordshire........ 127
Cranhurst Books, London NW 160
Fifteenth Century Bookshop (The), East Sussex. 104
First Edition, The, Essex 109
Foster Bookshop (Paul), London SW............. 167
Harrington (Adrian), London W................... 173
Island Books, Devon................................ 85
Jean Hedger, Berks................................. 55
Key Books (Sarah), Cambridgeshire............... 64
Little Stour Books, Kent 136
Lucius Books, North Yorkshire 197
Minster Gate Bookshop, North Yorkshire 197
Preston Book Company, Lancashire 144
R. & A. Books, East Sussex 101
Rye Old Books, East Sussex 104
St Mary's Books & Prints, Lincolnshire 152
Trinity Rare Books, Co. Leitrim 266
World War II Books, Surrey 234

- RAISTRICK, ARTHUR
Anthony Vickers Books, North Yorkshire 195
Crosby Nethercott Books, London O 180
Grove Bookshop (The), North Yorkshire 195

- RAND, AYN
Webb Books (John), South Yorkshire............. 221

- RANKIN, IAN
Annie's Books, South Yorkshire 221
Apocalypse, Surrey 232
Cranhurst Books, London NW 160
Fiction First, Cheshire 69
Intech Books, Northumberland 201
James M Pickhard (Rare Books), Leics........... 145
Simpson (Dave), Central 268
Surprise Books, Gloucestershire 113
Trinity Rare Books, Co. Leitrim 266
Wayside Books and Cards, Oxfordshire 206

- RANSOME, ARTHUR
Adrem Books, Herts 130
Annie's Books, South Yorkshire 221
Bookmark (Children's Books), Wiltshire.......... 253
Bookshop on the Heath, The, London SE 163
Boris Books, Somerset 216
Chalmers Hallam (E.), Hampshire................. 125
Children's Bookshop (The), Herefordshire........ 127
Cranhurst Books, London NW 160
Cygnet Books, East Yorkshire..................... 107
Draca Books, West Yorkshire 248
Farringdon (J.M.), Swansea........................ 291
Fifteenth Century Bookshop (The), East Sussex. 104
First Edition, The, Essex 109
Heppa (Christopher), Essex 108
Island Books, Devon................................ 85
Key Books (Sarah), Cambridgeshire............... 64
Kirkland Books, Cumbria 78
Old Station Pottery & Bookshop (The), Norfolk 191
R. & A. Books, East Sussex 101
Schutte (David), Hampshire........................ 124
Trinity Rare Books, Co. Leitrim 266

- RATCLIFFE, DOROTHY UNA
Grove Bookshop (The), North Yorkshire 195
Trinity Rare Books, Co. Leitrim 266

- READ, MISS
Adrem Books, Herts 130
Annie's Books, South Yorkshire 221
Baker - Books for the Collector (Colin), Devon. 89
Bilski (Gill), Buckinghamshire 61
Bookmark (Children's Books), Wiltshire.......... 253
Boris Books, Somerset 216
Brown-Studies, Strathclyde.......................... 277
Clent Books, Worcestershire 255
Country Books, Derbyshire 82
Cygnet Books, East Yorkshire...................... 107
Fifteenth Century Bookshop (The), East Sussex. 104
Intech Books, Northumberland 201
Old Station Pottery & Bookshop (The), Norfolk 191
Trinity Rare Books, Co. Leitrim 266

- RICE, ANNE
Annie's Books, South Yorkshire 221
Fiction First, Cheshire 69
Old Celtic Bookshop (The), Devon................ 87
Simpson (Dave), Central 268
Surprise Books, Gloucestershire.................... 113
Trinity Rare Books, Co. Leitrim 266

- RICHARDS, FRANK
Adrem Books, Herts 130
Bookmark (Children's Books), Wiltshire.......... 253
Booth (Booksearch Service), (Geoff), Cheshire... 68
Children's Bookshop (The), Herefordshire........ 127
Cranhurst Books, London NW 160
D. & M. Books, West Yorkshire.................... 249
Draca Books, West Yorkshire....................... 248
Fifteenth Century Bookshop (The), East Sussex. 104
Heppa (Christopher), Essex 108
Intech Books, Northumberland 201
R. & A. Books, East Sussex 101
Schutte (David), Hampshire.......................... 124
Trinity Rare Books, Co. Leitrim 266
Wright (Norman), Dorset 95

- ROBINSON, HEATH W.
Adrem Books, Herts 130
Bookmark (Children's Books), Wiltshire.......... 253
Cranhurst Books, London NW 160
Fifteenth Century Bookshop (The), East Sussex. 104
Jean Hedger, Berks................................... 55
Myra Dean Illustated Books, Powys 287
R. & A. Books, East Sussex 101
Rye Old Books, East Sussex 104

- ROHMER, SAX
Trinity Rare Books, Co. Leitrim 266
Zardoz Books, Wiltshire.............................. 254

- ROLFE, F.
Doolin Dinghy Books, Co. Clare 262
Ellis, Bookseller (Peter), London WC 177

- ROLT, L.T.C.
Anthony Vickers Books, North Yorkshire 195
Baldwin (M. & M.), Worcestershire 255

Bird Books (Nigel), Ceredigion..................... 283
Boox-Box (The), Shropshire 212
Bott, (Bookdealers) Ltd., (Martin), Greater
    Manchester 118
Crosby Nethercott Books, London O 180
Dales and Lakes Book Centre, Cumbria......... 79
Island Books, Devon................................. 85
Liddle (Steve), Bristol 58
Randall (Tom), Somerset............................ 218
Robert Humm & Co, Lincolnshire 152
Trinity Rare Books, Co. Leitrim 266

- ROSSETTI, C.
Adrem Books, Herts 130
Cox Rare Books (Charles), Cornwall.............. 73
Dolphin Books, Suffolk.............................. 225
Fifteenth Century Bookshop (The), East Sussex. 104
Hodgkins and Company Limited (Ian),
    Gloucestershire 116
R. & A. Books, East Sussex 101
Tiger Books, Kent.................................... 136

- ROWLING, J.K.
Apocalypse, Surrey 232
Cranhurst Books, London NW 160
Draca Books, West Yorkshire....................... 248
Fifteenth Century Bookshop (The), East Sussex. 104
Harrington (Adrian), London W................... 173
Intech Books, Northumberland 201
James M Pickhard (Rare Books), Leics........... 145
Modern First Editions, West Yorkshire........... 247
R. & A. Books, East Sussex 101
St Mary's Books & Prints, Lincolnshire 152
Simpson (Dave), Central 268
Trinity Rare Books, Co. Leitrim 266

- RUSHDIE, SALMAN
Adrem Books, Herts 130
Booth (Booksearch Service), (Geoff), Cheshire... 68
Dolphin Books, Suffolk.............................. 225
Norton Books, North Yorkshire 192
R. & A. Books, East Sussex 101
Simpson (Dave), Central 268
Trinity Rare Books, Co. Leitrim 266

- RUSKIN, JOHN
Adrem Books, Herts 130
Apocalypse, Surrey 232
Brock Books, North Yorkshire..................... 192
Cox Rare Books (Charles), Cornwall.............. 73
Hodgkins and Company Limited (Ian),
    Gloucestershire 116
Island Books, Devon................................. 85
Jarndyce Antiquarian Booksellers, London WC. 177
Kirkland Books, Cumbria............................ 78
R. & A. Books, East Sussex 101
Rosley Books, Cumbria.............................. 81
Shacklock Books (David), Suffolk 226
Solitaire Books, Somerset............................ 216
Tiger Books, Kent.................................... 136

- RUSSELL, BERTRAND
Adrem Books, Herts 130
Island Books, Devon................................. 85
PsychoBabel Books & Journals, Oxfordshire..... 205

R. & A. Books, East Sussex 101

- RUSSELL, W
Karen Millward, Co. Cork.......................... 263

- SABATINI, R.
Adrem Books, Herts 130
Dusty Books, Powys 290
Eggeling Books (John), West Yorkshire 249
Fifteenth Century Bookshop (The), East Sussex. 104
Greta Books, Durham 97
Lucius Books, North Yorkshire.................... 197
Tiger Books, Kent.................................. 136

- SACKVILLE-WEST, VITA
Adrem Books, Herts 130
Apocalypse, Surrey 232
Booth (Booksearch Service), (Geoff), Cheshire... 68
Bow Windows Book Shop, East Sussex 103
Ellis, Bookseller (Peter), London WC 177
Evans Books (Paul), West Sussex 243
Fifteenth Century Bookshop (The), East Sussex. 104
Island Books, Devon................................ 85
Tiger Books, Kent.................................. 136
Trinity Rare Books, Co. Leitrim 266

- SASSOON, SIEGFRIED
Adrem Books, Herts 130
Anglo-American Rare Books, Surrey.............. 232
Booth (Booksearch Service), (Geoff), Cheshire... 68
Ellis, Bookseller (Peter), London WC 177
Fifteenth Century Bookshop (The), East Sussex. 104
Island Books, Devon................................ 85
R. & A. Books, East Sussex 101
Roz Hulse, Conwy 284
Trinity Rare Books, Co. Leitrim 266

- SAVILLE, M.
Adrem Books, Herts 130
Ardis Books, Hampshire 126
Beck (John), East Sussex 103
Bilski (Gill), Buckinghamshire 61
Bookmark (Children's Books), Wiltshire.......... 253
Bookpassage (The), Shropshire..................... 212
Boris Books, Somerset 216
Children's Bookshop (The), Herefordshire........ 127
Fifteenth Century Bookshop (The), East Sussex. 104
Green Meadow Books, Cornwall 74
Key Books (Sarah), Cambridgeshire............... 64
Lewis First Editions, Kent 136
Little Stour Books, Kent 136
Old Station Pottery & Bookshop (The), Norfolk 191
Schutte (David), Hampshire........................ 124
TP Children's Bookshop, West Yorkshire........ 245

- SAYERS, DOROTHY
Adrem Books, Herts 130
Annie's Books, South Yorkshire 221
Avonworld Books, Somerset........................ 216
Booth (Booksearch Service), (Geoff), Cheshire... 68
Cranhurst Books, London NW 160
Fifteenth Century Bookshop (The), East Sussex. 104
Island Books, Devon................................ 85
Lucius Books, North Yorkshire.................... 197
Ming Books, Dumfries & Galloway 270

Modern First Editions, West Yorkshire........... 247
R. & A. Books, East Sussex 101
Rosley Books, Cumbria 81
Trinity Rare Books, Co. Leitrim 266

- SEARLE, RONALD
Adrem Books, Herts 130
Allinson (Frank & Stella), Warwickshire 236
Bookmark (Children's Books), Wiltshire.......... 253
Bookshop on the Heath, The, London SE 163
Cranhurst Books, London NW 160
Eclectica, London SE 164
Facet Books, Dorset................................ 91
Fifteenth Century Bookshop (The), East Sussex. 104
Intech Books, Northumberland 201

- SELOUS, FREDERICK
Edmund Pollinger Rare Books, London SW..... 166
Preston Book Company, Lancashire 144

- SENDAK, MAURICE
Bookmark (Children's Books), Wiltshire.......... 253
Children's Bookshop (The), Herefordshire........ 127
Cranhurst Books, London NW 160
Fifteenth Century Bookshop (The), East Sussex. 104
Intech Books, Northumberland 201
Jean Hedger, Berks................................. 55
Myra Dean Illustated Books, Powys 287
R. & A. Books, East Sussex 101

- SERVICE, ROBERT W.
Booth (Booksearch Service), (Geoff), Cheshire... 68
Fifteenth Century Bookshop (The), East Sussex. 104

- SEYMOUR, JOHN
Coch-y-Bonddu Books, Powys 290
Dolphin Books, Suffolk............................. 225
Mount's Bay Books, Cornwall 74

- SHAKESPEARE, WILLIAM
Apocalypse, Surrey 232
Bennett & Kerr Books, Oxfordshire 205
Byre Books, Dumfries & Galloway................ 270
Chaucer Head Bookshop, Warwickshire.......... 237
Fifteenth Century Bookshop (The), East Sussex. 104
First Edition, The, Essex 109
Modern First Editions, West Yorkshire........... 247
Myra Dean Illustated Books, Powys 287
Period & Classical Collections, East Sussex 103
R. & A. Books, East Sussex 101
Simpson (Dave), Central 268
Trinity Rare Books, Co. Leitrim 266
Uncle Phil's Books, West Midlands 239

- SHAW, GEORGE BERNARD
Adrem Books, Herts 130
Apocalypse, Surrey 232
Booth (Booksearch Service), (Geoff), Cheshire... 68
Brock Books, North Yorkshire..................... 192
Carraig Books Ltd., Co. Dublin 263
Dolphin Books, Suffolk............................. 225
Doolin Dinghy Books, Co. Clare 262
Ellis, Bookseller (Peter), London WC 177
Fifteenth Century Bookshop (The), East Sussex. 104
Quentin Books Ltd, Essex 108

R. & A. Books, East Sussex 101
Simpson (Dave), Central 268

- SHELLEY, PERCY B

Adrem Books, Herts 130
Alec–Smith Books (Alex), East Yorkshire 107
Michael Rogers, Wiltshire 251
Tiger Books, Kent 136

- SHEPARD, E.H.

Adrem Books, Herts 130
Bookmark (Children's Books), Wiltshire 253
Booth (Booksearch Service), (Geoff), Cheshire... 68
Fifteenth Century Bookshop (The), East Sussex. 104
Jean Hedger, Berks 55
Key Books (Sarah), Cambridgeshire 64
R. & A. Books, East Sussex 101

- SHUTE, NEVILLE

Adrem Books, Herts 130
Booth (Booksearch Service), (Geoff), Cheshire... 68
Boris Books, Somerset 216
Dusty Books, Powys 290
Eggeling Books (John), West Yorkshire 249
Fifteenth Century Bookshop (The), East Sussex. 104
Greta Books, Durham 97
Intech Books, Northumberland 201
Lewis First Editions, Kent 136
Lucius Books, North Yorkshire 197
Modern First Editions, West Yorkshire........... 247
Orb's Bookshop, Grampian.......................... 273
Portus Books, Hampshire 122
R. & A. Books, East Sussex 101
Simpson (Dave), Central 268
The Sanctuary Bookshop, Dorset 94
Trinity Rare Books, Co. Leitrim 266
Webb Books (John), South Yorkshire............. 221

- SIMENON, GEORGES

Adrem Books, Herts 130
Apocalypse, Surrey 232
Bass (Ben), Wiltshire 251
James M Pickhard (Rare Books), Leics........... 145
Lucius Books, North Yorkshire 197
Ming Books, Dumfries & Galloway 270
Simpson (Dave), Central 268
Treasure Trove Books, Leics....................... 146
Trinity Rare Books, Co. Leitrim 266
Wayside Books and Cards, Oxfordshire 206
Williams (Bookdealer), (Richard), North Lincs.. 153

- SITWELL FAMILY

Adrem Books, Herts 130
Apocalypse, Surrey 232
Booth (Booksearch Service), (Geoff), Cheshire... 68
Carraig Books Ltd., Co. Dublin 263
Ellis, Bookseller (Peter), London WC 177
Fifteenth Century Bookshop (The), East Sussex. 104
Island Books, Devon............................... 85
Simpson (Dave), Central 268
Trinity Rare Books, Co. Leitrim 266

- SMITH, GUY N.

Adrem Books, Herts 130

- SMITH, WILBUR

Adrem Books, Herts 130
Annie's Books, South Yorkshire 221
Booth (Booksearch Service), (Geoff), Cheshire... 68
James M Pickhard (Rare Books), Leics........... 145
Oak Tree Press, Oxfordshire 207
R. & A. Books, East Sussex 101
Simpson (Dave), Central 268
Surprise Books, Gloucestershire 113
Trinity Rare Books, Co. Leitrim 266

- SNAFFLES

Adrem Books, Herts 130
Chalmers Hallam (E.), Hampshire 125

- SOLZHENITSYN, ALEXANDER

Adrem Books, Herts 130
Apocalypse, Surrey 232
Booth (Booksearch Service), (Geoff), Cheshire... 68
R. & A. Books, East Sussex 101
Trinity Rare Books, Co. Leitrim 266

- SOMERVILLE & ROSS

Adrem Books, Herts 130
Booth (Booksearch Service), (Geoff), Cheshire... 68
Darkwood Books, Co. Cork 263
Fifteenth Century Bookshop (The), East Sussex. 104
Greta Books, Durham 97
Tiger Books, Kent 136
Trinity Rare Books, Co. Leitrim 266

- SPARE, AUSTIN O.

Apocalypse, Surrey 232
Inner Bookshop (The), Oxfordshire............... 208
Lucius Books, North Yorkshire 197

- SPARE, AUSTIN OSMAN

Apocalypse, Surrey 232
Atlantis Bookshop, London WC................... 176
Inner Bookshop (The), Oxfordshire............... 208
Occultique, Northants.............................. 199
Trinity Rare Books, Co. Leitrim 266

- SPARK, MURIEL

Adrem Books, Herts 130
Booth (Booksearch Service), (Geoff), Cheshire... 68
Criterion Books, London O......................... 181
Dolphin Books, Suffolk 225
Fifteenth Century Bookshop (The), East Sussex. 104
Simpson (Dave), Central 268
Trinity Rare Books, Co. Leitrim 266

- STEADMAN, RALPH

Adrem Books, Herts 130
Barmby (C. & A.J.), Kent.......................... 140
Dylans Bookstore, Swansea........................ 291
Fifteenth Century Bookshop (The), East Sussex. 104
Lucius Books, North Yorkshire 197
Myra Dean Illustated Books, Powys 287

- STEGNER, WALLACE

Booth (Booksearch Service), (Geoff), Cheshire... 68

- STEIN, GERTRUDE

Adrem Books, Herts 130

Norton Books, North Yorkshire 192
R. & A. Books, East Sussex 101
Trinity Rare Books, Co. Leitrim 266

- STEINBECK, JOHN
Adrem Books, Herts 130
Bookworms Paradise Ltd., West Sussex 242
Booth (Booksearch Service), (Geoff), Cheshire... 68
Fifteenth Century Bookshop (The), East Sussex. 104
Trinity Rare Books, Co. Leitrim 266

- STEINER, RUDOLF
Anthroposophical Books, Gloucestershire 116
Dolphin Books, Suffolk.............................. 225
Inner Bookshop (The), Oxfordshire................ 208
Needham Books, (Russell), Somerset.............. 219
Trinity Rare Books, Co. Leitrim 266

- STENDHAL
Apocalypse, Surrey 232
Fifteenth Century Bookshop (The), East Sussex. 104

- STERNE, L
Adrem Books, Herts 130
Spelman (Ken), North Yorkshire 198

- STEVENSON, ROBERT LOUIS
Adrem Books, Herts 130
Apocalypse, Surrey 232
Bookmark (Children's Books), Wiltshire.......... 253
Bookshop on the Heath, The, London SE 163
Booth (Booksearch Service), (Geoff), Cheshire... 68
Criterion Books, London O........................ 181
Dolphin Books, Suffolk.............................. 225
Fifteenth Century Bookshop (The), East Sussex. 104
First Edition, The, Essex 109
Greta Books, Durham 97
Jean Hedger, Berks 55
Jonkers Rare Books, Oxfordshire 207
Olynthiacs, Shropshire 213
Parrott (Jeremy), London E........................ 154
R. & A. Books, East Sussex 101
Simpson (Dave), Central 268
Trinity Rare Books, Co. Leitrim 266

- STOKER, B.
Modern First Editions, West Yorkshire........... 247
R. & A. Books, East Sussex 101
Rider Haggard Society (The), Tyne and Wear... 235
Trinity Rare Books, Co. Leitrim 266

- STRACHEY, LYTTON
Adrem Books, Herts 130
Evans Books (Paul), West Sussex 243
Fifteenth Century Bookshop (The), East Sussex. 104
R. & A. Books, East Sussex 101

- STRATTON PORTER, GENE
Fifteenth Century Bookshop (The), East Sussex. 104
Greta Books, Durham 97

- STREET, A.G.
Baker - Books for the Collector (Colin), Devon. 89
Books for Content, Herefordshire.................. 127
Dolphin Books, Suffolk.............................. 225

Greta Books, Durham 97

- STRINDBERG, A.
Adrem Books, Herts 130
R. & A. Books, East Sussex 101

- SWIFT, J
Island Books, Devon 85
R. & A. Books, East Sussex 101
Tiger Books, Kent.................................... 136
Trinity Rare Books, Co. Leitrim 266

- SWINBURNE, A.C.
Adrem Books, Herts 130
Cameron House Books, Isle of Wight............. 133
Cox Rare Books (Charles), Cornwall............. 73
Fifteenth Century Bookshop (The), East Sussex. 104
Hodgkins and Company Limited (Ian),
   Gloucestershire 116
R. & A. Books, East Sussex 101

- TANGYE, D.
Annie's Books, South Yorkshire 221
Baker - Books for the Collector (Colin), Devon. 89
Bass (Ben), Wiltshire 251
Bonython Bookshop, Cornwall..................... 75
Bosco Books, Cornwall 72
Emjay Books, Surrey................................. 231
Fifteenth Century Bookshop (The), East Sussex. 104
Green Meadow Books, Cornwall 74
Intech Books, Northumberland 201
Island Books, Devon 85
Just Books, Cornwall 75
Kelpie's Books, Fife................................. 271
R. & A. Books, East Sussex 101

- TENNYSON, LORD ALFRED
Adrem Books, Herts 130
Apocalypse, Surrey 232
Cameron House Books, Isle of Wight............. 133
Cox Rare Books (Charles), Cornwall............. 73
Fifteenth Century Bookshop (The), East Sussex. 104
First Edition, The, Essex 109

- THACKERY, WILLIAM M.
Apocalypse, Surrey 232
Dolphin Books, Suffolk.............................. 225
Fifteenth Century Bookshop (The), East Sussex. 104
First Edition, The, Essex 109
Park Gallery & Bookshop (The), Northants 200
R. & A. Books, East Sussex 101
Simpson (Dave), Central 268

- THELWELL, N
Adrem Books, Herts 130
Annie's Books, South Yorkshire 221
Bookstand, Dorset.................................... 94
Country Books, Derbyshire 82
Fifteenth Century Bookshop (The), East Sussex. 104
Myra Dean Illustated Books, Powys 287

- THEROUX, P.
Adrem Books, Herts 130
Dolphin Books, Suffolk.............................. 225
Fifteenth Century Bookshop (The), East Sussex. 104

R. & A. Books, East Sussex 101
Trinity Rare Books, Co. Leitrim 266

- THIRKELL, ANGELA
Adrem Books, Herts 130
Bookmark (Children's Books), Wiltshire.......... 253
Booth (Booksearch Service), (Geoff), Cheshire... 68
Boris Books, Somerset 216
Fifteenth Century Bookshop (The), East Sussex. 104

- THOMAS, DYLAN
Adrem Books, Herts 130
Annie's Books, South Yorkshire 221
Boz Books, Powys................................... 287
Cofion Books, Pembrokeshire 286
Criterion Books, London O......................... 181
Dylans Bookstore, Swansea........................ 291
Fifteenth Century Bookshop (The), East Sussex. 104
R. & A. Books, East Sussex 101
Trinity Rare Books, Co. Leitrim 266

- THOMAS, EDWARD
Canon Gate Books, West Sussex................... 243
Dylans Bookstore, Swansea........................ 291
Karen Millward, Co. Cork 263
Smith Books (Keith), Herefordshire 128
Tiger Books, Kent 136

- THOMPSON, ERNEST E.
Adrem Books, Herts 130
Annie's Books, South Yorkshire 221

- THOMPSON-SETON, ERNEST E.
Adrem Books, Herts 130
Annie's Books, South Yorkshire 221
Fifteenth Century Bookshop (The), East Sussex. 104
Green Meadow Books, Cornwall 74

- THOREAU, HENRY DAVID
Adrem Books, Herts 130
Evans Books (Paul), West Sussex 243

- THORNDIKE, RUSSELL
Fifteenth Century Bookshop (The), East Sussex. 104
James M Pickhard (Rare Books), Leics........... 145

- THURBER, JAMES
Adrem Books, Herts 130
Fifteenth Century Bookshop (The), East Sussex. 104
Island Books, Devon............................... 85
Portus Books, Hampshire 122

- TOKLAS, ALICE B.
Adrem Books, Herts 130
Fifteenth Century Bookshop (The), East Sussex. 104
Norton Books, North Yorkshire 192

- TOLKIEN, J.R.R.
Adrem Books, Herts 130
Annie's Books, South Yorkshire 221
Bookworms Paradise Ltd., West Sussex 242
Cranhurst Books, London NW 160
Daeron's Books, Buckinghamshire................. 62
Fifteenth Century Bookshop (The), East Sussex. 104
First Edition, The, Essex 109

Foster Bookshop (Paul), London SW 167
Green Meadow Books, Cornwall 74
Harrington (Adrian), London W................... 173
Island Books, Devon............................... 85
James M Pickhard (Rare Books), Leics........... 145
Key Books (Sarah), Cambridgeshire............... 64
Lucius Books, North Yorkshire 197
Modern First Editions, West Yorkshire.......... 247
R. & A. Books, East Sussex 101
Rosley Books, Cumbria 81
Simpson (Dave), Central 268
Thorntons of Oxford Ltd., Oxfordshire.......... 206
Trinity Rare Books, Co. Leitrim 266

- TOLSTOY, LEO
Adrem Books, Herts 130
Delectus Books, London WC....................... 176
Fifteenth Century Bookshop (The), East Sussex. 104
R. & A. Books, East Sussex 101
Tiger Books, Kent 136

- TOURTEL, M
Beck (John), East Sussex 103
Bookmark (Children's Books), Wiltshire.......... 253
Boris Books, Somerset 216
Children's Bookshop (The), Herefordshire........ 127
Cranhurst Books, London NW 160
Craobh Rua Books, Co. Armagh.................. 260
Fifteenth Century Bookshop (The), East Sussex. 104
First Edition, The, Essex 109
Jean Hedger, Berks 55
R. & A. Books, East Sussex 101

- TOWNSEND WARNER, SYLVIA
Dolphin Books, Suffolk............................. 225
Lymelight Books & Prints, Dorset................. 93
Stinton (Judith), Dorset............................ 92

- TRAVERN, B.
Adrem Books, Herts 130

- TROLLOPE, ANTHONY
Adrem Books, Herts 130
Ash Rare Books, London SW....................... 166
Beaton (Richard), East Sussex..................... 103
Bookshop on the Heath, The, London SE 163
Booth (Booksearch Service), (Geoff), Cheshire... 68
Boris Books, Somerset 216
Fifteenth Century Bookshop (The), East Sussex. 104
Quentin Books Ltd, Essex.......................... 108
Sen Books, Hampshire............................. 126
Tiger Books, Kent 136
Trinity Rare Books, Co. Leitrim 266

- TUDOR, TASHA
Bookmark (Children's Books), Wiltshire.......... 253
Fifteenth Century Bookshop (The), East Sussex. 104
Myra Dean Illustated Books, Powys 287

- TULLY, JIM
Loretta Lay Books, London NW 161

- TWAIN, MARK
Adrem Books, Herts 130
Dolphin Books, Suffolk............................. 225

Fifteenth Century Bookshop (The), East Sussex. 104
First Edition, The, Essex 109
Harrington (Adrian), London W.................... 173
Parrott (Jeremy), London E........................ 154
R. & A. Books, East Sussex 101
Simpson (Dave), Central 268
Tiger Books, Kent.................................... 136
Trinity Rare Books, Co. Leitrim 266

- UPFIELD, ARTHUR
Loretta Lay Books, London NW 161

- UTTLEY, ALISON
Annie's Books, South Yorkshire 221
Bookmark (Children's Books), Wiltshire.......... 253
Boris Books, Somerset 216
Children's Bookshop (The), Herefordshire........ 127
Country Books, Derbyshire.......................... 82
Fifteenth Century Bookshop (The), East Sussex. 104
Green Meadow Books, Cornwall 74
Jean Hedger, Berks.................................. 55
R. & A. Books, East Sussex 101
Rosley Books, Cumbria 81
Scarthin Books, Derbyshire 82
Simpson (Dave), Central 268

- VAN LOON, H.
Booth (Booksearch Service), (Geoff), Cheshire... 68
Dolphin Books, Suffolk.............................. 225

- VAN VOGT, A. E.
Bookworms Paradise Ltd., West Sussex 242
Orb's Bookshop, Grampian.......................... 273
Trinity Rare Books, Co. Leitrim 266

- VERNE, JULES
Adrem Books, Herts 130
Annie's Books, South Yorkshire 221
Booth (Booksearch Service), (Geoff), Cheshire... 68
Cox, Andrew, Shropshire............................ 214
Fifteenth Century Bookshop (The), East Sussex. 104
Parrott (Jeremy), London E........................ 154
R. & A. Books, East Sussex 101
Tiger Books, Kent.................................... 136
Trinity Rare Books, Co. Leitrim 266

- VONNEGUT, KURT
Adrem Books, Herts 130
Cranhurst Books, London NW 160
Trinity Rare Books, Co. Leitrim 266

- WAINWRIGHT, ALFRED
Adrem Books, Herts 130
Anthony Vickers Books, North Yorkshire 195
Country Books, Derbyshire.......................... 82
Fifteenth Century Bookshop (The), East Sussex. 104
Intech Books, Northumberland 201
Jane & John Kinnaird, Cumbria 78
Kirkland Books, Cumbria........................... 78

- WAINWRIGHT, ARTHUR
Adrem Books, Herts 130
Kirkland Books, Cumbria........................... 78
R. & A. Books, East Sussex 101

- WALLACE, EDGAR
Adrem Books, Herts 130
Book For All Reasons (A.), Suffolk............... 228
Bookshop on the Heath, The, London SE 163
Bookworms Paradise Ltd., West Sussex 242
Dolphin Books, Suffolk............................. 225
Eggeling Books (John), West Yorkshire 249
Fifteenth Century Bookshop (The), East Sussex. 104
McGee (Terence J.), London O 180
Mercat Books, Highland 274
R. & A. Books, East Sussex 101
Simpson (Dave), Central 268
Trinity Rare Books, Co. Leitrim 266
Williams (Bookdealer), (Richard), North Lincs.. 153
Zardoz Books, Wiltshire 254

- WALMSLEY, LEO
Adrem Books, Herts 130
Fifteenth Century Bookshop (The), East Sussex. 104
Intech Books, Northumberland 201

- WALSH, M.
Darkwood Books, Co. Cork........................ 263
Greta Books, Durham 97
Logie Steading Bookshop, Grampian 273

- WATKINS, VERNON
Apocalypse, Surrey 232
Dylans Bookstore, Swansea........................ 291
Riderless Horse Books, Norfolk................... 186

- WATKINS-PITCHFORD, DENYS ('B.B.')
Adrem Books, Herts 130
Baker - Books for the Collector (Colin), Devon. 89
Baker (Gerald), Bristol.............................. 60
Bookmark (Children's Books), Wiltshire.......... 253
Bookshop on the Heath, The, London SE 163
Booth (Booksearch Service), (Geoff), Cheshire... 68
Boris Books, Somerset 216
Chalmers Hallam (E.), Hampshire................. 125
Children's Bookshop (The), Herefordshire........ 127
Coch-y-Bonddu Books, Powys 290
Country Books, Derbyshire.......................... 82
Deverell Books, Bristol 59
Fifteenth Century Bookshop (The), East Sussex. 104
Heppa (Christopher), Essex 108
Intech Books, Northumberland 201
Island Books, Devon................................ 85
James M Pickhard (Rare Books), Leics........... 145
Key Books (Sarah), Cambridgeshire............... 64
Lucius Books, North Yorkshire 197
Martin (Brian), Surrey 231
McEwan Fine Books, Grampian.................... 272
River Reads Bookshop, Devon...................... 90
St Mary's Books & Prints, Lincolnshire 152
Shakeshaft (Dr. B.), Cheshire...................... 71
Trinity Rare Books, Co. Leitrim 266
Yesterday Tackle & Books, Dorset 92

- WAUGH, EVELYN
Adrem Books, Herts 130
C J Renwick Books, Powys......................... 287
Carraig Books Ltd., Co. Dublin 263
Island Books, Devon................................ 85
Simpson (Dave), Central 268

- WEBB, MARY
Adrem Books, Herts 130
Boris Books, Somerset 216
R. & A. Books, East Sussex 101
Simpson (Dave), Central 268
Trinity Rare Books, Co. Leitrim 266
Woodbine Books, West Yorkshire 245

- WELCH, R.
Adrem Books, Herts 130
Fifteenth Century Bookshop (The), East Sussex. 104
Key Books (Sarah), Cambridgeshire............... 64

- WELCOME, JOHN
Adrem Books, Herts 130
Eggeling Books (John), West Yorkshire 249

- WELLS, H.G.
Adrem Books, Herts 130
Antique Map and Bookshop (The), Dorset 94
Doolin Dinghy Books, Co. Clare 262
Fantastic Literature, Essex 110
Fifteenth Century Bookshop (The), East Sussex. 104
First Edition, The, Essex 109
Foster Bookshop (Paul), London SW............. 167
Harrington (Adrian), London W................... 173
R. & A. Books, East Sussex 101
RGS Books, Surrey 234
Simpson (Dave), Central 268
Tiger Books, Kent................................... 136
Trinity Rare Books, Co. Leitrim 266

- WENDELL HOLMES, OLIVER
Roz Hulse, Conwy 284

- WHARTON, EDITH
Adrem Books, Herts 130
Apocalypse, Surrey 232
Doolin Dinghy Books, Co. Clare 262
Norton Books, North Yorkshire 192
Tiger Books, Kent................................... 136

- WHEATLEY, DENNIS
Adrem Books, Herts 130
Annie's Books, South Yorkshire 221
Apocalypse, Surrey 232
Bookstand, Dorset................................... 94
Broadwater Books, Hampshire 125
Cranhurst Books, London NW 160
Dolphin Books, Suffolk............................. 225
Fifteenth Century Bookshop (The), East Sussex. 104
Heckmondwike Book Shop, West Yorkshire 249
Island Books, Devon 85
James M Pickhard (Rare Books), Leics........... 145
Lucius Books, North Yorkshire 197
Orb's Bookshop, Grampian......................... 273
R. & A. Books, East Sussex 101
Simpson (Dave), Central 268
Surprise Books, Gloucestershire 113
Trinity Rare Books, Co. Leitrim 266

- WHITE, GILBERT
Adrem Books, Herts 130
Country Books, Derbyshire......................... 82
Fifteenth Century Bookshop (The), East Sussex. 104

Island Books, Devon 85
Sen Books, Hampshire.............................. 126

- WHITE, T.H.
Adrem Books, Herts 130
Coch-y-Bonddu Books, Powys 290
Fifteenth Century Bookshop (The), East Sussex. 104
Gildas Books, Cheshire 68
John Underwood Antiquarian Books, Norfolk.. 189
Trinity Rare Books, Co. Leitrim 266

- WHITMAN, W.
R. & A. Books, East Sussex 101
Trinity Rare Books, Co. Leitrim 266

- WILDE, OSCAR
Annie's Books, South Yorkshire 221
Apocalypse, Surrey 232
Brock Books, North Yorkshire..................... 192
Courtwood Books, Co. Laois....................... 265
Cox Rare Books (Charles), Cornwall............. 73
Doolin Dinghy Books, Co. Clare 262
Fifteenth Century Bookshop (The), East Sussex. 104
First Edition, The, Essex 109
Foster Bookshop (Paul), London SW............. 167
Harrington (Adrian), London W................... 173
Karen Millward, Co. Cork.......................... 263
R. & A. Books, East Sussex 101
Trinity Rare Books, Co. Leitrim 266

- WILLIAMS, CHARLES
Booth (Booksearch Service), (Geoff), Cheshire... 68
Eggeling Books (John), West Yorkshire 249
Riderless Horse Books, Norfolk.................... 186
Rosley Books, Cumbria 81
Trinity Rare Books, Co. Leitrim 266

- WILLIAMS, TENNESSEE
R. & A. Books, East Sussex 101
Trinity Rare Books, Co. Leitrim 266
Tsbbooks, London SW 169

- WILLIAMSON, HENRY
Adrem Books, Herts 130
Booth (Booksearch Service), (Geoff), Cheshire... 68
Dolphin Books, Suffolk............................. 225
Fifteenth Century Bookshop (The), East Sussex. 104
Grahame Thornton, Bookseller, Dorset.......... 93
Grove Bookshop (The), North Yorkshire 195
Heppa (Christopher), Essex 108
Island Books, Devon 85
Old Station Pottery & Bookshop (The), Norfolk 191
R. & A. Books, East Sussex 101
Rickaro Books, West Yorkshire.................... 246
River Reads Bookshop, Devon...................... 90
Tarka Books, Devon................................. 84
Trinity Rare Books, Co. Leitrim 266

- WILSON, COLIN
Adrem Books, Herts 130
Apocalypse, Surrey 232
Booth (Booksearch Service), (Geoff), Cheshire... 68
Gildas Books, Cheshire 68
Loretta Lay Books, London NW 161
Michael Rogers, Wiltshire.......................... 251

Star Lord Books, Greater Manchester 119
Yarwood Rare Books (Edward), G Manchester. 118

- WODEHOUSE, P.G.
Adrem Books, Herts 130
Annie's Books, South Yorkshire 221
Bass (Ben), Wiltshire 251
Boris Books, Somerset 216
Cranhurst Books, London NW 160
Fifteenth Century Bookshop (The), East Sussex. 104
First Edition, The, Essex 109
Harrington (Adrian), London W................... 173
Heppa (Christopher), Essex 108
Intech Books, Northumberland 201
Island Books, Devon................................. 85
Jonkers Rare Books, Oxfordshire 207
Little Stour Books, Kent 136
Lucius Books, North Yorkshire.................... 197
Mercat Books, Highland 274
N V Books, Warwickshire........................... 236
Not Just Books, Dorset.............................. 94
Olynthiacs, Shropshire 213
Orb's Bookshop, Grampian......................... 273
R. & A. Books, East Sussex 101
Simpson (Dave), Central 268
Trinity Rare Books, Co. Leitrim 266
Williams Rare Books (Nigel), London WC 179

- WOLFE, THOMAS
Adrem Books, Herts 130
Idle Genius Books, London N 157
R. & A. Books, East Sussex 101
Trinity Rare Books, Co. Leitrim 266

- WOODEFORD, PARSON JAMES
Country Books, Derbyshire.......................... 82
Fifteenth Century Bookshop (The), East Sussex. 104

- WOOLF, LEONARD
Evans Books (Paul), West Sussex 243
Fifteenth Century Bookshop (The), East Sussex. 104

- WOOLF, VIRGINIA
Adrem Books, Herts 130
Annie's Books, South Yorkshire 221
Bookbox, Gloucestershire 115
Booth (Booksearch Service), (Geoff), Cheshire... 68
Bow Windows Book Shop, East Sussex 103
Evans Books (Paul), West Sussex 243
Fifteenth Century Bookshop (The), East Sussex. 104
First Edition, The, Essex 109
Foster Bookshop (Paul), London SW.............. 167
Island Books, Devon................................. 85
Jonkers Rare Books, Oxfordshire 207
Lucius Books, North Yorkshire.................... 197
Modern First Editions, West Yorkshire........... 247
Orb's Bookshop, Grampian......................... 273
R. & A. Books, East Sussex 101
Tiger Books, Kent................................... 136
Trinity Rare Books, Co. Leitrim 266
Words Etcetera Bookshop, Dorset................. 93

- WORDSWORTH, WILLIAM
Adrem Books, Herts 130
Alec–Smith Books (Alex), East Yorkshire........ 107

Apocalypse, Surrey 232
Dolphin Books, Suffolk.............................. 225
Fifteenth Century Bookshop (The), East Sussex. 104
Island Books, Devon................................. 85
Jane & John Kinnaird, Cumbria 78
Kirkland Books, Cumbria............................ 78
R. & A. Books, East Sussex 101
Tiger Books, Kent................................... 136

- WYNDHAM, JOHN
Adrem Books, Herts 130
Annie's Books, South Yorkshire 221
James M Pickhard (Rare Books), Leics........... 145

- YARBRO, CHELSEA QUINN
Adrem Books, Herts 130

- YATES, DORNFORD
Adrem Books, Herts 130
Book For All Reasons (A.), Suffolk............... 228
Booth (Booksearch Service), (Geoff), Cheshire... 68
Boris Books, Somerset 216
Fifteenth Century Bookshop (The), East Sussex. 104
Heppa (Christopher), Essex 108
Island Books, Devon................................. 85
Trinity Rare Books, Co. Leitrim 266

- YEATS, W.B.
Apocalypse, Surrey 232
Carraig Books Ltd., Co. Dublin 263
Courtwood Books, Co. Laois....................... 265
Craobh Rua Books, Co. Armagh 260
Criterion Books, London O......................... 181
Delectus Books, London WC........................ 176
Read Ireland, Co. Dublin 264
Tiger Books, Kent................................... 136
Trinity Rare Books, Co. Leitrim 266

- YEE, CHIANG
Booth (Booksearch Service), (Geoff), Cheshire... 68
Eclectica, London SE 164
Eggeling Books (John), West Yorkshire 249
Greta Books, Durham 97

- YOUNG, FRANCIS BRETT
Adrem Books, Herts 130
Boris Books, Somerset 216
Clent Books, Worcestershire 255
Orb's Bookshop, Grampian......................... 273
Sedgeberrow Books, Worcestershire 256

- ZOLA, EMILE
Apocalypse, Surrey 232
Beaton (Richard), East Sussex..................... 103
Cranhurst Books, London NW 160
Tiger Books, Kent................................... 136
Trinity Rare Books, Co. Leitrim 266

AUTHORS
- AUSTRALIAN
Eggeling Books (John), West Yorkshire 249

- BRITISH
Annie's Books, South Yorkshire 221
Beaton (Richard), East Sussex..................... 103

Booth (Booksearch Service), (Geoff), Cheshire... 68
Cranhurst Books, London NW 160
Eggeling Books (John), West Yorkshire 249
Glasheen-Books, Surrey 231
Harvest Books, Lancashire 144
Intech Books, Northumberland 201
Island Books, Devon 85
Oak Tree Press, Oxfordshire 207
R. & A. Books, East Sussex 101
Shakeshaft (Dr. B.), Cheshire 71
Stinton (Judith), Dorset 92
Valentine Rare Books, London W 175

- LOCAL

Atholl Fine Books, Tayside 280
Bookpassage (The), Shropshire 212
Chapter Two, London SE 163
Colonsay Bookshop, Isle of Colonsay 275
Eggeling Books (John), West Yorkshire 249
Esoteric Dreams Bookshop, Cumbria 77
Facet Books, Dorset 91
Farquharson, (Hilary), Tayside 280
Fifteenth Century Bookshop (The), East Sussex. 104
Hay Castle, Powys 288
hullbooks.com, East Yorkshire 106
Intech Books, Northumberland 201
Joel Segal Books, Devon 86
Just Books, Cornwall 75
MK Book Services, Cambridgeshire 66
Stinton (Judith), Dorset 92
The Sanctuary Bookshop, Dorset 94

- NATIONAL

Booth (Booksearch Service), (Geoff), Cheshire... 68
Joel Segal Books, Devon 86
Oak Tree Press, Oxfordshire 207

- WOMEN

Al Saqi Books, London W 171
Backfold Books, Herefordshire 127
Books & Bygones (Pam Taylor), West Midlands 240
Cofion Books, Pembrokeshire 286
Crawford (Elizabeth), London EC 155
dgbbooks, West Sussex 244
Dolphin Books, Suffolk 225
Dylans Bookstore, Swansea 291
Eggeling Books (John), West Yorkshire 249
Elaine Lonsdale Books, West Yorkshire 247
Esoteric Dreams Bookshop, Cumbria 77
Fifteenth Century Bookshop (The), East Sussex. 104
Hobgoblin Books, Hampshire 125
Intech Books, Northumberland 201
Joel Segal Books, Devon 86
John L Capes (Books Maps & Prints), North
   Yorkshire 196
Johnson Rare Book Collections (C.R.),
   London NW 161
Lane Books (Shirley), Isle of Wight 134
Maghreb Bookshop (The), London WC 177
McCrone (Audrey), Isle of Arran 274
Oak Tree Press, Oxfordshire 207
Park Gallery & Bookshop (The), Northants 200
Quaritch Ltd., (Bernard), London W 174
Reading Lasses, Dumfries & Galloway 270
Robert Temple, London N 158

Scrivener's Books & Bookbinding, Derbyshire... 82
Stevens (Joan), Cambridgeshire 65
Susanne Schulz-Falster Rare Books, London N. 158
Symes Books (Naomi), Cheshire 71
Tiger Books, Kent 136
Treasure Trove Books, Leics 146
Tucker (Alan & Joan), Gloucestershire 116
Willmott Bookseller (Nicholas), Cardiff 281

AUTISM
Westons, Herts 132

AUTOBIOGRAPHY
Abacus Gallery, Staffordshire 224
Addyman Books, Powys 287
Adrem Books, Herts 130
Annie's Books, South Yorkshire 221
Anthony Spranger, Wiltshire 252
Antiques on High, Oxfordshire 207
Any Old Books, Hampshire 121
Apocalypse, Surrey 232
Archer (Steve), London O 180
Backfold Books, Herefordshire 127
Bell (Peter), Lothian 275
Beware of the Leopard, Bristol 58
Black Five Books, Shropshire 214
Bob Mallory (Books), Derbyshire 83
Bodders Books, Shropshire 212
Bookroom (The), Surrey 233
Books, Oxfordshire 205
Books, Kent 137
books2books, Devon 88
BOOKS4U, Flintshire 284
Bookworms Paradise Ltd., West Sussex 242
Booth (Booksearch Service), (Geoff), Cheshire... 68
Brad Books, Essex 110
Catalyst Booksearch Services, Devon 87
Chaucer Bookshop, Kent 136
Cheshire Book Centre, Cheshire 69
Childrens Bookshop, West Yorkshire 247
Church Street Books, Norfolk 186
Clements (R.W.), London O 181
Clent Books, Worcestershire 255
Cofion Books, Pembrokeshire 286
Cornucopia Books, Lincolnshire 151
Crabtree (Mrs. C.), Greater Manchester 120
Dalbeattie Books, Dumfries & Galloway 269
Darkwood Books, Co. Cork 263
Dave Jelfs, Devon 85
Debbage (John), Norfolk 189
Discovery Bookshop, Carmarthenshire 281
Dolphin Books, Suffolk 225
Draca Books, West Yorkshire 248
Family-Favourites, East Yorkshire 106
Fifteenth Century Bookshop (The), East Sussex. 104
firstpagebooks, Norfolk 189
G. C. Books Ltd., Dumfries & Galloway 270
George St. Books, Derbyshire 83
Grahame Thornton, Bookseller, Dorset 93
Great Oak Bookshop (The), Powys 289
Hab Books, London W 172
Hambleton Books, North Yorkshire 196
Hurst (Jenny), Kent 137
Jack and Molly's Trading Co 90
Jade Mountain Bookshop, Hampshire 125

Joel Segal Books, Devon 86
Karen Millward, Co. Cork........................ 263
Kyrios Books, Nottinghamshire.................... 203
Little Bookshop (The), Greater Manchester...... 119
Lyng Heath Books, Norfolk 190
Lyngheath Books, Norfolk......................... 188
Marine and Cannon Books, Cheshire 69
McCrone (Audrey), Isle of Arran 274
MilitaryHistoryBooks.com, Kent................... 137
Murphy (C.J.), Norfolk............................. 189
Norton Books, North Yorkshire 192
Oopalba Books, Cheshire........................... 71
Orb's Bookshop, Grampian......................... 273
Park Gallery & Bookshop (The), Northants 200
Parker Books (Mike), Cambridgeshire 64
Poetry Bookshop (The), Powys.................... 289
Portus Books, Hampshire 122
Price (R.D.M. & I.M.) (Books), G Manchester.. 120
R. & A. Books, East Sussex 101
Reading Lasses, Dumfries & Galloway 270
Reads, Dorset 95
Richard Thornton Books, London N 158
Richmond Books, North Yorkshire 194
Robert Temple, London N.......................... 158
Roland Books, Kent 138
Rothwell & Dunworth, Somerset 217
Samovar Books, Co. Dublin....................... 264
Savona Books, Lincolnshire........................ 151
Sax Books, Suffolk................................. 228
Scrivener's Books & Bookbinding, Derbyshire... 82
SETI Books, West Midlands........................ 239
Stalagluft Books, Tyne and Wear.................. 235
Sturford Books, Wiltshire 254
Tarka Books, Devon 84
Tiffin (Tony and Gill), Durham 97
Treasure Island (The), Greater Manchester....... 119
Trinity Rare Books, Co. Leitrim 266
Uncle Phil's Books, West Midlands 239
Wheen O'Books, Borders........................... 267
Wiend Books, Lancashire 143
Willmott Bookseller (Nicholas), Cardiff........... 281

AUTOGRAPHS

Baron (H.), London NW........................... 160
Bertram Rota Ltd., London WC 176
Book Business (The), London W 171
Books & Bygones (Pam Taylor), West Midlands 240
Bookshop (The), Norfolk 191
Bookstand, Dorset.................................. 94
Bristow & Garland, Hampshire 123
Chas J. Sawyer, Kent 140
Cox Music (Lisa), Devon........................... 86
Cox Rare Books (Charles), Cornwall.............. 73
Davids Ltd., (Roy), Oxfordshire 208
Farahar & Dupre (Clive & Sophie), Wiltshire ... 251
Finch Rare Books Ltd. (Simon), London W..... 172
firstpagebooks, Norfolk............................ 189
Ford (Richard), London W......................... 172
Franks Booksellers, Greater Manchester.......... 119
Harrington Antiquarian Bookseller (Peter),
   London SW...................................... 167
Ken's Paper Collectables, Buckinghamshire 62
M. and A.C. Thompson, Norfolk.................. 191
Maggs Brothers Limited, London W.............. 173
Marine & Cannon Books, Cheshire 71

Marine and Cannon Books, Cheshire 69
Modern Firsts Etc, Lancashire 142
Neil Summersgill, Lancashire 142
Oak Tree Press, Oxfordshire 207
Quaritch Ltd., (Bernard), London W............. 174
Rassam (Paul), London NW 161
Riderless Horse Books, Norfolk.................... 186
Silverman (Michael), London SE 165
Stevens (Joan), Cambridgeshire.................... 65
Treasure Island (The), Greater Manchester....... 119
Trinity Rare Books, Co. Leitrim 266
Watkins (R.G.), Somerset 215
Wilson (Manuscripts) Ltd., (John), Glos.......... 114

AUTOLITHOGRAPHY

Dolphin Books, Suffolk............................ 225
Temperley (David), West Midlands............... 238

AUTOMATA

Randall (Tom), Somerset........................... 218
Weiner (Graham), London N 158

AUTOMOBILIA/AUTOMOTIVE

Annie's Books, South Yorkshire 221
Bob Mallory (Books), Derbyshire.................. 83
Brad Books, Essex.................................. 110
Burroughs (Andrew), Lincolnshire 152
Cofion Books, Pembrokeshire 286
Cornucopia Books, Lincolnshire 151
Cowley, Auto–in–Print (John), Essex.............. 108
Elmo Books, West Sussex 243
Falconwood Transport & Military Bookshop,
   London O....................................... 183
Fifteenth Century Bookshop (The), East Sussex. 104
Hay Castle, Powys................................. 288
Intech Books, Northumberland 201
J & J Burgess Booksellers, Cambridgeshire....... 64
Jade Mountain Bookshop, Hampshire 125
Joel Segal Books, Devon 86
McCrone (Audrey), Isle of Arran 274
Merseyside Books, Merseyside..................... 185
Morris Secondhand & Antiquarian
   Books (Chris), Oxfordshire...................... 208
R. & A. Books, East Sussex 101
Roadmaster Books, Kent........................... 136
Stroh (M.A.), London E 154
Weiner (Graham), London N 158
Wiend Books, Lancashire 143

AVANT-GARDE

Norton Books, North Yorkshire 192
R. & A. Books, East Sussex 101
Riderless Horse Books, Norfolk.................... 186
Sclanders (Beatbooks), (Andrew), London EC... 155
Trinity Rare Books, Co. Leitrim 266
Woburn Books, London N 159
Worlds End Bookshop, London SW 169

AVIATION

Addyman Books, Powys............................ 287
Adrem Books, Herts 130
All Books, Essex 111
Anchor Books, Lincolnshire 149
Annie's Books, South Yorkshire 221
Anthony Vickers Books, North Yorkshire 195

Armchair Auctions, Hampshire 121
Askew Books (Vernon), Wiltshire................. 251
Avedikian Rare Books, Somerset 216
Aviabooks, Gloucestershire 114
Backfold Books, Herefordshire.................... 127
Baldwin (M. & M.), Worcestershire 255
Bancroft (David G.), Isle of Wight 133
Barbican Bookshop, North Yorkshire............. 196
Barely Read Books, Kent 141
Barnes (Peter), Wiltshire............................ 253
Beware of the Leopard, Bristol..................... 58
Black Five Books, Shropshire 214
Books Afloat, Dorset.................................. 96
Books Bought & Sold, Surrey 231
books2books, Devon.................................. 88
Bookshelf – Aviation Books, West Sussex....... 241
Bookshop (The), Norfolk 191
BookShop, The, Dumfries & Galloway 270
Bookworms, Norfolk................................. 186
Booth (Booksearch Service), (Geoff), Cheshire... 68
Bott, (Bookdealers) Ltd., (Martin), Greater
   Manchester 118
Brad Books, Essex 110
Brewin Books Ltd., Warwickshire 237
Broadhurst of Southport Ltd., Merseyside 185
Camilla's Bookshop, East Sussex 101
Castle Bookshop, Essex.............................. 108
Chelifer Books, Cumbria 80
Cheshire Book Centre, Cheshire................... 69
Chevin Books, West Yorkshire..................... 249
Church Street Books, Norfolk...................... 186
Clevedon Books, Somerset 217
Cobbles Books, Somerset............................ 217
Cobweb Books, North Yorkshire 194
Cocks (Brian), Cambridgeshire 67
Cofion Books, Pembrokeshire 286
Cornucopia Books, Lincolnshire 151
Cotswold Internet Books, Gloucestershire........ 113
Coulthurst (Richard), Greater Manchester 120
Cox (Geoff), Devon 90
Dandy Lion Editions, Surrey 233
D'Arcy Books, Wiltshire............................. 252
Darkwood Books, Co. Cork......................... 263
Debbage (John), Norfolk............................ 189
Duck (William), Hampshire......................... 124
Eastgate Bookshop, East Yorkshire 106
Edwards (London) Limited (Francis),
   London WC 176
Falconwood Transport & Military Bookshop,
   London O 183
Family-Favourites, East Yorkshire................. 106
Farnborough Gallery, Hampshire................... 122
Fifteenth Century Bookshop (The), East Sussex. 104
Fylde Books, Lancashire 144
G&S Books, Kent 138
Gallimaufry Books, Herts 131
Good for Books, Lincolnshire 149
Grant, Lothian 276
Hall's Bookshop, Kent............................... 140
Harlequin Books, Bristol 59
Harris (George J.), Co. Derry 260
Hay Castle, Powys.................................... 288
Helion & Company, West Midlands 239
High Street Books, Devon 86
Horsham Rare Books, West Sussex 242

Internet Bookshop UK Ltd., Gloucestershire 113
Invicta Bookshop, Berks............................. 56
Island Books, Devon................................. 85
J & J Burgess Booksellers, Cambridgeshire....... 64
J.B. Books, Berks.................................... 57
Jade Mountain Bookshop, Hampshire 125
Joel Segal Books, Devon 86
Keegan's Bookshop, Berks.......................... 57
Keel Row Bookshop, Tyne and Wear 235
Kerr (Norman), Cumbria 77
Kingfisher Book Service, Nottinghamshire 204
Lawrence Books, Nottinghamshire 203
Libris (Weston) Books, Somerset 216
Lost Books, Northants................................ 200
M. and A.C. Thompson, Norfolk.................. 191
Malvern Bookshop (The), Worcestershire 255
Marine & Cannon Books, Cheshire 71
Marine and Cannon Books, Cheshire 69
Meekins Books (Paul), Warwickshire.............. 237
Mercat Books, Highland 274
Milestone Books, Devon 89
Military Parade Bookshop, Wiltshire.............. 252
MilitaryHistoryBooks.com, Kent................... 137
Morley Case, Hampshire 125
N1 Books, East Sussex 105
Nelson (Elizabeth), Suffolk......................... 226
Phelps (Michael), West Sussex...................... 242
Postings, Surrey 233
Prior (Michael), Lincolnshire 152
R. & A. Books, East Sussex 101
Richmond Books, North Yorkshire 194
Robert Humm & Co, Lincolnshire 152
Rowan (H. & S.J.), Dorset.......................... 91
Scrivener's Books & Bookbinding, Derbyshire... 82
Sedgeberrow Books, Worcestershire 256
Smith Maritime Aviation Books (Frank),
   Tyne and Wear.................................... 235
Soldridge Books Ltd, Hampshire 124
Spooner (John E.), Dorset 91
Stour Books, Dorset.................................. 95
Stroh (M.A.), London E 154
Sub Aqua Prints and Books, Hampshire 123
Suffolk Rare Books, Suffolk 229
Tarka Books, Devon.................................. 84
Thin Read Line, Merseyside 184
Tilston (Stephen E.), London SE................... 165
Treasure Chest Books, Suffolk 226
Treasure Island (The), Greater Manchester....... 119
Vanstone - Aviation Books, (Derek), Suffolk 229
Wadard Books, Kent 137
War & Peace Books, Hampshire 122
Weiner (Graham), London N 158
Westwood Books Ltd, Cumbria 80
Wheen O'Books, Borders............................ 267
Wiend Books, Lancashire 143
World War Books, Kent 141
Yeoman Books, Lothian 277

AWARD WINNERS

books2books, Devon.................................. 88
James M Pickhard (Rare Books), Leics........... 145
Modern First Editions, London O 181

AYURVEDA

Inner Bookshop (The), Oxfordshire............... 208

Joel Segal Books, Devon 86

BACTERIOLOGY
Bernard Dixon and Kath Adams, London O.... 182
Parkinsons Books, Merseyside...................... 185
Phelps (Michael), West Sussex...................... 242
R M Books, Herts.................................... 132
Savona Books, Lincolnshire......................... 151
Stroh (M.A.), London E 154
Turret House, Norfolk............................... 191
Westons, Herts 132

BAMBOO
Park (Mike), London O 182

BANKING & INSURANCE
Abrahams (Mike), Staffordshire.................... 223
Chris Porter Books, Norfolk........................ 186
Collectables (W.H.), Suffolk 229
Debbage (John), Norfolk............................ 189
Drury Rare Books (John), Essex.................... 110
Prospect House Books, Co. Down.................. 261
Quaritch Ltd., (Bernard), London W.............. 174
Rainford (Sheila), Herts 129
Susanne Schulz-Falster Rare Books, London N. 158

BEAT WRITERS
Addyman Books, Powys............................. 287
Delectus Books, London WC....................... 176
Ellis, Bookseller (Peter), London WC 177
Joel Segal Books, Devon 86
Kenny's Bookshop & Art Galleries Ltd., Co. Galway
265
Michael Rogers, Wiltshire.......................... 251
Needham Books, (Russell), Somerset.............. 219
Orlando Booksellers, Lincolnshire 150
Poetry Bookshop (The), Powys..................... 289
Price (R.W.), Nottinghamshire 203
Riderless Horse Books, Norfolk.................... 186
Sclanders (Beatbooks), (Andrew), London EC... 155
Trinity Rare Books, Co. Leitrim 266
Woburn Books, London N 159
Words Etcetera Bookshop, Dorset.................. 93
Worlds End Bookshop, London SW 169
Zardoz Books, Wiltshire............................ 254

BEER
Delectus Books, London WC....................... 176
Joel Segal Books, Devon 86
R. & A. Books, East Sussex 101
Sax Books, Suffolk 228
Stroh (M.A.), London E 154
Thorne (John), Essex................................ 109

BEES & BEEKEEPING
Muttonchop Manuscripts, West Sussex 242

BELLE-LETTRES
Apocalypse, Surrey 232
Delectus Books, London WC....................... 176
Derek Stirling Bookseller, Kent 141
Fortune Green Books, London NW............... 160
Grahame Thornton, Bookseller, Dorset.......... 93
Joel Segal Books, Devon 86
Robert Temple, London N.......................... 158

Trinity Rare Books, Co. Leitrim 266

BELL-RINGING (CAMPANOLOGY)
Belfry Books, Nottinghamshire..................... 203
Birchden Books, London E 154
Church Green Books, Oxfordshire................. 210
Country Books, Derbyshire 82
Farringdon (J.M.), Swansea......................... 291
Hadfield (G.K.), Cumbria 79
Island Books, Devon................................ 85
R. & A. Books, East Sussex 101
S Mary's Books & Prints, Lincolnshire 152

BIBLES
Addyman Books, Powys............................. 287
Apocalypse, Surrey 232
Ardis Books, Hampshire 126
Barbican Bookshop, North Yorkshire............. 196
Bardsley's Books, Suffolk.......................... 225
Beckham Books Ltd., Suffolk 229
Bernstein (Nicholas), London W 171
Bookshop on the Heath, The, London SE 163
Butler Rare Books, Buckinghamshire 61
Chandos Books, Devon............................. 85
Chapter Two, London SE........................... 163
Cobnar Books, Kent 141
Copnal Books, Cheshire 69
Courtenay Bookroom, Oxfordshire................ 205
Demetzy Books, Oxfordshire 206
Derek Stirling Bookseller, Kent 141
Du Ry Medieval Manuscripts (Marc–Antoine),
  London W... 172
ECR Books, Dorset................................. 92
Fishburn Books, London NW....................... 160
G. C. Books Ltd., Dumfries & Galloway 270
Gage Postal Books, Essex 111
Golden Age Books, Worcestershire................ 256
Harrington Antiquarian Bookseller (Peter),
  London SW....................................... 167
Hava Books, London SE............................ 164
Hennessey Bookseller (Ray), East Sussex 100
Hilton (Books) (P.J.), London W 173
Humber Books, Lincolnshire 148
Island Books, Devon................................ 85
Jade Mountain Bookshop, Hampshire............. 125
Kirkman Ltd., (Robert), Bedfordshire............ 54
Leo Cadogan, London N 157
Martin (Books and Pictures), (Brian P.), Surrey. 231
Michael Graves-Johnston, London SW 168
Oasis Booksearch, Cambridgeshire................ 67
Paper Moon Books, Gloucestershire 116
Pendleburys Bookshop, London N 158
Preston Book Company, Lancashire 144
Prospect House Books, Co. Down.................. 261
R. & A. Books, East Sussex 101
Roscrea Bookshop & Newsagents,
  Co. Tipperary 266
Rosemary Pugh Books, Wiltshire 253
Rosley Books, Cumbria 81
S.P.C.K., Bristol 59
St Philip's Books, Oxfordshire..................... 208
Samovar Books, Co. Dublin........................ 264
Scrivener's Books & Bookbinding, Derbyshire... 82
Spooner & Co, Somerset............................ 219
Trinity Rare Books, Co. Leitrim 266

Tuft (Patrick), London O 181
Walker Fine Books (Steve), Dorset 92

BIBLICAL STUDIES

Beckham Books Ltd., Suffolk 229
Bunyan Books, Bedfordshire......................... 53
Butler Rare Books, Buckinghamshire 61
Chapter Two, London SE........................... 163
Discovery Bookshop, Carmarthenshire........... 281
Dolphin Books, Suffolk.............................. 225
Fishburn Books, London NW...................... 160
G. C. Books Ltd., Dumfries & Galloway........ 270
Gage Postal Books, Essex 111
Golden Age Books, Worcestershire................ 256
J.E. Burns Booksellers, Merseyside 185
Jade Mountain Bookshop, Hampshire 125
Leo Cadogan, London N 157
Oasis Booksearch, Cambridgeshire................. 67
Parkinsons Books, Merseyside...................... 185
Pendleburys Bookshop, London N 158
Pittville Books, Gloucestershire.................... 113
PsychoBabel Books & Journals, Oxfordshire..... 205
R. & A. Books, East Sussex 101
Rosley Books, Cumbria 81
S.P.C.K., Bristol 59
St Philip's Books, Oxfordshire..................... 208
Samovar Books, Co. Dublin....................... 264
Spooner & Co, Somerset 219
Walker Fine Books (Steve), Dorset 92

BIBLIOGRAPHY

Acanthophyllum Books, Wirral 184
Alec–Smith Books (Alex), East Yorkshire........ 107
Ash Rare Books, London SW...................... 166
Askew (Vernon), Wiltshire.......................... 251
Barry McKay Rare Books, Cumbria.............. 76
Bettridge (Gordon), Fife............................ 271
Bianco Library, West Sussex....................... 241
Bookcase, Cumbria.................................. 76
Brinded (Scott), Kent 138
Broadhurst of Southport Ltd., Merseyside 185
Butler Rare Books, Buckinghamshire 61
Caledonia Books, Strathclyde...................... 278
Chas J. Sawyer, Kent 140
Childrens Bookshop, West Yorkshire 247
Cooper Hay Rare Books, Strathclyde............. 278
Cox Old & Rare Books (Claude), Suffolk 227
Dew (Roderick), East Sussex 101
Ford (Richard), London W 172
Forest Books, Nottinghamshire 204
Fortune Green Books, London NW................ 160
Fotheringam (Alex), Northumberland 201
Howes Bookshop, East Sussex 102
Island Books, Devon................................ 85
Jackson (M.W.), Wiltshire.......................... 254
Joel Segal Books, Devon 86
Madoc Books, Conwy 284
Maggs Brothers Limited, London W 173
Marlborough Rare Books Ltd., London W...... 173
Mills Rare Books (Adam), Cambridgeshire 64
MK Book Services, Cambridgeshire............... 66
Modern First Editions, West Yorkshire........... 247
Moorhead Books, West Yorkshire................. 245
Mulyan (Don), Merseyside.......................... 185
O'Connor Fine Books, Lancashire................. 144

Parrott (Jeremy), London E......................... 154
Quaritch Ltd., (Bernard), London W.............. 174
Quentin Books Ltd, Essex........................... 108
R. & A. Books, East Sussex 101
RGS Books, Surrey 234
Robert Temple, London N.......................... 158
Seydi Rare Books (Sevin), London NW 161
Smith Books, (Sally), Suffolk 226
Solitaire Books, Somerset........................... 216
Spooner & Co, Somerset 219
Stroh (M.A.), London E 154
Sue Lowell Natural History Books, London W . 175
Susanne Schulz-Falster Rare Books, London N. 158
Taylor & Son (Peter), Herts........................ 132
Taylor Rare Books (Michael), Norfolk 187
The Sanctuary Bookshop, Dorset.................. 94
Thornber (Peter M.), North Yorkshire............ 195
Tuft (Patrick), London O 181
Unsworth's Booksellers, Suffolk................... 225
Ventnor Rare Books, Isle of Wight............... 134
Wakeman Books (Frances), Nottinghamshire.... 204
Williams (Bookdealer), (Richard), N Lincs....... 153
Wykeham Books, London SW 170
Yates Antiquarian Books (Tony), Leics........... 146

BIBLIOPHILY

Cox Old & Rare Books (Claude), Suffolk 227
Ford (Richard), London W 172
Hilton (Books) (P.J.), London W 173
Island Books, Devon................................ 85
Jean Hedger, Berks 55
Quaritch Ltd., (Bernard), London W.............. 174
Stalagluft Books, Tyne and Wear.................. 235
Stroh (M.A.), London E 154
Thornber (Peter M.), North Yorkshire............ 195

BICYCLES AND CYCLING

Ampersand Books, Norfolk......................... 189
Kingfisher Book Service, Nottinghamshire 204

BINDINGS

Abacus Gallery, Staffordshire....................... 224
Addyman Annexe (The), Powys.................... 287
Addyman Books, Powys............................. 287
Adrem Books, Herts 130
Allsop (Duncan M.), Warwickshire................ 237
Atholl Fine Books, Tayside 280
Barry McKay Rare Books, Cumbria.............. 76
Bates & Hindmarch, West Yorkshire.............. 248
Baxter (Steve), Surrey 233
Bayntun (George), Somerset 215
Beckham Books Ltd., Suffolk 229
Bernstein (Nicholas), London W 171
Booklore, Leics....................................... 146
Bookshop on the Heath, The, London SE 163
Bunyan Books, Bedfordshire....................... 53
Camilla's Bookshop, East Sussex 101
Chandos Books, Devon............................. 85
Chapter & Verse, Lincolnshire 150
Chas J. Sawyer, Kent 140
Classic Bindings Ltd, London SW 166
Cobnar Books, Kent 141
Cooper Hay Rare Books, Strathclyde............. 278
Courtney & Hoff, North Yorkshire................ 197
Cox Old & Rare Books (Claude), Suffolk 227

Cumming Limited (A. & Y.), East Sussex 104
David (G.), Cambridgeshire 63
Davis, Antiquarian Books (Guy), Notts 204
de Beaumont (Robin), London SW 166
De Burca Rare Books, Co. Dublin 264
Demetzy Books, Oxfordshire 206
Design Gallery 1850-1950 (The), Kent 141
Eclectica, London SE 164
Edwards (London) Limited (Francis),
   London WC 176
Elgar (Raymond), East Sussex 99
Ely Books, Cambridgeshire 65
Eton Antique Bookshop, Berks 57
Finch Rare Books Ltd. (Simon), London W..... 172
Fine Books at Ilkley, West Yorkshire 247
Fletcher (H.M.), Herts 131
Forest Books, Nottinghamshire 204
Foster Bookshop (Paul), London SW 167
Fosters Bookshop, London W 172
Frew Limited (Robert), London SW 167
Garbett Antiquarian Books (Michael),
   Gloucestershire 115
Golden Books Group, Devon 85
Grove Bookshop (The), North Yorkshire 195
Hall's Bookshop, Kent 140
Harrington Antiquarian Bookseller (Peter),
   London SW 167
Hava Books, London SE 164
Hay Castle, Powys 288
Hereward Books, Cambridgeshire 66
Heritage, West Midlands 238
Hodgkins and Company Limited (Ian),
   Gloucestershire 116
Horsham Rare Books, West Sussex 242
Howes Bookshop, East Sussex 102
Island Books, Devon 85
J.E. Burns Booksellers, Merseyside 185
Junk & Spread Eagle, London SE 164
Kay Books, London W 173
Kemp Bookseller, Michael S, G Manchester 118
Kings Bookshop Callander, Central 268
Kirkman Ltd., (Robert), Bedfordshire 54
Liddle (Steve), Bristol 58
Madoc Books, Conwy 284
Maggs Brothers Limited, London W 173
Mair Wilkes Books, Fife 271
Malvern Bookshop (The), Worcestershire 255
Marlborough Rare Books Ltd., London W 173
Martin (Books and Pictures), (Brian P.), Surrey. 231
Martin (Brian), Surrey 231
Maynard & Bradley, Leics 146
McConnell Fine Books, Kent 137
Moore (C.R.), Shropshire 213
Moorhead Books, West Yorkshire 245
Moorside Books, Lancashire 143
Muttonchop Manuscripts, West Sussex 242
N1 Books, East Sussex 105
Neil Summersgill, Lancashire 142
Offa's Dyke Books, Shropshire 213
Old Town Bookshop (The), Lothian 276
Paper Moon Books, Gloucestershire 116
Petworth Antique Market (Bookroom),
   W Sussex 244
Poetry Bookshop (The), Powys 289
Pordes Books Ltd., (Henry), London WC 177

PsychoBabel Books & Journals, Oxfordshire..... 205
Quentin Books Ltd, Essex 108
R. & A. Books, East Sussex 101
Red Star Books, Herts 129
Richard Thornton Books, London N 158
Roger Collicott Books, Cornwall 74
Russell (Charles), London SW 169
St Mary's Books & Prints, Lincolnshire 152
Scrivener's Books & Bookbinding, Derbyshire... 82
Seydi Rare Books (Sevin), London NW 161
Sotheran Limited (Henry), London W 175
Staniland (Booksellers), Lincolnshire 152
Sterling Books, Somerset 220
Studio (The), Strathclyde 278
Temperley (David), West Midlands 238
Thorntons of Oxford Ltd., Oxfordshire 206
Trinity Rare Books, Co. Leitrim 266
Turton (John), Durham 98
Vandeleur Antiquarian Books, Surrey 231
Ventnor Rare Books, Isle of Wight 134
Woodbine Books, West Yorkshire 245
Yates Antiquarian Books (Tony), Leics 146

BIOCHEMISTRY

Bernard Dixon and Kath Adams, London O.... 182
Parkinsons Books, Merseyside 185
Phelps (Michael), West Sussex 242
R M Books, Herts 132
Stroh (M.A.), London E 154
Turret House, Norfolk 191
Westons, Herts 132

BIOGRAPHY

Abacus Gallery, Staffordshire 224
Adrem Books, Herts 130
Alexander's Books, Warwickshire 237
Annie's Books, South Yorkshire 221
Anthony Spranger, Wiltshire 252
Antiquary Ltd., (Bar Bookstore),
   North Yorkshire 194
Antiques on High, Oxfordshire 207
Applin (Malcolm), Berks 55
Archer (Steve), London O 180
Arden Books & Cosmographia, Warwickshire... 236
Askew Books (Vernon), Wiltshire 251
Aurora Books Ltd, Lothian 275
Backfold Books, Herefordshire 127
baconboooks, London WC 176
Baldwin's Scientific Books, Essex 111
Barcombe Services, Essex 108
Bass (Ben), Wiltshire 251
Bell (Peter), Lothian 275
Bianco Library, West Sussex 241
Black Five Books, Shropshire 214
Blythswood Bookshop, Highland 274
Bob Mallory (Books), Derbyshire.................. 83
Bodders Books, Shropshire 212
Bookroom (The), Surrey 233
Books Antiques & Collectables, Devon 90
books2books, Devon 88
Bookworms, Norfolk 186
Bookworms Paradise Ltd., West Sussex 242
Booth (Booksearch Service), (Geoff), Cheshire... 68
Bosco Books, Cornwall 72
Bosorne Books, Cornwall 75

Brad Books, Essex.................................... 110
Brighton Books, East Sussex........................ 99
Brimstones, East Sussex 104
Broadhurst of Southport Ltd., Merseyside 185
Brock Books, North Yorkshire..................... 192
Caledonia Books, Strathclyde..................... 278
Carnforth Bookshop (The), Lancashire 142
Carraig Books Ltd., Co. Dublin 263
Catalyst Booksearch Services, Devon............. 87
Chalmers Hallam (E.), Hampshire................ 125
Charles Bossom, Cambridgeshire.................. 65
Chaucer Bookshop, Kent.......................... 136
Childrens Bookshop, West Yorkshire 247
Church Street Books, Norfolk..................... 186
Classic Bindings Ltd, London SW 166
Clements (R.W.), London O....................... 181
Clent Books, Worcestershire...................... 255
Clifford Elmer Books Ltd., Cheshire 68
Coach House Books, Worcestershire 256
Cobbles Books, Somerset.......................... 217
Cobweb Books, North Yorkshire.................. 194
Cofion Books, Pembrokeshire 286
Cornucopia Books, Lincolnshire 151
Crabtree (Mrs. C.), Greater Manchester 120
Criterion Books, London O....................... 181
Dales & Lakes Book Centre, Cumbria........... 79
Dandy Lion Editions, Surrey 233
Darkwood Books, Co. Cork....................... 263
Debbage (John), Norfolk........................... 189
dgbbooks, West Sussex 244
Discovery Bookshop, Carmarthenshire............ 281
Dolphin Books, Suffolk............................. 225
Doolin Dinghy Books, Co. Clare 262
Draca Books, West Yorkshire...................... 248
Eastleach Books, Berks 56
Elaine Lonsdale Books, West Yorkshire.......... 247
Ellis, Bookseller (Peter), London WC 177
Ely Books, Cambridgeshire 65
Esoteric Dreams Bookshop, Cumbria 77
Family-Favourites, East Yorkshire................. 106
Fifteenth Century Bookshop (The), East Sussex. 104
Ford Books (David), Herts 130
Francis, S. L., Sussex............................... 103
Frost (Richard), Herts 129
Garfi Books, Powys 291
George St. Books, Derbyshire 83
Gladstone Books, Lincolnshire 150
Good for Books, Lincolnshire 149
Graham (John), Dorset............................. 96
Grahame Thornton, Bookseller, Dorset.......... 93
Great Hall Bookshop, Buckinghamshire......... 61
Great Oak Bookshop (The), Powys 289
Green Meadow Books, Cornwall 74
Hab Books, London W............................. 172
Hall's Bookshop, Kent.............................. 140
Hambleton Books, North Yorkshire 196
Handley (Christopher), Tyne and Wear........... 235
Hawley (C.L.), North Yorkshire 195
Heraldry Today, Wiltshire.......................... 253
Hilton (Books) (P.J.), London W 173
Hollett and Son (R.F.G.), Cumbria 79
Holmes Books (Harry), East Yorkshire........... 107
Horsham Rare Books, West Sussex 242
Hughes (Ms. Sonia A.), Monmouthshire 286
Hurst (Jenny), Kent 137

Jade Mountain Bookshop, Hampshire 125
Joel Segal Books, Devon 86
Karen Millward, Co. Cork.......................... 263
Kingsmere Books, Bedfordshire 53
Little Bookshop (The), Greater Manchester...... 119
Little Bookshop (The), Cumbria 80
Lyng Heath Books, Norfolk........................ 190
Lyngheath Books, Norfolk......................... 188
Maggy Browne, Lincolnshire 148
Malvern Bookshop (The), Worcestershire 255
Martin's Books, Powys 290
McCaughtrie (K.A.), North Yorkshire........... 192
McCrone (Audrey), Isle of Arran.................. 274
Michael J Carroll, Co. Cork 263
Missing Books, Essex 109
Modlock (Lilian), Dorset............................ 93
Mogul Diamonds, West Midlands 240
Mr. Pickwick of Towcester, Northants........... 199
Murch Booksend, (Herbert), London SE......... 165
Nineteenth Century Books, Oxfordshire 209
Norton Books, North Yorkshire 192
O'Brien Books & Photo Gallery, Co. Limerick.. 266
O'Donoghue Books, Powys 289
Olynthiacs, Shropshire 213
Oopalba Books, Cheshire 71
Orb's Bookshop, Grampian........................ 273
Paperbacks Plus, Bristol 59
Park Gallery & Bookshop (The), Northants 200
Parrott Books, Oxfordshire 209
Pauline Harries Books, Hampshire 123
Peter M Daly, Hampshire 126
Poetry Bookshop (The), Powys..................... 289
Pooks Motor Books, Leics.......................... 146
Portobello Books, London W 174
Price (R.D.M. & I.M.) (Books),
  Greater Manchester 120
Primrose Hill Books, London NW 161
Pringle Booksellers (Andrew), Lothian 277
Quentin Books Ltd, Essex.......................... 108
R. & A. Books, East Sussex 101
Reading Lasses, Dumfries & Galloway 270
Reads, Dorset 95
Richmond Books, North Yorkshire 194
Robert Temple, London N.......................... 158
Roland Books, Kent 138
Roundstone Books, Lancashire..................... 143
Samovar Books, Co. Dublin 264
Saunders (Tom), Caerphilly 281
Savona Books, Lincolnshire........................ 151
SETI Books, West Midlands........................ 239
Shacklock Books (David), Suffolk 226
Shakeshaft (Dr. B.), Cheshire 71
Slightly Foxed on Gloucester Road, London SW 167
Smith Books, (Sally), Suffolk 226
Spenceley Books (David), West Yorkshire........ 248
Stalagluft Books, Tyne and Wear.................. 235
Star Lord Books, Greater Manchester 119
Stern Antiquarian Bookseller (Jeffrey), North
  Yorkshire... 198
Strathtay Antiquarian - Secondhand Books,
  Tayside 280
Stroma Books, Borders 267
Sturford Books, Wiltshire 254
The Sanctuary Bookshop, Dorset.................. 94
Tiffin (Tony and Gill), Durham 97

Tilston (Stephen E.), London SE.................... 165
Tombland Bookshop, Norfolk 190
Trevorrow (Edwin), Herts........................... 129
Trinity Rare Books, Co. Leitrim 266
Uncle Phil's Books, West Midlands 239
War & Peace Books, Hampshire................... 122
Wayside Books and Cards, Oxfordshire 206
Wheen O'Books, Borders........................... 267
Whitfield (Ken), Essex 110
Willmott Bookseller (Nicholas), Cardiff.......... 281
Words Etcetera Bookshop, Dorset................. 93
Worlds End Bookshop, London SW 169
Yarwood Rare Books (Edward),
    Greater Manchester 118

BIOLOGY - GENERAL
Alba Books, Grampian 273
Arden, Bookseller (C.), Powys...................... 287
Austwick Hall Books, North Yorkshire........... 192
Barcombe Services, Essex........................... 108
Baron - Scientific Book Sales (P.J.), Somerset ... 216
Bernard Dixon and Kath Adams, London O.... 182
Bracton Books, Cambridgeshire.................... 63
Gladstone Books, Lincolnshire 150
Lymelight Books & Prints, Dorset................. 93
Mogul Diamonds, West Midlands................. 240
Orb's Bookshop, Grampian......................... 273
Orchid Book Distributors, Co. Clare.............. 262
Parkinsons Books, Merseyside...................... 185
Pittville Books, Gloucestershire 113
Pollak (P.M.), Devon 88
Prospect House Books, Co. Down................. 261
Quaritch Ltd., (Bernard), London W.............. 174
R M Books, Herts................................... 132
R. & A. Books, East Sussex 101
Roosterbooks, Northants............................ 199
Smith (David & Lynn), London O 181
Tarka Books, Devon................................. 84
Transformer, Dumfries & Galloway 270
Turret House, Norfolk.............................. 191
Westons, Herts....................................... 132
Woodside Books, Kent 135
Wyseby House Books, Berks 55

BIOLOGY - MARINE
Lymelight Books & Prints, Dorset................. 93
Periplus Books, Buckinghamshire.................. 62
Westons, Herts....................................... 132
Woodside Books, Kent 135

BLACK STUDIES
Afar Books International, West Midlands........ 238
Black Voices, Merseyside............................ 184
Bookshop (The), Greater Manchester 118
Hylton Booksearch, Merseyside 184
R. & A. Books, East Sussex 101
Reading Lasses, Dumfries & Galloway 270
Spurrier (Nick), Kent 137
Stevens (Joan), Cambridgeshire.................... 65
Woburn Books, London N 159
Yesterday's Books, Dorset 92

BOHEMIANISM
R. & A. Books, East Sussex 101
Trinity Rare Books, Co. Leitrim 266

BOOK ARTS
Alauda Books, Cumbria............................. 76
Barry McKay Rare Books, Cumbria.............. 76
Bertram Rota Ltd., London WC 176
Bruce Holdsworth Books, East Sussex 105
Chalk (Old & Out of Print Books)
    (Christine M.), West Midlands 238
Collinge & Clark, London WC..................... 176
Cornucopia Books, Lincolnshire 151
Ford (Richard), London W 172
Jackdaw Books, Norfolk 188
Mannwaring (M.G.), Bristol 59
Myra Dean Illustated Books, Powys 287
R. & A. Books, East Sussex 101
Stevens (Joan), Cambridgeshire..................... 65
Susanne Schulz-Falster Rare Books, London N. 158
Woodbine Books, West Yorkshire................. 245
Wykeham Books, London SW 170

BOOK AUCTIONS
Hay Castle, Powys.................................. 288

BOOK OF HOURS
Addyman Books, Powys............................. 287
Butler Rare Books, Buckinghamshire 61
Du Ry Medieval Manuscripts (Marc–Antoine),
    London W 172
Island Books, Devon 85
John Underwood Antiquarian Books, Norfolk .. 189
R. & A. Books, East Sussex 101

BOOKBINDING
Alauda Books, Cumbria............................. 76
Barry McKay Rare Books, Cumbria.............. 76
Beverley Old Bookshop, East Yorkshire.......... 106
Bunyan Books, Bedfordshire....................... 53
Chandos Books, Devon.............................. 85
Chas J. Sawyer, Kent 140
Cheshire Book Centre, Cheshire................... 69
Coupland (Terry W.), Staffordshire............... 223
Cox Old & Rare Books (Claude), Suffolk 227
Elgar (Raymond), East Sussex...................... 99
Family-Favourites, East Yorkshire................. 106
Forest Books, Nottinghamshire 204
Intech Books, Northumberland 201
Island Books, Devon 85
Paper Pleasures, Somerset 218
R. & A. Books, East Sussex 101
Scrivener's Books & Bookbinding, Derbyshire... 82
Spooner & Co, Somerset 219
Stroh (M.A.), London E 154
Sue Lowell Natural History Books, London W . 175
Trinity Rare Books, Co. Leitrim 266
Walker Fine Books (Steve), Dorset................. 92
Wykeham Books, London SW 170

BOOKER PRIZE
Firsts in Print, Somerset 219
Oak Tree Press, Oxfordshire....................... 207

BOOKS ABOUT BOOKS
Addyman Books, Powys............................. 287
Alec–Smith Books (Alex), East Yorkshire........ 107
Andron (G.W.), London N 156
Bardsley's Books, Suffolk........................... 225

Bates Books, London O 180
Besleys Books, Suffolk 225
Bettridge (Gordon), Fife 271
Book Palace (The), London SE 163
Bracton Books, Cambridgeshire 63
Brinded (Scott), Kent 138
Butler Rare Books, Buckinghamshire 61
Chandos Books, Devon.............................. 85
Chapter & Verse, Lincolnshire..................... 150
Cofion Books, Pembrokeshire 286
Collinge & Clark, London WC..................... 176
Cooper Hay Rare Books, Strathclyde 278
Cowley, Bookdealer (K.W.), Somerset 217
Cox Old & Rare Books (Claude), Suffolk 227
Deverell Books, Bristol 59
Double - B - Books Ltd, Somerset................ 59
Eastgate Bookshop, East Yorkshire 106
Family-Favourites, East Yorkshire................ 106
Ford (Richard), London W 172
Forest Books, Nottinghamshire 204
Freeman's Corner Shop, Norfolk 189
Glasheen-Books, Surrey 231
Green Meadow Books, Cornwall 74
Hava Books, London SE............................ 164
Hylton Booksearch, Merseyside 184
Island Books, Devon................................ 85
Jean Hedger, Berks................................. 55
Joel Segal Books, Devon 86
Madoc Books, Conwy 284
Malvern Bookshop (The), Worcestershire 255
Mills Rare Books (Adam), Cambridgeshire 64
Mr. Pickwick of Towcester, Northants........... 199
Myra Dean Illustated Books, Powys 287
Nineteenth Century Books, Oxfordshire 209
Parrott (Jeremy), London E........................ 154
Prospect House Books, Co. Down................. 261
Quentin Books Ltd, Essex.......................... 108
R. & A. Books, East Sussex 101
RGS Books, Surrey 234
Roadmaster Books, Kent............................ 136
Scott (Peter), East Sussex........................... 104
Seabreeze Books, Lancashire....................... 144
Solitaire Books, Somerset.......................... 216
Spooner & Co, Somerset 219
Stroh (M.A.), London E 154
Susanne Schulz-Falster Rare Books, London N. 158
Thornber (Peter M.), North Yorkshire............ 195
Trinity Rare Books, Co. Leitrim 266
Unsworth's Booksellers, Suffolk................... 225
Updike Rare Books (John), Lothian 277
Wakeman Books (Frances), Nottinghamshire.... 204
Walker Fine Books (Steve), Dorset 92
Williams (Bookdealer), (Richard), N Lincs 153
Wilson (James), Herts............................... 129
Wykeham Books, London SW 170
Yates Antiquarian Books (Tony), Leics........... 146
Zardoz Books, Wiltshire............................ 254

BOOKS IN GREEK

Butler Rare Books, Buckinghamshire 61
Hall's Bookshop, Kent.............................. 140
Hellenic Bookservices, London NW 161
Joel Segal Books, Devon 86
Quaritch Ltd., (Bernard), London W.............. 174
Seydi Rare Books (Sevin), London NW 161

Thorntons of Oxford Ltd., Oxfordshire........... 206

BOTANY

Acanthophyllum Books, Wirral 184
Adrem Books, Herts 130
Alauda Books, Cumbria............................. 76
Antique Map and Bookshop (The), Dorset 94
Arden, Bookseller (C.), Powys..................... 287
Ashwell Books, Wiltshire........................... 252
Austwick Hall Books, North Yorkshire........... 192
Aviabooks, Gloucestershire 114
Baldwin's Scientific Books, Essex 111
Baron - Scientific Book Sales (P.J.), Somerset ... 216
Bernard Dixon and Kath Adams, London O.... 182
Besleys Books, Suffolk 225
Bianco Library, West Sussex....................... 241
Blest (Peter), Kent 138
Brown (Books) (P.R.), Durham 98
Burden Ltd., (Clive A.), Herts.................... 131
Calluna Books, Dorset.............................. 95
Camilla's Bookshop, East Sussex 101
Cornucopia Books, Lincolnshire 151
Court Hay Books, West Midlands................. 239
Dales & Lakes Book Centre, Cumbria 79
Dene Barn Books & Prints, Somerset 219
Dolphin Books, Suffolk............................. 225
Elizabeth Ferguson, Grampian 272
Frost (Richard), Herts 129
Goodyer (Nicholas), London N 157
Harrington Antiquarian Bookseller (Peter),
    London SW.. 167
Hollingshead (Chris), London O 182
Inner Bookshop (The), Oxfordshire............... 208
Ivelet Books Ltd., Surrey.......................... 233
Joel Segal Books, Devon 86
Kennedy (Peter), Surrey 234
Lymelight Books & Prints, Dorset................ 93
Madoc Books, Conwy 284
Mandalay Bookshop, London SW 168
Mannwaring (M.G.), Bristol 59
Martin (Books and Pictures), (Brian P.), Surrey. 231
Martin (Brian), Surrey 231
Martin's Books, Powys 290
Mobbs (A.J.), West Midlands 239
Old Town Bookshop (The), Lothian 276
Orchid Book Distributors, Co. Clare.............. 262
Park (Mike), London O 182
Parkinsons Books, Merseyside...................... 185
Pemberley Books, Buckinghamshire 62
Peter M Daly, Hampshire........................... 126
Phelps (Michael), West Sussex..................... 242
Prospect House Books, Co. Down................. 261
Quaritch Ltd., (Bernard), London W.............. 174
R. & A. Books, East Sussex 101
Reeves Technical Books, North Yorkshire 195
Roz Hulse, Conwy 284
Savona Books, Lincolnshire......................... 151
Steven Simpson Books, Norfolk 190
Sue Lowell Natural History Books, London W . 175
Summerfield Books Ltd, Cumbria 79
Tant Yn Ellen Books, Powys 290
Thin Read Line, Merseyside 184
Treasure Trove Books, Leics....................... 146
Trinity Rare Books, Co. Leitrim 266
Westons, Herts 132

Woodside Books, Kent 135
Wyseby House Books, Berks 55

BRAZILIANA
Hodgson (Judith), London W 173
Orssich (Paul), London SW 169

BREWING
Anthony Vickers Books, North Yorkshire 195
Bernard Dixon and Kath Adams, London O.... 182
Cornucopia Books, Lincolnshire 151
Country Books, Derbyshire 82
Debbage (John), Norfolk 189
Joel Segal Books, Devon 86
Lucas (Richard), London NW...................... 161
Past & Present Books, Gloucestershire 114
Phelps (Michael), West Sussex...................... 242
R. & A. Books, East Sussex 101
Secondhand Bookshop, The, Kent................. 140
Stroh (M.A.), London E 154
Thorne (John), Essex................................ 109

BRIDGE
Annie's Books, South Yorkshire 221
Beaver Booksearch, Suffolk 225
Dunstan Books, Dorset.............................. 91
Erian Books, London N............................. 156
Glenbower Books, Co. Dublin 264
Joel Segal Books, Devon 86
R. & A. Books, East Sussex 101
R. S. & P. A. Scowen, London O 181
Reeves Technical Books, North Yorkshire 195
Tilston (Stephen E.), London SE................... 165

BRITISH ART & DESIGN
Art Book Company, (The), Suffolk................ 227
Batterham (David), London W...................... 171
Books & Things, London W......................... 171
Bruce Holdsworth Books, East Sussex 105
Butts Books (Mary), Berks.......................... 56
C J Renwick Books, Powys.......................... 287
Cornucopia Books, Lincolnshire 151
Hay Castle, Powys................................... 288
Jean Hedger, Berks 55
Joel Segal Books, Devon 86
Mannwaring (M.G.), Bristol 59
Nelson (Elizabeth), Suffolk.......................... 226
Pagan Limited (Hugh), Hampshire 122
Portus Books, Hampshire 122
Stevens (Joan), Cambridgeshire..................... 65
Treasure Island (The), Greater Manchester....... 119
Trinity Rare Books, Co. Leitrim 266
Woodbine Books, West Yorkshire.................. 245

BRITISH BOOKS
Annie's Books, South Yorkshire 221
Apocalypse, Surrey 232
Blackwell's Rare Books, Oxfordshire.............. 208
Books at Star Dot Star, West Midlands 240
books2books, Devon................................. 88
Burmester (James), Bristol.......................... 58
C J Renwick Books, Powys.......................... 287
Cornucopia Books, Lincolnshire 151
Darkwood Books, Co. Cork 263
First Edition, The, Essex 109

Gildas Books, Cheshire.............................. 68
Ian Marr Rare Books, Cornwall 73
Island Books, Devon................................ 85
Joel Segal Books, Devon 86
McCrone (Audrey), Isle of Arran 274
O'Flynn Books, North Yorkshire.................. 197
Parkinsons Books, Merseyside....................... 185
Portus Books, Hampshire 122
R. & A. Books, East Sussex 101
Rickaro Books, West Yorkshire..................... 246
Robert Temple, London N.......................... 158
Roberts Books, Strathclyde 279
Samovar Books, Co. Dublin 264
Trinity Rare Books, Co. Leitrim 266
Uncle Phil's Books, West Midlands 239
Wheen O'Books, Borders............................ 267

BROADCASTING
Anthony Spranger, Wiltshire........................ 252
Apocalypse, Surrey 232
Cornucopia Books, Lincolnshire 151
Dolphin Books, Suffolk............................. 225
Greenroom Books, West Yorkshire 247
Joel Segal Books, Devon 86
Kelly Books Ltd, Devon............................. 89
Kent T. G., Surrey 230
Morris Secondhand & Antiquarian
  Books (Chris), Oxfordshire...................... 208
R. & A. Books, East Sussex 101
Saintfield Antiques & Fine Books, Co. Down ... 261
Stroh (M.A.), London E 154
Weiner (Graham), London N 158
Wood (Peter), Cambridgeshire....................... 65
Yesterday's News, Conwy.......................... 283

BROADSIDES - LETTERPRESS
Aitchison (Lesley), Bristol 58
Burmester (James), Bristol.......................... 58
Derek Stirling Bookseller, Kent 141
Kenny's Bookshop & Art Galleries Ltd.,
  Co. Galway 265
Knowles - Antiquary (Roger J.), Staffordshire... 223
Oak Tree Press, Oxfordshire 207
Yates Antiquarian Books (Tony), Leics.......... 146

BUILDING & CONSTRUCTION
Amwell Book Company, London EC.............. 155
Brown-Studies, Strathclyde......................... 277
Buckland Books, West Sussex 243
Darkwood Books, Co. Cork........................ 263
Elton Engineering Books, London W 172
Greta Books, Durham 97
Inch's Books, Kent 137
Joel Segal Books, Devon 86
N1 Books, East Sussex 105
Pagan Limited (Hugh), Hampshire 122
Parkinsons Books, Merseyside....................... 185
Reeves Technical Books, North Yorkshire 195
Roberts Books, Strathclyde 279
Scrivener's Books & Bookbinding, Derbyshire... 82
Staniland (Booksellers), Lincolnshire 152
Stobart Davies Limited, Carmarthenshire 282
Trinders' Fine Tools, Suffolk 226
Trinity Rare Books, Co. Leitrim 266
Upper–Room Books, Somerset....................... 217

Wheen O'Books, Borders............................ 267
Whistler's Books, London SW 169

BULL FIGHTING
Askew Books (Vernon), Wiltshire................. 251
Books on Spain, London O......................... 182
Craobh Rua Books, Co. Armagh................. 260
Orssich (Paul), London SW....................... 169
R. & A. Books, East Sussex 101

BUSES/TRAMS
Addyman Books, Powys............................. 287
Anvil Books, West Midlands 239
Barbican Bookshop, North Yorkshire............ 196
Books at Star Dot Star, West Midlands 240
Booth (Booksearch Service), (Geoff), Cheshire... 68
Bott, (Bookdealers) Ltd., (Martin), Greater
    Manchester 118
Browse Books, Lancashire 143
Cavern Books, Cheshire 70
Classic Crime Collections, Greater Manchester.. 119
Coulthurst (Richard), Greater Manchester 120
Cox (Geoff), Devon 90
Dales & Lakes Book Centre, Cumbria........... 79
Dales and Lakes Book Centre, Cumbria......... 79
Dinnages Transport Publishing, East Sussex 103
Falconwood Transport & Military Bookshop,
    London O.. 183
Fifteenth Century Bookshop (The), East Sussex. 104
Jade Mountain Bookshop, Hampshire 125
Joel Segal Books, Devon 86
Knowles (John), Norfolk 187
Milestone Books, Devon 89
R. & A. Books, East Sussex 101
Randall (Tom), Somerset........................... 218
Roadmaster Books, Kent............................ 136
Robert Humm & Co, Lincolnshire 152
Roland Books, Kent 138
Rolling Stock Books, Greater Manchester........ 120
Saintfield Antiques & Fine Books, Co. Down ... 261
Salway Books, Essex 112
Simon Lewis Transport Books, Gloucestershire . 114
Vintage Motorshop, West Yorkshire 245
Yesteryear Railwayana, Kent...................... 139

BUSHMEN
Chalmers Hallam (E.), Hampshire 125

BUSINESS STUDIES
Ardis Books, Hampshire 126
Barcombe Services, Essex........................... 108
Boer (Louise), Arthurian Books, Powys 287
Cornucopia Books, Lincolnshire 151
Esoteric Dreams Bookshop, Cumbria 77
Quaritch Ltd., (Bernard), London W............. 174
Reading Lasses, Dumfries & Galloway 270
Roland Books, Kent 138
Stern Antiquarian Bookseller (Jeffrey), North
    Yorkshire.. 198

BYZANTIUM
Askew Books (Vernon), Wiltshire................. 251
Bennett & Kerr Books, Oxfordshire............... 205
Caliver Books, Essex 109
Hellenic Bookservices, London NW 161

Joel Segal Books, Devon 86
Joppa Books Ltd., Surrey 230
Michael Graves-Johnston, London SW 168
Quest Books, East Yorkshire 107
Samovar Books, Co. Dublin........................ 264
Thorntons of Oxford Ltd., Oxfordshire........... 206
Trotter Books (John), London N 158
Unsworth's Booksellers, Suffolk................... 225
Whitchurch Books Ltd., Cardiff................... 281

CALLIGRAPHY
Apocalypse, Surrey 232
Barry McKay Rare Books, Cumbria.............. 76
Bettridge (Gordon), Fife 271
Cheshire Book Centre, Cheshire................... 69
Collinge & Clark, London WC.................... 176
Good for Books, Lincolnshire...................... 149
Hay Cinema Bookshop Ltd., Powys.............. 288
Joel Segal Books, Devon 86
John Underwood Antiquarian Books, Norfolk.. 189
Larkham Books (Patricia), Gloucestershire....... 117
Oopalba Books, Cheshire........................... 71
Print Matters, London SE........................... 165
R. & A. Books, East Sussex 101
Scrivener's Books & Bookbinding, Derbyshire... 82
Spenceley Books (David), West Yorkshire....... 248
Susanne Schulz-Falster Rare Books, London N. 158
Taylor Rare Books (Michael), Norfolk 187
Treasure Island (The), Greater Manchester....... 119
Whittle, Bookseller (Avril), Cumbria 80
Young (D. & J.), Powys............................ 291

CANADIANA
Antique Prints of the World, London N.......... 156
McEwan Fine Books, Grampian................... 272
Preston Book Company, Lancashire 144
Whistler (R.A.), East Sussex 99
Yesterday's News, Conwy.......................... 283

CANALS/INLAND WATERWAYS
Abrahams (Mike), Staffordshire................... 223
Addyman Books, Powys............................. 287
Aitchison (Lesley), Bristol 58
Al Saqi Books, London W.......................... 171
Anchor Books, Lincolnshire 149
Anthony Vickers Books, North Yorkshire 195
Anvil Books, West Midlands 239
Archer (Steve), London O 180
Arden Books & Cosmographia, Warwickshire... 236
Backfold Books, Herefordshire.................... 127
Baldwin (M. & M.), Worcestershire 255
Barbican Bookshop, North Yorkshire............. 196
Bianco Library, West Sussex....................... 241
Bird Books (Nigel), Ceredigion 283
Books Afloat, Dorset................................ 96
BookShop, The, Dumfries & Galloway........... 270
Bott, (Bookdealers) Ltd., (Martin), Greater
    Manchester 118
Cavern Books, Cheshire 70
Cheshire Book Centre, Cheshire................... 69
Childrens Bookshop, West Yorkshire 247
Classic Crime Collections, Greater Manchester.. 119
Clevedon Books, Somerset 217
Cornucopia Books, Lincolnshire 151
Cottage Books, Leics................................ 145

Coulthurst (Richard), Greater Manchester 120
Country Books, Derbyshire 82
Cox (Geoff), Devon 90
Crosby Nethercott Books, London O 180
Dales and Lakes Book Centre, Cumbria 79
Duck (William), Hampshire 124
Eastcote Bookshop (The), London O 180
Fifteenth Century Bookshop (The), East Sussex. 104
Good for Books, Lincolnshire 149
Hay Castle, Powys 288
Hennessey Bookseller (Ray), East Sussex 100
Island Books, Devon 85
Jade Mountain Bookshop, Hampshire 125
Joel Segal Books, Devon 86
K.S.C. Books, Cheshire 70
Keith Langford, London E 154
Kerr (Norman), Cumbria 77
Knowles - Antiquary (Roger J.), Staffordshire ... 223
Liddle (Steve), Bristol 58
Marcet Books, London SE 164
Merseyside Books, Merseyside 185
Nevis Railway Bookshops (The Antique &
  Book Collector), Wiltshire 252
Nicolas - Antiquarian Bookseller, London N 157
R. & A. Books, East Sussex 101
Roadmaster Books, Kent 136
Robert Humm & Co, Lincolnshire 152
Rochdale Book Company, Greater Manchester . 120
Rolling Stock Books, Greater Manchester 120
Salway Books, Essex 112
Scrivener's Books & Bookbinding, Derbyshire ... 82
Skyrack Books, West Yorkshire 247
Tony Pollastrone Railway Books, Wiltshire 251
Trinity Rare Books, Co. Leitrim 266
Winchester Bookshop (The), Hampshire 126

CAPITALISM

Quaritch Ltd., (Bernard), London W 174
Spurrier (Nick), Kent 137

CARICATURE

Apocalypse, Surrey 232
Batterham (David), London W 171
Derek Stirling Bookseller, Kent 141
Hogan (F. & J.), London N 157
InterCol London, London N 157
Joel Segal Books, Devon 86
Keith Langford, London E 154
N1 Books, East Sussex 105
Tooley, Adams & Co, Oxfordshire 209
Trinity Rare Books, Co. Leitrim 266

CARPETS
- GENERAL

Abington Books, Suffolk 227
Apocalypse, Surrey 232
Barmby (C. & A.J.), Kent 140
Byrom Textile Bookroom (Richard), Lancashire 142
Crosby (Simon), East Sussex 102
Don Kelly Books, London W 172
Heneage Art Books (Thomas), London SW 168
Joel Segal Books, Devon 86
Judith Mansfield, West Yorkshire 249
Potterton Books, North Yorkshire 196
Stroh (M.A.), London E 154

Trinders' Fine Tools, Suffolk 226

- ORIENTAL

Abington Books, Suffolk 227
Apocalypse, Surrey 232

CARRIAGES & DRIVING

Country Books, Derbyshire 82
Joel Segal Books, Devon 86
Keeble Antiques, Somerset 218
Pennymead Books, North Yorkshire 193
Phenotype Books, Cumbria 79
R. & A. Books, East Sussex 101
Stroh (M.A.), London E 154

CARTOGRAPHY

Alauda Books, Cumbria 76
Altea Antique Maps & Books, London W 171
Anthony Vickers Books, North Yorkshire 195
Archer (David), Powys 290
Booth (Booksearch Service), (Geoff), Cheshire... 68
Burden Ltd., (Clive A.), Herts 131
Chas J. Sawyer, Kent 140
Clevedon Books, Somerset 217
Frew Limited (Robert), London SW 167
Heritage, West Midlands 238
Hogan (F. & J.), London N 157
InterCol London, London N 157
Joel Segal Books, Devon 86
Marcet Books, London SE 164
O'Flynn Books, North Yorkshire 197
O'Flynn Books, North Yorkshire 197
Pennymead Books, North Yorkshire 193
Shapero Rare Books (Bernard J.), London W ... 175
Stalagluft Books, Tyne and Wear 235
Taney Books, Co. Dublin 263
Tim Bryers Ltd, London WC 178
Tooley, Adams & Co, Oxfordshire 209

CARTOONS

Apocalypse, Surrey 232
Book Palace (The), London SE 163
Cheshire Book Centre, Cheshire 69
D. & M. Books, West Yorkshire 249
Dales & Lakes Book Centre, Cumbria 79
Facet Books, Dorset 91
First Edition, The, Essex 109
Goldman (Paul), Dorset 94
InterCol London, London N 157
Jade Mountain Bookshop, Hampshire 125
Joel Segal Books, Devon 86
Longden (George), Cheshire 70
N1 Books, East Sussex 105
Print Matters, London SE 165
R. & A. Books, East Sussex 101
Wright (Norman), Dorset 95

CATALOGUES RAISONNÉ

Apocalypse, Surrey 232
Ars Artis, Oxfordshire 207
Art Book Company, (The), Suffolk 227
Barlow (Vincent G.), Hampshire 125
Book Palace (The), London SE 163
Facet Books, Dorset 91
Heneage Art Books (Thomas), London SW 168

Old Town Bookshop (The), Lothian 276
Print Matters, London SE............................. 165
Reeves Technical Books, North Yorkshire 195
Studio Bookshop, East Sussex...................... 100

CATERING & HOTEL MANAGEMENT
Gardener & Cook, London SW.................... 167

CATS
Annie's Books, South Yorkshire 221
Apocalypse, Surrey 232
Archivist (The), Devon.............................. 90
Backfold Books, Herefordshire.................... 127
Bookmark (Children's Books), Wiltshire.......... 253
Brad Books, Essex.................................. 110
Cat Lit, Somerset 218
Cheshire Book Centre, Cheshire................... 69
Cornucopia Books, Lincolnshire 151
Crabtree (Mrs. C.), Greater Manchester 120
Dalbeattie Books, Dumfries & Galloway 269
Dales & Lakes Book Centre, Cumbria............ 79
Fifteenth Century Bookshop (The), East Sussex. 104
Green Meadow Books, Cornwall 74
Jade Mountain Bookshop, Hampshire............ 125
Joel Segal Books, Devon 86
Kelpie's Books, Fife 271
Mayhew (Veronica), Berks 57
Ming Books, Dumfries & Galloway 270
Old Station Pottery & Bookshop (The), Norfolk 191
Oopalba Books, Cheshire........................... 71
R. & A. Books, East Sussex 101
Roland Books, Kent 138
Saint Swithin's Illustrated & Children's Books,
   London W 174
Stella Books, Monmouthshire 286
Tarka Books, Devon................................ 84

CATTLEMEN
Americanabooksuk, Cumbria........................ 76
Country Books, Derbyshire 82
Hodgson (Books) (Richard J.), North Yorks 196
Phenotype Books, Cumbria 79

CELTICA
Addyman Books, Powys............................. 287
Atlantis Bookshop, London WC.................... 176
Byre Books, Dumfries & Galloway................ 270
Colin Hancock, Ceredigion 282
Colonsay Bookshop, Isle of Colonsay............. 275
Cymric Books, Berks............................... 56
Delectus Books, London WC....................... 176
Ellwood Editions, Wiltshire 253
Gildas Books, Cheshire 68
Green Man Books, East Sussex 101
Hyland (C.P.), Co. Cork 263
Joel Segal Books, Devon 86
Madoc Books, Conwy 284
McCrone (Audrey), Isle of Arran 274
Michael J Carroll, Co. Cork....................... 263
Minster Gate Bookshop, North Yorkshire 197
Old Celtic Bookshop (The), Devon 87
Orb's Bookshop, Grampian......................... 273
PsychoBabel Books & Journals, Oxfordshire..... 205
R. & A. Books, East Sussex 101
Trinity Rare Books, Co. Leitrim 266

CEMETERIES
Birchden Books, London E 154
Joel Segal Books, Devon 86
Orb's Bookshop, Grampian......................... 273
R. & A. Books, East Sussex 101

CENSORSHIP
R. & A. Books, East Sussex 101
Susanne Schulz-Falster Rare Books, London N. 158

CERAMICS
Abacus Gallery, Staffordshire...................... 224
Addyman Books, Powys............................. 287
Anthony Vickers Books, North Yorkshire 195
Art Reference Books, Hampshire 124
Aviabooks, Gloucestershire 114
Axe Rare & Out of Print Books (Richard),
   North Yorkshire 193
Barmby (C. & A.J.), Kent.......................... 140
Bookroom (The), Surrey............................ 233
Books, Kent 137
Brad Books, Essex.................................. 110
Bruce Holdsworth Books, East Sussex 105
Buckland Books, West Sussex 243
Clark (Nigel A.), London SE....................... 163
Cofion Books, Pembrokeshire 286
Cornucopia Books, Lincolnshire 151
Cover to Cover, Merseyside........................ 185
Hay Castle, Powys.................................. 288
Heneage Art Books (Thomas), London SW 168
Joel Segal Books, Devon 86
McEwan Fine Books, Grampian.................... 272
Milestone Publications Goss & Crested China,
   Hampshire 123
Nelson (Elizabeth), Suffolk........................ 226
Potterton Books, North Yorkshire................. 196
R. & A. Books, East Sussex 101
Reference Works Ltd., Dorset...................... 95
Silver Trees Books, West Midlands................ 238
Stroh (M.A.), London E 154
Uncle Phil's Books, West Midlands 239
Whitchurch Books Ltd., Cardiff.................... 281

CHARITY
Cornucopia Books, Lincolnshire 151
Oak Tree Press, Oxfordshire....................... 207
R. & A. Books, East Sussex 101
Reading Lasses, Dumfries & Galloway 270

CHEMISTRY
Barcombe Services, Essex........................... 108
Baron - Scientific Book Sales (P.J.), Somerset ... 216
Bernard Dixon and Kath Adams, London O.... 182
Dean Byass, Bristol................................. 60
Gladstone Books, Lincolnshire 150
Glenbower Books, Co. Dublin 264
Parkinsons Books, Merseyside...................... 185
Phelps (Michael), West Sussex..................... 242
Pickering & Chatto, London W.................... 174
Prospect House Books, Co. Down................. 261
PsychoBabel Books & Journals, Oxfordshire..... 205
R M Books, Herts.................................. 132
R. & A. Books, East Sussex 101
Roosterbooks, Northants............................ 199
Stroh (M.A.), London E 154

Transformer, Dumfries & Galloway 270
Turret House, Norfolk 191
Weiner (Graham), London N 158
Westons, Herts 132
Westwood Books Ltd, Cumbria 80

CHESS
Addyman Books, Powys 287
Barcombe Services, Essex 108
Bowers Chess Suppliers (Francis),
   Cambridgeshire 67
Caissa Books, Surrey 233
Cheshire Book Centre, Cheshire 69
Glenbower Books, Co. Dublin 264
Joel Segal Books, Devon 86
Peterson (Tony), Essex 111
R. & A. Books, East Sussex 101
R. S. & P. A. Scowen, London O 181
Roger Treglown, Cheshire 70
Saunders (Tom), Caerphilly 281
Scrivener's Books & Bookbinding, Derbyshire ... 82
Uncle Phil's Books, West Midlands 239
Westwood Books Ltd, Cumbria 80
Whistler's Books, London SW 169
Yates Antiquarian Books (Tony),
   Leics 146

CHILDREN'S
- GENERAL
A. & R. Booksearch, Cornwall 73
AA1 Books, Dumfries & Galloway 269
Abrahams (Mike), Staffordshire 223
Addyman Books, Powys 287
Adrem Books, Herts 130
Alexander's Books, Warwickshire 237
Allinson (Frank & Stella), Warwickshire 236
Altshuler (Jean), Cumbria 78
Andrew Morton (Books), Powys 287
Annie's Books, South Yorkshire 221
Anthony Whittaker, Kent 135
Antiques on High, Oxfordshire 207
Anwoth Books Ltd, Dumfries & Galloway 269
Apocalypse, Surrey 232
Arden Books & Cosmographia, Warwickshire ... 236
Armitage (Booksearch), (Kate), Devon 84
Aurora Books Ltd, Lothian 275
Autolycus, Shropshire 212
Backfold Books, Herefordshire 127
baconboooks, London WC 176
Badger Books, Somerset 219
Baker - Books for the Collector (Colin), Devon . 89
Barely Read Books, Kent 141
Bates Books, London O 180
Bayntun (George), Somerset 215
Beck (John), East Sussex 103
Beckham Books Ltd., Suffolk 229
Beverley Old Bookshop, East Yorkshire 106
Biblipola, London NW 160
Bilski (Gill), Buckinghamshire 61
Black Cat Bookshop, Leics 147
Black Five Books, Shropshire 214
Blacket Books, Lothian 276
Book Business (The), London W 171
Book House (The), Cumbria 76
Book Palace (The), London SE 163

Bookbarrow, Cambridgeshire 63
Bookmark (Children's Books), Wiltshire 253
Bookroom (The), Surrey 233
Books & Collectables Ltd., Cambridgeshire 63
Books Antiques & Collectables, Devon 90
Books At The Barras, Lanarkshire 278
Books Bought & Sold, Surrey 231
books2books, Devon 88
Bookseller (The), Cumbria 79
Bookshop at the Plain, Lincolnshire 149
Bookshop on the Heath, The, London SE 163
Bookworms, Norfolk 186
Bookworms Paradise Ltd., West Sussex 242
Border Bookshop, West Yorkshire 249
Boris Books, Somerset 216
Brazenhead Ltd., Norfolk 188
Bridport Old Books, Dorset 92
Bright (P.G.), Cambridgeshire 65
Brighton Books, East Sussex 99
Broadhurst of Southport Ltd., Merseyside 185
Broadleaf Books, Torfaen 292
Browning Books, Torfaen 292
Butler Rare Books, Buckinghamshire 61
Butts Books (Mary), Berks 56
Byre Books, Dumfries & Galloway 270
Camilla's Bookshop, East Sussex 101
Canterbury Bookshop (The), Kent 136
Catalyst Booksearch Services, Devon 87
Chandos Books, Devon 85
Chapter Two, London SE 163
Charles Bossom, Cambridgeshire 65
Charlie Byrne's Bookshop, Co. Galway 265
Childrens Bookshop, West Yorkshire 247
Children's Bookshop (The), Herefordshire 127
Churchgate Books, Suffolk 226
Clear (Mrs. Patricia), Surrey 230
Clements (R.W.), London O 181
Cobweb Books, North Yorkshire 194
Cofion Books, Pembrokeshire 286
Collectables (W.H.), Suffolk 229
Cornell Books, Gloucestershire 117
Cotswold Internet Books, Gloucestershire 113
Countrymans Gallery (The), Leics 145
Coupland (Terry W.), Staffordshire 223
Cranhurst Books, London NW 160
Cygnet Books, East Yorkshire 107
D. & M. Books, West Yorkshire 249
Dalbeattie Books, Dumfries & Galloway 269
Dales & Lakes Book Centre, Cumbria 79
Dandy Lion Editions, Surrey 233
D'Arcy Books, Wiltshire 252
David (G.), Cambridgeshire 63
David Flint, Hampshire 124
Dennys Sanders & Greene Ltd, East Sussex 100
Deverell Books, Bristol 59
Dolphin Books, Suffolk 225
Doolin Dinghy Books, Co. Clare 262
Doorbar (P. & D.), Gwynedd 285
Dormouse Bookshop (The), Norfolk 189
Draca Books, West Yorkshire 248
Drummond Pleasures of Past Times (David),
   London WC 176
Eastcote Bookshop (The), London O 180
Eclectica, London SE 164
ECR Books, Dorset 92

Elizabeth Ferguson, Grampian 272
Ellis, Bookseller (Peter), London WC 177
Esoteric Dreams Bookshop, Cumbria 77
Everett (Richard), Norfolk 187
Everett (Richard, at the Southwold Antiques
  Centre), Suffolk 229
Facet Books, Dorset................................. 91
Ferguson (Elizabeth), Grampian 272
Fifteenth Century Bookshop (The), East Sussex. 104
First State Books, London W 172
firstpagebooks, Norfolk............................. 189
Firsts in Print, Somerset 219
Ford Books (David), Herts 130
Foster Bookshop (Paul), London SW 167
Fosters Bookshop, London W 172
Franks Booksellers, Greater Manchester.......... 119
Freya Books & Antiques, Norfolk................. 189
Furneaux Books (Lee), Devon...................... 89
Game Advice, Oxfordshire 208
Gander, (Jacques), Gloucestershire................ 114
Garfi Books, Powys 291
Gemini–Books, Shropshire 214
George St. Books, Derbyshire 83
Good Books, Shropshire 213
Good for Books, Lincolnshire 149
Grahame Thornton, Bookseller, Dorset........... 93
Green Meadow Books, Cornwall 74
Greer (Robin), London SW......................... 167
Hall's Bookshop, Kent.............................. 140
Hambleton Books, North Yorkshire 196
Hancock (Peter), West Sussex 241
Harrington (Adrian), London W................... 173
Harrington Antiquarian Bookseller (Peter),
  London SW... 167
Harvest Books, Lancashire.......................... 144
Hawley (C.L.), North Yorkshire 195
HCB Wholesale, Powys 288
Heppa (Christopher), Essex 108
Heywood Hill Limited (G.), London W 173
Hodgkins and Company Limited (Ian), Glos 116
Hollett and Son (R.F.G.), Cumbria 79
Holtom (Christopher), Gloucestershire............ 115
Hornsey's, North Yorkshire......................... 194
Hurst (Jenny), Kent 137
Hylton Booksearch, Merseyside 184
Innes Books, Shropshire............................. 212
Intech Books, Northumberland 201
Internet Bookshop UK Ltd., Gloucestershire 113
Jack and Molly's Trading Co...................... 90
Jackson (M.W.), Wiltshire.......................... 254
Jade Mountain Bookshop, Hampshire 125
Jane & John Kinnaird, Cumbria 78
Jane Badger Books, Northants 199
Jane Jones Books, Grampian 273
JB Books & Collectables, West Sussex 243
Jean Hedger, Berks................................. 55
Jenny Hurst, Kent 138
Joel Segal Books, Devon 86
John Underwood Antiquarian Books, Norfolk.. 189
Jolly Good Read (A.), Tayside 279
Jonkers Rare Books, Oxfordshire 207
Junk & Spread Eagle, London SE 164
K Books, Cheshire.................................. 70
Karen Millward, Co. Cork.......................... 263
Katesbooks, Devon.................................. 85

Katnap Arts, Norfolk............................... 190
Keel Row Bookshop, Tyne and Wear 235
Kellow Books, Oxfordshire 206
Kelpie's Books, Fife 271
Keswick Bookshop, Cumbria 78
Kevin S. Ogilvie Modern First Editions,
  Grampian 272
Key Books (Sarah), Cambridgeshire............... 64
Kineton Nooks, Warwickshire...................... 236
Kingfisher Book Service, Nottinghamshire 204
Kirkpatrick (Robert J.), London W 173
Lake (David), Norfolk.............................. 190
Leabeck Books, Oxfordshire........................ 208
Leaf Ends, Northumberland 202
Little Stour Books, Kent 136
Lloyd-Davies (Sue), Carmarthenshire 282
Lucius Books, North Yorkshire.................... 197
M. and A.C. Thompson, Norfolk.................. 191
Macbuiks, North Yorkshire......................... 193
Mainly Fiction, Cheshire 68
Malvern Bookshop (The), Worcestershire 255
March House Books, Somerset...................... 217
Marchpane, London WC............................ 177
Martin (Books and Pictures), (Brian P.), Surrey. 231
Martin (Brian), Surrey 231
Mason (Mary), Oxfordshire 205
McCrone (Audrey), Isle of Arran 274
McNaughtan's Bookshop, Lothian 276
Mellon's Books, East Sussex........................ 101
Minster Gate Bookshop, North Yorkshire 197
Modlock (Lilian), Dorset 93
Moorhead Books, West Yorkshire 245
Much Ado Books, East Sussex 99
Murphy (C.J.), Norfolk............................. 189
Myra Dean Illustated Books, Powys 287
New Strand, The, Herefordshire 127
Old Celtic Bookshop (The), Devon 87
Old Hall Bookshop (The), Northants 199
Old Station Pottery & Bookshop (The),
  Norfolk... 191
Old Town Bookshop (The), Lothian 276
Oopalba Books, Cheshire............................ 71
Paperbacks Plus, Bristol 59
Park Gallery & Bookshop (The), Northants 200
Parrott Books, Oxfordshire 209
Penny Farthing, The, Lothian 277
Period & Classical Collections, East Sussex 103
Peter Lyons Books, Gloucestershire 113
Peter's Bookshop, Norfolk 190
Pickering Bookshop, North Yorkshire 196
Porcupine Books, London O 181
Price (R.W.), Nottinghamshire 203
Priestpopple Books, Northumberland 201
Pyecroft (Ruth), Gloucestershire 116
Quaritch Ltd., (Bernard), London W.............. 174
R. & A. Books, East Sussex 101
Richard Thornton Books, London N 158
Rickaro Books, West Yorkshire..................... 246
Ripping Yarns, London N 158
River Reads Bookshop, Devon...................... 90
Robert Temple, London N.......................... 158
Roberts Fine Books (Julian), Lincolnshire........ 151
Robertson Books, Lothian 277
Rochdale Book Company, Greater Manchester . 120
Roland Books, Kent 138

Roscrea Bookshop & Newsagents, Co. Tipperary 266
Rose's Books, Powys 289
Ross & Company Ltd., (Louise), Worcs 255
Roundstone Books, Lancashire 143
Rowan House Books, Surrey 231
Rye Old Books, East Sussex 104
Ryeland Books, Northants 199
St Mary's Books & Prints, Lincolnshire 152
Saint Swithin's Illustrated & Children's Books, London W 174
Saintfield Antiques & Fine Books, Co. Down ... 261
Saunders (Tom), Caerphilly 281
Savage (Keith A.), Suffolk 228
Schutte (David), Hampshire 124
Scrivener's Books & Bookbinding, Derbyshire... 82
Seabreeze Books, Lancashire 144
Sesemann (Julia), Kent 135
Shakeshaft (Dr. B.), Cheshire 71
Sharpe (Mary), Somerset 219
Shelley (E. & J.), Buckinghamshire 61
Sillan Books, Co. Cavan 262
Silver Trees Books, West Midlands 238
Simpson (Dave), Central 268
Sims (Sue), Dorset 91
Sleepy Elephant Books & Artefacts, Cumbria ... 80
Slightly Foxed on Gloucester Road, London SW 167
Smith Books, (Sally), Suffolk 226
Sotheran Limited (Henry), London W 175
Staffs Bookshop (The), Staffordshire 223
Stansbury (Rosemary), Devon 88
Stella Books, Monmouthshire 286
Stepping Stones Bookshop, North Yorkshire 193
Stinton (Judith), Dorset 92
Stothert Old Books, Cheshire 68
Strathtay Antiquarian - Secondhand Books, Tayside 280
Stroma Books, Borders 267
Surprise Books, Gloucestershire 113
Tant Yn Ellen Books, Powys 290
Tarka Books, Devon 84
The End Bookshop, Devon 88
The Old Abbey Bookshop, Co. Down 261
The Old Children's Bookshelf, Lothian 277
Tiffin (Tony and Gill), Durham 97
Till's Bookshop, Lothian 277
TP Children's Bookshop, West Yorkshire 245
Transformer, Dumfries & Galloway 270
Treasure Trove Books, Leics 146
Trinity Rare Books, Co. Leitrim 266
Tucker (Alan & Joan), Gloucestershire 116
Uncle Phil's Books, West Midlands 239
Updike Rare Books (John), Lothian 277
Wadard Books, Kent 137
Westwood Books Ltd, Cumbria 80
Wheen O'Books, Borders 267
Wilbraham (J. & S.), London NW 162
Words Etcetera Bookshop, Dorset 93
Wright (Norman), Dorset 95
Wychwood Books, Gloucestershire 116
Xanadu Books, Durham 98
Yorkshire Relics, West Yorkshire 246

- EARLY TITLES

Addyman Books, Powys 287

Autolycus, Shropshire 212
Beck (John), East Sussex 103
Biblipola, London NW 160
Blackwell's Rare Books, Oxfordshire 208
Bookmark (Children's Books), Wiltshire 253
Butler Rare Books, Buckinghamshire 61
Charles Bossom, Cambridgeshire 65
Children's Bookshop (The), Herefordshire 127
Cox Old & Rare Books (Claude), Suffolk 227
Cygnet Books, East Yorkshire 107
David Flint, Hampshire 124
Elizabeth Ferguson, Grampian 272
Facet Books, Dorset 91
Ferguson (Elizabeth), Grampian 272
First Edition, The, Essex 109
Glenbower Books, Co. Dublin 264
Hambleton Books, North Yorkshire 196
JB Books & Collectables, West Sussex 243
Jean Hedger, Berks 55
Joel Segal Books, Devon 86
Kelpie's Books, Fife 271
Lake (David), Norfolk 190
March House Books, Somerset 217
Martin (Brian), Surrey 231
McCrone (Audrey), Isle of Arran 274
Mercat Books, Highland 274
Minster Gate Bookshop, North Yorkshire 197
Old Celtic Bookshop (The), Devon 87
Oopalba Books, Cheshire 71
Penny Farthing, The, Lothian 277
Period & Classical Collections, East Sussex 103
R. & A. Books, East Sussex 101
Richard Thornton Books, London N 158
Ripping Yarns, London N 158
Roberts Fine Books (Julian), Lincolnshire 151
Scrivener's Books & Bookbinding, Derbyshire... 82
Seydi Rare Books (Sevin), London NW 161
Smith Books, (Sally), Suffolk 226
Talisman Books, Cheshire 70
Tiffin (Tony and Gill), Durham 97
Treasure Trove Books, Leics 146
Uncle Phil's Books, West Midlands 239
Wadard Books, Kent 137
Wheen O'Books, Borders 267
Yates Antiquarian Books (Tony), Leics 146

- ILLUSTRATED

A. & R. Booksearch, Cornwall 73
Addyman Books, Powys 287
Adrem Books, Herts 130
Allinson (Frank & Stella), Warwickshire 236
Amwell Book Company, London EC 155
Annie's Books, South Yorkshire 221
Apocalypse, Surrey 232
Art Reference Books, Hampshire 124
Autolycus, Shropshire 212
Backfold Books, Herefordshire 127
Baker - Books for the Collector (Colin), Devon . 89
Barely Read Books, Kent 141
Barlow (Vincent G.), Hampshire 125
Bates Books, London O 180
Bath Old Books, Somerset 215
Bayntun (George), Somerset 215
Beck (John), East Sussex 103
Biblipola, London NW 160

Birmingham Books, West Midlands 238
Black Cat Bookshop, Leics 147
Blackwell's Rare Books, Oxfordshire.............. 208
Book Palace (The), London SE 163
Bookmark (Children's Books), Wiltshire.......... 253
Books & Things, London W....................... 171
books2books, Devon............................... 88
BOOKS4U, Flintshire.............................. 284
Bookseller (The), Cumbria 79
Bookstand, Dorset 94
Boris Books, Somerset 216
Bow Windows Book Shop, East Sussex 103
Brazenhead Ltd., Norfolk 188
Bridport Old Books, Dorset 92
Brock Books, North Yorkshire..................... 192
Browning Books, Torfaen 292
Bunyan Books, Bedfordshire........................ 53
Butler Rare Books, Buckinghamshire 61
Butts Books (Mary), Berks......................... 56
Camilla's Bookshop, East Sussex 101
Chalk (Old & Out of Print Books)
  (Christine M.), West Midlands 238
Charles Bossom, Cambridgeshire................... 65
Children's Bookshop (The), Herefordshire........ 127
Chris Phillips, Wiltshire............................ 252
Cobweb Books, North Yorkshire 194
Cofion Books, Pembrokeshire 286
Cooper Hay Rare Books, Strathclyde............. 278
Cox Old & Rare Books (Claude), Suffolk 227
Cox, Andrew, Shropshire........................... 214
Cygnet Books, East Yorkshire...................... 107
D. & M. Books, West Yorkshire.................... 249
Dales & Lakes Book Centre, Cumbria 79
Dandy Lion Editions, Surrey 233
Demetzy Books, Oxfordshire 206
Deverell Books, Bristol............................. 59
Doorbar (P. & D.), Gwynedd 285
Draca Books, West Yorkshire...................... 248
Eastwood Books (David), Cornwall 72
Elizabeth Ferguson, Grampian 272
Ellis, Bookseller (Peter), London WC 177
Embleton (Paul), Essex 111
Facet Books, Dorset 91
Ferguson (Elizabeth), Grampian 272
Fifteenth Century Bookshop (The), East Sussex. 104
Fine Books at Ilkley, West Yorkshire 247
Foster Bookshop (Paul), London SW............. 167
Fosters Bookshop, London W 172
Green Meadow Books, Cornwall 74
Greer (Robin), London SW......................... 167
Hennessey Bookseller (Ray), East Sussex 100
Ian Briddon, Derbyshire............................ 82
Intech Books, Northumberland 201
Jackson (M.W.), Wiltshire.......................... 254
Jane & John Kinnaird, Cumbria 78
JB Books & Collectables, West Sussex 243
Jean Hedger, Berks................................. 55
Joel Segal Books, Devon 86
John Underwood Antiquarian Books, Norfolk.. 189
Jonkers Rare Books, Oxfordshire 207
Junk & Spread Eagle, London SE................. 164
Katesbooks, Devon................................. 85
Kernaghans, Merseyside 185
Kineton Nooks, Warwickshire...................... 236
Lake (David), Norfolk 190

Liddle (Steve), Bristol 58
Lloyd-Davies (Sue), Carmarthenshire 282
Lucius Books, North Yorkshire..................... 197
Lymelight Books & Prints, Dorset................. 93
Macbuiks, North Yorkshire......................... 193
Mannwaring (M.G.), Bristol 59
March House Books, Somerset..................... 217
Martin (Books and Pictures), (Brian P) Surrey . 231
Martin (Brian), Surrey 231
McCrone (Audrey), Isle of Arran.................. 274
Minster Gate Bookshop, North Yorkshire 197
Myra Dean Illustated Books, Powys 287
N1 Books, East Sussex 105
Oasis Booksearch, Cambridgeshire................. 67
Old Celtic Bookshop (The), Devon............... 87
Oopalba Books, Cheshire............................ 71
Park Gallery & Bookshop (The), Northants 200
Penny Farthing, The, Lothian 277
Pittville Books, Gloucestershire.................... 113
Portobello Books, London W 174
Print Matters, London SE........................... 165
R. & A. Books, East Sussex 101
Rhodes, Bookseller (Peter), Hampshire 125
Richard Thornton Books, London N 158
Ripping Yarns, London N 158
Roberts Fine Books (Julian), Lincolnshire........ 151
Roscrea Bookshop & Newsagents,
  Co. Tipperary 266
Rose's Books, Powys................................ 289
Saint Swithin's Illustrated & Children's Books,
  London W 174
Scrivener's Books & Bookbinding, Derbyshire... 82
Shakeshaft (Dr. B.), Cheshire....................... 71
Stepping Stones Bookshop, North Yorkshire 193
Stroma Books, Borders 267
Studio (The), Strathclyde 278
Tant Yn Ellen Books, Powys 290
The Old Children's Bookshelf, Lothian 277
Thorntons of Oxford Ltd., Oxfordshire........... 206
Tiffin (Tony and Gill), Durham 97
TP Children's Bookshop, West Yorkshire 245
Treasure Trove Books, Leics 146
Trinity Rare Books, Co. Leitrim 266
Uncle Phil's Books, West Midlands 239
Wadard Books, Kent 137
Wheen O'Books, Borders........................... 267
Worlds End Bookshop, London SW 169
Xanadu Books, Durham 98
Yates Antiquarian Books (Tony), Leics........... 146

CHRISTMAS

Addyman Books, Powys............................. 287
Childrens Bookshop, West Yorkshire 247
Cygnet Books, East Yorkshire...................... 107
Dolphin Books, Suffolk............................. 225
Green Meadow Books, Cornwall 74
Joel Segal Books, Devon 86
Nostalgia Unlimited, Merseyside................... 184
Oasis Booksearch, Cambridgeshire................. 67
R. & A. Books, East Sussex 101
Roscrea Bookshop & Newsagents,
  Co. Tipperary 266
Saint Swithin's Illustrated & Children's Books,
  London W 174
Samovar Books, Co. Dublin........................ 264

Tarka Books, Devon 84
Uncle Phil's Books, West Midlands 239

CHURCHILLIANA

Annie's Books, South Yorkshire 221
Anthony Spranger, Wiltshire 252
Askew Books (Vernon), Wiltshire 251
Barely Read Books, Kent 141
Barn Books, Buckinghamshire 61
Baxter (Steve), Surrey 233
BookShop, The, Dumfries & Galloway 270
Cheshire Book Centre, Cheshire 69
Cofion Books, Pembrokeshire 286
Craobh Rua Books, Co. Armagh 260
Dolphin Books, Suffolk 225
First Edition, The, Essex 109
Foster Bookshop (Paul), London SW 167
Grahame Thornton, Bookseller, Dorset 93
Guildmaster Books, Cheshire 70
Harrington (Adrian), London W 173
Harrington Antiquarian Bookseller (Peter),
   London SW 167
Hay Castle, Powys 288
Island Books, Devon 85
Joel Segal Books, Devon 86
Lymelight Books & Prints, Dorset 93
Mellon's Books, East Sussex 101
Portus Books, Hampshire 122
R. & A. Books, East Sussex 101
Seabreeze Books, Lancashire 144
Shacklock Books (David), Suffolk 226
Sotheran Limited (Henry), London W 175
Uncle Phil's Books, West Midlands 239
Updike Rare Books (John), Lothian 277
Wadard Books, Kent 137
White (C.R.), London W 175
Yesterday's News, Conwy 283

CINEMA/FILM

Abbey Books, Cornwall 73
Anthony Spranger, Wiltshire 252
Apocalypse, Surrey 232
Armstrong's Books & Collectables, Leics 145
Bardsley's Books, Suffolk 225
Barn Books, Buckinghamshire 61
Beware of the Leopard, Bristol 58
Bob Mallory (Books), Derbyshire 83
Book Palace (The), London SE 163
Bookroom (The), Surrey 233
Books, Denbighshire 284
Books & Collectables Ltd., Cambridgeshire 63
books2books, Devon 88
Bookshop (The), Norfolk 191
BookShop, The, Dumfries & Galloway 270
Bookworms Paradise Ltd., West Sussex 242
Brighton Books, East Sussex 99
Byre Books, Dumfries & Galloway 270
Caledonia Books, Strathclyde 278
Camilla's Bookshop, East Sussex 101
Capel Mawr Collectors Centre, Gwynedd 285
Catalyst Booksearch Services, Devon 87
Chapter & Verse, Lincolnshire 150
Cheshire Book Centre, Cheshire 69
Cofion Books, Pembrokeshire 286
Cover to Cover, Merseyside 185

Cowley, Bookdealer (K.W.), Somerset 217
Dales & Lakes Book Centre, Cumbria 79
Darkwood Books, Co. Cork 263
Decorum Books, London N 156
Delectus Books, London WC 176
Dolphin Books, Suffolk 225
Eastcote Bookshop (The), London O 180
Evans (Mark), Lincolnshire 151
Fifteenth Century Bookshop (The), East Sussex . 104
firstpagebooks, Norfolk 189
Fitzsimons (Anne), Cumbria 76
Ford Books (David), Herts 130
Fossgate Books, North Yorkshire 197
Franks Booksellers, Greater Manchester 119
Greenroom Books, West Yorkshire 247
Hambleton Books, North Yorkshire 196
Hancock & Monks Music Emporium, Powys ... 288
Hay Castle, Powys 288
Hay Cinema Bookshop Ltd., Powys 288
HCB Wholesale, Powys 288
Jade Mountain Bookshop, Hampshire 125
Joel Segal Books, Devon 86
Judd Books, London WC 177
Junk & Spread Eagle, London SE 164
Kent T. G., Surrey 230
Kingfisher Book Service, Nottinghamshire 204
Kirkman Ltd., (Robert), Bedfordshire 54
McGee (Terence J.), London O 180
Mellon's Books, East Sussex 101
Modlock (Lilian), Dorset 93
Moon's Bookshop (Michael), Cumbria 80
Morris Secondhand & Antiquarian Books
   (Chris), Oxfordshire 208
My Back Pages, London SW 168
Nevitsky (Philip), Greater Manchester 119
O'Brien Books & Photo Gallery, Co. Limerick .. 266
Paramor (C.D.), Suffolk 228
Pickering Bookshop, North Yorkshire 196
Pordes Books Ltd., (Henry), London WC 177
Portobello Books, London W 174
Priestpopple Books, Northumberland 201
Print Matters, London SE 165
PsychoBabel Books & Journals, Oxfordshire 205
R. & A. Books, East Sussex 101
Reads, Dorset 95
Roland Books, Kent 138
Saintfield Antiques & Fine Books, Co. Down ... 261
Sclanders (Beatbooks), (Andrew), London EC ... 155
Scrivener's Books & Bookbinding, Derbyshire ... 82
Sleepy Elephant Books & Artefacts, Cumbria ... 80
Stroma Books, Borders 267
Sugen & Co., North Yorkshire 193
Tarka Books, Devon 84
Terence Kaye - Bookseller, London NW 161
Theatreshire Books, North Yorkshire 192
Till's Bookshop, Lothian 277
Treasure Chest Books, Suffolk 226
Waxfactor, East Sussex 100
Whittle, Bookseller (Avril), Cumbria 80
Williams (Bookdealer), (Richard), N Lincs 153
Wood (Peter), Cambridgeshire 65
Worlds End Bookshop, London SW 169
Wright (Norman), Dorset 95
Yesterday's News, Conwy 283
Zardoz Books, Wiltshire 254

CIRCUS

Addyman Books, Powys............................ 287
Apocalypse, Surrey 232
Cover to Cover, Merseyside........................ 185
Decorum Books, London N 156
Drummond Pleasures of Past Times (David),
  London WC 176
Fitzsimons (Anne), Cumbria....................... 76
R. & A. Books, East Sussex 101
St Swithin's Illustrated & Children's
  Books, London W 174
Terence Kaye - Bookseller, London NW 161
Webster (D.), Strathclyde......................... 279

CITIES

- GENERAL

Amwell Book Company, London EC............. 155
Annie's Books, South Yorkshire 221
Duck (William), Hampshire........................ 124
Inch's Books, Kent 137
Island Books, Devon 85
Joel Segal Books, Devon 86
Keith Langford, London E 154
Marlborough Rare Books Ltd., London W...... 173
O'Flynn Books, North Yorkshire................. 197
R. & A. Books, East Sussex 101

- CITY OF LONDON

Altea Antique Maps & Books, London W....... 171
Apocalypse, Surrey 232
Ash Rare Books, London SW...................... 166
Bookroom (The), Surrey........................... 233
Camilla's Bookshop, East Sussex 101
Charles Bossom, Cambridgeshire.................. 65
Chas J. Sawyer, Kent 140
Cofion Books, Pembrokeshire 286
Derek Stirling Bookseller, Kent 141
Dolphin Books, Suffolk............................ 225
Fifteenth Century Bookshop (The), East Sussex. 104
Fosters Bookshop, London W 172
InterCol London, London N 157
Island Books, Devon............................... 85
Joel Segal Books, Devon 86
Junk & Spread Eagle, London SE 164
Marcet Books, London SE.......................... 164
Marlborough Rare Books Ltd., London W...... 173
Missing Books, Essex 109
Muttonchop Manuscripts, West Sussex 242
Oopalba Books, Cheshire........................... 71
Portobello Books, London W 174
PsychoBabel Books & Journals, Oxfordshire..... 205
R. & A. Books, East Sussex 101
Roland Books, Kent 138
Stalagluft Books, Tyne and Wear................. 235
Uncle Phil's Books, West Midlands 239

- NEW YORK CITY AND BROOKLYN

R. & A. Books, East Sussex 101

CIVIL ENGINEERING

Camden Books, Somerset 215
Cox (Geoff), Devon 90
Duck (William), Hampshire........................ 124
Joel Segal Books, Devon 86
Parkinsons Books, Merseyside..................... 185

Phelps (Michael), West Sussex..................... 242
Reeves Technical Books, North Yorkshire 195
Stroh (M.A.), London E 154
Weiner (Graham), London N 158
Westons, Herts.................................... 132
Wheen O'Books, Borders........................... 267
Winchester Bookshop (The), Hampshire.......... 126

CIVIL RIGHTS

Left on The Shelf, Cumbria........................ 78
R. & A. Books, East Sussex 101

CLASSICAL STUDIES

Apocalypse, Surrey 232
BookShop, The, Dumfries & Galloway........... 270
Camden Books, Somerset 215
Carnforth Bookshop (The), Lancashire 142
Charlie Byrne's Bookshop, Co. Galway......... 265
Chthonios Books, East Sussex 102
Classics Bookshop (The), Oxfordshire........... 205
Cornucopia Books, Lincolnshire 151
Cotswold Internet Books, Gloucestershire........ 113
Crouch Rare Books, Surrey........................ 232
Grahame Thornton, Bookseller, Dorset.......... 93
Hall's Bookshop, Kent 140
Hellenic Bookservices, London NW 161
Hill (Peter), Hampshire 122
Howes Bookshop, East Sussex 102
Joel Segal Books, Devon 86
Kings Bookshop Callander, Central 268
Lamb (R.W.), Suffolk............................. 228
Michael Graves-Johnston, London SW 168
Much Binding, Norfolk............................ 186
O'Flynn Books, North Yorkshire................. 197
Olynthiacs, Shropshire 213
Parkinsons Books, Merseyside..................... 185
Pittville Books, Gloucestershire................... 113
Poole (William), London W 174
PsychoBabel Books & Journals, Oxfordshire..... 205
Quest Books, East Yorkshire 107
R. & A. Books, East Sussex 101
Sandpiper Books Ltd., London SW 169
Scrivener's Books & Bookbinding, Derbyshire... 82
Seydi Rare Books (Sevin), London NW 161
Staniland (Booksellers), Lincolnshire 152
Thorntons of Oxford Ltd., Oxfordshire.......... 206
Tim Bryers Ltd, London WC 178
Unsworth's Booksellers, Suffolk................... 225
Winchester Bookshop (The), Hampshire.......... 126
Winghale Books, Lincolnshire 152
Wizard Books, Cambridgeshire.................... 67

CLASSICS, THE

Addyman Books, Powys............................ 287
Adrem Books, Herts 130
Any Old Books, Hampshire 121
Apocalypse, Surrey 232
Bayntun (George), Somerset 215
Beware of the Leopard, Bristol 58
Butler Rare Books, Buckinghamshire 61
C J Renwick Books, Powys....................... 287
Charlie Byrne's Bookshop, Co. Galway.......... 265
Cornucopia Books, Lincolnshire 151
Dolphin Books, Suffolk............................ 225
Elstree Books, Herts.............................. 130

Fifteenth Century Bookshop (The), East Sussex. 104
Hancock (Peter), West Sussex 241
Joel Segal Books, Devon 86
Just Books, Cornwall 75
Martin (Books and Pictures), (Brian P)., Surrey. 231
Michael Graves-Johnston, London SW 168
N1 Books, East Sussex 105
O'Flynn Books, North Yorkshire 197
Print Matters, London SE............................ 165
PsychoBabel Books & Journals, Oxfordshire.... 205
Quaritch Ltd., (Bernard), London W.............. 174
R. & A. Books, East Sussex 101
Staniland (Booksellers), Lincolnshire 152
Tarka Books, Devon 84
Till's Bookshop, Lothian 277
Uncle Phil's Books, West Midlands 239
Unsworth's Booksellers, Suffolk.................... 225
Winchester Bookshop (The), Hampshire.......... 126

CLIMATOLOGY
Cornucopia Books, Lincolnshire 151
Joel Segal Books, Devon 86
Phelps (Michael), West Sussex...................... 242
R. & A. Books, East Sussex 101
Weiner (Graham), London N 158
Westons, Herts.. 132

COASTAL DEFENCE
Earth Science Books, Wiltshire 252
MilitaryHistoryBooks.com, Kent.................... 137
R. & A. Books, East Sussex 101

COCKFIGHTING
Blest (Peter), Kent 138
Chalmers Hallam (E.), Hampshire 125
Coch-y-Bonddu Books, Powys 290
Country Books, Derbyshire 82
Home Farm Books, Warwickshire.................. 236
Kilgour (Sporting Books) (Ian), Leics 147
Phenotype Books, Cumbria 79
R. & A. Books, East Sussex 101
Thomas (Barry), Ceredigion 282

COFFEE
Kenya Books, East Sussex 100
R. & A. Books, East Sussex 101
Stroh (M.A.), London E 154
Susanne Schulz-Falster Rare Books, London N. 158

COLLECTABLES
Annie's Books, South Yorkshire 221
Apocalypse, Surrey................................... 232
Avonworld Books, Somerset......................... 216
Bates Books, London O 180
BC Books, Cheshire.................................. 69
Book Palace (The), London SE 163
Bookmark (Children's Books), Wiltshire.......... 253
books2books, Devon 88
Bookworms Paradise Ltd., West Sussex 242
Booth (Booksearch Service), (Geoff), Cheshire... 68
Chalk (Old & Out of Print Books) (Christine M.),
   West Midlands 238
Clark (Nigel A.), London SE........................ 163
Cofion Books, Pembrokeshire 286
Collectors Carbooks, Northants.................... 199

Cornucopia Books, Lincolnshire 151
Cover to Cover, Merseyside.......................... 185
Darkwood Books, Co. Cork 263
Debbage (John), Norfolk 189
Don Kelly Books, London W 172
Exeter's Antiques Centre on the Quay, Devon... 86
First Edition, The, Essex 109
Green Meadow Books, Cornwall 74
Hylton Booksearch, Merseyside 184
InterCol London, London N 157
Joel Segal Books, Devon 86
Kingfisher Book Service, Nottinghamshire 204
Milestone Publications Goss & Crested China,
   Hampshire 123
Oak Tree Press, Oxfordshire 207
Paul Hoare, Cornwall................................ 74
R. & A. Books, East Sussex 101
Randall (Tom), Somerset............................ 218
Read - Gorleston Books, (C.&J.), Norfolk 187
Spink, London WC 178
Tarka Books, Devon 84
Thorntons of Oxford Ltd., Oxfordshire........... 206
Uncle Phil's Books, West Midlands 239
Wiend Books, Lancashire 143

COLLECTING
Abrahams (Mike), Staffordshire..................... 223
Ancient Art Books, London SW 166
Annie's Books, South Yorkshire 221
Antiques on High, Oxfordshire...................... 207
Apocalypse, Surrey................................... 232
Art Reference Books, Hampshire 124
Barmby (C. & A.J.), Kent............................ 140
Barn Books, Buckinghamshire....................... 61
Bianco Library, West Sussex......................... 241
Booth (Booksearch Service), (Geoff), Cheshire... 68
Browzers, Greater Manchester....................... 118
Buckland Books, West Sussex 243
Chalk (Old & Out of Print Books) (Christine M.),
   West Midlands 238
Clark (Nigel A.), London SE........................ 163
Cofion Books, Pembrokeshire 286
Collectors Corner, Wiltshire......................... 253
Cornucopia Books, Lincolnshire 151
Crabtree (Mrs. C.), Greater Manchester 120
Debbage (John), Norfolk............................. 189
Don Kelly Books, London W 172
Embleton (Paul), Essex 111
Fifteenth Century Bookshop (The), East Sussex. 104
Forest Books of Manchester, Cheshire............. 70
Green Meadow Books, Cornwall 74
Hanshan Tang Books, London SW 167
Heneage Art Books (Thomas), London SW 168
Hollett and Son (R.F.G.), Cumbria 79
InterCol London, London N 157
Joel Segal Books, Devon 86
Junk & Spread Eagle, London SE 164
Kingfisher Book Service, Nottinghamshire 204
Martin (Books and Pictures), (Brian P.), Surrey. 231
Milestone Publications Goss & Crested China,
   Hampshire 123
Modern First Editions, West Yorkshire........... 247
Nostalgia Unlimited, Merseyside.................... 184
Print Matters, London SE............................ 165
R. & A. Books, East Sussex 101

Read - Gorleston Books, (C.&J.), Norfolk 187
Restormel Books, Worcs 257
Spink, London WC 178
Thin Read Line, Merseyside 184
Trinders' Fine Tools, Suffolk 226
Uncle Phil's Books, West Midlands 239
Westwood Books Ltd, Cumbria.................... 80
Wiend Books, Lancashire 143

COLONIAL

Afar Books International, West Midlands........ 238
Bickford-Smith (G.) (formerly Snowden Smith
    Books), Surrey 232
Caliver Books, Essex 109
Collectables (W.H.), Suffolk 229
Eggeling Books (John), West Yorkshire 249
Empire Books, North Yorkshire 197
G. C. Books Ltd., Dumfries & Galloway........ 270
Knowles - Antiquary (Roger J.), Staffordshire... 223
Maghreb Bookshop (The), London WC......... 177
Mandalay Bookshop, London SW 168
MilitaryHistoryBooks.com, Kent.................. 137
Pennymead Books, North Yorkshire 193
Peter M Daly, Hampshire.......................... 126
Price (R.D.M. & I.M.) (Books),
    Greater Manchester 120
R. & A. Books, East Sussex 101
White (C.R.), London W........................... 175
Winghale Books, Lincolnshire 152
Woolcott Books, Dorset............................ 92

COLOUR-PLATE

Artco, Nottinghamshire............................ 204
Aurelian Books, London NW 160
Besleys Books, Suffolk 225
Bianco Library, West Sussex...................... 241
Black Cat Books, Norfolk.......................... 187
Bolton Books, Hampshire.......................... 121
Charles Bossom, Cambridgeshire.................. 65
Chas J. Sawyer, Kent 140
Clevedon Books, Somerset 217
Corvus Books, Buckinghamshire................... 61
Eastcote Bookshop (The), London O 180
Frew Limited (Robert), London SW 167
Goodyer (Nicholas), London N 157
Grayling (David A.H.), Cumbria 78
Halson Books, Cheshire 71
Harrington (Adrian), London W.................. 173
Harrington Antiquarian Bookseller (Peter),
    London SW....................................... 167
Hodgkins and Company Limited (Ian),
    Gloucestershire 116
Hodgson (Books) (Richard J.), N Yorks 196
Hollett and Son (R.F.G.), Cumbria 79
Joel Segal Books, Devon 86
Lake (David), Norfolk 190
Lymelight Books & Prints, Dorset................ 93
Madoc Books, Conwy 284
Mannwaring (M.G.), Bristol 59
Marlborough Rare Books Ltd., London W 173
Marshall Rare Books (Bruce), Gloucestershire... 113
Martin (Brian), Surrey 231
Maynard & Bradley, Leics 146
Moorhead Books, West Yorkshire................. 245
Myra Dean Illustated Books, Powys 287

Paul Hoare, Cornwall............................... 74
Peter M Daly, Hampshire.......................... 126
Preston Book Company, Lancashire 144
R. & A. Books, East Sussex 101
Roz Hulse, Conwy 284
Sephton (A.F.), London W 174
Shapero Rare Books (Bernard J.), London W... 175
Temperley (David), West Midlands.............. 238
Thorntons of Oxford Ltd., Oxfordshire........... 206
Wilson (James), Herts............................... 129

COMEDY

Addyman Books, Powys............................ 287
Annie's Books, South Yorkshire 221
baconboooks, London WC 176
Books Only, Suffolk................................ 226
Booth (Booksearch Service), (Geoff), Cheshire... 68
Cornucopia Books, Lincolnshire 151
Dales & Lakes Book Centre, Cumbria............ 79
Facet Books, Dorset................................ 91
firstpagebooks, Norfolk............................ 189
Goldman (Paul), Dorset............................ 94
Greenroom Books, West Yorkshire 247
Joel Segal Books, Devon 86
McGee (Terence J.), London O 180
Old Station Pottery & Bookshop (The), Norfolk 191
Price (R.W.), Nottinghamshire 203
R. & A. Books, East Sussex 101

COMIC BOOKS & ANNUALS

Abrahams (Mike), Staffordshire................... 223
Annie's Books, South Yorkshire 221
Bates Books, London O 180
Beck (John), East Sussex 103
Black Cat Bookshop, Leics 147
Book Palace (The), London SE 163
Bookmark (Children's Books), Wiltshire.......... 253
Books & Collectables Ltd., Cambridgeshire...... 63
Bookworms Paradise Ltd., West Sussex 242
Booth (Booksearch Service), (Geoff), Cheshire... 68
Border Bookshop, West Yorkshire 249
Broadhurst of Southport Ltd., Merseyside 185
Camilla's Bookshop, East Sussex 101
Cheshire Book Centre, Cheshire.................... 69
Cofion Books, Pembrokeshire 286
Cygnet Books, East Yorkshire..................... 107
D. & M. Books, West Yorkshire................... 249
Dales & Lakes Book Centre, Cumbria............ 79
Dawlish Books, Devon 86
Draca Books, West Yorkshire...................... 248
Elizabeth Ferguson, Grampian 272
Facet Books, Dorset................................ 91
Fifteenth Century Bookshop (The), East Sussex. 104
firstpagebooks, Norfolk............................ 189
Franks Booksellers, Greater Manchester.......... 119
Hambleton Books, N Yorks 196
Intech Books, Northumberland 201
Jean Hedger, Berks 55
Joel Segal Books, Devon 86
K Books, Cheshire.................................. 70
Key Books (Sarah), Cambridgeshire............... 64
Longden (George), Cheshire 70
M. and A.C. Thompson, Norfolk.................. 191
Murphy (C.J.), Norfolk 189
Nostalgia Unlimited, Merseyside 184

Old Celtic Bookshop (The), Devon 87
Paul Hoare, Cornwall 74
Pickering Bookshop, N Yorks 196
Print Matters, London SE 165
Pyecroft (Ruth), Gloucestershire 116
R. & A. Books, East Sussex 101
Readers World, West Midlands 238
Ripping Yarns, London N 158
Savage (Keith A.), Suffolk 228
Scrivener's Books & Bookbinding, Derbyshire... 82
Sesemann (Julia), Kent 135
The Old Children's Bookshelf, Lothian 277
Tilleys Vintage Magazine Shop, Derbyshire 82
Tilleys Vintage Magazine Shop, S Yorks 222
Till's Bookshop, Lothian 277
Towers (Mark), Lancashire 143
Wheen O'Books, Borders 267
Wright (Norman), Dorset 95
Yesterday's News, Conwy 283
Yorkshire Relics, West Yorkshire 246

COMICS

Ardis Books, Hampshire 126
Armstrong's Books & Collectables, Leics 145
Bates Books, London O 180
Beck (John), East Sussex 103
Black Cat Bookshop, Leics 147
Book Palace (The), London SE 163
Bookbarrow, Cambridgeshire 63
Bookmark (Children's Books), Wiltshire 253
Books & Collectables Ltd., Cambridgeshire 63
Bookshop (The), Norfolk 191
Bookworms Paradise Ltd., West Sussex 242
Border Bookshop, West Yorkshire 249
Capel Mawr Collectors Centre, Gwynedd 285
Cofion Books, Pembrokeshire 286
Collectables (W.H.), Suffolk 229
Cranhurst Books, London NW 160
D. & M. Books, West Yorkshire 249
Facet Books, Dorset 91
First Edition, The, Essex 109
Intech Books, Northumberland 201
Ken's Paper Collectables, Buckinghamshire 62
Longden (George), Cheshire 70
M. and A.C. Thompson, Norfolk 191
McGee (Terence J.), London O 180
Nostalgia Unlimited, Merseyside 184
Print Matters, London SE 165
Pyecroft (Ruth), Gloucestershire 116
Savage (Keith A.), Suffolk 228
The Old Children's Bookshelf, Lothian 277
Tilleys Vintage Magazine Shop, S Yorks 222
Towers (Mark), Lancashire 143
Tsbbooks, London SW 169
Wiend Books, Lancashire 143
Wright (Norman), Dorset 95
Yesterday's News, Conwy 283
Yorkshire Relics, West Yorkshire 246

COMMERCE - GENERAL

Ardis Books, Hampshire 126
Cornucopia Books, Lincolnshire 151
Leo Cadogan, London N 157
Quaritch Ltd., (Bernard), London W 174
Robert Humm & Co, Lincolnshire 152

Susanne Schulz-Falster Rare Books, London N . 158
Uncle Phil's Books, West Midlands 239

COMMERCIAL VEHICLES

Bott, (Bookdealers) Ltd., (Martin), Greater
    Manchester 118
Brad Books, Essex 110
Cox (Geoff), Devon 90
Dinnages Transport Publishing, East Sussex 103
Fifteenth Century Bookshop (The), East Sussex. 104
Joel Segal Books, Devon 86
Kenneth Ball, East Sussex 100
R. & A. Books, East Sussex 101
Randall (Tom), Somerset 218
Roadmaster Books, Kent 136

COMMUNICATION

Apocalypse, Surrey 232
Barcombe Services, Essex 108
Cornucopia Books, Lincolnshire 151
Joel Segal Books, Devon 86
R. & A. Books, East Sussex 101
Weiner (Graham), London N 158

COMMUNISM

Delectus Books, London WC 176
G. C. Books Ltd., Dumfries & Galloway 270
Hab Books, London W 172
Hylton Booksearch, Merseyside 184
J.E. Burns Booksellers, Merseyside 185
Joel Segal Books, Devon 86
Left on The Shelf, Cumbria 78
Northern Herald Books, West Yorkshire 245
Parkinsons Books, Merseyside 185
PsychoBabel Books & Journals, Oxfordshire 205
R. & A. Books, East Sussex 101
Reading Lasses, Dumfries & Galloway 270
Red Star Books, Herts 129
Roz Hulse, Conwy 284
Samovar Books, Co. Dublin 264

COMPANY HISTORY

Aardvark Books, Wiltshire 254
Bell (Peter), Lothian 275
Bott, (Bookdealers) Ltd., (Martin), Greater
    Manchester 118
Byrom Textile Bookroom (Richard), Lancashire 142
Cheshire Book Centre, Cheshire 69
Clevedon Books, Somerset 217
Cornucopia Books, Lincolnshire 151
Crosby Nethercott Books, London O 180
Debbage (John), Norfolk 189
Delph Books, Greater Manchester 120
Dolphin Books, Suffolk 225
Good for Books, Lincolnshire 149
Handsworth Books, Essex 112
Hindsight Books, Herts 131
Island Books, Devon 85
Joel Segal Books, Devon 86
Kellow Books, Oxfordshire 206
R. & A. Books, East Sussex 101
Randall (Tom), Somerset 218
Roadmaster Books, Kent 136
Robert Humm & Co, Lincolnshire 152
Rochdale Book Company, Greater Manchester . 120

Roland Books, Kent 138
Saintfield Antiques & Fine Books, Co. Down ... 261
Salway Books, Essex 112
Spurrier (Nick), Kent 137
Uncle Phil's Books, West Midlands 239
Whistler's Books, London SW 169

COMPUTING
Adrem Books, Herts 130
Annie's Books, S Yorks 221
Apocalypse, Surrey 232
Ardis Books, Hampshire 126
Barcombe Services, Essex 108
Beware of the Leopard, Bristol 58
Cornucopia Books, Lincolnshire 151
Crabtree (Mrs. C.), Greater Manchester 120
Game Advice, Oxfordshire 208
Jade Mountain Bookshop, Hampshire 125
Old Celtic Bookshop (The), Devon 87
Plurabelle Books, Cambridgeshire................. 65
Quaritch Ltd., (Bernard), London W.............. 174
R. & A. Books, East Sussex 101
Roland Books, Kent 138
Roscrea Bookshop & Newsagents,
    Co. Tipperary 266
Stern Antiquarian Bookseller (Jeffrey), N Yorks 198
Stroh (M.A.), London E 154
Tarka Books, Devon 84
Treasure Island (The), Greater Manchester....... 119
Westons, Herts 132
Woodland Books, Devon............................ 84

CONCHOLOGY
(SEE ALSO MALACOLOGY)
Acanthophyllum Books, Wirral 184
Earth Science Books, Wiltshire 252
Joel Segal Books, Devon 86
Parkinsons Books, Merseyside...................... 185
Peter M Daly, Hampshire............................ 126
R. & A. Books, East Sussex 101
Sub Aqua Prints and Books, Hampshire 123

CONSERVATION
Acanthophyllum Books, Wirral 184
Arden, Bookseller (C.), Powys...................... 287
Aurelian Books, London NW 160
Calluna Books, Dorset............................... 95
Coch-y-Bonddu Books, Powys 290
Colonsay Bookshop, Isle of Colonsay............. 275
Demar Books (Grant), Kent......................... 140
Earth Science Books, Wiltshire 252
Heneage Art Books (Thomas), London SW 168
Joel Segal Books, Devon 86
Martin (Books and Pictures), (Brian P.), Surrey . 231
Newgate Books and Translations,
    Northumberland 201
Peter M Daly, Hampshire............................ 126
Phillip Robbins of Warwick, Warwickshire 237
R. & A. Books, East Sussex 101
Roadmaster Books, Kent............................. 136
Trinders' Fine Tools, Suffolk 226

CONSPIRACY
Apocalypse, Surrey 232
SETI Books, West Midlands........................ 239

COOKERY - PROFESSIONAL
Addyman Books, Powys.............................. 287
baconboooks, London WC 176
Bookroom (The), Surrey............................. 233
Books & Bygones, Berks 57
Books at Star Dot Star, West Midlands 240
Bookworms Paradise Ltd., West Sussex 242
Cooking = The Books, Gloucestershire 115
Cover to Cover, Merseyside......................... 185
Dolphin Books, Suffolk.............................. 225
Edwards, Fiona, Nottinghamshire 203
Gardener & Cook, London SW..................... 167
Island Books, Devon................................. 85
Joel Segal Books, Devon 86
Marcet Books, London SE........................... 164
Oopalba Books, Cheshire............................ 71
R & B Graham Trading, Cornwall 73
Uncle Phil's Books, West Midlands 239
Wheen O'Books, Borders............................ 267

COOKERY/GASTRONOMY
A. & R. Booksearch, Cornwall..................... 73
Abacus Gallery, Staffordshire....................... 224
Abrahams (Mike), Staffordshire.................... 223
Addyman Books, Powys.............................. 287
Al Saqi Books, London W 171
Alexander's Books, Warwickshire.................. 237
Apocalypse, Surrey 232
Armstrong's Books & Collectables, Leics 145
Autumn Leaves, Lincolnshire....................... 150
Axe Rare & Out of Print Books (Richard),
    N Yorks 193
Backfold Books, Herefordshire 127
baconboooks, London WC 176
Beckham Books Ltd., Suffolk 229
Biff Books and Records, S Yorks.................. 221
Black Cat Books, Norfolk........................... 187
Bookbox, Gloucestershire 115
Books, Oxfordshire.................................. 205
Books & Bygones, Berks 57
Books & Collectables Ltd., Cambridgeshire...... 63
Books at Star Dot Star, West Midlands 240
Books for Content, Herefordshire................... 127
Books Only, Suffolk................................. 226
Bosorne Books, Cornwall 75
Brown-Studies, Strathclyde.......................... 277
Burmester (James), Bristol.......................... 58
Capel Mawr Collectors Centre, Gwynedd 285
Carningli Centre, Pembrokeshire................... 286
Chandos Books, Devon.............................. 85
Chantrey Books, S Yorks 222
Charlie Byrne's Bookshop, Co. Galway........... 265
Clarke (Janet), Somerset............................. 215
Cobnar Books, Kent 141
Cooking = The Books, Gloucestershire 115
Cooks Books, East Sussex 99
Cotswold Internet Books, Gloucestershire 113
Country Books, Derbyshire.......................... 82
Cover to Cover, Merseyside......................... 185
Crabtree (Mrs. C.), Greater Manchester 120
Dales & Lakes Book Centre, Cumbria............. 79
D'Arcy Books, Wiltshire............................. 252
Deeside Books, Grampian............................ 272
Delectus Books, London WC........................ 176
Discovery Bookshop, Carmarthenshire............ 281

Dolphin Books, Suffolk.............................. 225
Dusty Books, Powys 290
Edwards, Fiona, Nottinghamshire 203
Elmfield Books, West Midlands.................... 238
Esoteric Dreams Bookshop, Cumbria 77
Fifteenth Century Bookshop (The), East Sussex. 104
Ford Books (David), Herts 130
Fox Books (J. & J.), Kent........................... 139
Gardener & Cook, London SW.................... 167
Garfi Books, Powys 291
Garwood & Voigt, Kent............................. 139
Good for Books, Lincolnshire 149
Grahame Thornton, Bookseller, Dorset........... 93
Gresham Books, Somerset 217
Hall's Bookshop, Kent.............................. 140
Harrington (Adrian), London W................... 173
Hay Cinema Bookshop Ltd., Powys.............. 288
HCB Wholesale, Powys............................. 288
Internet Bookshop UK Ltd., Gloucestershire ... 113
Invicta Bookshop, Berks............................ 56
Island Books, Devon................................ 85
Jade Mountain Bookshop, Hampshire 125
Jenny Hurst, Kent 138
Joel Segal Books, Devon 86
Lamb's Tales Books, Devon 87
Lucas (Richard), London NW...................... 161
Maggs Brothers Limited, London W.............. 173
Mannwaring (M.G.), Bristol 59
Maynard & Bradley, Leics 146
McNaughtan's Bookshop, Lothian 276
Mellon's Books, East Sussex....................... 101
Modlock (Lilian), Dorset............................ 93
Moorhead Books, West Yorkshire................. 245
Much Ado Books, East Sussex..................... 99
Oopalba Books, Cheshire........................... 71
Parrott Books, Oxfordshire 209
Peter M Daly, Hampshire........................... 126
Price (John), London N 158
Quaritch Ltd., (Bernard), London W.............. 174
Queen Victoria PH, Torfaen 292
R & B Graham Trading, Cornwall 73
R. & A. Books, East Sussex 101
Rainford (Sheila), Herts 129
River Reads Bookshop, Devon...................... 90
Roberts Fine Books (Julian), Lincolnshire........ 151
Roland Books, Kent 138
Sax Books, Suffolk 228
Scrivener's Books & Bookbinding, Derbyshire... 82
Seeber (Liz), East Sussex 102
Sleepy Elephant Books & Artefacts, Cumbria ... 80
Slightly Foxed on Gloucester Road, London SW 167
Smith (Clive), Essex 109
Stroma Books, Borders 267
Susanne Schulz-Falster Rare Books, London N. 158
Talisman Books, Cheshire........................... 70
Tant Yn Ellen Books, Powys 290
Tarka Books, Devon 84
Tilston (Stephen E.), London SE................... 165
Trinity Rare Books, Co. Leitrim 266
Uncle Phil's Books, West Midlands 239
Wadard Books, Kent 137
Wheen O'Books, Borders............................ 267
Whitchurch Books Ltd., Cardiff.................... 281
Whittle, Bookseller (Avril), Cumbria 80
Wychwood Books, Gloucestershire 116

Yates Antiquarian Books (Tony), Leics........... 146

CORNISH

Aitchison (Lesley), Bristol 58
Annie's Books, S Yorks 221
Apocalypse, Surrey 232
Bosorne Books, Cornwall 75

CORNISH HISTORY

Aitchison (Lesley), Bristol 58
Baker - Books for the Collector (Colin), Devon. 89
Bosorne Books, Cornwall 75
Dartmoor Book Gallery, Devon 87
Ian Marr Rare Books, Cornwall 73

COSMOLOGY

Apocalypse, Surrey 232
Inner Bookshop (The), Oxfordshire................ 208
Joel Segal Books, Devon 86
Moorside Books, Lancashire........................ 143
Stroh (M.A.), London E 154
Westons, Herts 132

COUNSELLING

Apocalypse, Surrey 232
Fifteenth Century Bookshop (The), East Sussex. 104
Inner Bookshop (The), Oxfordshire................ 208
Joel Segal Books, Devon 86
Oast Books, Kent 136
Outcast Books, Herefordshire...................... 127
Reading Lasses, Dumfries & Galloway 270

COUNTERCULTURE

Atlas, London N..................................... 156
Black Cat Bookshop, Leics 147
Capel Mawr Collectors Centre, Gwynedd 285
Church Street Books, Norfolk...................... 186
Invisible Books, East Sussex 100
McGee (Terence J.), London O 180
Michael Rogers, Wiltshire 251
Poetry Bookshop (The), Powys..................... 289
Print Matters, London SE........................... 165
Sclanders (Beatbooks), (Andrew), London EC... 155

COUNTIES IN ENGLAND

Aitchison (Lesley), Bristol 58
Allsop (Duncan M.), Warwickshire................ 237
Ambra Books, Bristol................................ 58
Antique Map and Bookshop (The), Dorset 94
baconboooks, London WC 176
Clarke Books (David), Somerset 218
Coach House Books, Worcs 256
Cofion Books, Pembrokeshire 286
Cox Old & Rare Books (Claude), Suffolk 227
Dandy Lion Editions, Surrey 233
Debbage (John), Norfolk............................ 189
Grahame Thornton, Bookseller, Dorset........... 93
Jane & John Kinnaird, Cumbria 78
Kemp Bookseller, Michael S, G Manchester..... 118
Knowles - Antiquary (Roger J.), Staffordshire... 223
Lion Books, Worcs 255
Martin (Books and Pictures), (Brian P.), Surrey. 231
Martin (Brian), Surrey 231
Old Station Pottery & Bookshop (The), Norfolk 191
Park Gallery & Bookshop (The), Northants 200

COUNTRIES
- GENERAL
Antique Prints of the World, London N.......... 156
Aurora Books Ltd, Lothian........................ 275
Barn Books, Buckinghamshire...................... 61
Blackwell's Rare Books, Oxfordshire.............. 208
Books Only, Suffolk............................... 226
Brad Books, Essex................................. 110
Cofion Books, Pembrokeshire...................... 286
Cotswold Internet Books, Gloucestershire........ 113
Dolphin Books, Suffolk............................ 225
Fifteenth Century Bookshop (The), East Sussex. 104
Ford Books (David), Herts 130
Freeman's Corner Shop, Norfolk 189
Glasheen-Books, Surrey 231
Good for Books, Lincolnshire...................... 149
Grahame Thornton, Bookseller, Dorset.......... 93
Harrington Antiquarian Bookseller (Peter),
  London SW....................................... 167
J & J Burgess Booksellers, Cambridgeshire....... 64
Jack and Molly's Trading Co....................... 90
Jade Mountain Bookshop, Hampshire 125
Joel Segal Books, Devon 86
O'Flynn Books, N Yorks............................ 197
Peter M Daly, Hampshire.......................... 126
R. & A. Books, East Sussex 101
Wheen O'Books, Borders........................... 267
Winchester Bookshop (The), Hampshire.......... 126

- AFGHANISTAN
Antique Prints of the World, London N.......... 156
Bates & Hindmarch, West Yorkshire.............. 248
Ctesiphon Books, Greater Manchester 120
David Warnes Books, Herefordshire 128
Eggeling Books (John), West Yorkshire 249
Joppa Books Ltd., Surrey 230
Peter M Daly, Hampshire.......................... 126
R. & A. Books, East Sussex 101
Traveller's Bookshelf (The), Somerset 218
Verandah Books, Dorset 95

- AFRICA
Acanthophyllum Books, Wirral 184
Afar Books International, West Midlands........ 238
Allsworth Rare Books Ltd., London SW......... 166
Apocalypse, Surrey 232
Ayre (Peter J.), Somerset 219
Barn Books, Buckinghamshire...................... 61
Bickford-Smith (G.) (formerly Snowden Smith
  Books), Surrey 232
Black Voices, Merseyside 184
Bonham (J. & S.L.), London W 171
Bookbarrow, Cambridgeshire...................... 63
Bracton Books, Cambridgeshire.................... 63
Bunyan Books, Bedfordshire....................... 53
Chalmers Hallam (E.), Hampshire................. 125
Chapter Two, London SE.......................... 163
Chas J. Sawyer, Kent 140
Coch-y-Bonddu Books, Powys 290
Deeside Books, Grampian.......................... 272
Dolphin Books, Suffolk............................ 225
Empire Books, N Yorks............................ 197
Folios Limited, London SW 167
G. C. Books Ltd., Dumfries & Galloway......... 270
Grayling (David A.H.), Cumbria 78

Halewood & Sons, Lancashire...................... 144
Hall, (Anthony C.) Antiquarian Bookseller,
  London O.. 183
Harrington Antiquarian Bookseller (Peter),
  London SW....................................... 167
Heritage Books, Isle of Wight 133
Kenya Books, East Sussex 100
Knowles - Antiquary (Roger J.), Staffordshire... 223
Lawson & Company (E.M.), Oxfordshire 206
Marble Hill Books, Outer London................. 182
Michael Graves-Johnston, London SW 168
Oak Tree Press, Oxfordshire 207
Oopalba Books, Cheshire........................... 71
Penny Farthing, The, Lothian 277
Peter M Daly, Hampshire.......................... 126
Popeley (Frank T.), Cambridgeshire............... 67
Post–Horn Books, N Yorks 192
Probsthain (Arthur), London WC 178
Quaritch Ltd., (Bernard), London W............. 174
R. & A. Books, East Sussex 101
Roland Books, Kent 138
Wheen O'Books, Borders........................... 267
Wiend Books, Lancashire 143
Woolcott Books, Dorset............................ 92
Yesterday's Books, Dorset 92

- ALASKA
Cavendish Rare Books, London N 156
David Warnes Books, Herefordshire 128
Glacier Books, Tayside 280
R. & A. Books, East Sussex 101

- ALBANIA
Antique Prints of the World, London N.......... 156
de Visser Books, Cambridgeshire.................. 63
Joppa Books Ltd., Surrey 230
Peter M Daly, Hampshire.......................... 126
Traveller's Bookshelf (The), Somerset 218

- ALGERIA
Apocalypse, Surrey 232
Ctesiphon Books, Greater Manchester 120
Joppa Books Ltd., Surrey 230

- AMERICAS, THE
Americanabooksuk, Cumbria....................... 76
Bracton Books, Cambridgeshire.................... 63
Glacier Books, Tayside 280
Halewood & Sons, Lancashire...................... 144
Hodgson (Judith), London W 173
Knowles - Antiquary (Roger J.), Staffordshire... 223
Lawson & Company (E.M.), Oxfordshire 206
Quaritch Ltd., (Bernard), London W............. 174
R. & A. Books, East Sussex 101

- ANDORRA
Books on Spain, London O......................... 182
Orssich (Paul), London SW 169
Peter M Daly, Hampshire.......................... 126

- ANTARCTIC, THE
Bluntisham Books, Cambridgeshire................ 63
Bonham (J. & S.L.), London W 171
Cavendish Rare Books, London N 156
Chalmers Hallam (E.), Hampshire................. 125

Craobh Rua Books, Co. Armagh.................. 260
Fifteenth Century Bookshop (The), East Sussex. 104
Glacier Books, Tayside 280
Harrington Antiquarian Bookseller (Peter),
    London SW... 167
Hill (Peter), Hampshire 122
Libris (Weston) Books, Somerset 216
Marble Hill Books, Outer London................. 182
McEwan Fine Books, Grampian.................... 272
Peter M Daly, Hampshire........................... 126
Prospect House Books, Co. Down................. 261
R. & A. Books, East Sussex 101

- ARABIA
Allsworth Rare Books Ltd., London SW......... 166
Apocalypse, Surrey 232
Bonham (J. & S.L.), London W 171
Clarke Books (David), Somerset 218
Ctesiphon Books, Greater Manchester 120
David Warnes Books, Herefordshire 128
Delectus Books, London WC....................... 176
Eastern Traveller (The), Somerset................. 219
Folios Limited, London SW 167
Joppa Books Ltd., Surrey 230
P. and P. Books, Worcs 256
Peter M Daly, Hampshire........................... 126
Quest Books, East Yorkshire 107
Traveller's Bookshelf (The), Somerset 218

- ARABIAN PENINSULA
Acanthophyllum Books, Wirral 184
Bickford-Smith (G.) (formerly Snowden Smith
    Books), Surrey 232
Clarke Books (David), Somerset 218
Ctesiphon Books, Greater Manchester 120
Joppa Books Ltd., Surrey 230
Moorside Books, Lancashire........................ 143
P. and P. Books, Worcs 256
Peter M Daly, Hampshire........................... 126
Watkins (R.G.), Somerset 215

- ARCTIC, THE
Bluntisham Books, Cambridgeshire................ 63
Bonham (J. & S.L.), London W 171
Cavendish Rare Books, London N 156
Chalmers Hallam (E.), Hampshire................. 125
Craobh Rua Books, Co. Armagh.................. 260
Deeside Books, Grampian........................... 272
Fifteenth Century Bookshop (The), East Sussex. 104
Glacier Books, Tayside 280
Harrington Antiquarian Bookseller (Peter),
    London SW... 167
Hill (Peter), Hampshire 122
J & J Burgess Booksellers, Cambridgeshire....... 64
McEwan Fine Books, Grampian.................... 272
Peter M Daly, Hampshire........................... 126
Prospect House Books, Co. Down................. 261
R. & A. Books, East Sussex 101
Roz Hulse, Conwy 284

- ARGENTINA
Hodgson (Judith), London W 173
R. & A. Books, East Sussex 101

- ARMENIA
Antique Prints of the World, London N.......... 156
David Warnes Books, Herefordshire 128
Joppa Books Ltd., Surrey 230
Traveller's Bookshelf (The), Somerset 218

- ASCENSION ISLANDS
MK Book Services, Cambridgeshire............... 66

- ASIA
Acanthophyllum Books, Wirral 184
Allsworth Rare Books Ltd., London SW......... 166
Bates & Hindmarch, West Yorkshire.............. 248
Bickford-Smith (G.) (formerly Snowden Smith
    Books), Surrey 232
Bonham (J. & S.L.), London W 171
Bracton Books, Cambridgeshire.................... 63
Canon Gate Books, West Sussex................... 243
Cavendish Rare Books, London N 156
Chapter Two, London SE............................ 163
Ctesiphon Books, Greater Manchester 120
David Warnes Books, Herefordshire 128
Eastern Traveller (The), Somerset................. 219
Empire Books, N Yorks.............................. 197
Glacier Books, Tayside 280
Grayling (David A.H.), Cumbria 78
Hall, (Anthony C.) Antiquarian Bookseller,
    London O... 183
Joppa Books Ltd., Surrey 230
Mandalay Bookshop, London SW 168
Penny Farthing, The, Lothian 277
Peter M Daly, Hampshire........................... 126
Post–Horn Books, N Yorks 192
Rayner (Hugh Ashley), Somerset 215
Traveller's Bookshelf (The), Somerset 218

- ASIA MINOR
Ctesiphon Books, Greater Manchester 120
Joppa Books Ltd., Surrey 230
Peter M Daly, Hampshire........................... 126
Quest Books, East Yorkshire 107
Seydi Rare Books (Sevin), London NW 161
Traveller's Bookshelf (The), Somerset 218

- ATLANTIC OCEAN
Empire Books, N Yorks.............................. 197

- AUSTRALASIA
Antique Prints of the World, London N.......... 156
Bonham (J. & S.L.), London W 171
Cavendish Rare Books, London N 156
Empire Books, N Yorks.............................. 197
Knowles - Antiquary (Roger J.), Staffordshire... 223
Lawson & Company (E.M.), Oxfordshire 206
Michael Graves-Johnston, London SW 168
Preston Book Company, Lancashire 144
R. & A. Books, East Sussex 101
Roz Hulse, Conwy 284

- AUSTRALIA
Bonham (J. & S.L.), London W 171
Empire Books, N Yorks.............................. 197
Halewood & Sons, Lancashire...................... 144
Moore (Peter), Cambridgeshire..................... 64
R. & A. Books, East Sussex 101

Roz Hulse, Conwy 284

- AUSTRIA
de Visser Books, Cambridgeshire................... 63
R. & A. Books, East Sussex 101

- AZORES, THE
Empire Books, N Yorks............................ 197
Hodgson (Judith), London W 173

- BAHAMAS, THE
Pennymead Books, N Yorks........................ 193

- BALKANS, THE
Bickford-Smith (G.) (formerly Snowden Smith
   Books), Surrey 232
David Warnes Books, Herefordshire 128
de Visser Books, Cambridgeshire................... 63
Joppa Books Ltd., Surrey 230
Marijana Dworski Books, Powys 288
Peter M Daly, Hampshire.......................... 126
Quest Books, East Yorkshire 107
Thorntons of Oxford Ltd., Oxfordshire........... 206
Traveller's Bookshelf (The), Somerset 218
White Eagle Books, London NW.................. 162

- BALTIC STATES
Baldwin (Jack), Strathclyde 278
de Visser Books, Cambridgeshire................... 63
MK Book Services, Cambridgeshire............... 66
Peter M Daly, Hampshire.......................... 126
Traveller's Bookshelf (The), Somerset 218

- BALUCHISTAN
Joppa Books Ltd., Surrey 230

- BELGIUM
R. & A. Books, East Sussex 101

- BERMUDA
Leapman Ltd. (G. & R.), Herts 130
Lymelight Books & Prints, Dorset................. 93
Pennymead Books, N Yorks........................ 193

- BHUTAN
Glacier Books, Tayside 280
Rayner (Hugh Ashley), Somerset 215

- BOLIVIA
Hodgson (Judith), London W 173

- BRAZIL
Hodgson (Judith), London W 173
R. & A. Books, East Sussex 101

- BRITISH NORTH BORNEO
Eastgate Bookshop, East Yorkshire 106
Empire Books, N Yorks............................ 197
Park (Mike), London O 182

- BULGARIA
de Visser Books, Cambridgeshire................... 63
Joppa Books Ltd., Surrey 230
R. & A. Books, East Sussex 101

- BURMA
Mandalay Bookshop, London SW 168
MK Book Services, Cambridgeshire............... 66
Peter M Daly, Hampshire.......................... 126
Rayner (Hugh Ashley), Somerset 215
Verandah Books, Dorset 95

- CANADA
Apocalypse, Surrey 232
Chalmers Hallam (E.), Hampshire................. 125
Empire Books, N Yorks............................ 197
Glacier Books, Tayside 280
R. & A. Books, East Sussex 101

- CARIBBEAN, THE
Afar Books International, West Midlands........ 238
Allsworth Rare Books Ltd., London SW......... 166
Black Voices, Merseyside 184
Burton–Garbett (A.), London O 182
Craobh Rua Books, Co. Armagh.................. 260
Empire Books, N Yorks............................ 197
Knowles - Antiquary (Roger J.), Staffordshire... 223
Leapman Ltd. (G. & R.), Herts 130
Norton Books, N Yorks............................ 192
Pennymead Books, N Yorks........................ 193
Peter M Daly, Hampshire.......................... 126

- CENTRAL AMERICA
Books on Spain, London O......................... 182
Burton–Garbett (A.), London O 182
Chalmers Hallam (E.), Hampshire................. 125
Glacier Books, Tayside 280
Hylton Booksearch, Merseyside 184
Orssich (Paul), London SW........................ 169

- CENTRAL ASIA
Al Saqi Books, London W.......................... 171
Allsworth Rare Books Ltd., London SW......... 166
Bates & Hindmarch, West Yorkshire............. 248
Beaumont Travel Books, London SE 163
Bickford-Smith (G.) (formerly Snowden Smith
   Books), Surrey 232
Bonham (J. & S.L.), London W 171
Cavendish Rare Books, London N 156
Chalmers Hallam (E.), Hampshire................. 125
David Warnes Books, Herefordshire 128
Glacier Books, Tayside 280
Grayling (David A.H.), Cumbria 78
Hanshan Tang Books, London SW 167
Hunter and Krageloh, Derbyshire 83
Hylton Booksearch, Merseyside 184
Joppa Books Ltd., Surrey 230
Peter M Daly, Hampshire.......................... 126
Rayner (Hugh Ashley), Somerset 215
Riddell (Peter), East Yorkshire 106
Traveller's Bookshelf (The), Somerset 218
White Eagle Books, London NW.................. 162

- CENTRAL EAST EUROPE
de Visser Books, Cambridgeshire................... 63
Glacier Books, Tayside 280
Hylton Booksearch, Merseyside 184
Modern First Editions, West Yorkshire........... 247
Peter M Daly, Hampshire.......................... 126

- CHANNEL ISLANDS, THE
Books and Things, Channel Islands 258
Cornucopia Books, Lincolnshire 151
Paul Hoare, Cornwall 74
Portus Books, Hampshire 122
R. & A. Books, East Sussex 101

- CHINA
Allsworth Rare Books Ltd., London SW 166
Bickford-Smith (G.) (formerly Snowden Smith
   Books), Surrey 232
Bonham (J. & S.L.), London W 171
Bow Windows Book Shop, East Sussex 103
Cavendish Rare Books, London N 156
Ctesiphon Books, Greater Manchester 120
Empire Books, N Yorks............................. 197
Fine Books Oriental, London W14 172
Glacier Books, Tayside 280
Hanshan Tang Books, London SW 167
Hobgoblin Books, Hampshire 125
Mandalay Bookshop, London SW 168
Peter M Daly, Hampshire........................... 126
R. & A. Books, East Sussex 101
Transformer, Dumfries & Galloway 270
Traveller's Bookshelf (The), Somerset 218

- CUBA
Books on Spain, London O.......................... 182
Hodgson (Judith), London W 173
Pennymead Books, N Yorks........................ 193

- CYPRUS
Antique Prints of the World, London N.......... 156
Askew Books (Vernon), Wiltshire.................. 251
Crouch Rare Books, Surrey......................... 232
Hellenic Bookservices, London NW 161
Joppa Books Ltd., Surrey 230
Kalligraphia (formerly Charmouth
   Bounty Books), Isle of Wight.................... 133
Nicolas - Antiquarian Bookseller, London N.... 157
Quest Books, East Yorkshire 107
R. & A. Books, East Sussex 101
White Eagle Books, London NW.................. 162

- CZECH REPUBLIC
de Visser Books, Cambridgeshire.................. 63
R. & A. Books, East Sussex 101

- DOMINICAN REPUBLIC
Pennymead Books, N Yorks........................ 193

- EAST AFRICA
Chalmers Hallam (E.), Hampshire................. 125
Coch-y-Bonddu Books, Powys 290
Kenya Books, East Sussex 100
Peter M Daly, Hampshire........................... 126
Preston Book Company, Lancashire 144
Samovar Books, Co. Dublin........................ 264
White (C.R.), London W............................ 175
Yesterday's Books, Dorset 92

- EAST EUROPE
Apocalypse, Surrey 232
de Visser Books, Cambridgeshire.................. 63
Dolphin Books, Suffolk.............................. 225

Hab Books, London W............................... 172
Hall, (Anthony C.) Antiquarian Bookseller,
   London O.. 183
Hylton Booksearch, Merseyside 184
Orbis Books (London) Ltd., London W 173
Peter M Daly, Hampshire........................... 126
R. & A. Books, East Sussex 101

- EAST MEDITERRANEAN, THE
Joppa Books Ltd., Surrey 230
Paul Hoare, Cornwall................................ 74
Quest Books, East Yorkshire 107
Seydi Rare Books (Sevin), London NW 161

- EAST TIMOR
Hylton Booksearch, Merseyside 184

- EGYPT
Afar Books International, West Midlands........ 238
Apocalypse, Surrey 232
Atlantis Bookshop, London WC 176
Chalmers Hallam (E.), Hampshire................. 125
Ctesiphon Books, Greater Manchester 120
Eastern Traveller (The), Somerset.................. 219
Joppa Books Ltd., Surrey 230
Oasis Booksearch, Cambridgeshire................. 67
Occultique, Northants................................ 199
P. and P. Books, Worcs 256
Quest Books, East Yorkshire 107
R. & A. Books, East Sussex 101
Samovar Books, Co. Dublin........................ 264
Trotter Books (John), London N 158
Yesterday's Books, Dorset 92

- ENGLAND
Anthony Vickers Books, N Yorks 195
Barn Books, Shropshire.............................. 214
Bell (Peter), Lothian................................. 275
Bonython Bookshop, Cornwall..................... 75
Broadwater Books, Hampshire 125
Chapman (Neville), Lancashire..................... 144
Cofion Books, Pembrokeshire 286
Cornell Books, Gloucestershire..................... 117
Cornucopia Books, Lincolnshire 151
Cox (Geoff), Devon 90
Debbage (John), Norfolk............................ 189
Grove Bookshop (The), N Yorks 195
Hava Books, London SE............................. 164
Island Books, Devon 85
Martin (Brian), Surrey 231
McCrone (Audrey), Isle of Arran 274
Missing Books, Essex 109
Oakwood Books, Gloucestershire 115
Park Gallery & Bookshop (The), Northants 200
Paul Hoare, Cornwall................................ 74
Peter M Daly, Hampshire........................... 126
R. & A. Books, East Sussex 101
Read - Gorleston Books, (C.&J.), Norfolk 187
Rickaro Books, West Yorkshire.................... 246
Roberts Books, Strathclyde 279
Samovar Books, Co. Dublin........................ 264
SETI Books, West Midlands........................ 239
Wadard Books, Kent 137
Wheen O'Books, Borders............................ 267

- ESTONIA
de Visser Books, Cambridgeshire.................. 63

- ETHIOPIA
Apocalypse, Surrey 232
Chalmers Hallam (E.), Hampshire................. 125
Craobh Rua Books, Co. Armagh.................. 260
Ctesiphon Books, Greater Manchester 120
Grayling (David A.H.), Cumbria 78
Joppa Books Ltd., Surrey 230
Traveller's Bookshelf (The), Somerset 218
Yesterday's Books, Dorset 92

- EUROPE
Antique Prints of the World, London N.......... 156
Glacier Books, Tayside 280
owenbooks65, Conwy................................ 283
Paul Hoare, Cornwall................................ 74
Penny Farthing, The, Lothian 277
Peter M Daly, Hampshire........................... 126
Prospect House Books, Co. Down................. 261
PsychoBabel Books & Journals, Oxfordshire..... 205
R. & A. Books, East Sussex 101
York (Graham), Devon............................... 86

- FALKLANDS, THE
Bluntisham Books, Cambridgeshire................ 63
Craobh Rua Books, Co. Armagh.................. 260
Empire Books, N Yorks.............................. 197
Miles Apart, Suffolk.................................. 228
R. & A. Books, East Sussex 101

- FAR EAST, THE
Beaumont Travel Books, London SE 163
Bickford-Smith (G.) (formerly Snowden Smith
  Books), Surrey 232
Cavendish Rare Books, London N 156
Chalmers Hallam (E.), Hampshire................. 125
Kingswood Books, Dorset 94
Marble Hill Books, Outer London................. 182
Oxley (Laurence), Hampshire...................... 121
Peter M Daly, Hampshire........................... 126
Quaritch Ltd., (Bernard), London W............. 174
R. & A. Books, East Sussex 101
Robert G Sawers Ltd, London NW............... 161
Traveller's Bookshelf (The), Somerset 218

- FIJI
Bonham (J. & S.L.), London W 171
Empire Books, N Yorks.............................. 197
Michael Graves-Johnston, London SW 168

- FINLAND
R. & A. Books, East Sussex 101

- FORMOSA
Ctesiphon Books, Greater Manchester 120

- FRANCE
Glacier Books, Tayside 280
Hava Books, London SE............................. 164
Kenya Books, East Sussex 100
Owen (J.V.), Conwy.................................. 284
owenbooks65, Conwy................................ 283
R. & A. Books, East Sussex 101

Roscrea Bookshop & Newsagents,
  Co. Tipperary 266
Seydi Rare Books (Sevin), London NW 161
Taylor & Son (Peter), Herts........................ 132

- GERMANY
de Visser Books, Cambridgeshire.................. 63
Helion & Company, West Midlands 239
R. & A. Books, East Sussex 101
Trotter Books (John), London N 158

- GIBRALTAR
Annie's Books, S Yorks 221
Books on Spain, London O......................... 182
Chapter Two, London SE............................ 163
Orssich (Paul), London SW 169
R. & A. Books, East Sussex 101

- GREAT BRITAIN
Beckham Books Ltd., Suffolk 229
Booth (Booksearch Service), (Geoff), Cheshire... 68
Broadwater Books, Hampshire 125
Catalyst Booksearch Services, Devon............. 87
Clarke Books (David), Somerset 218
Cofion Books, Pembrokeshire 286
Copperplate Antique Maps and Prints, Herts.... 132
Dolphin Books, Suffolk.............................. 225
G. C. Books Ltd., Dumfries & Galloway......... 270
Glacier Books, Tayside 280
J and J Books, Lincolnshire........................ 149
Jackdaw Books, Norfolk 188
Joel Segal Books, Devon 86
Kalligraphia (formerly Charmouth
  Bounty Books), Isle of Wight.................... 133
Karen Millward, Co. Cork.......................... 263
Lymelight Books & Prints, Dorset................ 93
Madoc Books, Conwy 284
Martin (Books and Pictures), (Brian P.),
  Surrey.. 231
Oopalba Books, Cheshire........................... 71
Orb's Bookshop, Grampian......................... 273
Parkinsons Books, Merseyside...................... 185
Peter M Daly, Hampshire........................... 126
PsychoBabel Books & Journals, Oxfordshire..... 205
R. & A. Books, East Sussex 101
Richmond Books, N Yorks.......................... 194
Samovar Books, Co. Dublin........................ 264
Shakeshaft (Dr. B.), Cheshire...................... 71
Whitchurch Books Ltd., Cardiff.................... 281

- GREAT LAKES, THE
R. & A. Books, East Sussex 101

- GREECE
Antique Prints of the World, London N.......... 156
Ballantyne–Way (Roger), Suffolk 228
Crouch Rare Books, Surrey......................... 232
Hellenic Bookservices, London NW 161
Kalligraphia (formerly Charmouth
  Bounty Books), Isle of Wight.................... 133
Morris Secondhand & Antiquarian Books
  (Chris), Oxfordshire 208
Nicolas - Antiquarian Bookseller, London N 157
Old Station Pottery & Bookshop (The), Norfolk 191
Quest Books, East Yorkshire 107

R. & A. Books, East Sussex 101
Seydi Rare Books (Sevin), London NW 161
Traveller's Bookshelf (The), Somerset 218

- GREENLAND
Bluntisham Books, Cambridgeshire................ 63
Glacier Books, Tayside 280
R. & A. Books, East Sussex 101

- GUATEMALA
Orssich (Paul), London SW 169
R. & A. Books, East Sussex 101

- HAITI
Pennymead Books, N Yorks....................... 193

- HAWAII
R. & A. Books, East Sussex 101

- HIMALAYAS, THE
Chalmers Hallam (E.), Hampshire................ 125
David Warnes Books, Herefordshire 128
Glacier Books, Tayside 280
Grayling (David A.H.), Cumbria 78
Hanshan Tang Books, London SW 167
Hunter and Krageloh, Derbyshire 83
Kabristan Archives, Shropshire.................... 214
Peter M Daly, Hampshire.......................... 126
R. & A. Books, East Sussex 101
Rayner (Hugh Ashley), Somerset 215
Traveller's Bookshelf (The), Somerset 218
Verandah Books, Dorset 95
White Eagle Books, London NW.................. 162

- HOLY LAND, THE
baconbooks, London WC 176
Beckham Books Ltd., Suffolk 229
Ctesiphon Books, Greater Manchester 120
Folios Limited, London SW 167
P. and P. Books, Worcs 256
R. & A. Books, East Sussex 101
Samovar Books, Co. Dublin 264
Trotter Books (John), London N 158

- HONG KONG
Allsworth Rare Books Ltd., London SW......... 166
Antique Prints of the World, London N.......... 156
Ctesiphon Books, Greater Manchester 120
R. & A. Books, East Sussex 101

- HUNGARY
de Visser Books, Cambridgeshire.................. 63
Parrott (Jeremy), London E........................ 154
R. & A. Books, East Sussex 101

- ICELAND
Bluntisham Books, Cambridgeshire................ 63
Fine Books Oriental, London W14 172
Glacier Books, Tayside 280
R. & A. Books, East Sussex 101

- INDIA
Bates & Hindmarch, West Yorkshire.............. 248
Beaumont Travel Books, London SE 163
Bonham (J. & S.L.), London W 171

Bonython Bookshop, Cornwall..................... 75
Canon Gate Books, West Sussex.................. 243
Catalyst Booksearch Services, Devon............. 87
Chalmers Hallam (E.), Hampshire................ 125
David Warnes Books, Herefordshire 128
Donovan Military Books (Tom), East Sussex.... 99
Empire Books, N Yorks............................ 197
G. C. Books Ltd., Dumfries & Galloway........ 270
Glacier Books, Tayside 280
Jackdaw Books, Norfolk 188
Jackson (M.W.), Wiltshire.......................... 254
Kabristan Archives, Shropshire.................... 214
Mandalay Bookshop, London SW 168
My Back Pages, London SW 168
Oxley (Laurence), Hampshire...................... 121
Peter M Daly, Hampshire.......................... 126
Rayner (Hugh Ashley), Somerset 215
Rhodes, Bookseller (Peter), Hampshire 125
Roland Books, Kent 138
Traveller's Bookshelf (The), Somerset 218
Verandah Books, Dorset 95
Woolcott Books, Dorset 92

- INDIAN OCEAN, THE
Empire Books, N Yorks............................ 197
Kenya Books, East Sussex 100
R. & A. Books, East Sussex 101

- INDONESIA
Park (Mike), London O 182
R. & A. Books, East Sussex 101

- IRAN
Antique Prints of the World, London N.......... 156
Bates & Hindmarch, West Yorkshire.............. 248
Ctesiphon Books, Greater Manchester 120
David Warnes Books, Herefordshire 128
Joppa Books Ltd., Surrey 230
Quest Books, East Yorkshire 107
R. & A. Books, East Sussex 101
Traveller's Bookshelf (The), Somerset 218
White Eagle Books, London NW.................. 162

- IRAQ
Bates & Hindmarch, West Yorkshire.............. 248
Bickford-Smith (G.) (formerly Snowden Smith
Books), Surrey 232
Ctesiphon Books, Greater Manchester 120
Joppa Books Ltd., Surrey 230
R. & A. Books, East Sussex 101
Traveller's Bookshelf (The), Somerset 218

- IRELAND
Abbey Books, Cornwall 73
Apocalypse, Surrey 232
Armchair Books, Lothian 275
Barnacle Books, County Fermanagh 261
Carraig Books Ltd., Co. Dublin 263
Celtic Bookshop (The), Co. Limerick 266
Courtwood Books, Co. Laois....................... 265
Darkwood Books, Co. Cork........................ 263
De Burca Rare Books, Co. Dublin 264
Delectus Books, London WC....................... 176
Doolin Dinghy Books, Co. Clare 262
Foyle Books, Co. Derry 260

Greene's Bookshop Ltd, Co. Dublin 264
Grove Bookshop (The), N Yorks 195
Hyland (C.P.), Co. Cork 263
Hylton Booksearch, Merseyside 184
J.E. Burns Booksellers, Merseyside 185
Jackson (M.W.), Wiltshire........................... 254
JIRI Books, Co. Antrim............................. 260
Kabristan Archives, Shropshire.................... 214
Karen Millward, Co. Cork 263
Kenya Books, East Sussex 100
Keogh's Books, Gloucestershire 115
Kernaghans, Merseyside............................. 185
Lyonshill Books, Co. Dublin 265
Michael J Carroll, Co. Cork 263
Oasis Booksearch, Cambridgeshire............... 67
Prospect House Books, Co. Down................ 261
R. & A. Books, East Sussex 101
Read Ireland, Co. Dublin 264
Red Star Books, Herts 129
Roscrea Bookshop & Newsagents,
   Co. Tipperary 266
Rowan (P. & B.), Co. Antrim 260
Rye Old Books, East Sussex 104
Schull Books, Co. Cork 262
Skelton (Tony), Kent................................ 140
Spenceley Books (David), West Yorkshire........ 248
Stokes Books, Co. Dublin........................... 264
Taney Books, Co. Dublin 263
Whelan (P. & F.), Kent.............................. 140

- ISLE OF MAN
Craobh Rua Books, Co. Armagh.................. 260
Garretts Antiquarian Books, Isle of Man........ 259
Kernaghans, Merseyside............................. 185
Mulyan (Don), Merseyside.......................... 185
R. & A. Books, East Sussex 101

- ISLE OF WIGHT
Apocalypse, Surrey 232
Cameron House Books, Isle of Wight............. 133
Curtle Mead Books, Isle of Wight................. 133
Heritage Books, Isle of Wight 133
Portus Books, Hampshire 122
R. & A. Books, East Sussex 101

- ISLES OF SCILLY
R. & A. Books, East Sussex 101

- ISRAEL
baconboooks, London WC 176
Ctesiphon Books, Greater Manchester 120
Fishburn Books, London NW....................... 160
R. & A. Books, East Sussex 101
Samovar Books, Co. Dublin........................ 264

- ITALY
Apocalypse, Surrey 232
Campbell (Fiona), London SE 163
Derek Stirling Bookseller, Kent 141
Empire Books, N Yorks............................. 197
Glacier Books, Tayside 280
Hava Books, London SE............................ 164
McGee (Terence J.), London O 180
R. & A. Books, East Sussex 101
Seydi Rare Books (Sevin), London NW 161

Spelman (Ken), N Yorks............................ 198
Susanne Schulz-Falster Rare Books, London N. 158

- JAPAN
Allsworth Rare Books Ltd., London SW......... 166
Bow Windows Book Shop, East Sussex 103
Burebank Books, Norfolk........................... 186
Empire Books, N Yorks............................. 197
Fine Books Oriental, London W14................. 172
Hanshan Tang Books, London SW 167
Hobgoblin Books, Hampshire 125
Orb's Bookshop, Grampian......................... 273
R. & A. Books, East Sussex 101
Robert G Sawers Ltd, London NW................ 161
Roberts Books, Strathclyde 279
Transformer, Dumfries & Galloway 270
Traveller's Bookshelf (The), Somerset 218

- KENYA
Ayre (Peter J.), Somerset 219
Bonham (J. & S.L.), London W 171
Chalmers Hallam (E.), Hampshire 125
Kenya Books, East Sussex 100
Peter M Daly, Hampshire 126
Popeley (Frank T.), Cambridgeshire............... 67
R. & A. Books, East Sussex 101
White (C.R.), London W............................ 175
Yesterday's Books, Dorset 92

- KOREA
Allsworth Rare Books Ltd., London SW......... 166
Ctesiphon Books, Greater Manchester 120
Empire Books, N Yorks............................. 197
Fine Books Oriental, London W14................. 172
Hanshan Tang Books, London SW 167
R. & A. Books, East Sussex 101
Transformer, Dumfries & Galloway 270
Traveller's Bookshelf (The), Somerset 218

- LADAKH
Bates & Hindmarch, West Yorkshire............. 248
Chalmers Hallam (E.), Hampshire 125
Glacier Books, Tayside 280
Grayling (David A.H.), Cumbria 78
Hunter and Krageloh, Derbyshire 83
Kabristan Archives, Shropshire.................... 214
Rayner (Hugh Ashley), Somerset 215

- LAOS
Empire Books, N Yorks............................. 197
Traveller's Bookshelf (The), Somerset 218

- LAPLAND
R. & A. Books, East Sussex 101

- LATIN AMERICA
Baldwin (Jack), Strathclyde 278
Books on Spain, London O.......................... 182
Chalmers Hallam (E.), Hampshire 125
Delectus Books, London WC....................... 176
Hodgson (Judith), London W 173
Hünersdorff Rare Books, London SW 168
Marble Hill Books, Outer London................. 182
Quaritch Ltd., (Bernard), London W.............. 174
R. & A. Books, East Sussex 101

- LATVIA
de Visser Books, Cambridgeshire................... 63
R. & A. Books, East Sussex 101

- LEBANON
Joppa Books Ltd., Surrey 230
Trotter Books (John), London N 158

- LITHUANIA
de Visser Books, Cambridgeshire................... 63
R. & A. Books, East Sussex 101

- MADEIRA
Chas J. Sawyer, Kent 140
Hodgson (Judith), London W 173
Orssich (Paul), London SW 169
Pennymead Books, N Yorks 193
R. & A. Books, East Sussex 101

- MALAYA
Empire Books, N Yorks.............................. 197
R. & A. Books, East Sussex 101
Traveller's Bookshelf (The), Somerset 218

- MALAYSIA
Beardsley (A.E.), Nottinghamshire.................. 204
Bonham (J. & S.L.), London W 171
Eastgate Bookshop, East Yorkshire 106
Empire Books, N Yorks.............................. 197
Joppa Books Ltd., Surrey 230
R. & A. Books, East Sussex 101
Traveller's Bookshelf (The), Somerset 218

- MALTA
Joppa Books Ltd., Surrey 230
Nicolas - Antiquarian Bookseller, London N 157
R. & A. Books, East Sussex 101

- MAURITIUS
Antique Prints of the World, London N.......... 156
Chas J. Sawyer, Kent 140
R. & A. Books, East Sussex 101

- MELANESIA
Bonham (J. & S.L.), London W 171
Books, Denbighshire 284
Bracton Books, Cambridgeshire.................... 63
Broadwater Books, Hampshire...................... 125
Chalmers Hallam (E.), Hampshire.................. 125
Modern First Editions, London O................. 181
Wayside Books and Cards, Oxfordshire 206

- MESOPOTAMIA
Bonham (J. & S.L.), London W 171
Ctesiphon Books, Greater Manchester 120
Joppa Books Ltd., Surrey 230
Quest Books, East Yorkshire 107

- MEXICO
Baldwin (Jack), Strathclyde 278
Bardsley's Books, Suffolk........................... 225
Books on Spain, London O.......................... 182
Burton–Garbett (A.), London O 182
Delectus Books, London WC....................... 176
L.M.S. Books, Herts 131

Modern First Editions, London O................. 181
Orssich (Paul), London SW 169
R. & A. Books, East Sussex 101

- MIDDLE EAST, THE
Beaumont Travel Books, London SE 163
Bickford-Smith (G.) (formerly Snowden Smith
  Books), Surrey 232
Chalmers Hallam (E.), Hampshire.................. 125
Chapter Two, London SE........................... 163
Clarke Books (David), Somerset 218
David Warnes Books, Herefordshire 128
Delectus Books, London WC....................... 176
Fishburn Books, London NW...................... 160
Hall, (Anthony C.) Antiquarian Bookseller,
  London O.. 183
Hylton Booksearch, Merseyside 184
J.C. Deyong Books (Previously of
  Snowden Smith Books), London SW 168
Joppa Books Ltd., Surrey 230
Kingswood Books, Dorset 94
Maghreb Bookshop (The), London WC.......... 177
Old Station Pottery & Bookshop (The), Norfolk 191
P. and P. Books, Worcs 256
Penny Farthing, The, Lothian 277
Peter M Daly, Hampshire........................... 126
Quaritch Ltd., (Bernard), London W.............. 174
Quest Books, East Yorkshire 107
R. & A. Books, East Sussex 101
Ryeland Books, Northants 199
Thorntons of Oxford Ltd., Oxfordshire.......... 206
Traveller's Bookshelf (The), Somerset 218
Trotter Books (John), London N 158
White Eagle Books, London NW.................. 162

- MONGOLIA
Chalmers Hallam (E.), Hampshire.................. 125
Ctesiphon Books, Greater Manchester 120
Grayling (David A.H.), Cumbria 78
R. & A. Books, East Sussex 101
Rayner (Hugh Ashley), Somerset 215
Traveller's Bookshelf (The), Somerset 218

- MONTE CARLO
R. & A. Books, East Sussex 101

- MOROCCO
Books on Spain, London O.......................... 182
Ctesiphon Books, Greater Manchester 120
Glacier Books, Tayside 280
Joppa Books Ltd., Surrey 230
Orssich (Paul), London SW 169
R. & A. Books, East Sussex 101
Traveller's Bookshelf (The), Somerset 218
Yesterday's Books, Dorset 92

- NATAL
Chalmers Hallam (E.), Hampshire.................. 125
Kenya Books, East Sussex 100
R. & A. Books, East Sussex 101
Yesterday's Books, Dorset 92

- NEAR EAST, THE
Bickford-Smith (G.) (formerly Snowden Smith
  Books), Surrey 232

Kingswood Books, Dorset 94
Marble Hill Books, Outer London................. 182
Peter M Daly, Hampshire........................... 126
Quest Books, East Yorkshire 107
R. & A. Books, East Sussex 101
Seydi Rare Books (Sevin), London NW 161
Thorntons of Oxford Ltd., Oxfordshire........... 206
Traveller's Bookshelf (The), Somerset 218

- NEPAL
Bonham (J. & S.L.), London W 171
Chalmers Hallam (E.), Hampshire................. 125
David Warnes Books, Herefordshire 128
Glacier Books, Tayside 280
Hunter and Krageloh, Derbyshire 83
Little Bookshop (The), Cumbria 80
R. & A. Books, East Sussex 101
Rayner (Hugh Ashley), Somerset 215
Traveller's Bookshelf (The), Somerset 218
Verandah Books, Dorset 95

- NETHERLANDS, THE
R. & A. Books, East Sussex 101

- NEW ZEALAND
Belfry Books, Nottinghamshire..................... 203
Empire Books, N Yorks............................. 197
Moore (Peter), Cambridgeshire..................... 64
Preston Book Company, Lancashire 144
R. & A. Books, East Sussex 101

- NICARAGUA
Orssich (Paul), London SW 169
R. & A. Books, East Sussex 101

- NORTH AFRICA
Chalmers Hallam (E.), Hampshire................. 125
Joppa Books Ltd., Surrey 230
Maghreb Bookshop (The), London WC.......... 177
Peter M Daly, Hampshire........................... 126
R. & A. Books, East Sussex 101
Samovar Books, Co. Dublin........................ 264
Traveller's Bookshelf (The), Somerset 218
Yesterday's Books, Dorset 92

- NORTH EAST ASIA
Bickford-Smith (G.) (formerly Snowden Smith
    Books), Surrey 232
Chalmers Hallam (E.), Hampshire................. 125
R. & A. Books, East Sussex 101
Traveller's Bookshelf (The), Somerset 218

- NORTH WEST FRONTIER PROVINCE
Bonham (J. & S.L.), London W 171
David Warnes Books, Herefordshire 128
Rayner (Hugh Ashley), Somerset 215
Verandah Books, Dorset 95

- NORWAY
Apocalypse, Surrey 232
Glacier Books, Tayside 280
Mulyan (Don), Merseyside.......................... 185
R. & A. Books, East Sussex 101

- ORIENT, THE
Bickford-Smith (G.) (formerly Snowden Smith
    Books), Surrey 232
Quaritch Ltd., (Bernard), London W.............. 174
R. & A. Books, East Sussex 101
Rayner (Hugh Ashley), Somerset 215

- PACIFIC NORTH WEST, THE
Michael Graves-Johnston, London SW 168

- PACIFIC, THE
Chalmers Hallam (E.), Hampshire................. 125
Empire Books, N Yorks............................. 197
Michael Graves-Johnston, London SW 168
Moore (Peter), Cambridgeshire..................... 64
Quaritch Ltd., (Bernard), London W.............. 174
R. & A. Books, East Sussex 101

- PAKISTAN
Catalyst Booksearch Services, Devon.............. 87
Glacier Books, Tayside 280
R. & A. Books, East Sussex 101
Rayner (Hugh Ashley), Somerset 215
Traveller's Bookshelf (The), Somerset 218
Verandah Books, Dorset 95

- PALESTINE
Ctesiphon Books, Greater Manchester 120
Joppa Books Ltd., Surrey 230
R. & A. Books, East Sussex 101
Samovar Books, Co. Dublin........................ 264
Traveller's Bookshelf (The), Somerset 218

- PANAMA CANAL
Pennymead Books, N Yorks........................ 193
R. & A. Books, East Sussex 101

- PAPUA NEW GUINEA
Bonham (J. & S.L.), London W 171
Michael Graves-Johnston, London SW 168
Moore (Peter), Cambridgeshire..................... 64
Traveller's Bookshelf (The), Somerset 218

- PHILIPPINES, THE
Hodgson (Judith), London W 173
Orssich (Paul), London SW 169
R. & A. Books, East Sussex 101
Traveller's Bookshelf (The), Somerset 218

- POLAND
Bardsley's Books, Suffolk........................... 225
de Visser Books, Cambridgeshire.................. 63
Orbis Books (London) Ltd., London W 173
R. & A. Books, East Sussex 101

- POLAR
Allinson (Frank & Stella), Warwickshire 236
Bluntisham Books, Cambridgeshire............... 63
Bonham (J. & S.L.), London W 171
Glacier Books, Tayside 280
J & J Burgess Booksellers, Cambridgeshire....... 64
Lymelight Books & Prints, Dorset................. 93
McEwan Fine Books, Grampian.................... 272
R. & A. Books, East Sussex 101
Riddell (Peter), East Yorkshire 106

Roz Hulse, Conwy 284
White (C.R.), London W 175

- POLYNESIA
Bracton Books, Cambridgeshire 63
Chalmers Hallam (E.), Hampshire 125
Empire Books, N Yorks 197
R. & A. Books, East Sussex 101

- PORTUGAL
Annie's Books, South Yorkshire 221
Baldwin (Jack), Strathclyde 278
Books on Spain, London O 182
Hodgson (Judith), London W 173
Orssich (Paul), London SW 169
R. & A. Books, East Sussex 101
York (Graham), Devon 86

- PUERTO RICO
Orssich (Paul), London SW 169
Pennymead Books, N Yorks 193
R. & A. Books, East Sussex 101

- PUNJAB
Grayling (David A.H.), Cumbria 78
R. & A. Books, East Sussex 101
Rayner (Hugh Ashley), Somerset 215

- PYRENEES, THE
Bass (Ben), Wiltshire 251
Glacier Books, Tayside 280
Orssich (Paul), London SW 169
R. & A. Books, East Sussex 101

- RAJASTHAN
Chalmers Hallam (E.), Hampshire 125
R. & A. Books, East Sussex 101
Rayner (Hugh Ashley), Somerset 215

- ROMANIA
de Visser Books, Cambridgeshire 63
R. & A. Books, East Sussex 101
Traveller's Bookshelf (The), Somerset 218

- RUSSIA
Baldwin (Jack), Strathclyde 278
de Visser Books, Cambridgeshire 63
Delectus Books, London WC 176
Hab Books, London W 172
Hall, (Anthony C.) Antiquarian Bookseller,
London O 183
Left on The Shelf, Cumbria 78
Orbis Books (London) Ltd., London W 173
Orb's Bookshop, Grampian 273
Penny Farthing, The, Lothian 277
Quaritch Ltd., (Bernard), London W 174
R. & A. Books, East Sussex 101
Thorntons of Oxford Ltd., Oxfordshire 206
Traveller's Bookshelf (The), Somerset 218
White Eagle Books, London NW 162

- SAHARA, THE
Apocalypse, Surrey 232
Chalmers Hallam (E.), Hampshire 125
Grayling (David A.H.), Cumbria 78

Joppa Books Ltd., Surrey 230
Kenya Books, East Sussex 100
R. & A. Books, East Sussex 101
Yesterday's Books, Dorset 92

- SANTO DOMINGO
Pennymead Books, N Yorks 193

- SARAWAK
Eastgate Bookshop, East Yorkshire 106
Empire Books, N Yorks 197
R. & A. Books, East Sussex 101
Traveller's Bookshelf (The), Somerset 218

- SCANDINAVIA
Chapter Two, London SE 163
Glacier Books, Tayside 280
R. & A. Books, East Sussex 101

- SCOTLAND
Alba Books, Grampian 273
Armchair Books, Lothian 275
Atholl Fine Books, Tayside 280
Bell (Peter), Lothian 275
Benny Gillies Books Ltd, Dumfries & Galloway 268
Broadwater Books, Hampshire 125
Byre Books, Dumfries & Galloway 270
Clifford Milne Books, Grampian 272
Colonsay Bookshop, Isle of Colonsay 275
Cooper Hay Rare Books, Strathclyde 278
Cornell Books, Gloucestershire 117
Cornucopia Books, Lincolnshire 151
Creaking Shelves, Highland 274
David Houston - Bookseller, London E 154
Elizabeth Ferguson, Grampian 272
Farquharson, (Hilary), Tayside 280
Ferguson (Elizabeth), Grampian 272
Freader's Books, Tayside 279
G. C. Books Ltd., Dumfries & Galloway 270
Glacier Books, Tayside 280
Grampian Books, Grampian 273
Greta Books, Durham 97
Holmes Books (Harry), East Yorkshire 107
Hughes Rare Books (Spike), Borders 267
Hutchison (Books) (Larry), Fife 271
Iona Bookshop (The), Isle of Iona 275
Joel Segal Books, Devon 86
Last Century Books, Borders 267
Leakey's Bookshop, Highland 274
Loch Croispol Bookshop & Restaurant,
Highland 273
McCrone (Audrey), Isle of Arran 274
McNaughtan's Bookshop, Lothian 276
Mercat Books, Highland 274
Mr. Mac, Dumfries & Galloway 269
Oakwood Books, Gloucestershire 115
Oopalba Books, Cheshire 71
Orb's Bookshop, Grampian 273
Portus Books, Hampshire 122
Prospect House Books, Co. Down 261
R. & A. Books, East Sussex 101
Read - Gorleston Books, (C.&J.), Norfolk 187
Roberts Books, Strathclyde 279
Samovar Books, Co. Dublin 264
Stroma Books, Borders 267

Wheen O'Books, Borders............................ 267
Wilson (David), Buckinghamshire 61
Worlds End Bookshop, London SW 169

- SEYCHELLES, THE
Chas J. Sawyer, Kent 140
R. & A. Books, East Sussex 101
Yesterday's Books, Dorset 92

- SIAM
Antique Prints of the World, London N.......... 156
R. & A. Books, East Sussex 101
Traveller's Bookshelf (The), Somerset 218

- SIBERIA
Bonham (J. & S.L.), London W 171
Orb's Bookshop, Grampian........................ 273
Peter M Daly, Hampshire.......................... 126
R. & A. Books, East Sussex 101

- SINGAPORE
Allsworth Rare Books Ltd., London SW......... 166
Empire Books, N Yorks............................. 197
R. & A. Books, East Sussex 101

- SOUTH AFRICA
Barn Books, Buckinghamshire..................... 61
Boer War Books, N Yorks.......................... 197
Bonham (J. & S.L.), London W 171
Chalmers Hallam (E.), Hampshire................. 125
Chas J. Sawyer, Kent 140
Delectus Books, London WC...................... 176
Empire Books, N Yorks............................. 197
Grayling (David A.H.), Cumbria 78
Kenya Books, East Sussex 100
Oak Tree Press, Oxfordshire...................... 207
Price (R.D.M. & I.M.) (Books), G Manchester.. 120
R. & A. Books, East Sussex 101
Samovar Books, Co. Dublin........................ 264
Smith (Ray), Herts 129

- SOUTH AMERICA
Baldwin (Jack), Strathclyde 278
Bonham (J. & S.L.), London W 171
Books on Spain, London O........................ 182
Burton–Garbett (A.), London O 182
Chalmers Hallam (E.), Hampshire................. 125
Hodgson (Judith), London W 173
Hünersdorff Rare Books, London SW 168
Orssich (Paul), London SW........................ 169
Peter M Daly, Hampshire.......................... 126
R. & A. Books, East Sussex 101

- SOUTH ATLANTIC ISLANDS
Empire Books, N Yorks............................. 197
Miles Apart, Suffolk................................. 228
MK Book Services, Cambridgeshire............... 66
R. & A. Books, East Sussex 101

- SOUTH EAST ASIA
Bickford-Smith (G.) (formerly Snowden Smith
  Books), Surrey 232
Chalmers Hallam (E.), Hampshire................. 125
David Warnes Books, Herefordshire 128
Eastgate Bookshop, East Yorkshire 106

Grayling (David A.H.), Cumbria 78
Hanshan Tang Books, London SW 167
Mandalay Bookshop, London SW 168
Peter M Daly, Hampshire.......................... 126
R. & A. Books, East Sussex 101
Transformer, Dumfries & Galloway.............. 270
Traveller's Bookshelf (The), Somerset 218
Verandah Books, Dorset 95

- SOUTH EAST EUROPE
de Visser Books, Cambridgeshire.................. 63
R. & A. Books, East Sussex 101

- SOUTH PACIFIC ISLANDS
Bonham (J. & S.L.), London W 171
Chalmers Hallam (E.), Hampshire................. 125
Empire Books, N Yorks............................. 197
R. & A. Books, East Sussex 101

- SPAIN
Baldwin (Jack), Strathclyde 278
Bass (Ben), Wiltshire 251
Books on Spain, London O........................ 182
Hodgson (Judith), London W 173
Orssich (Paul), London SW........................ 169
Peter M Daly, Hampshire.......................... 126
R. & A. Books, East Sussex 101
Studio Bookshop, East Sussex..................... 100
York (Graham), Devon.............................. 86

- SRI LANKA
Antique Prints of the World, London N.......... 156
Chalmers Hallam (E.), Hampshire................. 125
Empire Books, N Yorks............................. 197
R. & A. Books, East Sussex 101
Rayner (Hugh Ashley), Somerset 215
Verandah Books, Dorset 95

- STRAITS SETTLEMENTS, THE
Empire Books, N Yorks............................. 197
Traveller's Bookshelf (The), Somerset 218

- SUDAN
Bonham (J. & S.L.), London W 171
Chalmers Hallam (E.), Hampshire................. 125
Ctesiphon Books, Greater Manchester 120
Joppa Books Ltd., Surrey 230
P. and P. Books, Worcs 256
Peter M Daly, Hampshire........................... 126
R. & A. Books, East Sussex 101
Traveller's Bookshelf (The), Somerset 218
Yesterday's Books, Dorset 92

- SURINAM
Pennymead Books, N Yorks........................ 193

- SWEDEN
R. & A. Books, East Sussex 101

- SWITZERLAND
Cavendish Rare Books, London N 156
Glacier Books, Tayside 280
Hunter and Krageloh, Derbyshire 83
R. & A. Books, East Sussex 101

- SYRIA

Bonham (J. & S.L.), London W 171
Ctesiphon Books, Greater Manchester 120
Joppa Books Ltd., Surrey 230
R. & A. Books, East Sussex 101
Traveller's Bookshelf (The), Somerset 218

- TANZANIA

Ayre (Peter J.), Somerset 219
Chalmers Hallam (E.), Hampshire 125
Kenya Books, East Sussex 100
Popeley (Frank T.), Cambridgeshire 67
White (C.R.), London W 175
Yesterday's Books, Dorset 92

- TIBET

Bates & Hindmarch, West Yorkshire.............. 248
Bonham (J. & S.L.), London W 171
Canon Gate Books, West Sussex................... 243
Cavendish Rare Books, London N 156
Chalmers Hallam (E.), Hampshire 125
Craobh Rua Books, Co. Armagh 260
Ctesiphon Books, Greater Manchester 120
David Warnes Books, Herefordshire 128
Glacier Books, Tayside 280
Hanshan Tang Books, London SW 167
Hunter and Krageloh, Derbyshire 83
Inner Bookshop (The), Oxfordshire................ 208
Penny Farthing, The, Lothian 277
Peter M Daly, Hampshire........................... 126
R. & A. Books, East Sussex 101
Rayner (Hugh Ashley), Somerset 215
Traveller's Bookshelf (The), Somerset 218
Verandah Books, Dorset 95
White Eagle Books, London NW 162

- TRISTAN DA CUNHA

Bickford-Smith (G.) (formerly Snowden Smith
　Books), Surrey 232
Empire Books, N Yorks.............................. 197

- TURKEY

Antique Prints of the World, London N 156
Arslan Books Etc., East Sussex..................... 99
Bonham (J. & S.L.), London W 171
Ctesiphon Books, Greater Manchester 120
Joppa Books Ltd., Surrey 230
Nicolas - Antiquarian Bookseller, London N.... 157
Quest Books, East Yorkshire 107
R. & A. Books, East Sussex 101
Seydi Rare Books (Sevin), London NW 161
Traveller's Bookshelf (The), Somerset 218

- U.S.A.

Americanabooksuk, Cumbria........................ 76
Glacier Books, Tayside 280
Little Stour Books, Kent 136
Marble Hill Books, Outer London................. 182
Preston Book Company, Lancashire 144
PsychoBabel Books & Journals, Oxfordshire..... 205
R. & A. Books, East Sussex 101
Roland Books, Kent 138
Roz Hulse, Conwy 284
Shakeshaft (Dr. B.), Cheshire...................... 71

- UGANDA

Bonham (J. & S.L.), London W 171
Chalmers Hallam (E.), Hampshire 125
Kenya Books, East Sussex 100
Michael Graves-Johnston, London SW 168
Popeley (Frank T.), Cambridgeshire.............. 67
R. & A. Books, East Sussex 101
White (C.R.), London W............................ 175
Yesterday's Books, Dorset 92

- VIETNAM

Bates Books, London O 180
R. & A. Books, East Sussex 101
Traveller's Bookshelf (The), Somerset 218

- WALES

Browning Books, Torfaen........................... 292
Capital Bookshop, Cardiff 281
Carningli Centre, Pembrokeshire 286
Castle Bookshop, Powys............................ 290
Cofion Books, Pembrokeshire 286
Colin Hancock, Ceredigion 282
Colwyn Books, Conwy 283
Cornell Books, Gloucestershire 117
Cymric Books, Berks................................ 56
Dylans Bookstore, Swansea 291
Fifteenth Century Bookshop (The), East Sussex. 104
Gildas Books, Cheshire 68
Glacier Books, Tayside 280
Great Oak Bookshop (The), Powys 289
Island Books, Devon 85
Madoc Books, Conwy 284
Modern Welsh Publications Ltd., Merseyside.... 184
Oakwood Books, Gloucestershire 115
R. & A. Books, East Sussex 101
Read - Gorleston Books, (C.&J.), Norfolk 187
Siop Lyfrau'r Hen Bost, Gwynedd 285
Stella Books, Monmouthshire 286
Thomas (E. Wyn), Conwy 284
Whitchurch Books Ltd., Cardiff.................... 281
Ystwyth Books, Ceredigion 282

- WEST AFRICA

Antique Prints of the World, London N 156
Bonham (J. & S.L.), London W 171
Chalmers Hallam (E.), Hampshire 125
Empire Books, N Yorks............................. 197
Kenya Books, East Sussex 100
Michael Graves-Johnston, London SW 168
Oopalba Books, Cheshire........................... 71
Peter M Daly, Hampshire........................... 126
R. & A. Books, East Sussex 101
Yesterday's Books, Dorset 92

- WEST INDIES, THE

Bonham (J. & S.L.), London W 171
Empire Books, N Yorks............................. 197
Leapman Ltd. (G. & R.), Herts 130
Pennymead Books, N Yorks........................ 193
R. & A. Books, East Sussex 101
Roz Hulse, Conwy 284

- WESTERN CAPE

R. & A. Books, East Sussex 101
Yesterday's Books, Dorset 92

- YUKON
Chalmers Hallam (E.), Hampshire 125

- ZULULAND
Antique Prints of the World, London N 156
Chalmers Hallam (E.), Hampshire 125
Kenya Books, East Sussex 100
R. & A. Books, East Sussex 101
Yesterday's Books, Dorset 92

COUNTRY HOUSES
Apocalypse, Surrey 232
Art Reference Books, Hampshire 124
Cornucopia Books, Lincolnshire 151
Dales & Lakes Book Centre, Cumbria 79
Debbage (John), Norfolk 189
Fifteenth Century Bookshop (The), East Sussex. 104
Jackdaw Books, Norfolk 188
Lighthouse Books (The), Dorset 92
Mannwaring (M.G.), Bristol 59
Marlborough Rare Books Ltd., London W 173
Martin (Brian), Surrey 231
Old Town Bookshop (The), Lothian 276
R. & A. Books, East Sussex 101
Spenceley Books (David), West Yorkshire 248
Staniland (Booksellers), Lincolnshire 152
Trinity Rare Books, Co. Leitrim 266

COUNTY - LOCAL
Abacus Books, Greater Manchester 118
Ambra Books, Bristol 58
Anthony Vickers Books, N Yorks 195
Barn Books, Shropshire 214
Bath Old Books, Somerset 215
Benny Gillies Books Ltd, Dumfries & Galloway 268
Black Cat Bookshop, Leics 147
Blackwell's Rare Books, Oxfordshire 208
Bonython Bookshop, Cornwall 75
Bookpassage (The), Shropshire 212
Bosorne Books, Cornwall 75
Bunyan Books, Bedfordshire 53
Bury Bookshop, Suffolk 225
Canon Gate Books, West Sussex 243
Cassidy (Bookseller) (P.), Lincolnshire 151
Churchgate Books, Suffolk 226
Clark (Nigel A.), London SE 163
Cobnar Books, Kent 141
Colin Hancock, Ceredigion 282
Cornucopia Books, Lincolnshire 151
Country Books, Derbyshire 82
Cox, Andrew, Shropshire 214
Dales & Lakes Book Centre, Cumbria 79
Dandy Lion Editions, Surrey 233
Debbage (John), Norfolk 189
Delph Books, Greater Manchester 120
Eagle Bookshop (The), Bedfordshire 53
Fifteenth Century Bookshop (The), East Sussex. 104
Glasheen-Books, Surrey 231
Grahame Thornton, Bookseller, Dorset 93
Grampian Books, Grampian 273
Hall's Bookshop, Kent 140
Inner Bookshop (The), Oxfordshire 208
Island Books, Devon 85
Jade Mountain Bookshop, Hampshire 125
John Clifford, Dorset 92

Martin (Books and Pictures), (Brian P.), Surrey. 231
Martin (Brian), Surrey 231
MK Book Services, Cambridgeshire 66
Oakwood Books, Gloucestershire 115
Old Station Pottery & Bookshop (The), Norfolk 191
Peter M Daly, Hampshire 126
Portus Books, Hampshire 122
Post–Horn Books, N Yorks 192
R & B Graham Trading, Cornwall 73
Read - Gorleston Books, (C.&J.), Norfolk 187
Roger Collicott Books, Cornwall 74
Sax Books, Suffolk 228
Spooner & Co, Somerset 219
Uncle Phil's Books, West Midlands 239
Whitchurch Books Ltd., Cardiff 281
York (Graham), Devon 86

COURTESY
Black Cat Books, Norfolk 187
Burmester (James), Bristol 58
Weininger Antiquarian Books (Eva M.),
London NW 161

COWBOYS
Americanabooksuk, Cumbria 76
Annie's Books, S Yorks 221
Joel Segal Books, Devon 86
Phenotype Books, Cumbria 79
R. & A. Books, East Sussex 101
Wheen O'Books, Borders 267
Williams (Bookdealer), (Richard), North Lincs .. 153

CRAFTS
Andrew Morton (Books), Powys 287
Annie's Books, S Yorks 221
Apocalypse, Surrey 232
Arden Books & Cosmographia, Warwickshire ... 236
Backfold Books, Herefordshire 127
Baldwin (M. & M.), Worcs 255
Barn Books, Buckinghamshire 61
Books for Content, Herefordshire 127
Brad Books, Essex 110
Brock Books, N Yorks 192
Browse Books, Lancashire 143
Bruce Holdsworth Books, East Sussex 105
Cavern Books, Cheshire 70
Cheshire Book Centre, Cheshire 69
Cornucopia Books, Lincolnshire 151
Cottage Books, Leics 145
Country Books, Derbyshire 82
Cover to Cover, Merseyside 185
Crabtree (Mrs. C.), Greater Manchester 120
Crouch Rare Books, Surrey 232
Dalbeattie Books, Dumfries & Galloway 269
Dales & Lakes Book Centre, Cumbria 79
Design Gallery 1850-1950 (The), Kent 141
Discovery Bookshop, Carmarthenshire 281
DPE Books, Devon 87
Dusty Books, Powys 290
Fifteenth Century Bookshop (The), East Sussex. 104
Footrope Knots, Suffolk 227
Ford Books (David), Herts 130
Furneaux Books (Lee), Devon 89
George St. Books, Derbyshire 83
Gladstone Books, Lincolnshire 150

Good for Books, Lincolnshire 149
Grahame Thornton, Bookseller, Dorset 93
Hay Castle, Powys 288
J & J Burgess Booksellers, Cambridgeshire 64
Jade Mountain Bookshop, Hampshire 125
Joel Segal Books, Devon 86
Judith Mansfield, West Yorkshire.................. 249
Just Books, Cornwall 75
Macbuiks, N Yorks 193
McCrone (Audrey), Isle of Arran 274
N1 Books, East Sussex 105
Portus Books, Hampshire 122
Priestpopple Books, Northumberland 201
R. & A. Books, East Sussex 101
Reeves Technical Books, N Yorks 195
Scrivener's Books & Bookbinding, Derbyshire... 82
Sleepy Elephant Books & Artefacts, Cumbria ... 80
Smith Books (Keith), Herefordshire 128
Smith Books, (Sally), Suffolk 226
Sterling Books, Somerset 220
Stobart Davies Limited, Carmarthenshire 282
Tarka Books, Devon 84
The Sanctuary Bookshop, Dorset 94
Treasure Island (The), Greater Manchester 119
Trigon Books, Dorset 95
Trinders' Fine Tools, Suffolk 226
Upper–Room Books, Somerset 217
Wheen O'Books, Borders 267
Whittle, Bookseller (Avril), Cumbria 80
Young (D. & J.), Powys 291

CRIME (TRUE)

Abrahams (Mike), Staffordshire 223
Biff Books and Records, S Yorks 221
Bolland Books, Bedfordshire 53
Bookworms Paradise Ltd., West Sussex 242
Booth (Booksearch Service), (Geoff), Cheshire... 68
Catalyst Booksearch Services, Devon 87
Cavern Books, Cheshire 70
Chapter Two, London SE 163
Charles Bossom, Cambridgeshire 65
Cheshire Book Centre, Cheshire 69
Classic Crime Collections, Greater Manchester .. 119
Clifford Elmer Books Ltd., Cheshire 68
Crimes Ink, London E 154
Dunstan Books, Dorset 91
Eastcote Bookshop (The), London O 180
Eastgate Bookshop, East Yorkshire 106
Fifteenth Century Bookshop (The), East Sussex. 104
ForensicSearch, Herts 131
Garfi Books, Powys 291
HCB Wholesale, Powys 288
Hylton Booksearch, Merseyside 184
Intech Books, Northumberland 201
J & J Burgess Booksellers, Cambridgeshire 64
Jade Mountain Bookshop, Hampshire 125
Joel Segal Books, Devon 86
John Underwood Antiquarian Books, Norfolk .. 189
Just Books, Cornwall 75
Kingfisher Book Service, Nottinghamshire 204
Loretta Lay Books, London NW 161
Maggy Browne, Lincolnshire 148
McCaughtrie (K.A.), N Yorks 192
McCrone (Audrey), Isle of Arran 274
Ming Books, Dumfries & Galloway 270

Murder & Mayhem, Powys 288
Porter Bookshop (The), S Yorks 222
R M Books, Herts 132
R. & A. Books, East Sussex 101
Roland Books, Kent 138
Roscrea Bookshop & Newsagents,
    Co. Tipperary 266
Ruebotham (Kirk), Cheshire 71
Simply Read Books, East Sussex 100
Star Lord Books, Greater Manchester 119
Tarka Books, Devon 84
Treasure Trove Books, Leics 146
Undercover Books, Lincolnshire 152
Wayside Books and Cards, Oxfordshire 206
Whitehall Books, East Sussex 103
Wiend Books, Lancashire 143
Williams (Bookdealer), (Richard), N Lincs 153
Yesterday's News, Conwy 283
Zardoz Books, Wiltshire 254

CRIMINAL LAW

Delectus Books, London WC 176
Hylton Booksearch, Merseyside 184
Leo Cadogan, London N 157
Pittville Books, Gloucestershire 113
R. & A. Books, East Sussex 101
Williams (Bookdealer), (Richard), N Lincs 153

CRIMINOLOGY

Bolland Books, Bedfordshire 53
Chesters (G. & J.), Staffordshire 224
Clifford Elmer Books Ltd., Cheshire 68
Craobh Rua Books, Co. Armagh 260
Crimes Ink, London E 154
Delectus Books, London WC 176
Garfi Books, Powys 291
hullbooks.com, East Yorkshire 106
Hylton Booksearch, Merseyside 184
Joel Segal Books, Devon 86
Loretta Lay Books, London NW 161
Murder & Mayhem, Powys 288
R M Books, Herts 132
R. & A. Books, East Sussex 101
Reading Lasses, Dumfries & Galloway 270
Roscrea Bookshop & Newsagents,
    Co. Tipperary 266
Savona Books, Lincolnshire 151
Transformer, Dumfries & Galloway 270
Undercover Books, Lincolnshire 152
Whitehall Books, East Sussex 103
Williams (Bookdealer), (Richard), N Lincs 153

CRITICAL THEORY

Joel Segal Books, Devon 86
Price (John), London N 158
Reading Lasses, Dumfries & Galloway 270
Woburn Books, London N 159

CROCHET

Annie's Books, S Yorks 221
Browse Books, Lancashire 143
Byrom Textile Bookroom (Richard), Lancashire 142
Cover to Cover, Merseyside 185
Joel Segal Books, Devon 86
Judith Mansfield, West Yorkshire 249

R. & A. Books, East Sussex 101
Sleepy Elephant Books & Artefacts, Cumbria ... 80
Whittle, Bookseller (Avril), Cumbria 80
Young (D. & J.), Powys............................. 291

CRUSTACEA
Joel Segal Books, Devon 86
Parkinsons Books, Merseyside..................... 185
Savona Books, Lincolnshire........................ 151

CRYPTOGRAPHY
Baldwin (M. & M.), Worcs 255
Bookworms Paradise Ltd., West Sussex 242
Joel Segal Books, Devon 86
Quaritch Ltd., (Bernard), London W............. 174
Susanne Schulz-Falster Rare Books, London N. 158

CRYPTOZOOLOGY
Atlantis Bookshop, London WC.................... 176
Gildas Books, Cheshire 68
Inner Bookshop (The), Oxfordshire............... 208
Randall (Tom), Somerset........................... 218
SETI Books, West Midlands........................ 239
Wizard Books, Cambridgeshire.................... 67

CULTS
Inner Bookshop (The), Oxfordshire............... 208
Joel Segal Books, Devon 86
R. & A. Books, East Sussex 101
Samovar Books, Co. Dublin........................ 264
Woburn Books, London N 159

CULTURAL STUDIES
Kenya Books, East Sussex 100
Left on The Shelf, Cumbria......................... 78
Pittville Books, Gloucestershire.................... 113
PsychoBabel Books & Journals, Oxfordshire..... 205
Spurrier (Nick), Kent 137
Woburn Books, London N 159

CULTURE
- FOREIGN
Books on Spain, London O.......................... 182
Joel Segal Books, Devon 86
Pittville Books, Gloucestershire.................... 113
Print Matters, London SE........................... 165
Transformer, Dumfries & Galloway............... 270
Wadard Books, Kent 137
Weininger Antiquarian Books (Eva M.),
   London NW....................................... 161
Woburn Books, London N 159

- NATIONAL
Colin Hancock, Ceredigion 282
De Burca Rare Books, Co. Dublin 264
Guildmaster Books, Cheshire....................... 70
Joel Segal Books, Devon 86
Leakey's Bookshop, Highland 274
Orb's Bookshop, Grampian......................... 273
Pittville Books, Gloucestershire.................... 113
Print Matters, London SE........................... 165
Samovar Books, Co. Dublin........................ 264
Stokes Books, Co. Dublin........................... 264
Weininger Antiquarian Books (Eva M.)
   London NW....................................... 161

Woburn Books, London N 159

- POPULAR
Apocalypse, Surrey 232
Book Palace (The), London SE 163
Bookshop (The), Greater Manchester 118
Hava Books, London SE............................. 164
Joel Segal Books, Devon 86
Print Matters, London SE........................... 165
Pyecroft (Ruth), Gloucestershire 116
R. & A. Books, East Sussex 101
Reid of Liverpool, Merseyside...................... 184
Woburn Books, London N 159

CUNEIFORM STUDIES
Thorntons of Oxford Ltd., Oxfordshire........... 206

CURIOSA
Delectus Books, London WC........................ 176
Edmund Pollinger Rare Books, London SW..... 166
Eggeling Books (John), West Yorkshire 249
Price (John), London N 158
R. & A. Books, East Sussex 101
Susanne Schulz-Falster Rare Books, London N. 158

CURIOSITIES
Bernstein (Nicholas), London W 171
Don Kelly Books, London W 172
Dylans Bookstore, Swansea......................... 291
N1 Books, East Sussex 105
R. & A. Books, East Sussex 101

CURRENT AFFAIRS
R. & A. Books, East Sussex 101
Woburn Books, London N 159

CUSTOMS & EXCISE
Cox (Geoff), Devon 90

CYBERNETICS
Dylans Bookstore, Swansea......................... 291
Stroh (M.A.), London E 154

D.I.Y. (DO IT YOURSELF)
Annie's Books, S Yorks 221
Barcombe Services, Essex............................ 108
Brown-Studies, Strathclyde.......................... 277
Carningli Centre, Pembrokeshire................... 286
Cornucopia Books, Lincolnshire 151
Cover to Cover, Merseyside......................... 185
Jade Mountain Bookshop, Hampshire 125
Junk & Spread Eagle, London SE................. 164
Larkham Books (Patricia), Gloucestershire....... 117
McCrone (Audrey), Isle of Arran.................. 274
R. & A. Books, East Sussex 101
Reeves Technical Books, N Yorks................. 195
Roscrea Bookshop & Newsagents,
   Co. Tipperary 266
Stobart Davies Limited, Carmarthenshire 282
Tarka Books, Devon................................. 84
Trinity Rare Books, Co. Leitrim 266
Uncle Phil's Books, West Midlands 239

DADAISM
Delectus Books, London WC........................ 176

Joel Segal Books, Devon 86
R. & A. Books, East Sussex 101

DANCE
Addyman Books, Powys............................. 287
Annie's Books, S Yorks 221
Anthony Spranger, Wiltshire....................... 252
Baxter - Books (Eddie), Somerset 220
Brock Books, N Yorks 192
Byre Books, Dumfries & Galloway 270
Cofion Books, Pembrokeshire 286
Cornucopia Books, Lincolnshire 151
Cover to Cover, Merseyside........................ 185
Dance Books Ltd, Hampshire 121
Dooley (Rosemary), Cumbria 77
Fifteenth Century Bookshop (The), East Sussex. 104
Fitzsimons (Anne), Cumbria 76
Greenroom Books, West Yorkshire 247
Hylton Booksearch, Merseyside 184
Joel Segal Books, Devon 86
Paramor (C.D.), Suffolk 228
Quadrille at Delehar, London W................... 174
R. & A. Books, East Sussex 101
Travis & Emery Music Bookshop, London WC 178

DARWINISM
Lymelight Books & Prints, Dorset................. 93
Quaritch Ltd., (Bernard), London W.............. 174

DEATH & FUNERALS
Delectus Books, London WC....................... 176
Inner Bookshop (The), Oxfordshire................ 208
R. & A. Books, East Sussex 101

DEATH, DYING, BEREAVEMENT & LOSS
Beckham Books Ltd., Suffolk 229

DECORATIVE ART
Amwell Book Company, London EC.............. 155
Antiques on High, Oxfordshire..................... 207
Apocalypse, Surrey 232
Art Reference Books, Hampshire 124
Ballantyne–Way (Roger), Suffolk 228
Barlow (Vincent G.), Hampshire................... 125
Barmby (C. & A.J.), Kent.......................... 140
Books & Things, London W........................ 171
Bruce Holdsworth Books, East Sussex 105
Buckland Books, West Sussex 243
Butts Books (Mary), Berks......................... 56
Chalk (Old & Out of Print Books)
  (Christine M.), West Midlands 238
Cornucopia Books, Lincolnshire 151
Cover to Cover, Merseyside........................ 185
Decorum Books, London N 156
Don Kelly Books, London W 172
Duck (William), Hampshire........................ 124
Foster (Stephen), London NW 160
Goodyer (Nicholas), London N..................... 157
Heneage Art Books (Thomas), London SW 168
Hodgkins and Company Limited (Ian),
  Gloucestershire 116
Jackdaw Books, Norfolk 188
Jane & John Kinnaird, Cumbria 78
Jean Hedger, Berks................................. 55
Joel Segal Books, Devon 86

Judith Mansfield, West Yorkshire................. 249
Junk & Spread Eagle, London SE................. 164
Keswick Bookshop, Cumbria...................... 78
Milestone Publications Goss & Crested China,
  Hampshire 123
N1 Books, East Sussex 105
Old Town Bookshop (The), Lothian 276
Pagan Limited (Hugh), Hampshire 122
Phelan Books, Co. Dublin 264
Portobello Books, London W 174
Potterton Books, N Yorks 196
R. & A. Books, East Sussex 101
Reference Works Ltd., Dorset...................... 95
Saint Swithin's Illustrated & Children's Books,
  London W 174
Studio (The), Strathclyde 278
Tasburgh Books, Norfolk 190
Temperley (David), West Midlands................ 238
Trinders' Fine Tools, Suffolk 226
Uncle Phil's Books, West Midlands 239
Whittle, Bookseller (Avril), Cumbria 80
Worlds End Bookshop, London SW 169
Wyseby House Books, Berks 55

DEEP SEA DIVING
Green Ltd. (G.L.), Herts 131
Larkham Books (Patricia), Gloucestershire....... 117
Lost Books, Northants............................. 200
Marine and Cannon Books, Cheshire 69
McLaren Books Ltd, Strathclyde 279
R. & A. Books, East Sussex 101
Rods Books, Devon................................ 88
Stroh (M.A.), London E 154
Sub Aqua Prints and Books, Hampshire 123

DEMOGRAPHY
Quaritch Ltd., (Bernard), London W.............. 174
R. & A. Books, East Sussex 101
Woburn Books, London N 159

DENTISTRY
Quaritch Ltd., (Bernard), London W.............. 174
R. & A. Books, East Sussex 101
Rebecca Hardie Rare Books, London W......... 171
Weiner (Graham), London N 158

DESIGN
Amwell Book Company, London EC.............. 155
Apocalypse, Surrey 232
Art Book Company, (The), Suffolk................ 227
Art Reference Books, Hampshire 124
Ballantyne–Way (Roger), Suffolk 228
Bianco Library, West Sussex....................... 241
Blaenavon Books, Torfaen 292
Broadleaf Books, Torfaen 292
Brock Books, N Yorks 192
Bruce Holdsworth Books, East Sussex 105
C J Renwick Books, Powys........................ 287
Cover to Cover, Merseyside........................ 185
David Flint, Hampshire 124
Decorum Books, London N 156
Don Kelly Books, London W 172
Duck (William), Hampshire........................ 124
Finch Rare Books Ltd. (Simon), London W..... 172
Greenroom Books, West Yorkshire 247

IDEA, London EC 155
Inch's Books, Kent 137
Jane & John Kinnaird, Cumbria 78
Jean Hedger, Berks 55
Joel Segal Books, Devon 86
Malvern Bookshop (The), Worcs 255
Martin - Bookseller (Colin), East Yorkshire 107
O'Flynn Books, N Yorks 197
Quaritch Ltd., (Bernard), London W 174
R. & A. Books, East Sussex 101
Ray Rare and Out of Print Books (Janette),
    N Yorks 198
Sleepy Elephant Books & Artefacts, Cumbria ... 80
Stobart Davies Limited, Carmarthenshire 282
Trinders' Fine Tools, Suffolk 226
Uncle Phil's Books, West Midlands 239
Whittle, Bookseller (Avril), Cumbria 80
Woburn Books, London N 159
Woodbine Books, West Yorkshire 245

DIARIES
Country Books, Derbyshire 82
Dolphin Books, Suffolk 225
Fifteenth Century Bookshop (The), East Sussex. 104
Handley (Christopher), Tyne and Wear 235
Jackdaw Books, Norfolk 188
Joel Segal Books, Devon 86
Lawrence Books, Nottinghamshire 203
Piccadilly Rare Books, East Sussex 105
R. & A. Books, East Sussex 101
Wembdon Books, Somerset 216

DICTIONARIES
Addyman Books, Powys 287
Alec–Smith Books (Alex), East Yorkshire 107
Annie's Books, S Yorks 221
Apocalypse, Surrey 232
Askew Books (Vernon), Wiltshire 251
Backfold Books, Herefordshire 127
baconboooks, London WC 176
Bernstein (Nicholas), London W 171
Books & Bygones (Pam Taylor), West Midlands 240
BOOKS4U, Flintshire 284
Chandos Books, Devon 85
Church Street Books, Norfolk 186
Colin Hancock, Ceredigion 282
Cornucopia Books, Lincolnshire 151
Courtenay Bookroom, Oxfordshire 205
Delectus Books, London WC 176
Derek Stirling Bookseller, Kent 141
Fifteenth Century Bookshop (The), East Sussex. 104
Hava Books, London SE 164
Jade Mountain Bookshop, Hampshire 125
Joel Segal Books, Devon 86
Karen Thomson, Oxfordshire 209
Kenya Books, East Sussex 100
Madoc Books, Conwy 284
Murphy (C.J.), Norfolk 189
Portobello Books, London W 174
Price (John), London N 158
PsychoBabel Books & Journals, Oxfordshire 205
Quaritch Ltd., (Bernard), London W 174
R. & A. Books, East Sussex 101
Sax Books, Suffolk 228
Scrivener's Books & Bookbinding, Derbyshire... 82

Seydi Rare Books (Sevin), London NW 161
Thorntons of Oxford Ltd., Oxfordshire 206
Walker Fine Books (Steve), Dorset 92
Yates Antiquarian Books (Tony), Leics 146

DINOSAURS
Baldwin's Scientific Books, Essex 111
Joel Segal Books, Devon 86
Kelpie's Books, Fife 271
R. & A. Books, East Sussex 101

DIRECTORIES
- GENERAL
Heritage, West Midlands 238
Joel Segal Books, Devon 86
Roger Collicott Books, Cornwall 74
Sparkes (Books) (Ray), Staffordshire 224

- BRITISH
Chapter & Verse, Lincolnshire 150
Craobh Rua Books, Co. Armagh 260
Dadd, Stephen, Kent 135
Debbage (John), Norfolk 189
Delph Books, Greater Manchester 120
Facet Books, Dorset 91
Joel Segal Books, Devon 86
Kemp Bookseller, Michael S, G Manchester 118
PsychoBabel Books & Journals, Oxfordshire 205
Sparkes (Books) (Ray), Staffordshire 224

DISNEYANA
Book Palace (The), London SE 163
Cygnet Books, East Yorkshire 107
Fifteenth Century Bookshop (The), East Sussex. 104
First Edition, The, Essex 109
Green Meadow Books, Cornwall 74
Print Matters, London SE 165
R. & A. Books, East Sussex 101
Roscrea Bookshop & Newsagents,
    Co. Tipperary 266
Stroh (M.A.), London E 154

DIVINING
Inner Bookshop (The), Oxfordshire 208
Joel Segal Books, Devon 86
Magis Books, Leics 146
McCrone (Audrey), Isle of Arran 274
Occultique, Northants 199
Wizard Books, Cambridgeshire 67

DOCUMENTS
- GENERAL
Apocalypse, Surrey 232
Collectables (W.H.), Suffolk 229
Farahar & Dupre (Clive & Sophie), Wiltshire ... 251
Ford (Richard), London W 172
Junk & Spread Eagle, London SE 164
Knowles - Antiquary (Roger J.), Staffordshire ... 223
Mayfly Ephemera, London W 173
Silverman (Michael), London SE 165
Wilson (Manuscripts) Ltd., (John), Glos 114

DOGS
Annie's Books, S Yorks 221
Apocalypse, Surrey 232

Backfold Books, Herefordshire 127
Bookworms Paradise Ltd., West Sussex 242
Cat Lit, Somerset 218
Chalmers Hallam (E.), Hampshire 125
Coch-y-Bonddu Books, Powys 290
Cornucopia Books, Lincolnshire 151
Country Books, Derbyshire 82
Countrymans Gallery (The), Leics 145
Crabtree (Mrs. C.), Greater Manchester 120
Dales & Lakes Book Centre, Cumbria 79
Debbage (John), Norfolk 189
Discovery Bookshop, Carmarthenshire............ 281
Dolphin Books, Suffolk.............................. 225
Doorbar (P. & D.), Gwynedd 285
Fifteenth Century Bookshop (The), East Sussex. 104
Fylde Books, Lancashire 144
Green Meadow Books, Cornwall 74
Halson Books, Cheshire 71
Head (John & Judith), Wiltshire 253
Home Farm Books, Warwickshire.................. 236
Intech Books, Northumberland 201
Jane Jones Books, Grampian 273
Joel Segal Books, Devon 86
Kelpie's Books, Fife.................................. 271
Kilgour (Sporting Books) (Ian), Leics 147
London & Sussex Antiquarian Book &
    Print Services, East Sussex....................... 101
Martin (Books and Pictures), (Brian P.), Surrey. 231
McInnes (P.F. & J.R.), Dorset 91
Oopalba Books, Cheshire............................ 71
Peel (Valerie), Berks 56
Priestpopple Books, Northumberland 201
R. & A. Books, East Sussex 101
Roger Collicott Books, Cornwall 74
Roland Books, Kent 138
Rolfe (John), London SE............................ 165
Sleepy Elephant Books & Artefacts, Cumbria ... 80
Stella Books, Monmouthshire 286
Tarka Books, Devon.................................. 84
Treasure Trove Books, Leics........................ 146
Wheen O'Books, Borders............................ 267
Whittle, Bookseller (Avril), Cumbria 80
Wright Trace Books, West Midlands............... 239

DOLLS & DOLLS' HOUSES

Addyman Books, Powys.............................. 287
Apocalypse, Surrey 232
Art Reference Books, Hampshire 124
BC Books, Cheshire 69
Bookmark (Children's Books), Wiltshire.......... 253
Bookworms Paradise Ltd., West Sussex 242
Cover to Cover, Merseyside......................... 185
Discovery Bookshop, Carmarthenshire............ 281
Elizabeth Ferguson, Grampian 272
Joel Segal Books, Devon 86
Oopalba Books, Cheshire............................ 71
R. & A. Books, East Sussex 101
Roadmaster Books, Kent............................ 136
Saint Swithin's Illustrated & Children's Books,
    London W 174
Sleepy Elephant Books & Artefacts, Cumbria ... 80
Staffs Bookshop (The), Staffordshire 223
Stroh (M.A.), London E 154
Twigg (Keith), Staffordshire........................ 224
Whittle, Bookseller (Avril), Cumbria 80

DOMESTICITY

Reading Lasses, Dumfries & Galloway 270
Susan Taylor Books, West Yorkshire 247
Whittle, Bookseller (Avril), Cumbria 80

DRAMA

Addyman Books, Powys.............................. 287
Alexander's Books, Warwickshire.................. 237
Apocalypse, Surrey 232
Autumn Leaves, Lincolnshire....................... 150
babelog.books, Herefordshire 127
Bookbox, Glos 115
Brighton Books, East Sussex........................ 99
Brock Books, N Yorks 192
Byre Books, Dumfries & Galloway................ 270
Caledonia Books, Strathclyde 278
Catalyst Booksearch Services, Devon.............. 87
Chaucer Head Bookshop, Warwickshire.......... 237
Clements (R.W.), London O 181
Cox Rare Books (Charles), Cornwall.............. 73
Dales & Lakes Book Centre, Cumbria............ 79
Darkwood Books, Co. Cork 263
Delectus Books, London WC........................ 176
Draca Books, West Yorkshire 248
Fifteenth Century Bookshop (The), East Sussex. 104
Forest Books of Manchester, Cheshire............ 70
Greenroom Books, West Yorkshire 247
Joel Segal Books, Devon 86
Judd Books, London WC............................ 177
Junk & Spread Eagle, London SE 164
Kent T. G., Surrey 230
Mellon's Books, East Sussex 101
Paramor (C.D.), Suffolk 228
Pordes Books Ltd., (Henry), London WC........ 177
PsychoBabel Books & Journals, Oxfordshire..... 205
Quaritch Ltd., (Bernard), London W.............. 174
R. & A. Books, East Sussex 101
Robert Temple, London N........................... 158
Roundstone Books, Lancashire 143
SaBeRo Books, London SW......................... 169
Terence Kaye - Bookseller, London NW 161
Theatreshire Books, N Yorks....................... 192
Till's Bookshop, Lothian 277
Travis & Emery Music Bookshop, London WC 178
Trinity Rare Books, Co. Leitrim 266
Updike Rare Books (John), Lothian 277
Willmott Bookseller (Nicholas), Cardiff........... 281
Woburn Books, London N 159

DRAWING

Annie's Books, S Yorks 221
Apocalypse, Surrey 232
Book Palace (The), London SE 163
Bookworms Paradise Ltd., West Sussex 242
Booth (Booksearch Service), (Geoff), Cheshire... 68
Crabtree (Mrs. C.), Greater Manchester 120
Fifteenth Century Bookshop (The), East Sussex. 104
Jean Hedger, Berks 55
Joel Segal Books, Devon 86
Print Matters, London SE........................... 165
R. & A. Books, East Sussex 101
Treasure Island (The), Greater Manchester....... 119

DRUGS

Bernard Dixon and Kath Adams, London O.... 182

Delectus Books, London WC........................ 176
Joel Segal Books, Devon 86
Parkinsons Books, Merseyside..................... 185
R M Books, Herts.................................... 132
Weiner (Graham), London N 158
Westons, Herts....................................... 132
Woburn Books, London N 159

DYES
Cover to Cover, Merseyside........................ 185
Joel Segal Books, Devon 86
Judith Mansfield, West Yorkshire.................. 249
N1 Books, East Sussex 105
Parkinsons Books, Merseyside..................... 185
Sleepy Elephant Books & Artefacts, Cumbria ... 80
Weiner (Graham), London N 158

EARLY IMPRINTS
Barry McKay Rare Books, Cumbria.............. 76
Blackwell's Rare Books, Oxfordshire.............. 208
Butler Rare Books, Buckinghamshire 61
Cobnar Books, Kent 141
David (G.), Cambridgeshire......................... 63
Derek Stirling Bookseller, Kent 141
Edwards (Christopher), Oxfordshire 209
Finch Rare Books Ltd. (Simon), London W..... 172
Golden Books Group, Devon 85
House of Figgis Ltd (The), Co. Galway 265
Junk & Spread Eagle, London SE................. 164
Leo Cadogan, London N 157
Maggs Brothers Limited, London W.............. 173
Martin (Books and Pictures), (Brian P.), Surrey . 231
Modern First Editions, West Yorkshire........... 247
Pickering & Chatto, London W.................... 174
Quaritch Ltd., (Bernard), London W.............. 174
Roger Treglown, Cheshire.......................... 70
Seydi Rare Books (Sevin), London NW 161
Susanne Schulz-Falster Rare Books, London N. 158
Tim Bryers Ltd, London WC 178
Unsworth's Booksellers, Suffolk................... 225
Woburn Books, London N 159

EARTH MYSTERIES
Abrahams (Mike), Staffordshire.................... 223
Atlantis Bookshop, London WC................... 176
Byre Books, Dumfries & Galloway................ 270
Chthonios Books, East Sussex..................... 102
Cofion Books, Pembrokeshire 286
Country Books, Derbyshire 82
Fifteenth Century Bookshop (The), East Sussex. 104
Gildas Books, Cheshire 68
Green Man Books, East Sussex 101
Inner Bookshop (The), Oxfordshire................ 208
J & J Burgess Booksellers, Cambridgeshire....... 64
Joel Segal Books, Devon 86
McCrone (Audrey), Isle of Arran.................. 274
Occultique, Northants.............................. 199
Pyecroft (Ruth), Glos 116
R. & A. Books, East Sussex 101
SETI Books, West Midlands........................ 239
Star Lord Books, Greater Manchester 119
Woburn Books, London N 159

EARTH SCIENCES
Andrew Hunter Rare Books, London SW 166

Baldwin's Scientific Books, Essex 111
Dean Byass, Bristol................................. 60
Jay Books, Lothian.................................. 276
Kalligraphia (formerly Charmouth Bounty
  Books), Isle of Wight............................. 133
Knowles - Antiquary (Roger J.), Staffordshire... 223
Orchid Book Distributors, Co. Clare.............. 262
Parkinsons Books, Merseyside..................... 185
Periplus Books, Buckinghamshire.................. 62
Pollak (P.M.), Devon 88
PsychoBabel Books & Journals, Oxfordshire..... 205
R. & A. Books, East Sussex 101
Roberts Books, Strathclyde 279
Roger Collicott Books, Cornwall 74
Weiner (Graham), London N 158
Westons, Herts....................................... 132
Woburn Books, London N 159

EASTER
R. & A. Books, East Sussex 101
S Swithin's Illustrated & Children's Books,
  London W 174
Samovar Books, Co. Dublin........................ 264

EASTERN PHILOSOPHY
Annie's Books, S Yorks 221
Apocalypse, Surrey 232
Art Book Company, (The), Suffolk................ 227
Bookbarrow, Cambridgeshire....................... 63
Chthonios Books, East Sussex..................... 102
Cofion Books, Pembrokeshire 286
Fifteenth Century Bookshop (The), East Sussex. 104
Gladstone Books, Lincolnshire 150
Inner Bookshop (The), Oxfordshire................ 208
Joel Segal Books, Devon 86
Occultique, Northants.............................. 199
Orchid Book Distributors, Co. Clare.............. 262
Parkinsons Books, Merseyside..................... 185
Portobello Books, London W 174
PsychoBabel Books & Journals, Oxfordshire..... 205
R. & A. Books, East Sussex 101
Star Lord Books, Greater Manchester 119
Till's Bookshop, Lothian 277

**ECCLESIASTICAL HISTORY
& ARCHITECTURE**
Apocalypse, Surrey 232
Barbican Bookshop, N Yorks 196
Bardsley's Books, Suffolk........................... 225
Beckham Books Ltd., Suffolk...................... 229
Bell (Peter), Lothian................................ 275
Bennett & Kerr Books, Oxfordshire............... 205
Berwick Books, Lincolnshire....................... 150
Birchden Books, London E 154
Carter, (Brian), Oxfordshire....................... 210
Cheshire Book Centre, Cheshire................... 69
Cofion Books, Pembrokeshire 286
Courtney & Hoff, N Yorks 197
Crouch Rare Books, Surrey 232
Edwards (Alan & Margaret), Kent 141
Fifteenth Century Bookshop (The), East Sussex. 104
Frost (Richard), Herts 129
Gage Postal Books, Essex 111
Hall's Bookshop, Kent.............................. 140
Haskell (R.H. & P.), Dorset 94

Hedgerow Books, S Yorks 221
Island Books, Devon 85
Joel Segal Books, Devon 86
Kyrios Books, Nottinghamshire 203
Leo Cadogan, London N 157
Mannwaring (M.G.), Bristol 59
Michael J Carroll, Co. Cork 263
Olynthiacs, Shropshire 213
Pagan Limited (Hugh), Hampshire 122
Pendleburys Bookshop, London N 158
R. & A. Books, East Sussex 101
Rosemary Pugh Books, Wiltshire 253
S.P.C.K., Bristol 59
St Philip's Books, Oxfordshire 208
Salsus Books, Worcs 256
Samovar Books, Co. Dublin 264
Scrivener's Books & Bookbinding, Derbyshire... 82
South Downs Book Service, West Sussex......... 243
Spenceley Books (David), West Yorkshire........ 248
Spooner & Co, Somerset 219
Staniland (Booksellers), Lincolnshire 152
Taylor & Son (Peter), Herts........................ 132
Thornber (Peter M.), N Yorks 195
Turton (John), Durham 98
Uncle Phil's Books, West Midlands 239
Whitchurch Books Ltd., Cardiff.................... 281
Winghale Books, Lincolnshire 152

ECCLESIOLOGY

Beckham Books Ltd., Suffolk 229
Bell (Peter), Lothian................................ 275
Chapter Two, London SE............................ 163
Leo Cadogan, London N 157
Winghale Books, Lincolnshire 152

ECOLOGY

Acanthophyllum Books, Wirral 184
Arden, Bookseller (C.), Powys...................... 287
Baron - Scientific Book Sales (P.J.), Somerset ... 216
Bernard Dixon and Kath Adams, London O.... 182
Brown-Studies, Strathclyde......................... 277
Calluna Books, Dorset 95
Cornucopia Books, Lincolnshire 151
Dolphin Books, Suffolk 225
Hawley (C.L.), N Yorks............................ 195
Inner Bookshop (The), Oxfordshire............... 208
Joel Segal Books, Devon 86
Orb's Bookshop, Grampian......................... 273
Orchid Book Distributors, Co. Clare.............. 262
Parkinsons Books, Merseyside...................... 185
R. & A. Books, East Sussex 101
Rosemary Pugh Books, Wiltshire 253
Woburn Books, London N 159
Woodside Books, Kent 135
Wyseby House Books, Berks 55

ECONOMICS

Barcombe Services, Essex............................ 108
Bernstein (Nicholas), London W 171
Bloomsbury Bookshop, London O 181
Burmester (James), Bristol.......................... 58
Camden Books, Somerset 215
Chesters (G. & J.), Staffordshire 224
Clifton Books, Essex 111
Cornucopia Books, Lincolnshire 151

Darkwood Books, Co. Cork........................ 263
Delectus Books, London WC....................... 176
Drury Rare Books (John), Essex................... 110
Edwards (London) Limited (Francis),
  London WC.. 176
Edwards in Hay-on-Wye (Francis), Powys 288
Foster Bookshop (Paul), London SW............. 167
Gladstone Books, Lincolnshire 150
Glenbower Books, Co. Dublin 264
Hamish Riley-Smith, Norfolk....................... 191
Harrington Antiquarian Bookseller (Peter),
  London SW.. 167
Hay Cinema Bookshop Ltd., Powys............... 288
Herb Tandree Philosophy Books, Glos 116
Jade Mountain Bookshop, Hampshire............ 125
Jarndyce Antiquarian Booksellers, London WC. 177
Lawson & Company (E.M.), Oxfordshire 206
Lee Rare Books (Rachel), Bristol 59
Left on The Shelf, Cumbria......................... 78
Leo Cadogan, London N 157
Maghreb Bookshop (The), London WC.......... 177
Northern Herald Books, West Yorkshire........ 245
Parkinsons Books, Merseyside...................... 185
Pickering & Chatto, London W 174
Pollak (P.M.), Devon 88
Price (John), London N 158
PsychoBabel Books & Journals, Oxfordshire..... 205
Quaritch Ltd., (Bernard), London W............. 174
R. & A. Books, East Sussex 101
Rainford (Sheila), Herts 129
Reading Lasses, Dumfries & Galloway 270
Rowan (P. & B.), Co. Antrim 260
Spurrier (Nick), Kent 137
Staniland (Booksellers), Lincolnshire 152
Stern Antiquarian Bookseller (Jeffrey),
  N Yorks 198
Susanne Schulz-Falster Rare Books, London N. 158
Webb Books (John), S Yorks........................ 221
Wetherell (Frances), Cambridgeshire 65
Woburn Books, London N 159

EDUCATION & SCHOOL

Alba Books, Grampian 273
Anthony Spranger, Wiltshire........................ 252
Apocalypse, Surrey 232
Barcombe Services, Essex............................ 108
Black Five Books, Shropshire 214
Burmester (James), Bristol.......................... 58
Cofion Books, Pembrokeshire 286
Cornucopia Books, Lincolnshire 151
Delectus Books, London WC....................... 176
Delph Books, Greater Manchester................. 120
Drury Rare Books (John), Essex................... 110
Game Advice, Oxfordshire 208
Holtom (Christopher), Glos......................... 115
hullbooks.com, East Yorkshire 106
Jarndyce Antiquarian Booksellers, London WC. 177
Joel Segal Books, Devon 86
Kirkpatrick (Robert J.), London W 173
McGee (Terence J.), London O 180
Oopalba Books, Cheshire............................ 71
Parkinsons Books, Merseyside...................... 185
Pickering & Chatto, London W 174
Price (John), London N 158
Priestpopple Books, Northumberland 201

PsychoBabel Books & Journals, Oxfordshire..... 205
Quaritch Ltd., (Bernard), London W.............. 174
R. & A. Books, East Sussex 101
Reading Lasses, Dumfries & Galloway 270
Roland Books, Kent 138
Rutland Bookshop (The), Rutland 211
Saunders (Tom), Caerphilly 281
The Old Children's Bookshelf, Lothian 277
Tiffin (Tony and Gill), Durham 97
Transformer, Dumfries & Galloway............... 270
Wise (Derek), East Sussex.......................... 104
Yates Antiquarian Books (Tony), Leics........... 146

EGYPTOLOGY
Afar Books International, West Midlands........ 238
Alpha Books, London N............................ 156
Apocalypse, Surrey 232
Atlantis Bookshop, London WC................... 176
Books B.C., London O 180
Byre Books, Dumfries & Galloway................ 270
Cavern Books, Cheshire 70
Chthonios Books, East Sussex 102
Cofion Books, Pembrokeshire 286
Crouch Rare Books, Surrey......................... 232
Delectus Books, London WC....................... 176
Dolphin Books, Suffolk............................. 225
Ford Books (David), Herts 130
G&S Books, Kent 138
Good for Books, Lincolnshire 149
Hylton Booksearch, Merseyside 184
J.E. Burns Booksellers, Merseyside 185
Joel Segal Books, Devon 86
Kingswood Books, Dorset 94
My Back Pages, London SW 168
Occultique, Northants............................... 199
P. and P. Books, Worcs 256
Parkinsons Books, Merseyside...................... 185
Peter M Daly, Hampshire 126
Prospect House Books, Co. Down................. 261
R. & A. Books, East Sussex 101
Scrivener's Books & Bookbinding, Derbyshire... 82
Sue Lowell Natural History Books, London W . 175
Treasure Island (The), Greater Manchester....... 119
Treasure Trove Books, Leics........................ 146
Uncle Phil's Books, West Midlands 239
Whitchurch Books Ltd., Cardiff.................... 281
Wiend Books, Lancashire 143
Yesterday's Books, Dorset 92

ELECTIONS
Woburn Books, London N 159

ELECTRICITY & GAS
Elton Engineering Books, London W 172
Weiner (Graham), London N 158
Westons, Herts...................................... 132

ELECTRONICS
R. & A. Books, East Sussex 101
Westons, Herts...................................... 132
Whistler's Books, London SW 169

EMBLEMATA
John Underwood Antiquarian Books, Norfolk.. 189
Parikian, Rare Books (Diana), London W 174

Seydi Rare Books (Sevin), London NW 161

EMBROIDERY
Addyman Books, Powys............................. 287
Annie's Books, S Yorks 221
Apocalypse, Surrey 232
Black Cat Books, Norfolk.......................... 187
Browse Books, Lancashire 143
Byrom Textile Bookroom (Richard), Lancashire 142
Camilla's Bookshop, East Sussex 101
Cofion Books, Pembrokeshire 286
Cornucopia Books, Lincolnshire 151
Cover to Cover, Merseyside......................... 185
Crabtree (Mrs. C.), Greater Manchester 120
Don Kelly Books, London W 172
DPE Books, Devon 87
Edwards, Fiona, Nottinghamshire 203
Fifteenth Century Bookshop (The), East Sussex. 104
Hay Castle, Powys................................... 288
Hennessey Bookseller (Ray), East Sussex 100
Joel Segal Books, Devon 86
Judith Mansfield, West Yorkshire.................. 249
Just Books, Cornwall 75
McCrone (Audrey), Isle of Arran.................. 274
Old Bookshop (The), West Midlands 240
Oopalba Books, Cheshire 71
Park Gallery & Bookshop (The), Northants 200
R. & A. Books, East Sussex 101
Reading Lasses, Dumfries & Galloway 270
Scrivener's Books & Bookbinding, Derbyshire... 82
Sleepy Elephant Books & Artefacts, Cumbria ... 80
Smith Books (Keith), Herefordshire 128
Traveller's Bookshelf (The), Somerset 218
Trinders' Fine Tools, Suffolk 226
Uncle Phil's Books, West Midlands 239
Warnes (Felicity J.), London O 180
Wheen O'Books, Borders........................... 267
Whittle, Bookseller (Avril), Cumbria 80
Young (D. & J.), Powys............................ 291

ENAMEL
Cover to Cover, Merseyside......................... 185
Joel Segal Books, Devon 86
R. & A. Books, East Sussex 101

ENCYCLOPAEDIAS
Apocalypse, Surrey 232
Cornucopia Books, Lincolnshire 151
Frew Limited (Robert), London SW 167
PsychoBabel Books & Journals, Oxfordshire..... 205
Quaritch Ltd., (Bernard), London W.............. 174
R. & A. Books, East Sussex 101
Susanne Schulz-Falster Rare Books, London N. 158

ENERGY
- GENERAL
Coulthurst (Richard), Greater Manchester 120
Parkinsons Books, Merseyside...................... 185
R. & A. Books, East Sussex 101
Westons, Herts...................................... 132

- ALTERNATIVE
Coulthurst (Richard), Greater Manchester 120
Inner Bookshop (The), Oxfordshire................ 208
R. & A. Books, East Sussex 101

Westons, Herts 132

- FUELS

Coulthurst (Richard), Greater Manchester 120
R. & A. Books, East Sussex 101
Stroh (M.A.), London E 154
Westons, Herts 132

- POWER

Coulthurst (Richard), Greater Manchester 120
R. & A. Books, East Sussex 101
Westons, Herts 132

ENGINEERING

Baron - Scientific Book Sales (P.J.), Somerset ... 216
Bianco Library, West Sussex 241
Book House (The), Cumbria......................... 76
BookShop, The, Dumfries & Galloway........... 270
Bott, (Bookdealers) Ltd., (Martin), Greater
    Manchester 118
Clevedon Books, Somerset 217
Courtwood Books, Co. Laois........................ 265
Cox (Geoff), Devon 90
Elton Engineering Books, London W 172
Falconwood Transport & Military Bookshop,
    London O 183
Gaskell Rare Books (Roger), Cambridgeshire ... 66
Hylton Booksearch, Merseyside 184
Just Books, Cornwall 75
K.S.C. Books, Cheshire............................. 70
Kerr (Norman), Cumbria........................... 77
Parkinsons Books, Merseyside...................... 185
Phelps (Michael), West Sussex...................... 242
PsychoBabel Books & Journals, Oxfordshire..... 205
R. & A. Books, East Sussex 101
Robert Humm & Co, Lincolnshire 152
Roberts Books, Strathclyde 279
Roosterbooks, Northants............................ 199
Salway Books, Essex 112
Savona Books, Lincolnshire......................... 151
Stroh (M.A.), London E 154
Theatreshire Books, N Yorks........................ 192
Treasure Island (The), Greater Manchester....... 119
Trinders' Fine Tools, Suffolk 226
Weiner (Graham), London N 158
Westons, Herts 132
Wheen O'Books, Borders............................ 267
Whistler's Books, London SW 169

ENGINEERING - ELECTRICAL

Elton Engineering Books, London W 172
Oopalba Books, Cheshire............................ 71
Treasure Island (The), Greater Manchester....... 119
Westons, Herts 132

ENGLISH

Apocalypse, Surrey 232
babelog.books, Herefordshire 127
Burmester (James), Bristol.......................... 58
Cornucopia Books, Lincolnshire 151
Dales & Lakes Book Centre, Cumbria............. 79
Fifteenth Century Bookshop (The), East Sussex. 104
Hawley (C.L.), N Yorks.............................. 195
Joel Segal Books, Devon 86
Kenya Books, East Sussex 100

Leo Cadogan, London N 157
Olynthiacs, Shropshire 213
Pittville Books, Glos................................ 113
Price (John), London N 158
Quaritch Ltd., (Bernard), London W.............. 174
R. & A. Books, East Sussex 101
Wheen O'Books, Borders............................ 267

ENGRAVING

Apocalypse, Surrey 232
Besleys Books, Suffolk 225
Chapter & Verse, Lincolnshire...................... 150
Collinge & Clark, London WC...................... 176
Heritage, West Midlands 238
Lymelight Books & Prints, Dorset................. 93
Mulyan (Don), Merseyside.......................... 185
Myra Dean Illustated Books, Powys 287
R. & A. Books, East Sussex 101
Robin Doughty - Fine Books, West Midlands... 238
Stroh (M.A.), London E 154
Susanne Schulz-Falster Rare Books, London N. 158
Webb Books (John), S Yorks........................ 221
Woodbine Books, West Yorkshire................. 245

ENTERTAINMENT - GENERAL

Annie's Books, S Yorks 221
Apocalypse, Surrey 232
Aurora Books Ltd, Lothian.......................... 275
Autumn Leaves, Lincolnshire....................... 150
Bookshop (The), Norfolk 191
Byre Books, Dumfries & Galloway................. 270
Cavern Books, Cheshire............................. 70
Cofion Books, Pembrokeshire 286
DaSilva Puppet Books, Dorset 93
Discovery Bookshop, Carmarthenshire........... 281
Dolphin Books, Suffolk 225
Greenroom Books, West Yorkshire 247
Jade Mountain Bookshop, Hampshire 125
Joel Segal Books, Devon 86
Junk & Spread Eagle, London SE................. 164
Katnap Arts, Norfolk................................ 190
Kent T. G., Surrey 230
Kingfisher Book Service, Nottinghamshire 204
M. and A.C. Thompson, Norfolk.................... 191
Nevitsky (Philip), Greater Manchester 119
Paramor (C.D.), Suffolk 228
Pyecroft (Ruth), Glos 116
R. & A. Books, East Sussex 101
Roland Books, Kent 138
Stroma Books, Borders 267
Terence Kaye - Bookseller, London NW 161
Till's Bookshop, Lothian 277
Wheen O'Books, Borders............................ 267
Whitfield (Ken), Essex 110
Wood (Peter), Cambridgeshire...................... 65
Yesterday's News, Conwy........................... 283

ENTOMOLOGY

Arden, Bookseller (C.), Powys 287
Aurelian Books, London NW 160
Aviabooks, Glos 114
Besleys Books, Suffolk 225
Blest (Peter), Kent 138
Calluna Books, Dorset.............................. 95
Demar Books (Grant), Kent........................ 140

Edmund Pollinger Rare Books, London SW..... 166
Joel Segal Books, Devon 86
Lymelight Books & Prints, Dorset................. 93
Mobbs (A.J.), West Midlands 239
Orb's Bookshop, Grampian.......................... 273
Parkinsons Books, Merseyside....................... 185
Pemberley Books, Buckinghamshire 62
Pendleside Books, Lancashire....................... 143
Peter M Daly, Hampshire............................ 126
Phillip Robbins of Warwick, Warwickshire 237
Pollak (P.M.), Devon 88
R M Books, Herts...................................... 132
R. & A. Books, East Sussex 101
Tant Yn Ellen Books, Powys 290
Thin Read Line, Merseyside 184
Trotter Books (John), London N 158
Weiner (Graham), London N 158
Woodside Books, Kent 135

ENVIRONMENT, THE

Barcombe Services, Essex............................ 108
Country Books, Derbyshire 82
Dolphin Books, Suffolk............................... 225
Fifteenth Century Bookshop (The), East Sussex. 104
Hylton Booksearch, Merseyside 184
Joel Segal Books, Devon 86
Newgate Books and Translations,
   Northumberland 201
Parkinsons Books, Merseyside....................... 185
Peter M Daly, Hampshire............................ 126
Post–Horn Books, N Yorks 192
R. & A. Books, East Sussex 101
Reading Lasses, Dumfries & Galloway 270
Westons, Herts... 132

EROTICA

Annie's Books, S Yorks 221
Apocalypse, Surrey 232
Delectus Books, London WC........................ 176
Edmund Pollinger Rare Books, London SW..... 166
Eggeling Books (John), West Yorkshire 249
Good for Books, Lincolnshire 149
High Street Books, Devon 86
Hylton Booksearch, Merseyside 184
InterCol London, London N 157
Joel Segal Books, Devon 86
N1 Books, East Sussex 105
Occultique, Northants................................. 199
Paper Pleasures, Somerset 218
Price (John), London N 158
Price (R.W.), Nottinghamshire 203
R. & A. Books, East Sussex 101
Tsbbooks, London SW................................ 169
Zardoz Books, Wiltshire.............................. 254

ESKIMOS

R. & A. Books, East Sussex 101

ESOTERIC

Alpha Books, London N.............................. 156
Armchair Books, Lothian 275
Berwick Books, Lincolnshire........................ 150
Beware of the Leopard, Bristol...................... 58
Bookbarrow, Cambridgeshire........................ 63
Caduceus Books, Leics............................... 145

Chthonios Books, East Sussex....................... 102
Cofion Books, Pembrokeshire 286
Dawlish Books, Devon 86
Eastcote Bookshop (The), London O 180
Esoteric Dreams Bookshop, Cumbria 77
Fifteenth Century Bookshop (The), East Sussex. 104
Green Man Books, East Sussex 101
Greensleeves, Oxfordshire 206
High Street Books, Devon 86
Inner Bookshop (The), Oxfordshire................ 208
Invisible Books, East Sussex 100
Joel Segal Books, Devon 86
Magis Books, Leics.................................... 146
Main Point Books, Lothian 276
Needham Books, (Russell), Somerset.............. 219
Occultique, Northants................................. 199
Old Aberdeen Bookshop, Grampian 272
Old Station Pottery & Bookshop (The), Norfolk 191
Orchid Book Distributors, Co. Clare.............. 262
Pittville Books, Glos.................................. 113
PsychoBabel Books & Journals, Oxfordshire..... 205
Pyecroft (Ruth), Glos 116
R. & A. Books, East Sussex 101
Reid of Liverpool, Merseyside 184
Roger Treglown, Cheshire............................ 70
Roosterbooks, Northants.............................. 199
SETI Books, West Midlands......................... 239
Star Lord Books, Greater Manchester 119
Watkins Books Ltd., London WC................... 179
Waxfactor, East Sussex 100
Woburn Books, London N 159
Worlds End Bookshop, London SW 169

ESPIONAGE

AA1 Books, Dumfries & Galloway................ 269
Baldwin (M. & M.), Worcs 255
Bolland Books, Bedfordshire........................ 53
Burroughs (Andrew), Lincolnshire 152
Corfe Books, Surrey................................... 230
Crimes Ink, London E................................ 154
Dennys Sanders & Greene Ltd, East Sussex 100
Dolphin Books, Suffolk............................... 225
Grahame Thornton, Bookseller, Dorset........... 93
Hylton Booksearch, Merseyside 184
Island Books, Devon.................................. 85
Loretta Lay Books, London NW 161
Lost Books, Northants................................ 200
MilitaryHistoryBooks.com, Kent.................... 137
Ming Books, Dumfries & Galloway 270
Murphy (C.J.), Norfolk............................... 189
Price (R.W.), Nottinghamshire 203
R. & A. Books, East Sussex 101
Transformer, Dumfries & Galloway 270
Trinity Rare Books, Co. Leitrim 266
Undercover Books, Lincolnshire 152
Wayside Books and Cards, Oxfordshire 206
Williams (Bookdealer), (Richard), North Lincs.. 153

ETHICS

Apocalypse, Surrey 232
Gladstone Books, Lincolnshire 150
Hawley (C.L.), N Yorks.............................. 195
Joel Segal Books, Devon 86
Parkinsons Books, Merseyside....................... 185
PsychoBabel Books & Journals, Oxfordshire..... 205

R. & A. Books, East Sussex 101
Reading Lasses, Dumfries & Galloway 270
Samovar Books, Co. Dublin 264
Star Lord Books, Greater Manchester 119
Woburn Books, London N 159

ETHNOBOTANY
Atlantis Bookshop, London WC 176
Kenya Books, East Sussex 100
Park (Mike), London O 182
Westons, Herts 132

ETHNOGRAPHY
Bickford-Smith (G.) (formerly Snowden
  Smith Books), Surrey 232
Bracton Books, Cambridgeshire 63
Butcher (Pablo), Oxfordshire 206
Campbell Hewson Books (R.), Fife 271
Chalmers Hallam (E.), Hampshire 125
Delectus Books, London WC 176
Dennys Sanders & Greene Ltd, East Sussex 100
Empire Books, N Yorks 197
J.C. Deyong Books (Previously of Snowden
  Smith Books), London SW 168
Joel Segal Books, Devon 86
Kenya Books, East Sussex 100
Maghreb Bookshop (The), London WC 177
Michael Graves-Johnston, London SW 168
Nakota Curios, East Sussex 102
Reading Lasses, Dumfries & Galloway 270
Traveller's Bookshelf (The), Somerset 218
Woburn Books, London N 159
Yesterday's Books, Dorset 92

ETHNOLOGY
Allsworth Rare Books Ltd., London SW 166
Anwoth Books Ltd, Dumfries & Galloway 269
Craobh Rua Books, Co. Armagh 260
Delectus Books, London WC 176
Inner Bookshop (The), Oxfordshire 208
J.C. Deyong Books (Previously of Snowden
  Smith Books), London SW 168
Kenya Books, East Sussex 100
Maghreb Bookshop (The), London WC 177
Mandalay Bookshop, London SW 168
Randall (Tom), Somerset 218
Sue Lowell Natural History Books, London W . 175
Woburn Books, London N 159

ETIQUETTE
Apocalypse, Surrey 232
Black Cat Books, Norfolk 187
Lucas (Richard), London NW 161
R. & A. Books, East Sussex 101
Weininger Antiquarian Books (Eva M.),
  London NW 161

EUROPEAN BOOKS
Baldwin (Jack), Strathclyde 278
Hava Books, London SE 164
Joel Segal Books, Devon 86
Leo Cadogan, London N 157
PsychoBabel Books & Journals, Oxfordshire 205
Quaritch Ltd., (Bernard), London W 174
R. & A. Books, East Sussex 101

Seydi Rare Books (Sevin), London NW 161
Thorntons of Oxford Ltd., Oxfordshire 206
Woburn Books, London N 159

EUROPEAN STUDIES
PsychoBabel Books & Journals, Oxfordshire 205
R. & A. Books, East Sussex 101
Studio Bookshop, East Sussex 100
Winghale Books, Lincolnshire 152
Woburn Books, London N 159

EVOLUTION
Arden, Bookseller (C.), Powys 287
Austwick Hall Books, N Yorks 192
Baldwin's Scientific Books, Essex 111
Bernard Dixon and Kath Adams, London O 182
Bracton Books, Cambridgeshire 63
Earth Science Books, Wiltshire 252
Gladstone Books, Lincolnshire 150
Humanist Book Services, Cornwall 72
Ice House Books, Wiltshire 254
Joel Segal Books, Devon 86
Kalligraphia (formerly Charmouth Bounty
  Books), Isle of Wight 133
Lymelight Books & Prints, Dorset 93
Martin (Books and Pictures), (Brian P.), Surrey . 231
Parkinsons Books, Merseyside 185
Quaritch Ltd., (Bernard), London W 174
R M Books, Herts 132
R. & A. Books, East Sussex 101
Star Lord Books, Greater Manchester 119
Turret House, Norfolk 191
Wayside Books and Cards, Oxfordshire 206

EXAMINATION PAPERS
Apocalypse, Surrey 232

EXHIBITIONS
Batterham (David), London W 171
R. & A. Books, East Sussex 101
Studio Bookshop, East Sussex 100
Weiner (Graham), London N 158

EX-LIBRIS
Cox Old & Rare Books (Claude), Suffolk 227
Darkwood Books, Co. Cork 263
Derek Stirling Bookseller, Kent 141
Heraldry Today, Wiltshire 253
Heritage, West Midlands 238
Hodgson (Books) (Richard J.), N Yorks 196
Joel Segal Books, Devon 86
Murphy (C.J.), Norfolk 189
Reeves Technical Books, N Yorks 195
RGS Books, Surrey 234
Stalagluft Books, Tyne and Wear 235
Woburn Books, London N 159

EXOTIC BOOKS
Oak Tree Press, Oxfordshire 207
R. & A. Books, East Sussex 101
Woburn Books, London N 159

EX-PAT LITERATURE
Norton Books, N Yorks 192

EXPEDITIONS

Americanabooksuk, Cumbria...................... 76
Brad Books, Essex..................................... 110
Cavendish Rare Books, London N 156
Craobh Rua Books, Co. Armagh.................. 260
Dolphin Books, Suffolk.............................. 225
Gildas Books, Cheshire.............................. 68
Jarvis Books, Derbyshire 83
Joel Segal Books, Devon 86
Kineton Nooks, Warwickshire..................... 236
Mandalay Bookshop, London SW 168
Peter M Daly, Hampshire........................... 126
R. & A. Books, East Sussex 101
Samovar Books, Co. Dublin........................ 264

EXPLORATION
- GENERAL

Americanabooksuk, Cumbria...................... 76
Austwick Hall Books, N Yorks 192
Barn Books, Buckinghamshire..................... 61
BookShop, The, Dumfries & Galloway 270
Byre Books, Dumfries & Galloway 270
C J Renwick Books, Powys......................... 287
Chalmers Hallam (E.), Hampshire 125
Coch-y-Bonddu Books, Powys 290
Ctesiphon Books, Greater Manchester 120
Dolphin Books, Suffolk.............................. 225
Empire Books, N Yorks.............................. 197
Garfi Books, Powys 291
Glacier Books, Tayside 280
Jarvis Books, Derbyshire 83
Joel Segal Books, Devon 86
Just Books, Cornwall 75
Kenya Books, East Sussex 100
Kingswood Books, Dorset 94
Kirkland Books, Cumbria............................ 78
Lost Books, Northants................................ 200
Mandalay Bookshop, London SW 168
Marble Hill Books, Outer London................. 182
Martin (Brian), Surrey 231
Mercat Books, Highland 274
O'Flynn Books, N Yorks............................. 197
O'Reilly - Mountain Books (John), Derbyshire.. 83
Peter M Daly, Hampshire........................... 126
Pinnacle Books, Lothian............................. 276
Preston Book Company, Lancashire 144
R. & A. Books, East Sussex ... 101
Saintfield Antiques & Fine Books, Co. Down ... 261
Samovar Books, Co. Dublin........................ 264
Wheen O'Books, Borders............................ 267
White (C.R.), London W............................. 175

- POLAR REGIONS

Bluntisham Books, Cambridgeshire............... 63
Fifteenth Century Bookshop (The), East Sussex. 104
Jarvis Books, Derbyshire 83
Joel Segal Books, Devon 86
Kineton Nooks, Warwickshire..................... 236
Lost Books, Northants................................ 200
O'Reilly - Mountain Books (John), Derbyshire.. 83
Peter M Daly, Hampshire........................... 126
R. & A. Books, East Sussex 101
Roz Hulse, Conwy 284

EXPLOSIVES

Stroh (M.A.), London E 154
Weiner (Graham), London N 158

EXPRESSIONISM

R. & A. Books, East Sussex 101
Woburn Books, London N 159

FABLES

Bookmark (Children's Books), Wiltshire.......... 253
Byre Books, Dumfries & Galloway................ 270
Country Books, Derbyshire 82
Cover to Cover, Merseyside........................ 185
Derek Stirling Bookseller, Kent 141
Eggeling Books (John), West Yorkshire 249
Fifteenth Century Bookshop (The), East Sussex. 104
First Edition, The, Essex 109
Gildas Books, Cheshire.............................. 68
Holtom (Christopher), Glos......................... 115
Jean Hedger, Berks................................... 55
Junk & Spread Eagle, London SE................. 164
R. & A. Books, East Sussex 101
Williams Rare Books (Nigel), London WC 179

FAIRGROUNDS

Anthony Vickers Books, N Yorks 195
Cottage Books, Leics................................. 145
Country Books, Derbyshire 82
Cover to Cover, Merseyside........................ 185
Decorum Books, London N 156
R. & A. Books, East Sussex 101
Randall (Tom), Somerset............................ 218
Stroh (M.A.), London E 154
Terence Kaye - Bookseller, London NW 161

FAIRY/FOLK TALES

Apocalypse, Surrey 232
Bates Books, London O 180
Bookmark (Children's Books), Wiltshire.......... 253
Books & Things, London W........................ 171
Byre Books, Dumfries & Galloway................ 270
Children's Bookshop (The), Herefordshire....... 127
Cornucopia Books, Lincolnshire 151
Country Books, Derbyshire 82
Cover to Cover, Merseyside........................ 185
Cox, Andrew, Shropshire............................ 214
Dales & Lakes Book Centre, Cumbria 79
Delectus Books, London WC....................... 176
Derek Stirling Bookseller, Kent 141
Eclectica, London SE 164
Eggeling Books (John), West Yorkshire 249
Fifteenth Century Bookshop (The), East Sussex. 104
First Edition, The, Essex 109
Fosters Bookshop, London W 172
Gildas Books, Cheshire.............................. 68
Harvest Books, Lancashire.......................... 144
Jean Hedger, Berks................................... 55
Joel Segal Books, Devon 86
Just Books, Cornwall 75
McCrone (Audrey), Isle of Arran 274
Minster Gate Bookshop, N Yorks................. 197
Myra Dean Illustated Books, Powys 287
Orb's Bookshop, Grampian......................... 273
Peter M Daly, Hampshire........................... 126
Print Matters, London SE........................... 165

R. & A. Books, East Sussex 101
Randall (Tom), Somerset............................ 218
Seydi Rare Books (Sevin), London NW 161

FAMILY
Gildas Books, Cheshire.............................. 68
Jackdaw Books, Norfolk 188
Reading Lasses, Dumfries & Galloway 270

FAMOUS PEOPLE
- GENERAL
Annie's Books, S Yorks 221
books2books, Devon................................. 88
Booth (Booksearch Service), (Geoff), Cheshire... 68
Brad Books, Essex................................... 110
Catalyst Booksearch Services, Devon.............. 87
Cofion Books, Pembrokeshire 286
Crabtree (Mrs. C.), Greater Manchester 120
Discovery Bookshop, Carmarthenshire............ 281
Dolphin Books, Suffolk.............................. 225
Fifteenth Century Bookshop (The), East Sussex. 104
Gladstone Books, Lincolnshire 150
J & J Burgess Booksellers, Cambridgeshire....... 64
Joel Segal Books, Devon 86
Karen Millward, Co. Cork........................... 263
MilitaryHistoryBooks.com, Kent.................... 137
R. & A. Books, East Sussex 101

- BADEN POWELL, LORD & LADY R.S.S.
R. & A. Books, East Sussex 101

- BEATLES, THE
firstpagebooks, Norfolk.............................. 189
R. & A. Books, East Sussex 101

- CHURCHILL, SIR WINSTON
Annie's Books, S Yorks 221
Antique Map and Bookshop (The), Dorset 94
Apocalypse, Surrey 232
Booth (Booksearch Service), (Geoff), Cheshire... 68
Cofion Books, Pembrokeshire 286
Dolphin Books, Suffolk.............................. 225
First Edition, The, Essex 109
Gladstone Books, Lincolnshire 150
Grahame Thornton, Bookseller, Dorset.......... 93
Island Books, Devon................................. 85
Kineton Nooks, Warwickshire...................... 236
Kirkman Ltd., (Robert), Bedfordshire............. 54
Little Stour Books, Kent 136
Lost Books, Northants............................... 200
Lymelight Books & Prints, Dorset................. 93
McCrone (Audrey), Isle of Arran 274
Mellon's Books, East Sussex 101
Preston Book Company, Lancashire 144
R. & A. Books, East Sussex 101
Sax Books, Suffolk 228
Uncle Phil's Books, West Midlands 239
White (C.R.), London W............................ 175

- CONAN DOYLE, SIR ARTHUR
First Edition, The, Essex 109
Preston Book Company, Lancashire 144
R. & A. Books, East Sussex 101

- CONNERY, SEAN
R. & A. Books, East Sussex 101

- ENTERTAINERS
Annie's Books, S Yorks 221
Apocalypse, Surrey 232
Booth (Booksearch Service), (Geoff), Cheshire... 68
Cofion Books, Pembrokeshire 286
Dolphin Books, Suffolk.............................. 225
First Edition, The, Essex 109
Hylton Booksearch, Merseyside 184
R. & A. Books, East Sussex 101
SETI Books, West Midlands......................... 239

- KENNEDY, JOHN F
Apocalypse, Surrey 232
Barn Books, Buckinghamshire...................... 61
Bolland Books, Bedfordshire....................... 53
Clifford Elmer Books Ltd., Cheshire 68
K Books, Cheshire................................... 70
R. & A. Books, East Sussex 101
SETI Books, West Midlands......................... 239

- MONROE, MARILYN
Booth (Booksearch Service), (Geoff), Cheshire... 68
R. & A. Books, East Sussex 101
Simply Read Books, East Sussex................... 100
Whittle, Bookseller (Avril), Cumbria 80

- NELSON & LADY HAMILTON, LORD
Annie's Books, S Yorks 221
Chapter Two, London SE........................... 163
Debbage (John), Norfolk 189
Marine & Cannon Books, Cheshire 71
Marine and Cannon Books, Cheshire 69
Martin (Brian), Surrey 231
Old Station Pottery & Bookshop (The), Norfolk 191
R. & A. Books, East Sussex 101

- PITT, WILLIAM (THE YOUNGER)
R. & A. Books, East Sussex 101

- STANLEY, W.M.
Kenya Books, East Sussex 100

- WAGNER, RICHARD
Apocalypse, Surrey 232
R. & A. Books, East Sussex 101

- WORDSWORTH, WILLIAM
Country Books, Derbyshire......................... 82
Island Books, Devon................................. 85
R. & A. Books, East Sussex 101

FARMING & LIVESTOCK
Backfold Books, Herefordshire..................... 127
Barn Books, Shropshire............................. 214
Besleys Books, Suffolk.............................. 225
Books for Content, Herefordshire.................. 127
Carningli Centre, Pembrokeshire.................. 286
Chantrey Books, S Yorks 222
Cheshire Book Centre, Cheshire................... 69
Clarke Books (David), Somerset 218
Cornucopia Books, Lincolnshire 151
Country Books, Derbyshire......................... 82

Debbage (John), Norfolk 189
Farquharson, (Hilary), Tayside 280
Fifteenth Century Bookshop (The), East Sussex. 104
Gladstone Books, Lincolnshire 150
Greta Books, Durham 97
Hodgson (Books) (Richard J.), N Yorks 196
Jane Jones Books, Grampian 273
Joel Segal Books, Devon 86
Kelpie's Books, Fife 271
Kilgour (Sporting Books) (Ian), Leics 147
Martin (Books and Pictures), (Brian P.), Surrey. 231
Mayhew (Veronica), Berks 57
Muttonchop Manuscripts, West Sussex 242
Old Station Pottery & Bookshop (The), Norfolk 191
Phenotype Books, Cumbria 79
R. & A. Books, East Sussex 101
Rutland Bookshop (The), Rutland 211
Scrivener's Books & Bookbinding, Derbyshire... 82
Stroh (M.A.), London E 154
Thornber (Peter M.), N Yorks 195
Westons, Herts 132

FARRIERS

Austwick Hall Books, N Yorks 192
Country Books, Derbyshire 82
Debbage (John), Norfolk 189
Martin (Books and Pictures), (Brian P.), Surrey. 231
Phenotype Books, Cumbria 79
R. & A. Books, East Sussex 101
Rutland Bookshop (The), Rutland 211

FASHION & COSTUME

Abrahams (Mike), Staffordshire 223
Art Reference Books, Hampshire 124
Backfold Books, Herefordshire 127
Ballantyne–Way (Roger), Suffolk 228
Barn Books, Buckinghamshire 61
Batterham (David), London W 171
Black Cat Books, Norfolk 187
Bookroom (The), Surrey 233
Byrom Textile Bookroom (Richard), Lancashire 142
Caliver Books, Essex 109
Cheshire Book Centre, Cheshire 69
Cornucopia Books, Lincolnshire 151
Cover to Cover, Merseyside 185
Crabtree (Mrs. C.), Greater Manchester 120
Derek Stirling Bookseller, Kent 141
Duncan & Reid, Lothian 276
Dyson (Anthony), West Midlands 239
Forest Books of Manchester, Cheshire 70
Garfi Books, Powys 291
Goodyer (Nicholas), London N 157
Greenroom Books, West Yorkshire 247
Gresham Books, Somerset 217
IDEA, London EC 155
Joel Segal Books, Devon 86
Lighthouse Books (The), Dorset 92
Meekins Books (Paul), Warwickshire 237
My Back Pages, London SW 168
N1 Books, East Sussex 105
Photo Books International, London WC 177
Pordes Books Ltd., (Henry), London WC 177
Portobello Books, London W 174
PsychoBabel Books & Journals, Oxfordshire 205
R. & A. Books, East Sussex 101

Read - Gorleston Books, (C.&J.), Norfolk 187
Reading Lasses, Dumfries & Galloway 270
Roland Books, Kent 138
Sleepy Elephant Books & Artefacts, Cumbria ... 80
Stroh (M.A.), London E 154
Trinders' Fine Tools, Suffolk 226
Warnes (Felicity J.), London O 180
Whittle, Bookseller (Avril), Cumbria 80
Worlds End Bookshop, London SW 169
Young (D. & J.), Powys 291

FEMINISM

Delectus Books, London WC 176
Dolphin Books, Suffolk 225
Dylans Bookstore, Swansea 291
Fortune Green Books, London NW 160
Game Advice, Oxfordshire 208
Hylton Booksearch, Merseyside 184
Joel Segal Books, Devon 86
Judd Books, London WC 177
Lane Books (Shirley), Isle of Wight 134
Quaritch Ltd., (Bernard), London W 174
R. & A. Books, East Sussex 101
Reading Lasses, Dumfries & Galloway 270
Red Star Books, Herts 129
Rosemary Pugh Books, Wiltshire 253
Spurrier (Nick), Kent 137
Stevens (Joan), Cambridgeshire 65
Susan Taylor Books, West Yorkshire 247
Symes Books (Naomi), Cheshire 71
Till's Bookshop, Lothian 277
Treasure Trove Books, Leics 146
Willmott Bookseller (Nicholas), Cardiff 281
Woburn Books, London N 159
Yesterday's News, Conwy 283

FICTION
- GENERAL

A. & R. Booksearch, Cornwall 73
Abacus Gallery, Staffordshire 224
Abbey Books, Cornwall 73
Addyman Books, Powys 287
ahbooks, Merseyside 184
Alister & Garon Books, Cambridgeshire 63
Allinson (Frank & Stella), Warwickshire 236
Anglo-American Rare Books, Surrey 232
Annie's Books, S Yorks 221
Antique Map and Bookshop (The), Dorset 94
Antiques on High, Oxfordshire 207
Any Old Books, Hampshire 121
Apocalypse, Surrey 232
Applin (Malcolm), Berks 55
Aurora Books Ltd, Lothian 275
Autumn Leaves, Lincolnshire 150
babelog.books, Herefordshire 127
Backfold Books, Herefordshire 127
Bass (Ben), Wiltshire 251
Beaton (Richard), East Sussex 103
Beckham Books Ltd., Suffolk 229
Bernstein (Nicholas), London W 171
Berwick Books, Lincolnshire 150
Beware of the Leopard, Bristol 58
Black Cat Bookshop, Leics 147
Black Five Books, Shropshire 214
Blackwell's Rare Books, Oxfordshire 208

Book For All Reasons (A.), Suffolk 228
Book House (The), Cumbria........................ 76
Bookcase, Cumbria................................ 76
Bookpassage (The), Shropshire.................... 212
Books & Collectables Ltd., Cambridgeshire...... 63
Books Afloat, Dorset.............................. 96
Books and Beans, Grampian 272
Books Antiques & Collectables, Devon 90
books2books, Devon............................... 88
BOOKS4U, Flintshire.............................. 284
Bookworm (The), Lothian 276
Booth (Booksearch Service), (Geoff), Cheshire... 68
Bosco Books, Cornwall............................ 72
Bowie Books & Collectables, East Yorkshire 107
Boz Books, Powys................................. 287
Brad Books, Essex................................ 110
Brighton Books, East Sussex...................... 99
Broadhurst of Southport Ltd., Merseyside 185
Caledonia Books, Strathclyde..................... 278
Capel Mawr Collectors Centre, Gwynedd 285
Carnforth Bookshop (The), Lancashire 142
Carningli Centre, Pembrokeshire.................. 286
Catalyst Booksearch Services, Devon............. 87
Cecilia Marsden, Surrey 232
Celtic Bookshop (The), Co. Limerick 266
Chalk (Old & Out of Print Books)
   (Christine M.), West Midlands 238
Charles Bossom, Cambridgeshire.................. 65
Charlie Byrne's Bookshop, Co. Galway........... 265
Chaucer Bookshop, Kent.......................... 136
Cheshire Book Centre, Cheshire.................. 69
Chris Adam Smith Modern First Editions,
   West Sussex................................... 243
Church Street Books, Norfolk..................... 186
Clarke Books (David), Somerset 218
Clements (R.W.), London O....................... 181
Clent Books, Worcs 255
Cobbles Books, Somerset......................... 217
Cofion Books, Pembrokeshire 286
Colwyn Books, Conwy 283
Coopercollectablebooks, Hampshire 123
Corfe Books, Surrey.............................. 230
Cox Rare Books (Charles), Cornwall.............. 73
Crabtree (Mrs. C.), Greater Manchester 120
Crimes Ink, London E............................ 154
Dales & Lakes Book Centre, Cumbria............ 79
D'Arcy Books, Wiltshire.......................... 252
Dartmoor Bookshop (The), Devon................ 84
Dennys Sanders & Greene Ltd, East Sussex 100
dgbbooks, West Sussex 244
Dolphin Books, Suffolk........................... 225
Doolin Dinghy Books, Co. Clare 262
Dormouse Bookshop (The), Norfolk 189
Eastcote Bookshop (The), London O 180
Eggeling Books (John), West Yorkshire 249
Elaine Lonsdale Books, West Yorkshire 247
Ellis, Bookseller (Peter), London WC 177
Ellwood Editions, Wiltshire...................... 253
Esoteric Dreams Bookshop, Cumbria 77
Fiction First, Cheshire 69
Fifteenth Century Bookshop (The), East Sussex. 104
Fireside Bookshop, Cumbria....................... 81
First Edition, The, Essex 109
First State Books, London W 172
Firsts in Print, Somerset 219

Ford Books (David), Herts 130
Fortune Green Books, London NW............... 160
Fossgate Books, N Yorks.......................... 197
Freeman's Corner Shop, Norfolk 189
Freya Books & Antiques, Norfolk................ 189
Gemini–Books, Shropshire 214
George St. Books, Derbyshire 83
Gladstone Books, Lincolnshire 150
Glasheen-Books, Surrey 231
Glenbower Books, Co. Dublin 264
Great Hall Bookshop, Buckinghamshire.......... 61
Greta Books, Durham 97
Grove Bookshop (The), N Yorks 195
Hab Books, London W............................ 172
Hall's Bookshop, Kent 140
Hambleton Books, N Yorks 196
Harrington (Adrian), London W................... 173
Hay Cinema Bookshop Ltd., Powys............... 288
Heckmondwike Book Shop, West Yorkshire 249
Hilton (Books) (P.J.), London W 173
Hurst (Jenny), Kent 137
Hylton Booksearch, Merseyside 184
Ian McKelvie Bookseller, London N............. 157
Innes Books, Shropshire 212
Intech Books, Northumberland 201
J & J Burgess Booksellers, Cambridgeshire....... 64
Jade Mountain Bookshop, Hampshire 125
Jenny Hurst, Kent............................... 138
Joel Segal Books, Devon 86
John L Capes (Books Maps & Prints), N Yorks 196
Just Books, Cornwall 75
K Books, Cheshire................................ 70
Kellow Books, Oxfordshire 206
Kim's Bookshop, West Sussex.................... 242
Kim's Bookshop, West Sussex.................... 241
Kingfisher Book Service, Nottinghamshire 204
L.M.S. Books, Herts 131
Last Century Books, Borders 267
Lewis (J.T. & P.), Cornwall...................... 73
Little Bookshop (The), Greater Manchester...... 119
Little Stour Books, Kent 136
M. and A.C. Thompson, Norfolk.................. 191
Maggy Browne, Lincolnshire 148
Main Point Books, Lothian........................ 276
Marble Hill Books, Outer London................ 182
Marine Workshop Bookshop, Dorset 93
Martin's Books, Powys 290
Modern First Editions, London O................. 181
Moffat Book Exchange, Dumfries & Galloway.. 269
Mr. Pickwick of Towcester, Northants........... 199
Much Ado Books, East Sussex 99
Mundy (David), Herts 129
Murphy (C.J.), Norfolk........................... 189
Neil's Books, London NW........................ 161
New Strand, The, Herefordshire 127
Oak Tree Press, Oxfordshire 207
O'Brien Books & Photo Gallery, Co. Limerick.. 266
O'Flynn Books, N Yorks.......................... 197
O'Flynn Books, N Yorks.......................... 197
Olynthiacs, Shropshire 213
Pamona Books, Lancashire 144
Paperbacks Plus, Bristol 59
Park Gallery & Bookshop (The), Northants 200
Parker Books (Mike), Cambridgeshire 64
Period & Classical Collections, East Sussex 103

Peter M Daly, Hampshire............................ 126
Peter's Bookshop, Norfolk 190
Pickering Bookshop, N Yorks...................... 196
Poor Richard's Books, Suffolk 226
Portobello Books, London W 174
Price (R.D.M. & I.M.) (Books), G Manchester.. 120
Price (R.W.), Nottinghamshire 203
Pyecroft (Ruth), Glos 116
Quaritch Ltd., (Bernard), London W.............. 174
Quinto of Charing Cross Road, London WC ... 178
R. & A. Books, East Sussex 101
Reading Lasses, Dumfries & Galloway 270
Reaveley Books, Devon 87
RGS Books, Surrey 234
Richmond Books, N Yorks........................... 194
Ripping Yarns, London N 158
Robert (Leslie), London W 174
Robert Temple, London N........................... 158
Roberts Fine Books (Julian), Lincolnshire....... 151
Roland Books, Kent 138
Roundstone Books, Lancashire...................... 143
Rutland Bookshop (The), Rutland 211
Rye Old Books, East Sussex 104
Savery Books, East Sussex 100
Sax Books, Suffolk 228
Seabreeze Books, Lancashire........................ 144
Shacklock Books (David), Suffolk 226
Shakeshaft (Dr. B.), Cheshire....................... 71
Simpson (Dave), Central 268
Sleepy Elephant Books & Artefacts, Cumbria ... 80
Slightly Foxed on Gloucester Road, London SW 167
Smith Books, (Sally), Suffolk 226
Sol Books, Devon 84
Spooner & Co, Somerset 219
Strathtay Antiquarian - Secondhand
  Books, Tayside 280
Sturford Books, Wiltshire 254
Surprise Books, Glos................................ 113
Tarka Books, Devon 84
Thistle Books, Strathclyde........................... 278
Thomas (E. Wyn), Conwy 284
Till's Bookshop, Lothian 277
Tilston (Stephen E.), London SE................... 165
Tindley & Chapman, London WC 178
Treasure Trove Books, Leics........................ 146
Trevorrow (Edwin), Herts 129
Trinity Rare Books, Co. Leitrim 266
Ventnor Rare Books, Isle of Wight............... 134
Vokes Books Ltd., N Yorks 194
Ward (R.F. & C.), Norfolk 187
Warrington Book Loft (The), Cheshire 71
Wealden Books, Kent 138
Wheen O'Books, Borders............................ 267
Whitfield (Ken), Essex 110
Williams (Bookdealer), (Richard), N Lincs....... 153
Williams Rare Books (Nigel), London WC 179
Willmott Bookseller (Nicholas), Cardiff.......... 281
Winchester Bookshop (The), Hampshire......... 126
Woburn Books, London N 159
Worlds End Bookshop, London SW 169
Yarborough House Bookshop, Shropshire 212
Zardoz Books, Wiltshire............................. 254

- 18TH CENTURY

Bookworms Paradise Ltd., West Sussex 242

Burmester (James), Bristol........................... 58
Derek Stirling Bookseller, Kent 141
Jarndyce Antiquarian Booksellers, London WC. 177
Joel Segal Books, Devon 86
Johnson Rare Book Collections (C.R.),
  London NW 161
Price (John), London N 158
Quaritch Ltd., (Bernard), London W.............. 174
Robert Temple, London N........................... 158
Seydi Rare Books (Sevin), London NW 161
Tiger Books, Kent.................................... 136
Valentine Rare Books, London W................. 175

- ADVENTURE

Annie's Books, S Yorks 221
Apocalypse, Surrey 232
Bookpassage (The), Shropshire..................... 212
Dolphin Books, Suffolk 225
Eggeling Books (John), West Yorkshire 249
Hylton Booksearch, Merseyside 184
Innes Books, Shropshire............................. 212
Jack and Molly's Trading Co....................... 90
Joel Segal Books, Devon 86
Post Mortem Books, West Sussex 242
R. & A. Books, East Sussex 101
Robert Temple, London N........................... 158
Roland Books, Kent 138
Simpson (Dave), Central 268
Spike's Books, N Yorks 192
Surprise Books, Glos 113
Tarka Books, Devon 84
Wheen O'Books, Borders............................ 267
Williams (Bookdealer), (Richard), N Lincs....... 153
Zardoz Books, Wiltshire............................. 254

- CRIME, DETECTIVE, SPY, THRILLERS

AA1 Books, Dumfries & Galloway................ 269
Abbey Books, Cornwall 73
Annie's Books, S Yorks 221
Antique Map and Bookshop (The), Dorset 94
Any Old Books, Hampshire 121
Apocalypse, Surrey 232
Armstrong's Books & Collectables, Leics......... 145
Berwick Books, Lincolnshire........................ 150
Beware of the Leopard, Bristol..................... 58
Birmingham Books, West Midlands 238
Black Cat Bookshop, Leics 147
Book Business (The), London W 171
Bookbarrow, Cambridgeshire........................ 63
Bookpassage (The), Shropshire..................... 212
Books and Beans, Grampian 272
books2books, Devon 88
Bookshop on the Heath, The, London SE 163
Bookworm (The), Lothian 276
Bookworms Paradise Ltd., West Sussex 242
Booth (Booksearch Service), (Geoff), Cheshire... 68
Catalyst Booksearch Services, Devon.............. 87
Cecilia Marsden, Surrey 232
Chris Adam Smith Modern First Editions,
  West Sussex... 243
Classic Crime Collections, Greater Manchester.. 119
Cotswold Internet Books, Glos..................... 113
Cowley, Bookdealer (K.W.), Somerset 217
Crimes Ink, London E............................... 154
Dolphin Books, Suffolk.............................. 225

Dunstan Books, Dorset 91
Dyson (Anthony), West Midlands 239
Eggeling Books (John), West Yorkshire 249
Enigma Books, Wiltshire 252
Esoteric Dreams Bookshop, Cumbria 77
Fantastic Literature, Essex 110
Fiction First, Cheshire 69
First Edition, The, Essex 109
firstpagebooks, Norfolk 189
Firsts in Print, Somerset 219
Framlingham Bookshop, Suffolk 227
Garfi Books, Powys 291
George St. Books, Derbyshire 83
HCB Wholesale, Powys 288
Heckmondwike Book Shop, West Yorkshire 249
Heppa (Christopher), Essex 108
Hight (Norman F.), Glamorgan 285
Hill (John S.), Devon 86
Hylton Booksearch, Merseyside 184
Ian McKelvie Bookseller, London N 157
Innes Books, Shropshire 212
Island Books, Devon 85
J & J Burgess Booksellers, Cambridgeshire 64
J and J Books, Lincolnshire 149
Jade Mountain Bookshop, Hampshire 125
Joel Segal Books, Devon 86
John Gorton Booksearch, East Sussex 105
John L Capes (Books Maps & Prints),
  N Yorks 196
Junk & Spread Eagle, London SE 164
K Books, Cheshire 70
Kelpie's Books, Fife 271
Kent (Books) (Mrs. A.), Suffolk 227
Kevin S. Ogilvie Modern First Editions,
  Grampian 272
Lucius Books, N Yorks 197
Mainly Fiction, Cheshire 68
McCaughtrie (K.A.), N Yorks 192
McGee (Terence J.), London O 180
Ming Books, Dumfries & Galloway 270
Modern First Editions, West Yorkshire 247
Murder & Mayhem, Powys 288
Newgate Books and Translations,
  Northumberland 201
Old Celtic Bookshop (The), Devon 87
Orb's Bookshop, Grampian 273
Paperbacks Plus, Bristol 59
Porcupine Books, London O 181
Post Mortem Books, West Sussex 242
Price (R.W.), Nottinghamshire 203
Pyecroft (Ruth), Glos 116
R. & A. Books, East Sussex 101
Reading Lasses, Dumfries & Galloway 270
Reaveley Books, Devon 87
Richmond Books, N Yorks 194
Robert (Leslie), London W 174
Robert Temple, London N 158
Roland Books, Kent 138
Roscrea Bookshop & Newsagents,
  Co. Tipperary 266
Ruebotham (Kirk), Cheshire 71
Savery Books, East Sussex 100
Sax Books, Suffolk 228
Simpson (Dave), Central 268
Spike's Books, N Yorks 192

Star Lord Books, Greater Manchester 119
Surprise Books, Glos 113
Sutcliffe (Mark), West Yorkshire 248
Tarka Books, Devon 84
The Glass Key, West Yorkshire 246
The Sanctuary Bookshop, Dorset 94
Till's Bookshop, Lothian 277
Tindley & Chapman, London WC 178
TP Children's Bookshop, West Yorkshire 245
Transformer, Dumfries & Galloway 270
Treasure Trove Books, Leics 146
Uncle Phil's Books, West Midlands 239
Vokes (Jeremiah), Durham 97
Ward (R.F. & C.), Norfolk 187
Wayside Books and Cards, Oxfordshire 206
Wheen O'Books, Borders 267
Wiend Books, Lancashire 143
Williams (Bookdealer), (Richard), N Lincs 153
Zardoz Books, Wiltshire 254

- FANTASY, HORROR

AA1 Books, Dumfries & Galloway 269
Annie's Books, S Yorks 221
Apocalypse, Surrey 232
Armstrong's Books & Collectables, Leics 145
Beware of the Leopard, Bristol 58
Birmingham Books, West Midlands 238
Black Cat Bookshop, Leics 147
Bookpassage (The), Shropshire 212
Books and Beans, Grampian 272
Books B.C., London O 180
Bookworm (The), Lothian 276
Bookworms Paradise Ltd., West Sussex 242
Booth (Booksearch Service), (Geoff), Cheshire... 68
Cowley, Bookdealer (K.W.), Somerset 217
Crimes Ink, London E 154
Daeron's Books, Buckinghamshire 62
Dalby (Richard), N Yorks 195
Eggeling Books (John), West Yorkshire 249
Enigma Books, Wiltshire 252
Fantastic Literature, Essex 110
Fantasy Centre, London N 156
Fiction First, Cheshire 69
Firsts in Print, Somerset 219
Gildas Books, Cheshire 68
HCB Wholesale, Powys 288
Hight (Norman F.), Glamorgan 285
Hylton Booksearch, Merseyside 184
Interstellar Master Traders, Lancashire 143
Joel Segal Books, Devon 86
Lucius Books, N Yorks 197
McGee (Terence J.), London O 180
Ming Books, Dumfries & Galloway 270
Modern First Editions, London O 181
Murder & Mayhem, Powys 288
Occultique, Northants 199
Old Celtic Bookshop (The), Devon 87
Orb's Bookshop, Grampian 273
Paperbacks Plus, Bristol 59
Porcupine Books, London O 181
Price (R.W.), Nottinghamshire 203
Pyecroft (Ruth), Glos 116
R. & A. Books, East Sussex 101
Richmond Books, N Yorks 194
Robert Temple, London N 158

Roland Books, Kent 138
Ruebotham (Kirk), Cheshire 71
SaBeRo Books, London SW 169
Sensawunda Books, Cheshire 68
Simpson (Dave), Central 268
Solaris Books, East Yorkshire 106
Spike's Books, N Yorks 192
Surprise Books, Glos 113
Tarka Books, Devon 84
The Glass Key, West Yorkshire 246
Till's Bookshop, Lothian 277
Transformer, Dumfries & Galloway 270
Uncle Phil's Books, West Midlands 239
Williams (Bookdealer), (Richard), N Lincs 153
Zardoz Books, Wiltshire 254

- GAY FICTION
Delectus Books, London WC 176
PsychoBabel Books & Journals, Oxfordshire 205
R. & A. Books, East Sussex 101
Tsbbooks, London SW 169

- HISTORICAL
Americanabooksuk, Cumbria 76
Annie's Books, S Yorks 221
Any Old Books, Hampshire 121
Apocalypse, Surrey 232
Black Cat Bookshop, Leics 147
Black Five Books, Shropshire 214
Bookpassage (The), Shropshire 212
Bookworms Paradise Ltd., West Sussex 242
Boris Books, Somerset 216
Chris Adam Smith Modern First Editions,
    West Sussex 243
Clarke Books (David), Somerset 218
Dolphin Books, Suffolk 225
Eggeling Books (John), West Yorkshire 249
Enscot Books, London SE 164
Fantastic Literature, Essex 110
First Edition, The, Essex 109
Firsts in Print, Somerset 219
Heppa (Christopher), Essex 108
Hylton Booksearch, Merseyside 184
Jack and Molly's Trading Co 90
John L Capes (Books Maps & Prints), N Yorks 196
Keel Row Bookshop, Tyne and Wear 235
Ming Books, Dumfries & Galloway 270
Orb's Bookshop, Grampian 273
R. & A. Books, East Sussex 101
Reaveley Books, Devon 87
Richmond Books, N Yorks 194
Robert (Leslie), London W 174
Robert Temple, London N 158
Roland Books, Kent 138
Simpson (Dave), Central 268
Spike's Books, N Yorks 192
Sturford Books, Wiltshire 254
Surprise Books, Glos 113
Tarka Books, Devon 84
Trevorrow (Edwin), Herts 129
Uncle Phil's Books, West Midlands 239
Wheen O'Books, Borders 267
Williams (Bookdealer), (Richard),
    North Lincolnshire 153
Williams Rare Books (Nigel), London WC 179

Zardoz Books, Wiltshire 254

- PONY NOVELS
Jane Badger Books, Northants 199

- ROMANTIC
Annie's Books, S Yorks 221
Black Cat Bookshop, Leics 147
Bookpassage (The), Shropshire 212
Bookworms Paradise Ltd., West Sussex 242
Eggeling Books (John), West Yorkshire 249
Mandalay Bookshop, London SW 168
Orb's Bookshop, Grampian 273
Price (R.W.), Nottinghamshire 203
R. & A. Books, East Sussex 101
Spike's Books, N Yorks 192
Tarka Books, Devon 84
Wheen O'Books, Borders 267
Williams (Bookdealer), (Richard),
    North Lincolnshire 153

- SCIENCE FICTION
AA1 Books, Dumfries & Galloway 269
Abbey Books, Cornwall 73
Altshuler (Jean), Cumbria 78
Annie's Books, S Yorks 221
Apocalypse, Surrey 232
Armchair Books, Lothian 275
Armstrong's Books & Collectables, Leics 145
Backfold Books, Herefordshire 127
Beckham Books Ltd., Suffolk 229
Beware of the Leopard, Bristol 58
Birmingham Books, West Midlands 238
Black Cat Bookshop, Leics 147
Bookbarrow, Cambridgeshire 63
Bookpassage (The), Shropshire 212
Books & Bygones (Pam Taylor), West Midlands 240
Books and Beans, Grampian 272
Books B.C., London O 180
books2books, Devon 88
Bookworm (The), Lothian 276
Bookworms Paradise Ltd., West Sussex 242
Booth (Booksearch Service), (Geoff), Cheshire... 68
Carningli Centre, Pembrokeshire 286
Cecilia Marsden, Surrey 232
Cofion Books, Pembrokeshire 286
Cold Tonnage Books, Surrey 234
Cowley, Bookdealer (K.W.), Somerset 217
Crimes Ink, London E 154
Daeron's Books, Buckinghamshire 62
Discovery Bookshop, Carmarthenshire 281
Driffield Bookshop (The), East Yorkshire 106
Eggeling Books (John), West Yorkshire 249
Fantastic Literature, Essex 110
Fantasy Centre, London N 156
Fiction First, Cheshire 69
firstpagebooks, Norfolk 189
Gildas Books, Cheshire 68
Glasheen-Books, Surrey 231
Heckmondwike Book Shop, West Yorkshire 249
Hight (Norman F.), Glamorgan 285
Hill (John S.), Devon 86
Idle Genius Books, London N 157
Interstellar Master Traders, Lancashire 143
Joel Segal Books, Devon 86

K Books, Cheshire.................................. 70
Lucius Books, N Yorks............................ 197
Ming Books, Dumfries & Galloway.............. 270
Modern First Editions, London O................ 181
Orb's Bookshop, Grampian........................ 273
Paperbacks Plus, Bristol 59
Porcupine Books, London O 181
Price (R.W.), Nottinghamshire 203
Print Matters, London SE.......................... 165
Pyecroft (Ruth), Glos 116
R. & A. Books, East Sussex 101
Reid of Liverpool, Merseyside..................... 184
Robert Temple, London N.......................... 158
Rods Books, Devon................................. 88
Roland Books, Kent 138
Ruebotham (Kirk), Cheshire....................... 71
SaBeRo Books, London SW........................ 169
Sensawunda Books, Cheshire...................... 68
Simpson (Dave), Central 268
Solaris Books, East Yorkshire..................... 106
Spike's Books, N Yorks 192
Surprise Books, Glos............................... 113
Tarka Books, Devon................................ 84
The Glass Key, West Yorkshire.................... 246
The Sanctuary Bookshop, Dorset.................. 94
Till's Bookshop, Lothian 277
Transformer, Dumfries & Galloway.............. 270
Treasure Trove Books, Leics....................... 146
Trevorrow (Edwin), Herts.......................... 129
Uncle Phil's Books, West Midlands 239
Ward (R.F. & C.), Norfolk 187
Waxfactor, East Sussex 100
Wayside Books and Cards, Oxfordshire 206
Wiend Books, Lancashire 143
Williams (Bookdealer), (Richard), N Lincs....... 153
Zardoz Books, Wiltshire........................... 254

- SUPERNATURAL

Annie's Books, S Yorks 221
Apocalypse, Surrey 232
Bookworms Paradise Ltd., West Sussex 242
Chris Adam Smith Modern First Editions,
    West Sussex...................................... 243
Dalby (Richard), N Yorks 195
Eggeling Books (John), West Yorkshire 249
Enigma Books, Wiltshire........................... 252
Fantastic Literature, Essex 110
Gildas Books, Cheshire 68
Green Man Books, East Sussex 101
J & J Burgess Booksellers, Cambridgeshire....... 64
John L Capes (Books Maps & Prints), N Yorks 196
Occultique, Northants.............................. 199
Porcupine Books, London O 181
R. & A. Books, East Sussex 101
Robert Temple, London N.......................... 158
Ruebotham (Kirk), Cheshire....................... 71
Surprise Books, Glos............................... 113
Tarka Books, Devon................................ 84
The Glass Key, West Yorkshire.................... 246
Williams (Bookdealer), (Richard), N Lincs....... 153
Zardoz Books, Wiltshire........................... 254

- WESTERNS

AA1 Books, Dumfries & Galloway................. 269
Americanabooksuk, Cumbria....................... 76
Annie's Books, S Yorks 221
Black Cat Bookshop, Leics 147
Bookworms Paradise Ltd., West Sussex 242
Crimes Ink, London E............................... 154
firstpagebooks, Norfolk............................ 189
Ming Books, Dumfries & Galloway.............. 270
Price (R.W.), Nottinghamshire 203
R. & A. Books, East Sussex 101
Rods Books, Devon................................. 88
Roscrea Bookshop & Newsagents,
    Co. Tipperary 266
Spike's Books, N Yorks 192
Surprise Books, Glos............................... 113
Tarka Books, Devon................................ 84
Ward (R.F. & C.), Norfolk 187
Wheen O'Books, Borders........................... 267
Williams (Bookdealer), (Richard), N Lincs....... 153
Zardoz Books, Wiltshire........................... 254

- WOMEN

Apocalypse, Surrey 232
Applin (Malcolm), Berks 55
Black Cat Bookshop, Leics 147
Boris Books, Somerset 216
Burmester (James), Bristol......................... 58
Cheshire Book Centre, Cheshire................... 69
Eggeling Books (John), West Yorkshire 249
Elaine Lonsdale Books, West Yorkshire.......... 247
Fortune Green Books, London NW................ 160
Jarndyce Antiquarian Booksellers, London WC. 177
Joel Segal Books, Devon 86
L.M.S. Books, Herts 131
Paperbacks Plus, Bristol 59
Poor Richard's Books, Suffolk 226
PsychoBabel Books & Journals, Oxfordshire..... 205
R. & A. Books, East Sussex 101
Reading Lasses, Dumfries & Galloway 270
Robert Temple, London N.......................... 158
Stevens (Joan), Cambridgeshire.................... 65
Susan Taylor Books, West Yorkshire.............. 247
Symes Books (Naomi), Cheshire 71
Tarka Books, Devon................................ 84
Tiger Books, Kent 136
Tindley & Chapman, London WC 178
Treasure Trove Books, Leics....................... 146
Wheen O'Books, Borders........................... 267
Williams (Bookdealer), (Richard), N Lincs....... 153
Yesterday's News, Conwy.......................... 283

- YOUNG ADULT MYSTERY
& ADVENTURE SERIES

Annie's Books, S Yorks 221
Apocalypse, Surrey 232
Bookmark (Children's Books), Wiltshire.......... 253
Bookroom (The), Surrey............................ 233
Children's Bookshop (The), Herefordshire........ 127
Chris Adam Smith Modern First Editions,
    West Sussex...................................... 243
Green Meadow Books, Cornwall 74
Porcupine Books, London O 181
R. & A. Books, East Sussex 101
Reaveley Books, Devon............................ 87
Robert (Leslie), London W 174
Wheen O'Books, Borders........................... 267
Williams (Bookdealer), (Richard), N Lincs....... 153

FICTIONAL CHARACTERS
Annie's Books, S Yorks 221
Apocalypse, Surrey 232
Fifteenth Century Bookshop (The), East Sussex. 104
R. & A. Books, East Sussex 101

FILM AND TELEVISION TIE-INS
Annie's Books, S Yorks 221
Black Cat Bookshop, Leics 147
books2books, Devon 88
Dolphin Books, Suffolk 225
Hambleton Books, N Yorks 196
Hurst (Jenny), Kent 137
Morris Secondhand & Antiquarian
  Books (Chris), Oxfordshire 208
Star Lord Books, Greater Manchester 119

FINANCE - GENERAL
Aurora Books Ltd, Lothian 275
Barcombe Services, Essex 108
Beware of the Leopard, Bristol 58
Hylton Booksearch, Merseyside 184
Quaritch Ltd., (Bernard), London W 174
Reid of Liverpool, Merseyside 184

FINE & RARE
Allsop (Duncan M.), Warwickshire 237
Amwell Book Company, London EC 155
Antique Map and Bookshop (The), Dorset 94
Arden, Bookseller (C.), Powys 287
Ardis Books, Hampshire 126
Atholl Fine Books, Tayside 280
Baldwin's Scientific Books, Essex 111
Barnacle Books, County Fermanagh 261
Barry McKay Rare Books, Cumbria 76
Baxter (Steve), Surrey 233
Blackwell's Rare Books, Oxfordshire 208
Books at Star Dot Star, West Midlands 240
Books on Spain, London O 182
Bookshop on the Heath, The, London SE 163
Booth (Booksearch Service), (Geoff), Cheshire... 68
Bristow & Garland, Hampshire 123
Broadhurst of Southport Ltd., Merseyside 185
Brock Books, N Yorks 192
Burmester (James), Bristol 58
Byblos Antiquarian & Rare Book, Hampshire .. 122
Camden Books, Somerset 215
Carnforth Bookshop (The), Lancashire 142
Cobnar Books, Kent 141
Cobweb Books, N Yorks 194
Colin Hancock, Ceredigion 282
Cooper Hay Rare Books, Strathclyde 278
Cox Rare Books (Charles), Cornwall 73
Dartmoor Bookshop (The), Devon 84
David (G.), Cambridgeshire 63
Dean Byass, Bristol 60
Drury Rare Books (John), Essex 110
Eastwood Books (David), Cornwall 72
Ellwood Editions, Wiltshire 253
Farquharson, (Hilary), Tayside 280
Fletcher (H.M.), Herts 131
Foster (Stephen), London NW 160
Fosters Bookshop, London W 172
Gardener & Cook, London SW 167
Golden Books Group, Devon 85

Grahame (Major Iain), Suffolk 225
Grayling (David A.H.), Cumbria 78
Green Man Books, East Sussex 101
Harrington (Adrian), London W 173
Harrington Antiquarian Bookseller
  (Peter), London SW 167
Hava Books, London SE 164
Heath (A.R.), Bristol 59
Heritage, West Midlands 238
Hughes Rare Books (Spike), Borders 267
Hutchison (Books) (Larry), Fife 271
Ian Briddon, Derbyshire 82
Ian McKelvie Bookseller, London N 157
Island Books, Devon 85
Joel Segal Books, Devon 86
Johnson Rare Book Collections (C.R.),
  London NW 161
Jones (Andrew), Suffolk 227
Kenny's Bookshop & Art Galleries Ltd.,
  Co. Galway 265
Kernaghans, Merseyside 185
Kerr (Norman), Cumbria 77
Kilgarriff (Raymond), East Sussex 105
Kirkman Ltd., (Robert), Bedfordshire 54
Lost Books, Northants 200
Lucius Books, N Yorks 197
Madoc Books, Conwy 284
Mair Wilkes Books, Fife 271
Marble Hill Books, Outer London 182
Marks Limited (Barrie), London N 157
Martin (Books and Pictures), (Brian P.), Surrey. 231
Martin (Brian), Surrey 231
Modern First Editions, West Yorkshire 247
N V Books, Warwickshire 236
Oak Tree Press, Oxfordshire 207
Offa's Dyke Books, Shropshire 213
O'Flynn Books, N Yorks 197
Orlando Booksellers, Lincolnshire 150
Parikian, Rare Books (Diana), London W 174
Parkinsons Books, Merseyside 185
Paul Hoare, Cornwall 74
Poetry Bookshop (The), Powys 289
Pollak (P.M.), Devon 88
Poole (William), London W 174
Quaritch Ltd., (Bernard), London W 174
R. & A. Books, East Sussex 101
Reeves Technical Books, N Yorks 195
Robert Temple, London N 158
Rochdale Book Company, Greater Manchester . 120
Rosley Books, Cumbria 81
Rowan (P. & B.), Co. Antrim 260
Roz Hulse, Conwy 284
Rutland Bookshop (The), Rutland 211
Rye Old Books, East Sussex 104
St Mary's Books & Prints, Lincolnshire 152
Saintfield Antiques & Fine Books, Co. Down ... 261
Stalagluft Books, Tyne and Wear 235
Stern Antiquarian Bookseller (Jeffrey),
  N Yorks 198
Susanne Schulz-Falster Rare Books, London N. 158
Taylor & Son (Peter), Herts 132
Temperley (David), West Midlands 238
Thorntons of Oxford Ltd., Oxfordshire 206
Tim Bryers Ltd, London WC 178
Trinity Rare Books, Co. Leitrim 266

Unsworth's Booksellers, Suffolk 225
Updike Rare Books (John), Lothian 277
Valentine Rare Books, London W 175
Venables (Morris & Juliet), Bristol 59
Woburn Books, London N 159
Woodbine Books, West Yorkshire 245
Words Etcetera Bookshop, Dorset 93
Yates Antiquarian Books (Tony), Leics 146
York (Graham), Devon 86

FINE ART

Amwell Book Company, London EC 155
Apocalypse, Surrey 232
Ars Artis, Oxfordshire 207
Art Book Company, (The), Suffolk 227
Art Reference Books, Hampshire 124
Besleys Books, Suffolk 225
Book Palace (The), London SE 163
Bookroom (The), Surrey 233
Brock Books, N Yorks 192
Bruce Holdsworth Books, East Sussex 105
Chalk (Old & Out of Print Books)
  (Christine M.), West Midlands 238
Cooper Hay Rare Books, Strathclyde 278
Cornucopia Books, Lincolnshire 151
Cover to Cover, Merseyside 185
Decorum Books, London N 156
Dew (Roderick), East Sussex 101
Dolphin Books, Suffolk 225
Don Kelly Books, London W 172
Farnborough Gallery, Hampshire 122
Handsworth Books, Essex 112
Heneage Art Books (Thomas), London SW 168
Hollett and Son (R.F.G.), Cumbria 79
Jane & John Kinnaird, Cumbria 78
Joel Segal Books, Devon 86
Mannwaring (M.G.), Bristol 59
Marlborough Rare Books Ltd., London W 173
Myra Dean Illustrated Books, Powys 287
Nelson (Elizabeth), Suffolk 226
Pagan Limited (Hugh), Hampshire 122
Phelan Books, Co. Dublin 264
Pordes Books Ltd., (Henry), London WC 177
Potterton Books, N Yorks 196
Pugh Books (Ian K.), Worcs 256
R. & A. Books, East Sussex 101
Ray Rare and Out of Print Books
  (Janette), N Yorks 198
Sleepy Elephant Books & Artefacts, Cumbria ... 80
Spelman (Ken), N Yorks 198
Stroh (M.A.), London E 154
Sykes (Graham), West Yorkshire 249
Tasburgh Books, Norfolk 190
Trinders' Fine Tools, Suffolk 226
Webb Books (John), S Yorks 221
Whittle, Bookseller (Avril), Cumbria 80
Woburn Books, London N 159
Wyseby House Books, Berks 55

FINE LEATHER BINDINGS
(SEE ALSO FINE & RARE)

Antique Map and Bookshop (The), Dorset 94
Atholl Fine Books, Tayside 280
Bayntun (George), Somerset 215
Booklore, Leics 146

C J Renwick Books, Powys 287
Eastwood Books (David), Cornwall 72
Ely Books, Cambridgeshire 65
First Edition, The, Essex 109
Foster (Stephen), London NW 160
Foster Bookshop (Paul), London SW 167
Fosters Bookshop, London W 172
Freeman's Corner Shop, Norfolk 189
Grove Bookshop (The), N Yorks 195
Hava Books, London SE 164
Kenny's Bookshop & Art Galleries Ltd.,
  Co. Galway 265
Kirkman Ltd., (Robert), Bedfordshire 54
Madoc Books, Conwy 284
Martin (Books and Pictures), (Brian P.), Surrey . 231
Mercat Books, Highland 274
Quaritch Ltd., (Bernard), London W 174
R. & A. Books, East Sussex 101
Red Star Books, Herts 129
Rosley Books, Cumbria 81
Saintfield Antiques & Fine Books, Co. Down ... 261
Staniland (Booksellers), Lincolnshire 152
Winchester Bookshop (The), Hampshire 126
Woodbine Books, West Yorkshire 245
Yates Antiquarian Books (Tony), Leics 146

FINE PRINTING

Apocalypse, Surrey 232
Ballantyne–Way (Roger), Suffolk 228
Bardsley's Books, Suffolk 225
Barlow (Vincent G.), Hampshire 125
Barry McKay Rare Books, Cumbria 76
Blackwell's Rare Books, Oxfordshire 208
Books & Things, London W 171
Bookstand, Dorset 94
Colin Hancock, Ceredigion 282
Collinge & Clark, London WC 176
Cox Old & Rare Books (Claude), Suffolk 227
Dales & Lakes Book Centre, Cumbria 79
Macfarlane (Mr. H.), Essex 111
Maggs Brothers Limited, London W 173
Mills Rare Books (Adam), Cambridgeshire 64
Myra Dean Illustrated Books, Powys 287
Oak Tree Press, Oxfordshire 207
Pordes Books Ltd., (Henry), London WC 177
Price (John), London N 158
R. & A. Books, East Sussex 101
Seydi Rare Books (Sevin), London NW 161
Solitaire Books, Somerset 216
Susanne Schulz-Falster Rare Books, London N. 158
Taylor Rare Books (Michael), Norfolk 187
Tucker (Alan & Joan), Glos 116
Updike Rare Books (John), Lothian 277
Woodbine Books, West Yorkshire 245

FIRE & FIRE FIGHTERS

Chris Porter Books, Norfolk 186
Cox (Geoff), Devon 90
Maggy Browne, Lincolnshire 148
R. & A. Books, East Sussex 101
St Swithin's Illustrated & Children's Books,
  London W 174
Theatreshire Books, N Yorks 192

FIREARMS/GUNS

Americanabooksuk, Cumbria 76
Bookworm (The), Lothian 276
Cader Idris Books, Powys 290
Caliver Books, Essex 109
Camilla's Bookshop, East Sussex 101
Chalmers Hallam (E.), Hampshire 125
Cornucopia Books, Lincolnshire 151
Duck (William), Hampshire 124
Farnborough Gallery, Hampshire 122
Greta Books, Durham 97
Guildmaster Books, Cheshire 70
Hay Castle, Powys 288
Helion & Company, West Midlands 239
Heneage Art Books (Thomas), London SW 168
Home Farm Books, Warwickshire 236
Joel Segal Books, Devon 86
Kilgour (Sporting Books) (Ian), Leics 147
Lost Books, Northants 200
Martin (Brian), Surrey 231
Meekins Books (Paul), Warwickshire 237
MilitaryHistoryBooks.com, Kent 137
Muttonchop Manuscripts, West Sussex 242
N1 Books, East Sussex 105
Prospect Books, Conwy 283
R. & A. Books, East Sussex 101
Ramrod Antiques, N Yorks 195
River Reads Bookshop, Devon 90
Stroh (M.A.), London E 154
Trinders' Fine Tools, Suffolk 226
Vinovium Books, Durham 97

FIRST EDITIONS

Allinson (Frank & Stella), Warwickshire 236
Amwell Book Company, London EC 155
Annie's Books, S Yorks 221
Anthony Sillem, East Sussex 102
Antiques on High, Oxfordshire 207
Apocalypse, Surrey 232
Ardis Books, Hampshire 126
Armchair Books, Lothian 275
Ash Rare Books, London SW 166
Aurora Books Ltd, Lothian 275
Autolycus, Shropshire 212
Avonworld Books, Somerset 216
Barnacle Books, County Fermanagh 261
Bass (Ben), Wiltshire 251
Bates Books, London O 180
Bath Old Books, Somerset 215
Baxter (Steve), Surrey 233
Bayntun (George), Somerset 215
BC Books, Cheshire 69
Beck (John), East Sussex 103
Bertram Rota Ltd., London WC 176
Berwick Books, Lincolnshire 150
Bibliophile Books, London E 154
Biblipola, London NW 160
Blackwell's Rare Books, Oxfordshire 208
Blythswood Bookshop, Highland 274
Book Business (The), London W 171
Book Gallery (The), Cornwall 74
Books & Collectables Ltd., Cambridgeshire 63
Books Only, Suffolk 226
books2books, Devon 88
Bookshop (The), Co. Donegal 263

Bookshop on the Heath, The, London SE 163
Booth (Booksearch Service), (Geoff), Cheshire... 68
Bowie Books & Collectables, East Yorkshire 107
Brighton Books, East Sussex 99
Castle Bookshop, Essex 108
Chapter & Verse, Lincolnshire 150
Cheshire Book Centre, Cheshire 69
Cobweb Books, N Yorks 194
Coopercollectablebooks, Hampshire 123
Cox Rare Books (Charles), Cornwall 73
Craobh Rua Books, Co. Armagh 260
Criterion Books, London O 181
Darkwood Books, Co. Cork 263
Deeside Books, Grampian 272
Dennys Sanders & Greene Ltd, East Sussex 100
Dolphin Books, Suffolk 225
Eastcote Bookshop (The), London O 180
Eastwood Books (David), Cornwall 72
Elaine Lonsdale Books, West Yorkshire 247
Ellis, Bookseller (Peter), London WC 177
Ely Books, Cambridgeshire 65
English (Toby), Oxfordshire 209
Enigma Books, Wiltshire 252
Evergreen Livres, Glos 116
Family-Favourites, East Yorkshire 106
Farnborough Gallery, Hampshire 122
Fiction First, Cheshire 69
Fifteenth Century Bookshop (The), East Sussex. 104
First State Books, London W 172
firstpagebooks, Norfolk 189
Firsts in Print, Somerset 219
Ford Books (David), Herts 130
Foster (Stephen), London NW 160
Foster Bookshop (Paul), London SW 167
Fosters Bookshop, London W 172
Frost (Richard), Herts 129
Gekoski (R.A.), London WC 177
Gildas Books, Cheshire 68
Glyn's Books, Shropshire 212
Greta Books, Durham 97
Hambleton Books, N Yorks 196
Harrington (Adrian), London W 173
Harrington Antiquarian Bookseller (Peter),
   London SW 167
Hava Books, London SE 164
Heppa (Christopher), Essex 108
Hill (John S.), Devon 86
Hylton Booksearch, Merseyside 184
Ian Briddon, Derbyshire 82
Ian McKelvie Bookseller, London N 157
Innes Books, Shropshire 212
Intech Books, Northumberland 201
Island Books, Devon 85
Jackdaw Books, Norfolk 188
Jarndyce Antiquarian Booksellers, London WC. 177
Joel Segal Books, Devon 86
John Underwood Antiquarian Books, Norfolk .. 189
Junk & Spread Eagle, London SE 164
K Books, Cheshire 70
Karen Millward, Co. Cork 263
Katnap Arts, Norfolk 190
Kendall–Carpenter (Tim), G Manchester 119
Keswick Bookshop, Cumbria 78
Kevin S. Ogilvie Modern First Editions,
   Grampian 272

Kineton Nooks, Warwickshire........................ 236
Kirkman Ltd., (Robert), Bedfordshire............ 54
L.M.S. Books, Herts 131
Leabeck Books, Oxfordshire 208
Little Stour Books, Kent 136
Lloyd-Davies (Sue), Carmarthenshire 282
Lucius Books, N Yorks................................ 197
Mainly Fiction, Cheshire 68
Marcet Books, London SE............................ 164
Martin (Books and Pictures), (Brian P.), Surrey. 231
Martin's Books, Powys 290
Mellon's Books, East Sussex 101
Ming Books, Dumfries & Galloway 270
Modern First Editions, London O................. 181
Modern Firsts Etc, Lancashire 142
Murphy (C.J.), Norfolk.............................. 189
Myra Dean Illustated Books, Powys 287
N V Books, Warwickshire............................ 236
Oak Tree Press, Oxfordshire 207
O'Flynn Books, N Yorks............................. 197
Palladour Books, Hampshire 125
Pamona Books, Lancashire 144
Penny Farthing, The, Lothian 277
Period & Classical Collections, East Sussex 103
Pickering Bookshop, N Yorks....................... 196
Poetry Bookshop (The), Powys 289
Price (R.W.), Nottinghamshire 203
Primrose Hill Books, London NW 161
Quaritch Ltd., (Bernard), London W............. 174
R. & A. Books, East Sussex 101
Rassam (Paul), London NW 161
Reading Lasses, Dumfries & Galloway 270
Riderless Horse Books, Norfolk.................... 186
Robert (Leslie), London W 174
Robert Temple, London N........................... 158
Rosley Books, Cumbria 81
Rowan House Books, Surrey 231
Roz Hulse, Conwy 284
Ruebotham (Kirk), Cheshire......................... 71
Sansovino Books, West Sussex 244
Scrivener's Books & Bookbinding, Derbyshire... 82
Sensawunda Books, Cheshire 68
Shakeshaft (Dr. B.), Cheshire 71
Shelley (E. & J.), Buckinghamshire 61
Skelton (Tony), Kent................................. 140
Slightly Foxed on Gloucester Road, London SW 167
Stevens (Joan), Cambridgeshire...................... 65
Surprise Books, Glos 113
Sutcliffe (Mark), West Yorkshire................... 248
Sykes (Graham), West Yorkshire 249
The Glass Key, West Yorkshire..................... 246
Thorntons of Oxford Ltd., Oxfordshire........... 206
Tiffin (Tony and Gill), Durham 97
Till's Bookshop, Lothian 277
Tindley & Chapman, London WC 178
Trevorrow (Edwin), Herts........................... 129
Trinity Rare Books, Co. Leitrim 266
Updike Rare Books (John), Lothian 277
Ward (R.F. & C.), Norfolk.......................... 187
Waterfield's, Oxfordshire 209
Webb Books (John), S Yorks........................ 221
Wheen O'Books, Borders............................ 267
Williams (Bookdealer), (Richard), N Lincs 153
Williams Rare Books (Nigel), London WC 179
Winchester Bookshop (The), Hampshire.......... 126

Woburn Books, London N 159
Woodbine Books, West Yorkshire................ 245

FISHERIES

Chalmers Hallam (E.), Hampshire................. 125
Coch-y-Bonddu Books, Powys 290
Garfi Books, Powys 291
Head (John & Judith), Wiltshire 253
hullbooks.com, East Yorkshire 106
Joel Segal Books, Devon 86
Martin (Books and Pictures), (Brian P.), Surrey. 231
McLaren Books Ltd, Strathclyde 279
Parkinsons Books, Merseyside....................... 185
Steven Simpson Books, Norfolk 190
Westons, Herts...................................... 132

FISHES

Alauda Books, Cumbria............................. 76
Atholl Fine Books, Tayside 280
Chalmers Hallam (E.), Hampshire................. 125
Coch-y-Bonddu Books, Powys 290
Cofion Books, Pembrokeshire 286
Cornucopia Books, Lincolnshire 151
Edmund Pollinger Rare Books, London SW..... 166
Head (John & Judith), Wiltshire 253
Joel Segal Books, Devon 86
Martin (Books and Pictures), (Brian P.), Surrey. 231
Martin (Brian), Surrey 231
Parkinsons Books, Merseyside....................... 185
Peter M Daly, Hampshire........................... 126
R. & A. Books, East Sussex 101
River Reads Bookshop, Devon...................... 90
Steven Simpson Books, Norfolk 190
Sub Aqua Prints and Books, Hampshire 123

FLAGS

Joel Segal Books, Devon 86
Marine & Cannon Books, Cheshire 71
Marine and Cannon Books, Cheshire 69
R. & A. Books, East Sussex 101

FLORA & FAUNA

Acanthophyllum Books, Wirral 184
Alauda Books, Cumbria............................. 76
Antique Map and Bookshop (The), Dorset 94
Baldwin's Scientific Books, Essex 111
Besleys Books, Suffolk 225
Calluna Books, Dorset.............................. 95
Carningli Centre, Pembrokeshire................... 286
Coch-y-Bonddu Books, Powys 290
Crabtree (Mrs. C.), Greater Manchester 120
Dales & Lakes Book Centre, Cumbria 79
Edmund Pollinger Rare Books, London SW..... 166
Fifteenth Century Bookshop (The), East Sussex. 104
Garfi Books, Powys 291
Grahame Thornton, Bookseller, Dorset........... 93
Inner Bookshop (The), Oxfordshire 208
J & J Burgess Booksellers, Cambridgeshire....... 64
Jay Books, Lothian.................................. 276
Joel Segal Books, Devon 86
Kenya Books, East Sussex 100
Kingfisher Book Service, Nottinghamshire 204
Langford Press, Lincolnshire........................ 151
Mandalay Bookshop, London SW 168
Mercat Books, Highland 274

O'Flynn Books, N Yorks............................ 197
Orb's Bookshop, Grampian......................... 273
Parkinsons Books, Merseyside..................... 185
Peter M Daly, Hampshire........................... 126
Prospect House Books, Co. Down................. 261
R. & A. Books, East Sussex 101
Roger Collicott Books, Cornwall 74
Shakeshaft (Dr. B.), Cheshire...................... 71
Shearwater Books, Northumberland............... 201
Summerfield Books Ltd, Cumbria 79
Treasure Island (The), Greater Manchester...... 119
Westons, Herts 132
Wheen O'Books, Borders........................... 267
Woodside Books, Kent 135

FLOWER ARRANGING

Blest (Peter), Kent 138
Court Hay Books, West Midlands................. 239
Crabtree (Mrs. C.), Greater Manchester 120
Farnborough Gallery, Hampshire.................. 122
Joel Segal Books, Devon 86
Park (Mike), London O 182
R. & A. Books, East Sussex 101
Reading Lasses, Dumfries & Galloway 270
Roadmaster Books, Kent............................ 136

FOLIO SOCIETY, THE

Antique Map and Bookshop (The), Dorset 94
Ardis Books, Hampshire 126
Avery (Alan), N Yorks 194
Backfold Books, Herefordshire.................... 127
Barbican Bookshop, N Yorks 196
Bath Old Books, Somerset 215
Birmingham Books, West Midlands............... 238
Bookbox, Glos 115
BOOKS4U, Flintshire............................... 284
Booth (Booksearch Service), (Geoff), Cheshire... 68
Bonython Bookshop, Cornwall..................... 75
Camilla's Bookshop, East Sussex 101
Cheshire Book Centre, Cheshire................... 69
Chevin Books, West Yorkshire..................... 249
Coach House Books, Worcs 256
Cobbles Books, Somerset........................... 217
Cofion Books, Pembrokeshire 286
Dales & Lakes Book Centre, Cumbria............ 79
Dandy Lion Editions, Surrey 233
Discovery Bookshop, Carmarthenshire........... 281
Dolphin Books, Suffolk............................. 225
Eastgate Bookshop, East Yorkshire 106
Ellwood Editions, Wiltshire 253
Fifteenth Century Bookshop (The), East Sussex. 104
Fisher & Sperr, London N.......................... 157
Ford Books (David), Herts 130
Fossgate Books, N Yorks........................... 197
Fosters Bookshop, London W 172
G. C. Books Ltd., Dumfries & Galloway......... 270
Good for Books, Lincolnshire...................... 149
Hab Books, London W.............................. 172
Hava Books, London SE............................ 164
Island Books, Devon................................ 85
JB Books & Collectables, West Sussex 243
Joel Segal Books, Devon 86
Junk & Spread Eagle, London SE................. 164
Lighthouse Books (The), Dorset 92
My Back Pages, London SW 168

Myra Dean Illustated Books, Powys 287
New Strand, The, Herefordshire 127
O'Brien Books & Photo Gallery, Co. Limerick.. 266
O'Connor Fine Books, Lancashire................. 144
Old Station Pottery & Bookshop (The), Norfolk 191
Park Gallery & Bookshop (The), Northants 200
Parrott Books, Oxfordshire 209
Pauline Harries Books, Hampshire 123
Penny Farthing, The, Lothian 277
Piccadilly Rare Books, East Sussex 105
Poetry Bookshop (The), Powys 289
Portobello Books, London W 174
PsychoBabel Books & Journals, Oxfordshire..... 205
R. & A. Books, East Sussex 101
Richmond Books, N Yorks.......................... 194
Ross Old Books & Prints, Herefordshire 128
Sax Books, Suffolk 228
Scrivener's Books & Bookbinding, Derbyshire... 82
Shacklock Books (David), Suffolk 226
Sleepy Elephant Books & Artefacts, Cumbria ... 80
Tasburgh Books, Norfolk 190
Tiffin (Tony and Gill), Durham 97
Treasure Trove Books, Leics........................ 146
Trinity Rare Books, Co. Leitrim 266
Westwood Books (Mark), Powys 289
Westwood Books Ltd, Cumbria.................... 80
Whittle, Bookseller (Avril), Cumbria 80

FOLKLORE

Alpha Books, London N............................ 156
Apocalypse, Surrey 232
Books, Denbighshire................................ 284
Books on Spain, London O......................... 182
Bracton Books, Cambridgeshire.................... 63
Byre Books, Dumfries & Galloway................ 270
Caduceus Books, Leics.............................. 145
Cottage Books, Leics................................ 145
Country Books, Derbyshire 82
Daeron's Books, Buckinghamshire................. 62
Dales & Lakes Book Centre, Cumbria............ 79
Dancing Goat Bookshop (The), Norfolk 187
Delectus Books, London WC....................... 176
Doolin Dinghy Books, Co. Clare 262
DPE Books, Devon 87
Edwards (London) Limited (Francis),
    London WC 176
Edwards in Hay–on–Wye (Francis), Powys 288
Elizabeth Ferguson, Grampian 272
Ellwood Editions, Wiltshire 253
Fifteenth Century Bookshop (The), East Sussex. 104
Gilbert (R.A.), Somerset............................ 219
Gildas Books, Cheshire............................. 68
Grampian Books, Grampian......................... 273
Green Man Books, East Sussex 101
Harvest Books, Lancashire.......................... 144
Hava Books, London SE............................ 164
Hobgoblin Books, Hampshire 125
Holtom (Christopher), Glos......................... 115
Hutchison (Books) (Larry), Fife................... 271
Inner Bookshop (The), Oxfordshire............... 208
Joel Segal Books, Devon 86
Lowe (John), Norfolk............................... 188
M. and A.C. Thompson, Norfolk.................. 191
Magis Books, Leics.................................. 146
Michael J Carroll, Co. Cork 263

Minster Gate Bookshop, N Yorks 197
Occultique, Northants 199
Orb's Bookshop, Grampian 273
Philip Hopper, Essex 110
R. & A. Books, East Sussex 101
Randall (Tom), Somerset 218
Thornber (Peter M.), N Yorks 195
Walker Fine Books (Steve), Dorset 92

FOOD & DRINK

Annie's Books, S Yorks 221
Apocalypse, Surrey 232
Arden Books & Cosmographia, Warwickshire... 236
Aurora Books Ltd, Lothian 275
Backfold Books, Herefordshire 127
Black Cat Books, Norfolk 187
Books & Bygones, Berks 57
Books at Star Dot Star, West Midlands 240
Capel Mawr Collectors Centre, Gwynedd 285
Chantrey Books, S Yorks 222
Clarke (Janet), Somerset 215
Collectable Books, London SE 163
Cooking = The Books, Glos 115
Cooks Books, East Sussex 99
Crabtree (Mrs. C.), Greater Manchester 120
Dales & Lakes Book Centre, Cumbria 79
Dusty Books, Powys 290
Edmund Pollinger Rare Books, London SW 166
Edwards, Fiona, Nottinghamshire 203
Elmfield Books, West Midlands 238
Fifteenth Century Bookshop (The), East Sussex. 104
Ford Books (David), Herts 130
Foster (Stephen), London NW 160
Gardener & Cook, London SW 167
Garfi Books, Powys 291
Gladstone Books, Lincolnshire 150
Grahame Thornton, Bookseller, Dorset 93
Gresham Books, Somerset 217
Hall's Bookshop, Kent 140
Hurst (Jenny), Kent 137
Ian Briddon, Derbyshire 82
Joel Segal Books, Devon 86
Junk & Spread Eagle, London SE 164
Lucas (Richard), London NW 161
Marcet Books, London SE 164
Mr. Mac, Dumfries & Galloway 269
Much Ado Books, East Sussex 99
N1 Books, East Sussex 105
New Strand, The, Herefordshire 127
Parkinsons Books, Merseyside 185
Quaritch Ltd., (Bernard), London W 174
R. & A. Books, East Sussex 101
Rebecca Hardie Rare Books, London W 171
Seeber (Liz), East Sussex 102
Sleepy Elephant Books & Artefacts, Cumbria ... 80
Stroh (M.A.), London E 154
Susanne Schulz-Falster Rare Books, London N. 158
The Glass Key, West Yorkshire 246
The Sanctuary Bookshop, Dorset 94
Weiner (Graham), London N 158
Wheen O'Books, Borders 267
Whittle, Bookseller (Avril), Cumbria 80

FORE-EDGE PAINTINGS

Chas J. Sawyer, Kent 140

Cox Old & Rare Books (Claude), Suffolk 227
Davis, Antiquarian Books (Guy), Notts 204
Game Advice, Oxfordshire 208
Harrington (Adrian), London W 173
Harrington Antiquarian Bookseller (Peter),
  London SW 167
Kirkman Ltd., (Robert), Bedfordshire 54
Poetry Bookshop (The), Powys 289

FOREIGN TEXTS

Anthony Neville, Kent 138
Apocalypse, Surrey 232
Artco, Nottinghamshire 204
Atlas, London N 156
Baldwin (Jack), Strathclyde 278
Books on Spain, London O 182
Classic Bindings Ltd, London SW 166
Crouch Rare Books, Surrey 232
Hab Books, London W 172
Hellenic Bookservices, London NW 161
Hesketh & Ward Ltd., London SW 168
Joel Segal Books, Devon 86
Midnight Oil Books, Fife 271
Needham Books, (Russell), Somerset 219
Orbis Books (London) Ltd., London W 173
Owen (J.V.), Conwy 284
owenbooks65, Conwy 283
Parikian, Rare Books (Diana), London W 174
Poetry Bookshop (The), Powys 289
Poole (William), London W 174
PsychoBabel Books & Journals, Oxfordshire 205
Robertshaw (John), Cambridgeshire 66
Roundstone Books, Lancashire 143
Sturford Books, Wiltshire 254
Thorntons of Oxford Ltd., Oxfordshire 206

FORESTRY

Besleys Books, Suffolk 225
Coch-y-Bonddu Books, Powys 290
Country Books, Derbyshire 82
Court Hay Books, West Midlands 239
Dales & Lakes Book Centre, Cumbria 79
Joel Segal Books, Devon 86
Kenya Books, East Sussex 100
Mandalay Bookshop, London SW 168
New Strand, The, Herefordshire 127
Park (Mike), London O 182
Parkinsons Books, Merseyside 185
R. & A. Books, East Sussex 101
Stobart Davies Limited, Carmarthenshire 282
Summerfield Books Ltd, Cumbria 79
Westons, Herts 132
Woodside Books, Kent 135

FOSSILS

Baldwin's Scientific Books, Essex 111
Cox, Andrew, Shropshire 214
Earth Science Books, Wiltshire 252
Inner Bookshop (The), Oxfordshire 208
J & J Burgess Booksellers, Cambridgeshire 64
Joel Segal Books, Devon 86
Kalligraphia (formerly Charmouth Bounty
  Books), Isle of Wight 133
Knowles - Antiquary (Roger J.), Staffordshire ... 223
Martin (Books and Pictures), (Brian P.), Surrey. 231

Parkinsons Books, Merseyside 185
Peter M Daly, Hampshire 126
R. & A. Books, East Sussex 101
Randall (Tom), Somerset 218
Roberts Books, Strathclyde 279
Roger Collicott Books, Cornwall 74
Savona Books, Lincolnshire 151
The Sanctuary Bookshop, Dorset 94
Westons, Herts 132

FOURTH WAY
Alpha Books, London N 156
Inner Bookshop (The), Oxfordshire 208
Needham Books, (Russell), Somerset 219

FREE THOUGHT
Church Street Books, Norfolk 186
Forder (R.W.), Hampshire 121
Humanist Book Services, Cornwall 72
Left on The Shelf, Cumbria 78
Northern Herald Books, West Yorkshire 245
Price (John), London N 158
Quaritch Ltd., (Bernard), London W 174
Stevens (Joan), Cambridgeshire 65
Turton (John), Durham 98
Webb Books (John), S Yorks 221
Woburn Books, London N 159

FREEMASONRY & ANTI-MASONRY
Alpha Books, London N 156
Bibliophile (The), S Yorks 221
Chapter Two, London SE 163
Chas J. Sawyer, Kent 140
Debbage (John), Norfolk 189
Fun in Books, Surrey 234
Gilbert (R.A.), Somerset 219
Hava Books, London SE 164
Inner Bookshop (The), Oxfordshire 208
InterCol London, London N 157
Occultique, Northants 199
R. & A. Books, East Sussex 101
Samovar Books, Co. Dublin 264
SETI Books, West Midlands 239
Treasure Island (The), Greater Manchester 119
Yesterday's News, Conwy 283

FRENCH FOREIGN LEGION, THE
Bookworms Paradise Ltd., West Sussex 242
Burroughs (Andrew), Lincolnshire 152
Rods Books, Devon 88
Wiend Books, Lancashire 143

FRENCH REVOLUTION PERIOD
PUBLICATIONS
Quaritch Ltd., (Bernard), London W 174

FREUDIANA
Apocalypse, Surrey 232
Barcombe Services, Essex 108
Delectus Books, London WC 176
Inner Bookshop (The), Oxfordshire 208
Joel Segal Books, Devon 86
Parkinsons Books, Merseyside 185
R M Books, Herts 132

FRUITARIANISM
Park (Mike), London O 182

FUNGI
Bernard Dixon and Kath Adams, London O 182
Calluna Books, Dorset 95
Court Hay Books, West Midlands 239
Edmund Pollinger Rare Books, London SW 166
Gardener & Cook, London SW 167
Joel Segal Books, Devon 86
Martin (Books and Pictures), (Brian P.), Surrey . 231
Martin (Brian), Surrey 231
Park (Mike), London O 182
Parkinsons Books, Merseyside 185
R. & A. Books, East Sussex 101
Summerfield Books Ltd, Cumbria 79
Woodside Books, Kent 135

FUR TRADE
Americanabooksuk, Cumbria 76

FURNITURE
Art Reference Books, Hampshire 124
Brock Books, N Yorks 192
Clark (Nigel A.), London SE 163
Cornucopia Books, Lincolnshire 151
Cover to Cover, Merseyside 185
Dales & Lakes Book Centre, Cumbria 79
Don Kelly Books, London W 172
Fifteenth Century Bookshop (The), East Sussex . 104
Foster (Stephen), London NW 160
Hadfield (G.K.), Cumbria 79
Heneage Art Books (Thomas), London SW 168
Joel Segal Books, Devon 86
Keith Langford, London E 154
N1 Books, East Sussex 105
Nelson (Elizabeth), Suffolk 226
Phillips of Hitchin (Antiques) Ltd., Herts 131
Portus Books, Hampshire 122
R. & A. Books, East Sussex 101
Reeves Technical Books, N Yorks 195
Scrivener's Books & Bookbinding, Derbyshire ... 82
Sleepy Elephant Books & Artefacts, Cumbria ... 80
Stobart Davies Limited, Carmarthenshire 282
Trinders' Fine Tools, Suffolk 226
Upper–Room Books, Somerset 217
Whittle, Bookseller (Avril), Cumbria 80

FURNITURE AND CABINET MAKING
Upper–Room Books, Somerset 217

FUTURISM
Cover to Cover, Merseyside 185
Delectus Books, London WC 176

GAMBLING
Amos (Denis W.), Herts 130
Delectus Books, London WC 176
Garwood & Voigt, Kent 139
InterCol London, London N 157
Joel Segal Books, Devon 86
Junk & Spread Eagle, London SE 164
Quaritch Ltd., (Bernard), London W 174
R. & A. Books, East Sussex 101
Susanne Schulz-Falster Rare Books, London N. 158

Yesterday's News, Conwy 283

GAMES

Annie's Books, S Yorks 221
Baron (Christopher), Cheshire 68
Ben–Nathan (Jack), London O 180
Bookmark (Children's Books), Wiltshire 253
Bowers Chess Suppliers (Francis),
  Cambridgeshire 67
Cheshire Book Centre, Cheshire 69
Cornucopia Books, Lincolnshire 151
Fifteenth Century Bookshop (The), East Sussex. 104
Game Advice, Oxfordshire 208
Garwood & Voigt, Kent 139
Green Meadow Books, Cornwall 74
InterCol London, London N 157
Joel Segal Books, Devon 86
R. & A. Books, East Sussex 101
R. S. & P. A. Scowen, London O 181
Saint Swithin's Illustrated & Children's Books,
  London W 174
Treasure Island (The), Greater Manchester 119

GANDHIANA

Inner Bookshop (The), Oxfordshire 208
Rayner (Hugh Ashley), Somerset 215

GARDENING

- GENERAL

Abacus Gallery, Staffordshire 224
Annie's Books, S Yorks 221
Apocalypse, Surrey 232
Arden Books & Cosmographia, Warwickshire... 236
Arden, Bookseller (C.), Powys 287
Ashwell Books, Wiltshire 252
Backfold Books, Herefordshire 127
Barn Books, Shropshire 214
Barnhill Books, Isle of Arran 274
Belfry Books, Nottinghamshire 203
Besleys Books, Suffolk 225
Bianco Library, West Sussex 241
Biff Books and Records, S Yorks 221
Blest (Peter), Kent 138
Book House (The), Cumbria 76
Bookbox, Glos 115
Bookroom (The), Surrey 233
Books, Denbighshire 284
Books & Collectables Ltd., Cambridgeshire 63
Books for Content, Herefordshire 127
Bosco Books, Cornwall 72
Brighton Books, East Sussex 99
Brown-Studies, Strathclyde 277
Browse Books, Lancashire 143
Bunyan Books, Bedfordshire 53
Camilla's Bookshop, East Sussex 101
Chantrey Books, S Yorks 222
Chaucer Bookshop, Kent 136
Cheshire Book Centre, Cheshire 69
Clark (M.R.), West Yorkshire 245
Clarke Books (David), Somerset 218
Court Hay Books, West Midlands 239
Crabtree (Mrs. C.), Greater Manchester 120
Dales & Lakes Book Centre, Cumbria 79
D'Arcy Books, Wiltshire 252
Dartmoor Bookshop (The), Devon 84

Discovery Bookshop, Carmarthenshire 281
Dolphin Books, Suffolk 225
Duck (William), Hampshire 124
Dusty Books, Powys 290
Elizabeth Ferguson, Grampian 272
Ellis, Bookseller (Peter), London WC 177
Esoteric Dreams Bookshop, Cumbria 77
Fifteenth Century Bookshop (The), East Sussex. 104
Ford Books (David), Herts 130
Furneaux Books (Lee), Devon 89
Gardener & Cook, London SW 167
Garfi Books, Powys 291
George St. Books, Derbyshire 83
GfB: the Colchester Bookshop, Essex 108
Glasheen-Books, Surrey 231
Good for Books, Lincolnshire 149
Goodyer (Nicholas), London N 157
HCB Wholesale, Powys 288
Hennessey Bookseller (Ray), East Sussex 100
Hollett and Son (R.F.G.), Cumbria 79
Hollingshead (Chris), London O 182
Hünersdorff Rare Books, London SW 168
Internet Bookshop UK Ltd., Glos 113
Ivelet Books Ltd., Surrey 233
J.E. Burns Booksellers, Merseyside 185
Jade Mountain Bookshop, Hampshire 125
Joel Segal Books, Devon 86
Junk & Spread Eagle, London SE 164
Just Books, Cornwall 75
Langford Press, Lincolnshire 151
Macbuiks, N Yorks 193
Mannwaring (M.G.), Bristol 59
Marble Hill Books, Outer London 182
Martin (Brian), Surrey 231
McCrone (Audrey), Isle of Arran 274
Ming Books, Dumfries & Galloway 270
My Back Pages, London SW 168
New Strand, The, Herefordshire 127
Oasis Booksearch, Cambridgeshire 67
Optimus Books Ltd, West Sussex 244
Paper Moon Books, Glos 116
Park (Mike), London O 182
Park Gallery & Bookshop (The), Northants 200
Parrott Books, Oxfordshire 209
Penny Farthing, The, Lothian 277
Peter M Daly, Hampshire 126
Portobello Books, London W 174
Potterton Books, N Yorks 196
Quaritch Ltd., (Bernard), London W 174
Queen Victoria PH, Torfaen 292
R. & A. Books, East Sussex 101
Rare & Racy, S Yorks 222
River Reads Bookshop, Devon 90
Roland Books, Kent 138
Rutland Bookshop (The), Rutland 211
Seeber (Liz), East Sussex 102
Silver Trees Books, West Midlands 238
Slightly Foxed on Gloucester Road, London SW 167
Staniland (Booksellers), Lincolnshire 152
Sue Lowell Natural History Books, London W . 175
Summerfield Books Ltd, Cumbria 79
Tant Yn Ellen Books, Powys 290
Tarka Books, Devon 84
Thin Read Line, Merseyside 184
Trinders' Fine Tools, Suffolk 226

Valerie Merritt, Worcs 256
Vokes Books Ltd., N Yorks 194
Wadard Books, Kent 137
Westwood Books Ltd, Cumbria.................... 80
Wheen O'Books, Borders........................... 267
Winchester Bookshop (The), Hampshire.......... 126
Wyseby House Books, Berks 55

- ORGANIC

Barn Books, Shropshire.............................. 214
Court Hay Books, West Midlands................. 239
Crabtree (Mrs. C.), Greater Manchester 120
Fifteenth Century Bookshop (The), East Sussex. 104
Inner Bookshop (The), Oxfordshire................ 208
Joel Segal Books, Devon 86
Macbuiks, N Yorks 193
R. & A. Books, East Sussex 101
Saracen Books, Derbyshire......................... 83
Wheen O'Books, Borders........................... 267

GEMMOLOGY

Baldwin's Scientific Books, Essex 111
Barmby (C. & A.J.), Kent............................ 140
Don Kelly Books, London W 172
Earth Science Books, Wiltshire..................... 252
Hadfield (G.K.), Cumbria 79
J.G. Natural History Books, Surrey 233
Joel Segal Books, Devon 86
Mandalay Bookshop, London SW 168
Nibris Books, London SW.......................... 169
Phelps (Michael), West Sussex...................... 242
R. & A. Books, East Sussex 101
Savona Books, Lincolnshire......................... 151
Trinders' Fine Tools, Suffolk 226

GENDER STUDIES

Delectus Books, London WC....................... 176
Hylton Booksearch, Merseyside 184
Joel Segal Books, Devon 86
Kenya Books, East Sussex 100
Pittville Books, Glos................................. 113
PsychoBabel Books & Journals, Oxfordshire..... 205
R. & A. Books, East Sussex 101
Reading Lasses, Dumfries & Galloway 270
Tsbbooks, London SW 169
Woburn Books, London N 159

GENEALOGY

Aitchison (Lesley), Bristol 58
Ambra Books, Bristol................................ 58
Annie's Books, S Yorks 221
Bell (Peter), Lothian................................. 275
Bookworms Paradise Ltd., West Sussex 242
Brewin Books Ltd., Warwickshire 237
Cofion Books, Pembrokeshire 286
De Burca Rare Books, Co. Dublin 264
Delph Books, Greater Manchester................. 120
Dennys Sanders & Greene Ltd, East Sussex 100
Farquharson, (Hilary), Tayside..................... 280
Grampian Books, Grampian......................... 273
Hawes Books, Norfolk............................... 190
Hay Cinema Bookshop Ltd., Powys............... 288
Heraldry Today, Wiltshire........................... 253
Heritage, West Midlands 238
Herne Bay Books, Kent 138

Hill Books (Alan), S Yorks 222
Hutchison (Books) (Larry), Fife.................... 271
Idle Booksellers (The), West Yorkshire 245
Island Books, Devon................................. 85
Joel Segal Books, Devon 86
Kabristan Archives, Shropshire..................... 214
Kent T. G., Surrey 230
Kingfisher Book Service, Nottinghamshire 204
Knowles - Antiquary (Roger J.), Staffordshire... 223
Moore (C.R.), Shropshire 213
Saintfield Antiques & Fine Books, Co. Down ... 261
Spooner & Co, Somerset 219
Thornber (Peter M.), N Yorks 195
Titford (John), Derbyshire 82
Townsend (John), Berks 57
Turton (John), Durham 98
Tyger Press, London N 158
Williams (Bookdealer), (Richard), N Lincs 153

GENETICS

Baldwin's Scientific Books, Essex 111
Bernard Dixon and Kath Adams, London O.... 182
Gladstone Books, Lincolnshire 150
Parkinsons Books, Merseyside...................... 185
R M Books, Herts.................................... 132
Stroh (M.A.), London E 154
Turret House, Norfolk............................... 191
Westons, Herts 132

GEOGRAPHY

Altea Antique Maps & Books, London W 171
Archer (David), Powys............................... 290
Barcombe Services, Essex........................... 108
Chesters (G. & J.), Staffordshire 224
Cornucopia Books, Lincolnshire 151
Earth Science Books, Wiltshire..................... 252
George St. Books, Derbyshire 83
Good for Books, Lincolnshire 149
Harrington Antiquarian Bookseller (Peter),
    London SW...................................... 167
Joel Segal Books, Devon 86
Kabristan Archives, Shropshire..................... 214
Kalligraphia (formerly Charmouth
    Bounty Books), Isle of Wight.................. 133
Maghreb Bookshop (The), London WC.......... 177
Peter M Daly, Hampshire............................ 126
R. & A. Books, East Sussex 101
Roadmaster Books, Kent............................ 136
Sparrow Books, West Yorkshire 245
Taney Books, Co. Dublin 263
Tooley, Adams & Co, Oxfordshire 209

GEOLOGY

Acanthophyllum Books, Wirral 184
Archer (David), Powys............................... 290
Austwick Hall Books, N Yorks 192
Baldwin's Scientific Books, Essex 111
Bernard Dixon and Kath Adams, London O.... 182
Bow Windows Book Shop, East Sussex 103
Cheshire Book Centre, Cheshire.................... 69
Chesters (G. & J.), Staffordshire 224
Clevedon Books, Somerset 217
Cofion Books, Pembrokeshire 286
Cornucopia Books, Lincolnshire 151
Cox (Geoff), Devon 90

Cox, Andrew, Shropshire.............................. 214
Dartmoor Book Gallery, Devon 87
Duck (William), Hampshire........................ 124
Earth Science Books, Wiltshire 252
Esoteric Dreams Bookshop, Cumbria 77
Geophysical Books, Kent............................ 139
Henly (John), West Sussex 244
Hollett and Son (R.F.G.), Cumbria 79
Joel Segal Books, Devon 86
K.S.C. Books, Cheshire.............................. 70
Kalligraphia (formerly Charmouth Bounty
  Books), Isle of Wight.............................. 133
Kingswood Books, Dorset 94
Knowles - Antiquary (Roger J.), Staffordshire... 223
Little Bookshop (The), Cumbria 80
Lymelight Books & Prints, Dorset................. 93
Park (Mike), London O 182
Parkinsons Books, Merseyside...................... 185
Periplus Books, Buckinghamshire.................. 62
Peter M Daly, Hampshire........................... 126
Phelps (Michael), West Sussex 242
Pollak (P.M.), Devon 88
R. & A. Books, East Sussex 101
Randall (Tom), Somerset............................ 218
Reads, Dorset 95
Roadmaster Books, Kent............................ 136
Roger Collicott Books, Cornwall 74
Sparrow Books, West Yorkshire 245
Stalagluft Books, Tyne and Wear.................. 235
Weiner (Graham), London N 158
Westwood Books Ltd, Cumbria..................... 80
Whitchurch Books Ltd., Cardiff.................... 281
Wiend Books, Lancashire 143

GEOPHYSICS

Baldwin's Scientific Books, Essex 111
Earth Science Books, Wiltshire 252
Geophysical Books, Kent............................ 139
Parkinsons Books, Merseyside...................... 185
Westons, Herts 132

GHOSTS

AA1 Books, Dumfries & Galloway................. 269
Apocalypse, Surrey 232
Bookworms Paradise Ltd., West Sussex 242
Cofion Books, Pembrokeshire 286
Cornucopia Books, Lincolnshire 151
Country Books, Derbyshire 82
Cowley, Bookdealer (K.W.), Somerset 217
Dalby (Richard), N Yorks 195
Enigma Books, Wiltshire 252
Esoteric Dreams Bookshop, Cumbria 77
Gildas Books, Cheshire 68
Inner Bookshop (The), Oxfordshire................ 208
Loretta Lay Books, London NW 161
Magis Books, Leics 146
Occultique, Northants............................... 199
R. & A. Books, East Sussex 101
Robert Temple, London N........................... 158
Roger Collicott Books, Cornwall 74
Sax Books, Suffolk 228
SETI Books, West Midlands......................... 239
Wizard Books, Cambridgeshire..................... 67

GLAMOUR

Book Palace (The), London SE 163
Fun in Books, Surrey 234
N1 Books, East Sussex 105
Nostalgia Publications Ltd., N Yorks 197
Paper Pleasures, Somerset 218
Print Matters, London SE........................... 165
R. & A. Books, East Sussex 101
Tilleys Vintage Magazine Shop, Derbyshire...... 82
Yesterday's News, Conwy........................... 283
Zardoz Books, Wiltshire............................ 254

GLASS

Ancient Art Books, London SW 166
Art Reference Books, Hampshire 124
Barmby (C. & A.J.), Kent........................... 140
Booth (Booksearch Service), (Geoff), Cheshire... 68
Clark (Nigel A.), London SE........................ 163
Cover to Cover, Merseyside......................... 185
Fifteenth Century Bookshop (The), East Sussex. 104
Heneage Art Books (Thomas), London SW 168
Joel Segal Books, Devon 86
R. & A. Books, East Sussex 101
Stained Glass Books, Kent.......................... 139
Stroh (M.A.), London E 154
Trinders' Fine Tools, Suffolk 226

GLOS

Keogh's Books, Glos................................. 115
Whitchurch Books Ltd., Cardiff.................... 281

GNOSTICS / GNOSTICISM

Chthonios Books, East Sussex...................... 102
Gilbert (R.A.), Somerset............................ 219
Hava Books, London SE............................. 164
J & J Burgess Booksellers, Cambridgeshire....... 64
Joel Segal Books, Devon 86
Minster Gate Bookshop, N Yorks.................. 197
Needham Books, (Russell), Somerset.............. 219
Occultique, Northants............................... 199
Rosemary Pugh Books, Wiltshire 253
S.P.C.K., Bristol 59

GOLD RUSH

Americanabooksuk, Cumbria........................ 76
Apocalypse, Surrey 232
Knowles - Antiquary (Roger J.), Staffordshire... 223
R. & A. Books, East Sussex 101

GOLDSMITHS

Don Kelly Books, London W 172
Joel Segal Books, Devon 86
R. & A. Books, East Sussex 101

GOTHIC REVIVAL

Design Gallery 1850-1950 (The), Kent 141
Don Kelly Books, London W 172
Haskell (R.H. & P.), Dorset 94
R. & A. Books, East Sussex 101

GRAND CANYON &
COLORADO RIVER, THE

Americanabooksuk, Cumbria........................ 76

GRAPHIC NOVELS

Book Palace (The), London SE 163
Print Matters, London SE........................... 165

GRAPHICS

Amwell Book Company, London EC............. 155
Barlow (Vincent G.), Hampshire................... 125
Book Palace (The), London SE 163
Burden (Derek), Surrey 232
Cornucopia Books, Lincolnshire 151
Joel Segal Books, Devon 86
Print Matters, London SE........................... 165
Whittle, Bookseller (Avril), Cumbria 80
Woburn Books, London N 159
Woodbine Books, West Yorkshire................. 245

GRAPHOLOGY

Inner Bookshop (The), Oxfordshire................ 208
Joel Segal Books, Devon 86
Magis Books, Leics.................................... 146
R. & A. Books, East Sussex 101

GRAVEYARDS

Kabristan Archives, Shropshire..................... 214
R. & A. Books, East Sussex 101

GUIDE BOOKS

Abrahams (Mike), Staffordshire.................... 223
Annie's Books, S Yorks 221
Apocalypse, Surrey 232
Arden Books & Cosmographia, Warwickshire... 236
Backfold Books, Herefordshire..................... 127
baconboooks, London WC 176
Baedekers & Murray Guides, S Yorks 221
Baker - Books for the Collector (Colin), Devon . 89
Brad Books, Essex.................................... 110
Cavern Books, Cheshire 70
Church Street Books, Norfolk 186
Clarke Books (David), Somerset 218
Collectables (W.H.), Suffolk 229
Cornucopia Books, Lincolnshire 151
Cox (Geoff), Devon 90
Dales & Lakes Book Centre, Cumbria........... 79
Derek Stirling Bookseller, Kent 141
Fifteenth Century Bookshop (The), East Sussex. 104
Hava Books, London SE............................. 164
Hellenic Bookservices, London NW 161
Hodgson (Books) (Richard J.), N Yorks 196
InterCol London, London N 157
Island Books, Devon................................. 85
Jarvis Books, Derbyshire 83
Joel Segal Books, Devon 86
Mandalay Bookshop, London SW 168
Martin (Brian), Surrey 231
Michael J Carroll, Co. Cork 263
O'Flynn Books, N Yorks............................. 197
Prospect House Books, Co. Down................. 261
R. & A. Books, East Sussex 101
Roger Collicott Books, Cornwall 74
Saintfield Antiques & Fine Books, Co. Down ... 261
Shacklock Books (David), Suffolk 226
Shapero Rare Books (Bernard J.), London W... 175
Trinders' Fine Tools, Suffolk 226
Trinity Rare Books, Co. Leitrim 266
Tyger Press, London N 158

GYNAECOLOGY

Alba Books, Grampian 273
Forest Books of Manchester, Cheshire........... 70
Parkinsons Books, Merseyside...................... 185
R M Books, Herts.................................... 132
Reading Lasses, Dumfries & Galloway 270
Rebecca Hardie Rare Books, London W 171

GYPSIES

2 Ravens, Cumbria................................... 78
A Holmes Books, Nottinghamshire............... 203
Abrahams (Mike), Staffordshire.................... 223
Apocalypse, Surrey 232
Coch-y-Bonddu Books, Powys 290
Cottage Books, Leics................................. 145
Country Books, Derbyshire 82
Cover to Cover, Merseyside......................... 185
Dales & Lakes Book Centre, Cumbria........... 79
Delectus Books, London WC....................... 176
Doorbar (P. & D.), Gwynedd 285
J.E. Burns Booksellers, Merseyside 185
Joel Segal Books, Devon 86
John Underwood Antiquarian Books, Norfolk.. 189
Just Books, Cornwall 75
R. & A. Books, East Sussex 101
Randall (Tom), Somerset............................ 218
White Eagle Books, London NW.................. 162
Winchester Bookshop (The), Hampshire.......... 126
York (Graham), Devon............................... 86

HAIRDRESSING

Black Cat Books, Norfolk........................... 187
Bookworms Paradise Ltd., West Sussex 242
Judith Mansfield, West Yorkshire.................. 249
R. & A. Books, East Sussex 101

HALLOWEEN

Inner Bookshop (The), Oxfordshire................ 208
Occultique, Northants................................ 199
R. & A. Books, East Sussex 101

HAND BOOKBINDING

Barry McKay Rare Books, Cumbria.............. 76
Eastgate Bookshop, East Yorkshire 106
John Underwood Antiquarian Books, Norfolk.. 189
Shearwater Books, Northumberland............... 201
Walker Fine Books (Steve), Dorset................ 92

HANDWRITING

Barry McKay Rare Books, Cumbria.............. 76
Joel Segal Books, Devon 86

HANDWRITTEN BOOKS

Apocalypse, Surrey 232
John Underwood Antiquarian Books, Norfolk.. 189
O'Flynn Books, N Yorks............................. 197

HEALTH

Annie's Books, S Yorks 221
Autumn Leaves, Lincolnshire....................... 150
Bookworms Paradise Ltd., West Sussex 242
Cheshire Book Centre, Cheshire.................... 69
Collectable Books, London SE...................... 163
Cornucopia Books, Lincolnshire 151
Country Books, Derbyshire 82

Crabtree (Mrs. C.), Greater Manchester 120
Dolphin Books, Suffolk................................ 225
Empire Books, N Yorks.............................. 197
Greensleeves, Oxfordshire 206
Hurst (Jenny), Kent 137
Inner Bookshop (The), Oxfordshire............... 208
Joel Segal Books, Devon 86
Orchid Book Distributors, Co. Clare.............. 262
Pickering & Chatto, London W..................... 174
R M Books, Herts...................................... 132
Reading Lasses, Dumfries & Galloway 270
Rebecca Hardie Rare Books, London W......... 171
River Reads Bookshop, Devon...................... 90
Roland Books, Kent 138
Roundstone Books, Lancashire..................... 143
SETI Books, West Midlands......................... 239
Till's Bookshop, Lothian 277
Woburn Books, London N 159

HEBRAICA

Beckham Books Ltd., Suffolk 229
Chapter Two, London SE............................. 163
Delectus Books, London WC........................ 176
Fishburn Books, London NW....................... 160
Joel Segal Books, Devon 86
Samovar Books, Co. Dublin 264
Thorntons of Oxford Ltd., Oxfordshire........... 206
Trotter Books (John), London N 158

HERALDRY

Aardvark Books, Wiltshire........................... 254
Bookshop on the Heath, The, London SE 163
Dennys Sanders & Greene Ltd, East Sussex 100
Heraldry Today, Wiltshire........................... 253
Heritage, West Midlands 238
Joel Segal Books, Devon 86
Marcet Books, London SE........................... 164
McEwan Fine Books, Grampian.................... 272
Milestone Publications Goss &
  Crested China, Hampshire 123
Moore (C.R.), Shropshire 213
N1 Books, East Sussex 105
R. & A. Books, East Sussex 101
RGS Books, Surrey 234
Sax Books, Suffolk 228
Scrivener's Books & Bookbinding, Derbyshire... 82
Spooner & Co, Somerset 219
Titford (John), Derbyshire 82
Townsend (John), Berks 57
Turton (John), Durham 98

HERBALISM

Blest (Peter), Kent 138
Bookworms Paradise Ltd., West Sussex 242
Brown-Studies, Strathclyde.......................... 277
Chantrey Books, S Yorks 222
Dolphin Books, Suffolk............................... 225
Edmund Pollinger Rare Books, London SW..... 166
Esoteric Dreams Bookshop, Cumbria 77
Fifteenth Century Bookshop (The), East Sussex. 104
Gardener & Cook, London SW...................... 167
Greensleeves, Oxfordshire 206
Guildmaster Books, Cheshire 70
Hollingshead (Chris), London O 182
Inner Bookshop (The), Oxfordshire............... 208

Joel Segal Books, Devon 86
Lucas (Richard), London NW....................... 161
Occultique, Northants................................ 199
Orchid Book Distributors, Co. Clare.............. 262
Park (Mike), London O 182
Peter M Daly, Hampshire............................ 126
Phelps (Michael), West Sussex..................... 242
Pollak (P.M.), Devon 88
R. & A. Books, East Sussex 101
Wadard Books, Kent 137
Woodside Books, Kent 135

HEREDITY

Joel Segal Books, Devon 86
Parkinsons Books, Merseyside...................... 185
R M Books, Herts...................................... 132
R. & A. Books, East Sussex 101

HERITAGE

Bodders Books, Shropshire.......................... 212
Cornucopia Books, Lincolnshire 151
Dolphin Books, Suffolk............................... 225
G. C. Books Ltd., Dumfries & Galloway......... 270
Joel Segal Books, Devon 86
R. & A. Books, East Sussex 101
Winchester Bookshop (The), Hampshire.......... 126

HERMETICISM

Alpha Books, London N.............................. 156
Chthonios Books, East Sussex 102
Inner Bookshop (The), Oxfordshire............... 208
Magis Books, Leics.................................... 146
Occultique, Northants................................ 199
Quaritch Ltd., (Bernard), London W............. 174
Star Lord Books, Greater Manchester 119

HERPETOLOGY

Blest (Peter), Kent 138
Calluna Books, Dorset................................ 95
J.G. Natural History Books, Surrey 233
Kenya Books, East Sussex 100
Mobbs (A.J.), West Midlands 239
Parkinsons Books, Merseyside...................... 185
Pemberley Books, Buckinghamshire 62
Steven Simpson Books, Norfolk 190
Westons, Herts 132

HIMALAYAN KINGDOMS

Cavendish Rare Books, London N 156
David Warnes Books, Herefordshire 128
Jarvis Books, Derbyshire 83
Kabristan Archives, Shropshire..................... 214
Peter M Daly, Hampshire............................ 126
Rayner (Hugh Ashley), Somerset 215
Verandah Books, Dorset 95
White Eagle Books, London NW................... 162
Winchester Bookshop (The), Hampshire.......... 126

HISPANICA

Baldwin (Jack), Strathclyde 278
Hava Books, London SE.............................. 164
Hodgson (Judith), London W 173
York (Graham), Devon................................ 86

HISTORY
- GENERAL

A. & H. Peasgood, Cambridgeshire 66
AA1 Books, Dumfries & Galloway................ 269
Abacus Gallery, Staffordshire........................ 224
Abbey Books, Cornwall 73
Addyman Books, Powys.............................. 287
Alexander's Books, Warwickshire.................. 237
Alister & Garon Books, Cambridgeshire.......... 63
All Books, Essex 111
Allinson (Frank & Stella), Warwickshire 236
Anchor Books, Lincolnshire 149
Andrew Morton (Books), Powys.................... 287
Annie's Books, S Yorks 221
Anthony Vickers Books, N Yorks 195
Antiquary Ltd., (Bar Bookstore), N Yorks...... 194
Antique Map and Bookshop (The), Dorset 94
Antiques on High, Oxfordshire..................... 207
Any Old Books, Hampshire 121
Apocalypse, Surrey 232
Arden Books & Cosmographia, Warwickshire... 236
Askew Books (Vernon), Wiltshire.................. 251
Aurora Books Ltd, Lothian.......................... 275
Autumn Leaves, Lincolnshire 150
Avonworld Books, Somerset........................ 216
Axe Rare & Out of Print Books (Richard),
    N Yorks.. 193
Backfold Books, Herefordshire..................... 127
baconboooks, London WC 176
Baker Limited (A.P. & R.),
    Dumfries & Galloway 269
Barbican Bookshop, N Yorks 196
Barcombe Services, Essex........................... 108
Bardsley's Books, Suffolk........................... 225
Barn Books, Buckinghamshire....................... 61
Barnes (Peter), Wiltshire 253
Bath Old Books, Somerset 215
Baxter (Steve), Surrey 233
Beardsell Books, West Yorkshire................... 246
Beckham Books Ltd., Suffolk 229
Bell (Peter), Lothian................................ 275
Bennett & Kerr Books, Oxfordshire 205
Beware of the Leopard, Bristol...................... 58
Biff Books and Records, S Yorks.................. 221
Black Five Books, Shropshire 214
Bodders Books, Shropshire......................... 212
Bookbox, Glos 115
Bookfare, Cumbria 80
Bookroom (The), Surrey............................. 233
Books, Denbighshire 284
Books & Bygones (Pam Taylor), West Midlands 240
Books & Collectables Ltd., Cambridgeshire...... 63
Books Antiques & Collectables, Devon 90
Books at Star Dot Star, West Midlands 240
Books Bought & Sold, Surrey 231
books2books, Devon................................ 88
Booksets.com Ltd, Shropshire 214
Bookshop (The), Greater Manchester 118
Bookshop (The), West Sussex 242
Bookshop at the Plain, Lincolnshire............... 149
Bookworm (The), Lothian 276
Bookworms, Norfolk................................ 186
Bookworms of Evesham, Worcs 257
Bosorne Books, Cornwall 75
Bracton Books, Cambridgeshire.................... 63

Brad Books, Essex................................... 110
Brimstones, East Sussex 104
Broadhurst of Southport Ltd., Merseyside 185
Broadwater Books, Hampshire 125
Browsers Bookshop, Cornwall...................... 72
C J Renwick Books, Powys......................... 287
Caledonia Books, Strathclyde...................... 278
Caliver Books, Essex................................ 109
Carnforth Bookshop (The), Lancashire 142
Carningli Centre, Pembrokeshire................... 286
Castle Hill Books, Herefordshire.................. 128
Catalyst Booksearch Services, Devon............. 87
Celtic Bookshop (The), Co. Limerick 266
Channel Islands Galleries Limited,
    Channel Islands 258
Charles Bossom, Cambridgeshire................... 65
Charlie Byrne's Bookshop, Co. Galway........... 265
Chaucer Bookshop, Kent 136
Cheshire Book Centre, Cheshire................... 69
Chesters (G. & J.), Staffordshire.................. 224
Clarendon Books, Leics............................. 145
Classic Bindings Ltd, London SW 166
Clements (R.W.), London O........................ 181
Clent Books, Worcs 255
Cobbles Books, Somerset........................... 217
Cobweb Books, N Yorks............................ 194
Colwyn Books, Conwy 283
Coombes (A.J.), Surrey 230
Corfe Books, Surrey................................ 230
Courtenay Bookroom, Oxfordshire 205
Cox Old & Rare Books (Claude), Suffolk 227
Crouch Rare Books, Surrey......................... 232
Dales & Lakes Book Centre, Cumbria........... 79
Dandy Lion Editions, Surrey 233
D'Arcy Books, Wiltshire............................ 252
Darkwood Books, Co. Cork 263
Davids Ltd., (Roy), Oxfordshire 208
Debbage (John), Norfolk............................ 189
Deeside Books, Grampian........................... 272
Dennys Sanders & Greene Ltd, East Sussex 100
Derek Stirling Bookseller, Kent 141
Dolphin Books, Suffolk............................. 225
Dormouse Bookshop (The), Norfolk 189
Double - B - Books Ltd, Somerset................. 59
Driffield Bookshop (The), East Yorkshire 106
Eagle Bookshop (The), Bedfordshire 53
Eastern Traveller (The), Somerset.................. 219
Eastleach Books, Berks 56
Edwards (Christopher), Oxfordshire 209
Edwards (London) Limited (Francis),
    London WC 176
Edwards in Hay–on–Wye (Francis), Powys 288
Elaine Lonsdale Books, West Yorkshire.......... 247
Ellis, Bookseller (Peter), London WC 177
Esoteric Dreams Bookshop, Cumbria 77
Eton Antique Bookshop, Berks 57
Farnborough Gallery, Hampshire................... 122
Fifteenth Century Bookshop (The), East Sussex. 104
Fireside Bookshop, Cumbria 81
Ford Books (David), Herts 130
Fossgate Books, N Yorks 197
Foster (Stephen), London NW 160
Freeman's Corner Shop, Norfolk 189
Frew Limited (Robert), London SW 167
Frost (Richard), Herts 129

Furneaux Books (Lee), Devon...................... 89
G. C. Books Ltd., Dumfries & Galloway........ 270
Garfi Books, Powys 291
George St. Books, Derbyshire 83
Gildas Books, Cheshire 68
Gladstone Books, Lincolnshire 150
Glasheen-Books, Surrey 231
Glenbower Books, Co. Dublin 264
Glyn's Books, Shropshire............................ 212
Golden Books Group, Devon 85
Good for Books, Lincolnshire 149
Graham (John), Dorset 96
Grahame Thornton, Bookseller, Dorset.......... 93
Great Hall Bookshop, Buckinghamshire.......... 61
Greta Books, Durham 97
Hall's Bookshop, Kent.............................. 140
Hambleton Books, N Yorks......................... 196
Handsworth Books, Essex.......................... 112
Hava Books, London SE............................ 164
Hawley (C.L.), N Yorks............................ 195
Hay Cinema Bookshop Ltd., Powys............... 288
HCB Wholesale, Powys............................. 288
Helion & Company, West Midlands 239
Heraldry Today, Wiltshire........................... 253
Heywood Hill Limited (G.), London W 173
Horsham Rare Books, West Sussex 242
Howes Bookshop, East Sussex 102
Hughes Rare Books (Spike), Borders............. 267
hullbooks.com, East Yorkshire 106
Hurst (Jenny), Kent 137
Hutchison (Books) (Larry), Fife.................... 271
Ice House Books, Wiltshire 254
J & J Burgess Booksellers, Cambridgeshire....... 64
Jackdaw Books, Norfolk 188
Jade Mountain Bookshop, Hampshire 125
Jane Jones Books, Grampian 273
JB Books & Collectables, West Sussex 243
Jenny Hurst, Kent 138
Joel Segal Books, Devon 86
John Clifford, Dorset................................. 92
Jones (Andrew), Suffolk 227
Judd Books, London WC............................ 177
Junk & Spread Eagle, London SE.................. 164
Just Books, Cornwall 75
Kalligraphia (formerly Charmouth Bounty
  Books), Isle of Wight.............................. 133
Karen Millward, Co. Cork 263
Katnap Arts, Norfolk 190
Keel Row Bookshop, Tyne and Wear 235
Keith Langford, London E 154
Kelsall (George), Greater Manchester............. 118
Kemp Bookseller, Michael S, G Manchester..... 118
Kilgarriff (Raymond), East Sussex................. 105
Kim's Bookshop, West Sussex...................... 242
Kim's Bookshop, West Sussex...................... 241
Kingfisher Book Service, Nottinghamshire 204
Knowles - Antiquary (Roger J.), Staffordshire... 223
Lawrence Millward, Nottinghamshire 203
Leabeck Books, Oxfordshire 208
Leo Cadogan, London N 157
Lewis (J.T. & P.), Cornwall 73
Libris (Weston) Books, Somerset 216
Little Bookshop (The), Greater Manchester...... 119
Lost Books, Northants............................... 200
Maggy Browne, Lincolnshire 148

Mannwaring (M.G.), Bristol 59
Marble Hill Books, Outer London................. 182
Marcet Books, London SE.......................... 164
Marijana Dworski Books, Powys 288
McCrone (Audrey), Isle of Arran 274
McNaughtan's Bookshop, Lothian 276
Meekins Books (Paul), Warwickshire............. 237
Mellon's Books, East Sussex....................... 101
Michael J Carroll, Co. Cork 263
MilitaryHistoryBooks.com, Kent.................. 137
Ming Books, Dumfries & Galloway 270
Modern Welsh Publications Ltd., Merseyside.... 184
Morgan (H.J.), Bedfordshire 54
Much Binding, Norfolk.............................. 186
Mundy (David), Herts 129
Murphy (C.J.), Norfolk............................. 189
My Back Pages, London SW 168
N1 Books, East Sussex 105
Nicolas - Antiquarian Bookseller, London N 157
Nineteenth Century Books, Oxfordshire 209
Nonsuch Books, Surrey............................. 234
Oasis Booksearch, Cambridgeshire................. 67
O'Brien Books & Photo Gallery, Co. Limerick .. 266
O'Flynn Books, N Yorks............................ 197
Old Bookshop (The), West Midlands 240
Old Town Bookshop (The), Lothian 276
Olynthiacs, Shropshire 213
Oopalba Books, Cheshire............................ 71
Parker Books (Mike), Cambridgeshire 64
Parkinsons Books, Merseyside...................... 185
Parrott Books, Oxfordshire 209
Pauline Harries Books, Hampshire 123
Period & Classical Collections, East Sussex 103
Peter Lyons Books, Glos 113
Peter M Daly, Hampshire........................... 126
Pickering Bookshop, N Yorks...................... 196
Polmorla Books, Cornwall 75
Pordes Books Ltd., (Henry), London WC....... 177
Portobello Books, London W 174
Pringle Booksellers (Andrew), Lothian............ 277
PsychoBabel Books & Journals, Oxfordshire..... 205
Quaritch Ltd., (Bernard), London W.............. 174
Quentin Books Ltd, Essex.......................... 108
Quinto of Charing Cross Road, London WC ... 178
Read - Gorleston Books, (C.&J.), Norfolk 187
Reading Lasses, Dumfries & Galloway 270
RGS Books, Surrey 234
Richard Thornton Books, London N 158
Richmond Books, N Yorks......................... 194
Rods Books, Devon................................. 88
Roland Books, Kent 138
Rothwell & Dunworth, Somerset 217
Roundstone Books, Lancashire..................... 143
St Philip's Books, Oxfordshire..................... 208
Saintfield Antiques & Fine Books, Co. Down ... 261
Samovar Books, Co. Dublin........................ 264
Saracen Books, Derbyshire.......................... 83
Sax Books, Suffolk 228
Scott (Peter), East Sussex.......................... 104
Scrivener's Books & Bookbinding,
  Derbyshire 82
Shacklock Books (David), Suffolk 226
Sillan Books, Co. Cavan............................ 262
Silverman (Michael), London SE 165
Singleton (Anthony), S Yorks 221

Slightly Foxed on Gloucester Road, London SW167
Smith Books (Keith), Herefordshire 128
Spelman (Ken), N Yorks 198
Spurrier (Nick), Kent 137
Staffs Bookshop (The), Staffordshire 223
Stalagluft Books, Tyne and Wear 235
Staniland (Booksellers), Lincolnshire 152
Star Lord Books, Greater Manchester 119
Stella Books, Monmouthshire 286
Sterling Books, Somerset 220
Stern Antiquarian Bookseller (Jeffrey), N Yorks 198
Stothert Old Books, Cheshire........................ 68
Sturford Books, Wiltshire 254
Sykes (Graham), West Yorkshire 249
Symes Books (Naomi), Cheshire 71
Tarka Books, Devon 84
The Glass Key, West Yorkshire..................... 246
Thistle Books, Strathclyde........................... 278
Thomas (E. Wyn), Conwy 284
Till's Bookshop, Lothian............................. 277
Tilston (Stephen E.), London SE................... 165
Titford (John), Derbyshire 82
Townsend (John), Berks 57
Treasure Trove Books, Leics........................ 146
Tuft (Patrick), London O 181
Tyger Press, London N 158
ULoveBooks, Devon................................. 90
Uncle Phil's Books, West Midlands 239
Unsworth's Booksellers, Suffolk.................... 225
Village Books, Norfolk 186
Waterfield's, Oxfordshire 209
Waxfactor, East Sussex 100
Westwood Books (Mark), Powys 289
Westwood Books Ltd, Cumbria..................... 80
Whig Books Ltd., Leics.............................. 147
Whitchurch Books Ltd., Cardiff..................... 281
Whitfield (Ken), Essex 110
Williams (Bookdealer), (Richard), N Lincs 153
Willmott Bookseller (Nicholas), Cardiff........... 281
Words Etcetera Bookshop, Dorset................. 93
Worlds End Bookshop, London SW 169
Yesterday's Books, Dorset 92
Yewtree Books, Cumbria............................ 78

- 19TH CENTURY

Aitchison (Lesley), Bristol 58
Americanabooksuk, Cumbria........................ 76
Annie's Books, S Yorks 221
Apocalypse, Surrey 232
Bell (Peter), Lothian................................. 275
Browsers Bookshop, Cornwall...................... 72
Burroughs (Andrew), Lincolnshire 152
Cox Rare Books (Charles), Cornwall.............. 73
Darkwood Books, Co. Cork 263
Debbage (John), Norfolk............................ 189
Derek Stirling Bookseller, Kent 141
Dolphin Books, Suffolk.............................. 225
Empire Books, N Yorks.............................. 197
Fifteenth Century Bookshop (The), East Sussex. 104
Hall's Bookshop, Kent................................ 140
Handsworth Books, Essex............................ 112
Helion & Company, West Midlands 239
hullbooks.com, East Yorkshire 106
J & J Burgess Booksellers, Cambridgeshire....... 64
Jackdaw Books, Norfolk 188

Joel Segal Books, Devon 86
Junk & Spread Eagle, London SE 164
Karen Millward, Co. Cork........................... 263
Lost Books, Northants................................ 200
MilitaryHistoryBooks.com, Kent.................... 137
Mulyan (Don), Merseyside........................... 185
N1 Books, East Sussex 105
Old Bookshop (The), West Midlands 240
Pittville Books, Glos................................. 113
PsychoBabel Books & Journals, Oxfordshire..... 205
R. & A. Books, East Sussex 101
SETI Books, West Midlands........................ 239
Symes Books (Naomi), Cheshire 71
Wheen O'Books, Borders............................ 267
Whitchurch Books Ltd., Cardiff..................... 281
Winghale Books, Lincolnshire 152

- 20TH CENTURY

Annie's Books, S Yorks 221
Backfold Books, Herefordshire 127
books2books, Devon................................. 88
Darkwood Books, Co. Cork 263
Debbage (John), Norfolk............................ 189
Dolphin Books, Suffolk.............................. 225
Empire Books, N Yorks.............................. 197
Fifteenth Century Bookshop (The), East Sussex. 104
Handsworth Books, Essex............................ 112
hullbooks.com, East Yorkshire 106
Joel Segal Books, Devon 86
Karen Millward, Co. Cork........................... 263
Kineton Nooks, Warwickshire....................... 236
MilitaryHistoryBooks.com, Kent.................... 137
Old Station Pottery & Bookshop (The), Norfolk 191
Park Gallery & Bookshop (The), Northants 200
Pittville Books, Glos................................. 113
PsychoBabel Books & Journals, Oxfordshire..... 205
R. & A. Books, East Sussex 101
Rods Books, Devon................................. 88
SETI Books, West Midlands........................ 239
Symes Books (Naomi), Cheshire 71
War & Peace Books, Hampshire.................... 122
Wheen O'Books, Borders............................ 267
Winghale Books, Lincolnshire 152
Woburn Books, London N 159
York Modern Books, N Yorks....................... 196

- AFRICAN

Kenya Books, East Sussex 100

- AMERICAN

Americanabooksuk, Cumbria........................ 76
Beckham Books Ltd., Suffolk....................... 229
Bookworms Paradise Ltd., West Sussex 242
Darkwood Books, Co. Cork 263
Dolphin Books, Suffolk.............................. 225
Fifteenth Century Bookshop (The), East Sussex. 104
Helion & Company, West Midlands 239
Joel Segal Books, Devon 86
PsychoBabel Books & Journals, Oxfordshire..... 205
Quentin Books Ltd, Essex........................... 108
Winghale Books, Lincolnshire 152

- AMERICAN REVOLUTION

Americanabooksuk, Cumbria........................ 76
Fifteenth Century Bookshop (The), East Sussex. 104

- ANARCHISM

Delectus Books, London WC......................... 176
Helion & Company, West Midlands 239
Northern Herald Books, West Yorkshire........ 245
Red Star Books, Herts............................... 129
Star Lord Books, Greater Manchester 119

- ANCIENT

Aviabooks, Glos 114
BC Books, Cheshire................................... 69
Black Five Books, Shropshire 214
Bloomsbury Bookshop, London O 181
Books B.C., London O 180
Bookworms Paradise Ltd., West Sussex 242
Byre Books, Dumfries & Galloway................ 270
Classics Bookshop (The), Oxfordshire............ 205
Crouch Rare Books, Surrey......................... 232
Fifteenth Century Bookshop (The), East Sussex. 104
Ford Books (David), Herts 130
GfB: the Colchester Bookshop, Essex 108
Gildas Books, Cheshire............................... 68
Golden Age Books, Worcs........................... 256
Handsworth Books, Essex........................... 112
Helion & Company, West Midlands 239
Joel Segal Books, Devon 86
Junk & Spread Eagle, London SE................. 164
Kingswood Books, Dorset 94
Meekins Books (Paul), Warwickshire............. 237
Michael Graves-Johnston, London SW 168
Michael J Carroll, Co. Cork 263
N1 Books, East Sussex 105
P. and P. Books, Worcs 256
Parkinsons Books, Merseyside...................... 185
Pittville Books, Glos.................................. 113
PsychoBabel Books & Journals, Oxfordshire..... 205
R. & A. Books, East Sussex 101
Rods Books, Devon................................... 88
Rosanda Books, Leics 146
SETI Books, West Midlands........................ 239
Stalagluft Books, Tyne and Wear................. 235
Thorntons of Oxford Ltd., Oxfordshire........... 206
Trotter Books (John), London N 158
Uncle Phil's Books, West Midlands 239
Unsworth's Booksellers, Suffolk................... 225
Walker Fine Books (Steve), Dorset................ 92
Whitchurch Books Ltd., Cardiff.................... 281
Winghale Books, Lincolnshire 152

- ARGENTINA

Baldwin (Jack), Strathclyde 278
Hodgson (Judith), London W 173
Orssich (Paul), London SW......................... 169

- AUSTRALIAN

Empire Books, N Yorks.............................. 197
Fifteenth Century Bookshop (The), East Sussex. 104
Joel Segal Books, Devon 86

- BERMUDAN

Pennymead Books, N Yorks......................... 193

- BRAZIL

Baldwin (Jack), Strathclyde 278
Hodgson (Judith), London W 173
Orssich (Paul), London SW......................... 169

- BRITISH

Aardvark Books, Wiltshire........................... 254
Aitchison (Lesley), Bristol 58
Annie's Books, S Yorks 221
Anthony Spranger, Wiltshire........................ 252
Apocalypse, Surrey 232
Ardis Books, Hampshire 126
Aviabooks, Glos 114
Barbican Bookshop, N Yorks 196
BC Books, Cheshire................................... 69
Beckham Books Ltd., Suffolk 229
Bell (Peter), Lothian................................. 275
Black Five Books, Shropshire 214
Blackpool Book Warehouse, Lancashire........... 142
BookShop, The, Dumfries & Galloway.......... 270
Bookworms Paradise Ltd., West Sussex 242
Brad Books, Essex.................................... 110
Burmester (James), Bristol.......................... 58
Chichester Bookshop (The), Herefordshire 241
Clarke Books (David), Somerset 218
Clifton Books, Essex 111
Cobbles Books, Somerset............................ 217
Coombes (A.J.), Surrey 230
Corder (Mark W.), Kent 139
Country Books, Derbyshire.......................... 82
Crabtree (Mrs. C.), Greater Manchester 120
Darkwood Books, Co. Cork........................ 263
Dolphin Books, Suffolk.............................. 225
Double - B - Books Ltd, Somerset................. 59
Ellis, Bookseller (Peter), London WC 177
Fifteenth Century Bookshop (The), East Sussex. 104
Garfi Books, Powys................................... 291
GfB: the Colchester Bookshop, Essex 108
Gildas Books, Cheshire 68
Guildmaster Books, Cheshire....................... 70
Hall's Bookshop, Kent 140
Handsworth Books, Essex........................... 112
Hawley (C.L.), N Yorks............................. 195
Helion & Company, West Midlands 239
High Street Books, Devon 86
Hornsey's, N Yorks 194
hullbooks.com, East Yorkshire 106
Island Books, Devon................................. 85
Jackdaw Books, Norfolk 188
JB Books & Collectables, West Sussex 243
Joel Segal Books, Devon 86
Junk & Spread Eagle, London SE................. 164
K.S.C. Books, Cheshire.............................. 70
Karen Millward, Co. Cork........................... 263
Liddle (Steve), Bristol 58
Lost Books, Northants............................... 200
Lowe (John), Norfolk 188
Madoc Books, Conwy 284
Maggy Browne, Lincolnshire 148
Marine and Cannon Books, Cheshire 69
Martin (Books and Pictures), (Brian P.), Surrey. 231
medievalbookshop, Herts............................ 132
Meekins Books (Paul), Warwickshire............. 237
Michael J Carroll, Co. Cork 263
Minster Gate Bookshop, N Yorks................. 197
Mulyan (Don), Merseyside.......................... 185
N1 Books, East Sussex 105
Niner (Marcus), Isle of Wight 133
Orb's Bookshop, Grampian.......................... 273
Pittville Books, Glos.................................. 113

Price (John), London N 158
Prospect House Books, Co. Down................. 261
R. & A. Books, East Sussex 101
Rods Books, Devon................................... 88
Roland Books, Kent 138
Rosanda Books, Leics 146
St Philip's Books, Oxfordshire..................... 208
Samovar Books, Co. Dublin 264
Saracen Books, Derbyshire.......................... 83
Sax Books, Suffolk 228
SETI Books, West Midlands......................... 239
Shakeshaft (Dr. B.), Cheshire....................... 71
Spenceley Books (David), West Yorkshire....... 248
Spurrier (Nick), Kent 137
Stalagluft Books, Tyne and Wear 235
Stella Books, Monmouthshire 286
Studio Bookshop, East Sussex...................... 100
Symes Books (Naomi), Cheshire 71
Taylor & Son (Peter), Herts......................... 132
Uncle Phil's Books, West Midlands 239
Unsworth's Booksellers, Suffolk 225
Wheen O'Books, Borders............................ 267
Whitchurch Books Ltd., Cardiff.................... 281
Wiend Books, Lancashire 143
York Modern Books, N Yorks...................... 196

- BRITISH EMPIRE, THE

Annie's Books, S Yorks 221
Antique Prints of the World, London N.......... 156
Apocalypse, Surrey 232
Bookworms Paradise Ltd., West Sussex 242
Burroughs (Andrew), Lincolnshire 152
Caliver Books, Essex 109
Dolphin Books, Suffolk.............................. 225
Empire Books, N Yorks............................. 197
Fifteenth Century Bookshop (The), East Sussex. 104
G. C. Books Ltd., Dumfries & Galloway......... 270
Joel Segal Books, Devon 86
Kenya Books, East Sussex 100
Lost Books, Northants............................... 200
Marine and Cannon Books, Cheshire 69
Martin (Books and Pictures), (Brian P.), Surrey. 231
N1 Books, East Sussex 105
Pennymead Books, N Yorks........................ 193
Peter M Daly, Hampshire........................... 126
Price (John), London N 158
R. & A. Books, East Sussex 101
Rayner (Hugh Ashley), Somerset 215
Saracen Books, Derbyshire.......................... 83
SETI Books, West Midlands......................... 239
Uncle Phil's Books, West Midlands 239
Wheen O'Books, Borders............................ 267
Winghale Books, Lincolnshire 152

- BYZANTINE

Bennett & Kerr Books, Oxfordshire 205
Camden Books, Somerset 215
Helion & Company, West Midlands 239
Kingswood Books, Dorset 94
Olynthiacs, Shropshire 213
Rosanda Books, Leics 146
St Philip's Books, Oxfordshire..................... 208
Samovar Books, Co. Dublin........................ 264
Unsworth's Booksellers, Suffolk 225

- CANADIAN

Empire Books, N Yorks............................. 197

- CARIBBEAN

Empire Books, N Yorks............................. 197
Pennymead Books, N Yorks........................ 193
Woburn Books, London N 159

- CHURCH

Cofion Books, Pembrokeshire 286
Hornsey's, N Yorks 194
Rosley Books, Cumbria 81
Thorntons of Oxford Ltd., Oxfordshire........... 206

- COLONIAL

Burroughs (Andrew), Lincolnshire 152
Caliver Books, Essex 109
Dolphin Books, Suffolk.............................. 225
Fifteenth Century Bookshop (The), East Sussex. 104
Joel Segal Books, Devon 86
Kabristan Archives, Shropshire..................... 214
Kenya Books, East Sussex 100
Lost Books, Northants............................... 200
Michael Graves-Johnston, London SW 168
N1 Books, East Sussex 105
Pennymead Books, N Yorks........................ 193
Peter M Daly, Hampshire........................... 126
Winghale Books, Lincolnshire 152

- DESIGN

Apocalypse, Surrey 232
Art Reference Books, Hampshire 124
Ballantyne–Way (Roger), Suffolk 228
Black Cat Books, Norfolk........................... 187
C J Renwick Books, Powys......................... 287
Don Kelly Books, London W 172
Ellis, Bookseller (Peter), London WC 177
Inch's Books, Kent 137
Joel Segal Books, Devon 86
Judith Mansfield, West Yorkshire.................. 249
R. & A. Books, East Sussex 101
Sleepy Elephant Books & Artefacts, Cumbria ... 80
Woburn Books, London N 159

- DEVELOPMENT OF
TRANS-MISSISSIPPI WEST

Americanabooksuk, Cumbria....................... 76

- DUTCH EAST INDIA COMPANY

Drury Rare Books (John), Essex.................... 110

- ECONOMIC THOUGHT

Drury Rare Books (John), Essex.................... 110
Empire Books, N Yorks............................. 197
Hamish Riley-Smith, Norfolk....................... 191
Leo Cadogan, London N 157
Northern Herald Books, West Yorkshire......... 245
Parkinsons Books, Merseyside...................... 185
Quaritch Ltd., (Bernard), London W.............. 174
Susanne Schulz-Falster Rare Books, London N. 158
Winghale Books, Lincolnshire 152
Woburn Books, London N 159

- EUROPEAN

Apocalypse, Surrey 232
Beckham Books Ltd., Suffolk 229
Bennett & Kerr Books, Oxfordshire 205
Bloomsbury Bookshop, London O 181
Books on Spain, London O.......................... 182
Broadwater Books, Hampshire..................... 125
de Visser Books, Cambridgeshire................... 63
Dolphin Books, Suffolk.............................. 225
Empire Books, N Yorks.............................. 197
Fifteenth Century Bookshop (The), East Sussex. 104
Helion & Company, West Midlands 239
Joel Segal Books, Devon 86
Leo Cadogan, London N 157
medievalbookshop, Herts............................ 132
Park Gallery & Bookshop (The), Northants 200
Parkinsons Books, Merseyside...................... 185
Roland Books, Kent 138
Rosanda Books, Leics 146
St Philip's Books, Oxfordshire 208
Seydi Rare Books (Sevin), London NW 161
Symes Books (Naomi), Cheshire 71
Taylor & Son (Peter), Herts......................... 132
Unsworth's Booksellers, Suffolk.................... 225
Winghale Books, Lincolnshire 152
York (Graham), Devon.............................. 86

- FAMILY

Aitchison (Lesley), Bristol 58
Annie's Books, S Yorks 221
Atholl Fine Books, Tayside 280
Bookworms Paradise Ltd., West Sussex 242
Country Books, Derbyshire 82
Delph Books, Greater Manchester................. 120
Fifteenth Century Bookshop (The), East Sussex. 104
Jackdaw Books, Norfolk 188
Joel Segal Books, Devon 86
McEwan Fine Books, Grampian..................... 272
Symes Books (Naomi), Cheshire 71
Thornber (Peter M.), N Yorks 195
Turton (John), Durham 98
Tyger Press, London N 158

- GREEK

Crouch Rare Books, Surrey.......................... 232
Michael Graves-Johnston, London SW 168
Rosanda Books, Leics 146

- GUILDS & LIVERY COMPANIES

Chas J. Sawyer, Kent 140
Joel Segal Books, Devon 86

- HAWAIIAN

Mulyan (Don), Merseyside........................... 185

- IMPERIAL RUSSIA

Cox (Geoff), Devon 90
Dolphin Books, Suffolk.............................. 225
Joel Segal Books, Devon 86
Marijana Dworski Books, Powys 288
White Eagle Books, London NW 162

- INDUSTRIAL

Anvil Books, West Midlands 239
Baldwin (M. & M.), Worcs 255

Barbican Bookshop, N Yorks 196
Blanchfield (John), West Yorkshire................ 248
Book House (The), Cumbria......................... 76
Books & Bygones (Pam Taylor), West Midlands . 240
Bott, (Bookdealers) Ltd., (Martin),
   Greater Manchester 118
Clevedon Books, Somerset 217
Coulthurst (Richard), Greater Manchester 120
Cox (Geoff), Devon 90
Crosby Nethercott Books, London O 180
Dales and Lakes Book Centre, Cumbria.......... 79
Delph Books, Greater Manchester.................. 120
Graham (John), Dorset............................... 96
Hall, (Anthony C.) Antiquarian Bookseller,
   London O 183
Hedgerow Books, S Yorks 221
Helion & Company, West Midlands 239
Hindsight Books, Herts.............................. 131
Hutchison (Books) (Larry), Fife.................... 271
Jackdaw Books, Norfolk 188
Joel Segal Books, Devon 86
John L Capes (Books Maps & Prints),
   N Yorks.. 196
Kelsall (George), Greater Manchester 118
N1 Books, East Sussex 105
Parkinsons Books, Merseyside...................... 185
Phelps (Michael), West Sussex..................... 242
R. & A. Books, East Sussex 101
Rainford (Sheila), Herts 129
Randall (Tom), Somerset............................ 218
Roadmaster Books, Kent 136
Robert Humm & Co, Lincolnshire 152
Rochdale Book Company, G Manchester........ 120
Rolling Stock Books, Greater Manchester........ 120
Salway Books, Essex 112
Scarthin Books, Derbyshire 82
Skyrack Books, West Yorkshire..................... 247
Spurrier (Nick), Kent 137
Stalagluft Books, Tyne and Wear.................. 235
Stroh (M.A.), London E 154
Symes Books (Naomi), Cheshire 71
Tony Pollastrone Railway Books, Wiltshire...... 251
Trinders' Fine Tools, Suffolk 226
Tyger Press, London N 158
Westons, Herts....................................... 132
Whitchurch Books Ltd., Cardiff.................... 281
Winghale Books, Lincolnshire 152
Wizard Books, Cambridgeshire..................... 67
Ystwyth Books, Ceredigion 282

- IRISH

Abbey Books, Cornwall 73
Ann & Mike Conry, Worcs......................... 257
Apocalypse, Surrey 232
Armchair Books, Lothian 275
Bloomsbury Bookshop, London O 181
Book Business (The), London W 171
Celtic Bookshop (The), Co. Limerick 266
Colonsay Bookshop, Isle of Colonsay............. 275
Craobh Rua Books, Co. Armagh 260
Darkwood Books, Co. Cork........................ 263
Delectus Books, London WC....................... 176
Doolin Dinghy Books, Co. Clare 262
Fifteenth Century Bookshop (The), East Sussex. 104
Foyle Books, Co. Derry 260

Gildas Books, Cheshire 68
Grove Bookshop (The), N Yorks 195
Helion & Company, West Midlands 239
House of Figgis Ltd (The), Co. Galway 265
J.E. Burns Booksellers, Merseyside 185
JIRI Books, Co. Antrim 260
Joel Segal Books, Devon 86
Kabristan Archives, Shropshire 214
Karen Millward, Co. Cork 263
Kenny's Bookshop & Art Galleries Ltd.,
    Co. Galway 265
Kenya Books, East Sussex 100
Keogh's Books, Glos 115
Lyonshill Books, Co. Dublin 265
Michael J Carroll, Co. Cork 263
Prospect House Books, Co. Down 261
R. & A. Books, East Sussex 101
Read Ireland, Co. Dublin 264
Roscrea Bookshop & Newsagents,
    Co. Tipperary 266
Rowan (P. & B.), Co. Antrim 260
Saintfield Antiques & Fine Books, Co. Down ... 261
Schull Books, Co. Cork 262
Stokes Books, Co. Dublin 264
Taylor & Son (Peter), Herts 132

- JEWISH
Chapter Two, London SE 163
Delectus Books, London WC 176

- LABOUR/ RADICAL MOVEMENTS
Berwick Books, Lincolnshire 150
Bloomsbury Bookshop, London O 181
Cox Rare Books (Charles), Cornwall 73
Delectus Books, London WC 176
Drury Rare Books (John), Essex 110
Fifteenth Century Bookshop (The), East Sussex . 104
Helion & Company, West Midlands 239
J.E. Burns Booksellers, Merseyside 185
Jackdaw Books, Norfolk 188
Joel Segal Books, Devon 86
Left on The Shelf, Cumbria 78
Northern Herald Books, West Yorkshire 245
PsychoBabel Books & Journals, Oxfordshire 205
Quaritch Ltd., (Bernard), London W 174
R. & A. Books, East Sussex 101
Reading Lasses, Dumfries & Galloway 270
Red Star Books, Herts 129
Spurrier (Nick), Kent 137
Star Lord Books, Greater Manchester 119
Symes Books (Naomi), Cheshire 71
Woburn Books, London N 159

- LIBRARY
Sillan Books, Co. Cavan 262

- LOCAL
Abrahams (Mike), Staffordshire 223
Ambra Books, Bristol 58
Ampersand Books, Norfolk 189
Antiquary Ltd., (Bar Bookstore), N Yorks 194
Arden Books & Cosmographia, Warwickshire ... 236
Atholl Fine Books, Tayside 280
Barbican Bookshop, N Yorks 196
Barn Books, Shropshire 214

Bear Island Books, Cardiff 281
Beardsell Books, West Yorkshire 246
Beckham Books Ltd., Suffolk 229
Bell (Peter), Lothian 275
Beverley Old Bookshop, East Yorkshire 106
Black Five Books, Shropshire 214
Blore's Bookshop (Geoffrey), Nottinghamshire .. 204
Bonython Bookshop, Cornwall 75
Book For All Reasons (A.), Suffolk 228
Bookshop (The), Co. Donegal 263
Brazenhead Ltd., Norfolk 188
Brown (Books) (P.R.), Durham 98
Browning Books, Torfaen 292
Browsers Bookshop, Cornwall 72
Burebank Books, Norfolk 186
Bury Bookshop, Suffolk 225
Carlton Books, Norfolk 189
Carnforth Bookshop (The), Lancashire 142
Castle Bookshop, Essex 108
Castle Hill Books, Herefordshire 128
Chapman (Neville), Lancashire 144
Chaucer Bookshop, Kent 136
Clarendon Books, Leics 145
Clark (Nigel A.), London SE 163
Colin Hancock, Ceredigion 282
Colonsay Bookshop, Isle of Colonsay 275
Compass Books, Devon 85
Coombes (A.J.), Surrey 230
Copperplate Antique Maps and Prints, Herts.... 132
Cornucopia Books, Lincolnshire 151
Cottage Books, Leics 145
Country Books, Derbyshire 82
Courtwood Books, Co. Laois 265
Cox (Geoff), Devon 90
Daeron's Books, Buckinghamshire 62
Dobson (Bob), Lancashire 142
Dormouse Bookshop (The), Norfolk 189
Eastgate Bookshop, East Yorkshire 106
Elaine Lonsdale Books, West Yorkshire 247
Ellis, Bookseller (Peter), London WC 177
Empire Books, North Yorkshire 197
Fifteenth Century Bookshop (The), East Sussex. 104
Forest Books of Manchester, Cheshire 70
Fosters Bookshop, London W 172
Freeman's Corner Shop, Norfolk 189
G. C. Books Ltd., Dumfries & Galloway 270
Garretts Antiquarian Books, Isle of Man 259
Gildas Books, Cheshire 68
Glenwood Books, Surrey 234
Good for Books, Lincolnshire 149
Graham (John), Dorset 96
Guisborough Bookshop (The), North Yorkshire 192
Handsworth Books, Essex 112
Hawes Books, Norfolk 190
Hawley (C.L.), North Yorkshire 195
Helion & Company, West Midlands 239
Hicks (Ronald C.), Cornwall 73
Horsham Rare Books, West Sussex 242
Hughes Rare Books (Spike), Borders 267
hullbooks.com, East Yorkshire 106
Idle Booksellers (The), West Yorkshire 245
Iona Bookshop (The), Isle of Iona 275
J.C. Books, Devon 87
Jackdaw Books, Norfolk 188
Joel Segal Books, Devon 86

John Barton, Hampshire 126
Just Books, Cornwall 75
Karen Millward, Co. Cork......................... 263
Kenny's Bookshop & Art Galleries Ltd.,
  Co. Galway...................................... 265
Kingfisher Book Service, Nottinghamshire 204
Kingsgate Books & Prints, Hampshire............ 126
Letterbox Books, Nottinghamshire 203
Liddle (Steve), Bristol 58
Martin (Brian), Surrey 231
Michael J Carroll, Co. Cork 263
Missing Books, Essex 109
MK Book Services, Cambridgeshire............... 66
Mogul Diamonds, West Midlands 240
Moon's Bookshop (Michael), Cumbria 80
Oakwood Books, Glos.............................. 115
Old Bookshelf (The), Strathclyde................... 278
Old Bookshop (The), West Midlands 240
Orb's Bookshop, Grampian......................... 273
Ouse Valley Books, Bedfordshire 54
Peter M Daly, Hampshire........................... 126
Peter White, Hampshire 121
Polmorla Books, Cornwall 75
R. & A. Books, East Sussex 101
Randall (Tom), Somerset............................ 218
Rare & Racy, S Yorks.............................. 222
Richard Thornton Books, London N 158
Rickaro Books, West Yorkshire.................... 246
Roadmaster Books, Kent............................ 136
Roberts Books, Strathclyde 279
Rods Books, Devon................................. 88
Rose Books, Greater Manchester 119
Ross Old Books & Prints, Herefordshire 128
Salway Books, Essex 112
Samovar Books, Co. Dublin........................ 264
Scarthin Books, Derbyshire 82
Sedgeberrow Books, Worcs 256
SETI Books, West Midlands 239
Sillan Books, Co. Cavan............................ 262
Siop Lyfrau'r Hen Bost, Gwynedd 285
Skyrack Books, West Yorkshire.................... 247
Smith Books (Keith), Herefordshire 128
Spooner & Co, Somerset............................ 219
Stacpoole (George), Co. Limerick.................. 266
Stinton (Judith), Dorset............................. 92
Studio (The), Strathclyde 278
Suffolk Rare Books, Suffolk 229
Symes Books (Naomi), Cheshire 71
Taylor & Son (Peter), Herts........................ 132
Turton (John), Durham 98
Tyger Press, London N 158
Wealden Books, Kent............................... 138
Wheen O'Books, Borders........................... 267
Whitchurch Books Ltd., Cardiff.................... 281
Yates Antiquarian Books (Tony), Leics........... 146

- MAFEKING

Empire Books, North Yorkshire 197

- MIDDLE AGES

Alexander's Books, Warwickshire................... 237
Apocalypse, Surrey 232
Baker Limited (A.P. & R.),
  Dumfries & Galloway............................. 269
Bennett & Kerr Books, Oxfordshire 205

Blackpool Book Warehouse, Lancashire.......... 142
Bloomsbury Bookshop, London O 181
Bookshop at the Plain, Lincolnshire............... 149
Caliver Books, Essex 109
Camden Books, Somerset 215
Dolphin Books, Suffolk............................. 225
Fifteenth Century Bookshop (The), East Sussex. 104
Green Man Books, East Sussex 101
Handsworth Books, Essex 112
Helion & Company, West Midlands 239
Jackdaw Books, Norfolk 188
Joel Segal Books, Devon 86
Kingswood Books, Dorset 94
medievalbookshop, Herts 132
Meekins Books (Paul), Warwickshire.............. 237
Michael J Carroll, Co. Cork 263
Minster Gate Bookshop, North Yorkshire 197
N1 Books, East Sussex 105
Rosanda Books, Leics 146
Spenceley Books (David), West Yorkshire........ 248
Taylor & Son (Peter), Herts........................ 132
Thorntons of Oxford Ltd., Oxfordshire........... 206
Uncle Phil's Books, West Midlands 239
Unsworth's Booksellers, Suffolk................... 225
Winghale Books, Lincolnshire 152
Wizard Books, Cambridgeshire..................... 67

- MINING

Bott, (Bookdealers) Ltd., (Martin),
  Greater Manchester 118
Crosby Nethercott Books, London O 180
Dartmoor Book Gallery, Devon 87
Whitchurch Books Ltd., Cardiff.................... 281

- MODERN

Annie's Books, S Yorks 221
Baker Limited (A.P. & R.),
  Dumfries & Galloway............................. 269
Barcombe Services, Essex........................... 108
Bloomsbury Bookshop, London O 181
Bookshop at the Plain, Lincolnshire............... 149
Fifteenth Century Bookshop (The), East Sussex. 104
Joel Segal Books, Devon 86
Maggy Browne, Lincolnshire 148
Michael J Carroll, Co. Cork 263
Rosanda Books, Leics 146
SETI Books, West Midlands........................ 239
Symes Books (Naomi), Cheshire 71
Unsworth's Booksellers, Suffolk................... 225
Wizard Books, Cambridgeshire..................... 67

- NAPOLEONIC

Apocalypse, Surrey 232
Baker Limited (A.P. & R.),
  Dumfries & Galloway............................. 269
Blackpool Book Warehouse, Lancashire.......... 142
Dolphin Books, Suffolk............................. 225
Fifteenth Century Bookshop (The), East Sussex. 104
Green Ltd. (G.L.), Herts 131
Marine & Cannon Books, Cheshire 71
Marine and Cannon Books, Cheshire 69
N1 Books, East Sussex 105
Solaris Books, East Yorkshire 106
Sutcliffe (Victor), Norfolk......................... 187
Taylor & Son (Peter), Herts........................ 132

Trotman (Ken), Cambridgeshire 66
Wizard Books, Cambridgeshire..................... 67

- NATIONAL

Apocalypse, Surrey 232
Baker Limited (A.P. & R.),
    Dumfries & Galloway............................ 269
Bell (Peter), Lothian............................... 275
Bloomsbury Bookshop, London O 181
Carnforth Bookshop (The), Lancashire 142
Cox (Geoff), Devon 90
Craobh Rua Books, Co. Armagh.................. 260
Davidson Books, Co. Down 261
De Burca Rare Books, Co. Dublin 264
Doolin Dinghy Books, Co. Clare 262
Fifteenth Century Bookshop (The), East Sussex. 104
Fuchsia Books, Co. Wexford 266
Graham (John), Dorset............................. 96
Hawes Books, Norfolk.............................. 190
Helion & Company, West Midlands 239
Hughes Rare Books (Spike), Borders............. 267
Joel Segal Books, Devon 86
Kingswood Books, Dorset 94
Pringle Booksellers (Andrew), Lothian 277
Siop y Morfa, Denbighshire 284
Thistle Books, Strathclyde.......................... 278
Whelan (P. & F.), Kent............................. 140
Winghale Books, Lincolnshire 152
Wizard Books, Cambridgeshire..................... 67
Woolcott Books, Dorset............................ 92

- OTTOMAN EMPIRE

Antique Prints of the World, London N.......... 156
Empire Books, North Yorkshire 197
Joppa Books Ltd., Surrey 230
Seydi Rare Books (Sevin), London NW 161

- PHOTOGRAPHY

Apocalypse, Surrey 232
Ballantyne–Way (Roger), Suffolk 228
Dally (Andrew), Powys 289
Jill Howell, East Sussex 102
Joel Segal Books, Devon 86
Print Matters, London SE.......................... 165
Quaritch Ltd., (Bernard), London W.............. 174
R. & A. Books, East Sussex 101
Rayner (Hugh Ashley), Somerset 215
Stroh (M.A.), London E 154

- POSTAL

Apocalypse, Surrey 232
Empire Books, North Yorkshire 197
Joel Segal Books, Devon 86
Pennymead Books, North Yorkshire 193
Postings, Surrey..................................... 233
R. & A. Books, East Sussex 101

- PUERTO RICO

Pennymead Books, North Yorkshire 193

- REFORMATION

Apocalypse, Surrey 232
Bloomsbury Bookshop, London O 181
Chapter Two, London SE........................... 163
Dolphin Books, Suffolk............................. 225

Fifteenth Century Bookshop (The), East Sussex. 104
Handsworth Books, Essex........................... 112
Joel Segal Books, Devon 86
Leo Cadogan, London N 157
medievalbookshop, Herts........................... 132
Pendleburys Bookshop, London N 158
St Philip's Books, Oxfordshire...................... 208
Samovar Books, Co. Dublin........................ 264
Unsworth's Booksellers, Suffolk 225
Wizard Books, Cambridgeshire..................... 67

- RENAISSANCE, THE

All Books, Essex 111
Apocalypse, Surrey 232
Art Reference Books, Hampshire 124
Bennett & Kerr Books, Oxfordshire 205
Caliver Books, Essex 109
Dolphin Books, Suffolk............................. 225
Fifteenth Century Bookshop (The), East Sussex. 104
Handsworth Books, Essex........................... 112
Helion & Company, West Midlands 239
Jackdaw Books, Norfolk 188
Joel Segal Books, Devon 86
Leo Cadogan, London N 157
medievalbookshop, Herts........................... 132
R. & A. Books, East Sussex 101
Seydi Rare Books (Sevin), London NW 161
Spenceley Books (David), West Yorkshire........ 248
Taylor & Son (Peter), Herts........................ 132
Thorntons of Oxford Ltd., Oxfordshire........... 206
Unsworth's Booksellers, Suffolk 225
Winghale Books, Lincolnshire 152

- ROMAN

Annie's Books, S Yorks 221
Apocalypse, Surrey 232
Aviabooks, Glos 114
Brock Books, North Yorkshire 192
C J Renwick Books, Powys 287
Caliver Books, Essex 109
Crouch Rare Books, Surrey......................... 232
Fifteenth Century Bookshop (The), East Sussex. 104
Handsworth Books, Essex........................... 112
Helion & Company, West Midlands 239
Joel Segal Books, Devon 86
N1 Books, East Sussex 105
R. & A. Books, East Sussex 101
Rosanda Books, Leics 146
Stalagluft Books, Tyne and Wear.................. 235
Unsworth's Booksellers, Suffolk 225

- RUSSIAN IMPERIAL

Caliver Books, Essex 109
Cox (Geoff), Devon 90
Darkwood Books, Co. Cork......................... 263
de Visser Books, Cambridgeshire................... 63
Dolphin Books, Suffolk............................. 225
Marijana Dworski Books, Powys 288
R. & A. Books, East Sussex 101
Thorntons of Oxford Ltd., Oxfordshire........... 206
Wizard Books, Cambridgeshire..................... 67

- SCIENCE

Barcombe Services, Essex........................... 108
Bernard Dixon and Kath Adams, London O.... 182

Dean Byass, Bristol 60
Empire Books, North Yorkshire 197
Handsworth Books, Essex 112
Jackdaw Books, Norfolk 188
Joel Segal Books, Devon 86
Kingswood Books, Dorset 94
Moorside Books, Lancashire 143
Orb's Bookshop, Grampian 273
Park (Mike), London O 182
Parkinsons Books, Merseyside 185
Polczynski (Udo K.H.), Powys 289
Roberts Books, Strathclyde 279
Seydi Rare Books (Sevin), London NW 161
Taylor & Son (Peter), Herts 132
Turret House, Norfolk 191
Weiner (Graham), London N 158
Westons, Herts 132

- SCOTTISH
Atholl Fine Books, Tayside 280
Bell (Peter), Lothian 275
Bloomsbury Bookshop, London O 181
Byre Books, Dumfries & Galloway 270
Caliver Books, Essex 109
Colonsay Bookshop, Isle of Colonsay 275
Cooper Hay Rare Books, Strathclyde 278
Creaking Shelves, Highland 274
Darkwood Books, Co. Cork 263
Delectus Books, London WC 176
Dolphin Books, Suffolk 225
Elizabeth Ferguson, Grampian 272
Farquharson, (Hilary), Tayside 280
Ferguson (Elizabeth), Grampian 272
Fifteenth Century Bookshop (The), East Sussex. 104
Grampian Books, Grampian 273
Greta Books, Durham 97
Handsworth Books, Essex 112
Joel Segal Books, Devon 86
Loch Croispol Bookshop & Restaurant,
    Highland 273
McCrone (Audrey), Isle of Arran 274
Mercat Books, Highland 274
Orb's Bookshop, Grampian 273
R. & A. Books, East Sussex 101
Rosanda Books, Leics 146
Samovar Books, Co. Dublin 264
Stalagluft Books, Tyne and Wear 235
Thistle Books, Strathclyde 278
Till's Bookshop, Lothian 277
Wheen O'Books, Borders 267

- SOUTH AFRICA
Barn Books, Buckinghamshire 61
Boer War Books, North Yorkshire 197
Caliver Books, Essex 109
Chalmers Hallam (E.), Hampshire 125
Delectus Books, London WC 176
Hawley (C.L.), North Yorkshire 195
Kenya Books, East Sussex 100
Yesterday's Books, Dorset 92

- SPANISH CIVIL WAR
Baldwin (Jack), Strathclyde 278
Bass (Ben), Wiltshire 251
Delectus Books, London WC 176

Fifteenth Century Bookshop (The), East Sussex. 104
Left on The Shelf, Cumbria 78
Meekins Books (Paul), Warwickshire 237
Orssich (Paul), London SW 169
Red Star Books, Herts 129

- SPORTS
Annie's Books, S Yorks 221
Bermondsey Basement Bookstore, London SE .. 163
Collectors Carbooks, Northants 199
Joel Segal Books, Devon 86
Old Bookshop (The), West Midlands 240

- TROTSKYISM
Left on The Shelf, Cumbria 78
Northern Herald Books, West Yorkshire 245
R. & A. Books, East Sussex 101
Red Star Books, Herts 129

- U.S. COLONIAL
Americanabooksuk, Cumbria 76

- WOMEN
Burmester (James), Bristol 58
Dolphin Books, Suffolk 225
Drury Rare Books (John), Essex 110
Elaine Lonsdale Books, West Yorkshire 247
Fifteenth Century Bookshop (The), East Sussex. 104
Karen Millward, Co. Cork 263
Northern Herald Books, West Yorkshire 245
Price (John), London N 158
Reading Lasses, Dumfries & Galloway 270
Scorpio Books, Suffolk 225
Spenceley Books (David), West Yorkshire 248
Symes Books (Naomi), Cheshire 71
Woburn Books, London N 159

HISTORY OF CIVILISATION
Apocalypse, Surrey 232
Camden Books, Somerset 215
Crouch Rare Books, Surrey 232
Fifteenth Century Bookshop (The), East Sussex. 104
Helion & Company, West Midlands 239
Karen Millward, Co. Cork 263
N1 Books, East Sussex 105
R. & A. Books, East Sussex 101
Star Lord Books, Greater Manchester 119
Treadwell's Books, London WC 178

HISTORY OF IDEAS
Apocalypse, Surrey 232
Bernard Dixon and Kath Adams, London O 182
Bernstein (Nicholas), London W 171
Clevedon Books, Somerset 217
Dean Byass, Bristol 60
Drury Rare Books (John), Essex 110
Eagle Bookshop (The), Bedfordshire 53
Fifteenth Century Bookshop (The), East Sussex. 104
Game Advice, Oxfordshire 208
Gildas Books, Cheshire 68
Helion & Company, West Midlands 239
Herb Tandree Philosophy Books, Glos 116
Lee Rare Books (Rachel), Bristol 59
Leo Cadogan, London N 157
Mair Wilkes Books, Fife 271

Parkinsons Books, Merseyside...................... 185
Pendleburys Bookshop, London N 158
Phillips (Nigel), Hampshire........................... 122
Price (John), London N 158
Quaritch Ltd., (Bernard), London W.............. 174
St Philip's Books, Oxfordshire...................... 208
Seydi Rare Books (Sevin), London NW 161
Star Lord Books, Greater Manchester 119
Taylor & Son (Peter), Herts........................ 132
Treadwell's Books, London WC 178
Weininger Antiquarian Books (Eva M.),
  London NW.. 161
Westwood Books Ltd, Cumbria................... 80

HOBBIES

Annie's Books, S Yorks 221
Charles Bossom, Cambridgeshire................... 65
Cheshire Book Centre, Cheshire.................... 69
Cornucopia Books, Lincolnshire 151
Cover to Cover, Merseyside........................ 185
Dales & Lakes Book Centre, Cumbria........... 79
DPE Books, Devon 87
Esoteric Dreams Bookshop, Cumbria 77
Fifteenth Century Bookshop (The), East Sussex. 104
Joel Segal Books, Devon 86
McCrone (Audrey), Isle of Arran 274
Oopalba Books, Cheshire........................... 71
R. & A. Books, East Sussex 101
Reeves Technical Books, North Yorkshire 195
River Reads Bookshop, Devon...................... 90
Treasure Island (The), Greater Manchester...... 119
Wheen O'Books, Borders........................... 267

HOLOCAUST

Bookshop (The), Greater Manchester 118
Booth (Booksearch Service), (Geoff), Cheshire... 68
Fishburn Books, London NW...................... 160
Helion & Company, West Midlands 239
Island Books, Devon................................ 85
Joel Segal Books, Devon 86
MilitaryHistoryBooks.com, Kent.................... 137
Rosemary Pugh Books, Wiltshire 253
Samovar Books, Co. Dublin....................... 264
SETI Books, West Midlands........................ 239
Trotter Books (John), London N 158
White Eagle Books, London NW.................. 162
World War Books, Kent 141

HOLY LAND

Criterion Books, London O........................ 181

HOME IMPROVEMENTS

Annie's Books, S Yorks 221
Uncle Phil's Books, West Midlands 239

HOMEOPATHY'

Crabtree (Mrs. C.), Greater Manchester 120
Dales & Lakes Book Centre, Cumbria........... 79
Edmund Pollinger Rare Books, London SW..... 166
Esoteric Dreams Bookshop, Cumbria 77
Fifteenth Century Bookshop (The), East Sussex. 104
Greensleeves, Oxfordshire 206
Inner Bookshop (The), Oxfordshire.............. 208
Joel Segal Books, Devon 86
Magis Books, Leics................................ 146

Occultique, Northants............................... 199
Orchid Book Distributors, Co. Clare.............. 262
Phelps (Michael), West Sussex...................... 242
R. & A. Books, East Sussex 101
Rebecca Hardie Rare Books, London W......... 171
Scrivener's Books & Bookbinding, Derbyshire... 82
Till's Bookshop, Lothian 277

HOMOSEXUALITY & LESBIANISM

Bookshop (The), Greater Manchester 118
Delectus Books, London WC...................... 176
Esoteric Dreams Bookshop, Cumbria 77
Gay's The Word, London WC..................... 177
Ian Briddon, Derbyshire............................ 82
Joel Segal Books, Devon 86
Judd Books, London WC.......................... 177
Paper Pleasures, Somerset.......................... 218
R. & A. Books, East Sussex 101
Reading Lasses, Dumfries & Galloway 270
Till's Bookshop, Lothian 277
Tsbbooks, London SW 169
Woburn Books, London N 159

HORIZON WRITERS

Criterion Books, London O........................ 181

HOROLOGY

Anthony Vickers Books, North Yorkshire 195
Barmby (C. & A.J.), Kent.......................... 140
Baron (Christopher), Cheshire..................... 68
Blackpool Book Warehouse, Lancashire.......... 142
Cheshire Book Centre, Cheshire.................... 69
Clark (Nigel A.), London SE...................... 163
Cornucopia Books, Lincolnshire 151
Delph Books, Greater Manchester................. 120
Engaging Gear Ltd., Essex......................... 108
Formby Antiques (Jeffrey), Glos 115
Hadfield (G.K.), Cumbria.......................... 79
Joel Segal Books, Devon 86
Nibris Books, London SW.......................... 169
Rogers Turner Books, London SE................. 165
Scrivener's Books & Bookbinding, Derbyshire... 82
Sue Lowell Natural History Books, London W . 175
Trinders' Fine Tools, Suffolk 226
Wadard Books, Kent 137

HORSES

Annie's Books, S Yorks 221
Bob Mallory (Books), Derbyshire.................. 83
Bookworms Paradise Ltd., West Sussex 242
Browzers, Greater Manchester...................... 118
Cofion Books, Pembrokeshire 286
Cornucopia Books, Lincolnshire 151
Country Books, Derbyshire......................... 82
Dales & Lakes Book Centre, Cumbria........... 79
Darkwood Books, Co. Cork........................ 263
Discovery Bookshop, Carmarthenshire............ 281
Fifteenth Century Bookshop (The), East Sussex. 104
Garfi Books, Powys 291
Grove Bookshop (The), North Yorkshire 195
Hünersdorff Rare Books, London SW 168
Jane Badger Books, Northants 199
JB Books & Collectables, West Sussex 243
Joel Segal Books, Devon 86
Karen Millward, Co. Cork......................... 263

Kelpie's Books, Fife 271
Kennedy & Farley, East Sussex 104
Phenotype Books, Cumbria 79
R. & A. Books, East Sussex 101

HORTICULTURE

Barn Books, Shropshire 214
Besleys Books, Suffolk 225
Black Five Books, Shropshire 214
Blest (Peter), Kent 138
Books for Content, Herefordshire 127
Burmester (James), Bristol 58
Clarke Books (David), Somerset 218
Coach House Books, Worcs 256
Court Hay Books, West Midlands 239
Dales & Lakes Book Centre, Cumbria 79
Dolphin Books, Suffolk 225
Eastcote Bookshop (The), London O 180
Evergreen Livres, Glos 116
Fifteenth Century Bookshop (The), East Sussex. 104
Gardener & Cook, London SW 167
Garfi Books, Powys 291
Hollingshead (Chris), London O 182
Hünersdorff Rare Books, London SW 168
Joel Segal Books, Devon 86
Mobbs (A.J.), West Midlands 239
Orb's Bookshop, Grampian 273
Park (Mike), London O 182
Parkinsons Books, Merseyside 185
Peter M Daly, Hampshire 126
Phelps (Michael), West Sussex 242
Pollak (P.M.), Devon 88
Pugh Books (Ian K.), Worcs 256
R. & A. Books, East Sussex 101
Spelman (Ken), North Yorkshire 198
Summerfield Books Ltd, Cumbria 79
Thin Read Line, Merseyside 184
Trigon Books, Dorset 95
Uncle Phil's Books, West Midlands 239
Valerie Merritt, Worcs 256
Vokes Books Ltd., North Yorkshire 194
Westons, Herts 132

HOSPITALS

Bernard Dixon and Kath Adams, London O.... 182
Empire Books, North Yorkshire 197
J & J Burgess Booksellers, Cambridgeshire 64
Jackdaw Books, Norfolk 188
PsychoBabel Books & Journals, Oxfordshire 205
R M Books, Herts 132
R. & A. Books, East Sussex 101
Westons, Herts 132

HOUSEKEEPING

Black Cat Books, Norfolk 187
Country Books, Derbyshire 82
DPE Books, Devon 87
Fifteenth Century Bookshop (The), East Sussex. 104
HCB Wholesale, Powys 288
R. & A. Books, East Sussex 101
Sleepy Elephant Books & Artefacts, Cumbria ... 80
Susan Taylor Books, West Yorkshire 247

HUDSON BAY COMPANY

Americanabooksuk, Cumbria 76

HUMANISM

Books Only, Suffolk 226
Chthonios Books, East Sussex 102
Forder (R.W.), Hampshire 121
Humanist Book Services, Cornwall 72
Jackdaw Books, Norfolk 188
Northern Herald Books, West Yorkshire 245
Parkinsons Books, Merseyside 185
Poole (William), London W 174
R. & A. Books, East Sussex 101
Unsworth's Booksellers, Suffolk 225
Woburn Books, London N 159

HUMANITIES

Apocalypse, Surrey 232
Aurora Books Ltd, Lothian 275
Bristol Books, Bristol 60
Crouch Rare Books, Surrey 232
Drury Rare Books (John), Essex 110
Fireside Bookshop, Cumbria 81
Forest Books of Manchester, Cheshire 70
Hawley (C.L.), North Yorkshire 195
hullbooks.com, East Yorkshire 106
Joel Segal Books, Devon 86
Lee Rare Books (Rachel), Bristol 59
Maghreb Bookshop (The), London WC 177
Parkinsons Books, Merseyside 185
Pickering & Chatto, London W 174
Pittville Books, Glos 113
Plurabelle Books, Cambridgeshire 65
Porter Bookshop (The), S Yorks 222
Quaritch Ltd., (Bernard), London W 174
Reading Lasses, Dumfries & Galloway 270
Samovar Books, Co. Dublin 264
Star Lord Books, Greater Manchester 119
Till's Bookshop, Lothian 277
Unsworth's Booksellers, Suffolk 225
Waterfield's, Oxfordshire 209
Woburn Books, London N 159

HUMOUR

Annie's Books, S Yorks 221
Apocalypse, Surrey 232
Autumn Leaves, Lincolnshire 150
BC Books, Cheshire 69
Black Five Books, Shropshire 214
Bob Mallory (Books), Derbyshire 83
Book Palace (The), London SE 163
Books Only, Suffolk 226
Bookstand, Dorset 94
Browse Books, Lancashire 143
Carningli Centre, Pembrokeshire 286
Chapter & Verse, Lincolnshire 150
Cheshire Book Centre, Cheshire 69
Cofion Books, Pembrokeshire 286
Cornucopia Books, Lincolnshire 151
Dales & Lakes Book Centre, Cumbria 79
Dolphin Books, Suffolk 225
Eastcote Bookshop (The), London O 180
Eggeling Books (John), West Yorkshire 249
Fifteenth Century Bookshop (The), East Sussex. 104
Fun in Books, Surrey 234
Goldman (Paul), Dorset 94
Grahame Thornton, Bookseller, Dorset 93
Hay Castle, Powys 288

Hughes (Ms. Sonia A.), Monmouthshire 286
Ian Briddon, Derbyshire............................ 82
Jade Mountain Bookshop, Hampshire 125
Jenny Hurst, Kent 138
Joel Segal Books, Devon 86
Kelpie's Books, Fife 271
Poetry Bookshop (The), Powys..................... 289
Print Matters, London SE........................... 165
Scrivener's Books & Bookbinding, Derbyshire... 82
Uncle Phil's Books, West Midlands 239
Wayside Books and Cards, Oxfordshire 206
Willmott Bookseller (Nicholas), Cardiff........... 281
Yesterday's News, Conwy........................... 283

HYDROGRAPHY
Earth Science Books, Wiltshire 252
Jackdaw Books, Norfolk 188
Phelps (Michael), West Sussex...................... 242

HYMNOLOGY
ECR Books, Dorset 92
Humber Books, Lincolnshire 148
Oasis Booksearch, Cambridgeshire................. 67
Parkinsons Books, Merseyside...................... 185
Rosemary Pugh Books, Wiltshire 253
Samovar Books, Co. Dublin........................ 264
Spooner & Co, Somerset 219
Stalagluft Books, Tyne and Wear.................. 235
Travis & Emery Music Bookshop, London WC 178

HYPNOTISM
Magis Books, Leics................................. 146
Occultique, Northants............................... 199
Phelps (Michael), West Sussex...................... 242
R. & A. Books, East Sussex 101

I-CHING
Atlantis Bookshop, London WC.................... 176
Inner Bookshop (The), Oxfordshire................ 208
Joel Segal Books, Devon 86

ICHTHYOLOGY
Chalmers Hallam (E.), Hampshire 125
Martin (Books and Pictures), (Brian P.), Surrey. 231
Parkinsons Books, Merseyside...................... 185
Pollak (P.M.), Devon 88
Steven Simpson Books, Norfolk 190
Sub Aqua Prints and Books, Hampshire 123

ICONOGRAPHY
Bardsley's Books, Suffolk.......................... 225
Baron (H.), London NW............................ 160
Bennett & Kerr Books, Oxfordshire 205
Foster (Stephen), London NW 160
Parikian, Rare Books (Diana), London W 174
Rosemary Pugh Books, Wiltshire 253

ILLUMINATED MANUSCRIPTS
Bardsley's Books, Suffolk.......................... 225
Bennett & Kerr Books, Oxfordshire 205
Birchden Books, London E 154
Bookstand, Dorset.................................. 94
Butler Rare Books, Buckinghamshire 61
Collectables (W.H.), Suffolk 229
Cox Old & Rare Books (Claude), Suffolk 227

Derek Stirling Bookseller, Kent 141
Du Ry Medieval Manuscripts (Marc–Antoine),
London W 172
John Underwood Antiquarian Books, Norfolk.. 189
Maggs Brothers Limited, London W.............. 173
Quaritch Ltd., (Bernard), London W.............. 174
Taylor & Son (Peter), Herts....................... 132

ILLUSTRATED
- GENERAL
Alastor Rare Books, Hampshire 124
Alexander's Books, Warwickshire.................. 237
Anthony Neville, Kent.............................. 138
Anthony Whittaker, Kent 135
Antique Map and Bookshop (The), Dorset 94
Antiques on High, Oxfordshire..................... 207
Art Reference Books, Hampshire 124
Artco, Nottinghamshire............................. 204
Autolycus, Shropshire.............................. 212
Avonworld Books, Somerset 216
Baker - Books for the Collector (Colin), Devon. 89
Ballantyne–Way (Roger), Suffolk 228
Barlow (Vincent G.), Hampshire.................. 125
Barry McKay Rare Books, Cumbria 76
Bates Books, London O 180
Batterham (David), London W..................... 171
Bayntun (George), Somerset 215
Beck (John), East Sussex 103
Bermondsey Basement Bookstore, London SE .. 163
Besleys Books, Suffolk 225
Bettridge (Gordon), Fife........................... 271
Beverley Old Bookshop, East Yorkshire.......... 106
Bolton Books, Hampshire 121
Book Palace (The), London SE 163
Bookmark (Children's Books), Wiltshire.......... 253
Books Bought & Sold, Surrey 231
books2books, Devon 88
Bookstand, Dorset.................................. 94
Boxwood Books & Prints, Somerset............... 219
Bright (P.G.), Cambridgeshire 65
Brighton Books, East Sussex....................... 99
Burden (Derek), Surrey 232
Burden Ltd., (Clive A.), Herts..................... 131
Butts Books (Mary), Berks......................... 56
Bygone Books, Isles of Scotland 275
Cameron House Books, Isle of Wight............. 133
Camilla's Bookshop, East Sussex 101
Canterbury Bookshop (The), Kent 136
Chalk (Old & Out of Print Books)
(Christine M.), West Midlands 238
Charles Bossom, Cambridgeshire................... 65
Chris Phillips, Wiltshire............................ 252
Cobweb Books, North Yorkshire 194
Cooper Hay Rare Books, Strathclyde 278
Coupland (Terry W.), Staffordshire................ 223
Cox Old & Rare Books (Claude), Suffolk 227
Criterion Books, London O......................... 181
Cumming Limited (A. & Y.), East Sussex........ 104
D'Arcy Books, Wiltshire............................ 252
David (G.), Cambridgeshire......................... 63
de Beaumont (Robin), London SW 166
Derek Stirling Bookseller, Kent 141
Deverell Books, Bristol 59
Doorbar (P. & D.), Gwynedd 285
DPE Books, Devon 87

Drummond Pleasures of Past Times (David),
London WC 176
Eastcote Bookshop (The), London O 180
Eastwood Books (David), Cornwall 72
Eclectica, London SE 164
Elmfield Books, West Midlands.................... 238
Elstree Books, Herts........................... 130
Ely Books, Cambridgeshire 65
Embleton (Paul), Essex 111
Erian Books, London N........... 156
Everett (Richard), Norfolk 187
Ferdinando (Steven), Somerset 218
Ferguson (Elizabeth), Grampian 272
Fifteenth Century Bookshop (The), East Sussex. 104
Fletcher (H.M.), Herts....................... 131
Fosters Bookshop, London W 172
Frew Limited (Robert), London SW 167
Golden Goose Books, Lincolnshire............... 150
Goldman (Paul), Dorset 94
Goodyer (Nicholas), London N.................. 157
Green Meadow Books, Cornwall 74
Grove Bookshop (The), North Yorkshire 195
Hanborough Books, Oxfordshire.................. 208
Harrington (Adrian), London W.................. 173
Harrington Antiquarian Bookseller (Peter),
London SW............. 167
Harvest Books, Lancashire........................ 144
Harwich Old Books, Essex...................... 109
Hatchard & Daughters, West Yorkshire 246
Hava Books, London SE...................... 164
Hennessey Bookseller (Ray), East Sussex 100
Heppa (Christopher), Essex 108
Hereward Books, Cambridgeshire.................. 66
Heywood Hill Limited (G.), London W 173
Hodgkins and Company Limited (Ian), Glos 116
Hodgson (Books) (Richard J.), N Yorks 196
Hughes (Ms. Sonia A.), Monmouthshire......... 286
Hummingbird Books, Herefordshire............... 128
Innes Books, Shropshire........................... 212
Island Books, Devon.............................. 85
Jane & John Kinnaird, Cumbria 78
JB Books & Collectables, West Sussex 243
Jean Hedger, Berks 55
Jermy & Westerman, Nottinghamshire............ 204
Joel Segal Books, Devon 86
Junk & Spread Eagle, London SE................. 164
Katharine House Gallery, Wiltshire 252
Kennedy (Peter), Surrey......................... 234
Kerr (Norman), Cumbria 77
Keswick Bookshop, Cumbria.................... 78
Key Books (Sarah), Cambridgeshire............. 64
Kineton Nooks, Warwickshire.................... 236
Leabeck Books, Oxfordshire 208
Leigh Gallery Books, Essex 110
Lenton (Alfred), Leics........................... 145
Little Stour Books, Kent 136
Lloyd-Davies (Sue), Carmarthenshire 282
Lucius Books, North Yorkshire 197
Lymelight Books & Prints, Dorset............... 93
March House Books, Somerset..................... 217
Marchpane, London WC......................... 177
Marks Limited (Barrie), London N............... 157
Marlborough Rare Books Ltd., London W....... 173
Martin Bookshop & Gallery (Richard), Hants... 123
Mason (Mary), Oxfordshire....................... 205

Maynard & Bradley, Leics 146
McCrone (Audrey), Isle of Arran 274
Mereside Books, Cheshire........................ 70
Mills Rare Books (Adam), Cambridgeshire 64
Minster Gate Bookshop, North Yorkshire 197
Modlock (Lilian), Dorset......................... 93
Myra Dean Illustated Books, Powys 287
Newcastle Bookshop At Haltwhistle,
Northumberland 201
Nonsuch Books, Surrey........................... 234
Oak Tree Press, Oxfordshire....................... 207
O'Flynn Books, North Yorkshire.................. 197
O'Flynn Books, North Yorkshire.................. 197
Old Town Bookshop (The), Lothian 276
Period & Classical Collections, East Sussex 103
Peter M Daly, Hampshire........................ 126
Poetry Bookshop (The), Powys.................... 289
Print Matters, London SE........................ 165
Pugh Books (Ian K.), Worcs...................... 256
R. & A. Books, East Sussex 101
Rees & O'Neill Rare Books, London WC........ 178
Ripping Yarns, London N........................ 158
Rising Tide Books, Fife........................... 270
Robin Doughty - Fine Books, West Midlands... 238
Rochdale Book Company, G Manchester........ 120
Rose's Books, Powys............................. 289
Ross & Company Ltd., (Louise), Worcs.......... 255
Rowan House Books, Surrey 231
Roz Hulse, Conwy 284
Rye Old Books, East Sussex 104
Sabin (Printed Works) (P.R. & V.), Kent........ 135
St Mary's Books & Prints, Lincolnshire 152
Scrivener's Books & Bookbinding, Derbyshire... 82
Sephton (A.F.), London W....................... 174
Sesemann (Julia), Kent.......................... 135
Seydi Rare Books (Sevin), London NW 161
Shakeshaft (Dr. B.), Cheshire..................... 71
Sharpe (Mary), Somerset 219
Shelley (E. & J.), Buckinghamshire 61
Sillan Books, Co. Cavan.......................... 262
Sims Reed Limited, London SW.................. 169
Slightly Foxed on Gloucester Road, London SW 167
Sotheran Limited (Henry), London W 175
Stevens (Joan), Cambridgeshire................... 65
Stothert Old Books, Cheshire..................... 68
Stour Bookshop, Dorset.......................... 95
Taylor Rare Books (Michael), Norfolk 187
Temperley (David), West Midlands................ 238
Updike Rare Books (John), Lothian 277
Wheen O'Books, Borders......................... 267
Whitehall Books, East Sussex..................... 103
Whittle, Bookseller (Avril), Cumbria 80
Woodbine Books, West Yorkshire................. 245
Words Etcetera Bookshop, Dorset................. 93
Xanadu Books, Durham 98
Yates Antiquarian Books (Tony), Leics........... 146
York Modern Books, North Yorkshire........... 196

- 19TH & 20TH CENTURY

Antique Map and Bookshop (The), Dorset 94
Atholl Fine Books, Tayside 280
Ballantyne–Way (Roger), Suffolk 228
Barlow (Vincent G.), Hampshire.................. 125
Blackwell's Rare Books, Oxfordshire 208
Books & Things, London W....................... 171

books2books, Devon.................................. 88
Brazenhead Ltd., Norfolk 188
Chantrey Books, S Yorks 222
Cornucopia Books, Lincolnshire 151
Courtwood Books, Co. Laois...................... 265
Deverell Books, Bristol 59
Eclectica, London SE 164
Ellis, Bookseller (Peter), London WC 177
Fifteenth Century Bookshop (The), East Sussex. 104
Foster Bookshop (Paul), London SW 167
Fosters Bookshop, London W 172
Goldman (Paul), Dorset 94
Greer (Robin), London SW......................... 167
Hava Books, London SE............................ 164
Island Books, Devon................................ 85
Jane & John Kinnaird, Cumbria 78
Jean Hedger, Berks................................. 55
Joel Segal Books, Devon 86
Liddle (Steve), Bristol 58
Myra Dean Illustated Books, Powys 287
O'Flynn Books, North Yorkshire.................. 197
Paul Hoare, Cornwall............................... 74
Period & Classical Collections, East Sussex 103
Print Matters, London SE........................... 165
R. & A. Books, East Sussex 101
Robin Doughty - Fine Books, West Midlands... 238
Taylor Rare Books (Michael), Norfolk 187
Wheen O'Books, Borders........................... 267
Woodbine Books, West Yorkshire................. 245

ILLUSTRATORS

Barlow (Vincent G.), Hampshire................... 125
Bookmark (Children's Books), Wiltshire.......... 253
books2books, Devon................................ 88
Brown-Studies, Strathclyde......................... 277
Chantrey Books, S Yorks 222
Cornucopia Books, Lincolnshire 151
Deverell Books, Bristol 59
Embleton (Paul), Essex 111
Fifteenth Century Bookshop (The), East Sussex. 104
Greer (Robin), London SW......................... 167
Jean Hedger, Berks................................. 55
Mannwaring (M.G.), Bristol 59
Martin (Books and Pictures), (Brian P.), Surrey. 231
Martin (Brian), Surrey 231
Minster Gate Bookshop, North Yorkshire 197
Myra Dean Illustated Books, Powys 287
Print Matters, London SE........................... 165
Shelley (E. & J.), Buckinghamshire 61
Woodbine Books, West Yorkshire................. 245

IMAGINARY VOYAGES

Eggeling Books (John), West Yorkshire 249
Quaritch Ltd., (Bernard), London W.............. 174
Susanne Schulz-Falster Rare Books, London N. 158

IMMIGRATION

Empire Books, North Yorkshire 197
Fishburn Books, London NW...................... 160
Woburn Books, London N 159

IMMUNOLOGY

Bernard Dixon and Kath Adams, London O.... 182
Parkinsons Books, Merseyside..................... 185
R M Books, Herts.................................. 132

Westons, Herts 132

IMPRINTS

Seydi Rare Books (Sevin), London NW 161
Woburn Books, London N 159

INCUNABULA

Andrew Hunter Rare Books, London SW 166
Butler Rare Books, Buckinghamshire 61
De Burca Rare Books, Co. Dublin 264
Fletcher (H.M.), Herts.............................. 131
Pickering & Chatto, London W 174
Quaritch Ltd., (Bernard), London W.............. 174
Seydi Rare Books (Sevin), London NW 161

INDOLOGY

Rayner (Hugh Ashley), Somerset 215

INDUSTRIAL DESIGN

Ballantyne–Way (Roger), Suffolk 228
Cornucopia Books, Lincolnshire 151
Joel Segal Books, Devon 86
N1 Books, East Sussex 105
Westons, Herts...................................... 132
Whitchurch Books Ltd., Cardiff.................... 281

INDUSTRIAL RELATIONS

Northern Herald Books, West Yorkshire......... 245
PsychoBabel Books & Journals, Oxfordshire..... 205
Spurrier (Nick), Kent 137

INDUSTRY

Anvil Books, West Midlands 239
Blanchfield (John), West Yorkshire............... 248
Book House (The), Cumbria....................... 76
Bott, (Bookdealers) Ltd., (Martin), Greater
    Manchester 118
Byrom Textile Bookroom (Richard), Lancashire 142
Cheshire Book Centre, Cheshire................... 69
Chris Porter Books, Norfolk....................... 186
Clevedon Books, Somerset 217
Cornucopia Books, Lincolnshire 151
Country Books, Derbyshire 82
Cox (Geoff), Devon 90
Debbage (John), Norfolk........................... 189
Duck (William), Hampshire........................ 124
Elton Engineering Books, London W 172
Empire Books, North Yorkshire 197
Keel Row Bookshop, Tyne and Wear 235
Parkinsons Books, Merseyside..................... 185
Past & Present Books, Glos........................ 114
PsychoBabel Books & Journals, Oxfordshire..... 205
Rainford (Sheila), Herts........................... 129
Robert Humm & Co, Lincolnshire 152
Rochdale Book Company, Greater Manchester . 120
Stroh (M.A.), London E 154
Westons, Herts...................................... 132
Whistler's Books, London SW 169
Whitchurch Books Ltd., Cardiff.................... 281
Wiend Books, Lancashire 143

INSTITUTIONS

G. C. Books Ltd., Dumfries & Galloway......... 270
Joel Segal Books, Devon 86

INTERIOR DESIGN

Annie's Books, S Yorks 221
Ballantyne–Way (Roger), Suffolk 228
Barlow (Vincent G.), Hampshire 125
Batterham (David), London W 171
Black Cat Books, Norfolk 187
Buckland Books, West Sussex 243
Cornucopia Books, Lincolnshire 151
Don Kelly Books, London W 172
Foster (Stephen), London NW 160
Haskell (R.H. & P.), Dorset 94
Heneage Art Books (Thomas), London SW 168
Hornsey's, North Yorkshire 194
Joel Segal Books, Devon 86
Judd Books, London WC 177
Judith Mansfield, West Yorkshire 249
Keswick Bookshop, Cumbria 78
Martin - Bookseller (Colin), East Yorkshire 107
N1 Books, East Sussex 105
Pagan Limited (Hugh), Hampshire 122
Phillips of Hitchin (Antiques) Ltd., Herts........ 131
Portobello Books, London W 174
Potterton Books, North Yorkshire 196
Ray Rare and Out of Print Books (Janette),
    North Yorkshire 198
Sleepy Elephant Books & Artefacts, Cumbria ... 80
Slightly Foxed on Gloucester Road, London SW 167
Staniland (Booksellers), Lincolnshire 152
Trinders' Fine Tools, Suffolk 226
Uncle Phil's Books, West Midlands 239
Whittle, Bookseller (Avril), Cumbria 80

INTERNATIONAL AFFAIRS

Al Saqi Books, London W 171
Bickford-Smith (G.) (formerly Snowden Smith
    Books), Surrey 232
Brimstones, East Sussex 104
Empire Books, North Yorkshire 197
Game Advice, Oxfordshire 208
Melvin Tenner, London W 173
PsychoBabel Books & Journals, Oxfordshire..... 205

INVENTORS & INVENTIONS

Bernard Dixon and Kath Adams, London O.... 182
Elton Engineering Books, London W 172
Gildas Books, Cheshire 68
Joel Segal Books, Devon 86
McGee (Terence J.), London O 180
N1 Books, East Sussex 105
Stroh (M.A.), London E 154
Westons, Herts 132

INVESTMENTS

Barcombe Services, Essex............................ 108
Quaritch Ltd., (Bernard), London W.............. 174

IRIDOLOGY

Inner Bookshop (The), Oxfordshire................ 208
Orchid Book Distributors, Co. Clare 262

IRISH HISTORY & LITERATURE

Barnacle Books, County Fermanagh 261
Charlie Byrne's Bookshop, Co. Galway........... 265
Kenny's Bookshop & Art Galleries Ltd.,
    Co. Galway 265

Kenya Books, East Sussex 100
Keogh's Books, Glos................................. 115
Robert Temple, London N........................... 158
Rowan (P. & B.), Co. Antrim 260
Schull Books, Co. Cork 262

IRISH INTEREST

Anglo-American Rare Books, Surrey.............. 232
Ann & Mike Conry, Worcs.......................... 257
Backfold Books, Herefordshire 127
Barcombe Services, Essex............................ 108
Barnacle Books, County Fermanagh 261
Bath Old Books, Somerset 215
Books Ulster, Co. Down 261
Bookshop (The), Greater Manchester 118
Bookshop (The), Co. Donegal....................... 263
Bott, (Bookdealers) Ltd., (Martin), Greater
    Manchester 118
Byre Books, Dumfries & Galloway................ 270
Caledonia Books, Strathclyde....................... 278
Camilla's Bookshop, East Sussex 101
Carraig Books Ltd., Co. Dublin 263
Cecilia Marsden, Surrey 232
Chapter Two, London SE............................ 163
Charlie Byrne's Bookshop, Co. Galway........... 265
Clements (R.W.), London O 181
Country Books, Derbyshire 82
Courtwood Books, Co. Laois........................ 265
Cover to Cover, Merseyside.......................... 185
Craobh Rua Books, Co. Armagh................... 260
Darkwood Books, Co. Cork......................... 263
Davidson Books, Co. Down.......................... 261
De Burca Rare Books, Co. Dublin 264
Delectus Books, London WC........................ 176
Doolin Dinghy Books, Co. Clare 262
Drury Rare Books (John), Essex.................... 110
Dublin Bookbrowsers, Co. Dublin.................. 265
Ferdinando (Steven), Somerset 218
Fuchsia Books, Co. Wexford 266
G. C. Books Ltd., Dumfries & Galloway........ 270
Glenbower Books, Co. Dublin 264
Gowan Books (John), Co. Fermanagh............. 261
Greene's Bookshop Ltd, Co. Dublin 264
Grove Bookshop (The), North Yorkshire 195
Harris (George J.), Co. Derry 260
House of Figgis Ltd (The), Co. Galway 265
Hyland (C.P.), Co. Cork 263
J.E. Burns Booksellers, Merseyside 185
Jackdaw Books, Norfolk 188
Jackson (M.W.), Wiltshire........................... 254
JIRI Books, Co. Antrim.............................. 260
Joel Segal Books, Devon 86
Karen Millward, Co. Cork 263
Kenny's Bookshop & Art Galleries Ltd.,
    Co. Galway 265
Kenya Books, East Sussex 100
Kernaghans, Merseyside 185
Lighthouse Books (The), Dorset 92
Lyonshill Books, Co. Dublin 265
My Back Pages, London SW 168
O'Brien Books & Photo Gallery,
    Co. Limerick..................................... 266
Poetry Bookshop (The), Powys..................... 289
R. & A. Books, East Sussex 101
Read Ireland, Co. Dublin 264

Roscrea Bookshop & Newsagents,
Co. Tipperary 266
Rowan (P. & B.), Co. Antrim 260
Rye Old Books, East Sussex 104
SaBeRo Books, London SW......................... 169
Saintfield Antiques & Fine Books, Co. Down ... 261
Samovar Books, Co. Dublin......................... 264
Schull Books, Co. Cork 262
Sillan Books, Co. Cavan............................. 262
Stokes Books, Co. Dublin............................ 264
The Old Abbey Bookshop, Co. Down 261
Trinity Rare Books, Co. Leitrim 266
Updike Rare Books (John), Lothian 277
Whelan (P. & F.), Kent............................... 140
Woburn Books, London N 159

ISLANDS
Dolphin Books, Suffolk.............................. 225
Georgina Hobhouse, Argyll......................... 274
Miles Apart, Suffolk.................................. 228

JAPANOLOGY
Alexander's Books, Warwickshire.................. 237

JEWELLERY
Art Reference Books, Hampshire 124
Barmby (C. & A.J.), Kent............................ 140
Bookworms Paradise Ltd., West Sussex 242
Cover to Cover, Merseyside.......................... 185
Design Gallery 1850-1950 (The), Kent 141
Don Kelly Books, London W 172
Edmund Pollinger Rare Books, London SW..... 166
Hay Castle, Powys.................................... 288
Heneage Art Books (Thomas), London SW 168
Joel Segal Books, Devon 86
Judith Mansfield, West Yorkshire.................. 249
Nelson (Elizabeth), Suffolk 226
Nibris Books, London SW 169
Orchid Book Distributors, Co. Clare 262
Potterton Books, North Yorkshire................. 196
R. & A. Books, East Sussex 101
Sleepy Elephant Books & Artefacts, Cumbria ... 80
Trinders' Fine Tools, Suffolk 226
Warnes (Felicity J.), London O 180
Whittle, Bookseller (Avril), Cumbria 80

JOURNALISM
Archivist (The), Devon............................... 90
Barcombe Services, Essex............................ 108
Bob Mallory (Books), Derbyshire.................. 83
Books at Star Dot Star, West Midlands 240
Cornucopia Books, Lincolnshire 151
Kelly Books Ltd, Devon.............................. 89
Pastmasters, Derbyshire.............................. 83
Uncle Phil's Books, West Midlands 239
Williams (Bookdealer), (Richard), N Lincs 153

JOURNALS
- GENERAL
Baldwin's Scientific Books, Essex 111
Batterham (David), London W...................... 171
Bettridge (Gordon), Fife............................. 271
Booksets.com Ltd, Shropshire 214
Derek Stirling Bookseller, Kent 141
Dolphin Books, Suffolk.............................. 225

Fifteenth Century Bookshop (The), East Sussex. 104
Good for Books, Lincolnshire 149
Handley (Christopher), Tyne and Wear.......... 235
Joel Segal Books, Devon 86
Karen Millward, Co. Cork 263
Kenneth Ball, East Sussex........................... 100
PsychoBabel Books & Journals, Oxfordshire..... 205
Robert Temple, London N........................... 158
Siop Lyfrau'r Hen Bost, Gwynedd 285
Stroh (M.A.), London E 154
Turton (John), Durham 98
Wayside Books and Cards, Oxfordshire 206
Williams (Bookdealer), (Richard), N Lincs 153

- MARITIME
Joel Segal Books, Devon 86

JUDAICA
de Visser Books, Cambridgeshire................... 63
Delectus Books, London WC........................ 176
Fishburn Books, London NW....................... 160
Golden Age Books, Worcs........................... 256
Inner Bookshop (The), Oxfordshire............... 208
Joel Segal Books, Devon 86
Nautical Antique Centre (The), Dorset 96
Needham Books, (Russell), Somerset.............. 219
Occultique, Northants................................ 199
Pordes Books Ltd., (Henry), London WC........ 177
Rosemary Pugh Books, Wiltshire 253
Saint Swithin's Illustrated & Children's Books,
London W 174
Samovar Books, Co. Dublin......................... 264
Thorntons of Oxford Ltd., Oxfordshire........... 206
Trotter Books (John), London N 158
Woburn Books, London N 159
Yesterday's News, Conwy........................... 283

JUNGIANA
Apocalypse, Surrey 232
Inner Bookshop (The), Oxfordshire............... 208
Joel Segal Books, Devon 86

JUVENILE
Annie's Books, S Yorks 221
Barry McKay Rare Books, Cumbria 76
Beck (John), East Sussex 103
Blackwell's Rare Books, Oxfordshire 208
Bookmark (Children's Books), Wiltshire.......... 253
Bookworms Paradise Ltd., West Sussex 242
Canterbury Bookshop (The), Kent 136
Charles Bossom, Cambridgeshire................... 65
Childrens Bookshop, West Yorkshire 247
Children's Bookshop (The), Herefordshire....... 127
Cooper Hay Rare Books, Strathclyde 278
Coupland (Terry W.), Staffordshire................ 223
Elizabeth Ferguson, Grampian 272
Ferguson (Elizabeth), Grampian 272
Fifteenth Century Bookshop (The), East Sussex. 104
Foster Bookshop (Paul), London SW............. 167
Freya Books & Antiques, Norfolk................. 189
Game Advice, Oxfordshire 208
Holtom (Christopher), Glos......................... 115
Jackdaw Books, Norfolk............................. 188
Jean Hedger, Berks 55
Joel Segal Books, Devon 86

K Books, Cheshire.................................... 70
Kirkpatrick (Robert J.), London W 173
Korn (M. Eric), London N 157
Martin (Brian), Surrey 231
Mason (Mary), Oxfordshire........................ 205
Myra Dean Illustated Books, Powys 287
R. & A. Books, East Sussex 101
Robert Temple, London N.......................... 158
Roscrea Bookshop & Newsagents,
   Co. Tipperary 266
Saint Swithin's Illustrated & Children's Books,
   London W 174
Sesemann (Julia), Kent.............................. 135
Shacklock Books (David), Suffolk 226
Smith Books, (Sally), Suffolk 226
Stour Bookshop, Dorset............................. 95
The Old Children's Bookshelf, Lothian 277
Wheen O'Books, Borders........................... 267

KABBALA/CABBALA/CABALA

Atlantis Bookshop, London WC.................... 176
Book Business (The), London W 171
Bygone Books, Isles of Scotland 275
Chthonios Books, East Sussex..................... 102
Fishburn Books, London NW....................... 160
Inner Bookshop (The), Oxfordshire............... 208
Magis Books, Leics.................................. 146
Needham Books, (Russell), Somerset............. 219
Occultique, Northants............................... 199
Star Lord Books, Greater Manchester 119
Trotter Books (John), London N 158

KNITTING

Annie's Books, S Yorks 221
Apocalypse, Surrey 232
Autumn Leaves, Lincolnshire...................... 150
Black Cat Books, Norfolk.......................... 187
Brown-Studies, Strathclyde......................... 277
Browse Books, Lancashire 143
Byrom Textile Bookroom (Richard), Lancashire 142
Cover to Cover, Merseyside......................... 185
Dolphin Books, Suffolk.............................. 225
DPE Books, Devon 87
Fifteenth Century Bookshop (The), East Sussex. 104
Gallimaufry Books, Herts 131
Joel Segal Books, Devon 86
Judith Mansfield, West Yorkshire.................. 249
Reading Lasses, Dumfries & Galloway 270
Sleepy Elephant Books & Artefacts, Cumbria ... 80
Treasure Island (The), Greater Manchester....... 119
Warnes (Felicity J.), London O 180
Wheen O'Books, Borders............................ 267
Whittle, Bookseller (Avril), Cumbria 80
Young (D. & J.), Powys............................. 291

KU KLUX KLAN

Loretta Lay Books, London NW 161

LACE

Black Cat Books, Norfolk........................... 187
Byrom Textile Bookroom (Richard), Lancashire 142
Cover to Cover, Merseyside......................... 185
Ely Books, Cambridgeshire 65
Fifteenth Century Bookshop (The), East Sussex. 104
Heneage Art Books (Thomas), London SW 168

Hennessey Bookseller (Ray), East Sussex 100
Joel Segal Books, Devon 86
Judith Mansfield, West Yorkshire.................. 249
Reading Lasses, Dumfries & Galloway 270
Sleepy Elephant Books & Artefacts, Cumbria ... 80
Warnes (Felicity J.), London O 180
Whittle, Bookseller (Avril), Cumbria 80
York (Graham), Devon.............................. 86
Young (D. & J.), Powys............................. 291

LANDSCAPE

Apocalypse, Surrey 232
Arden, Bookseller (C.), Powys..................... 287
Burebank Books, Norfolk........................... 186
Cornucopia Books, Lincolnshire 151
Cottage Books, Leics................................ 145
Duck (William), Hampshire......................... 124
Haskell (R.H. & P.), Dorset 94
Hollingshead (Chris), London O 182
Hünersdorff Rare Books, London SW 168
Inch's Books, Kent 137
Joel Segal Books, Devon 86
Karen Millward, Co. Cork.......................... 263
Marlborough Rare Books Ltd., London W...... 173
Modlock (Lilian), Dorset............................ 93
Park (Mike), London O 182
R. & A. Books, East Sussex 101
Ray Rare and Out of Print Books (Janette),
   North Yorkshire 198
Spelman (Ken), North Yorkshire 198

LANGUAGES
- AFRICAN

Chapter Two, London SE............................ 163
J.C. Deyong Books (Previously of Snowden
   Smith Books), London SW 168
Kenya Books, East Sussex 100
Marijana Dworski Books, Powys 288
Michael Graves-Johnston, London SW 168
owenbooks65, Conwy............................... 283
Yesterday's Books, Dorset 92

- ANCIENT

Blackwell's Rare Books, Oxfordshire.............. 208
C J Renwick Books, Powys......................... 287
Chapter Two, London SE............................ 163
Classics Bookshop (The), Oxfordshire............ 205
Hava Books, London SE............................ 164
Leo Cadogan, London N 157
Marijana Dworski Books, Powys 288
Michael Graves-Johnston, London SW 168
Parkinsons Books, Merseyside...................... 185
Pittville Books, Glos................................ 113
Price (John), London N 158
Samovar Books, Co. Dublin........................ 264
Seydi Rare Books (Sevin), London NW 161
Unsworth's Booksellers, Suffolk.................... 225

- FOREIGN

Al Saqi Books, London W.......................... 171
Annie's Books, S Yorks 221
Apocalypse, Surrey 232
Autumn Leaves, Lincolnshire....................... 150
Baldwin (Jack), Strathclyde 278
Book House (The), Cumbria........................ 76

Bookcase, Cumbria 76
Books on Spain, London O 182
Carnforth Bookshop (The), Lancashire 142
Crouch Rare Books, Surrey 232
Fifteenth Century Bookshop (The), East Sussex. 104
George St. Books, Derbyshire 83
Hab Books, London W 172
Hava Books, London SE 164
Hodgson (Judith), London W 173
Hünersdorff Rare Books, London SW 168
Joel Segal Books, Devon 86
Korn (M. Eric), London N 157
Leo Cadogan, London N 157
Mandalay Bookshop, London SW 168
Marijana Dworski Books, Powys 288
Oopalba Books, Cheshire 71
Owen (J.V.), Conwy 284
owenbooks65, Conwy 283
Parkinsons Books, Merseyside 185
Priestpopple Books, Northumberland 201
Robertshaw (John), Cambridgeshire 66
Roundstone Books, Lancashire 143
Scrivener's Books & Bookbinding, Derbyshire... 82
Stokes Books, Co. Dublin 264
Tarka Books, Devon 84
Thorntons of Oxford Ltd., Oxfordshire 206
Transformer, Dumfries & Galloway 270

- NATIONAL
Book House (The), Cumbria 76
BOOKS4U, Flintshire 284
Browning Books, Torfaen 292
Chapter Two, London SE 163
Colin Hancock, Ceredigion 282
Derek Stirling Bookseller, Kent 141
Doolin Dinghy Books, Co. Clare 262
Hünersdorff Rare Books, London SW 168
Hyland (C.P.), Co. Cork 263
Joel Segal Books, Devon 86
Kenya Books, East Sussex 100
Leo Cadogan, London N 157
Marijana Dworski Books, Powys 288
owenbooks65, Conwy 283
Spenceley Books (David), West Yorkshire 248
Treasure Island (The), Greater Manchester 119
Walker Fine Books (Steve), Dorset 92

- PIDGIN AND CREOLE
Chapter Two, London SE 163
Joel Segal Books, Devon 86
Kenya Books, East Sussex 100
Marijana Dworski Books, Powys 288
Michael Graves-Johnston, London SW 168
Yesterday's Books, Dorset 92

LAW
- GENERAL
Armstrong's Books & Collectables, Leics 145
Aurora Books Ltd, Lothian 275
Crimes Ink, London E 154
Dean Byass, Bristol 60
Drury Rare Books (John), Essex 110
Edwards (London) Limited (Francis),
   London WC 176
Edwards in Hay–on–Wye (Francis), Powys 288

Karen Millward, Co. Cork 263
Leo Cadogan, London N 157
Period & Classical Collections, East Sussex 103
Pittville Books, Glos 113
PsychoBabel Books & Journals, Oxfordshire 205
Quaritch Ltd., (Bernard), London W 174
Roscrea Bookshop & Newsagents,
   Co. Tipperary 266
Susanne Schulz-Falster Rare Books, London N. 158
Thornber (Peter M.), North Yorkshire 195
Undercover Books, Lincolnshire 152
Unsworth's Booksellers, Suffolk 225
Wayside Books and Cards, Oxfordshire 206
Webb Books (John), S Yorks 221
Westfield Books, North Yorkshire 198
Wheen O'Books, Borders 267
Wildy & Sons Ltd, London WC 179

- CONSTITUTIONAL
Leo Cadogan, London N 157
Wildy & Sons Ltd, London WC 179

LEGAL PAPERWORK
Aitchison (Lesley), Bristol 58
Apocalypse, Surrey 232
John Underwood Antiquarian Books, Norfolk .. 189
Thornber (Peter M.), North Yorkshire 195

LENINISM
Northern Herald Books, West Yorkshire 245
Reading Lasses, Dumfries & Galloway 270
Woburn Books, London N 159

LEPIDOPTERA (BUTTERFLIES, MOTHS, INSECTS)
Aurelian Books, London NW 160
Lymelight Books & Prints, Dorset 93
Pollak (P.M.), Devon 88
Savona Books, Lincolnshire 151
Woodside Books, Kent 135

LEPIDOPTEROLOGY
Aurelian Books, London NW 160
Aviabooks, Glos 114
Edmund Pollinger Rare Books, London SW 166
Joel Segal Books, Devon 86
Park (Mike), London O 182
Pemberley Books, Buckinghamshire 62
Sue Lowell Natural History Books, London W . 175

LETTERING
Joel Segal Books, Devon 86
N1 Books, East Sussex 105
Taylor Rare Books (Michael), Norfolk 187
Woodbine Books, West Yorkshire 245

LETTERS
Baron (H.), London NW 160
Charles Bossom, Cambridgeshire 65
Davids Ltd., (Roy), Oxfordshire 208
Evans Books (Paul), West Sussex 243
Farahar & Dupre (Clive & Sophie), Wiltshire ... 251
Fifteenth Century Bookshop (The), East Sussex. 104
Gekoski (R.A.), London WC 177
Good for Books, Lincolnshire 149

Hodgkins and Company Limited (Ian), Glos 116
James Fergusson Books & Manuscripts,
  London W 173
Joel Segal Books, Devon 86
Just Books, Cornwall 75
Lawrence Books, Nottinghamshire 203
Maggs Brothers Limited, London W 173
Marine & Cannon Books, Cheshire 71
Marine and Cannon Books, Cheshire 69
Neil Summersgill, Lancashire 142
Poetry Bookshop (The), Powys..................... 289
Reading Lasses, Dumfries & Galloway 270
Robert Temple, London N.......................... 158
Scrivener's Books & Bookbinding, Derbyshire... 82
Silverman (Michael), London SE 165

LIBERTARIANISM
Joel Segal Books, Devon 86
Woburn Books, London N 159

LIBRARIES - EVERYMAN'S LIBRARY
Charles Bossom, Cambridgeshire................... 65
Fifteenth Century Bookshop (The), East Sussex. 104
Hava Books, London SE............................ 164
Island Books, Devon................................. 85
Joel Segal Books, Devon 86
Just Books, Cornwall 75
Williams (Bookdealer), (Richard), N Lincs 153

LIBRARY SCIENCE
PsychoBabel Books & Journals, Oxfordshire..... 205
Smith Books, (Sally), Suffolk 226
Westons, Herts 132

LIMITED EDITIONS
- GENERAL
Apocalypse, Surrey 232
Artco, Nottinghamshire............................. 204
Ballantyne–Way (Roger), Suffolk 228
Barlow (Vincent G.), Hampshire.................... 125
Besleys Books, Suffolk 225
Blackwell's Rare Books, Oxfordshire.............. 208
BOOKS4U, Flintshire................................ 284
Bookstand, Dorset................................... 94
Chapter & Verse, Lincolnshire..................... 150
Coach House Books, Worcs 256
Collinge & Clark, London WC..................... 176
Cox Old & Rare Books (Claude), Suffolk 227
Eastwood Books (David), Cornwall 72
Ellis, Bookseller (Peter), London WC 177
Fiction First, Cheshire 69
Hanborough Books, Oxfordshire................... 208
Harwich Old Books, Essex 109
Hava Books, London SE............................ 164
Hollett and Son (R.F.G.), Cumbria 79
Island Books, Devon................................. 85
JB Books & Collectables, West Sussex 243
Kenny's Bookshop & Art Galleries Ltd.,
  Co. Galway 265
Kirkman Ltd., (Robert), Bedfordshire............. 54
Lucius Books, North Yorkshire 197
Mannwaring (M.G.), Bristol 59
Marks Limited (Barrie), London N 157
Martin (Books and Pictures), (Brian P.), Surrey. 231
Martin (Brian), Surrey 231

Mills Rare Books (Adam), Cambridgeshire 64
Modern First Editions, London Outer 181
Myra Dean Illustated Books, Powys 287
N V Books, Warwickshire.......................... 236
Oak Tree Press, Oxfordshire 207
Paul Hoare, Cornwall............................... 74
Print Matters, London SE.......................... 165
Reaveley Books, Devon 87
Riderless Horse Books, Norfolk 186
Robert Temple, London N.......................... 158
Roz Hulse, Conwy 284
Rye Old Books, East Sussex 104
Sabin (Printed Works) (P.R. & V.), Kent........ 135
Scrivener's Books & Bookbinding, Derbyshire... 82
Seabreeze Books, Lancashire 144
Stevens (Joan), Cambridgeshire.................... 65
Talisman Books, Cheshire.......................... 70
Thorntons of Oxford Ltd., Oxfordshire........... 206
Tucker (Alan & Joan), Glos 116
Updike Rare Books (John), Lothian 277
Woburn Books, London N 159
Woodbine Books, West Yorkshire.................. 245
Words Etcetera Bookshop, Dorset................. 93

- CLUB BOOKS
First Edition, The, Essex 109
Island Books, Devon................................. 85
Jackdaw Books, Norfolk 188
Myra Dean Illustated Books, Powys 287
Roz Hulse, Conwy 284

LINGUISTICS
Baldwin (Jack), Strathclyde 278
Barcombe Services, Essex........................... 108
Bates Books, London Outer 180
Beaumont Travel Books, London SE 163
Chesters (G. & J.), Staffordshire 224
Delectus Books, London WC....................... 176
Derek Stirling Bookseller, Kent 141
Game Advice, Oxfordshire 208
Hava Books, London SE............................ 164
Joel Segal Books, Devon 86
Judd Books, London WC........................... 177
Kenya Books, East Sussex 100
Mandalay Bookshop, London SW 168
Midnight Oil Books, Fife............................ 271
Olynthiacs, Shropshire 213
Oopalba Books, Cheshire........................... 71
Parkinsons Books, Merseyside...................... 185
Plurabelle Books, Cambridgeshire.................. 65
PsychoBabel Books & Journals, Oxfordshire..... 205
Reading Lasses, Dumfries & Galloway 270
Roundstone Books, Lancashire...................... 143
Staniland (Booksellers), Lincolnshire 152
Thorntons of Oxford Ltd., Oxfordshire............ 206
Westons, Herts 132
York (Graham), Devon.............................. 86

LITERACY
Bosorne Books, Cornwall 75
Oopalba Books, Cheshire........................... 71

LITERARY CRITICISM
Alec–Smith Books (Alex), East Yorkshire 107
Ann & Mike Conry, Worcs......................... 257

Apocalypse, Surrey 232
Applin (Malcolm), Berks 55
Autumn Leaves, Lincolnshire........................ 150
Axe Rare & Out of Print Books (Richard),
  North Yorkshire 193
Bennett & Kerr Books, Oxfordshire 205
Biff Books and Records, S Yorks.................. 221
Boer (Louise), Arthurian Books, Powys 287
Bookcase, Cumbria 76
Books, Denbighshire 284
BOOKS4U, Flintshire................................ 284
Bracton Books, Cambridgeshire.................... 63
Broadhurst of Southport Ltd., Merseyside 185
Caledonia Books, Strathclyde....................... 278
Charles Bossom, Cambridgeshire.................... 65
Charlie Byrne's Bookshop, Co. Galway........... 265
Chaucer Bookshop, Kent............................ 136
Chesters (G. & J.), Staffordshire 224
Clarendon Books, Leics.............................. 145
Clevedon Books, Somerset 217
Coach House Books, Worcs 256
Cobbles Books, Somerset........................... 217
Darkwood Books, Co. Cork........................ 263
Delectus Books, London WC....................... 176
Dolphin Books, Suffolk 225
Dyson (Anthony), West Midlands 239
Ellis, Bookseller (Peter), London WC 177
Ellwood Editions, Wiltshire 253
Fifteenth Century Bookshop (The), East Sussex. 104
Fisher & Sperr, London N.......................... 157
Fortune Green Books, London NW............... 160
Freeman's Corner Shop, Norfolk 189
Frost (Richard), Herts 129
George St. Books, Derbyshire 83
GfB: the Colchester Bookshop, Essex 108
Handsworth Books, Essex........................... 112
Hawkes (James), London............................ 164
Hawley (C.L.), North Yorkshire 195
Hellenic Bookservices, London NW 161
Ian McKelvie Bookseller, London N............... 157
Innes Books, Shropshire............................. 212
Island Books, Devon 85
Jackdaw Books, Norfolk 188
Joel Segal Books, Devon 86
Kingsgate Books & Prints, Hampshire............ 126
Marcet Books, London SE........................... 164
Nineteenth Century Books, Oxfordshire 209
Oopalba Books, Cheshire............................ 71
Parkinsons Books, Merseyside...................... 185
Parrott (Jeremy), London E......................... 154
Parrott Books, Oxfordshire 209
Poetry Bookshop (The), Powys..................... 289
Polmorla Books, Cornwall 75
Pordes Books Ltd., (Henry), London WC........ 177
PsychoBabel Books & Journals, Oxfordshire..... 205
R. & A. Books, East Sussex 101
Reading Lasses, Dumfries & Galloway 270
Red Star Books, Herts.............................. 129
Riderless Horse Books, Norfolk.................... 186
Robert Temple, London N........................... 158
Rosley Books, Cumbria 81
Roundstone Books, Lancashire...................... 143
Rutland Bookshop (The), Rutland 211
Rye Old Books, East Sussex 104
Saintfield Antiques & Fine Books, Co. Down ... 261

Samovar Books, Co. Dublin........................ 264
Scrivener's Books & Bookbinding, Derbyshire... 82
Staniland (Booksellers), Lincolnshire 152
Stevens (Joan), Cambridgeshire..................... 65
Studio Bookshop, East Sussex...................... 100
Symes Books (Naomi), Cheshire 71
The Glass Key, West Yorkshire.................... 246
Tombland Bookshop, Norfolk 190
Tucker (Alan & Joan), Glos 116
Uncle Phil's Books, West Midlands 239
Venables (Morris & Juliet), Bristol................ 59
Waterfield's, Oxfordshire 209
Whitehall Books, East Sussex....................... 103
Woburn Books, London N 159
Yesterday's News, Conwy........................... 283

LITERARY TRAVEL

Al Saqi Books, London W........................... 171
Amwell Book Company, London EC.............. 155
Ann & Mike Conry, Worcs 257
Anthony Sillem, East Sussex....................... 102
Archer (Steve), London Outer 180
Askew Books (Vernon), Wiltshire.................. 251
Books on Spain, London Outer 182
Charlie Byrne's Bookshop, Co. Galway........... 265
Cobbles Books, Somerset............................ 217
Collectables (W.H.), Suffolk 229
Cox Rare Books (Charles), Cornwall.............. 73
Criterion Books, London Outer 181
Dolphin Books, Suffolk 225
Ellis, Bookseller (Peter), London WC 177
Fifteenth Century Bookshop (The), East Sussex. 104
Hodgkins and Company Limited (Ian), Glos 116
Ian McKelvie Bookseller, London N.............. 157
Joel Segal Books, Devon 86
Keith Langford, London E 154
Nineteenth Century Books, Oxfordshire 209
Orb's Bookshop, Grampian.......................... 273
PsychoBabel Books & Journals, Oxfordshire..... 205
R. & A. Books, East Sussex 101
Rayner (Hugh Ashley), Somerset 215
Robert Temple, London N........................... 158
The Glass Key, West Yorkshire.................... 246
Tiger Books, Kent.................................. 136
Trinity Rare Books, Co. Leitrim 266
Tucker (Alan & Joan), Glos 116
War & Peace Books, Hampshire.................... 122
Yesterday's Books, Dorset 92
York (Graham), Devon.............................. 86
York Modern Books, North Yorkshire........... 196

LITERATURE
- GENERAL

A. & H. Peasgood, Cambridgeshire 66
Abbey Books, Cornwall 73
Addyman Annexe (The), Powys.................... 287
Addyman Books, Powys............................. 287
Alba Books, Grampian.............................. 273
Alexander's Books, Warwickshire.................. 237
Alister & Garon Books, Cambridgeshire.......... 63
Allinson (Frank & Stella), Warwickshire 236
Andrew Hunter Rare Books, London SW 166
Andrew Morton (Books), Powys.................... 287
Anglo-American Rare Books, Surrey.............. 232
Ann & Mike Conry, Worcs........................ 257

Anthony Sillem, East Sussex 102
Antiquary Ltd., (Bar Bookstore),
  North Yorkshire 194
Antique Map and Bookshop (The), Dorset 94
Apocalypse, Surrey 232
Archer (Steve), London Outer 180
Archivist (The), Devon.............................. 90
Armchair Books, Lothian 275
Artco, Nottinghamshire.............................. 204
Aurora Books Ltd, Lothian......................... 275
Autolycus, Shropshire................................ 212
Autumn Leaves, Lincolnshire....................... 150
Avonworld Books, Somerset........................ 216
Axe Rare & Out of Print Books (Richard),
  North Yorkshire 193
babelog.books, Herefordshire....................... 127
Barbican Bookshop, North Yorkshire............. 196
Bass (Ben), Wiltshire 251
Bath Old Books, Somerset 215
Baxter (Steve), Surrey 233
Bayntun (George), Somerset 215
BC Books, Cheshire 69
Beaton (Richard), East Sussex..................... 103
Beckham Books Ltd., Suffolk 229
Bernstein (Nicholas), London W 171
Bertram Rota Ltd., London WC 176
Beware of the Leopard, Bristol 58
Black Five Books, Shropshire 214
Blackwell's Rare Books, Oxfordshire.............. 208
Book Business (The), London W 171
Books & Collectables Ltd., Cambridgeshire...... 63
Books & Things, London W......................... 171
Books on Spain, London Outer 182
books2books, Devon.................................. 88
BOOKS4U, Flintshire................................ 284
Bookshop (The), Norfolk 191
Bookshop at the Plain, Lincolnshire............... 149
Bookworms, Norfolk.................................. 186
Bookworms of Evesham, Worcs 257
Booth (Booksearch Service), (Geoff), Cheshire... 68
Boris Books, Somerset 216
Bow Windows Book Shop, East Sussex 103
Bowie Books & Collectables, East Yorkshire 107
Boz Books, Powys..................................... 287
Bracton Books, Cambridgeshire..................... 63
Brazenhead Ltd., Norfolk 188
Bright (P.G.), Cambridgeshire 65
Brinded (Scott), Kent 138
Bristol Books, Bristol 60
Broadhurst of Southport Ltd., Merseyside 185
Brock Books, North Yorkshire...................... 192
Burmester (James), Bristol........................... 58
Butts Books (Mary), Berks.......................... 56
C J Renwick Books, Powys.......................... 287
Caledonia Books, Strathclyde....................... 278
Camden Books, Somerset 215
Carnforth Bookshop (The), Lancashire 142
Charles Bossom, Cambridgeshire.................... 65
Charlie Byrne's Bookshop, Co. Galway.......... 265
Chaucer Bookshop, Kent............................. 136
Cheshire Book Centre, Cheshire.................... 69
Chevin Books, West Yorkshire...................... 249
Chris Phillips, Wiltshire.............................. 252
Church Street Books, Norfolk....................... 186
Clarendon Books, Leics.............................. 145

Clements (R.W.), London Outer 181
Cobbles Books, Somerset............................ 217
Cobweb Books, North Yorkshire................... 194
Cofion Books, Pembrokeshire 286
Cox Old & Rare Books (Claude), Suffolk 227
Cox Rare Books (Charles), Cornwall.............. 73
Craobh Rua Books, Co. Armagh................... 260
Criterion Books, London Outer 181
Crouch Rare Books, Surrey.......................... 232
Cumming Limited (A. & Y.), East Sussex 104
Dalby (Richard), North Yorkshire.................. 195
Dales & Lakes Book Centre, Cumbria............ 79
D'Arcy Books, Wiltshire............................. 252
Darkwood Books, Co. Cork.......................... 263
Dartmoor Book Gallery, Devon 87
Dave Jelfs, Devon 85
David (G.), Cambridgeshire.......................... 63
Davidson Books, Co. Down 261
De Burca Rare Books, Co. Dublin 264
Dean Byass, Bristol................................... 60
Dennys Sanders & Greene Ltd, East Sussex 100
Derek Stirling Bookseller, Kent 141
Dolphin Books, Suffolk............................... 225
Doolin Dinghy Books, Co. Clare 262
Driffield Bookshop (The), East Yorkshire 106
Duncan & Reid, Lothian.............................. 276
Dyson (Anthony), West Midlands 239
Eastwood Books (David), Cornwall 72
Edrich (I.D.), London E.............................. 154
Edwards (Christopher), Oxfordshire............... 209
Edwards (London) Limited (Francis),
  London WC 176
Edwards in Hay–on–Wye (Francis), Powys 288
Elaine Lonsdale Books, West Yorkshire.......... 247
Ellis, Bookseller (Peter), London WC 177
Esoteric Dreams Bookshop, Cumbria 77
Eton Antique Bookshop, Berks 57
Evans Books (Paul), West Sussex 243
Farahar & Dupre (Clive & Sophie), Wiltshire ... 251
Ferdinando (Steven), Somerset 218
Fifteenth Century Bookshop (The), East Sussex. 104
Finch Rare Books Ltd. (Simon), London W..... 172
First Edition, The, Essex 109
Firsts in Print, Somerset 219
Fortune Green Books, London NW................ 160
Fossgate Books, North Yorkshire 197
Foster (Stephen), London NW 160
Foster Bookshop (Paul), London SW 167
Fosters Bookshop, London W 172
Fotheringham (Alex), Northumberland 201
Frew Limited (Robert), London SW 167
Furneaux Books (Lee), Devon....................... 89
G. C. Books Ltd., Dumfries & Galloway........ 270
George Gregory, Somerset 215
GfB: the Colchester Bookshop, Essex 108
Gibbs Books, (Jonathan), Worcs.................... 256
Gilbert and Son (H.M.), Hampshire............... 126
Glenbower Books, Co. Dublin 264
Glyn's Books, Shropshire............................. 212
Goldman (Paul), Dorset 94
Good for Books, Lincolnshire 149
Grahame Thornton, Bookseller, Dorset........... 93
Grove Bookshop (The), North Yorkshire 195
Hall's Bookshop, Kent................................ 140
Harrington (Adrian), London W.................... 173

Harrington Antiquarian Bookseller (Peter),
  London SW.. 167
Hart (John), Norfolk.................................... 186
Harvest Books, Lancashire.......................... 144
Harwich Old Books, Essex.......................... 109
Hava Books, London SE.............................. 164
Hawkes (James), London.............................. 164
Hennessey Bookseller (Ray), East Sussex......... 100
Heppa (Christopher), Essex.......................... 108
Heywood Hill Limited (G.), London W 173
Hollett and Son (R.F.G.), Cumbria 79
Holmes Books (Harry), East Yorkshire........... 107
House of Figgis Ltd (The), Co. Galway 265
Howes Bookshop, East Sussex 102
Hünersdorff Rare Books, London SW............ 168
Hughes Rare Books (Spike), Borders.............. 267
Hurst (Jenny), Kent 137
Hutchison (Books) (Larry), Fife.................... 271
Ian McKelvie Bookseller, London N 157
Idle Genius Books, London N 157
Innes Books, Shropshire.............................. 212
Jackson (M.W.), Wiltshire........................... 254
Jarndyce Antiquarian Booksellers, London WC. 177
JB Books & Collectables, West Sussex 243
Jermy & Westerman, Nottinghamshire........... 204
Joel Segal Books, Devon 86
Johnson Rare Book Collections (C.R.),
  London NW.. 161
Jonkers Rare Books, Oxfordshire.................. 207
Judd Books, London WC 177
Just Books, Cornwall 75
Karen Millward, Co. Cork.......................... 263
Katnap Arts, Norfolk................................. 190
Kilgarriff (Raymond), East Sussex................ 105
Killeen (John), North Yorkshire................... 193
Kingsgate Books & Prints, Hampshire........... 126
Kirkman Ltd., (Robert), Bedfordshire............. 54
L.M.S. Books, Herts 131
Lawson & Company (E.M.), Oxfordshire 206
Leabeck Books, Oxfordshire........................ 208
Leigh Gallery Books, Essex 110
Lenton (Alfred), Leics............................... 145
Leo Cadogan, London N 157
Liddle (Steve), Bristol 58
Lloyd-Davies (Sue), Carmarthenshire 282
Lymelight Books & Prints, Dorset................. 93
M. and A.C. Thompson, Norfolk................... 191
Madoc Books, Conwy................................ 284
Maghreb Bookshop (The), London WC.......... 177
Main Point Books, Lothian......................... 276
Malvern Bookshop (The), Worcs 255
Mannwaring (M.G.), Bristol........................ 59
Marks Limited (Barrie), London N................ 157
Marlborough Rare Books Ltd., London W 173
Martin (Books and Pictures), (Brian P.), Surrey. 231
Martin (Brian), Surrey 231
McCarty, Bookseller (M.E.),
  Dumfries & Galloway 270
McCarty, Bookseller (M.E.), Western Isles....... 275
McCrone (Audrey), Isle of Arran.................. 274
McNaughtan's Bookshop, Lothian 276
Mermaid Books (Burlingham), Norfolk........... 191
Mills Rare Books (Adam), Cambridgeshire 64
Minster Gate Bookshop, North Yorkshire 197
Morgan (H.J.), Bedfordshire........................ 54

Mr. Pickwick of Towcester, Northants............ 199
Murch Booksend, (Herbert), London SE......... 165
Murphy (C.J.), Norfolk.............................. 189
Needham Books, (Russell), Somerset.............. 219
Niner (Marcus), Isle of Wight 133
Nineteenth Century Books, Oxfordshire 209
Nonsuch Books, Surrey.............................. 234
Norton Books, North Yorkshire.................... 192
Oak Tree Press, Oxfordshire........................ 207
O'Brien Books & Photo Gallery, Co. Limerick.. 266
Offa's Dyke Books, Shropshire..................... 213
O'Flynn Books, North Yorkshire................... 197
Old Aberdeen Bookshop, Grampian 272
Old Bookshop (The), West Midlands 240
Old Town Bookshop (The), Lothian 276
Oopalba Books, Cheshire............................ 71
Orangeberry Books, Oxfordshire................... 207
Orlando Booksellers, Lincolnshire 150
Over-Sands Books, Cumbria........................ 77
Palladium Books, Hampshire 125
Paper Moon Books, Glos 116
Paper Pleasures, Somerset 218
Parker Books (Mike), Cambridgeshire 64
Parrott (Jeremy), London E......................... 154
Pauline Harries Books, Hampshire 123
Period & Classical Collections, East Sussex 103
Peter's Bookshop, Norfolk 190
Pickering & Chatto, London W..................... 174
Plurabelle Books, Cambridgeshire................. 65
Polmorla Books, Cornwall 75
Poor Richard's Books, Suffolk 226
Porter Bookshop (The), S Yorks................... 222
Price (John), London N 158
Pringle Booksellers (Andrew), Lothian 277
PsychoBabel Books & Journals, Oxfordshire..... 205
Quaritch Ltd., (Bernard), London W............. 174
Quest Booksearch, Cambridgeshire 65
Quinto of Charing Cross Road, London WC ... 178
R. & A. Books, East Sussex 101
Rainford (Sheila), Herts 129
Rassam (Paul), London NW 161
Reaveley Books, Devon 87
Rees & O'Neill Rare Books, London WC........ 178
Richard Thornton Books, London N 158
Richmond Books, North Yorkshire 194
Riderless Horse Books, Norfolk.................... 186
Ripping Yarns, London N........................... 158
Robert Temple, London N.......................... 158
Roberts Fine Books (Julian), Lincolnshire........ 151
Robin Doughty - Fine Books, West Midlands... 238
Rosley Books, Cumbria 81
Ross & Company Ltd., (Louise), Worcs.......... 255
Roundstone Books, Lancashire...................... 143
Rowan (P. & B.), Co. Antrim 260
Rye Old Books, East Sussex 104
St Philip's Books, Oxfordshire...................... 208
Saintfield Antiques & Fine Books, Co. Down ... 261
Samovar Books, Co. Dublin......................... 264
Sansovino Books, West Sussex 244
Scott (Peter), East Sussex 104
Scrivener's Books & Bookbinding, Derbyshire... 82
Shakespeare Books (Colin), Staffordshire......... 223
Sharpe (Mary), Somerset 219
Shelley (E. & J.), Buckinghamshire 61
Silverman (Michael), London SE 165

Simpson (Dave), Central 268
Siop Lyfrau'r Hen Bost, Gwynedd 285
Siop y Morfa, Denbighshire 284
Skelton (Tony), Kent.............................. 140
Slightly Foxed on Gloucester Road, London SW 167
Sotheran Limited (Henry), London W 175
Spelman (Ken), North Yorkshire 198
Staffs Bookshop (The), Staffordshire 223
Staniland (Booksellers), Lincolnshire 152
Stern Antiquarian Bookseller (Jeffrey),
    North Yorkshire 198
Stevens (Joan), Cambridgeshire.................... 65
Stinton (Judith), Dorset........................... 92
Stokes Books, Co. Dublin........................ 264
Stone Trough Books, North Yorkshire 198
Sturford Books, Wiltshire 254
Surprise Books, Glos.............................. 113
Symes Books (Naomi), Cheshire 71
Talisman Books, Cheshire.......................... 70
Tiffin (Tony and Gill), Durham 97
Tiger Books, Kent................................ 136
Till's Bookshop, Lothian 277
Tindley & Chapman, London WC 178
Treasure Trove Books, Leics...................... 146
Trevorrow (Edwin), Herts......................... 129
Trinity Rare Books, Co. Leitrim 266
Tucker (Alan & Joan), Glos 116
Uncle Phil's Books, West Midlands 239
Unsworth's Booksellers, Suffolk................... 225
Updike Rare Books (John), Lothian 277
Valentine Rare Books, London W 175
Venables (Morris & Juliet), Bristol................. 59
Ventnor Rare Books, Isle of Wight............... 134
Walden Books, London NW 161
Walker Fine Books (Steve), Dorset............... 92
War & Peace Books, Hampshire................... 122
Waterfield's, Oxfordshire 209
Waxfactor, East Sussex 100
Westcountry Oldbooks, Devon..................... 90
Wetherell (Frances), Cambridgeshire 65
Wheen O'Books, Borders........................... 267
Whig Books Ltd., Leics........................... 147
Whitehall Books, East Sussex..................... 103
Wilbraham (J. & S.), London NW 162
Williams Rare Books (Nigel), London WC 179
Willmott Bookseller (Nicholas), Cardiff........... 281
Wise (Derek), East Sussex......................... 104
Wizard Books, Cambridgeshire..................... 67
Woburn Books, London N 159
Worlds End Bookshop, London SW 169
Wychwood Books, Glos............................ 116
Yesterday's Books, Dorset 92
Yesterday's News, Conwy.......................... 283

- 17TH C

Bennett & Kerr Books, Oxfordshire 205
Burmester (James), Bristol.......................... 58
Cobnar Books, Kent 141
Dean Byass, Bristol................................. 60
Derek Stirling Bookseller, Kent 141
Fifteenth Century Bookshop (The), East Sussex. 104
Joel Segal Books, Devon 86
Leo Cadogan, London N 157
Quaritch Ltd., (Bernard), London W.............. 174
Robert Temple, London N.......................... 158

Rosley Books, Cumbria 81
Seydi Rare Books (Sevin), London NW 161
Stevens (Joan), Cambridgeshire.................... 65
Walker Fine Books (Steve), Dorset 92
Yates Antiquarian Books (Tony), Leics........... 146

- 19TH C

Alec–Smith Books (Alex), East Yorkshire 107
Atholl Fine Books, Tayside 280
babelog.books, Herefordshire 127
Beaton (Richard), East Sussex..................... 103
Bell (Peter), Lothian............................... 275
Book Business (The), London W 171
Boris Books, Somerset 216
Boz Books, Powys.................................. 287
Burmester (James), Bristol.......................... 58
Cox Rare Books (Charles), Cornwall............... 73
Derek Stirling Bookseller, Kent 141
Dolphin Books, Suffolk............................ 225
Elaine Lonsdale Books, West Yorkshire 247
Ellis, Bookseller (Peter), London WC 177
Fifteenth Century Bookshop (The), East Sussex. 104
First Edition, The, Essex 109
Fortune Green Books, London NW................ 160
Foster Bookshop (Paul), London SW 167
Glenwood Books, Surrey........................... 234
Jarndyce Antiquarian Booksellers, London WC. 177
JB Books & Collectables, West Sussex 243
Joel Segal Books, Devon 86
John L Capes (Books Maps & Prints),
    North Yorkshire 196
Keith Langford, London E 154
Kenny's Bookshop & Art Galleries Ltd.,
    Co. Galway 265
Marble Hill Books, Outer London................. 182
Quaritch Ltd., (Bernard), London W.............. 174
R. & A. Books, East Sussex 101
Robert Temple, London N.......................... 158
Rosley Books, Cumbria 81
Seydi Rare Books (Sevin), London NW 161
Sillan Books, Co. Cavan........................... 262
The Glass Key, West Yorkshire.................... 246
Valentine Rare Books, London W 175
Walden Books, London NW 161
Wheen O'Books, Borders........................... 267
Wizard Books, Cambridgeshire..................... 67
Yates Antiquarian Books (Tony), Leics........... 146

- AFRICAN

Eggeling Books (John), West Yorkshire 249
Hawley (C.L.), North Yorkshire 195
Joel Segal Books, Devon 86
Kenya Books, East Sussex 100
Stevens (Joan), Cambridgeshire.................... 65

- AFRICAN-AMERICAN

Black Voices, Merseyside........................... 184
Chalmers Hallam (E.), Hampshire................. 125
Eggeling Books (John), West Yorkshire 249
Joel Segal Books, Devon 86
Stevens (Joan), Cambridgeshire.................... 65
Woburn Books, London N 159

- CANADIAN

Eggeling Books (John), West Yorkshire 249

Fifteenth Century Bookshop (The), East Sussex. 104
Joel Segal Books, Devon 86
Stevens (Joan), Cambridgeshire..................... 65

- DISPENSATIONAL CHRISTIAN

Beckham Books Ltd., Suffolk 229
Chapter Two, London SE.......................... 163

- FRENCH

Anthony Sillem, East Sussex....................... 102
Apocalypse, Surrey 232
Baldwin (Jack), Strathclyde 278
Delectus Books, London WC....................... 176
Fifteenth Century Bookshop (The), East Sussex. 104
Joel Segal Books, Devon 86
PsychoBabel Books & Journals, Oxfordshire..... 205
Quaritch Ltd., (Bernard), London W.............. 174
Seydi Rare Books (Sevin), London NW 161
Thorntons of Oxford Ltd., Oxfordshire........... 206

- GERMAN

Joel Segal Books, Devon 86
PsychoBabel Books & Journals, Oxfordshire..... 205
Quaritch Ltd., (Bernard), London W.............. 174
Seydi Rare Books (Sevin), London NW 161
Thorntons of Oxford Ltd., Oxfordshire........... 206

- IRISH

Ann & Mike Conry, Worcs......................... 257
Cecilia Marsden, Surrey 232
Celtic Bookshop (The), Co. Limerick 266
Charlie Byrne's Bookshop, Co. Galway........... 265
Courtwood Books, Co. Laois....................... 265
Delectus Books, London WC....................... 176
Doolin Dinghy Books, Co. Clare 262
Eggeling Books (John), West Yorkshire 249
Ellis, Bookseller (Peter), London WC............. 177
Fifteenth Century Bookshop (The), East Sussex. 104
Foster Bookshop (Paul), London SW.............. 167
Foyle Books, Co. Derry 260
Glenbower Books, Co. Dublin 264
House of Figgis Ltd (The), Co. Galway 265
Ian McKelvie Bookseller, London N.............. 157
Jackson (M.W.), Wiltshire.......................... 254
Joel Segal Books, Devon 86
Karen Millward, Co. Cork......................... 263
Kenny's Bookshop & Art Galleries Ltd.,
  Co. Galway 265
Lyonshill Books, Co. Dublin 265
Maggs Brothers Limited, London W.............. 173
Pittville Books, Glos............................... 113
Rowan (P. & B.), Co. Antrim 260
Schull Books, Co. Cork 262
Skelton (Tony), Kent................................ 140
Stokes Books, Co. Dublin.......................... 264

- NEW ZEALAND

Eggeling Books (John), West Yorkshire 249
Joel Segal Books, Devon 86

- PROLETARIAN

Left on The Shelf, Cumbria........................ 78
Northern Herald Books, West Yorkshire......... 245

- SCOTTISH

Armchair Books, Lothian 275
Atholl Fine Books, Tayside 280
Byre Books, Dumfries & Galloway............... 270
Cheshire Book Centre, Cheshire.................... 69
Cooper Hay Rare Books, Strathclyde 278
Cox Rare Books (Charles), Cornwall.............. 73
David Houston - Bookseller, London E 154
Delectus Books, London WC....................... 176
Dolphin Books, Suffolk............................ 225
Dunkheld Antiques, Tayside....................... 279
Ferguson (Elizabeth), Grampian 272
Fifteenth Century Bookshop (The), East Sussex. 104
Grampian Books, Grampian........................ 273
Greta Books, Durham 97
Hutchison (Books) (Larry), Fife................... 271
Ian McKelvie Bookseller, London N............. 157
Jane Jones Books, Grampian 273
Joel Segal Books, Devon 86
Loch Croispol Bookshop & Restaurant,
  Highland 273
McCrone (Audrey), Isle of Arran.................. 274
Mercat Books, Highland 274
Orb's Bookshop, Grampian........................ 273
Price (John), London N 158
R. & A. Books, East Sussex 101
Roberts Books, Strathclyde 279
Stroma Books, Borders 267
Thistle Books, Strathclyde......................... 278
Till's Bookshop, Lothian 277
Wheen O'Books, Borders........................... 267

- SOUTH AFRICAN

Black Voices, Merseyside 184
Chalmers Hallam (E.), Hampshire................. 125
Criterion Books, London Outer 181
Eggeling Books (John), West Yorkshire 249
Kenya Books, East Sussex 100
Oak Tree Press, Oxfordshire 207
Stevens (Joan), Cambridgeshire..................... 65
Yesterday's Books, Dorset 92

- SPANISH

Baldwin (Jack), Strathclyde 278
Hodgson (Judith), London W 173
Joel Segal Books, Devon 86
Orssich (Paul), London SW........................ 169
PsychoBabel Books & Journals, Oxfordshire..... 205
Quaritch Ltd., (Bernard), London W.............. 174
Sturford Books, Wiltshire 254
York (Graham), Devon.............................. 86

- VICTORIAN

Antique Map and Bookshop (The), Dorset 94
Apocalypse, Surrey 232
Beaton (Richard), East Sussex..................... 103
Bell (Peter), Lothian................................ 275
Brock Books, North Yorkshire..................... 192
Burmester (James), Bristol.......................... 58
Cox Rare Books (Charles), Cornwall.............. 73
Delectus Books, London WC....................... 176
Derek Stirling Bookseller, Kent 141
Dolphin Books, Suffolk............................ 225
Eggeling Books (John), West Yorkshire 249
Elaine Lonsdale Books, West Yorkshire......... 247

Ely Books, Cambridgeshire 65
Enigma Books, Wiltshire 252
Fifteenth Century Bookshop (The), East Sussex. 104
Jarndyce Antiquarian Booksellers, London WC. 177
Joel Segal Books, Devon 86
Parrott (Jeremy), London E........................... 154
PsychoBabel Books & Journals, Oxfordshire..... 205
Quaritch Ltd., (Bernard), London W.............. 174
Quest Booksearch, Cambridgeshire 65
R. & A. Books, East Sussex 101
Robert Temple, London N............................ 158
Rosley Books, Cumbria 81
Seabreeze Books, Lancashire......................... 144
Smith Books, (Sally), Suffolk 226
South Downs Book Service, West Sussex........ 243
Symes Books (Naomi), Cheshire 71
Tiger Books, Kent...................................... 136
Valentine Rare Books, London W................. 175
Wheen O'Books, Borders............................. 267

- WESTERN AMERICAN

Americanabooksuk, Cumbria......................... 76
Fifteenth Century Bookshop (The), East Sussex. 104
Stevens (Joan), Cambridgeshire..................... 65

LITERATURE IN TRANSLATION

AA1 Books, Dumfries & Galloway................ 269
Atlas, London N...................................... 156
babelog.books, Herefordshire 127
Books on Spain, London Outer 182
Burmester (James), Bristol........................... 58
Chthonios Books, East Sussex....................... 102
Eggeling Books (John), West Yorkshire 249
Fifteenth Century Bookshop (The), East Sussex. 104
Hab Books, London W.............................. 172
Hava Books, London SE............................. 164
Ian McKelvie Bookseller, London N.............. 157
Joel Segal Books, Devon 86
Modern Welsh Publications Ltd., Merseyside.... 184
Parrott (Jeremy), London E.......................... 154
PsychoBabel Books & Journals, Oxfordshire..... 205
Quaritch Ltd., (Bernard), London W.............. 174
Riderless Horse Books, Norfolk..................... 186
Robert Temple, London N............................ 158
Rosley Books, Cumbria 81
Roundstone Books, Lancashire...................... 143
Stevens (Joan), Cambridgeshire..................... 65
Tiger Books, Kent 136
Tucker (Alan & Joan), Glos 116
Updike Rare Books (John), Lothian 277

LITURGICS

Beckham Books Ltd., Suffolk 229
Bennett & Kerr Books, Oxfordshire 205
St Philip's Books, Oxfordshire...................... 208

LOCAL HISTORY

Aitchison (Lesley), Bristol 58
Apocalypse, Surrey 232
Bookbarrow, Cambridgeshire........................ 63
Brewin Books Ltd., Warwickshire 237
Charles Bossom, Cambridgeshire................... 65
Debbage (John), Norfolk............................. 189
Elaine Lonsdale Books, West Yorkshire.......... 247
Furneaux Books (Lee), Devon....................... 89

Lyonshill Books, Co. Dublin 265
Madoc Books, Conwy 284
MK Book Services, Cambridgeshire............... 66
Oakwood Books, Glos................................ 115
Richmond Books, North Yorkshire 194
Ross Old Books & Prints, Herefordshire 128
Whitchurch Books Ltd., Cardiff.................... 281

LOCAL STUDIES
- LINCOLNSHIRE

Gladstone Books, Lincolnshire 150
Island Books, Devon 85
Kemp Bookseller, Michael S, G Manchester..... 118
Maggy Browne, Lincolnshire 148

- SUSSEX

Fifteenth Century Bookshop (The), East Sussex. 104
Joel Segal Books, Devon 86
Martin (Books and Pictures), (Brian P.), Surrey. 231
Mellon's Books, East Sussex......................... 101
Muttonchop Manuscripts, West Sussex 242
Portus Books, Hampshire 122
R. & A. Books, East Sussex 101

LOCKS & LOCKSMITHS

Baron (Christopher), Cheshire 68
Stroh (M.A.), London E 154

LOGGING/LUMBERING

Reeves Technical Books, North Yorkshire 195

LOGIC

Barcombe Services, Essex............................ 108
Joel Segal Books, Devon 86
Parkinsons Books, Merseyside....................... 185
Pittville Books, Glos.................................. 113
Quaritch Ltd., (Bernard), London W.............. 174

LONDON

Annie's Books, S Yorks............................... 221
Arthur Hook, Bristol.................................. 58
Charles Bossom, Cambridgeshire................... 65
Delectus Books, London WC........................ 176
Fosters Bookshop, London W 172
Hava Books, London SE.............................. 164
Martin (Books and Pictures), (Brian P.), Surrey. 231
Nonsuch Books, Surrey............................... 234
Oopalba Books, Cheshire............................ 71
PsychoBabel Books & Journals, Oxfordshire..... 205

LOST CIVILISATIONS

Apocalypse, Surrey 232
Bookworms Paradise Ltd., West Sussex 242
Byre Books, Dumfries & Galloway 270
Fifteenth Century Bookshop (The), East Sussex. 104
R. & A. Books, East Sussex 101

MAFIA

Bolland Books, Bedfordshire........................ 53
Booth (Booksearch Service), (Geoff), Cheshire... 68
Clifford Elmer Books Ltd., Cheshire 68
Loretta Lay Books, London NW 161

MAGAZINES & PERIODICALS
- GENERAL
Anglo-American Rare Books, Surrey............. 232
Annie's Books, S Yorks 221
Apocalypse, Surrey 232
Art Reference Books, Hampshire 124
Barnes (Peter), Wiltshire........................... 253
Bianco Library, West Sussex....................... 241
Black Cat Bookshop, Leics 147
Book Palace (The), London SE 163
Books & Collectables Ltd., Cambridgeshire..... 63
Books & Things, London W........................ 171
Border Bookshop, West Yorkshire 249
Bracton Books, Cambridgeshire.................... 63
Cornucopia Books, Lincolnshire 151
Derek Stirling Bookseller, Kent 141
Eggeling Books (John), West Yorkshire 249
Fosters Bookshop, London W 172
Franks Booksellers, G Manchester 119
Green Meadow Books, Cornwall 74
Ken's Paper Collectables, Buckinghamshire...... 62
Lloyd-Davies (Sue), Carmarthenshire 282
Mr. Pickwick of Towcester, Northants........... 199
Mulyan (Don), Merseyside.......................... 185
Norton Books, North Yorkshire 192
Nostalgia Publications Ltd., North Yorkshire ... 197
Nostalgia Unlimited, Merseyside................... 184
Palladour Books, Hampshire 125
Paper Pleasures, Somerset 218
Peter Lyons Books, Glos 113
Phenotype Books, Cumbria 79
Poetry Bookshop (The), Powys 289
Reading Lasses, Dumfries & Galloway 270
Riderless Horse Books, Norfolk.................... 186
Ripping Yarns, London N 158
Robert Temple, London N.......................... 158
Tennis Collectables, Cheshire 68
The Sanctuary Bookshop, Dorset.................. 94
Tiger Books, Kent 136
Tilleys Vintage Magazine Shop, S Yorks 222
Tilleys Vintage Magazine Shop, Derbyshire...... 82
Tony Hutchinson, Surrey............................ 233
Updike Rare Books (John), Lothian 277
Williams (Bookdealer), (Richard), N Lincs....... 153
Williams Rare Books (Nigel), London WC 179
Woburn Books, London N 159
Words Etcetera Bookshop, Dorset................. 93
Yesterday's News, Conwy 283
Yorkshire Relics, West Yorkshire.................. 246

- WOMEN'S
Black Cat Books, Norfolk........................... 187
Cornucopia Books, Lincolnshire 151
Green Meadow Books, Cornwall 74
Judith Mansfield, West Yorkshire.................. 249
Tilleys Vintage Magazine Shop, Derbyshire...... 82

MAGIC & CONJURING
Abrahams (Mike), Staffordshire..................... 223
Annie's Books, S Yorks 221
Books & Bygones (Pam Taylor), West Midlands 240
Booth (Booksearch Service), (Geoff), Cheshire... 68
Cheshire Book Centre, Cheshire.................... 69
Drummond Pleasures of Past Times (David),
    London WC 176

Edmund Pollinger Rare Books, London SW..... 166
Elgar (Raymond), East Sussex...................... 99
Fitzsimons (Anne), Cumbria 76
Franks Booksellers, Greater Manchester.......... 119
Game Advice, Oxfordshire 208
Harrington (Adrian), London W................... 173
Joel Segal Books, Devon 86
Modern First Editions, West Yorkshire........... 247
N1 Books, East Sussex 105
Phillip Robbins of Warwick, Warwickshire 237
St Swithin's Illustrated & Children's Books,
    London W 174
Scrivener's Books & Bookbinding, Derbyshire... 82
Treasure Island (The), Greater Manchester....... 119
Wiend Books, Lancashire 143
Wizard Books, Cambridgeshire..................... 67

MAGIC LANTERNS
R. & A. Books, East Sussex 101
Stroh (M.A.), London E 154

MAGICK
Annie's Books, S Yorks 221
Atlantis Bookshop, London WC.................... 176
Bookworms Paradise Ltd., West Sussex 242
Bygone Books, Isles of Scotland 275
Delectus Books, London WC....................... 176
Inner Bookshop (The), Oxfordshire................ 208
Just Books, Cornwall 75
Old Celtic Bookshop (The), Devon................ 87
Star Lord Books, Greater Manchester 119
Treasure Island (The), Greater Manchester....... 119

MAGNETICISM
Magis Books, Leics................................... 146
Pollak (P.M.), Devon 88
R. & A. Books, East Sussex 101
Stroh (M.A.), London E 154
Weiner (Graham), London N 158

MALACOLOGY
Earth Science Books, Wiltshire..................... 252
Parkinsons Books, Merseyside...................... 185
Pollak (P.M.), Devon 88

MAMMALS
Annie's Books, S Yorks 221
Austwick Hall Books, North Yorkshire........... 192
Bookworms Paradise Ltd., West Sussex 242
Calluna Books, Dorset............................... 95
Dales & Lakes Book Centre, Cumbria........... 79
Fifteenth Century Bookshop (The), East Sussex. 104
Joel Segal Books, Devon 86
Martin (Books and Pictures), (Brian P.), Surrey. 231
Martin (Brian), Surrey............................... 231
Mobbs (A.J.), West Midlands 239
Parkinsons Books, Merseyside...................... 185
Pemberley Books, Buckinghamshire 62
Peter M Daly, Hampshire........................... 126
R. & A. Books, East Sussex 101
Westons, Herts....................................... 132
Woodside Books, Kent 135

MANAGEMENT
Annie's Books, S Yorks 221

Bob Mallory (Books), Derbyshire.................... 83
Cornucopia Books, Lincolnshire 151
Northern Herald Books, West Yorkshire......... 245
Reading Lasses, Dumfries & Galloway 270

MANUALS
Cornucopia Books, Lincolnshire 151
MilitaryHistoryBooks.com, Kent.................... 137
Phillip Robbins of Warwick, Warwickshire 237

MANUALS - SEAMANSHIP
(SEE ALSO UNDER SEAMANSHIP)
Cheshire Book Centre,Cheshire..................... 69
Footrope Knots, Suffolk.............................. 227
Greta Books, Durham 97
Island Books, Devon................................ 85
Joel Segal Books, Devon 86
Marine & Cannon Books, Cheshire 71
Marine and Cannon Books, Cheshire 69
Milestone Books, Devon............................ 89
Nautical Antique Centre (The), Dorset 96
Phillip Robbins of Warwick, Warwickshire 237
Sea Chest Nautical Bookshop (The), Devon 88

MANUFACTURING
Debbage (John), Norfolk............................. 189
Parkinsons Books, Merseyside...................... 185
PsychoBabel Books & Journals, Oxfordshire..... 205
Susanne Schulz-Falster Rare Books, London N. 158

MANUSCRIPTS
Aitchison (Lesley), Bristol 58
Andrew Hunter Rare Books, London SW 166
Apocalypse, Surrey 232
Bertram Rota Ltd., London WC 176
Bookstand, Dorset................................... 94
Bristow & Garland, Hampshire 123
Butler Rare Books, Buckinghamshire 61
Cox Music (Lisa), Devon........................... 86
Cox Rare Books (Charles), Cornwall.............. 73
Davids Ltd., (Roy), Oxfordshire 208
De Burca Rare Books, Co. Dublin 264
Dean Byass, Bristol.................................. 60
Debbage (John), Norfolk............................ 189
Derek Stirling Bookseller, Kent 141
Drury Rare Books (John), Essex................... 110
Farahar & Dupre (Clive & Sophie), Wiltshire ... 251
Finch Rare Books Ltd. (Simon), London W..... 172
Fogg Rare Books & Manuscripts (Sam),
  London W 172
Ford (Richard), London W 172
Gekoski (R.A.), London WC....................... 177
Heath (A.R.), Bristol................................ 59
Hodgson (Judith), London W 173
Humber Books, Lincolnshire 148
Ian Marr Rare Books, Cornwall 73
James Fergusson Books & Manuscripts,
  London W 173
Jarndyce Antiquarian Booksellers, London WC. 177
John Underwood Antiquarian Books, Norfolk.. 189
Kenny's Bookshop & Art Galleries Ltd.,
  Co. Galway 265
Ken's Paper Collectables, Buckinghamshire 62
Knowles - Antiquary (Roger J.), Staffordshire... 223
Kunkler Books (Paul), Cambridgeshire 64

Leo Cadogan, London N 157
Lucius Books, North Yorkshire..................... 197
Maggs Brothers Limited, London W.............. 173
Marine & Cannon Books, Cheshire 71
Marine and Cannon Books, Cheshire 69
Modern First Editions, West Yorkshire........... 247
Muttonchop Manuscripts, West Sussex 242
Neil Summersgill, Lancashire 142
Phillip Robbins of Warwick, Warwickshire 237
Pickering & Chatto, London W 174
Quaritch Ltd., (Bernard), London W.............. 174
Rassam (Paul), London NW 161
Riderless Horse Books, Norfolk.................... 186
Rowan (P. & B.), Co. Antrim 260
Seydi Rare Books (Sevin), London NW 161
Silverman (Michael), London SE 165
Spelman (Ken), North Yorkshire 198
Taylor & Son (Peter), Herts........................ 132
Townsend (John), Berks............................. 57
Tyger Press, London N.............................. 158
Williams Rare Books (Nigel), London WC 179
Wilson (Manuscripts) Ltd., (John), Glos.......... 114

MAORI
Empire Books, North Yorkshire 197

MAPS & MAPMAKING
Altea Antique Maps & Books, London W....... 171
Anthony Vickers Books, North Yorkshire 195
Arthur Hook, Bristol................................. 58
Baynton–Williams Gallery, West Sussex 241
Bookshop on the Heath, The, London SE 163
Bunyan Books, Bedfordshire........................ 53
Chas J. Sawyer, Kent 140
Chris Phillips, Wiltshire............................. 252
Colin Hancock, Ceredigion 282
Copperplate Antique Maps and Prints, Herts.... 132
Cornell Books, Glos................................. 117
Dartmoor Book Gallery, Devon 87
Debbage (John), Norfolk............................ 189
Empire Books, North Yorkshire 197
Fifteenth Century Bookshop (The), East Sussex. 104
Frew Limited (Robert), London SW 167
Garwood & Voigt, Kent............................. 139
Grahame Thornton, Bookseller, Dorset........... 93
Grove Bookshop (The), North Yorkshire 195
Harlequin Gallery, Lincolnshire 150
Jackdaw Books, Norfolk 188
Just Books, Cornwall 75
Kalligraphia (formerly Charmouth Bounty
  Books), Isle of Wight............................ 133
Lymelight Books & Prints, Dorset................. 93
Moorside Books, Lancashire........................ 143
Mulyan (Don), Merseyside......................... 185
Paper Pleasures, Somerset 218
Quaritch Ltd., (Bernard), London W.............. 174
Rayner (Hugh Ashley), Somerset 215
Robin Doughty - Fine Books, West Midlands... 238
Roz Hulse, Conwy 284
Sea Chest Nautical Bookshop (The), Devon 88
Shapero Rare Books (Bernard J.), London W ... 175
Stalagluft Books, Tyne and Wear.................. 235
Tim Bryers Ltd, London WC 178

MARINE BIOLOGY

Baldwin's Scientific Books, Essex 111
Pollak (P.M.), Devon 88
Sea Chest Nautical Bookshop (The), Devon 88
Steven Simpson Books, Norfolk 190
Sub Aqua Prints and Books, Hampshire 123
Westons, Herts 132
Woodside Books, Kent 135

MARINE SCIENCES

Arden, Bookseller (C.), Powys..................... 287
Cheshire Book Centre, Cheshire................... 69
Parkinsons Books, Merseyside..................... 185
Periplus Books, Buckinghamshire................. 62
Phillip Robbins of Warwick, Warwickshire 237
R. & A. Books, East Sussex 101
Sea Chest Nautical Bookshop (The), Devon 88
Sub Aqua Prints and Books, Hampshire 123
Thomas Rare Books, Suffolk 226

MARITIME/NAUTICAL
- GENERAL

Alba Books, Grampian 273
All Books, Essex 111
Altea Antique Maps & Books, London W 171
Anchor Books, Lincolnshire 149
Anthony Vickers Books, North Yorkshire 195
Anvil Books, West Midlands 239
Arden Books & Cosmographia, Warwickshire... 236
Argent (Alan), Isle of Wight 134
Aviabooks, Glos 114
Axe Rare & Out of Print Books (Richard),
    North Yorkshire 193
Baldwin (M. & M.), Worcs 255
Barbican Bookshop, North Yorkshire............. 196
Barmby (C. & A.J.), Kent........................... 140
Blackpool Book Warehouse, Lancashire.......... 142
Books Afloat, Dorset 96
Bosorne Books, Cornwall 75
Bott, (Bookdealers) Ltd., (Martin),
    Greater Manchester 118
Broadhurst of Southport Ltd., Merseyside 185
Browsers Bookshop, Cornwall...................... 72
Burebank Books, Norfolk 186
Burroughs (Andrew), Lincolnshire 152
Butterworth (Robert F.), Lancashire 144
Cavendish Rare Books, London N 156
Cheshire Book Centre, Cheshire................... 69
Clevedon Books, Somerset 217
Cofion Books, Pembrokeshire 286
Collectables (W.H.), Suffolk 229
Collectors Carbooks, Northants..................... 199
Colonsay Bookshop, Isle of Colonsay............. 275
Compass Books, Devon 85
Cornucopia Books, Lincolnshire 151
Cox (Geoff), Devon 90
Curtle Mead Books, Isle of Wight 133
D'Arcy Books, Wiltshire............................ 252
Dartmoor Bookshop (The), Devon 84
Debbage (John), Norfolk 189
Delectus Books, London WC........................ 176
Discovery Bookshop, Carmarthenshire............ 281
Dolphin Books, Suffolk............................. 225
Duck (William), Hampshire......................... 124
Elton Engineering Books, London W 172

Embleton (Paul), Essex 111
Falconwood Transport & Military Bookshop,
    London Outer 183
Fifteenth Century Bookshop (The), East Sussex. 104
Fireside Bookshop, Cumbria........................ 81
Fisher Nautical, East Sussex 99
Footrope Knots, Suffolk............................. 227
Fox Books (J. & J.), Kent........................... 139
Furneaux Books (Lee), Devon...................... 89
G. C. Books Ltd., Dumfries & Galloway......... 270
George St. Books, Derbyshire 83
Gerald Lee Maritime Books, East Sussex......... 105
Green Ltd. (G.L.), Herts 131
Greta Books, Durham 97
Guildmaster Books, Cheshire 70
Hall's Bookshop, Kent.............................. 140
Harlequin Books, Bristol 59
Harrington Antiquarian Bookseller (Peter),
    London SW..................................... 167
Hay Cinema Bookshop Ltd., Powys............... 288
Helion & Company, West Midlands 239
High Street Books, Devon 86
Holdenhurst Books, Dorset 91
Hummingbird Books, Herefordshire............... 128
Island Books, Devon................................ 85
J & J Burgess Booksellers, Cambridgeshire....... 64
Jackdaw Books, Norfolk 188
Joel Segal Books, Devon 86
John L Capes (Books Maps & Prints), N Yorks 196
Johnston's Marine Stores, Scotland................ 274
Just Books, Cornwall 75
Kalligraphia (formerly Charmouth Bounty
    Books), Isle of Wight........................... 133
Keegan's Bookshop, Berks 57
Kellow Books, Oxfordshire 206
Kerr (Norman), Cumbria 77
Kingfisher Book Service, Nottinghamshire 204
Kirkman Ltd., (Robert), Bedfordshire............. 54
Lamb's Tales Books, Devon 87
Larkham Books (Patricia), Glos..................... 117
Lawrence Books, Nottinghamshire 203
Lost Books, Northants.............................. 200
Marcet Books, London SE........................... 164
Marine & Cannon Books, Cheshire 71
Marine and Cannon Books, Cheshire 69
Marine Workshop Bookshop, Dorset 93
Martin Bookshop & Gallery (Richard), Hants... 123
McCarty, Bookseller (M.E.),
    Dumfries & Galloway 270
McCarty, Bookseller (M.E.), Western Isles....... 275
McCrone (Audrey), Isle of Arran 274
McLaren Books Ltd, Strathclyde 279
Michael J Carroll, Co. Cork 263
Milestone Books, Devon 89
Military Parade Bookshop, Wiltshire.............. 252
Mothergoose Bookshop, Isle of Wight............ 133
Mulyan (Don), Merseyside.......................... 185
My Back Pages, London SW........................ 168
Nautical Antique Centre (The), Dorset 96
Nelson (Elizabeth), Suffolk......................... 226
Oasis Booksearch, Cambridgeshire................. 67
Parrott Books, Oxfordshire 209
Peter M Daly, Hampshire........................... 126
Phillip Robbins of Warwick, Warwickshire 237
Piccadilly Rare Books, East Sussex 105

Portus Books, Hampshire 122
Pringle Booksellers (Andrew), Lothian 277
Prior (Michael), Lincolnshire 152
Quentin Books Ltd, Essex 108
R. & A. Books, East Sussex 101
Read - Gorleston Books, (C.&J.), Norfolk 187
Richmond Books, North Yorkshire 194
Roadmaster Books, Kent 136
Robert Humm & Co, Lincolnshire 152
Rods Books, Devon 88
Roz Hulse, Conwy 284
Saintfield Antiques & Fine Books, Co. Down ... 261
Sansovino Books, West Sussex 244
Sea Chest Nautical Bookshop (The), Devon 88
Simmonds (Anthony J.), London SE 165
Smith Maritime Aviation Books (Frank),
    Tyne and Wear 235
Stella Books, Monmouthshire 286
Stroma Books, Borders 267
Sub Aqua Prints and Books, Hampshire 123
Suffolk Rare Books, Suffolk 229
Taylor & Son (Peter), Herts 132
Thomas Rare Books, Suffolk 226
Tilston (Stephen E.), London SE 165
Treasure Island (The), G Manchester 119
Trinders' Fine Tools, Suffolk 226
Vanstone - Aviation Books, (Derek), Suffolk 229
War & Peace Books, Hampshire 122
Warsash Nautical Bookshop, Hampshire 126
Wiend Books, Lancashire 143
Wise (Derek), East Sussex 104
World War Books, Kent 141

- HISTORY
Aardvark Books, Wiltshire 254
Anchor Books, Lincolnshire 149
Annie's Books, S Yorks 221
Baynton–Williams Gallery, West Sussex 241
books2books, Devon 88
Bott, (Bookdealers) Ltd., (Martin), Greater
    Manchester 118
Browsers Bookshop, Cornwall 72
Catalyst Booksearch Services, Devon 87
Cornucopia Books, Lincolnshire 151
Cox (Geoff), Devon 90
Curtle Mead Books, Isle of Wight 133
Dales and Lakes Book Centre, Cumbria 79
Debbage (John), Norfolk 189
Deeside Books, Grampian 272
Falconwood Transport & Military Bookshop,
    London Outer 183
Fifteenth Century Bookshop (The), East Sussex. 104
Gerald Lee Maritime Books, East Sussex 105
Handsworth Books, Essex 112
Joel Segal Books, Devon 86
Keel Row Bookshop, Tyne and Wear 235
Leo Cadogan, London N 157
Lost Books, Northants 200
Marine & Cannon Books, Cheshire 71
Marine and Cannon Books, Cheshire 69
Martin Bookshop & Gallery (Richard), Hants... 123
McLaren Books Ltd, Strathclyde 279
Michael J Carroll, Co. Cork 263
MilitaryHistoryBooks.com, Kent 137
Oasis Booksearch, Cambridgeshire 67

Portus Books, Hampshire 122
Pringle Booksellers (Andrew), Lothian 277
R. & A. Books, East Sussex 101
Read - Gorleston Books, (C.&J.), Norfolk 187
Robert Humm & Co, Lincolnshire 152
Rods Books, Devon 88
Sax Books, Suffolk 228
Sea Chest Nautical Bookshop (The), Devon 88
Sub Aqua Prints and Books, Hampshire 123
Thomas Rare Books, Suffolk 226
Tilston (Stephen E.), London SE 165
Wadard Books, Kent 137

- LOG BOOKS
Aardvark Books, Wiltshire 254
Anchor Books, Lincolnshire 149
Curtle Mead Books, Isle of Wight 133
Gerald Lee Maritime Books, East Sussex 105
Hicks (Ronald C.), Cornwall 73
Marine & Cannon Books, Cheshire 71
Marine and Cannon Books, Cheshire 69
Martin Bookshop & Gallery (Richard), Hants... 123
McLaren Books Ltd, Strathclyde 279
Nautical Antique Centre (The), Dorset 96
Sea Chest Nautical Bookshop (The), Devon 88
Stroh (M.A.), London E 154
Thomas Rare Books, Suffolk 226
Tyger Press, London N 158
Warsash Nautical Bookshop, Hampshire 126

MARQUE HISTORIES
(SEE ALSO MOTORING)
Annie's Books, S Yorks 221
Burroughs (Andrew), Lincolnshire 152
Collectors Carbooks, Northants 199
Falconwood Transport & Military Bookshop,
    London Outer 183
Fylde Books, Lancashire 144
Joel Segal Books, Devon 86
Kenneth Ball, East Sussex 100
Knowles (John), Norfolk 187
Pooks Motor Books, Leics 146
Roadmaster Books, Kent 136

MARXISM
Books Only, Suffolk 226
Delectus Books, London WC 176
Hab Books, London W 172
J.E. Burns Booksellers, Merseyside 185
Joel Segal Books, Devon 86
Killeen (John), North Yorkshire 193
Left on The Shelf, Cumbria 78
Northern Herald Books, West Yorkshire 245
Parkinsons Books, Merseyside 185
Quaritch Ltd., (Bernard), London W 174
Reading Lasses, Dumfries & Galloway 270
Red Star Books, Herts 129
Spurrier (Nick), Kent 137
Susanne Schulz-Falster Rare Books, London N. 158
Treasure Trove Books, Leics 146
Woburn Books, London N 159

MATHEMATICS
Andrew Hunter Rare Books, London SW 166
Annie's Books, S Yorks 221

Baldwin's Scientific Books, Essex 111
Barcombe Services, Essex........................... 108
Baron - Scientific Book Sales (P.J.), Somerset ... 216
Camden Books, Somerset 215
Chesters (G. & J.), Staffordshire 224
Eagle Bookshop (The), Bedfordshire 53
Ely Books, Cambridgeshire 65
Esplin (David), Hampshire.......................... 124
Game Advice, Oxfordshire.......................... 208
GfB: the Colchester Bookshop, Essex 108
Glenbower Books, Co. Dublin 264
Hadfield (G.K.), Cumbria........................... 79
Holtom (Christopher), Glos......................... 115
Hurst (Jenny), Kent 137
Joel Segal Books, Devon 86
John Gorton Booksearch, East Sussex 105
Moorside Books, Lancashire........................ 143
Parkinsons Books, Merseyside...................... 185
Phelps (Michael), West Sussex 242
Pickering & Chatto, London W 174
PsychoBabel Books & Journals, Oxfordshire..... 205
Quaritch Ltd., (Bernard), London W.............. 174
Rebecca Hardie Rare Books, London W 171
Roberts Books, Strathclyde 279
Roosterbooks, Northants............................ 199
Stroh (M.A.), London E 154
Susanne Schulz-Falster Rare Books, London N. 158
Transformer, Dumfries & Galloway............... 270
Treasure Trove Books, Leics....................... 146
Turret House, Norfolk.............................. 191
Wayside Books and Cards, Oxfordshire 206
Westons, Herts...................................... 132
Westwood Books (Mark), Powys 289
Westwood Books Ltd, Cumbria.................... 80
Whistler's Books, London SW 169

MAYFLOWER VOYAGE OF 1620

R. & A. Books, East Sussex 101

MECHANICAL ENGINEERING

Brad Books, Essex................................... 110
Elton Engineering Books, London W 172
N1 Books, East Sussex 105
Parkinsons Books, Merseyside...................... 185
Phelps (Michael), West Sussex 242
Pollak (P.M.), Devon 88
Robert Humm & Co, Lincolnshire 152
Stroh (M.A.), London E 154
Treasure Island (The), Greater Manchester....... 119
Westons, Herts...................................... 132

MEDIA

Aurora Books Ltd, Lothian.......................... 275
Barcombe Services, Essex........................... 108
Cornucopia Books, Lincolnshire 151
Greenroom Books, West Yorkshire 247
Joel Segal Books, Devon 86
Judd Books, London WC 177
Kelly Books Ltd, Devon............................. 89
Morris Secondhand & Antiquarian Books
    (Chris), Oxfordshire 208
Murch Booksend, (Herbert), London SE......... 165
My Back Pages, London SW 168
Reading Lasses, Dumfries & Galloway 270
Woburn Books, London N 159

MEDICINE

Alba Books, Grampian 273
Andrew Hunter Rare Books, London SW 166
Axe Rare & Out of Print Books (Richard),
    North Yorkshire 193
Barcombe Services, Essex........................... 108
Baron - Scientific Book Sales (P.J.), Somerset ... 216
Bernard Dixon and Kath Adams, London Outer 182
Beware of the Leopard, Bristol..................... 58
Bibliophile (The), S Yorks.......................... 221
Bookshop (The), Co. Donegal....................... 263
Bracton Books, Cambridgeshire.................... 63
Catalyst Booksearch Services, Devon............. 87
Cheshire Book Centre, Cheshire................... 69
Childrens Bookshop, West Yorkshire 247
Collectable Books, London SE 163
Dean Byass, Bristol................................. 60
Delectus Books, London WC........................ 176
Dunstan Books, Dorset............................. 91
Edwards (London) Limited (Francis),
    London WC 176
Edwards in Hay-on-Wye (Francis), Powys 288
Erian Books, London N............................. 156
Finch Rare Books Ltd. (Simon), London W..... 172
Game Advice, Oxfordshire.......................... 208
Gaskell Rare Books (Roger), Cambridgeshire ... 66
Glenbower Books, Co. Dublin 264
Grahame Thornton, Bookseller, Dorset.......... 93
Hay Cinema Bookshop Ltd., Powys............... 288
Hünersdorff Rare Books, London SW 168
Jackdaw Books, Norfolk 188
Lawson & Company (E.M.), Oxfordshire 206
Much Binding, Norfolk............................. 186
Orchid Book Distributors, Co. Clare.............. 262
Outcast Books, Herefordshire...................... 127
Parkinsons Books, Merseyside...................... 185
Pemberley Books, Buckinghamshire 62
Phelps (Michael), West Sussex 242
Phillips (Nigel), Hampshire......................... 122
Pickering & Chatto, London W 174
Pollak (P.M.), Devon 88
Portobello Books, London W 174
Pratt (B.A. & C.W.M.), Herefordshire 128
Prospect House Books, Co. Down................. 261
PsychoBabel Books & Journals, Oxfordshire..... 205
Quaritch Ltd., (Bernard), London W.............. 174
Quinto of Charing Cross Road, London WC ... 178
Rebecca Hardie Rare Books, London W 171
R M Books, Herts................................... 132
Scrivener's Books & Bookbinding, Derbyshire... 82
Smith (Clive), Essex 109
Smith (David & Lynn), London Outer............ 181
Stern Antiquarian Bookseller (Jeffrey), N Yorks 198
Stroh (M.A.), London E 154
Treasure Island (The), Greater Manchester....... 119
Turret House, Norfolk.............................. 191
Village Books, Norfolk 186
Weiner (Graham), London N 158
Westons, Herts...................................... 132
Westwood Books (Mark), Powys 289
Westwood Books Ltd, Cumbria.................... 80
Wheen O'Books, Borders........................... 267
White (David), Cambridgeshire.................... 65
Woburn Books, London N 159
Worcester Rare Books, Worcs...................... 256

MEDICINE - HISTORY OF

Alba Books, Grampian 273
Andrew Hunter Rare Books, London SW 166
Baldwin's Scientific Books, Essex 111
Barcombe Services, Essex 108
Bernard Dixon and Kath Adams, London Outer 182
Cheshire Book Centre, Cheshire 69
Chesters (G. & J.), Staffordshire 224
Childrens Bookshop, West Yorkshire 247
Clevedon Books, Somerset 217
Dean Byass, Bristol 60
Erian Books, London N 156
Esplin (David), Hampshire 124
Fireside Bookshop, Cumbria 81
Forest Books of Manchester, Cheshire 70
Game Advice, Oxfordshire 208
Gladstone Books, Lincolnshire 150
Joel Segal Books, Devon 86
Kingswood Books, Dorset 94
London & Sussex Antiquarian Book &
  Print Services, East Sussex 101
Maggs Brothers Limited, London W 173
Mair Wilkes Books, Fife 271
Meekins Books (Paul), Warwickshire 237
Parkinsons Books, Merseyside 185
Pemberley Books, Buckinghamshire 62
Phelps (Michael), West Sussex 242
Pittville Books, Glos. 113
Pollak (P.M.), Devon 88
Pordes Books Ltd., (Henry), London WC 177
PsychoBabel Books & Journals, Oxfordshire 205
Quaritch Ltd., (Bernard), London W 174
R M Books, Herts 132
R. & A. Books, East Sussex 101
Rebecca Hardie Rare Books, London W 171
Rowan (P. & B.), Co. Antrim 260
Smith (David & Lynn), London Outer 181
Stroh (M.A.), London E 154
Sue Lowell Natural History Books, London W . 175
Taylor & Son (Peter), Herts. 132
Westons, Herts 132
Westwood Books (Mark), Powys 289
White (David), Cambridgeshire 65
Woburn Books, London N 159

MEDIEVAL

Alexander's Books, Warwickshire 237
Baker Limited (A.P. & R.),
  Dumfries & Galloway 269
Bennett & Kerr Books, Oxfordshire 205
Byre Books, Dumfries & Galloway 270
Camden Books, Somerset 215
Du Ry Medieval Manuscripts (Marc–Antoine),
  London W 172
Fifteenth Century Bookshop (The), East Sussex. 104
Gildas Books, Cheshire 68
Grampian Books, Grampian 273
Hobgoblin Books, Hampshire 125
Jackdaw Books, Norfolk 188
Joel Segal Books, Devon 86
John Underwood Antiquarian Books, Norfolk .. 189
Karen Thomson, Oxfordshire 209
Kingswood Books, Dorset 94
Lost Books, Northants 200
medievalbookshop, Herts 132

Meekins Books (Paul), Warwickshire 237
Michael J Carroll, Co. Cork 263
MilitaryHistoryBooks.com, Kent 137
N1 Books, East Sussex 105
Pittville Books, Glos. 113
Priestpopple Books, Northumberland 201
Quaritch Ltd., (Bernard), London W 174
St Philip's Books, Oxfordshire 208
Samovar Books, Co. Dublin 264
Sandpiper Books Ltd., London SW 169
Spenceley Books (David), West Yorkshire 248
Taylor & Son (Peter), Herts. 132
Unsworth's Booksellers, Suffolk 225
Winghale Books, Lincolnshire 152

MEMOIRS

Bell (Peter), Lothian 275
Brimstones, East Sussex 104
Cornucopia Books, Lincolnshire 151
Darkwood Books, Co. Cork 263
Discovery Bookshop, Carmarthenshire 281
Dolphin Books, Suffolk 225
Fifteenth Century Bookshop (The), East Sussex. 104
Hab Books, London W 172
Jackdaw Books, Norfolk 188
Joel Segal Books, Devon 86
Karen Millward, Co. Cork 263
Kirkpatrick (Robert J.), London W 173
London & Sussex Antiquarian Book &
  Print Services, East Sussex 101
Marine & Cannon Books, Cheshire 71
Marine and Cannon Books, Cheshire 69
Mr. Pickwick of Towcester, Northants 199
N V Books, Warwickshire 236
Robert Temple, London N 158
Samovar Books, Co. Dublin 264
Woburn Books, London N 159

MEMORABILIA

Annie's Books, S Yorks 221
Art Reference Books, Hampshire 124
Collectors Carbooks, Northants 199
Dally (Andrew), Powys 289
Embleton (Paul), Essex 111
First Edition, The, Essex 109
firstpagebooks, Norfolk 189
Kent T. G., Surrey 230
Morris Secondhand & Antiquarian Books
  (Chris), Oxfordshire 208
R. & A. Books, East Sussex 101
Tyger Press, London N 158
Woburn Books, London N 159

MEMORY/MNEMONICS

Quaritch Ltd., (Bernard), London W 174

METAPHYSICS

Alpha Books, London N 156
Barcombe Services, Essex 108
Chthonios Books, East Sussex 102
Greensleeves, Oxfordshire 206
Inner Bookshop (The), Oxfordshire 208
Needham Books, (Russell), Somerset 219
Old Celtic Bookshop (The), Devon 87
Price (John), London N 158

Quaritch Ltd., (Bernard), London W 174
R. & A. Books, East Sussex 101
SETI Books, West Midlands........................ 239
Star Lord Books, Greater Manchester 119
Trinity Rare Books, Co. Leitrim 266

METEOROLOGY
Joel Segal Books, Devon 86
Parkinsons Books, Merseyside...................... 185
Periplus Books, Buckinghamshire................. 62

MEXICANA
Baldwin (Jack), Strathclyde 278
Delectus Books, London WC........................ 176
Hodgson (Judith), London W 173
Orssich (Paul), London SW........................ 169

MICROBIOLOGY
Baldwin's Scientific Books, Essex 111
Bernard Dixon and Kath Adams, London Outer 182
Pollak (P.M.), Devon 88
R M Books, Herts.................................... 132
Savona Books, Lincolnshire........................ 151
Westons, Herts....................................... 132

MICROSCOPY
Baron (Christopher), Cheshire...................... 68
Bernard Dixon and Kath Adams, London Outer 182
Hadfield (G.K.), Cumbria 79
Phelps (Michael), West Sussex..................... 242
Pollak (P.M.), Devon 88
R M Books, Herts.................................... 132
Stroh (M.A.), London E 154
Turret House, Norfolk............................... 191
Westons, Herts....................................... 132

MILITARY
- GENERAL
Aardvark Books, Wiltshire.......................... 254
Abacus Gallery, Staffordshire...................... 224
Addyman Annexe (The), Powys..................... 287
Addyman Books, Powys............................. 287
Alauda Books, Cumbria............................. 76
Albion Books, West Midlands....................... 238
Allinson (Frank & Stella), Warwickshire 236
Americanabooksuk, Cumbria........................ 76
Anchor Books, Lincolnshire 149
Andrew Morton (Books), Powys.................... 287
Andron (G.W.), London N 156
Anglo-American Rare Books, Surrey.............. 232
Annie's Books, S Yorks 221
Antiquary Ltd., (Bar Bookstore), N Yorks....... 194
Antique Map and Bookshop (The), Dorset 94
Apocalypse, Surrey 232
Ardis Books, Hampshire 126
Armchair Auctions, Hampshire 121
Austen (Phillip), Lincolnshire 151
Aviabooks, Glos 114
Axe Rare & Out of Print Books (Richard),
  North Yorkshire 193
B D McManmon, Lancashire 144
Backfold Books, Herefordshire 127
Baldwin (M. & M.), Worcs 255
Barbican Bookshop, North Yorkshire............. 196
Barn Books, Buckinghamshire...................... 61

Barnes (Peter), Wiltshire............................ 253
Bath Old Books, Somerset 215
Biff Books and Records, S Yorks.................. 221
Big Bairn Books, Tayside 279
Blacket Books, Lothian.............................. 276
Blackpool Book Warehouse, Lancashire.......... 142
Boer War Books, North Yorkshire................. 197
Book Business (The), London W 171
Book For All Reasons (A.), Suffolk............... 228
Books, Denbighshire 284
Books & Collectables Ltd., Cambridgeshire...... 63
Books Bought & Sold, Surrey 231
Bookworm (The), Lothian........................... 276
Bookworms of Evesham, Worcs 257
Bookworms Paradise Ltd., West Sussex 242
Booth (Booksearch Service), (Geoff), Cheshire... 68
Bosco Books, Cornwall.............................. 72
Brazenhead Ltd., Norfolk 188
Brewin Books Ltd., Warwickshire 237
Broadhurst of Southport Ltd., Merseyside 185
Browsers Bookshop, Cornwall...................... 72
Bufo Books, Hampshire 125
Burroughs (Andrew), Lincolnshire................. 152
Cader Idris Books, Powys........................... 290
Caliver Books, Essex 109
Camilla's Bookshop, East Sussex 101
Cassidy (Bookseller) (P.), Lincolnshire 151
Cavern Books, Cheshire 70
Chaucer Bookshop, Kent............................ 136
Chelifer Books, Cumbria............................ 80
Cheshire Book Centre, Cheshire.................... 69
Chevin Books, West Yorkshire...................... 249
Clent Books, Worcs 255
Coach House Books, Worcs 256
Cobweb Books, North Yorkshire................... 194
Cofion Books, Pembrokeshire 286
Collectors Corner, Wiltshire........................ 253
Cornucopia Books, Lincolnshire 151
Cotswold Internet Books, Glos..................... 113
Cox (Geoff), Devon 90
Dalbeattie Books, Dumfries & Galloway 269
Dally (Andrew), Powys 289
D'Arcy Books, Wiltshire............................ 252
Dartmoor Bookshop (The), Devon 84
Debbage (John), Norfolk............................ 189
Deeside Books, Grampian........................... 272
Discovery Bookshop, Carmarthenshire............ 281
Donovan Military Books (Tom), East Sussex.... 99
Eastgate Bookshop, East Yorkshire 106
Edwards (London) Limited (Francis),
  London WC 176
Edwards in Hay–on–Wye (Francis), Powys 288
Embleton (Paul), Essex 111
Empire Books, North Yorkshire 197
Eton Antique Bookshop, Berks 57
Falconwood Transport & Military Bookshop,
  London Outer 183
Farnborough Gallery, Hampshire................... 122
Fifteenth Century Bookshop (The), East Sussex. 104
Fireside Bookshop, Cumbria........................ 81
Ford Books (David), Herts 130
Fox Books (J. & J.), Kent.......................... 139
Freeman's Corner Shop, Norfolk 189
G&S Books, Kent 138
G. C. Books Ltd., Dumfries & Galloway........ 270

Gallimaufry Books, Herts 131
Grahame Thornton, Bookseller, Dorset.......... 93
Grove Bookshop (The), North Yorkshire 195
Hall's Bookshop, Kent.............................. 140
Hancock (Peter), West Sussex 241
Harlequin Books, Bristol 59
Harris (George J.), Co. Derry 260
Heartland Old Books, Devon 89
Helion & Company, West Midlands 239
High Street Books, Devon 86
Hill (John S.), Devon 86
Holdenhurst Books, Dorset 91
Hünersdorff Rare Books, London SW 168
hullbooks.com, East Yorkshire 106
Hurst (Jenny), Kent 137
Hutchison (Books) (Larry), Fife................... 271
Internet Bookshop UK Ltd., Glos................. 113
Invicta Bookshop, Berks............................ 56
Island Books, Devon................................ 85
Jackdaw Books, Norfolk 188
Jenny Hurst, Kent................................... 138
Joel Segal Books, Devon 86
Just Books, Cornwall 75
Keegan's Bookshop, Berks.......................... 57
Keel Row Bookshop, Tyne and Wear 235
Kenya Books, East Sussex 100
Kingfisher Book Service, Nottinghamshire 204
Lamb's Tales Books, Devon 87
Last Century Books, Borders....................... 267
Lawrence Books, Nottinghamshire 203
Lost Books, Northants............................... 200
Malvern Bookshop (The), Worcs 255
Mandalay Bookshop, London SW 168
Marcet Books, London SE.......................... 164
Marine & Cannon Books, Cheshire 71
Marine and Cannon Books, Cheshire............. 69
Martin (Books and Pictures), (Brian P.), Surrey. 231
McCrone (Audrey), Isle of Arran.................. 274
Meekins Books (Paul), Warwickshire.............. 237
Military Bookworm, London SE.................... 164
MilitaryHistoryBooks.com, Kent................... 137
Morley Case, Hampshire 125
Mothergoose Bookshop, Isle of Wight 133
Mundy (David), Herts 129
My Back Pages, London SW........................ 168
N1 Books, East Sussex 105
Nelson (Elizabeth), Suffolk 226
Old Aberdeen Bookshop, Grampian 272
Palladour Books, Hampshire 125
Park Gallery & Bookshop (The), Northants 200
Parker Books (Mike), Cambridgeshire 64
Parlour Bookshop (The), Oxfordshire............. 206
Pedlar's Pack Books, Devon 84
Penny Farthing, The, Lothian 277
Peter M Daly, Hampshire........................... 126
Pringle Booksellers (Andrew), Lothian............ 277
Print Matters, London SE........................... 165
Prior (Michael), Lincolnshire 152
Quaritch Ltd., (Bernard), London W.............. 174
Queen Victoria PH, Torfaen 292
R. & A. Books, East Sussex 101
Ramrod Antiques, North Yorkshire................ 195
Read - Gorleston Books, (C.&J.), Norfolk 187
Readers World, West Midlands 238
Richard Thornton Books, London N 158

Rickaro Books, West Yorkshire.................... 246
Rods Books, Devon................................. 88
Saint Swithin's Illustrated & Children's Books,
  London W 174
Saintfield Antiques & Fine Books, Co. Down ... 261
Samovar Books, Co. Dublin........................ 264
Sansovino Books, West Sussex 244
Saracen Books, Derbyshire......................... 83
Savery Books, East Sussex 100
Schull Books, Co. Cork 262
Scrivener's Books & Bookbinding, Derbyshire... 82
Sea Chest Nautical Bookshop (The), Devon 88
Seabreeze Books, Lancashire........................ 144
Sedgeberrow Books, Worcs 256
Shacklock Books (David), Suffolk 226
Shakeshaft (Dr. B.), Cheshire...................... 71
Silver Trees Books, West Midlands................ 238
Smith (Clive), Essex 109
Smith Books (Keith), Herefordshire 128
Spink, London WC 178
Spooner (John E.), Dorset 91
Stalagluft Books, Tyne and Wear.................. 235
Stella Books, Monmouthshire 286
Stroma Books, Borders.............................. 267
Suffolk Rare Books, Suffolk 229
Sutcliffe (Victor), Norfolk 187
T V Coles Books, Cambridgeshire 67
Tarka Books, Devon................................. 84
The Sanctuary Bookshop, Dorset.................. 94
Tiffin (Tony and Gill), Durham.................... 97
Tilston (Stephen E.), London SE................... 165
Tombland Bookshop, Norfolk 190
Trotman (Ken), Cambridgeshire 66
Tyger Press, London N 158
Vanstone - Aviation Books, (Derek), Suffolk 229
Wadard Books, Kent 137
War & Peace Books, Hampshire 122
Warnes (Felicity J.), London Outer................ 180
Wembdon Books, Somerset......................... 216
Westwood Books Ltd, Cumbria..................... 80
Wheen O'Books, Borders............................ 267
Wiend Books, Lancashire 143
Wise (Derek), East Sussex.......................... 104
Wizard Books, Cambridgeshire..................... 67
Woolcott Books, Dorset............................. 92
World War Books, Kent 141
Worlds End Bookshop, London SW 169
Xanadu Books, Durham 98
Yeoman Books, Lothian............................. 277
Yesterday's News, Conwy........................... 283

- HISTORY

Aardvark Books, Wiltshire.......................... 254
Albion Books, West Midlands...................... 238
Americanabooksuk, Cumbria........................ 76
Anchor Books, Lincolnshire 149
Annie's Books, S Yorks 221
Antique Prints of the World, London N.......... 156
Antiques on High, Oxfordshire..................... 207
Any Old Books, Hampshire 121
Apocalypse, Surrey 232
Armchair Books, Lothian 275
Armitage (Booksearch), (Kate), Devon 84
Askew Books (Vernon), Wiltshire.................. 251
Austen (Phillip), Lincolnshire 151

Avedikian Rare Books, Somerset 216
Baldwin (M. & M.), Worcs 255
Barbican Bookshop, North Yorkshire............. 196
Barn Books, Buckinghamshire...................... 61
Barnes (Peter), Wiltshire............................ 253
Bates & Hindmarch, West Yorkshire.............. 248
Beaumont Travel Books, London SE 163
Black Five Books, Shropshire 214
Blackpool Book Warehouse, Lancashire......... 142
Boer War Books, North Yorkshire 197
Book For All Reasons (A.), Suffolk 228
Books Afloat, Dorset................................. 96
Books on Spain, London Outer 182
books2books, Devon 88
Bookshop on the Heath, The, London SE 163
Bookworm (The), Lothian 276
Bosorne Books, Cornwall 75
Burroughs (Andrew), Lincolnshire 152
Caliver Books, Essex 109
Carnforth Bookshop (The), Lancashire 142
Cassidy (Bookseller) (P.), Lincolnshire 151
Castle Bookshop, Essex............................. 108
Cavern Books, Cheshire 70
Chaucer Bookshop, Kent............................ 136
Chelifer Books, Cumbria 80
Cheshire Book Centre, Cheshire.................... 69
Chevin Books, West Yorkshire..................... 249
Churchgate Books, Suffolk.......................... 226
Cobbles Books, Somerset............................ 217
Corfe Books, Surrey................................. 230
Cornucopia Books, Lincolnshire 151
Cotswold Internet Books, Glos..................... 113
Cox (Geoff), Devon 90
Dally (Andrew), Powys 289
Dandy Lion Editions, Surrey 233
Darkwood Books, Co. Cork 263
Dartmoor Bookshop (The), Devon 84
David Warnes Books, Herefordshire 128
Debbage (John), Norfolk............................ 189
Deeside Books, Grampian........................... 272
Delph Books, Greater Manchester................. 120
Dolphin Books, Suffolk.............................. 225
Donovan Military Books (Tom), East Sussex.... 99
Dormouse Bookshop (The), Norfolk 189
Driffield Bookshop (The), East Yorkshire 106
Falconwood Transport & Military Bookshop,
    London Outer 183
Farnborough Gallery, Hampshire................... 122
Fifteenth Century Bookshop (The), East Sussex. 104
firstpagebooks, Norfolk............................. 189
Furneaux Books (Lee), Devon...................... 89
G. C. Books Ltd., Dumfries & Galloway......... 270
Gallimaufry Books, Herts 131
Garfi Books, Powys 291
George St. Books, Derbyshire 83
Grant, Lothian 276
Guildmaster Books, Cheshire 70
Handsworth Books, Essex........................... 112
Harlequin Books, Bristol 59
Harris (George J.), Co. Derry 260
Hay Cinema Bookshop Ltd., Powys............... 288
Helion & Company, West Midlands 239
Heppa (Christopher), Essex......................... 108
Hummingbird Books, Herefordshire............... 128
Island Books, Devon................................. 85

Jackson (M.W.), Wiltshire........................... 254
Joel Segal Books, Devon 86
Keegan's Bookshop, Berks........................... 57
Keel Row Bookshop, Tyne and Wear 235
Kellow Books, Oxfordshire 206
Kingfisher Book Service, Nottinghamshire 204
Knowles - Antiquary (Roger J.), Staffordshire... 223
Lost Books, Northants............................... 200
Mandalay Bookshop, London SW 168
Marble Hill Books, Outer London................. 182
Marcet Books, London SE........................... 164
Marine & Cannon Books, Cheshire 71
Marine and Cannon Books, Cheshire............. 69
McCrone (Audrey), Isle of Arran 274
Meekins Books (Paul), Warwickshire.............. 237
Mercat Books, Highland 274
Military Bookworm, London SE.................... 164
Military Parade Bookshop, Wiltshire.............. 252
MilitaryHistoryBooks.com, Kent................... 137
Morten (Booksellers) (E.J.), G Manchester...... 119
My Back Pages, London SW........................ 168
N1 Books, East Sussex 105
Not Just Books, Dorset.............................. 94
O'Brien Books & Photo Gallery, Co. Limerick.. 266
O'Flynn Books, North Yorkshire................... 197
Old Station Pottery & Bookshop (The), Norfolk 191
Orssich (Paul), London SW........................ 169
Paperbacks Plus, Bristol 59
Parrott Books, Oxfordshire 209
Peter M Daly, Hampshire........................... 126
Pordes Books Ltd., (Henry), London WC........ 177
Priestpopple Books, Northumberland 201
Prior (Michael), Lincolnshire 152
Queen Victoria PH, Torfaen 292
Quinto of Charing Cross Road, London WC ... 178
R. & A. Books, East Sussex 101
Richard Thornton Books, London N 158
Richmond Books, North Yorkshire 194
Robert Humm & Co, Lincolnshire 152
Rochdale Book Company, G Manchester........ 120
Rods Books, Devon.................................. 88
Roland Books, Kent................................. 138
Sax Books, Suffolk 228
Schull Books, Co. Cork 262
Scorpio Books, Suffolk 225
Solaris Books, East Yorkshire 106
Sutcliffe (Victor), Norfolk 187
T V Coles Books, Cambridgeshire 67
Taylor & Son (Peter), Herts........................ 132
Thin Read Line, Merseyside 184
Tiffin (Tony and Gill), Durham 97
Tilston (Stephen E.), London SE................... 165
Tombland Bookshop, Norfolk 190
Trotman (Ken), Cambridgeshire 66
Turton (John), Durham 98
Tyger Press, London N 158
Ventnor Rare Books, Isle of Wight 134
Village Books, Norfolk 186
Vokes Books Ltd., North Yorkshire............... 194
Wadard Books, Kent 137
War & Peace Books, Hampshire................... 122
Wheen O'Books, Borders............................ 267
Wizard Books, Cambridgeshire..................... 67
Words Etcetera Bookshop, Dorset................. 93
World War II Books, Surrey 234

Worlds End Bookshop, London SW 169
Yeoman Books, Lothian 277
Yesterday's News, Conwy 283
Zardoz Books, Wiltshire 254

- MODELLING

Aardvark Books, Wiltshire 254
Barn Books, Buckinghamshire 61
Bookworm (The), Lothian 276
Burroughs (Andrew), Lincolnshire 152
Chelifer Books, Cumbria 80
Falconwood Transport & Military Bookshop,
    London Outer 183
Gallimaufry Books, Herts 131
Island Books, Devon 85
Joel Segal Books, Devon 86
Marine & Cannon Books, Cheshire 71
Marine and Cannon Books, Cheshire 69
Meekins Books (Paul), Warwickshire 237
MilitaryHistoryBooks.com, Kent 137
Rods Books, Devon 88
Stalagluft Books, Tyne and Wear 235
Trotman (Ken), Cambridgeshire 66
World War Books, Kent 141

- UNIFORMS

Aardvark Books, Wiltshire 254
Bookworm (The), Lothian 276
Burroughs (Andrew), Lincolnshire 152
Caliver Books, Essex 109
Chelifer Books, Cumbria 80
Debbage (John), Norfolk 189
Fifteenth Century Bookshop (The), East Sussex. 104
Gallimaufry Books, Herts 131
Island Books, Devon 85
Joel Segal Books, Devon 86
Lost Books, Northants 200
Marine & Cannon Books, Cheshire 71
Marine and Cannon Books, Cheshire 69
Meekins Books (Paul), Warwickshire 237
MilitaryHistoryBooks.com, Kent 137
N1 Books, East Sussex 105
Print Matters, London SE 165
R. & A. Books, East Sussex 101
Rods Books, Devon 88
Schull Books, Co. Cork 262
Sea Chest Nautical Bookshop (The), Devon 88
Stalagluft Books, Tyne and Wear 235
Thin Read Line, Merseyside 184
Trotman (Ken), Cambridgeshire 66

MIND, BODY & SPIRIT

Abbey Books, Cornwall 73
Alister & Garon Books, Cambridgeshire 63
Annie's Books, S Yorks 221
Atlantis Bookshop, London WC 176
Backfold Books, Herefordshire 127
Blackpool Book Warehouse, Lancashire 142
Chthonios Books, East Sussex 102
Cofion Books, Pembrokeshire 286
Cornucopia Books, Lincolnshire 151
Dales & Lakes Book Centre, Cumbria 79
Dandy Lion Editions, Surrey 233
Discovery Bookshop, Carmarthenshire 281
DPE Books, Devon 87

Esoteric Dreams Bookshop, Cumbria 77
Fifteenth Century Bookshop (The), East Sussex. 104
Furneaux Books (Lee), Devon 89
J & J Burgess Booksellers, Cambridgeshire 64
Joel Segal Books, Devon 86
Just Books, Cornwall 75
Oasis Booksearch, Cambridgeshire 67
Occultique, Northants 199
Old Celtic Bookshop (The), Devon 87
Orchid Book Distributors, Co. Clare 262
Reading Lasses, Dumfries & Galloway 270
Richmond Books, North Yorkshire 194
Roosterbooks, Northants 199
Roundstone Books, Lancashire 143
Sedgeberrow Books, Worcs 256
SETI Books, West Midlands 239
Star Lord Books, Greater Manchester 119
Tarka Books, Devon 84
Till's Bookshop, Lothian 277
Treasure Trove Books, Leics 146
Trinity Rare Books, Co. Leitrim 266
Watkins Books Ltd., London WC 179

MINERALOGY

Baldwin's Scientific Books, Essex 111
Bookworms Paradise Ltd., West Sussex 242
Clevedon Books, Somerset 217
Cox (Geoff), Devon 90
Crabtree (Mrs. C.), Greater Manchester 120
Earth Science Books, Wiltshire 252
Henly (John), West Sussex 244
Joel Segal Books, Devon 86
Knowles - Antiquary (Roger J.), Staffordshire... 223
Nibris Books, London SW 169
Parkinsons Books, Merseyside 185
Phelps (Michael), West Sussex 242
R. & A. Books, East Sussex 101
Westons, Herts 132
Whitchurch Books Ltd., Cardiff 281

MINIATURE BOOKS

Apocalypse, Surrey 232
Bernstein (Nicholas), London W 171
Demetzy Books, Oxfordshire 206
G. C. Books Ltd., Dumfries & Galloway 270
Garbett Antiquarian Books (Michael), Glos 115
Hennessey Bookseller (Ray), East Sussex 100
Moorhead Books, West Yorkshire 245
R. & A. Books, East Sussex 101
RGS Books, Surrey 234
Roscrea Bookshop & Newsagents,
    Co. Tipperary 266
Scrivener's Books & Bookbinding, Derbyshire... 82
Temperley (David), West Midlands 238
Yates Antiquarian Books (Tony), Leics 146

MINING

Anthony Vickers Books, North Yorkshire 195
Book House (The), Cumbria 76
Bott, (Bookdealers) Ltd., (Martin),
    Greater Manchester 118
Browning Books, Torfaen 292
Browsers Bookshop, Cornwall 72
Collectables (W.H.), Suffolk 229
Cox (Geoff), Devon 90

Duck (William), Hampshire.......................... 124
Empire Books, North Yorkshire 197
G. C. Books Ltd., Dumfries & Galloway......... 270
Joel Segal Books, Devon 86
Just Books, Cornwall 75
Knowles - Antiquary (Roger J.), Staffordshire... 223
Past & Present Books, Glos......................... 114
Phelps (Michael), West Sussex...................... 242
Randall (Tom), Somerset............................. 218
Turton (John), Durham 98
Vinovium Books, Durham 97
Westons, Herts.. 132
Whitchurch Books Ltd., Cardiff.................... 281

MINORITY STUDIES
Al Saqi Books, London W........................... 171
Left on The Shelf, Cumbria......................... 78
Reading Lasses, Dumfries & Galloway 270
Samovar Books, Co. Dublin......................... 264

MISSIONARIES & MISSIONS
Beckham Books Ltd., Suffolk 229
Chapter Two, London SE............................ 163
Dolphin Books, Suffolk.............................. 225
G. C. Books Ltd., Dumfries & Galloway......... 270
Kenya Books, East Sussex 100
Oasis Booksearch, Cambridgeshire................ 67
Pendleburys Bookshop, London N 158
St Philip's Books, Oxfordshire..................... 208
Samovar Books, Co. Dublin......................... 264

MISSOURIANA
Americanabooksuk, Cumbria........................ 76

MODEL ENGINEERING
Bott, (Bookdealers) Ltd., (Martin),
   Greater Manchester 118
Cornucopia Books, Lincolnshire 151
Cover to Cover, Merseyside.......................... 185
Dales and Lakes Book Centre, Cumbria.......... 79
Robert Humm & Co, Lincolnshire 152
Sea Chest Nautical Bookshop (The), Devon 88
Stroh (M.A.), London E 154
Tony Hutchinson, Surrey............................. 233
Yesteryear Railwayana, Kent........................ 139

MODEL RAILWAYS
Bianco Library, West Sussex........................ 241
Bookworms Paradise Ltd., West Sussex 242
Bott, (Bookdealers) Ltd., (Martin), Greater
   Manchester 118
Cofion Books, Pembrokeshire 286
Cornucopia Books, Lincolnshire 151
Cover to Cover, Merseyside.......................... 185
Cox (Geoff), Devon 90
Dales and Lakes Book Centre, Cumbria.......... 79
Deeside Books, Grampian............................ 272
Falconwood Transport & Military Bookshop,
   London Outer 183
Fifteenth Century Bookshop (The), East Sussex. 104
Joel Segal Books, Devon 86
Milestone Books, Devon 89
R. & A. Books, East Sussex 101
Roadmaster Books, Kent............................. 136
Robert Humm & Co, Lincolnshire 152

Tony Hutchinson, Surrey............................. 233
Yesteryear Railwayana, Kent........................ 139

MODEL THEATRE
Cover to Cover, Merseyside.......................... 185
R. & A. Books, East Sussex 101

MODERN
First Edition, The, Essex 109
Joel Segal Books, Devon 86
Oak Tree Press, Oxfordshire 207
Surprise Books, Glos.................................. 113
Wheen O'Books, Borders............................. 267

MODERN ART
Ballantyne–Way (Roger), Suffolk 228
Booth (Booksearch Service), (Geoff), Cheshire... 68
Bruce Holdsworth Books, East Sussex 105
Cornucopia Books, Lincolnshire 151
Cover to Cover, Merseyside.......................... 185
Evans Books (Paul), West Sussex 243
Fifteenth Century Bookshop (The), East Sussex. 104
Joel Segal Books, Devon 86
Just Books, Cornwall 75
Lucius Books, North Yorkshire..................... 197
Myra Dean Illustated Books, Powys 287
R. & A. Books, East Sussex 101
Woburn Books, London N 159
Worlds End Bookshop, London SW 169

MODERN FIRST EDITIONS
Addyman Annexe (The), Powys..................... 287
Addyman Books, Powys.............................. 287
ahbooks, Merseyside 184
Allinson (Frank & Stella), Warwickshire 236
Amwell Book Company, London EC.............. 155
Anglo-American Rare Books, Surrey............... 232
Ann & Mike Conry, Worcs 257
Annie's Books, S Yorks 221
Antique Map and Bookshop (The), Dorset 94
Any Old Books, Hampshire 121
Apocalypse, Surrey 232
Archer (Steve), London Outer 180
Armitage (Booksearch), (Kate), Devon 84
Askew Books (Vernon), Wiltshire.................. 251
Autolycus, Shropshire................................ 212
Avonworld Books, Somerset........................ 216
babelog.books, Herefordshire....................... 127
Bass (Ben), Wiltshire................................ 251
BC Books, Cheshire 69
Bertram Rota Ltd., London WC 176
Bibliopola, London NW.............................. 160
Biblipola, London NW............................... 160
Blackwell's Rare Books, Oxfordshire............. 208
Book Business (The), London W 171
Bookcase, Cumbria................................... 76
Books, Oxfordshire................................... 205
Books & Things, London W......................... 171
Books Only, Suffolk 226
BOOKS4U, Flintshire................................ 284
Bookshop on the Heath, The, London SE 163
Bookstand, Dorset.................................... 94
Booth (Booksearch Service), (Geoff), Cheshire... 68
Boris Books, Somerset 216
Bow Windows Book Shop, East Sussex 103

Bowie Books & Collectables, East Yorkshire 107
Broadhurst of Southport Ltd., Merseyside 185
Caledonia Books, Strathclyde........................ 278
Cameron House Books, Isle of Wight.............. 133
Camilla's Bookshop, East Sussex 101
Castle Bookshop, Essex.............................. 108
Childrens Bookshop, West Yorkshire 247
Chris Adam Smith Modern First Editions,
    West Sussex 243
Chris Phillips, Wiltshire.............................. 252
Church Street Books, Norfolk...................... 186
Clifford Milne Books, Grampian.................... 272
Corfe Books, Surrey.................................. 230
Cornucopia Books, Lincolnshire 151
Criterion Books, London Outer 181
Dales & Lakes Book Centre, Cumbria............ 79
Dave Jelfs, Devon 85
Dolphin Books, Suffolk.............................. 225
Dormouse Bookshop (The), Norfolk 189
Driffield Bookshop (The), East Yorkshire 106
Elaine Lonsdale Books, West Yorkshire 247
Ellis, Bookseller (Peter), London WC 177
Ellwood Editions, Wiltshire 253
Enscot Books, London SE 164
Fifteenth Century Bookshop (The), East Sussex. 104
Finch Rare Books Ltd. (Simon), London W..... 172
First State Books, London W 172
firstpagebooks, Norfolk.............................. 189
Firsts in Print, Somerset 219
Foster Bookshop (Paul), London SW 167
Fosters Bookshop, London W 172
G&S Books, Kent 138
Gander, (Jacques), Glos 114
Gildas Books, Cheshire 68
Good for Books, Lincolnshire 149
Hava Books, London SE............................ 164
Heppa (Christopher), Essex 108
Hight (Norman F.), Glamorgan..................... 285
Hollett and Son (R.F.G.), Cumbria 79
House of Figgis Ltd (The), Co. Galway 265
Hylton Booksearch, Merseyside 184
Ian McKelvie Bookseller, London N.............. 157
Idle Genius Books, London N 157
Innes Books, Shropshire............................ 212
Intech Books, Northumberland 201
Island Books, Devon................................ 85
Jackson (M.W.), Wiltshire.......................... 254
Joel Segal Books, Devon 86
Jonkers Rare Books, Oxfordshire 207
K Books, Cheshire................................... 70
Katharine House Gallery, Wiltshire 252
Kendall–Carpenter (Tim), Greater Manchester .. 119
Kennedy & Farley, East Sussex 104
Kestrel Books, Powys............................... 288
Kevin S. Ogilvie Modern First Editions,
    Grampian 272
L.M.S. Books, Herts 131
Lewis (J.T. & P.), Cornwall........................ 73
Lewis First Editions, Kent 136
Little Stour Books, Kent 136
Lucius Books, North Yorkshire 197
Maggs Brothers Limited, London W.............. 173
Mainly Fiction, Cheshire 68
Mair Wilkes Books, Fife 271
Mannwaring (M.G.), Bristol 59

McCrone (Audrey), Isle of Arran.................. 274
Ming Books, Dumfries & Galloway............... 270
Modern First Editions, West Yorkshire........... 247
Modern First Editions, London Outer 181
Moore (Sue), Cornwall 73
Murphy (C.J.), Norfolk............................. 189
N V Books, Warwickshire........................... 236
Needham Books, (Russell), Somerset.............. 219
Neil's Books, London NW.......................... 161
Norton Books, North Yorkshire.................... 192
Oak Tree Press, Oxfordshire 207
O'Flynn Books, North Yorkshire 197
Orlando Booksellers, Lincolnshire 150
Parker Books (Mike), Cambridgeshire 64
Parrott (Jeremy), London E......................... 154
Peter Lyons Books, Glos 113
Peter White, Hampshire 121
Poetry Bookshop (The), Powys..................... 289
Pordes Books Ltd., (Henry), London WC........ 177
Portus Books, Hampshire 122
Price (R.W.), Nottinghamshire 203
Pringle Booksellers (Andrew), Lothian............ 277
R. & A. Books, East Sussex 101
Reading Lasses, Dumfries & Galloway 270
Reaveley Books, Devon 87
Rees & O'Neill Rare Books, London WC........ 178
Richard Thornton Books, London N 158
Rising Tide Books, Fife............................. 270
Robert (Leslie), London W 174
Robert Temple, London N.......................... 158
Roberts Fine Books (Julian), Lincolnshire........ 151
Rye Old Books, East Sussex 104
Seabreeze Books, Lancashire....................... 144
Shakeshaft (Dr. B.), Cheshire...................... 71
Shapero Rare Books (Bernard J.), London W... 175
Sillan Books, Co. Cavan............................ 262
Silver Trees Books, West Midlands................ 238
Simply Read Books, East Sussex.................. 100
Simpson (Dave), Central 268
Skelton (Tony), Kent................................ 140
Solaris Books, East Yorkshire 106
Strathtay Antiquarian - Secondhand Books,
    Tayside 280
Stroma Books, Borders 267
Surprise Books, Glos................................ 113
Talisman Books, Cheshire........................... 70
Thistle Books, Strathclyde.......................... 278
Thornber (Peter M.), North Yorkshire............. 195
Till's Bookshop, Lothian 277
Trevorrow (Edwin), Herts 129
Trigon Books, Dorset 95
Trinity Rare Books, Co. Leitrim 266
Walden Books, London NW 161
Warrender (Andrew), West Yorkshire.............. 249
Webb Books (John), S Yorks....................... 221
Wiend Books, Lancashire 143
Williams (Bookdealer), (Richard), N Lincs....... 153
Willmott Bookseller (Nicholas), Cardiff.......... 281
Woburn Books, London N 159
Words Etcetera Bookshop, Dorset................. 93
Wright Trace Books, West Midlands.............. 239
Wychwood Books, Glos............................. 116
York Modern Books, North Yorkshire............ 196

MONOGRAPHS

Apocalypse, Surrey 232
Barlow (Vincent G.), Hampshire 125
Campbell Art Books (Marcus), London SE 163
Coch-y-Bonddu Books, Powys 290
Heneage Art Books (Thomas), London SW 168
Parkinsons Books, Merseyside...................... 185
Trinders' Fine Tools, Suffolk 226
Walden Books, London NW 161

MOTORBIKES / MOTORCYCLES

Books, Kent 137
Bookworms Paradise Ltd., West Sussex 242
Chaters Motoring Booksellers, London Outer ... 181
Cheshire Book Centre, Cheshire.................... 69
Collectors Carbooks, Northants.................... 199
Cornucopia Books, Lincolnshire 151
Cox (Geoff), Devon 90
Dales & Lakes Book Centre, Cumbria............ 79
Elmo Books, West Sussex 243
Falconwood Transport & Military Bookshop,
    London Outer 183
Holdenhurst Books, Dorset 91
Joel Segal Books, Devon 86
Kenneth Ball, East Sussex........................... 100
Knowles (John), Norfolk 187
Main–Smith & Co. Ltd. (Bruce), Leics............ 146
Merlin Books, West Sussex 242
Peake (Robin), Lincolnshire......................... 152
Pooks Motor Books, Leics........................... 146
R. & A. Books, East Sussex 101
Roadmaster Books, Kent............................. 136
Simon Lewis Transport Books, Glos 114
Stroh (M.A.), London E 154
Uncle Phil's Books, West Midlands 239
Vintage Motorshop, West Yorkshire 245
Yeoman Books, Lothian 277

MOTORING

Abrahams (Mike), Staffordshire..................... 223
Allinson (Frank & Stella), Warwickshire 236
Annie's Books, S Yorks 221
Baldwin (M. & M.), Worcs 255
Books, Kent 137
Books & Collectables Ltd., Cambridgeshire...... 63
Books Bought & Sold, Surrey 231
books2books, Devon.................................. 88
Brewin Books Ltd., Warwickshire 237
Browse Books, Lancashire 143
Cavern Books, Cheshire 70
Chandos Books, Devon.............................. 85
Chaters Motoring Booksellers, London Outer ... 181
Cheshire Book Centre, Cheshire.................... 69
Chevin Books, West Yorkshire...................... 249
Chris Porter Books, Norfolk........................ 186
Cobweb Books, North Yorkshire 194
Cofion Books, Pembrokeshire 286
Collectors Carbooks, Northants 199
Corfe Books, Surrey.................................. 231
Cornucopia Books, Lincolnshire 151
Cowley, Auto–in–Print (John), Essex............. 108
Cox (Geoff), Devon 90
Discovery Bookshop, Carmarthenshire............ 281
Eastcote Bookshop (The), London Outer........ 180
Emjay Books, Surrey................................. 231

Falconwood Transport & Military Bookshop,
    London Outer 183
Fifteenth Century Bookshop (The),
    East Sussex 104
Ford Books (David), Herts 130
Fylde Books, Lancashire 144
Hames (Peter), Devon................................ 84
Harlequin Books, Bristol 59
Holdenhurst Books, Dorset 91
Janus Books, West Midlands 239
Joel Segal Books, Devon 86
Kenneth Ball, East Sussex........................... 100
Kerr (Norman), Cumbria 77
Knowles (John), Norfolk 187
McGlynn (John), Lancashire 142
Morris Secondhand & Antiquarian Books
    (Chris), Oxfordshire 208
Peake (Robin), Lincolnshire......................... 152
Pooks Motor Books, Leics........................... 146
R. & A. Books, East Sussex 101
Richard Thornton Books, London N 158
Roadmaster Books, Kent............................. 136
Roberts (Booksellers), (Ray), Staffordshire 224
Rochdale Book Company, Greater Manchester . 120
Roland Books, Kent 138
St Mary's Books & Prints, Lincolnshire 152
St Paul's Street Bookshop, Lincolnshire 152
Sax Books, Suffolk 228
Scrivener's Books & Bookbinding, Derbyshire... 82
Simon Lewis Transport Books, Glos 114
Smith Maritime Aviation Books (Frank),
    Tyne and Wear 235
Stella Books, Monmouthshire 286
Stour Bookshop, Dorset.............................. 95
Stroh (M.A.), London E 154
Vintage Motorshop, West Yorkshire 245
Volumes of Motoring, Glos.......................... 113
Yeoman Books, Lothian 277

MOUNTAIN MEN

Americanabooksuk, Cumbria........................ 76
Gildas Books, Cheshire 68
Glacier Books, Tayside 280
Jarvis Books, Derbyshire 83
Mercat Books, Highland 274
Pinnacle Books, Lothian............................. 276
Roz Hulse, Conwy 284

MOUNTAINS

Allinson (Frank & Stella), Warwickshire 236
Bonham (J. & S.L.), London W 171
Cavendish Rare Books, London N 156
Chalmers Hallam (E.), Hampshire 125
Craobh Rua Books, Co. Armagh................... 260
Creaking Shelves, Highland 274
Dales & Lakes Book Centre, Cumbria............ 79
David Warnes Books, Herefordshire 128
Deeside Books, Grampian............................ 272
Earth Science Books, Wiltshire 252
Ford Books (David), Herts 130
Gildas Books, Cheshire 68
Glacier Books, Tayside 280
Hunter and Krageloh, Derbyshire 83
Jackdaw Books, Norfolk 188
Jarvis Books, Derbyshire 83

Joel Segal Books, Devon 86
Marcet Books, London SE........................... 164
McCrone (Audrey), Isle of Arran 274
Mercat Books, Highland 274
O'Reilly - Mountain Books (John), Derbyshire.. 83
Page (David), Lothian 276
Pinnacle Books, Lothian............................ 276
R. & A. Books, East Sussex 101
Riddell (Peter), East Yorkshire 106

MOVEABLE & 3D
Bookmark (Children's Books), Wiltshire.......... 253
Fifteenth Century Bookshop (The), East Sussex. 104
Temperley (David), West Midlands................ 238

MOVIE & TELEVISION SCRIPTS
Apocalypse, Surrey 232
Byre Books, Dumfries & Galloway................ 270
Greenroom Books, West Yorkshire 247
Joel Segal Books, Devon 86
McGee (Terence J.), London Outer 180

MULTI-MEDIA
Campbell Art Books (Marcus), London SE...... 163
McGee (Terence J.), London Outer 180

MUSIC
- GENERAL
AA1 Books, Dumfries & Galloway................ 269
Abacus Gallery, Staffordshire...................... 224
Alba Secondhand Music, Strathclyde............. 278
Alister & Garon Books, Cambridgeshire.......... 63
Annie's Books, S Yorks 221
Anthony Spranger, Wiltshire....................... 252
Antiquary Ltd., (Bar Bookstore), N Yorks....... 194
Antiques on High, Oxfordshire..................... 207
Apocalypse, Surrey 232
Armstrong's Books & Collectables, Leics........ 145
Aurora Books Ltd, Lothian.......................... 275
Autumn Leaves, Lincolnshire....................... 150
Axe Rare & Out of Print Books (Richard),
  North Yorkshire 193
Bardsley's Books, Suffolk........................... 225
Barnes - Books (Lyndon), Shropshire 212
Baron (H.), London NW............................ 160
Bath Old Books, Somerset 215
Baxter - Books (Eddie), Somerset 220
Beware of the Leopard, Bristol..................... 58
Biff Books and Records, S Yorks.................. 221
Blackwell's Music Shop, Oxfordshire.............. 208
Bookcase, Cumbria.................................. 76
Books, Denbighshire 284
Books & Collectables Ltd., Cambridgeshire...... 63
books2books, Devon 88
Bookshop (The), Norfolk 191
Bookshop on the Heath, The, London SE 163
Bookworms, Norfolk................................ 186
Booth (Booksearch Service), (Geoff), Cheshire.. 68
Bosorne Books, Cornwall 75
Browne (Christopher I.), West Yorkshire........ 246
Byre Books, Dumfries & Galloway................ 270
Carnforth Bookshop (The), Lancashire 142
Carningli Centre, Pembrokeshire.................. 286
Chaucer Bookshop, Kent........................... 136
Cheshire Book Centre, Cheshire................... 69

Clapham (M. & B.), Hampshire.................... 124
Clements (R.W.), London Outer 181
Cofion Books, Pembrokeshire 286
Colin Hancock, Ceredigion 282
Dales & Lakes Book Centre, Cumbria........... 79
Darkwood Books, Co. Cork........................ 263
Davids Ltd., (Roy), Oxfordshire 208
Decorum Books, London N 156
Discovery Bookshop, Carmarthenshire............ 281
Dolphin Books, Suffolk............................. 225
Dooley (Rosemary), Cumbria 77
East Riding Books, East Yorkshire................ 107
Edwards, Fiona, Nottinghamshire 203
Elaine Lonsdale Books, West Yorkshire.......... 247
Elgar (Raymond), East Sussex..................... 99
Esoteric Dreams Bookshop, Cumbria 77
Evans (Mark), Lincolnshire 151
Fifteenth Century Bookshop (The), East Sussex. 104
Fitzsimons (Anne), Cumbria........................ 76
Ford Books (David), Herts 130
Forest Books of Manchester, Cheshire............ 70
Francis, S. L., Sussex............................... 103
Freeman's Corner Shop, Norfolk 189
George St. Books, Derbyshire 83
Gibbs Books, (Jonathan), Worcs................... 256
Good for Books, Lincolnshire 149
Goodden (Peter), Somerset......................... 215
Hancock & Monks Music Emporium, Powys ... 288
Handsworth Books, Essex........................... 112
Hay Cinema Bookshop Ltd., Powys................ 288
HCB Wholesale, Powys............................. 288
Hurst (Jenny), Kent 137
Internet Bookshop UK Ltd., Glos................. 113
Jade Mountain Bookshop, Hampshire 125
Jenny Hurst, Kent.................................. 138
Joel Segal Books, Devon 86
Judd Books, London WC 177
Just Books, Cornwall 75
Kent T. G., Surrey 230
Kim's Bookshop, West Sussex...................... 242
Kim's Bookshop, West Sussex...................... 241
M. and A.C. Thompson, Norfolk................... 191
Malvern Bookshop (The), Worcs................... 255
Marcet Books, London SE.......................... 164
Martin Music Books (Philip), North Yorkshire . 197
McGee (Terence J.), London Outer 180
Mogul Diamonds, West Midlands................. 240
Music By The Score, Cornwall..................... 72
Newgate Books and Translations,
  Northumberland 201
Old Book Company, (The), West Yorkshire 248
Oopalba Books, Cheshire........................... 71
Paramor (C.D.), Suffolk 228
Parrott Books, Oxfordshire 209
Pastmasters, Derbyshire............................ 83
Portobello Books, London W 174
Price (R.W.), Nottinghamshire 203
Priestpopple Books, Northumberland 201
Quinto of Charing Cross Road, London WC ... 178
Roland Books, Kent 138
St Mary's Books & Prints, Lincolnshire 152
Sax Books, Suffolk 228
Scarthin Books, Derbyshire 82
Sheet Music Warehouse (The), Devon 88
Sherlaw-Johnson (Austin), Oxfordshire 209

Slightly Foxed on Gloucester Road, London SW167
Staniland (Booksellers), Lincolnshire 152
Stern Antiquarian Bookseller (Jeffrey),
   North Yorkshire 198
Stevens (Joan), Cambridgeshire..................... 65
Tarka Books, Devon 84
The Sanctuary Bookshop, Dorset 94
Till's Bookshop, Lothian 277
Travis & Emery Music Bookshop, London WC 178
Uncle Phil's Books, West Midlands 239
Venables (Morris & Juliet), Bristol................. 59
Wiend Books, Lancashire 143
Willmott Bookseller (Nicholas), Cardiff.......... 281
Wood (Peter), Cambridgeshire...................... 65
Woodlands Books, West Yorkshire................ 249
Worlds End Bookshop, London SW 169

- **CHART HISTORIES & RESEARCH**
Decorum Books, London N 156
McGee (Terence J.), London Outer 180
Morris Secondhand & Antiquarian Books
   (Chris), Oxfordshire 208
Sheet Music Warehouse (The), Devon 88
Travis & Emery Music Bookshop, London WC 178

- **CLASSICAL**
Alba Secondhand Music, Strathclyde............. 278
Alexander's Books, Warwickshire.................. 237
Annie's Books, S Yorks 221
Barnes - Books (Lyndon), Shropshire 212
Bermondsey Basement Bookstore, London SE .. 163
Blackwell's Music Shop, Oxfordshire.............. 208
Bookworms Paradise Ltd., West Sussex 242
Boris Books, Somerset 216
Browne (Christopher I.), West Yorkshire......... 246
Chesters (G. & J.), Staffordshire 224
Decorum Books, London N 156
Delectus Books, London WC....................... 176
Dolphin Books, Suffolk............................. 225
Dooley (Rosemary), Cumbria 77
East Riding Books, East Yorkshire................ 107
Ely Books, Cambridgeshire 65
Fifteenth Century Bookshop (The), East Sussex. 104
Gibbs Books, (Jonathan), Worcs................... 256
Goodden (Peter), Somerset.......................... 215
Grahame Thornton, Bookseller, Dorset.......... 93
Hancock & Monks Music Emporium, Powys ... 288
Handsworth Books, Essex............................ 112
Jackdaw Books, Norfolk 188
Joel Segal Books, Devon 86
Kennedy & Farley, East Sussex 104
Keogh's Books, Glos................................. 115
Kingsmere Books, Bedfordshire 53
Marcan, Bookseller (Peter), London SE........... 164
Martin Music Books (Philip), North Yorkshire . 197
McGee (Terence J.), London Outer 180
Mogul Diamonds, West Midlands 240
Music By The Score, Cornwall 72
Musicalania, Norfolk................................ 188
Newgate Books and Translations,
   Northumberland 201
Pordes Books Ltd., (Henry), London WC........ 177
Reads, Dorset 95
Scrivener's Books & Bookbinding, Derbyshire... 82
Sheet Music Warehouse (The), Devon 88

Sherlaw-Johnson (Austin), Oxfordshire 209
Staniland (Booksellers), Lincolnshire 152
Travis & Emery Music Bookshop, London WC 178
Uncle Phil's Books, West Midlands 239
Venables (Morris & Juliet), Bristol................. 59
Willmott Bookseller (Nicholas), Cardiff.......... 281

- **COMPOSERS**
Alba Secondhand Music, Strathclyde............. 278
Anthony Spranger, Wiltshire....................... 252
Barnes - Books (Lyndon), Shropshire 212
Blackwell's Music Shop, Oxfordshire.............. 208
Bookworms Paradise Ltd., West Sussex 242
Boris Books, Somerset 216
Browne (Christopher I.), West Yorkshire......... 246
Dales & Lakes Book Centre, Cumbria............ 79
Decorum Books, London N 156
Dolphin Books, Suffolk............................. 225
Dooley (Rosemary), Cumbria 77
East Riding Books, East Yorkshire................ 107
Fifteenth Century Bookshop (The), East Sussex. 104
Glenbower Books, Co. Dublin 264
Goodden (Peter), Somerset.......................... 215
Hancock & Monks Music Emporium, Powys ... 288
Handsworth Books, Essex............................ 112
Joel Segal Books, Devon 86
Kingsmere Books, Bedfordshire 53
Marcet Books, London SE........................... 164
Martin Music Books (Philip), North Yorkshire . 197
McGee (Terence J.), London Outer 180
Mogul Diamonds, West Midlands 240
Music By The Score, Cornwall 72
Musicalania, Norfolk................................ 188
Price (John), London N 158
R. & A. Books, East Sussex 101
Sheet Music Warehouse (The), Devon 88
Sherlaw-Johnson (Austin), Oxfordshire 209
Staniland (Booksellers), Lincolnshire 152
Travis & Emery Music Bookshop, London WC 178
Venables (Morris & Juliet), Bristol................. 59
Whistler's Books, London SW 169
Willmott Bookseller (Nicholas), Cardiff.......... 281

- **COUNTRY & WESTERN**
A. & R. Booksearch, Cornwall..................... 73
Barnes - Books (Lyndon), Shropshire 212
Decorum Books, London N 156
Fifteenth Century Bookshop (The), East Sussex. 104
Joel Segal Books, Devon 86
Sheet Music Warehouse (The), Devon 88
Travis & Emery Music Bookshop, London WC 178

- **FOLK & IRISH FOLK**
Alba Secondhand Music, Strathclyde............. 278
Bookshop (The), Norfolk 191
Bookworms Paradise Ltd., West Sussex 242
Church Green Books, Oxfordshire................. 210
Country Books, Derbyshire 82
Dancing Goat Bookshop (The), Norfolk 187
Dooley (Rosemary), Cumbria 77
Fifteenth Century Bookshop (The), East Sussex. 104
Green Man Books, East Sussex 101
Handsworth Books, Essex............................ 112
Joel Segal Books, Devon 86
K.S.C. Books, Cheshire............................. 70

Karen Millward, Co. Cork 263
McGee (Terence J.), London Outer 180
Music By The Score, Cornwall 72
Paramor (C.D.), Suffolk 228
R. & A. Books, East Sussex 101
Randall (Tom), Somerset 218
Schull Books, Co. Cork 262
Sheet Music Warehouse (The), Devon 88
Sherlaw-Johnson (Austin), Oxfordshire 209
Travis & Emery Music Bookshop, London WC 178

- GILBERT & SULLIVAN
Alba Secondhand Music, Strathclyde.............. 278
Annie's Books, S Yorks 221
Brock Books, North Yorkshire 192
Browne (Christopher I.), West Yorkshire 246
Decorum Books, London N 156
Dolphin Books, Suffolk 225
Fifteenth Century Bookshop (The), East Sussex. 104
Goodden (Peter), Somerset 215
Greenroom Books, West Yorkshire 247
Hancock & Monks Music Emporium, Powys ... 288
Joel Segal Books, Devon 86
Martin Music Books (Philip), North Yorkshire . 197
Musicalania, Norfolk................................. 188
Paramor (C.D.), Suffolk 228
R. & A. Books, East Sussex 101
Sherlaw-Johnson (Austin), Oxfordshire 209
Theatreshire Books, North Yorkshire 192
Travis & Emery Music Bookshop, London WC 178

- GREGORIAN CHANTS
Alba Secondhand Music, Strathclyde.............. 278
Birchden Books, London E 154
Bookworms Paradise Ltd., West Sussex 242
Browne (Christopher I.), West Yorkshire 246
Decorum Books, London N 156
Dooley (Rosemary), Cumbria 77
East Riding Books, East Yorkshire................ 107
Goodden (Peter), Somerset 215
Hancock & Monks Music Emporium, Powys ... 288
Sheet Music Warehouse (The), Devon 88
Sherlaw-Johnson (Austin), Oxfordshire 209
Travis & Emery Music Bookshop, London WC 178

- ILLUSTRATED SHEET MUSIC
Alba Secondhand Music, Strathclyde.............. 278
Browne (Christopher I.), West Yorkshire 246
Decorum Books, London N 156
Elizabeth Ferguson, Grampian 272
Ferguson (Elizabeth), Grampian 272
Gibbs Books, (Jonathan), Worcs................... 256
Hancock & Monks Music Emporium, Powys ... 288
McGee (Terence J.), London Outer 180
Music By The Score, Cornwall 72
Paramor (C.D.), Suffolk 228
Sheet Music Warehouse (The), Devon 88
Sherlaw-Johnson (Austin), Oxfordshire 209
The Old Music Master, Bristol 60
Travis & Emery Music Bookshop, London WC 178

- JAZZ & BLUES
A. & R. Booksearch, Cornwall...................... 73
Barnes - Books (Lyndon), Shropshire 212
Baxter - Books (Eddie), Somerset 220

Bookroom (The), Surrey............................. 233
Bookworms Paradise Ltd., West Sussex 242
Courtyard Books, Glos 113
Decorum Books, London N 156
Delectus Books, London WC....................... 176
East Riding Books, East Yorkshire................ 107
Fifteenth Century Bookshop (The), East Sussex. 104
Fossgate Books, North Yorkshire 197
Hames (Peter), Devon................................ 84
Hancock & Monks Music Emporium, Powys ... 288
Handsworth Books, Essex........................... 112
Joel Segal Books, Devon 86
John L Capes (Books Maps & Prints), North
　　Yorkshire.. 196
Martin Music Books (Philip), North Yorkshire . 197
McGee (Terence J.), London Outer 180
My Back Pages, London SW........................ 168
R. & A. Books, East Sussex 101
SaBeRo Books, London SW........................ 169
Scorpio Books, Suffolk 225
Sheet Music Warehouse (The), Devon 88
Sherlaw-Johnson (Austin), Oxfordshire 209
Travis & Emery Music Bookshop, London WC 178

- MUSIC HALL
Bookworms Paradise Ltd., West Sussex 242
Browne (Christopher I.), West Yorkshire 246
Decorum Books, London N 156
Fitzsimons (Anne), Cumbria 76
Greenroom Books, West Yorkshire 247
Hancock & Monks Music Emporium, Powys ... 288
Joel Segal Books, Devon 86
McGee (Terence J.), London Outer 180
Music By The Score, Cornwall 72
Paramor (C.D.), Suffolk 228
R. & A. Books, East Sussex 101
SaBeRo Books, London SW........................ 169
Sheet Music Warehouse (The), Devon 88
Sherlaw-Johnson (Austin), Oxfordshire 209
Terence Kaye - Bookseller, London NW 161
Travis & Emery Music Bookshop, London WC 178

- MUSICIANS
Alba Secondhand Music, Strathclyde.............. 278
Anthony Spranger, Wiltshire........................ 252
Barnes - Books (Lyndon), Shropshire 212
Blackwell's Music Shop, Oxfordshire.............. 208
Bookworms Paradise Ltd., West Sussex 242
Browne (Christopher I.), West Yorkshire 246
Decorum Books, London N 156
Dooley (Rosemary), Cumbria 77
East Riding Books, East Yorkshire................ 107
Fifteenth Century Bookshop (The), East Sussex. 104
Furneaux Books (Lee), Devon...................... 89
Goodden (Peter), Somerset......................... 215
Hancock & Monks Music Emporium, Powys ... 288
Handsworth Books, Essex........................... 112
Joel Segal Books, Devon 86
John L Capes (Books Maps & Prints), North
　　Yorkshire.. 196
Martin Music Books (Philip), North Yorkshire . 197
McGee (Terence J.), London Outer 180
Mogul Diamonds, West Midlands.................. 240
Price (John), London N 158
R. & A. Books, East Sussex 101

Sheet Music Warehouse (The), Devon 88
Sherlaw-Johnson (Austin), Oxfordshire 209
Travis & Emery Music Bookshop, London WC 178
Willmott Bookseller (Nicholas), Cardiff.......... 281
Woodlands Books, West Yorkshire............... 249

- OPERA

Alba Secondhand Music, Strathclyde.............. 278
Anthony Spranger, Wiltshire........................ 252
Barnes - Books (Lyndon), Shropshire 212
Blackwell's Music Shop, Oxfordshire.............. 208
Bookworms Paradise Ltd., West Sussex 242
Browne (Christopher I.), West Yorkshire......... 246
Dales & Lakes Book Centre, Cumbria............ 79
Decorum Books, London N 156
Dooley (Rosemary), Cumbria 77
East Riding Books, East Yorkshire................ 107
Fifteenth Century Bookshop (The), East Sussex. 104
Fitzsimons (Anne), Cumbria........................ 76
Garwood & Voigt, Kent............................. 139
Greenroom Books, West Yorkshire 247
Hancock & Monks Music Emporium, Powys ... 288
Handsworth Books, Essex........................... 112
Hodgkins and Company Limited (Ian), Glos 116
Joel Segal Books, Devon 86
Marcet Books, London SE.......................... 164
Martin Music Books (Philip), North Yorkshire . 197
Music By The Score, Cornwall..................... 72
Musicalania, Norfolk............................... 188
Price (John), London N 158
R. & A. Books, East Sussex 101
Sheet Music Warehouse (The), Devon 88
Sherlaw-Johnson (Austin), Oxfordshire 209
Staniland (Booksellers), Lincolnshire 152
Travis & Emery Music Bookshop, London WC 178
Whistler's Books, London SW 169
Willmott Bookseller (Nicholas), Cardiff.......... 281

- ORCHESTRAL

Alba Secondhand Music, Strathclyde.............. 278
Annie's Books, S Yorks 221
Anthony Spranger, Wiltshire........................ 252
Barnes - Books (Lyndon), Shropshire 212
Bookworms Paradise Ltd., West Sussex 242
Browne (Christopher I.), West Yorkshire......... 246
Decorum Books, London N 156
East Riding Books, East Yorkshire................ 107
Fifteenth Century Bookshop (The), East Sussex. 104
Hancock & Monks Music Emporium, Powys ... 288
Handsworth Books, Essex........................... 112
Joel Segal Books, Devon 86
Martin Music Books (Philip), North Yorkshire . 197
Mogul Diamonds, West Midlands 240
Music By The Score, Cornwall..................... 72
R. & A. Books, East Sussex 101
Sheet Music Warehouse (The), Devon 88
Sherlaw-Johnson (Austin), Oxfordshire 209
Staniland (Booksellers), Lincolnshire 152
Travis & Emery Music Bookshop, London WC 178

- POLITICAL SONGS & BALLADS

Barry McKay Rare Books, Cumbria.............. 76
Browne (Christopher I.), West Yorkshire......... 246
Church Green Books, Oxfordshire................. 210
Decorum Books, London N 156

Left on The Shelf, Cumbria........................ 78
Music By The Score, Cornwall..................... 72
Randall (Tom), Somerset............................ 218
Sheet Music Warehouse (The), Devon 88
Sherlaw-Johnson (Austin), Oxfordshire 209
Travis & Emery Music Bookshop, London WC 178

- POPULAR

A. & R. Booksearch, Cornwall..................... 73
Apocalypse, Surrey 232
Barnes - Books (Lyndon), Shropshire 212
Black Cat Bookshop, Leics 147
Bookworms Paradise Ltd., West Sussex 242
Browne (Christopher I.), West Yorkshire......... 246
Dancing Goat Bookshop (The), Norfolk 187
Decorum Books, London N 156
Exeter's Antiques Centre on the Quay, Devon... 86
Fifteenth Century Bookshop (The), East Sussex. 104
firstpagebooks, Norfolk............................. 189
Furneaux Books (Lee), Devon...................... 89
Joel Segal Books, Devon 86
Kent T. G., Surrey 230
Martin Music Books (Philip), North Yorkshire . 197
McGee (Terence J.), London Outer 180
Morris Secondhand & Antiquarian Books
  (Chris), Oxfordshire 208
Music By The Score, Cornwall..................... 72
Musicalania, Norfolk............................... 188
Nevitsky (Philip), Greater Manchester 119
Pordes Books Ltd., (Henry), London WC....... 177
Pyecroft (Ruth), Glos 116
R. & A. Books, East Sussex 101
Sheet Music Warehouse (The), Devon 88
Sherlaw-Johnson (Austin), Oxfordshire 209
Travis & Emery Music Bookshop, London WC 178
Uncle Phil's Books, West Midlands 239
Whistler's Books, London SW 169
Willmott Bookseller (Nicholas), Cardiff.......... 281
Woburn Books, London N 159
Yorkshire Relics, West Yorkshire.................. 246

- PRINTED, SHEET MUSIC & SCORES

Alba Secondhand Music, Strathclyde.............. 278
Annie's Books, S Yorks 221
Apocalypse, Surrey 232
Bookworms Paradise Ltd., West Sussex 242
Boris Books, Somerset 216
Browne (Christopher I.), West Yorkshire......... 246
Carningli Centre, Pembrokeshire................... 286
Cornucopia Books, Lincolnshire 151
Cox Music (Lisa), Devon........................... 86
Decorum Books, London N 156
East Riding Books, East Yorkshire................ 107
Exeter's Antiques Centre on the Quay, Devon... 86
Gibbs Books, (Jonathan), Worcs................... 256
Hab Books, London W............................. 172
Hancock & Monks Music Emporium, Powys ... 288
Jade Mountain Bookshop, Hampshire 125
Joel Segal Books, Devon 86
Just Books, Cornwall 75
Martin Music Books (Philip), North Yorkshire . 197
Mogul Diamonds, West Midlands 240
Music By The Score, Cornwall..................... 72
Musicalania, Norfolk............................... 188
Paramor (C.D.), Suffolk 228

Sheet Music Warehouse (The), Devon 88
Sherlaw-Johnson (Austin), Oxfordshire 209
The Old Music Master, Bristol 60
The Sanctuary Bookshop, Dorset 94
Travis & Emery Music Bookshop, London WC 178
Willmott Bookseller (Nicholas), Cardiff 281

- ROCK & ROLL

A. & R. Booksearch, Cornwall 73
Barnes - Books (Lyndon), Shropshire 212
Bookpassage (The), Shropshire 212
Bookshop (The), Norfolk 191
Bookworms Paradise Ltd., West Sussex 242
Dancing Goat Bookshop (The), Norfolk 187
Decorum Books, London N 156
firstpagebooks, Norfolk 189
Gravity Books, Lincolnshire 149
Joel Segal Books, Devon 86
McGee (Terence J.), London Outer 180
Morris Secondhand & Antiquarian Books (Chris),
  Oxfordshire 208
Music By The Score, Cornwall 72
R. & A. Books, East Sussex 101
Roland Books, Kent 138
Sclanders (Beatbooks), (Andrew), London EC... 155
Sheet Music Warehouse (The), Devon 88
Sherlaw-Johnson (Austin), Oxfordshire 209
Till's Bookshop, Lothian 277
Travis & Emery Music Bookshop, London WC 178
Yorkshire Relics, West Yorkshire 246

- SHEET MUSIC

Alba Secondhand Music, Strathclyde.............. 278
Apocalypse, Surrey 232
Bookshop (The), Norfolk 191
Bookworms Paradise Ltd., West Sussex 242
Browne (Christopher I.), West Yorkshire......... 246
Carningli Centre, Pembrokeshire 286
Cofion Books, Pembrokeshire 286
Cornucopia Books, Lincolnshire 151
Decorum Books, London N 156
East Riding Books, East Yorkshire 107
Esoteric Dreams Bookshop, Cumbria 77
Ferguson (Elizabeth), Grampian 272
Forest Books, Rutland 211
Good Book Shop, The, Devon 90
Green Man Books, East Sussex 101
Hab Books, London W 172
Hancock & Monks Music Emporium, Powys ... 288
Joel Segal Books, Devon 86
Martin Music Books (Philip), North Yorkshire . 197
McGee (Terence J.), London Outer 180
Mogul Diamonds, West Midlands 240
Music By The Score, Cornwall 72
Park Gallery & Bookshop (The), Northants 200
Saintfield Antiques & Fine Books, Co. Down ... 261
Sheet Music Warehouse (The), Devon 88
Sherlaw-Johnson (Austin), Oxfordshire 209
Travis & Emery Music Bookshop, London WC 178
Willmott Bookseller (Nicholas), Cardiff 281

- SONGS & BALLADS

Alba Secondhand Music, Strathclyde.............. 278
Apocalypse, Surrey 232
Barnes - Books (Lyndon), Shropshire 212

Bookworms Paradise Ltd., West Sussex 242
Browne (Christopher I.), West Yorkshire......... 246
Decorum Books, London N 156
Fifteenth Century Bookshop (The), East Sussex. 104
Hancock & Monks Music Emporium, Powys ... 288
Joel Segal Books, Devon 86
McGee (Terence J.), London Outer 180
Mogul Diamonds, West Midlands 240
Music By The Score, Cornwall 72
Musicalania, Norfolk 188
Paramor (C.D.), Suffolk 228
Randall (Tom), Somerset 218
Sheet Music Warehouse (The), Devon 88
Sherlaw-Johnson (Austin), Oxfordshire 209
Travis & Emery Music Bookshop, London WC 178
Willmott Bookseller (Nicholas), Cardiff 281

- THEORY

Alba Secondhand Music, Strathclyde.............. 278
Bath Old Books, Somerset 215
Browne (Christopher I.), West Yorkshire......... 246
Decorum Books, London N 156
Dooley (Rosemary), Cumbria 77
East Riding Books, East Yorkshire 107
Fifteenth Century Bookshop (The), East Sussex. 104
Goodden (Peter), Somerset 215
Hancock & Monks Music Emporium, Powys ... 288
Joel Segal Books, Devon 86
Martin Music Books (Philip), North Yorkshire . 197
Mogul Diamonds, West Midlands 240
Music By The Score, Cornwall 72
Price (John), London N 158
Sheet Music Warehouse (The), Devon 88
Sherlaw-Johnson (Austin), Oxfordshire 209
Travis & Emery Music Bookshop, London WC 178
Willmott Bookseller (Nicholas), Cardiff 281

- WESTERNS

Decorum Books, London N 156
Sheet Music Warehouse (The), Devon 88
Sherlaw-Johnson (Austin), Oxfordshire 209
Travis & Emery Music Bookshop, London WC 178

MUSICAL INSTRUMENTS

Alba Secondhand Music, Strathclyde.............. 278
Apocalypse, Surrey 232
Barmby (C. & A.J.), Kent 140
Bookworms Paradise Ltd., West Sussex 242
Decorum Books, London N 156
Dooley (Rosemary), Cumbria 77
East Riding Books, East Yorkshire 107
Elgar (Raymond), East Sussex 99
Fifteenth Century Bookshop (The), East Sussex. 104
Goodden (Peter), Somerset 215
Hancock & Monks Music Emporium, Powys ... 288
Handsworth Books, Essex 112
Joel Segal Books, Devon 86
John L Capes (Books Maps & Prints), N Yorks 196
K.S.C. Books, Cheshire 70
Kitley (A.J.), Bristol 59
Martin Music Books (Philip), North Yorkshire . 197
Orchid Book Distributors, Co. Clare 262
Sherlaw-Johnson (Austin), Oxfordshire 209
Travis & Emery Music Bookshop, London WC 178
Trinders' Fine Tools, Suffolk 226

Willmott Bookseller (Nicholas), Cardiff........... 281

MUSICAL INSTRUMENTS - GUITARS
Bookpassage (The), Shropshire..................... 212
Bookworms Paradise Ltd., West Sussex 242
Decorum Books, London N 156
Fifteenth Century Bookshop (The), East Sussex. 104
K.S.C. Books, Cheshire............................ 70
Sherlaw-Johnson (Austin), Oxfordshire 209
Travis & Emery Music Bookshop, London WC 178

MUSICIANS
Alba Secondhand Music, Strathclyde.............. 278
Annie's Books, S Yorks 221
Anthony Spranger, Wiltshire....................... 252
Bookworms Paradise Ltd., West Sussex 242
Browne (Christopher I.), West Yorkshire......... 246
Dolphin Books, Suffolk............................ 225
Dooley (Rosemary), Cumbria 77
East Riding Books, East Yorkshire................ 107
Fifteenth Century Bookshop (The), East Sussex. 104
Goodden (Peter), Somerset......................... 215
Hancock & Monks Music Emporium, Powys ... 288
Joel Segal Books, Devon 86
Martin Music Books (Philip), North Yorkshire . 197
McGee (Terence J.), London Outer 180
Mogul Diamonds, West Midlands................. 240
R. & A. Books, East Sussex 101
Sheet Music Warehouse (The), Devon 88
Sherlaw-Johnson (Austin), Oxfordshire 209
Travis & Emery Music Bookshop, London WC 178
Willmott Bookseller (Nicholas), Cardiff........... 281

MYCOLOGY
baconboooks, London WC 176
Bernard Dixon and Kath Adams, London Outer 182
Coch-y-Bonddu Books, Powys 290
Hollingshead (Chris), London Outer 182
Joel Segal Books, Devon 86
Park (Mike), London Outer......................... 182
Parkinsons Books, Merseyside..................... 185
Pendleside Books, Lancashire...................... 143
R M Books, Herts 132
Savona Books, Lincolnshire........................ 151
Steven Simpson Books, Norfolk 190
Woodside Books, Kent 135

MYSTERIES
Annie's Books, S Yorks 221
Apocalypse, Surrey 232
Bookworms Paradise Ltd., West Sussex 242
Furneaux Books (Lee), Devon...................... 89
Gildas Books, Cheshire 68
Inner Bookshop (The), Oxfordshire................ 208
Joel Segal Books, Devon 86
L.M.S. Books, Herts 131
Ming Books, Dumfries & Galloway............... 270
Mostly Mysteries Bookstore, Lincolnshire........ 150
Occultique, Northants.............................. 199
R. & A. Books, East Sussex 101
Robert Temple, London N.......................... 158
Seabreeze Books, Lancashire....................... 144
Tiger Books, Kent.................................. 136
Wheen O'Books, Borders........................... 267
Wizard Books, Cambridgeshire.................... 67

MYSTICISM
Bardsley's Books, Suffolk.......................... 225
Beckham Books Ltd., Suffolk 229
Bookbarrow, Cambridgeshire....................... 63
Bygone Books, Isles of Scotland 275
Cavern Books, Cheshire 70
Esoteric Dreams Bookshop, Cumbria 77
Facet Books, Dorset................................ 91
Fifteenth Century Bookshop (The), East Sussex. 104
Green Man Books, East Sussex 101
Greensleeves, Oxfordshire 206
Hancock (Peter), West Sussex 241
Hava Books, London SE............................ 164
Inner Bookshop (The), Oxfordshire................ 208
Joel Segal Books, Devon 86
Magis Books, Leics................................. 146
Needham Books, (Russell), Somerset.............. 219
Occultique, Northants.............................. 199
Pendleburys Bookshop, London N 158
R. & A. Books, East Sussex 101
Reid of Liverpool, Merseyside..................... 184
Rosemary Pugh Books, Wiltshire 253
Samovar Books, Co. Dublin........................ 264
Star Lord Books, Greater Manchester 119
Wizard Books, Cambridgeshire.................... 67
Worlds End Bookshop, London SW 169

MYTHOLOGY
Alpha Books, London N 156
Apocalypse, Surrey 232
Atlantis Bookshop, London WC................... 176
Bookworms Paradise Ltd., West Sussex 242
Brad Books, Essex 110
Brighton Books, East Sussex....................... 99
Byre Books, Dumfries & Galloway................ 270
Cheshire Book Centre, Cheshire................... 69
Daeron's Books, Buckinghamshire................. 62
Esoteric Dreams Bookshop, Cumbria 77
Fifteenth Century Bookshop (The), East Sussex. 104
Galloway & Porter Limited, Cambridgeshire..... 64
Gildas Books, Cheshire 68
Green Man Books, East Sussex 101
Greensleeves, Oxfordshire 206
Inner Bookshop (The), Oxfordshire................ 208
Joel Segal Books, Devon 86
Karen Millward, Co. Cork......................... 263
Linton Books, Borders.............................. 267
Magis Books, Leics................................. 146
Occultique, Northants.............................. 199
R. & A. Books, East Sussex 101
Randall (Tom), Somerset........................... 218
SETI Books, West Midlands....................... 239
Seydi Rare Books (Sevin), London NW 161
Star Lord Books, Greater Manchester 119
Treadwell's Books, London WC 178
Watkins Books Ltd., London WC.................. 179
Wizard Books, Cambridgeshire.................... 67

NATIONAL GEOGRAPHIC
Bookworms Paradise Ltd., West Sussex 242
G. C. Books Ltd., Dumfries & Galloway......... 270
Hab Books, London W............................. 172
Orb's Bookshop, Grampian........................ 273
SaBeRo Books, London SW........................ 169
The Sanctuary Bookshop, Dorset................. 94

NATIONAL PARKS

Glacier Books, Tayside 280
Jane & John Kinnaird, Cumbria 78
R. & A. Books, East Sussex 101

NATIVE AMERICAN

Americanabooksuk, Cumbria 76
Bookworms Paradise Ltd., West Sussex 242
Byre Books, Dumfries & Galloway 270
Fifteenth Century Bookshop (The), East Sussex. 104
Hay Castle, Powys 288
Inner Bookshop (The), Oxfordshire 208
Joel Segal Books, Devon 86
Magis Books, Leics 146
Occultique, Northants 199
Optimus Books Ltd, West Sussex 244
Orchid Book Distributors, Co. Clare 262
SaBeRo Books, London SW 169

NATIVE CANADIAN

Americanabooksuk, Cumbria 76
Hay Castle, Powys 288
Joel Segal Books, Devon 86

NATURAL HEALTH

Annie's Books, S Yorks 221
Bookworms Paradise Ltd., West Sussex 242
Cheshire Book Centre, Cheshire 69
Clevedon Books, Somerset 217
Fifteenth Century Bookshop (The), East Sussex. 104
Greensleeves, Oxfordshire 206
Hay Cinema Bookshop Ltd., Powys 288
Joel Segal Books, Devon 86
Just Books, Cornwall 75
Occultique, Northants 199
R. & A. Books, East Sussex 101
Roundstone Books, Lancashire 143

NATURAL HISTORY

Abacus Books, Greater Manchester 118
Abacus Gallery, Staffordshire 224
Alauda Books, Cumbria 76
Allhalland Books, Devon 84
Allinson (Frank & Stella), Warwickshire 236
Andron (G.W.), London N 156
Annie's Books, S Yorks 221
Anthony Whittaker, Kent 135
Antique Map and Bookshop (The), Dorset 94
Antiques on High, Oxfordshire 207
Arden Books & Cosmographia, Warwickshire ... 236
Arden, Bookseller (C.), Powys 287
Armstrong's Books & Collectables, Leics 145
Aurelian Books, London NW 160
Austwick Hall Books, North Yorkshire 192
Autumn Leaves, Lincolnshire 150
Aviabooks, Glos 114
Axe Rare & Out of Print Books (Richard),
  North Yorkshire 193
Ayre (Peter J.), Somerset 219
Baker (Gerald), Bristol 60
Baldwin's Scientific Books, Essex 111
Barn Books, Buckinghamshire 61
Barnhill Books, Isle of Arran 274
Baron - Scientific Book Sales (P.J.), Somerset ... 216
Baron (Christopher), Cheshire 68

Bath Old Books, Somerset 215
Bernard Dixon and Kath Adams, London O.... 182
Besleys Books, Suffolk 225
Biblipola, London NW 160
Birdnet Optics Ltd., Derbyshire 82
Blest (Peter), Kent 138
Book Business (The), London W 171
Bookbarrow, Cambridgeshire 63
Bookcase, Cumbria 76
Books & Collectables Ltd., Cambridgeshire 63
Books and Things, Channel Islands 258
Bookworms, Norfolk 186
Bookworms Paradise Ltd., West Sussex 242
Bosorne Books, Cornwall 75
Bow Windows Book Shop, East Sussex 103
Broadhurst of Southport Ltd., Merseyside 185
Broadleaf Books, Torfaen 292
Brock Books, North Yorkshire 192
Burden Ltd., (Clive A.), Herts 131
Calluna Books, Dorset 95
Carlton Books, Norfolk 189
Carnforth Bookshop (The), Lancashire 142
Carningli Centre, Pembrokeshire 286
Castle Hill Books, Herefordshire 128
Chalmers Hallam (E.), Hampshire 125
Chandos Books, Devon 85
Channel Islands Galleries Limited,
  Channel Islands 258
Charlie Byrne's Bookshop, Co. Galway 265
Cheshire Book Centre, Cheshire 69
Chevin Books, West Yorkshire 249
Chris Phillips, Wiltshire 252
Clark (M.R.), West Yorkshire 245
Clarke Books (David), Somerset 218
Clent Books, Worcs 255
Cobbles Books, Somerset 217
Coch-y-Bonddu Books, Powys 290
Collectable Books, London SE 163
Colonsay Bookshop, Isle of Colonsay 275
Corvus Books, Buckinghamshire 61
Country Books, Derbyshire 82
Cox Old & Rare Books (Claude), Suffolk 227
Creaking Shelves, Highland 274
Cumming Limited (A. & Y.), East Sussex 104
Dales & Lakes Book Centre, Cumbria 79
Dandy Lion Editions, Surrey 233
D'Arcy Books, Wiltshire 252
Dartmoor Book Gallery, Devon 87
Dartmoor Bookshop (The), Devon 84
Dave Jelfs, Devon 85
David (G.), Cambridgeshire 63
Delectus Books, London WC 176
Demar Books (Grant), Kent 140
Dene Barn Books & Prints, Somerset 219
Dolphin Books, Suffolk 225
Dunkheld Antiques, Tayside 279
Earth Science Books, Wiltshire 252
Eastcote Bookshop (The), London O 180
ECR Books, Dorset 92
Edmund Pollinger Rare Books, London SW..... 166
Edwards (London) Limited (Francis),
  London WC 176
Edwards in Hay-on-Wye (Francis), Powys 288
Elizabeth Ferguson, Grampian 272
Elmfield Books, West Midlands 238

Evergreen Livres, Glos................................. 116
Fifteenth Century Bookshop (The), East Sussex. 104
Fine Books at Ilkley, West Yorkshire.............. 247
Fireside Bookshop, Cumbria......................... 81
firstpagebooks, Norfolk............................... 189
Ford Books (David), Herts 130
Freader's Books, Tayside 279
Freeman's Corner Shop, Norfolk 189
Frew Limited (Robert), London SW 167
Garfi Books, Powys 291
Georgina Hobhouse, Argyll.......................... 274
GfB: the Colchester Bookshop, Essex 108
Gibbard (A. & T.), East Sussex 101
Gillmark Gallery, Herts............................... 130
Gladstone Books, Lincolnshire 150
Glenbower Books, Co. Dublin 264
Goodyer (Nicholas), London N 157
Goodyer, Natural History Books (Eric), Leics... 146
Grahame (Major Iain), Suffolk...................... 225
Grayling (David A.H.), Cumbria 78
Hall's Bookshop, Kent................................ 140
Halson Books, Cheshire 71
Harrington (Adrian), London W.................... 173
Hawkridge Books, Derbyshire....................... 82
Hay Cinema Bookshop Ltd., Powys............... 288
Henly (John), West Sussex 244
Hereward Books, Cambridgeshire.................. 66
Heywood Hill Limited (G.), London W 173
Hodgson (Books) (Richard J.), N Yorks 196
Hollett and Son (R.F.G.), Cumbria 79
Hollingshead (Chris), London O 182
Home Farm Books, Warwickshire.................. 236
Hünersdorff Rare Books, London SW 168
Ice House Books, Wiltshire 254
Inner Bookshop (The), Oxfordshire................ 208
Island Books, Devon 85
Ivelet Books Ltd., Surrey............................ 233
Jackson (M.W.), Wiltshire........................... 254
Jane Jones Books, Grampian........................ 273
Jay Books, Lothian.................................... 276
JB Books & Collectables, West Sussex 243
Jenny Hurst, Kent..................................... 138
Joel Segal Books, Devon 86
Just Books, Cornwall 75
Kalligraphia (formerly Charmouth Bounty
    Books), Isle of Wight............................. 133
Katnap Arts, Norfolk................................. 190
Keeble Antiques, Somerset 218
Keel Row Bookshop, Tyne and Wear 235
Kellow Books, Oxfordshire 206
Kennedy (Peter), Surrey 234
Keogh's Books, Glos.................................. 115
Kernaghans, Merseyside.............................. 185
Kim's Bookshop, West Sussex...................... 241
Kim's Bookshop, West Sussex...................... 242
Kingsgate Books & Prints, Hampshire............ 126
Kingshead Books, Powys............................. 291
Kingsmere Books, Bedfordshire..................... 53
Kirkman Ltd., (Robert), Bedfordshire............. 54
Korn (M. Eric), London N 157
Langford Press, Lincolnshire........................ 151
Larkham Books (Patricia), Glos..................... 117
Lenton (Alfred), Leics................................ 145
Lymelight Books & Prints, Dorset................. 93
Malvern Bookshop (The), Worcs 255

Mannwaring (M.G.), Bristol 59
Marshall Rare Books (Bruce), Glos 113
Martin (Books and Pictures), (Brian P.), Surrey. 231
Martin (Brian), Surrey 231
Martin's Books, Powys 290
McCrone (Audrey), Isle of Arran.................. 274
McEwan Fine Books, Grampian..................... 272
McNaughtan's Bookshop, Lothian 276
Mobbs (A.J.), West Midlands 239
Moorhead Books, West Yorkshire.................. 245
Muse Bookshop (The), Gwynedd................... 285
Neil Summersgill, Lancashire 142
Nineteenth Century Books, Oxfordshire 209
O'Flynn Books, North Yorkshire.................... 197
Old Station Pottery & Bookshop (The), Norfolk 191
Old Town Bookshop (The), Lothian 276
Orb's Bookshop, Grampian.......................... 273
Page (David), Lothian 276
Pandion Books, North Yorkshire................... 194
Park (Mike), London O 182
Parrott Books, Oxfordshire 209
Pauline Harries Books, Hampshire 123
Pemberley Books, Buckinghamshire 62
Penny Farthing, The, Lothian....................... 277
Peregrine Books (Leeds), West Yorkshire........ 248
Peter M Daly, Hampshire............................ 126
Phelps (Michael), West Sussex...................... 242
Phillip Robbins of Warwick, Warwickshire 237
Pollak (P.M.), Devon 88
Pordes Books Ltd., (Henry), London WC........ 177
Portus Books, Hampshire............................ 122
Priestpopple Books, Northumberland 201
PsychoBabel Books & Journals, Oxfordshire..... 205
Quentin Books Ltd, Essex........................... 108
R. & A. Books, East Sussex 101
R.E. & G.B. Way, Suffolk 228
Read - Gorleston Books, (C.&J.), Norfolk 187
Richard Thornton Books, London N 158
River Reads Bookshop, Devon...................... 90
Roland Books, Kent 138
Roz Hulse, Conwy 284
Russell (Charles), London SW...................... 169
Rutland Bookshop (The), Rutland 211
Rye Old Books, East Sussex 104
Ryeland Books, Northants 199
St Ann's Books, Worcs 255
Saintfield Antiques & Fine Books, Co. Down ... 261
Saracen Books, Derbyshire........................... 83
Savona Books, Lincolnshire.......................... 151
Second Nature at Knapton Bookbarn, N Yorks 197
Shakeshaft (Dr. B.), Cheshire........................ 71
Shearwater Books, Northumberland................ 201
Slightly Foxed on Gloucester Road, London SW167
Smith (Clive), Essex 109
Smith Books, (Sally), Suffolk 226
Sotheran Limited (Henry), London W 175
Stella Books, Monmouthshire 286
Steven Simpson Books, Norfolk 190
Stone, (G.& R.), Borders 267
Stroma Books, Borders 267
Sue Lowell Natural History Books, London W . 175
Sykes (Graham), West Yorkshire 249
Tant Yn Ellen Books, Powys........................ 290
Tarka Books, Devon 84
Temperley (David), West Midlands................. 238

The Old Abbey Bookshop, Co. Down 261
Thomas (E. Wyn), Conwy 284
Tim Bryers Ltd, London WC 178
Trinity Rare Books, Co. Leitrim 266
Uncle Phil's Books, West Midlands 239
Vinovium Books, Durham 97
Vokes Books Ltd., North Yorkshire.............. 194
Wadard Books, Kent 137
Westons, Herts 132
Westwood Books Ltd, Cumbria.................... 80
Wheen O'Books, Borders........................... 267
Whistler (R.A.), East Sussex 99
Wilson (David), Buckinghamshire 61
Wise (Derek), East Sussex 104
Wizard Books, Cambridgeshire.................... 67
Woodbine Books, West Yorkshire................. 245
Woodside Books, Kent 135
Words Etcetera Bookshop, Dorset............... 93
Wychwood Books, Glos 116
Wyseby House Books, Berks 55

NATURAL SCIENCES

Alauda Books, Cumbria........................... 76
Arden, Bookseller (C.), Powys.................... 287
Austwick Hall Books, North Yorkshire........... 192
Barcombe Services, Essex....................... 108
Bernard Dixon and Kath Adams, London O.... 182
Cheshire Book Centre, Cheshire.................... 69
Cornucopia Books, Lincolnshire 151
Dartmoor Book Gallery, Devon 87
Demetzy Books, Oxfordshire 206
Earth Science Books, Wiltshire 252
Esplin (David), Hampshire.......................... 124
Fifteenth Century Bookshop (The), East Sussex. 104
J & J Burgess Booksellers, Cambridgeshire....... 64
Jackdaw Books, Norfolk 188
Joel Segal Books, Devon 86
Mannwaring (M.G.), Bristol 59
Mercat Books, Highland 274
Mobbs (A.J.), West Midlands 239
Moorside Books, Lancashire 143
Parkinsons Books, Merseyside...................... 185
Phelps (Michael), West Sussex 242
Pollak (P.M.), Devon 88
PsychoBabel Books & Journals, Oxfordshire..... 205
Quaritch Ltd., (Bernard), London W.............. 174
R M Books, Herts................................. 132
Rebecca Hardie Rare Books, London W 171
Savona Books, Lincolnshire....................... 151
Summerfield Books Ltd, Cumbria 79
Turret House, Norfolk............................. 191
Westons, Herts 132
Woburn Books, London N 159
Wyseby House Books, Berks 55

NATURE

Alauda Books, Cumbria........................... 76
Annie's Books, S Yorks 221
Blackpool Book Warehouse, Lancashire.......... 142
Calluna Books, Dorset............................. 95
Coch-y-Bonddu Books, Powys 290
Cornucopia Books, Lincolnshire 151
Dales & Lakes Book Centre, Cumbria............ 79
Demar Books (Grant), Kent....................... 140
Dolphin Books, Suffolk............................ 225

Fifteenth Century Bookshop (The), East Sussex. 104
Inner Bookshop (The), Oxfordshire............... 208
Joel Segal Books, Devon 86
Kelpie's Books, Fife.............................. 271
Kennedy & Farley, East Sussex 104
Kineton Nooks, Warwickshire...................... 236
Langford Press, Lincolnshire...................... 151
Mercat Books, Highland 274
Mobbs (A.J.), West Midlands 239
Peter M Daly, Hampshire 126
Pollak (P.M.), Devon 88
R. & A. Books, East Sussex 101
Second Nature at Knapton Bookbarn, N Yorks 197
Summerfield Books Ltd, Cumbria 79
Wheen O'Books, Borders........................... 267
Woodside Books, Kent 135

NATURISM

Delectus Books, London WC....................... 176
Green (Paul), Cambridgeshire 67
R. & A. Books, East Sussex 101

NAVAL

AA1 Books, Dumfries & Galloway............... 269
Alauda Books, Cumbria........................... 76
Anchor Books, Lincolnshire 149
Andron (G.W.), London N 156
Armchair Auctions, Hampshire 121
Aviabooks, Glos 114
Barnes (Peter), Wiltshire 253
Baynton–Williams Gallery, West Sussex 241
Book For All Reasons (A.), Suffolk 228
Bookends of Fowey, Cornwall 72
books2books, Devon............................... 88
Bookworm (The), Lothian 276
Bott, (Bookdealers) Ltd., (Martin), Greater
    Manchester 118
Broadhurst of Southport Ltd., Merseyside 185
Burroughs (Andrew), Lincolnshire 152
Camilla's Bookshop, East Sussex 101
Cavern Books, Cheshire 70
Cheshire Book Centre, Cheshire.................... 69
Chevin Books, West Yorkshire.................... 249
Cofion Books, Pembrokeshire 286
Corfe Books, Surrey............................... 230
Cornucopia Books, Lincolnshire 151
Cotswold Internet Books, Glos.................... 113
Cox (Geoff), Devon 90
Curtle Mead Books, Isle of Wight 133
Debbage (John), Norfolk.......................... 189
Delectus Books, London WC...................... 176
Dormouse Bookshop (The), Norfolk.............. 189
Edwards (London) Limited (Francis),
    London WC 176
Edwards in Hay–on–Wye (Francis), Powys 288
Elton Engineering Books, London W 172
Empire Books, North Yorkshire 197
Fifteenth Century Bookshop (The), East Sussex. 104
G&S Books, Kent 138
Gallimaufry Books, Herts 131
George St. Books, Derbyshire 83
Gerald Lee Maritime Books, East Sussex......... 105
Good for Books, Lincolnshire 149
Green Ltd. (G.L.), Herts 131
Handsworth Books, Essex......................... 112

Harris (George J.), Co. Derry 260
Helion & Company, West Midlands 239
High Street Books, Devon 86
Internet Bookshop UK Ltd., Glos 113
Invicta Bookshop, Berks 56
Island Books, Devon 85
J & J Burgess Booksellers, Cambridgeshire 64
Jackdaw Books, Norfolk 188
Jade Mountain Bookshop, Hampshire 125
Joel Segal Books, Devon 86
Keegan's Bookshop, Berks 57
Kingfisher Book Service, Nottinghamshire 204
Knowles - Antiquary (Roger J.), Staffordshire ... 223
Lost Books, Northants 200
Marcet Books, London SE 164
Marine & Cannon Books, Cheshire 71
Marine and Cannon Books, Cheshire 69
Martin Bookshop & Gallery (Richard), Hants ... 123
McCrone (Audrey), Isle of Arran 274
McLaren Books Ltd, Strathclyde 279
Meekins Books (Paul), Warwickshire 237
Milestone Books, Devon 89
MilitaryHistoryBooks.com, Kent 137
N1 Books, East Sussex 105
Nautical Antique Centre (The), Dorset 96
Not Just Books, Dorset 94
Prior (Michael), Lincolnshire 152
R. & A. Books, East Sussex 101
Robert Humm & Co, Lincolnshire 152
Rods Books, Devon 88
Sea Chest Nautical Bookshop (The), Devon 88
Simmonds (Anthony J.), London SE 165
Spooner (John E.), Dorset 91
Stalagluft Books, Tyne and Wear 235
Sub Aqua Prints and Books, Hampshire 123
Surprise Books, Glos 113
T V Coles Books, Cambridgeshire 67
Thin Read Line, Merseyside 184
Thomas Rare Books, Suffolk 226
Tilston (Stephen E.), London SE 165
Vanstone - Aviation Books, (Derek), Suffolk 229
Wadard Books, Kent 137
War & Peace Books, Hampshire 122
Warwick Leadley Gallery, London SE 165
Webb Books (John), S Yorks 221
Wheen O'Books, Borders 267
Wise (Derek), East Sussex 104
World War Books, Kent 141
World War II Books, Surrey 234
Yesterday's News, Conwy 283

NAVIGATION

Anvil Books, West Midlands 239
Books Afloat, Dorset 96
Cornucopia Books, Lincolnshire 151
Crabtree (Mrs. C.), Greater Manchester 120
Curtle Mead Books, Isle of Wight 133
Green Ltd. (G.L.), Herts 131
Jade Mountain Bookshop, Hampshire 125
Joel Segal Books, Devon 86
Keith Langford, London E 154
Marcet Books, London SE 164
Marine & Cannon Books, Cheshire 71
Marine and Cannon Books, Cheshire 69
McLaren Books Ltd, Strathclyde 279

Milestone Books, Devon 89
Nautical Antique Centre (The), Dorset 96
Quaritch Ltd., (Bernard), London W 174
R. & A. Books, East Sussex 101
Rods Books, Devon 88
Sea Chest Nautical Bookshop (The), Devon 88
Sub Aqua Prints and Books, Hampshire 123
Warsash Nautical Bookshop, Hampshire 126

NAVY, THE - GENERAL

Aardvark Books, Wiltshire 254
Anthony Spranger, Wiltshire 252
Bath Old Books, Somerset 215
Book For All Reasons (A.), Suffolk 228
Bookworms Paradise Ltd., West Sussex 242
C J Renwick Books, Powys 287
Curtle Mead Books, Isle of Wight 133
Debbage (John), Norfolk 189
Delectus Books, London WC 176
Empire Books, North Yorkshire 197
Falconwood Transport & Military Bookshop,
   London O 183
Fifteenth Century Bookshop (The), East Sussex . 104
Gerald Lee Maritime Books, East Sussex 105
Green Ltd. (G.L.), Herts 131
Jade Mountain Bookshop, Hampshire 125
Joel Segal Books, Devon 86
Keith Langford, London E 154
Marcet Books, London SE 164
Marine and Cannon Books, Cheshire 69
Martin Bookshop & Gallery (Richard), Hants ... 123
McLaren Books Ltd, Strathclyde 279
Milestone Books, Devon 89
N1 Books, East Sussex 105
Prior (Michael), Lincolnshire 152
R. & A. Books, East Sussex 101
Robert Humm & Co, Lincolnshire 152
Rods Books, Devon 88
Sea Chest Nautical Bookshop (The), Devon 88
Sub Aqua Prints and Books, Hampshire 123
War & Peace Books, Hampshire 122
Wheen O'Books, Borders 267
World War II Books, Surrey 234

- ROYAL NAVAL PATROL SERVICE

Book For All Reasons (A.), Suffolk 228
Gerald Lee Maritime Books, East Sussex 105
Green Ltd. (G.L.), Herts 131
Island Books, Devon 85
Rods Books, Devon 88
Sea Chest Nautical Bookshop (The), Devon 88

NEEDLEWORK

Alexander's Books, Warwickshire 237
Annie's Books, S Yorks 221
Apocalypse, Surrey 232
Arden Books & Cosmographia, Warwickshire ... 236
Axe Rare & Out of Print Books (Richard),
   North Yorkshire 193
Backfold Books, Herefordshire 127
Birchden Books, London E 154
Black Cat Books, Norfolk 187
Bookworms Paradise Ltd., West Sussex 242
Brock Books, North Yorkshire 192
Brown-Studies, Strathclyde 277

Byrom Textile Bookroom (Richard), Lancashire 142
Chevin Books, West Yorkshire...................... 249
Cofion Books, Pembrokeshire 286
Cover to Cover, Merseyside......................... 185
Crabtree (Mrs. C.), Greater Manchester 120
Don Kelly Books, London W 172
DPE Books, Devon 87
Edwards, Fiona, Nottinghamshire 203
Fifteenth Century Bookshop (The), East Sussex. 104
Good for Books, Lincolnshire....................... 149
Gresham Books, Somerset 217
Heneage Art Books (Thomas), London SW 168
Hennessey Bookseller (Ray), East Sussex 100
Joel Segal Books, Devon 86
Judith Mansfield, West Yorkshire.................. 249
McNaughtan's Bookshop, Lothian 276
Old Bookshop (The), West Midlands 240
R. & A. Books, East Sussex 101
Reading Lasses, Dumfries & Galloway 270
Scrivener's Books & Bookbinding, Derbyshire... 82
Sleepy Elephant Books & Artefacts, Cumbria ... 80
Smith Books (Keith), Herefordshire 128
Tilston (Stephen E.), London SE................... 165
Trinders' Fine Tools, Suffolk 226
Wheen O'Brooks, Borders........................... 267
Whittle, Bookseller (Avril), Cumbria 80

NEUROLOGY

Alba Books, Grampian 273
Barcombe Services, Essex........................... 108
Bernard Dixon and Kath Adams, London O.... 182
Erian Books, London N............................. 156
Game Advice, Oxfordshire 208
Mair Wilkes Books, Fife 271
Parkinsons Books, Merseyside...................... 185
Phelps (Michael), West Sussex...................... 242
Pollak (P.M.), Devon 88
R M Books, Herts.................................... 132
R. & A. Books, East Sussex 101
Rebecca Hardie Rare Books, London W......... 171
Turret House, Norfolk............................... 191
Westons, Herts 132

NEW AGE

2 Ravens, Cumbria 78
Abacus Gallery, Staffordshire....................... 224
Annie's Books, S Yorks 221
Chthonios Books, East Sussex 102
Dalbeattie Books, Dumfries & Galloway 269
Dawlish Books, Devon 86
DPE Books, Devon 87
Esoteric Dreams Bookshop, Cumbria 77
Furneaux Books (Lee), Devon....................... 89
Greensleeves, Oxfordshire 206
Inner Bookshop (The), Oxfordshire................ 208
Innes Books, Shropshire 212
Invisible Books, East Sussex 100
Joel Segal Books, Devon 86
Keel Row Bookshop, Tyne and Wear 235
Magis Books, Leics.................................. 146
Occultique, Northants............................... 199
Orchid Book Distributors, Co. Clare.............. 262
R. & A. Books, East Sussex 101
Roundstone Books, Lancashire...................... 143
SETI Books, West Midlands........................ 239

Star Lord Books, Greater Manchester 119
Till's Bookshop, Lothian 277
Trinity Rare Books, Co. Leitrim 266
Woburn Books, London N 159
Words Etcetera Bookshop, Dorset................. 93

NEW BOOKS

Al Saqi Books, London W.......................... 171
Americanabooksuk, Cumbria....................... 76
Birdnet Optics Ltd., Derbyshire 82
Brewin Books Ltd., Warwickshire 237
Browning Books, Torfaen........................... 292
Bruce Holdsworth Books, East Sussex 105
Camden Lock Books, London EC.................. 155
Chaters Motoring Booksellers, London O........ 181
Colwyn Books, Conwy 283
Cooking = The Books, Glos........................ 115
Dalbeattie Books, Dumfries & Galloway 269
Esoteric Dreams Bookshop, Cumbria 77
Gay's The Word, London WC...................... 177
George St. Books, Derbyshire 83
Green Man Books, East Sussex 101
Hambleton Books, North Yorkshire 196
Idler (The), Suffolk 227
J.C. Books, Devon................................... 87
J.G. Natural History Books, Surrey 233
Meekins Books (Paul), Warwickshire.............. 237
Print Matters, London SE........................... 165
R. & A. Books, East Sussex 101
Sillan Books, Co. Cavan 262
Siop Lyfrau'r Hen Bost, Gwynedd 285
Skyrack Books, West Yorkshire.................... 247
Slightly Foxed on Gloucester Road, London SW 167
Soccor Books Limited, Lincolnshire............... 148
Tarka Books, Devon................................. 84
Travel Bookshop (The), London W 175
Weobley Bookshop, Herefordshire................. 128
Wheeler's Bookshop, West Sussex 243

NEW NATURALIST

Alauda Books, Cumbria............................. 76
Antique Map and Bookshop (The), Dorset 94
Backfold Books, Herefordshire 127
Birdnet Optics Ltd., Derbyshire 82
Blest (Peter), Kent 138
Books and Things, Channel Islands 258
BOOKS4U, Flintshire............................... 284
BookShop, The, Dumfries & Galloway........... 270
Broadhurst of Southport Ltd., Merseyside 185
Calluna Books, Dorset.............................. 95
Chalmers Hallam (E.), Hampshire................. 125
Cheshire Book Centre, Cheshire.................... 69
Coch-y-Bonddu Books, Powys 290
Creaking Shelves, Highland 274
Dales & Lakes Book Centre, Cumbria........... 79
Demar Books (Grant), Kent......................... 140
Fifteenth Century Bookshop (The), East Sussex. 104
Ford Books (David), Herts 130
Hollett and Son (R.F.G.), Cumbria 79
J & J Burgess Booksellers, Cambridgeshire....... 64
Jackdaw Books, Norfolk 188
Jay Books, Lothian.................................. 276
Joel Segal Books, Devon 86
Just Books, Cornwall 75
Lymelight Books & Prints, Dorset................. 93

Martin (Books and Pictures), (Brian P.), Surrey. 231
Martin (Brian), Surrey 231
Muse Bookshop (The), Gwynedd 285
Park (Mike), London O 182
Pemberley Books, Buckinghamshire 62
Peter M Daly, Hampshire........................... 126
Polmorla Books, Cornwall 75
Poor Richard's Books, Suffolk 226
R. & A. Books, East Sussex 101
Roger Collicott Books, Cornwall 74
Second Nature at Knapton Bookbarn, N Yorks 197
St Ann's Books, Worcs 255
Scrivener's Books & Bookbinding, Derbyshire... 82
Shakeshaft (Dr. B.), Cheshire....................... 71
Shearwater Books, Northumberland............... 201
Sue Lowell Natural History Books, London W . 175
Summerfield Books Ltd, Cumbria 79
Westmoria Books (Mark), Powys 289
Westwood Books Ltd, Cumbria.................... 80
Whitchurch Books Ltd., Cardiff.................... 281
Woodside Books, Kent 135

NEW WORLD
Joel Segal Books, Devon 86

NEWBERY &
CALDECOTT AWARD-WINNERS
Fifteenth Century Bookshop (The), East Sussex. 104

NEWSPAPERS
Antique Prints of the World, London N.......... 156
Derek Stirling Bookseller, Kent 141
Early Times, Guernsey, Channel Islands.......... 258
John Underwood Antiquarian Books, Norfolk.. 189
Kelly Books Ltd, Devon............................. 89
Ken's Paper Collectables, Buckinghamshire 62
Knowles - Antiquary (Roger J.), Staffordshire... 223
Mr. Pickwick of Towcester, Northants............ 199
Mulyan (Don), Merseyside........................... 185
Nostalgia Unlimited, Merseyside................... 184
Tilleys Vintage Magazine Shop, Derbyshire...... 82
Yesterday's News, Conwy........................... 283

NON-FICTION
Abbey Books, Cornwall 73
Annie's Books, S Yorks 221
Apocalypse, Surrey 232
Ardis Books, Hampshire 126
baconboooks, London WC 176
Barcombe Services, Essex........................... 108
Bath Old Books, Somerset 215
books2books, Devon 88
Booth (Booksearch Service), (Geoff), Cheshire... 68
Carningli Centre, Pembrokeshire 286
Charles Bossom, Cambridgeshire................... 65
Clent Books, Worcs 255
Dolphin Books, Suffolk.............................. 225
Edwards, Fiona, Nottinghamshire 203
Fifteenth Century Bookshop (The), East Sussex. 104
Foster Bookshop (Paul), London SW 167
George St. Books, Derbyshire 83
HCB Wholesale, Powys.............................. 288
Joel Segal Books, Devon 86
Kingfisher Book Service, Nottinghamshire 204
Loretta Lay Books, London NW 161

Marble Hill Books, Outer London................. 182
MilitaryHistoryBooks.com, Kent................... 137
Mobbs (A.J.), West Midlands 239
Morris Secondhand & Antiquarian Books
  (Chris), Oxfordshire 208
Mount's Bay Books, Cornwall 74
Muttonchop Manuscripts, West Sussex 242
Orb's Bookshop, Grampian.......................... 273
Pittville Books, Glos................................. 113
R. & A. Books, East Sussex 101
Reading Lasses, Dumfries & Galloway 270
Sax Books, Suffolk 228
Sea Chest Nautical Bookshop (The), Devon 88
SETI Books, West Midlands......................... 239
Shakeshaft (Dr. B.), Cheshire....................... 71
Star Lord Books, Greater Manchester 119
Wheen O'Books, Borders............................ 267
Williams (Bookdealer), (Richard), N Lincs 153
Woburn Books, London N 159

NORFOLK
Book For All Reasons (A.), Suffolk 228

NOSTALGIA
Border Bookshop, West Yorkshire 249
Fifteenth Century Bookshop (The), East Sussex. 104
McGee (Terence J.), London O 180
Milestone Publications Goss & Crested China,
  Hampshire 123
Nostalgia Unlimited, Merseyside................... 184
Prior (Michael), Lincolnshire 152
Stalagluft Books, Tyne and Wear.................. 235
Till's Bookshop, Lothian 277
Yesterday's News, Conwy............................ 283

NOVELTY
Fifteenth Century Bookshop (The), East Sussex. 104
Green Meadow Books, Cornwall 74

NUCLEAR ISSUES
Delectus Books, London WC........................ 176
PsychoBabel Books & Journals, Oxfordshire..... 205
Westons, Herts 132
Woburn Books, London N 159

NUMEROLOGY
Inner Bookshop (The), Oxfordshire................ 208
Magis Books, Leics................................... 146

NUMISMATICS
Clark (Nigel A.), London SE 163
Heneage Art Books (Thomas), London SW 168
InterCol London, London N 157
Joel Segal Books, Devon 86
Parkinsons Books, Merseyside...................... 185
Spink, London WC 178
Taylor & Son (Peter), Herts........................ 132

NURSERY RHYMES
Country Books, Derbyshire 82
Fifteenth Century Bookshop (The), East Sussex. 104
First Edition, The, Essex 109
Green Meadow Books, Cornwall 74
JB Books & Collectables, West Sussex 243
Jean Hedger, Berks.................................. 55

Joel Segal Books, Devon 86
Lake (David), Norfolk................................ 190
R. & A. Books, East Sussex 101
Travis & Emery Music Bookshop, London WC 178

NURSES/DOCTORS
Game Advice, Oxfordshire........................... 208
London & Sussex Antiquarian Book & Print Services,
  East Sussex 101
Pollak (P.M.), Devon 88
PsychoBabel Books & Journals, Oxfordshire..... 205
R M Books, Herts..................................... 132
Reading Lasses, Dumfries & Galloway 270
Rebecca Hardie Rare Books, London W 171

OCCULT
Alpha Books, London N............................. 156
Anthroposophical Books, Glos...................... 116
Apocalypse, Surrey 232
Atlantis Bookshop, London WC................... 176
Berwick Books, Lincolnshire........................ 150
Bookbarrow, Cambridgeshire....................... 63
Books, Denbighshire.................................. 284
Bookworms Paradise Ltd., West Sussex 242
Bygone Books, Isles of Scotland 275
Byre Books, Dumfries & Galloway................ 270
Caduceus Books, Leics............................... 145
Cavern Books, Cheshire 70
Cheshire Book Centre, Cheshire.................... 69
Chthonios Books, East Sussex 102
Clegg (David), Staffordshire......................... 223
Cofion Books, Pembrokeshire 286
Dawlish Books, Devon 86
Delectus Books, London WC....................... 176
Enigma Books, Wiltshire 252
Esoteric Dreams Bookshop, Cumbria 77
Gilbert (R.A.), Somerset............................. 219
Gildas Books, Cheshire 68
Green Man Books, East Sussex 101
Greensleeves, Oxfordshire 206
Hava Books, London SE............................. 164
Hay Cinema Bookshop Ltd., Powys............... 288
Inner Bookshop (The), Oxfordshire................ 208
Invisible Books, East Sussex 100
J & J Burgess Booksellers, Cambridgeshire....... 64
Joel Segal Books, Devon 86
Loretta Lay Books, London NW 161
Lucius Books, North Yorkshire..................... 197
Magis Books, Leics................................... 146
Needham Books, (Russell), Somerset.............. 219
Occultique, Northants................................ 199
Old Celtic Bookshop (The), Devon 87
Philip Hopper, Essex 110
PsychoBabel Books & Journals, Oxfordshire..... 205
R. & A. Books, East Sussex 101
SETI Books, West Midlands......................... 239
Star Lord Books, G Manchester 119
Till's Bookshop, Lothian 277
Treadwell's Books, London WC 178
Treasure Chest Books, Suffolk 226
Victoria Bookshop (The), Devon................... 84
Walker Fine Books (Steve), Dorset 92
Watkins Books Ltd., London WC.................. 179
Waxfactor, East Sussex 100
Wizard Books, Cambridgeshire..................... 67

Worlds End Bookshop, London SW 169

OCEAN LINERS
Chas J. Sawyer, Kent 140
Cox (Geoff), Devon 90
Dales and Lakes Book Centre, Cumbria.......... 79
Fifteenth Century Bookshop (The), East Sussex. 104
Gerald Lee Maritime Books, East Sussex........ 105
Joel Segal Books, Devon 86
Marine & Cannon Books, Cheshire 71
Marine and Cannon Books, Cheshire 69
McLaren Books Ltd, Strathclyde 279
Milestone Books, Devon 89
Robert Humm & Co, Lincolnshire 152
Sea Chest Nautical Bookshop (The), Devon 88

OCEANOGRAPHY
Baldwin's Scientific Books, Essex 111
Parkinsons Books, Merseyside...................... 185
Periplus Books, Buckinghamshire.................. 62
Sea Chest Nautical Bookshop (The), Devon 88
Weiner (Graham), London N 158
Westons, Herts.. 132

ODD & UNUSUAL
Book Business (The), London W 171
Delectus Books, London WC....................... 176
Esoteric Dreams Bookshop, Cumbria 77
Facet Books, Dorset.................................. 91
Game Advice, Oxfordshire 208
Gildas Books, Cheshire 68
Gladstone Books, Lincolnshire 150
Glenbower Books, Co. Dublin 264
Good for Books, Lincolnshire 149
Hurst (Jenny), Kent 137
Just Books, Cornwall 75
Lewis (J.T. & P.), Cornwall......................... 73
Lighthouse Books (The), Dorset 92
Muttonchop Manuscripts, West Sussex 242
Occultique, Northants................................ 199
Old Station Pottery & Bookshop (The), Norfolk 191
Parkinsons Books, Merseyside...................... 185
Reid of Liverpool, Merseyside...................... 184
Roger Treglown, Cheshire........................... 70
Rutland Bookshop (The), Rutland 211
Williams (Bookdealer), (Richard), N Lincs....... 153
Woburn Books, London N 159

OIL INDUSTRY
High Street Books, Devon 86
Joel Segal Books, Devon 86
Mandalay Bookshop, London SW 168
Weiner (Graham), London N 158

OIL LAMPS
Don Kelly Books, London W 172
Weiner (Graham), London N 158

OLD WEST
Americanabooksuk, Cumbria........................ 76
Fifteenth Century Bookshop (The), East Sussex. 104
Joel Segal Books, Devon 86
Keel Row Bookshop, Tyne and Wear 235

ONLINE AUTHOR SIGNATURE SAMPLES

Greta Books, Durham 97

OPHTHALMOLOGY

Baldwin's Scientific Books, Essex 111
Parkinsons Books, Merseyside...................... 185
Pollak (P.M.), Devon 88
PsychoBabel Books & Journals, Oxfordshire..... 205
R M Books, Herts 132
Savona Books, Lincolnshire........................ 151
Weiner (Graham), London N 158
Westons, Herts 132

OPTICAL

Parkinsons Books, Merseyside...................... 185
Quaritch Ltd., (Bernard), London W.............. 174
Savona Books, Lincolnshire........................ 151
Stroh (M.A.), London E 154
Weiner (Graham), London N 158
Westons, Herts 132

ORDERS, DECORATIONS & MEDALS

Clark (Nigel A.), London SE...................... 163
Island Books, Devon 85
Joel Segal Books, Devon 86
MilitaryHistoryBooks.com, Kent................... 137

ORGANS

Birchden Books, London E 154
Joel Segal Books, Devon 86
Martin Music Books (Philip), North Yorkshire . 197
Travis & Emery Music Bookshop, London WC 178

ORIENTAL

Art Reference Books, Hampshire 124
Books, Denbighshire 284
Canon Gate Books, West Sussex................... 243
Crosby (Simon), East Sussex...................... 102
Hab Books, London W.............................. 172
Indoislamica, London SW.......................... 168
Joel Segal Books, Devon 86
Mandalay Bookshop, London SW 168
Probsthain (Arthur), London WC 178
R. & A. Books, East Sussex 101

ORNITHOLOGY

Alauda Books, Cumbria............................ 76
Anwoth Books Ltd, Dumfries & Galloway 269
Arden, Bookseller (C.), Powys..................... 287
Aviabooks, Glos 114
Barnhill Books, Isle of Arran 274
Besleys Books, Suffolk 225
Birdnet Optics Ltd., Derbyshire 82
Blackpool Book Warehouse, Lancashire.......... 142
Blest (Peter), Kent 138
Bookworms Paradise Ltd., West Sussex 242
Bosco Books, Cornwall 72
Brad Books, Essex 110
Brock Books, North Yorkshire..................... 192
Brown (Books) (P.R.), Durham 98
Calluna Books, Dorset............................. 95
Carlton Books, Norfolk 189
Coach House Books, Worcs 256
Coch-y-Bonddu Books, Powys 290

Cornucopia Books, Lincolnshire 151
Countrymans Gallery (The), Leics 145
Countryside Books, Hampshire 121
Dancing Goat Bookshop (The), Norfolk 187
Demar Books (Grant), Kent....................... 140
Dolphin Books, Suffolk............................ 225
Dunkheld Antiques, Tayside....................... 279
Edmund Pollinger Rare Books, London SW..... 166
Fifteenth Century Bookshop (The), East Sussex. 104
Goodyer (Nicholas), London N.................... 157
Hawkridge Books, Derbyshire..................... 82
Inner Bookshop (The), Oxfordshire............... 208
Internet Bookshop UK Ltd., Glos 113
Jane Jones Books, Grampian 273
Jay Books, Lothian 276
Joel Segal Books, Devon 86
Karen Millward, Co. Cork......................... 263
Kellow Books, Oxfordshire 206
Kirkman Ltd., (Robert), Bedfordshire............. 54
Langford Press, Lincolnshire...................... 151
Lymelight Books & Prints, Dorset................. 93
Mandalay Bookshop, London SW 168
Martin (Books and Pictures), (Brian P.), Surrey. 231
Martin (Brian), Surrey 231
Martin's Books, Powys 290
Mayhew (Veronica), Berks 57
McEwan Fine Books, Grampian................... 272
Mobbs (A.J.), West Midlands 239
Old Station Pottery & Bookshop (The), Norfolk 191
Pandion Books, North Yorkshire.................. 194
Park (Mike), London O 182
Parkinsons Books, Merseyside..................... 185
Pauline Harries Books, Hampshire 123
Pemberley Books, Buckinghamshire 62
Peter M Daly, Hampshire.......................... 126
Pollak (P.M.), Devon 88
Poor Richard's Books, Suffolk 226
Prospect House Books, Co. Down................. 261
R. & A. Books, East Sussex 101
Richard Thornton Books, London N 158
Rutland Bookshop (The), Rutland 211
St Ann's Books, Worcs 255
Shearwater Books, Northumberland............... 201
Staniland (Booksellers), Lincolnshire 152
Stella Books, Monmouthshire 286
Sue Lowell Natural History Books, London W . 175
Uncle Phil's Books, West Midlands 239
Wensum Books, Norfolk 190
Westons, Herts 132
Woodside Books, Kent 135
Wyseby House Books, Berks 55

OSTEOPATHY

Inner Bookshop (The), Oxfordshire............... 208
Phelps (Michael), West Sussex..................... 242
Pollak (P.M.), Devon 88
Rebecca Hardie Rare Books, London W......... 171

OTTOMAN EMPIRE

Arslan Books Etc., East Sussex.................... 99
Beaumont Travel Books, London SE 163
Collectables (W.H.), Suffolk 229
Empire Books, North Yorkshire 197
Indoislamica, London SW.......................... 168
Joppa Books Ltd., Surrey 230

Seydi Rare Books (Sevin), London NW 161

OUT-OF-PRINT
Apocalypse, Surrey 232
Aurora Books Ltd, Lothian.......................... 275
Black Cat Books, Norfolk........................... 187
Black Cat Bookshop, Leics 147
Book Business (The), London W 171
Book Mad, Lancashire............................... 142
Book Palace (The), London SE 163
Brad Books, Essex................................... 110
Chelifer Books, Cumbria 80
Clifford Elmer Books Ltd., Cheshire 68
Coch-y-Bonddu Books, Powys 290
Cornucopia Books, Lincolnshire 151
Cotswold Internet Books, Glos..................... 113
Country Books, Derbyshire 82
Crabtree (Mrs. C.), G Manchester 120
Dales & Lakes Book Centre, Cumbria........... 79
Dolphin Books, Suffolk.............................. 225
Fifteenth Century Bookshop (The), East Sussex. 104
Foster (Stephen), London NW 160
Foster Bookshop (Paul), London SW 167
Fosters Bookshop, London W 172
Glasheen-Books, Surrey 231
Glenbower Books, Co. Dublin 264
Good for Books, Lincolnshire 149
Hambleton Books, North Yorkshire 196
Hava Books, London SE............................ 164
Inner Bookshop (The), Oxfordshire............... 208
J & J Burgess Booksellers, Cambridgeshire....... 64
Jenny Hurst, Kent 138
Joel Segal Books, Devon 86
John Underwood Antiquarian Books, Norfolk .. 189
Just Books, Cornwall 75
Kingfisher Book Service, Nottinghamshire 204
London & Sussex Antiquarian Book &
   Print Services, East Sussex 101
Marine and Cannon Books, Cheshire 69
Orb's Bookshop, Grampian......................... 273
Park Gallery & Bookshop (The), Northants 200
Parkinsons Books, Merseyside...................... 185
Print Matters, London SE........................... 165
Reading Lasses, Dumfries & Galloway 270
Robert Temple, London N........................... 158
Samovar Books, Co. Dublin........................ 264
Sax Books, Suffolk 228
Schull Books, Co. Cork 262
Shakeshaft (Dr. B.), Cheshire...................... 71
Sol Books, Devon 84
Uncle Phil's Books, West Midlands 239
Volume Three, Central.............................. 268
Wheen O'Books, Borders............................ 267
Woburn Books, London N 159
Woodside Books, Kent 135

OUTDOORS
Clarke Books (David), Somerset 218
Dales & Lakes Book Centre, Cumbria........... 79
Fifteenth Century Bookshop (The), East Sussex. 104
Greta Books, Durham 97
Kelpie's Books, Fife................................. 271

OUTLAWS
Americanabooksuk, Cumbria....................... 76

Ian Marr Rare Books, Cornwall 73
Loretta Lay Books, London NW 161

OXFORD MOVEMENT
Beckham Books Ltd., Suffolk 229
Bell (Peter), Lothian................................ 275
Carter, (Brian), Oxfordshire....................... 210
Dolphin Books, Suffolk............................. 225
Morris Secondhand & Antiquarian Books
   (Chris), Oxfordshire 208
PsychoBabel Books & Journals, Oxfordshire..... 205
R. & A. Books, East Sussex 101
Rosemary Pugh Books, Wiltshire 253
S.P.C.K., Bristol 59
Samovar Books, Co. Dublin....................... 264

PACIFISM
Books Only, Suffolk................................. 226
Delectus Books, London WC....................... 176
Larkham Books (Patricia), Glos.................... 117
Left on The Shelf, Cumbria........................ 78
Spurrier (Nick), Kent 137
Woburn Books, London N 159
Yesterday's Books, Dorset 92
Yesterday's News, Conwy.......................... 283

PACKAGING
Debbage (John), Norfolk............................ 189

PADDLE BOATS
Bott, (Bookdealers) Ltd., (Martin),
   Greater Manchester 118
Cox (Geoff), Devon 90
Fifteenth Century Bookshop (The), East Sussex. 104
Gerald Lee Maritime Books, East Sussex......... 105
Marine & Cannon Books, Cheshire 71
Marine and Cannon Books, Cheshire 69
McLaren Books Ltd, Strathclyde 279
Robert Humm & Co, Lincolnshire 152
Sea Chest Nautical Bookshop (The), Devon 88
Yesteryear Railwayana, Kent...................... 139

PAGANISM
2 Ravens, Cumbria 78
Annie's Books, S Yorks 221
Atlantis Bookshop, London WC................... 176
Bygone Books, Isles of Scotland 275
Chthonios Books, East Sussex 102
Delectus Books, London WC....................... 176
Green Man Books, East Sussex 101
Inner Bookshop (The), Oxfordshire............... 208
Joel Segal Books, Devon 86
Occultique, Northants.............................. 199
R. & A. Books, East Sussex 101
Treasure Trove Books, Leics....................... 146

PAINTING
Annie's Books, S Yorks 221
Apocalypse, Surrey 232
Art Reference Books, Hampshire 124
Bookworms Paradise Ltd., West Sussex 242
Booth (Booksearch Service), (Geoff), Cheshire... 68
Butts Books (Mary), Berks......................... 56
Cheshire Book Centre, Cheshire................... 69
Cover to Cover, Merseyside........................ 185

Don Kelly Books, London W 172
Fifteenth Century Bookshop (The), East Sussex. 104
Heneage Art Books (Thomas), London SW 168
Jade Mountain Bookshop, Hampshire 125
Joel Segal Books, Devon 86
McCrone (Audrey), Isle of Arran 274
Modern Firsts Etc, Lancashire 142
Polmorla Books, Cornwall 75
Print Matters, London SE............................ 165
R. & A. Books, East Sussex 101
Treasure Island (The), G Manchester 119
Trinity Rare Books, Co. Leitrim 266

PALAEOGRAPHY

Bennett & Kerr Books, Oxfordshire 205
Brinded (Scott), Kent 138
Earth Science Books, Wiltshire 252
Gildas Books, Cheshire 68
Island Books, Devon 85
Leeds Bookseller, West Yorkshire 248

PALAEONTOLOGY

Acanthophyllum Books, Wirral 184
Baldwin's Scientific Books, Essex 111
Clevedon Books, Somerset 217
Cox, Andrew, Shropshire........................... 214
Earth Science Books, Wiltshire 252
Esoteric Dreams Bookshop, Cumbria 77
Henly (John), West Sussex 244
Island Books, Devon 85
Kalligraphia (formerly Charmouth Bounty
  Books), Isle of Wight............................. 133
Kenya Books, East Sussex 100
Kingswood Books, Dorset 94
Little Bookshop (The), Cumbria 80
Lymelight Books & Prints, Dorset 93
Parkinsons Books, Merseyside 185
Pemberley Books, Buckinghamshire 62
Peter M Daly, Hampshire........................... 126
Pollak (P.M.), Devon 88
Sykes (Graham), West Yorkshire 249
The Sanctuary Bookshop, Dorset.................. 94
Webb Books (John), S Yorks....................... 221
Weiner (Graham), London N 158
Whitchurch Books Ltd., Cardiff.................... 281

PALMISTRY & FORTUNE-TELLING

Alpha Books, London N 156
Cavern Books, Cheshire 70
Fifteenth Century Bookshop (The), East Sussex. 104
Good for Books, Lincolnshire 149
Inner Bookshop (The), Oxfordshire............... 208
Joel Segal Books, Devon 86
Magis Books, Leics.................................. 146
Occultique, Northants............................... 199
Old Book Company, (The), West Yorkshire 248
R. & A. Books, East Sussex 101
Treasure Island (The), Greater Manchester....... 119

PANTOMIME

Browne (Christopher I.), West Yorkshire......... 246
Paramor (C.D.), Suffolk 228
R. & A. Books, East Sussex 101

PAPER COLLECTABLES

Aitchison (Lesley), Bristol 58
Book Palace (The), London SE 163
Chas J. Sawyer, Kent 140
Derek Stirling Bookseller, Kent 141
Embleton (Paul), Essex 111
Green Meadow Books, Cornwall 74
Hava Books, London SE............................ 164
Joel Segal Books, Devon 86
John Underwood Antiquarian Books, Norfolk .. 189
Ken's Paper Collectables, Buckinghamshire 62
Murphy (C.J.), Norfolk............................. 189
Print Matters, London SE........................... 165
Randall (Tom), Somerset........................... 218
Stalagluft Books, Tyne and Wear................. 235
Wiend Books, Lancashire 143
Williams (Bookdealer), (Richard), N Lincs 153

PAPERBACKS 1940 - 1972

Backfold Books, Herefordshire..................... 127
Evergreen Livres, Glos.............................. 116

PAPERMAKING

Barry McKay Rare Books, Cumbria 76
Bettridge (Gordon), Fife............................ 271
Brinded (Scott), Kent 138
Coupland (Terry W.), Staffordshire................ 223
Cover to Cover, Merseyside........................ 185
Cox Old & Rare Books (Claude), Suffolk 227
Forest Books, Nottinghamshire 204
Joel Segal Books, Devon 86
R. & A. Books, East Sussex 101
Stroh (M.A.), London E 154
Wakeman Books (Frances), Nottinghamshire.... 204

PARAPSYCHOLOGY

Atlantis Bookshop, London WC 176
Cavern Books, Cheshire 70
Delectus Books, London WC....................... 176
Esoteric Dreams Bookshop, Cumbria 77
Greensleeves, Oxfordshire 206
Inner Bookshop (The), Oxfordshire............... 208
Joel Segal Books, Devon 86
Occultique, Northants............................... 199
SETI Books, West Midlands........................ 239

PARASITOLOGY

Bernard Dixon and Kath Adams, London O 182
Pollak (P.M.), Devon 88
Savona Books, Lincolnshire........................ 151

PARISH REGISTERS

Grampian Books, Grampian........................ 273
Island Books, Devon 85
Old Book Company, (The), West Yorkshire 248
Roadmaster Books, Kent............................ 136
Taylor & Son (Peter), Herts........................ 132
Townsend (John), Berks 57
Turton (John), Durham 98
Williams (Bookdealer), (Richard), N Lincs 153

PARKS AND GARDENS

Bermondsey Basement Bookstore, London SE .. 163
Besleys Books, Suffolk 225
Chantrey Books, S Yorks 222

Fifteenth Century Bookshop (The), East Sussex. 104
Joel Segal Books, Devon 86
Martin (Books and Pictures), (Brian P.)., Surrey. 231
Park (Mike), London O 182
Valerie Merritt, Worcs 256

PASSENGER LINERS
Bott, (Bookdealers) Ltd., (Martin),
   Greater Manchester 118
Cox (Geoff), Devon 90
Dales and Lakes Book Centre, Cumbria.......... 79
Falconwood Transport & Military Bookshop,
   London O 183
Fifteenth Century Bookshop (The), East Sussex. 104
Gerald Lee Maritime Books, East Sussex........ 105
Green Ltd. (G.L.), Herts 131
Joel Segal Books, Devon 86
Marine & Cannon Books, Cheshire 71
Marine and Cannon Books, Cheshire 69
McLaren Books Ltd, Strathclyde 279
R. & A. Books, East Sussex 101
Robert Humm & Co, Lincolnshire 152
Rods Books, Devon................................... 88

PATENTS
Stroh (M.A.), London E 154

PATHOLOGY
Parkinsons Books, Merseyside...................... 185
Phelps (Michael), West Sussex...................... 242
R M Books, Herts.................................... 132
Westons, Herts....................................... 132

PATRISTICS
Unsworth's Booksellers, Suffolk.................... 225

PERFORMING ARTS
Annie's Books, S Yorks 221
Anthony Spranger, Wiltshire........................ 252
Book Palace (The), London SE 163
Books & Bygones (Pam Taylor), West Midlands 240
Brock Books, North Yorkshire 192
Browne (Christopher I.), West Yorkshire........ 246
Catalyst Booksearch Services, Devon............. 87
Chaucer Bookshop, Kent............................ 136
Cofion Books, Pembrokeshire 286
Cornucopia Books, Lincolnshire 151
Cover to Cover, Merseyside......................... 185
Cox Rare Books (Charles), Cornwall.............. 73
D'Arcy Books, Wiltshire............................ 252
DaSilva Puppet Books, Dorset 93
Dolphin Books, Suffolk.............................. 225
Drummond Pleasures of Past Times (David),
   London WC 176
Fifteenth Century Bookshop (The), East Sussex. 104
Fitzsimons (Anne), Cumbria........................ 76
Franks Booksellers, Greater Manchester.......... 119
Garwood & Voigt, Kent............................. 139
Gibbs Books, (Jonathan), Worcs.................... 256
Greenroom Books, West Yorkshire 247
Hancock & Monks Music Emporium, Powys ... 288
Jarndyce Antiquarian Booksellers, London WC. 177
Joel Segal Books, Devon 86
Kent T. G., Surrey 230
Libris (Weston) Books, Somerset 216

M. and A.C. Thompson, Norfolk.................. 191
Malvern Bookshop (The), Worcs 255
Martin Music Books (Philip), North Yorkshire . 197
McCrone (Audrey), Isle of Arran 274
McGee (Terence J.), London O 180
N1 Books, East Sussex 105
Old Book Company, (The), West Yorkshire 248
Paramor (C.D.), Suffolk 228
Poor Richard's Books, Suffolk 226
Price (John), London N 158
Quadrille at Delehar, London W................... 174
R. & A. Books, East Sussex 101
Reads, Dorset 95
SaBeRo Books, London SW........................ 169
Scorpio Books, Suffolk 225
Scrivener's Books & Bookbinding, Derbyshire... 82
Stella Books, Monmouthshire 286
Terence Kaye - Bookseller, London NW 161
Theatreshire Books, North Yorkshire 192
Till's Bookshop, Lothian 277
Treasure Trove Books, Leics........................ 146
Uncle Phil's Books, West Midlands 239
Willmott Bookseller (Nicholas), Cardiff........... 281
Wood (Peter), Cambridgeshire...................... 65

PETROLEUM GEOLOGY
Earth Science Books, Wiltshire 252
Geophysical Books, Kent............................ 139
Joel Segal Books, Devon 86
Parkinsons Books, Merseyside...................... 185
Steven Simpson Books, Norfolk.................... 190
Weiner (Graham), London N 158
Westons, Herts....................................... 132

PETROLEUM TECHNOLOGY
Earth Science Books, Wiltshire 252
Geophysical Books, Kent............................ 139
Parkinsons Books, Merseyside...................... 185
Westons, Herts....................................... 132

PHARMACY/PHARMACOLOGY
Alba Books, Grampian 273
Andrew Hunter Rare Books, London SW 166
Baldwin's Scientific Books, Essex 111
Bernard Dixon and Kath Adams, London O.... 182
Empire Books, North Yorkshire 197
Old Book Company, (The), West Yorkshire 248
Orchid Book Distributors, Co. Clare.............. 262
Parkinsons Books, Merseyside...................... 185
Phelps (Michael), West Sussex...................... 242
Pickering & Chatto, London W 174
Quaritch Ltd., (Bernard), London W.............. 174
R M Books, Herts.................................... 132
Rebecca Hardie Rare Books, London W 171
Savona Books, Lincolnshire......................... 151
Smith (David & Lynn), London O 181
Westons, Herts....................................... 132
White (David), Cambridgeshire..................... 65

PHENOMENA
Joel Segal Books, Devon 86
SETI Books, West Midlands........................ 239

PHILATELY
32 Seconds, East Sussex 104

Clark (Nigel A.), London SE 163
Frost (Richard), Herts 129
Hodgson (Books) (Richard J.), North Yorkshire 196
Jackdaw Books, Norfolk 188
Joel Segal Books, Devon 86
Old Book Company, (The), West Yorkshire 248
Pennymead Books, North Yorkshire 193
Postings, Surrey 233
R. & A. Books, East Sussex 101
Spooner & Co, Somerset 219
Treasure Island (The), Greater Manchester....... 119

PHILOLOGY
Baldwin (Jack), Strathclyde 278
Bennett & Kerr Books, Oxfordshire 205
Delectus Books, London WC........................ 176
Derek Stirling Bookseller, Kent 141
Ice House Books, Wiltshire 254
Joel Segal Books, Devon 86
Karen Thomson, Oxfordshire........................ 209
Kenya Books, East Sussex 100
Midnight Oil Books, Fife............................ 271
Nineteenth Century Books, Oxfordshire 209
Old Book Company, (The), West Yorkshire 248
Olynthiacs, Shropshire 213
Parkinsons Books, Merseyside....................... 185
Polczynski (Udo K.H.), Powys 289
Price (John), London N 158
Seydi Rare Books (Sevin), London NW 161
Susanne Schulz-Falster Rare Books, London N. 158
Unsworth's Booksellers, Suffolk.................... 225

PHILOLOGY - GERMAN
Karen Thomson, Oxfordshire....................... 209

PHILOSOPHY
Abbey Books, Cornwall 73
Anthroposophical Books, Glos 116
Apocalypse, Surrey 232
Armchair Books, Lothian 275
Backfold Books, Herefordshire 127
Barcombe Services, Essex............................ 108
Bath Old Books, Somerset 215
Bell (Peter), Lothian................................. 275
Bloomsbury Bookshop, London O 181
Books, Denbighshire 284
Books Antiques & Collectables, Devon 90
Bookshop (The), Greater Manchester 118
Bookshop (The), Co. Donegal....................... 263
Brimstones, East Sussex 104
Caledonia Books, Strathclyde....................... 278
Camden Books, Somerset 215
Carter, (Brian), Oxfordshire........................ 210
Cheshire Book Centre, Cheshire.................... 69
Chesters (G. & J.), Staffordshire 224
Chthonios Books, East Sussex...................... 102
Classics Bookshop (The), Oxfordshire............. 205
Darkwood Books, Co. Cork......................... 263
Dean Byass, Bristol 60
Delectus Books, London WC........................ 176
Dolphin Books, Suffolk.............................. 225
Drury Rare Books (John), Essex.................... 110
Edwards (London) Limited (Francis),
London WC 176
Edwards in Hay–on–Wye (Francis), Powys 288

Fifteenth Century Bookshop (The), East Sussex. 104
Fireside Bookshop, Cumbria........................ 81
Fisher & Sperr, London N........................... 157
Game Advice, Oxfordshire.......................... 208
GfB: the Colchester Bookshop, Essex 108
Gladstone Books, Lincolnshire 150
Hamish Riley-Smith, Norfolk....................... 191
Handsworth Books, Essex............................ 112
Herb Tandree Philosophy Books, Glos 116
High Street Books, Devon 86
Hughes Rare Books (Spike), Borders.............. 267
Humanist Book Services, Cornwall 72
Hurst (Jenny), Kent 137
Jackdaw Books, Norfolk 188
Joel Segal Books, Devon 86
John Gorton Booksearch, East Sussex 105
Judd Books, London WC............................ 177
Killeen (John), North Yorkshire 193
Kyrios Books, Nottinghamshire.................... 203
Lee Rare Books (Rachel), Bristol 59
Leo Cadogan, London N 157
My Back Pages, London SW 168
Occultique, Northants................................ 199
O'Donoghue Books, Powys......................... 289
Old Book Company, (The), West Yorkshire 248
Orb's Bookshop, Grampian.......................... 273
Parkinsons Books, Merseyside....................... 185
Pauline Harries Books, Hampshire 123
Pendleburys Bookshop, London N 158
Pickering & Chatto, London W.................... 174
Pittville Books, Glos................................. 113
Plurabelle Books, Cambridgeshire.................. 65
Polczynski (Udo K.H.), Powys 289
Pordes Books Ltd., (Henry), London WC........ 177
Portobello Books, London W 174
Price (John), London N 158
PsychoBabel Books & Journals, Oxfordshire..... 205
Quaritch Ltd., (Bernard), London W.............. 174
Quinto of Charing Cross Road, London WC ... 178
R. & A. Books, East Sussex 101
Readers World, West Midlands 238
Reading Lasses, Dumfries & Galloway 270
Reads, Dorset 95
Roland Books, Kent 138
Roosterbooks, Northamptonshire.................... 199
Rosemary Pugh Books, Wiltshire 253
Rowan (P. & B.), Co. Antrim 260
St Philip's Books, Oxfordshire...................... 208
Samovar Books, Co. Dublin......................... 264
Savery Books, East Sussex 100
Scrivener's Books & Bookbinding, Derbyshire... 82
Seydi Rare Books (Sevin), London NW 161
Spurrier (Nick), Kent 137
Staniland (Booksellers), Lincolnshire 152
Stokes Books, Co. Dublin........................... 264
Susanne Schulz-Falster Rare Books, London N. 158
Tarka Books, Devon 84
Thorntons of Oxford Ltd., Oxfordshire........... 206
Till's Bookshop, Lothian............................ 277
Trade Priced Old Books, Powys.................... 289
Transformer, Dumfries & Galloway 270
Trinity Rare Books, Co. Leitrim 266
Trotter Books (John), London N 158
Uncle Phil's Books, West Midlands 239
Walden Books, London NW 161

Waterfield's, Oxfordshire 209
Webb Books (John), S Yorks........................ 221
Westwood Books (Mark), Powys 289
Wiend Books, Lancashire 143
Winchester Bookshop (The), Hampshire.......... 126
Winghale Books, Lincolnshire 152
Woburn Books, London N 159
Worcester Rare Books, Worcs....................... 256
Worlds End Bookshop, London SW 169
Yarwood Rare Books (Edward), G Manchester. 118

PHONOLOGY
Kenya Books, East Sussex 100

PHOTOGRAPHY
Abacus Gallery, Staffordshire....................... 224
Allsworth Rare Books Ltd., London SW......... 166
Amwell Book Company, London EC............. 155
Apocalypse, Surrey 232
Ars Artis, Oxfordshire 207
Aviabooks, Glos 114
Bermondsey Basement Bookstore, London SE .. 163
Blaenavon Books, Torfaen 292
Books, Denbighshire 284
Books & Collectables Ltd., Cambridgeshire...... 63
Books & Things, London W........................ 171
Books Only, Suffolk.................................. 226
Bookshop on the Heath, The, London SE 163
Brighton Books, East Sussex........................ 99
Broadleaf Books, Torfaen 292
Bruce Holdsworth Books, East Sussex 105
Butcher (Pablo), Oxfordshire 206
Camden Lock Books, London EC................. 155
Cameron House Books, Isle of Wight............. 133
Cavern Books, Cheshire 70
Cofion Books, Pembrokeshire 286
Collectables (W.H.), Suffolk 229
Cover to Cover, Merseyside......................... 185
Dally (Andrew), Powys 289
Derek Stirling Bookseller, Kent 141
Farahar & Dupre (Clive & Sophie), Wiltshire ... 251
Fifteenth Century Bookshop (The), East Sussex. 104
Finch Rare Books Ltd. (Simon), London W..... 172
Good for Books, Lincolnshire 149
Grays of Westminster, London SW 167
Hay Castle, Powys.................................... 288
Hill House Books, Devon 88
IDEA, London EC 155
Intech Books, Northumberland 201
Jade Mountain Bookshop, Hampshire 125
Jill Howell, East Sussex............................. 102
Joel Segal Books, Devon 86
Judd Books, London WC............................ 177
Keswick Bookshop, Cumbria 78
McGee (Terence J.), London O 180
Modern First Editions, West Yorkshire........... 247
N1 Books, East Sussex 105
O'Brien Books & Photo Gallery, Co. Limerick.. 266
Old Book Company, (The), West Yorkshire..... 248
Orlando Booksellers, Lincolnshire 150
Paper Pleasures, Somerset 218
Park Gallery & Bookshop (The), Northants 200
Peter Lyons Books, Glos 113
Photo Books International, London WC......... 177
Phototitles.com, Lincolnshire 151

Pollak (P.M.), Devon 88
Print Matters, London SE........................... 165
PsychoBabel Books & Journals, Oxfordshire..... 205
Quaritch Ltd., (Bernard), London W.............. 174
Ray Rare and Out of Print Books (Janette),
    North Yorkshire 198
Rayner (Hugh Ashley), Somerset 215
Rhodes, Bookseller (Peter), Hampshire 125
Solaris Books, East Yorkshire...................... 106
Soldridge Books Ltd, Hampshire 124
Stroh (M.A.), London E 154
Sykes (Graham), West Yorkshire 249
Tarka Books, Devon 84
Treasure Island (The), Greater Manchester....... 119
Uncle Phil's Books, West Midlands 239
Weiner (Graham), London N 158
Wiend Books, Lancashire 143
Woburn Books, London N 159
Worlds End Bookshop, London SW 169

PHRENOLOGY
Atlantis Bookshop, London WC.................... 176
Occultique, Northamptonshire....................... 199
Old Book Company, (The), West Yorkshire 248
Phelps (Michael), West Sussex 242
Rebecca Hardie Rare Books, London W......... 171

PHYSICAL CULTURE
Combat Arts Archive, Durham 97
Webster (D.), Strathclyde............................ 279

PHYSICS
Barcombe Services, Essex............................ 108
Camden Books, Somerset 215
Eagle Bookshop (The), Bedfordshire 53
Ely Books, Cambridgeshire 65
Esplin (David), Hampshire 124
Freader's Books, Tayside............................ 279
Gladstone Books, Lincolnshire 150
Moorside Books, Lancashire......................... 143
Old Book Company, (The), West Yorkshire 248
Parkinsons Books, Merseyside....................... 185
Phelps (Michael), West Sussex...................... 242
PsychoBabel Books & Journals, Oxfordshire..... 205
Quaritch Ltd., (Bernard), London W.............. 174
The Sanctuary Bookshop, Dorset.................. 94
Transformer, Dumfries & Galloway............... 270
Turret House, Norfolk 191
Wayside Books and Cards, Oxfordshire 206
Weiner (Graham), London N 158
Westons, Herts....................................... 132
Whistler's Books, London SW 169

PHYSIOLOGY
Barcombe Services, Essex............................ 108
Bernard Dixon and Kath Adams, London O.... 182
Gladstone Books, Lincolnshire 150
Old Book Company, (The), West Yorkshire 248
Parkinsons Books, Merseyside....................... 185
Phelps (Michael), West Sussex...................... 242
PsychoBabel Books & Journals, Oxfordshire..... 205
R M Books, Herts.................................... 132
R. & A. Books, East Sussex 101
Rebecca Hardie Rare Books, London W......... 171
Weiner (Graham), London N 158

Westons, Herts 132

PICTURE RESEARCH
Debbage (John), Norfolk 189

PIGS
Hodgson (Books) (Richard J.), North Yorkshire 196
Joel Segal Books, Devon 86
Kelpie's Books, Fife 271
Phenotype Books, Cumbria 79

PILGRIMS
Chapter Two, London SE 163
Joel Segal Books, Devon 86
R. & A. Books, East Sussex 101

PIONEERS
Americanabooksuk, Cumbria 76
Joel Segal Books, Devon 86

PIRATES
Book Palace (The), London SE 163
Cox (Geoff), Devon 90
Fifteenth Century Bookshop (The), East Sussex. 104
Joel Segal Books, Devon 86
Loretta Lay Books, London NW 161
Marine & Cannon Books, Cheshire 71
Marine and Cannon Books, Cheshire 69
McLaren Books Ltd, Strathclyde 279
Print Matters, London SE 165
R. & A. Books, East Sussex 101
Red Star Books, Herts 129
Sea Chest Nautical Bookshop (The), Devon 88
Treasure Island (The), Greater Manchester 119

PLANNING - CITY
Haskell (R.H. & P.), Dorset 94
Joel Segal Books, Devon 86

PLANT HUNTING
Abacus Books, Greater Manchester 118
Acanthophyllum Books, Wirral 184
Alauda Books, Cumbria 76
Anne Harris Books & Bags Booksearch, Devon 88
Arden, Bookseller (C.), Powys 287
Barnhill Books, Isle of Arran 274
Bernard Dixon and Kath Adams, London O 182
Besleys Books, Suffolk 225
Blest (Peter), Kent 138
Dales & Lakes Book Centre, Cumbria 79
Edmund Pollinger Rare Books, London SW 166
Fifteenth Century Bookshop (The), East Sussex. 104
Hollett and Son (R.F.G.), Cumbria 79
Hollingshead (Chris), London O 182
Hunter and Krageloh, Derbyshire 83
Joel Segal Books, Devon 86
Mandalay Bookshop, London SW 168
Martin (Brian), Surrey 231
McEwan Fine Books, Grampian 272
Page (David), Lothian 276
Park (Mike), London O 182
Peter M Daly, Hampshire 126
R. & A. Books, East Sussex 101
Summerfield Books Ltd, Cumbria 79
Traveller's Bookshelf (The), Somerset 218

Trinity Rare Books, Co. Leitrim 266
Valerie Merritt, Worcs 256
Westons, Herts 132

PLATO
Joel Segal Books, Devon 86
R. & A. Books, East Sussex 101
Seydi Rare Books (Sevin), London NW 161

PLAYS
Abbey Books, Cornwall 73
Amwell Book Company, London EC 155
Apocalypse, Surrey 232
babelog.books, Herefordshire 127
Books Antiques & Collectables, Devon 90
Bosorne Books, Cornwall 75
Brock Books, North Yorkshire 192
Byre Books, Dumfries & Galloway 270
Catalyst Booksearch Services, Devon 87
Charles Bossom, Cambridgeshire 65
Cheshire Book Centre, Cheshire 69
Church Street Books, Norfolk 186
Cofion Books, Pembrokeshire 286
Cox Rare Books (Charles), Cornwall 73
Delectus Books, London WC 176
Derek Stirling Bookseller, Kent 141
Draca Books, West Yorkshire 248
Fifteenth Century Bookshop (The), East Sussex. 104
G. C. Books Ltd., Dumfries & Galloway 270
Greenroom Books, West Yorkshire 247
Ian McKelvie Bookseller, London N 157
Jade Mountain Bookshop, Hampshire 125
Jarndyce Antiquarian Booksellers, London WC. 177
Joel Segal Books, Devon 86
Just Books, Cornwall 75
Maggs Brothers Limited, London W 173
Paramor (C.D.), Suffolk 228
Park Gallery & Bookshop (The), Northants 200
Pastmasters, Derbyshire 83
R. & A. Books, East Sussex 101
Reading Lasses, Dumfries & Galloway 270
Robert Temple, London N 158
Roundstone Books, Lancashire 143
Scrivener's Books & Bookbinding, Derbyshire... 82
Skelton (Tony), Kent 140
Stalagluft Books, Tyne and Wear 235
Surprise Books, Glos 113
The Sanctuary Bookshop, Dorset 94
Till's Bookshop, Lothian 277
Willmott Bookseller (Nicholas), Cardiff 281

POETRY
Abacus Gallery, Staffordshire 224
Addyman Books, Powys 287
Amwell Book Company, London EC 155
Anglo-American Rare Books, Surrey 232
Antiques on High, Oxfordshire 207
Anwoth Rare Books Ltd, Dumfries & Galloway 269
Any Old Books, Hampshire 121
Apocalypse, Surrey 232
Applin (Malcolm), Berks 55
Arden Books & Cosmographia, Warwickshire... 236
Armchair Books, Lothian 275
Ash Rare Books, London SW 166
babelog.books, Herefordshire 127

Backfold Books, Herefordshire 127
Barmby (C. & A.J.), Kent 140
Barnacle Books, County Fermanagh 261
Bayntun (George), Somerset 215
Big Bairn Books, Tayside 279
Bookroom (The), Surrey 233
Books, Oxfordshire 205
Books, Denbighshire 284
Books & Bygones (Pam Taylor), West Midlands 240
Books Antiques & Collectables, Devon 90
Bookstand, Dorset 94
Bookworms Paradise Ltd., West Sussex 242
Bosorne Books, Cornwall 75
Bracton Books, Cambridgeshire 63
Brad Books, Essex 110
Bridge Books, Cumbria 81
Brighton Books, East Sussex 99
Browse Books, Lancashire 143
Byre Books, Dumfries & Galloway 270
Cameron House Books, Isle of Wight 133
Campbell Art Books (Marcus), London SE 163
Carningli Centre, Pembrokeshire 286
Catalyst Booksearch Services, Devon 87
Cheshire Book Centre, Cheshire 69
Church Street Books, Norfolk 186
Classic Bindings Ltd, London SW 166
Clements (R.W.), London O 181
Clent Books, Worcs 255
Cofion Books, Pembrokeshire 286
Cox Rare Books (Charles), Cornwall 73
Criterion Books, London O 181
Dales & Lakes Book Centre, Cumbria 79
Dancing Goat Bookshop (The), Norfolk 187
Dandy Lion Editions, Surrey 233
D'Arcy Books, Wiltshire 252
Dave Jelfs, Devon 85
David (G.), Cambridgeshire 63
Delectus Books, London WC 176
Derek Stirling Bookseller, Kent 141
Dolphin Books, Suffolk 225
Eastcote Bookshop (The), London O 180
Edrich (I.D.), London E 154
Elaine Lonsdale Books, West Yorkshire 247
Ellis, Bookseller (Peter), London WC 177
Ellwood Editions, Wiltshire 253
Erian Books, London N 156
Eton Antique Bookshop, Berks 57
Fifteenth Century Bookshop (The), East Sussex . 104
Ford Books (David), Herts 130
Foster Bookshop (Paul), London SW 167
Francis, S. L., Sussex 103
GfB: the Colchester Bookshop, Essex 108
Gladstone Books, Lincolnshire 150
Good for Books, Lincolnshire 149
Grampian Books, Grampian 273
Green (Paul), Cambridgeshire 67
Hall's Bookshop, Kent 140
Hancock (Peter), West Sussex 241
Hava Books, London SE 164
Hellenic Bookservices, London NW 161
Hennessey Bookseller (Ray), East Sussex 100
Hurst (Jenny), Kent 137
Ian McKelvie Bookseller, London N 157
Innes Books, Shropshire 212
Jabberwock Books, Lincolnshire 149

Jackdaw Books, Norfolk 188
Jade Mountain Bookshop, Hampshire 125
JB Books & Collectables, West Sussex 243
Joel Segal Books, Devon 86
Just Books, Cornwall 75
Karen Millward, Co. Cork 263
Kendall–Carpenter (Tim), Greater Manchester .. 119
Kineton Nooks, Warwickshire 236
Kings Bookshop Callander, Central 268
Kingsgate Books & Prints, Hampshire 126
Kingsmere Books, Bedfordshire 53
Lawrence Books, Nottinghamshire 203
Libris (Weston) Books, Somerset 216
Little Bookshop (The), Greater Manchester 119
Loch Croispol Bookshop & Restaurant,
　Highland 273
Lymelight Books & Prints, Dorset 93
Main Point Books, Lothian 276
Malvern Bookshop (The), Worcs 255
Marine Workshop Bookshop, Dorset 93
Martin's Books, Powys 290
McCrone (Audrey), Isle of Arran 274
Mermaid Books (Burlingham), Norfolk 191
Modlock (Lilian), Dorset 93
Needham Books, (Russell), Somerset 219
Nineteenth Century Books, Oxfordshire 209
Old Book Company, (The), West Yorkshire 248
Orangeberry Books, Oxfordshire 207
Orlando Booksellers, Lincolnshire 150
Palladour Books, Hampshire 125
Paper Moon Books, Glos 116
Park Gallery & Bookshop (The), Northants 200
Peter Lyons Books, Glos 113
Poetry Bookshop (The), Powys 289
Polmorla Books, Cornwall 75
Poor Richard's Books, Suffolk 226
Price (John), London N 158
Primrose Hill Books, London NW 161
PsychoBabel Books & Journals, Oxfordshire 205
Quest Booksearch, Cambridgeshire 65
R & B Graham Trading, Cornwall 73
R. & A. Books, East Sussex 101
Reading Lasses, Dumfries & Galloway 270
Richmond Books, North Yorkshire 194
Riderless Horse Books, Norfolk 186
Ripping Yarns, London N 158
River Reads Bookshop, Devon 90
Robert Temple, London N 158
Roundstone Books, Lancashire 143
Rutland Bookshop (The), Rutland 211
Samovar Books, Co. Dublin 264
Scrivener's Books & Bookbinding, Derbyshire... 82
Seabreeze Books, Lancashire 144
Shelley (E. & J.), Buckinghamshire 61
Skelton (Tony), Kent 140
Slightly Foxed on Gloucester Road, London SW 167
Smith Books (Keith), Herefordshire 128
Staniland (Booksellers), Lincolnshire 152
Stevens (Joan), Cambridgeshire 65
Stone, (G.& R.), Borders 267
Stroma Books, Borders 267
Sturford Books, Wiltshire 254
Tant Yn Ellen Books, Powys 290
The Old Abbey Bookshop, Co. Down 261
Tiffin (Tony and Gill), Durham 97

Till's Bookshop, Lothian 277
Tilston (Stephen E.), London SE.................. 165
Tindley & Chapman, London WC 178
Tucker (Alan & Joan), Glos 116
Updike Rare Books (John), Lothian 277
Venables (Morris & Juliet), Bristol................ 59
War & Peace Books, Hampshire................... 122
Wheen O'Books, Borders........................... 267
Whittle, Bookseller (Avril), Cumbria 80
Willmott Bookseller (Nicholas), Cardiff........... 281
Woburn Books, London N 159
Woodbine Books, West Yorkshire................. 245
Words Etcetera Bookshop, Dorset.................. 93
Yates Antiquarian Books (Tony), Leics........... 146
Yesterday's News, Conwy........................... 283
Ystwyth Books, Ceredigion 282

POLICE

Bolland Books, Bedfordshire....................... 53
Delectus Books, London WC....................... 176
Loretta Lay Books, London NW.................. 161

POLICE FORCE HISTORIES

Anthony Vickers Books, North Yorkshire 195
Bolland Books, Bedfordshire....................... 53
Clifford Elmer Books Ltd., Cheshire 68
Crimes Ink, London E.............................. 154
Delph Books, Greater Manchester................. 120
Joel Segal Books, Devon 86
Kenya Books, East Sussex 100
Loretta Lay Books, London NW.................. 161
Maggy Browne, Lincolnshire 148
R. & A. Books, East Sussex 101
Roscrea Bookshop & Newsagents,
   Co. Tipperary 266
Undercover Books, Lincolnshire 152

POLITICAL HISTORY

Apocalypse, Surrey 232
Barn Books, Buckinghamshire...................... 61
Berwick Books, Lincolnshire....................... 150
Books at Star Dot Star, West Midlands 240
Brimstones, East Sussex 104
Cornucopia Books, Lincolnshire 151
Crabtree (Mrs. C.), Greater Manchester 120
Dolphin Books, Suffolk............................. 225
Drury Rare Books (John), Essex.................. 110
Fifteenth Century Bookshop (The), East Sussex. 104
G. C. Books Ltd., Dumfries & Galloway......... 270
Jarndyce Antiquarian Booksellers, London WC. 177
Joel Segal Books, Devon 86
Left on The Shelf, Cumbria........................ 78
Leo Cadogan, London N 157
Northern Herald Books, West Yorkshire......... 245
R. & A. Books, East Sussex 101
Reading Lasses, Dumfries & Galloway 270
Red Star Books, Herts.............................. 129
Star Lord Books, Greater Manchester 119
Woburn Books, London N 159

POLITICS

Al Saqi Books, London W........................... 171
Alexander's Books, Warwickshire.................. 237
Ann & Mike Conry, Worcs......................... 257
Apocalypse, Surrey 232

Barcombe Services, Essex........................... 108
Barn Books, Buckinghamshire...................... 61
Berwick Books, Lincolnshire....................... 150
Books, Denbighshire 284
Books at Star Dot Star, West Midlands 240
Bookshop (The), Greater Manchester 118
Brimstones, East Sussex 104
Catalyst Booksearch Services, Devon............. 87
Chas J. Sawyer, Kent 140
Chesters (G. & J.), Staffordshire 224
Church Street Books, Norfolk...................... 186
Cornucopia Books, Lincolnshire 151
Delectus Books, London WC....................... 176
Dolphin Books, Suffolk............................. 225
Drury Rare Books (John), Essex.................. 110
Dunstan Books, Dorset............................. 91
Esoteric Dreams Bookshop, Cumbria 77
Fifteenth Century Bookshop (The), East Sussex. 104
firstpagebooks, Norfolk............................ 189
Fossgate Books, North Yorkshire 197
G. C. Books Ltd., Dumfries & Galloway......... 270
Garfi Books, Powys 291
Hab Books, London W.............................. 172
Hambleton Books, North Yorkshire 196
Hurst (Jenny), Kent 137
Ice House Books, Wiltshire 254
Innes Books, Shropshire............................ 212
Internet Bookshop UK Ltd., Glos................. 113
Jackdaw Books, Norfolk 188
Jarndyce Antiquarian Booksellers, London WC. 177
Jenny Hurst, Kent 138
Judd Books, London WC 177
Just Books, Cornwall 75
Kelsall (George), Greater Manchester 118
Left on The Shelf, Cumbria........................ 78
Maggy Browne, Lincolnshire 148
Modern Welsh Publications Ltd., Merseyside.... 184
My Back Pages, London SW 168
Northern Herald Books, West Yorkshire......... 245
O'Donoghue Books, Powys......................... 289
Old Book Company, (The), West Yorkshire 248
Parkinsons Books, Merseyside...................... 185
Price (John), London N 158
Quaritch Ltd., (Bernard), London W.............. 174
R. & A. Books, East Sussex 101
Reading Lasses, Dumfries & Galloway 270
Reads, Dorset 95
Red Star Books, Herts 129
Roland Books, Kent 138
Rosemary Pugh Books, Wiltshire 253
Samovar Books, Co. Dublin........................ 264
Saracen Books, Derbyshire......................... 83
Saunders (Tom), Caerphilly........................ 281
Sparrow Books, West Yorkshire.................... 245
Spurrier (Nick), Kent 137
Staniland (Booksellers), Lincolnshire 152
Star Lord Books, Greater Manchester 119
Stroma Books, Borders.............................. 267
Till's Bookshop, Lothian 277
Tilston (Stephen E.), London SE.................. 165
Uncle Phil's Books, West Midlands 239
War & Peace Books, Hampshire................... 122
Webb Books (John), S Yorks....................... 221
Winghale Books, Lincolnshire...................... 152
Woburn Books, London N 159

POMOLOGY
Chantrey Books, S Yorks 222
Edmund Pollinger Rare Books, London SW..... 166
Hava Books, London SE............................ 164
Joel Segal Books, Devon 86
Park (Mike), London O 182
Valerie Merritt, Worcs.............................. 256

POP-UP, MOVABLE & CUT OUT
Annie's Books, S Yorks 221
Beck (John), East Sussex 103
Biblipola, London NW 160
Bookmark (Children's Books), Wiltshire.......... 253
Cheshire Book Centre, Cheshire.................... 69
Elizabeth Ferguson, Grampian 272
Ferguson (Elizabeth), Grampian 272
Fifteenth Century Bookshop (The), East Sussex. 104
Hava Books, London SE............................ 164
Intech Books, Northumberland 201
Jean Hedger, Berks 55
Joel Segal Books, Devon 86
Kernaghans, Merseyside............................ 185
Key Books (Sarah), Cambridgeshire............... 64
Martin (Books and Pictures), (Brian P.), Surrey. 231
Print Matters, London SE........................... 165
R. & A. Books, East Sussex 101
Rebecca Hardie Rare Books, London W 171
Saint Swithin's Illustrated & Children's Books,
  London W 174
Scrivener's Books & Bookbinding, Derbyshire... 82
Seabreeze Books, Lancashire....................... 144
Temperley (David), West Midlands................ 238
The Old Children's Bookshelf, Lothian 277

PORNOGRAPHY
Apocalypse, Surrey 232
Debbage (John), Norfolk............................ 189
Delectus Books, London WC........................ 176
R. & A. Books, East Sussex 101

POTTERY & GLASS
Abacus Books, Greater Manchester 118
Ancient Art Books, London SW.................... 166
Apocalypse, Surrey 232
Barn Books, Buckinghamshire...................... 61
Bookworms Paradise Ltd., West Sussex 242
Bruce Holdsworth Books, East Sussex 105
C J Renwick Books, Powys......................... 287
Clark (Nigel A.), London SE........................ 163
Cornucopia Books, Lincolnshire 151
Cover to Cover, Merseyside......................... 185
Don Kelly Books, London W 172
Fifteenth Century Bookshop (The), East Sussex. 104
Hay Castle, Powys................................... 288
Joel Segal Books, Devon 86
Mannwaring (M.G.), Bristol 59
Nelson (Elizabeth), Suffolk......................... 226
Old Book Company, (The), West Yorkshire 248
Orchid Book Distributors, Co. Clare.............. 262
R. & A. Books, East Sussex 101

POULTRY
Blest (Peter), Kent 138
Cheshire Book Centre, Cheshire.................... 69
Countrymans Gallery (The), Leics 145

Edmund Pollinger Rare Books, London SW..... 166
Hodgson (Books) (Richard J.), North Yorkshire 196
Joel Segal Books, Devon 86
Keith Langford, London E 154
Kelpie's Books, Fife................................. 271
Martin (Books and Pictures), (Brian P.), Surrey. 231
Martin (Brian), Surrey 231
Phenotype Books, Cumbria 79
R. & A. Books, East Sussex 101
Thomas (Barry), Ceredigion 282

PRAYER BOOKS
Annie's Books, S Yorks 221
Barbican Bookshop, North Yorkshire............. 196
Beckham Books Ltd., Suffolk 229
Chapter Two, London SE........................... 163
Fifteenth Century Bookshop (The), East Sussex. 104
Hilton (Books) (P.J.), London W 173
Jade Mountain Bookshop, Hampshire............. 125
Kyrios Books, Nottinghamshire.................... 203
Oasis Booksearch, Cambridgeshire................. 67
Paper Moon Books, Glos 116
Pendleburys Bookshop, London N 158
PsychoBabel Books & Journals, Oxfordshire..... 205
R. & A. Books, East Sussex 101
Roscrea Bookshop & Newsagents,
  Co. Tipperary 266
Rosemary Pugh Books, Wiltshire 253
S.P.C.K., Bristol 59
Samovar Books, Co. Dublin........................ 264
Stalagluft Books, Tyne and Wear.................. 235
Staniland (Booksellers), Lincolnshire 152

PRECIOUS METALS - SILVER
Art Reference Books, Hampshire................... 124
Cox (Geoff), Devon 90
Don Kelly Books, London W 172
Joel Segal Books, Devon 86
Nibris Books, London SW 169
R. & A. Books, East Sussex 101
Trinders' Fine Tools, Suffolk 226

PREHISTORY
Barcombe Services, Essex........................... 108
Fifteenth Century Bookshop (The), East Sussex. 104
Island Books, Devon................................ 85
Joel Segal Books, Devon 86
Kingswood Books, Dorset 94
Old Book Company, (The), West Yorkshire 248
Parkinsons Books, Merseyside...................... 185
SETI Books, West Midlands........................ 239

PRE-RAPHAELITES
Ballantyne–Way (Roger), Suffolk 228
Hornsey's, North Yorkshire........................ 194
Joel Segal Books, Devon 86
R. & A. Books, East Sussex 101
Robert Temple, London N.......................... 158

PRESIDENTIAL
Dolphin Books, Suffolk............................. 225
Hab Books, London W.............................. 172

PRINTED TEXTILES
Cover to Cover, Merseyside......................... 185

Don Kelly Books, London W 172
Joel Segal Books, Devon 86
Judith Mansfield, West Yorkshire.................. 249
N1 Books, East Sussex 105
R. & A. Books, East Sussex 101
Stroh (M.A.), London E 154
Weiner (Graham), London N 158

PRINTING

Andron (G.W.), London N 156
Atholl Fine Books, Tayside 280
Ballantyne–Way (Roger), Suffolk 228
Baynton–Williams Gallery, West Sussex 241
Bettridge (Gordon), Fife 271
Bibliophile (The), S Yorks.......................... 221
Boxwood Books & Prints, Somerset............... 219
Brinded (Scott), Kent 138
Collinge & Clark, London WC..................... 176
Coupland (Terry W.), Staffordshire................ 223
Cox Old & Rare Books (Claude), Suffolk 227
Early Times, Guernsey, Channel Islands.......... 258
ECR Books, Dorset................................. 92
Finch Rare Books Ltd. (Simon), London W..... 172
Forest Books, Nottinghamshire 204
Goldman (Paul), Dorset............................ 94
Hava Books, London SE............................ 164
Island Books, Devon................................ 85
Joel Segal Books, Devon 86
Judd Books, London WC 177
Leo Cadogan, London N 157
Macfarlane (Mr. H.), Essex 111
Mannwaring (M.G.), Bristol 59
Moore (C.R.), Shropshire 213
Myra Dean Illustated Books, Powys 287
O'Connor Fine Books, Lancashire 144
Old Book Company, (The), West Yorkshire 248
R. & A. Books, East Sussex 101
Robin Doughty - Fine Books, West Midlands... 238
Solitaire Books, Somerset........................... 216
Susanne Schulz-Falster Rare Books, London N. 158
Wakeman Books (Frances), Nottinghamshire.... 204
Worlds End Bookshop, London SW 169

PRINTING - NORTH OF
ENGLAND PROVINCIAL

Barry McKay Rare Books, Cumbria.............. 76
Early Times, Guernsey, Channel Islands.......... 258
Keel Row Bookshop, Tyne and Wear 235
Yates Antiquarian Books (Tony), Leics........... 146

PRINTING AND MIND OF MAN

Dean Byass, Bristol................................. 60
Foster Bookshop (Paul), London SW............ 167
Hamish Riley-Smith, Norfolk...................... 191
Myra Dean Illustated Books, Powys 287
Old Book Company, (The), West Yorkshire 248
Quaritch Ltd., (Bernard), London W............. 174
Seydi Rare Books (Sevin), London NW 161
Susanne Schulz-Falster Rare Books, London N. 158

PRIVATE PRESS

Anthony Neville, Kent.............................. 138
Artco, Nottinghamshire............................ 204
Askew Books (Vernon), Wiltshire................. 251
Ballantyne–Way (Roger), Suffolk 228

Barlow (Vincent G.), Hampshire.................. 125
Barry McKay Rare Books, Cumbria.............. 76
Bertram Rota Ltd., London WC 176
Besleys Books, Suffolk 225
Bettridge (Gordon), Fife........................... 271
Bibliopola, London NW............................ 160
Blackwell's Rare Books, Oxfordshire............. 208
Books & Things, London W........................ 171
Bookstand, Dorset.................................. 94
Bow Windows Book Shop, East Sussex 103
Boxwood Books & Prints, Somerset............... 219
Broadhurst of Southport Ltd., Merseyside 185
Bruce Holdsworth Books, East Sussex 105
Campbell Art Books (Marcus), London SE...... 163
Collinge & Clark, London WC..................... 176
Coupland (Terry W.), Staffordshire................ 223
Cox Old & Rare Books (Claude), Suffolk 227
Dylans Bookstore, Swansea........................ 291
Early Times, Guernsey, Channel Islands.......... 258
Eastcote Bookshop (The), London O 180
Ellis, Bookseller (Peter), London WC 177
Elstree Books, Herts................................ 130
Emjay Books, Surrey............................... 231
English (Toby), Oxfordshire........................ 209
Evans Books (Paul), West Sussex 243
Franks Booksellers, Greater Manchester.......... 119
Good Books, Shropshire 213
Hanborough Books, Oxfordshire................... 208
Heritage, West Midlands 238
Hodgkins and Company Limited (Ian), Glos 116
Hollett and Son (R.F.G.), Cumbria 79
Island Books, Devon............................... 85
Keeble Antiques, Somerset......................... 218
Macfarlane (Mr. H.), Essex 111
Mannwaring (M.G.), Bristol 59
Marks Limited (Barrie), London N................ 157
Martin's Books, Powys 290
Maynard & Bradley, Leics 146
Mills Rare Books (Adam), Cambridgeshire 64
Myra Dean Illustated Books, Powys 287
Oak Tree Press, Oxfordshire 207
O'Flynn Books, North Yorkshire................... 197
Old Book Company, (The), West Yorkshire 248
Poetry Bookshop (The), Powys..................... 289
R.E. & G.B. Way, Suffolk 228
Riderless Horse Books, Norfolk.................... 186
Robert Temple, London N.......................... 158
Robin Doughty - Fine Books, West Midlands... 238
Roz Hulse, Conwy 284
Sabin (Printed Works) (P.R. & V.), Kent........ 135
Sansovino Books, West Sussex 244
Slightly Foxed on Gloucester Road, London SW 167
Solitaire Books, Somerset........................... 216
Sotheran Limited (Henry), London W 175
Staniland (Booksellers), Lincolnshire 152
Sue Lowell Natural History Books, London W . 175
Taylor Rare Books (Michael), Norfolk 187
Updike Rare Books (John), Lothian 277
Wakeman Books (Frances), Nottinghamshire.... 204
Williams Rare Books (Nigel), London WC 179
Woburn Books, London N 159
Woodbine Books, West Yorkshire.................. 245
Words Etcetera Bookshop, Dorset................. 93
York Modern Books, North Yorkshire........... 196

PROOF COPIES

Bookworms Paradise Ltd., West Sussex 242
Broadhurst of Southport Ltd., Merseyside 185
Dolphin Books, Suffolk 225
Firsts in Print, Somerset 219
G. C. Books Ltd., Dumfries & Galloway......... 270
Hab Books, London W.............................. 172
Hylton Booksearch, Merseyside 184
Kendall–Carpenter (Tim), Greater Manchester .. 119
Marble Hill Books, Outer London................ 182
Richard Thornton Books, London N 158
Robert Temple, London N.......................... 158
Scrivener's Books & Bookbinding, Derbyshire... 82
Simpson (Dave), Central 268
Williams Rare Books (Nigel), London WC 179
Woburn Books, London N 159

PROSTITUTION

Delectus Books, London WC........................ 176

PROVINCES OF CANADA
- BRITISH COLUMBIA

Preston Book Company, Lancashire 144

- NEWFOUNDLAND

Preston Book Company, Lancashire 144

- ST. PIERRE ET MIQUELON

MK Book Services, Cambridgeshire............... 66

PSYCHIC

Alpha Books, London N............................ 156
Bookworms Paradise Ltd., West Sussex 242
Byre Books, Dumfries & Galloway................ 270
Cavern Books, Cheshire 70
Chthonios Books, East Sussex...................... 102
Dawlish Books, Devon 86
Discovery Bookshop, Carmarthenshire........... 281
Facet Books, Dorset................................. 91
Fifteenth Century Bookshop (The), East Sussex. 104
Gilbert (R.A.), Somerset........................... 219
Greensleeves, Oxfordshire 206
Hurst (Jenny), Kent 137
Inner Bookshop (The), Oxfordshire................ 208
Jenny Hurst, Kent 138
Joel Segal Books, Devon 86
Magis Books, Leics................................. 146
Occultique, Northamptonshire..................... 199
R. & A. Books, East Sussex....................... 101
SETI Books, West Midlands....................... 239
Wizard Books, Cambridgeshire.................... 67

PSYCHIC SURGERY

Magis Books, Leics................................. 146

PSYCHOANALYSIS

Alba Books, Grampian 273
Apocalypse, Surrey 232
Barcombe Services, Essex.......................... 108
Delectus Books, London WC....................... 176
Fifteenth Century Bookshop (The), East Sussex. 104
Game Advice, Oxfordshire......................... 208
Inner Bookshop (The), Oxfordshire................ 208
Joel Segal Books, Devon 86
Magis Books, Leics................................. 146

Oast Books, Kent..................................... 136
Outcast Books, Herefordshire...................... 127
Parkinsons Books, Merseyside..................... 185
PsychoBabel Books & Journals, Oxfordshire..... 205
Quentin Books Ltd, Essex.......................... 108
Reading Lasses, Dumfries & Galloway 270
Rosemary Pugh Books, Wiltshire 253
Savery Books, East Sussex 100
Treasure Trove Books, Leics....................... 146
Trinity Rare Books, Co. Leitrim 266
Westons, Herts 132
Woburn Books, London N 159

PSYCHOKINESIS

Atlantis Bookshop, London WC.................... 176
Inner Bookshop (The), Oxfordshire................ 208
Magis Books, Leics................................. 146

PSYCHOLOGY/PSYCHIATRY

Abbey Books, Cornwall 73
Alba Books, Grampian 273
Annie's Books, S Yorks 221
Barcombe Services, Essex.......................... 108
Beckham Books Ltd., Suffolk 229
Bernard Dixon and Kath Adams, London O.... 182
Bookworms Paradise Ltd., West Sussex 242
Bracton Books, Cambridgeshire.................... 63
Brimstones, East Sussex 104
Cheshire Book Centre, Cheshire................... 69
Chesters (G. & J.), Staffordshire.................. 224
Cofion Books, Pembrokeshire 286
Delectus Books, London WC....................... 176
Discovery Bookshop, Carmarthenshire........... 281
Erian Books, London N............................ 156
Fireside Bookshop, Cumbria....................... 81
Game Advice, Oxfordshire 208
GfB: the Colchester Bookshop, Essex 108
Greensleeves, Oxfordshire 206
Hawley (C.L.), North Yorkshire 195
Hurst (Jenny), Kent 137
Jade Mountain Bookshop, Hampshire 125
Joel Segal Books, Devon 86
Judd Books, London WC........................... 177
Mair Wilkes Books, Fife 271
Marathon Books, Lancashire....................... 142
Marine Workshop Bookshop, Dorset 93
Oast Books, Kent................................... 136
Occultique, Northamptonshire..................... 199
O'Donoghue Books, Powys 289
Orchid Book Distributors, Co. Clare.............. 262
Outcast Books, Herefordshire...................... 127
Parkinsons Books, Merseyside..................... 185
Phelps (Michael), West Sussex..................... 242
PsychoBabel Books & Journals, Oxfordshire..... 205
Quentin Books Ltd, Essex.......................... 108
R M Books, Herts................................... 132
Reading Lasses, Dumfries & Galloway 270
Reid of Liverpool, Merseyside..................... 184
Rosemary Pugh Books, Wiltshire 253
Savery Books, East Sussex 100
Scrivener's Books & Bookbinding, Derbyshire... 82
Spurrier (Nick), Kent 137
Transformer, Dumfries & Galloway............... 270
Treasure Trove Books, Leics....................... 146
Victoria Bookshop (The), Devon................... 84

Waxfactor, East Sussex 100
Westons, Herts 132
Westwood Books (Mark), Powys 289
Westwood Books Ltd, Cumbria.................... 80
Wizard Books, Cambridgeshire..................... 67
Woburn Books, London N 159
Worlds End Bookshop, London SW 169

PSYCHOTHERAPY

Alba Books, Grampian 273
Barcombe Services, Essex........................... 108
Delectus Books, London WC....................... 176
Dunstan Books, Dorset 91
Fifteenth Century Bookshop (The), East Sussex. 104
Game Advice, Oxfordshire 208
Greensleeves, Oxfordshire 206
Inner Bookshop (The), Oxfordshire............... 208
Joel Segal Books, Devon 86
Oast Books, Kent 136
Orchid Book Distributors, Co. Clare.............. 262
Outcast Books, Herefordshire....................... 127
Parkinsons Books, Merseyside...................... 185
PsychoBabel Books & Journals, Oxfordshire..... 205
Quentin Books Ltd, Essex........................... 108
Reading Lasses, Dumfries & Galloway 270
Rosemary Pugh Books, Wiltshire 253
Savery Books, East Sussex 100
Treasure Trove Books, Leics........................ 146
Westons, Herts 132
Woburn Books, London N 159

PUBLIC ADMINISTRATION

Reading Lasses, Dumfries & Galloway 270

PUBLIC HEALTH

Bernard Dixon and Kath Adams, London O.... 182
Gladstone Books, Lincolnshire 150
Joel Segal Books, Devon 86
Phelps (Michael), West Sussex..................... 242
R M Books, Herts...................................... 132
Reading Lasses, Dumfries & Galloway 270
Rebecca Hardie Rare Books, London W......... 171
Susanne Schulz-Falster Rare Books, London N. 158
Westons, Herts 132
Woburn Books, London N 159

PUBLIC HOUSES

Anthony Vickers Books, North Yorkshire 195
Debbage (John), Norfolk............................ 189
Joel Segal Books, Devon 86
Lucas (Richard), London NW...................... 161
Thornber (Peter M.), North Yorkshire............ 195
Thorne (John), Essex.................................. 109

PUBLIC SCHOOLS

Delph Books, Greater Manchester................ 120
Jackdaw Books, Norfolk 188
Joel Segal Books, Devon 86
Kirkpatrick (Robert J.), London W 173
Oopalba Books, Cheshire............................ 71
Reading Lasses, Dumfries & Galloway 270
Rutland Bookshop (The), Rutland 211
Thornber (Peter M.), North Yorkshire............ 195
Tiffin (Tony and Gill), Durham 97

Westwood Books Ltd, Cumbria.................... 80
Wise (Derek), East Sussex........................... 104

PUBLIC TRANSPORT

Bath Old Books, Somerset 215
Bott, (Bookdealers) Ltd., (Martin), Greater
  Manchester 118
Falconwood Transport & Military Bookshop,
  London O... 183
Jade Mountain Bookshop, Hampshire 125
Joel Segal Books, Devon 86
Roadmaster Books, Kent 136
Robert Humm & Co, Lincolnshire 152
Salway Books, Essex 112
Tony Pollastrone Railway Books, Wiltshire...... 251
Yesteryear Railwayana, Kent....................... 139

PUBLISHERS
- GENERAL

Adrem Books, Herts 130
Apocalypse, Surrey 232
Aurora Books Ltd, Lothian......................... 275
books2books, Devon.................................. 88
Dinnages Transport Publishing, East Sussex 103
Fifteenth Century Bookshop (The), East Sussex. 104
Ford (Richard), London W 172
G. C. Books Ltd., Dumfries & Galloway......... 270
HCB Wholesale, Powys.............................. 288
Jade Mountain Bookshop, Hampshire 125
Joel Segal Books, Devon 86
Poole (William), London W 174
Robert Temple, London N.......................... 158
Smith Books, (Sally), Suffolk 226
Wheen O'Books, Borders............................ 267
Zardoz Books, Wiltshire............................. 254

- ARABIS BOOKS

Al Saqi Books, London W........................... 171
Art Book Company, (The), Suffolk............... 227

- BATSFORD

Annie's Books, S Yorks 221
Cover to Cover, Merseyside......................... 185
Evergreen Livres, Glos............................... 116
Fifteenth Century Bookshop (The), East Sussex. 104
Heckmondwike Book Shop, West Yorkshire 249
Hennessey Bookseller (Ray), East Sussex 100
Island Books, Devon.................................. 85
Joel Segal Books, Devon 86
Portus Books, Hampshire 122
Roland Books, Kent 138
Samovar Books, Co. Dublin........................ 264

- BISON BOOKS (UNIVERSITY OF
  NEBRASKA)

Americanabooksuk, Cumbria....................... 76

- BLACK, A. & C.

Bolton Books, Hampshire........................... 121
Chapter Two, London SE............................ 163
Charles Bossom, Cambridgeshire................... 65
Fifteenth Century Bookshop (The), East Sussex. 104
Intech Books, Northumberland 201
Joel Segal Books, Devon 86
Missing Books, Essex 109

Paul Hoare, Cornwall 74
Shearwater Books, Northumberland............... 201
Tetbury Old Books, Glos............................. 117
Wheen O'Books, Borders............................. 267

- BLACKIE

Bookmark (Children's Books), Wiltshire.......... 253
Fifteenth Century Bookshop (The), East Sussex. 104
First Edition, The, Essex 109
Grampian Books, Grampian.......................... 273
Green Meadow Books, Cornwall 74
Jean Hedger, Berks................................... 55
Joel Segal Books, Devon 86
Studio (The), Strathclyde 278
Wheen O'Books, Borders............................. 267

- CHAMBERS

Maggy Browne, Lincolnshire 148
Wheen O'Books, Borders............................. 267

- CITY LIGHTS

Needham Books, (Russell), Somerset.............. 219

- COLLINS (CRIME CLB, THE)

Annie's Books, S Yorks 221
Lucius Books, North Yorkshire..................... 197
Ming Books, Dumfries & Galloway 270
Roland Books, Kent 138
Shearwater Books, Northumberland............... 201
Sutcliffe (Mark), West Yorkshire................... 248
Wheen O'Books, Borders............................. 267
Williams (Bookdealer), (Richard), North Lincolnshire
153

- CONWAY

Bott, (Bookdealers) Ltd., (Martin), Greater
Manchester 118

- CUNDALL, JOSEPH

Jean Hedger, Berks.................................. 55

- CURWEN PRESS

Collinge & Clark, London WC...................... 176
John L Capes (Books Maps & Prints), North
Yorkshire.. 196
Myra Dean Illustated Books, Powys 287
Solitaire Books, Somerset........................... 216

- DAVID & CHARLES

Ardis Books, Hampshire 126
Bott, (Bookdealers) Ltd., (Martin), Greater
Manchester 118
Cox (Geoff), Devon 90
Crosby Nethercott Books, London O 180
HCB Wholesale, Powys.............................. 288
Joel Segal Books, Devon 86
Roadmaster Books, Kent............................. 136
Robert Humm & Co, Lincolnshire 152

- EDINBURGH UNIVERSITY

Bell (Peter), Lothian................................. 275
Grampian Books, Grampian.......................... 273
Joel Segal Books, Devon 86

- FOULIS, T.N.

Bolton Books, Hampshire............................ 121
Cameron House Books, Isle of Wight............. 133
Fifteenth Century Bookshop (The), East Sussex. 104
Grampian Books, Grampian.......................... 273
Wheen O'Books, Borders............................. 267

- GHOST STORY PRESS

Fantastic Literature, Essex 110

- GOLLANCZ

Books Only, Suffolk.................................. 226
Joel Segal Books, Devon 86
PsychoBabel Books & Journals, Oxfordshire..... 205
Samovar Books, Co. Dublin......................... 264
Williams (Bookdealer), (Richard), N Lincs....... 153

- GUINNESS

books2books, Devon.................................. 88
Maggy Browne, Lincolnshire 148
Eclectica, London SE 164
Kingfisher Book Service, Nottinghamshire 204

- HACKER ART BOOKS

Art Book Company, (The), Suffolk................ 227

- HAKLUYT SOCIETY, THE

Joel Segal Books, Devon 86
Quaritch Ltd., (Bernard), London W.............. 174

- HARDING, PETER A

Dinnages Transport Publishing, East Sussex 103

- HAYNES PUBLISHING

Colwyn Books, Conwy 283
Joel Segal Books, Devon 86
Maggy Browne, Lincolnshire 148
Roland Books, Kent 138

- HOGARTH PRESS

Eastwood Books (David), Cornwall 72
Ellis, Bookseller (Peter), London WC 177
Evans Books (Paul), West Sussex 243
Fifteenth Century Bookshop (The), East Sussex. 104
Ian McKelvie Bookseller, London N.............. 157
Modern First Editions, West Yorkshire........... 247
Orlando Booksellers, Lincolnshire 150
PsychoBabel Books & Journals, Oxfordshire..... 205
Roz Hulse, Conwy 284

- INCLINE PRESS

Collinge & Clark, London WC...................... 176
Solitaire Books, Somerset........................... 216

- JANE'S MILITARY

Joel Segal Books, Devon 86
Maggy Browne, Lincolnshire 148
Robert Humm & Co, Lincolnshire 152

- JOSEPH LTD., MICHAEL

Annie's Books, S Yorks 221
Archivist (The), Devon............................... 90
Joel Segal Books, Devon 86

Samovar Books, Co. Dublin 264
Wheen O'Books, Borders 267

- KNOPF, A.A.
First Edition, The, Essex 109
Wheen O'Books, Borders 267

- LADYBIRD BOOKS
Annie's Books, S Yorks 221
Apocalypse, Surrey 232
Armchair Books, Lothian 275
Chapter Two, London SE 163
Dolphin Books, Suffolk 225
Dormouse Bookshop (The), Norfolk 189
Elizabeth Ferguson, Grampian 272
Exeter's Antiques Centre on the Quay, Devon... 86
Fifteenth Century Bookshop (The), East Sussex. 104
Green Meadow Books, Cornwall 74
Hawley (C.L.), North Yorkshire 195
Intech Books, Northumberland 201
Jade Mountain Bookshop, Hampshire 125
Joel Segal Books, Devon 86
Kelpie's Books, Fife 271
Key Books (Sarah), Cambridgeshire 64
Kineton Nooks, Warwickshire 236
Oasis Booksearch, Cambridgeshire 67
Old Station Pottery & Bookshop (The), Norfolk 191
Rose's Books, Powys 289
Shakeshaft (Dr. B.), Cheshire 71
Shearwater Books, Northumberland 201
Treasure Trove Books, Leics 146
Whitchurch Books Ltd., Cardiff 281
Wiend Books, Lancashire 143
Williams (Bookdealer), (Richard), N Lincs 153

- LAKESIDE CLASSICS
Americanabooksuk, Cumbria 76

- MARITIME & NAVAL INSTITUTE PRESS
Debbage (John), Norfolk 189
Sea Chest Nautical Bookshop (The), Devon 88

- NISTER
Embleton (Paul), Essex 111
Fifteenth Century Bookshop (The), East Sussex. 104
Jean Hedger, Berks 55
Lake (David), Norfolk 190

- OAKWOOD PRESS
Bott, (Bookdealers) Ltd., (Martin), Greater
  Manchester 118
Coulthurst (Richard), Greater Manchester 120
Crosby Nethercott Books, London O 180
Dales and Lakes Book Centre, Cumbria 79
Robert Humm & Co, Lincolnshire 152

- OBSERVERS BOOKS
Annie's Books, S Yorks 221
Backfold Books, Herefordshire 127
Baker - Books for the Collector (Colin), Devon. 89
Black Cat Bookshop, Leics 147
Dandy Lion Editions, Surrey 233
Fifteenth Century Bookshop (The), East Sussex. 104
Gallimaufry Books, Herts 131
Intech Books, Northumberland 201

Jade Mountain Bookshop, Hampshire 125
Joel Segal Books, Devon 86
Old Station Pottery & Bookshop (The), Norfolk 191
Stella Books, Monmouthshire 286
Whitchurch Books Ltd., Cardiff 281
Williams (Bookdealer), (Richard), N Lincs 153

- OXFORD UNIVERSITY PRESS
Annie's Books, S Yorks 221
BOOKS4U, Flintshire 284
Dolphin Books, Suffolk 225
Draca Books, West Yorkshire 248
Joel Segal Books, Devon 86
Myra Dean Illustated Books, Powys 287
PsychoBabel Books & Journals, Oxfordshire 205
Solitaire Books, Somerset 216
Wheen O'Books, Borders 267

- OXFORD WORLD'S CLASSICS
Criterion Books, London O 181
Elstree Books, Herts 130
PsychoBabel Books & Journals, Oxfordshire 205
Slightly Foxed on Gloucester Road, London SW 167

- PAN
Annie's Books, S Yorks 221
Bookbarrow, Cambridgeshire 63
Evergreen Livres, Glos 116
First Edition, The, Essex 109
Hab Books, London W 172
Heckmondwike Book Shop, West Yorkshire 249
Joel Segal Books, Devon 86
Ming Books, Dumfries & Galloway 270
Orlando Booksellers, Lincolnshire 150
Star Lord Books, Greater Manchester 119
Williams (Bookdealer), (Richard), N Lincs 153
Zardoz Books, Wiltshire 254

- PELICAN
Bass (Ben), Wiltshire 251
Books at the Warehouse, North Yorkshire 193
Evergreen Livres, Glos 116
Fifteenth Century Bookshop (The), East Sussex. 104
Heckmondwike Book Shop, West Yorkshire 249
Joel Segal Books, Devon 86
Orb's Bookshop, Grampian 273
Samovar Books, Co. Dublin 264
Star Lord Books, Greater Manchester 119
Wayside Books and Cards, Oxfordshire 206
Williams (Bookdealer), (Richard), N Lincs 153
Willmott Bookseller (Nicholas), Cardiff 281

- PENGUIN
Annie's Books, S Yorks 221
Arcadia, Oxfordshire 207
Armstrong's Books & Collectables, Leics 145
Backfold Books, Herefordshire 127
Bell (Peter), Lothian 275
Bettridge (Gordon), Fife 271
Black Cat Bookshop, Leics 147
Books at the Warehouse, North Yorkshire 193
Carningli Centre, Pembrokeshire 286
Evergreen Livres, Glos 116
Fifteenth Century Bookshop (The), East Sussex. 104
Grahame Thornton, Bookseller, Dorset 93

Hab Books, London W................................ 172
Heckmondwike Book Shop, West Yorkshire 249
J and J Books, Lincolnshire......................... 149
Jade Mountain Bookshop, Hampshire 125
Joel Segal Books, Devon 86
Ming Books, Dumfries & Galloway 270
Orb's Bookshop, Grampian.......................... 273
Orlando Booksellers, Lincolnshire 150
Price (R.W.), Nottinghamshire 203
PsychoBabel Books & Journals, Oxfordshire..... 205
Richmond Books, North Yorkshire 194
Shearwater Books, Northumberland............... 201
Skelton (Tony), Kent................................. 140
Star Lord Books, Greater Manchester 119
The Sanctuary Bookshop, Dorset.................. 94
Wayside Books and Cards, Oxfordshire 206
Williams (Bookdealer), (Richard), N Lincs....... 153
Willmott Bookseller (Nicholas), Cardiff........... 281
Zardoz Books, Wiltshire............................. 254

- PICKERING, WILLIAM
Cox Old & Rare Books (Claude), Suffolk 227
P. and P. Books, Worcs 256

- POYSERS
Birdnet Optics Ltd., Derbyshire 82
Calluna Books, Dorset............................... 95
Joel Segal Books, Devon 86
Shearwater Books, Northumberland............... 201

- PUFFIN
Annie's Books, S Yorks 221
Books at the Warehouse, North Yorkshire....... 193
Draca Books, West Yorkshire....................... 248
Evergreen Livres, Glos................................ 116
Fifteenth Century Bookshop (The), East Sussex. 104
Heckmondwike Book Shop, West Yorkshire 249
Jean Hedger, Berks.................................... 55
Joel Segal Books, Devon 86
Shearwater Books, Northumberland............... 201
Treasure Trove Books, Leics........................ 146
Williams (Bookdealer), (Richard), N Lincs....... 153
Willmott Bookseller (Nicholas), Cardiff........... 281

- ROUNDWOOD PRESS
Meekins Books (Paul), Warwickshire.............. 237

- SHELL GUIDES
Baker - Books for the Collector (Colin), Devon. 89
Baker (Gerald), Bristol............................... 60
Chris Phillips, Wiltshire.............................. 252
Island Books, Devon.................................. 85
J and J Books, Lincolnshire......................... 149
Joel Segal Books, Devon 86
Sea Chest Nautical Bookshop (The), Devon 88
Staniland (Booksellers), Lincolnshire 152
Whitchurch Books Ltd., Cardiff..................... 281
World War II Books, Surrey 234

- SMALL PRESS
Collinge & Clark, London WC...................... 176
Myra Dean Illustated Books, Powys 287
Norton Books, North Yorkshire.................... 192
Riderless Horse Books, Norfolk.................... 186
Samovar Books, Co. Dublin......................... 264

Woodbine Books, West Yorkshire................ 245

- SOUTHDOWN CLUB
Dinnages Transport Publishing, East Sussex 103

- STUDIO, THE
Apocalypse, Surrey 232
Books & Things, London W......................... 171
Eastwood Books (David), Cornwall 72
Joel Segal Books, Devon 86

- TAUCHNITZ
Beaton (Richard), East Sussex...................... 103
Williams (Bookdealer), (Richard), N Lincs....... 153

- THAMES & HUDSON
Annie's Books, S Yorks 221
Ardis Books, Hampshire 126
Joel Segal Books, Devon 86

- WARNES
Annie's Books, S Yorks 221
Everett (Richard), Norfolk 187
Everett (Richard, at the Southwold
    Antiques Centre), Suffolk.......................... 229
Hine (Anne), Somerset............................... 217
Intech Books, Northumberland 201
J and J Books, Lincolnshire......................... 149
Jean Hedger, Berks.................................... 55
Joel Segal Books, Devon 86
Shearwater Books, Northumberland............... 201
Wheen O'Books, Borders............................ 267

- WISDENS
Coach House Books, Worcs 256
Fifteenth Century Bookshop (The), East Sussex. 104
Grahame Thornton, Bookseller, Dorset........... 93
Joel Segal Books, Devon 86
PsychoBabel Books & Journals, Oxfordshire..... 205
St Mary's Books & Prints, Lincolnshire 152

PUBLISHING
Bettridge (Gordon), Fife............................. 271
Coupland (Terry W.), Staffordshire................ 223
Ford (Richard), London W 172
Kabristan Archives, Shropshire..................... 214
R. & A. Books, East Sussex 101
Roadmaster Books, Kent............................. 136
Smith Books, (Sally), Suffolk 226
Wakeman Books (Frances), Nottinghamshire.... 204

PULPS
Askew Books (Vernon), Wiltshire.................. 251
Book Palace (The), London SE 163
Bristol Books, Bristol 60
Cowley, Bookdealer (K.W.), Somerset 217
Delectus Books, London WC........................ 176
Eggeling Books (John), West Yorkshire 249
High Street Books, Devon 86
Trinity Rare Books, Co. Leitrim 266
Williams (Bookdealer), (Richard), N Lincs....... 153
Zardoz Books, Wiltshire............................. 254

PUNK FANZINES
Marchpane, London WC.............................. 177

Woburn Books, London N 159

PUPPETS & MARIONETTES
Cover to Cover, Merseyside.......................... 185
DaSilva Puppet Books, Dorset 93
Fitzsimons (Anne), Cumbria......................... 76
R. & A. Books, East Sussex 101
Saint Swithin's Illustrated & Children's Books,
London W 174
Westwood Books Ltd, Cumbria.................... 80

PUZZLES
Æenigma Designs (Books), Devon................. 86
Adrem Books, Herts 130
Jean Hedger, Berks.................................... 55
Saint Swithin's Illustrated & Children's Books,
London W 174

QUAKERS, THE
Beckham Books Ltd., Suffolk 229
Bookseeker, Tayside.................................. 280
Dales & Lakes Book Centre, Cumbria............ 79
Hollett and Son (R.F.G.), Cumbria 79
Joel Segal Books, Devon 86
R. & A. Books, East Sussex 101
Rosemary Pugh Books, Wiltshire 253
Woburn Books, London N 159

RADAR
Aardvark Books, Wiltshire........................... 254
Kelly Books Ltd, Devon.............................. 89
R. & A. Books, East Sussex 101
Sea Chest Nautical Bookshop (The), Devon 88
Stroh (M.A.), London E 154
Westons, Herts.. 132

RADICAL ISSUES
Forder (R.W.), Hampshire........................... 121
G. C. Books Ltd., Dumfries & Galloway......... 270
Left on The Shelf, Cumbria......................... 78
Northern Herald Books, West Yorkshire......... 245
Reading Lasses, Dumfries & Galloway 270
Red Star Books, Herts............................... 129
Spurrier (Nick), Kent 137
Star Lord Books, Greater Manchester 119
Woburn Books, London N 159

RADIO/WIRELESS
Bernard Dixon and Kath Adams, London O.... 182
Brad Books, Essex.................................... 110
Cover to Cover, Merseyside.......................... 185
Dormouse Bookshop (The), Norfolk 189
Fifteenth Century Bookshop (The), East Sussex. 104
Greenroom Books, West Yorkshire 247
Hambleton Books, North Yorkshire 196
Joel Segal Books, Devon 86
Kelly Books Ltd, Devon.............................. 89
Maggy Browne, Lincolnshire 148
McGee (Terence J.), London O 180
Old Book Company, (The), West Yorkshire 248
Orb's Bookshop, Grampian.......................... 273
R. & A. Books, East Sussex 101
Roland Books, Kent 138
Sea Chest Nautical Bookshop (The), Devon 88
Stroh (M.A.), London E 154

Transformer, Dumfries & Galloway............... 270
Weiner (Graham), London N 158
Whistler's Books, London SW 169

RADIOLOGY
Bernard Dixon and Kath Adams, London O.... 182
Parkinsons Books, Merseyside...................... 185
R M Books, Herts..................................... 132
R. & A. Books, East Sussex 101
Weiner (Graham), London N 158
Westons, Herts.. 132

RAILWAYS AND RAILROADS
Abacus Gallery, Staffordshire....................... 224
Acumen Books, Staffordshire....................... 224
Adrem Books, Herts 130
Anthony Vickers Books, North Yorkshire 195
Anvil Books, West Midlands 239
Apocalypse, Surrey 232
Arden Books & Cosmographia, Warwickshire... 236
Arthur Hook, Bristol................................. 58
Axe Rare & Out of Print Books (Richard),
North Yorkshire 193
Backfold Books, Herefordshire 127
Baker (Gerald), Bristol.............................. 60
Baldwin (M. & M.), Worcs 255
Barbican Bookshop, North Yorkshire............. 196
Bath Old Books, Somerset 215
Bianco Library, West Sussex........................ 241
Bird Books (Nigel), Ceredigion 283
Black Five Books, Shropshire 214
Book House (The), Cumbria......................... 76
Books, Kent 137
Books & Collectables Ltd., Cambridgeshire 63
Books Afloat, Dorset................................. 96
Books Bought & Sold, Surrey 231
BookShop, The, Dumfries & Galloway........... 270
Bookworms Paradise Ltd., West Sussex 242
Bosorne Books, Cornwall 75
Bott, (Bookdealers) Ltd., (Martin), Greater
Manchester 118
Brad Books, Essex.................................... 110
Brewin Books Ltd., Warwickshire 237
Broadhurst of Southport Ltd., Merseyside 185
Browning Books, Torfaen........................... 292
Bunyan Books, Bedfordshire........................ 53
Carningli Centre, Pembrokeshire................... 286
Cavern Books, Cheshire 70
Cheshire Book Centre, Cheshire.................... 69
Chevin Books, West Yorkshire..................... 249
Clarke Books (David), Somerset 218
Classic Crime Collections, Greater Manchester.. 119
Cobbles Books, Somerset............................ 217
Cobweb Books, North Yorkshire 194
Cofion Books, Pembrokeshire 286
Collectables (W.H.), Suffolk 229
Collectors Corner, Wiltshire........................ 253
Corfe Books, Surrey.................................. 230
Cornucopia Books, Lincolnshire 151
Coulthurst (Richard), Greater Manchester 120
Cox (Geoff), Devon 90
Crosby Nethercott Books, London O 180
Dales & Lakes Book Centre, Cumbria............ 79
Dales and Lakes Book Centre, Cumbria.......... 79
Dave Jelfs, Devon 85

Deeside Books, Grampian............................ 272
Delectus Books, London WC....................... 176
Dinnages Transport Publishing, East Sussex 103
Duck (William), Hampshire......................... 124
Eastcote Bookshop (The), London O 180
Edwards, Fiona, Nottinghamshire 203
Elton Engineering Books, London W 172
Esoteric Dreams Bookshop, Cumbria........... 77
Falconwood Transport & Military Bookshop,
     London O... 183
Farnborough Gallery, Hampshire.................. 122
Fifteenth Century Bookshop (The), East Sussex. 104
Garfi Books, Powys 291
Good Books, Shropshire 213
Grahame Thornton, Bookseller, Dorset.......... 93
Hambleton Books, North Yorkshire 196
Harlequin Books, Bristol 59
Hatchard & Daughters, West Yorkshire 246
Hay Castle, Powys 288
High Street Books, Devon 86
Howard Loftus Rail Books, S Yorks.............. 222
Internet Bookshop UK Ltd., Glos................. 113
Island Books, Devon.................................. 85
J.C. Books, Devon..................................... 87
Jade Mountain Bookshop, Hampshire 125
Joel Segal Books, Devon 86
Jones (Barry), West Sussex 242
Junk & Spread Eagle, London SE.................. 164
Just Books, Cornwall 75
Keegan's Bookshop, Berks 57
Kerr (Norman), Cumbria............................ 77
Kingfisher Book Service, Nottinghamshire 204
Kirkland Books, Cumbria............................ 78
Martin (Books and Pictures), (Brian P.), Surrey. 231
Martin (Brian), Surrey 231
Mercat Books, Highland 274
Milestone Books, Devon 89
My Back Pages, London SW 168
Nevis Railway Books, Oxfordshire 207
Nevis Railway Bookshops (The Antique &
     Book Collector), Wiltshire......................... 252
New Strand, The, Herefordshire 127
Newband (D.M.), Powys 290
Old Celtic Bookshop (The), Devon............... 87
Old Station Pottery & Bookshop (The), Norfolk 191
Over-Sands Books, Cumbria........................ 77
Park Gallery & Bookshop (The),
     Northamptonshire 200
Parlour Bookshop (The), Oxfordshire............. 206
Peter White, Hampshire 121
Postings, Surrey 233
R. & A. Books, East Sussex 101
Railway Book and Magazine Search, Berks...... 56
Railway Shop (The), Torfaen....................... 292
River Reads Bookshop, Devon...................... 90
Roadmaster Books, Kent............................. 136
Robert Humm & Co, Lincolnshire 152
Rochdale Book Company, Greater Manchester . 120
Roland Books, Kent 138
Rolling Stock Books, Greater Manchester........ 120
Roz Hulse, Conwy 284
Saint Swithin's Illustrated & Children's Books,
     London W 174
Salway Books, Essex 112
Sax Books, Suffolk 228

Scrivener's Books & Bookbinding, Derbyshire... 82
Sedgeberrow Books, Worcs 256
Simon Lewis Transport Books, Glos 114
Skyrack Books, West Yorkshire..................... 247
Soccor Books Limited, Lincolnshire 148
Staffs Bookshop (The), Staffordshire 223
Stella Books, Monmouthshire 286
Stroh (M.A.), London E 154
Suffolk Rare Books, Suffolk 229
Tony Pollastrone Railway Books, Wiltshire...... 251
Tozer Railway Books (Nick), West Yorkshire ... 247
Treasure Island (The), Greater Manchester....... 119
Trinders' Fine Tools, Suffolk 226
Uncle Phil's Books, West Midlands 239
Vailima Books, Dumfries & Galloway 269
Weiner (Graham), London N 158
Winchester Bookshop (The), Hampshire.......... 126
Wizard Books, Cambridgeshire...................... 67
Yesteryear Railwayana, Kent........................ 139
Yewtree Books, Cumbria............................. 78
Young (D. & J.), Powys 291

RATIONALISM
Forder (R.W.), Hampshire 121
Humanist Book Services, Cornwall 72
Joel Segal Books, Devon 86
Northern Herald Books, West Yorkshire......... 245
Woburn Books, London N 159

RECYCLING & WASTE MANAGEMENT
Coulthurst (Richard), Greater Manchester 120
Debbage (John), Norfolk............................. 189

REFERENCE
Adrem Books, Herts 130
Archivist (The), Devon............................... 90
Art Reference Books, Hampshire 124
Axe Rare & Out of Print Books (Richard),
     North Yorkshire 193
Books, Denbighshire 284
Corder (Mark W.), Kent 139
Cornucopia Books, Lincolnshire 151
Emjay Books, Surrey.................................. 231
Fifteenth Century Bookshop (The), East Sussex. 104
G. C. Books Ltd., Dumfries & Galloway......... 270
Hurst (Jenny), Kent 137
Joel Segal Books, Devon 86
Maggy Browne, Lincolnshire 148
New Strand, The, Herefordshire 127
R. & A. Books, East Sussex 101
Sax Books, Suffolk 228
Shacklock Books (David), Suffolk 226
Tooley, Adams & Co, Oxfordshire 209

REGISTERS
Brad Books, Essex..................................... 110
Delph Books, Greater Manchester.................. 120
Joel Segal Books, Devon 86
Thornber (Peter M.), North Yorkshire........... 195

RELIGION
- GENERAL
Adrem Books, Herts 130
Alpha Books, London N 156
Annie's Books, S Yorks 221

Armchair Books, Lothian 275
Aurora Books Ltd, Lothian........................ 275
Axe Rare & Out of Print Books (Richard),
    North Yorkshire 193
Barcombe Services, Essex........................ 108
Bardsley's Books, Suffolk........................... 225
Bath Old Books, Somerset 215
Beckham Books Ltd., Suffolk 229
Beware of the Leopard, Bristol 58
Blackwell's Rare Books, Oxfordshire 208
Blythswood Bookshop, Highland 274
Books, Denbighshire 284
Booksets.com Ltd, Shropshire 214
Bookshop at the Plain, Lincolnshire.............. 149
Bookworms Paradise Ltd., West Sussex 242
Bosorne Books, Cornwall 75
Bowie Books & Collectables, East Yorkshire 107
Brimstones, East Sussex 104
Broadwater Books, Hampshire 125
Bunyan Books, Bedfordshire........................ 53
Camilla's Bookshop, East Sussex 101
Canon Gate Books, West Sussex................... 243
Carningli Centre, Pembrokeshire 286
Carraig Books Ltd., Co. Dublin 263
Catalyst Booksearch Services, Devon.............. 87
Chapter Two, London SE........................... 163
Cheshire Book Centre, Cheshire................... 69
Church Street Books, Norfolk 186
Clegg (David), Staffordshire........................ 223
Cobweb Books, North Yorkshire 194
Cofion Books, Pembrokeshire 286
Collectable Books, London SE..................... 163
Colwyn Books, Conwy 283
D'Arcy Books, Wiltshire............................ 252
Ely Books, Cambridgeshire 65
Fifteenth Century Bookshop (The), East Sussex. 104
G. C. Books Ltd., Dumfries & Galloway......... 270
Gage Postal Books, Essex 111
Garfi Books, Powys 291
Geneva Books, London SW 167
Gilbert (R.A.), Somerset............................ 219
Gladstone Books, Lincolnshire 150
Glenbower Books, Co. Dublin 264
Golden Age Books, Worcs.......................... 256
Good for Books, Lincolnshire 149
Hall's Bookshop, Kent.............................. 140
Handsworth Books, Essex........................... 112
Hava Books, London SE............................ 164
Hawley (C.L.), North Yorkshire 195
Hay Cinema Bookshop Ltd., Powys............... 288
HCB Wholesale, Powys............................. 288
Herb Tandree Philosophy Books, Glos 116
Jade Mountain Bookshop, Hampshire 125
Joel Segal Books, Devon 86
Just Books, Cornwall 75
Kyrios Books, Nottinghamshire.................... 203
Last Century Books, Borders 267
Lewis (J.T. & P.), Cornwall........................ 73
Little Bookshop (The), Greater Manchester...... 119
Maggy Browne, Lincolnshire 148
medievalbookshop, Herts........................... 132
Much Binding, Norfolk............................. 186
Murphy (C.J.), Norfolk............................. 189
Needham Books, (Russell), Somerset.............. 219
Old Book Company, (The), West Yorkshire 248

Old Bookshop (The), West Midlands 240
Old Station Pottery & Bookshop (The), Norfolk 191
Parkinsons Books, Merseyside...................... 185
Parrott Books, Oxfordshire 209
Pauline Harries Books, Hampshire 123
Pendleburys Bookshop, London N 158
Pittville Books, Glos................................. 113
Portobello Books, London W 174
Price (John), London N 158
Priestpopple Books, Northumberland 201
Prospect House Books, Co. Down................. 261
PsychoBabel Books & Journals, Oxfordshire..... 205
Pyecroft (Ruth), Glos 116
R. & A. Books, East Sussex 101
Reading Lasses, Dumfries & Galloway 270
Robin Doughty - Fine Books, West Midlands... 238
Roland Books, Kent 138
Roscrea Bookshop & Newsagents,
    Co. Tipperary 266
Rosemary Pugh Books, Wiltshire 253
Rye Old Books, East Sussex 104
St Philip's Books, Oxfordshire...................... 208
Saintfield Antiques & Fine Books, Co. Down ... 261
Salsus Books, Worcs 256
Saunders (Tom), Caerphilly 281
Scott (Peter), East Sussex.......................... 104
Scrivener's Books & Bookbinding, Derbyshire... 82
Sillan Books, Co. Cavan............................ 262
Star Lord Books, Greater Manchester 119
Stroma Books, Borders.............................. 267
Tarka Books, Devon 84
The Sanctuary Bookshop, Dorset.................. 94
Treasure Trove Books, Leics....................... 146
Trinity Rare Books, Co. Leitrim 266
Uncle Phil's Books, West Midlands 239
Walker Fine Books (Steve), Dorset 92
Wayside Books and Cards, Oxfordshire 206
Westwood Books Ltd, Cumbria..................... 80
Wheen O'Books, Borders............................ 267
Wiend Books, Lancashire 143
Wizard Books, Cambridgeshire...................... 67
Worcester Rare Books, Worcs...................... 256

- ARAMAIC CHRISTIANITY

Collectable Books, London SE...................... 163
Michael Graves-Johnston, London SW 168
Thorntons of Oxford Ltd., Oxfordshire........... 206

- BRETHREN

Annie's Books, S Yorks 221
Chapter Two, London SE........................... 163
Copnal Books, Cheshire 69
Gage Postal Books, Essex 111

- BUDDHISM

Blackpool Book Warehouse, Lancashire.......... 142
Bookbarrow, Cambridgeshire........................ 63
Canon Gate Books, West Sussex................... 243
Delectus Books, London WC....................... 176
Hava Books, London SE............................ 164
Inner Bookshop (The), Oxfordshire................ 208
Joel Segal Books, Devon 86
Mandalay Bookshop, London SW 168
Needham Books, (Russell), Somerset.............. 219
Occultique, Northamptonshire...................... 199

Parrott (Jeremy), London E.......................... 154
Pendleburys Bookshop, London N 158
Trinity Rare Books, Co. Leitrim 266
Waxfactor, East Sussex 100

- CATHOLIC
Beckham Books Ltd., Suffolk 229
Bell (Peter), Lothian................................. 275
Bevan (John), Wiltshire.............................. 252
Britons Catholic Library, Co. Wexford 266
Carraig Books Ltd., Co. Dublin 263
Collectable Books, London SE 163
Craobh Rua Books, Co. Armagh 260
Delectus Books, London WC........................ 176
Dolphin Books, Suffolk.............................. 225
Gage Postal Books, Essex 111
Hilton (Books) (P.J.), London W 173
Joel Segal Books, Devon 86
Karen Millward, Co. Cork 263
Killeen (John), North Yorkshire 193
Oasis Booksearch, Cambridgeshire................. 67
Parkinsons Books, Merseyside...................... 185
Pendleburys Bookshop, London N 158
Prospect House Books, Co. Down................. 261
Roscrea Bookshop & Newsagents,
    Co. Tipperary 266
Rye Old Books, East Sussex 104
S.P.C.K., Bristol 59
St Philip's Books, Oxfordshire..................... 208
Salsus Books, Worcs 256
Samovar Books, Co. Dublin 264
Sims (Sue), Dorset................................... 91

- CHRISTIAN
Barbican Bookshop, North Yorkshire............. 196
Beckham Books Ltd., Suffolk 229
Bennett & Kerr Books, Oxfordshire............... 205
Berwick Books, Lincolnshire....................... 150
Bevan (John), Wiltshire.............................. 252
Black Five Books, Shropshire 214
Blythswood Bookshop, Highland 274
Bookshop (The), Co. Donegal...................... 263
Bookshop at the Plain, Lincolnshire.............. 149
Bookworm Alley, Devon 89
Canon Gate Books, West Sussex................... 243
Carnforth Bookshop (The), Lancashire 142
Carraig Books Ltd., Co. Dublin 263
Chapter Two, London SE 163
Chthonios Books, East Sussex...................... 102
Classic Bindings Ltd, London SW 166
Copnal Books, Cheshire 69
Crouch Rare Books, Surrey.......................... 232
Dolphin Books, Suffolk.............................. 225
Evangelical Bookshop, Co. Antrim 260
Facet Books, Dorset................................... 91
Fifteenth Century Bookshop (The), East Sussex. 104
Gage Postal Books, Essex 111
Golden Age Books, Worcs........................... 256
Greensleeves, Oxfordshire 206
Hab Books, London W............................... 172
Hava Books, London SE 164
Hilton (Books) (P.J.), London W 173
Holmes Books (Harry), East Yorkshire.......... 107
Humber Books, Lincolnshire 148
Inner Bookshop (The), Oxfordshire............... 208

Joel Segal Books, Devon 86
Karen Millward, Co. Cork.......................... 263
Kernaghans, Merseyside............................. 185
Kingsmere Books, Bedfordshire 53
Kirkman Ltd., (Robert), Bedfordshire............. 54
Kyrios Books, Nottinghamshire.................... 203
Leo Cadogan, London N 157
medievalbookshop, Herts............................ 132
Oasis Booksearch, Cambridgeshire................. 67
Orb's Bookshop, Grampian.......................... 273
Parkinsons Books, Merseyside...................... 185
Pendleburys Bookshop, London N 158
Price (John), London N 158
Prospect House Books, Co. Down................. 261
Roscrea Bookshop & Newsagents,
    Co. Tipperary 266
Rose Books, Greater Manchester 119
S.P.C.K., Bristol 59
S.P.C.K., Hampshire 126
St Philip's Books, Oxfordshire..................... 208
Salsus Books, Worcs 256
Samovar Books, Co. Dublin 264
Shacklock Books (David), Suffolk 226
Spooner & Co, Somerset 219
Stalagluft Books, Tyne and Wear.................. 235
Staniland (Booksellers), Lincolnshire 152
Thornber (Peter M.), North Yorkshire............ 195
Thorntons of Oxford Ltd., Oxfordshire........... 206
Trinity Rare Books, Co. Leitrim 266
Tuft (Patrick), London O 181
Victoria Bookshop (The), Devon................... 84
Walker Fine Books (Steve), Dorset 92
Wayside Books and Cards, Oxfordshire 206
Wheen O'Books, Borders............................. 267
Williams (Bookdealer), (Richard), N Lincs....... 153
Woburn Books, London N 159

- CHRISTIAN SPIRITISM
Stalagluft Books, Tyne and Wear.................. 235
Trinity Rare Books, Co. Leitrim 266

- CHRISTIANITY, SYRIAN ORTHODOX
Broadwater Books, Hampshire 125
Michael Graves-Johnston, London SW 168
Needham Books, (Russell), Somerset............. 219
Salsus Books, Worcs 256
Samovar Books, Co. Dublin 264
Trinity Rare Books, Co. Leitrim 266
Winghale Books, Lincolnshire 152

- CHURCH OF ENGLAND
Beckham Books Ltd., Suffolk 229
Bell (Peter), Lothian................................. 275
Broadwater Books, Hampshire 125
Collectable Books, London SE 163
Dolphin Books, Suffolk.............................. 225
Gage Postal Books, Essex 111
Hilton (Books) (P.J.), London W 173
Jackdaw Books, Norfolk 188
Joel Segal Books, Devon 86
Oasis Booksearch, Cambridgeshire................. 67
Olynthiacs, Shropshire 213
Parkinsons Books, Merseyside...................... 185
Pendleburys Bookshop, London N 158
Rye Old Books, East Sussex 104

S.P.C.K., Bristol 59
Stalagluft Books, Tyne and Wear 235
Williams (Bookdealer), (Richard), N Lincs 153
Woburn Books, London N 159

- COPTIC
Michael Graves-Johnston, London SW 168
P. and P. Books, Worcs 256

- DRUIDISM
Cymric Books, Berks 56

- HEBRAICA
baconboooks, London WC 176
Beckham Books Ltd., Suffolk 229
Chthonios Books, East Sussex 102
Delectus Books, London WC 176
Fishburn Books, London NW 160
Golden Age Books, Worcs 256
Hava Books, London SE 164
Joel Segal Books, Devon 86
Needham Books, (Russell), Somerset 219
Pendleburys Bookshop, London N 158
Samovar Books, Co. Dublin 264
Thorntons of Oxford Ltd., Oxfordshire 206
Trinity Rare Books, Co. Leitrim 266

- HINDI
Collectable Books, London SE 163
Inner Bookshop (The), Oxfordshire 208

- HINDU
Bookbarrow, Cambridgeshire 63
Delectus Books, London WC 176
Inner Bookshop (The), Oxfordshire 208
Needham Books, (Russell), Somerset 219
Pendleburys Bookshop, London N 158

- ISLAM
Al Saqi Books, London W 171
Beckham Books Ltd., Suffolk 229
Books on Spain, London O 182
Delectus Books, London WC 176
Folios Limited, London SW 167
Inner Bookshop (The), Oxfordshire 208
Joppa Books Ltd., Surrey 230
Kingswood Books, Dorset 94
Needham Books, (Russell), Somerset 219
Occultique, Northamptonshire 199
Pendleburys Bookshop, London N 158
Quaritch Ltd., (Bernard), London W 174
Samovar Books, Co. Dublin 264
Thorntons of Oxford Ltd., Oxfordshire 206
Trinity Rare Books, Co. Leitrim 266
Trotter Books (John), London N 158

- JAINISM
Collectable Books, London SE 163
Needham Books, (Russell), Somerset 219

- JEHOVAH'S WITNESSES
Golden Age Books, Worcs 256

- JESUITS, THE
Hodgson (Judith), London W 173

Pendleburys Bookshop, London N 158
St Philip's Books, Oxfordshire 208
Samovar Books, Co. Dublin 264
Trinity Rare Books, Co. Leitrim 266

- JEWISH
baconboooks, London WC 176
Beckham Books Ltd., Suffolk 229
Books on Spain, London O 182
Collectable Books, London SE 163
Delectus Books, London WC 176
Fishburn Books, London NW 160
Golden Age Books, Worcs 256
Inner Bookshop (The), Oxfordshire 208
Joel Segal Books, Devon 86
Needham Books, (Russell), Somerset 219
Occultique, Northamptonshire 199
Pendleburys Bookshop, London N 158
Samovar Books, Co. Dublin 264
Thorntons of Oxford Ltd., Oxfordshire 206
Trotter Books (John), London N 158
Woburn Books, London N 159

- METHODISM
Barbican Bookshop, North Yorkshire 196
Beckham Books Ltd., Suffolk 229
Bookshop at the Plain, Lincolnshire 149
Gage Postal Books, Essex 111
Humber Books, Lincolnshire 148
Joel Segal Books, Devon 86
MK Book Services, Cambridgeshire 66
Oasis Booksearch, Cambridgeshire 67
Parkinsons Books, Merseyside 185
Pendleburys Bookshop, London N 158
Price (John), London N 158
Rosley Books, Cumbria 81
S.P.C.K., Bristol 59
Samovar Books, Co. Dublin 264

- MORMONISM
Trinity Rare Books, Co. Leitrim 266

- MUSLIM
Al Saqi Books, London W 171
Collectable Books, London SE 163
Delectus Books, London WC 176
Joppa Books Ltd., Surrey 230
Needham Books, (Russell), Somerset 219
Occultique, Northamptonshire 199
Thorntons of Oxford Ltd., Oxfordshire 206

- NON CONFORMITY
Beckham Books Ltd., Suffolk 229
Chapter Two, London SE 163
Gage Postal Books, Essex 111
Humber Books, Lincolnshire 148
Joel Segal Books, Devon 86
Oasis Booksearch, Cambridgeshire 67
Parkinsons Books, Merseyside 185
Pendleburys Bookshop, London N 158
Price (John), London N 158
Richard Thornton Books, London N 158
S.P.C.K., Bristol 59
Samovar Books, Co. Dublin 264
Stalagluft Books, Tyne and Wear 235

- ORIENTAL

Canon Gate Books, West Sussex.................. 243
Chthonios Books, East Sussex...................... 102
Greensleeves, Oxfordshire 206
Inner Bookshop (The), Oxfordshire................ 208
Joel Segal Books, Devon 86
Needham Books, (Russell), Somerset.............. 219
Occultique, Northamptonshire...................... 199
Peter M Daly, Hampshire 126
Thorntons of Oxford Ltd., Oxfordshire........... 206
Trinity Rare Books, Co. Leitrim................... 266
Trotter Books (John), London N.................. 158

- PARSEEISM

Collectable Books, London SE..................... 163

- PRESBYTERIAN

Beckham Books Ltd., Suffolk 229
Bell (Peter), Lothian.............................. 275
Broadwater Books, Hampshire..................... 125
Pendleburys Bookshop, London N 158
Prospect House Books, Co. Down.................. 261
S.P.C.K., Bristol 59
Samovar Books, Co. Dublin........................ 264
Trinity Rare Books, Co. Leitrim................... 266
Wheen O'Books, Borders........................... 267

- PRE-VATICAN II CATHOLICISM

Parkinsons Books, Merseyside...................... 185
S.P.C.K., Bristol 59
St Philip's Books, Oxfordshire..................... 208
Samovar Books, Co. Dublin........................ 264
Stalagluft Books, Tyne and Wear.................. 235

- PROTESTANTISM

Beckham Books Ltd., Suffolk 229
Butler Rare Books, Buckinghamshire 61
Collectable Books, London SE..................... 163
Dolphin Books, Suffolk............................ 225
Gage Postal Books, Essex 111
Hilton (Books) (P.J.), London W 173
Humber Books, Lincolnshire 148
Joel Segal Books, Devon 86
Parkinsons Books, Merseyside...................... 185
Pendleburys Bookshop, London N 158
Price (John), London N 158
Prospect House Books, Co. Down.................. 261
S.P.C.K., Bristol 59
Samovar Books, Co. Dublin........................ 264
Spooner & Co, Somerset 219

- PURITANISM

Beckham Books Ltd., Suffolk 229
Gage Postal Books, Essex 111
Humber Books, Lincolnshire 148
Modern First Editions, West Yorkshire........... 247
Old Book Company, (The), West Yorkshire..... 248
Parkinsons Books, Merseyside...................... 185
S.P.C.K., Bristol 59
Samovar Books, Co. Dublin........................ 264
Spooner & Co, Somerset 219

- QUAKERS

Barbican Bookshop, North Yorkshire............. 196
Beckham Books Ltd., Suffolk 229

Bookseeker, Tayside................................ 280
Dales & Lakes Book Centre, Cumbria........... 79
Joel Segal Books, Devon 86
Post–Horn Books, North Yorkshire................ 192
Prospect House Books, Co. Down.................. 261
Robin Doughty - Fine Books, West Midlands... 238
Rosley Books, Cumbria 81
S.P.C.K., Bristol 59
Samovar Books, Co. Dublin........................ 264
Trinity Rare Books, Co. Leitrim................... 266

- SALVATION ARMY

Bookworm Alley, Devon 89
Collectable Books, London SE..................... 163
Dolphin Books, Suffolk............................ 225
Gage Postal Books, Essex 111
Prospect House Books, Co. Down.................. 261
Samovar Books, Co. Dublin........................ 264

- SIKH

Needham Books, (Russell), Somerset.............. 219
Trinity Rare Books, Co. Leitrim................... 266

- TAOISM

Chthonios Books, East Sussex...................... 102
Collectable Books, London SE..................... 163
Inner Bookshop (The), Oxfordshire................ 208
Joel Segal Books, Devon 86
Needham Books, (Russell), Somerset.............. 219
Occultique, Northamptonshire...................... 199

RELIGIOUS TEXTS

Apocalypse, Surrey 232
Beckham Books Ltd., Suffolk 229
Brimstones, East Sussex 104
Carraig Books Ltd., Co. Dublin 263
Chthonios Books, East Sussex...................... 102
Fifteenth Century Bookshop (The), East Sussex. 104
Foster Bookshop (Paul), London SW 167
Golden Age Books, Worcs.......................... 256
Hava Books, London SE............................ 164
Magis Books, Leics................................ 146
Needham Books, (Russell), Somerset.............. 219
Parkinsons Books, Merseyside...................... 185
Pendleburys Bookshop, London N 158
Rosemary Pugh Books, Wiltshire 253
Samovar Books, Co. Dublin........................ 264
Trotter Books (John), London N 158

REMAINDERS

Dalbeattie Books, Dumfries & Galloway 269
David (G.), Cambridgeshire......................... 63
Don Kelly Books, London W 172
HCB Wholesale, Powys............................. 288
Minster Gate Bookshop, North Yorkshire 197
Pendleburys Bookshop, London N 158
Westwood Books Ltd, Cumbria.................... 80

REVOLUTIONS

Dolphin Books, Suffolk............................ 225
Left on The Shelf, Cumbria........................ 78
Red Star Books, Herts............................. 129
Woburn Books, London N 159

RHETORIC
Price (John), London N 158

RHODESIANA
Chalmers Hallam (E.), Hampshire................. 125
Kenya Books, East Sussex 100
Smith (Ray), Herts 129

RIVER BOATS & RIVER MEN
Baldwin (M. & M.), Worcs 255
Cox (Geoff), Devon 90
Fifteenth Century Bookshop (The), East Sussex. 104
Joel Segal Books, Devon 86
Marine & Cannon Books, Cheshire 71
Marine and Cannon Books, Cheshire............. 69
McLaren Books Ltd, Strathclyde 279
Sea Chest Nautical Bookshop (The), Devon 88

RIVER THAMES
Apocalypse, Surrey 232
Baldwin (M. & M.), Worcs 255
Cornucopia Books, Lincolnshire 151
Elton Engineering Books, London W 172
Empire Books, North Yorkshire 197
Fifteenth Century Bookshop (The), East Sussex. 104
Island Books, Devon................................. 85
Marine and Cannon Books, Cheshire............. 69
Martin (Books and Pictures), (Brian P.), Surrey. 231
R. & A. Books, East Sussex 101
Salway Books, Essex 112
Sea Chest Nautical Bookshop (The), Devon 88
Tooley, Adams & Co, Oxfordshire 209

ROCK ART
Book Palace (The), London SE 163
Print Matters, London SE........................... 165
R. & A. Books, East Sussex 101
Whitchurch Books Ltd., Cardiff.................... 281

ROLE-PLAYING
SaBeRo Books, London SW........................ 169

ROMANCE
Annie's Books, S Yorks 221
Apocalypse, Surrey 232
Eggeling Books (John), West Yorkshire 249
First Edition, The, Essex 109
Wheen O'Books, Borders............................ 267

ROMANTICISM
Hawley (C.L.), North Yorkshire 195
Joel Segal Books, Devon 86
Price (John), London N 158
Quaritch Ltd., (Bernard), London W.............. 174
R. & A. Books, East Sussex 101
Robert Temple, London N........................... 158

ROPEMAKING & KNOTS
Chalmers Hallam (E.), Hampshire................. 125
Debbage (John), Norfolk............................. 189
Footrope Knots, Suffolk.............................. 227
Marine and Cannon Books, Cheshire............. 69
Mercat Books, Highland 274

ROSICRUCIANISM
Gildas Books, Cheshire.............................. 68
Green Man Books, East Sussex 101
Inner Bookshop (The), Oxfordshire............... 208
Magis Books, Leics................................... 146
Occultique, Northamptonshire...................... 199
SETI Books, West Midlands........................ 239

ROYALTY
- GENERAL
Annie's Books, S Yorks 221
Barn Books, Buckinghamshire...................... 61
Books & Collectables Ltd., Cambridgeshire...... 63
Bookworms Paradise Ltd., West Sussex 242
Dally (Andrew), Powys 289
Dolphin Books, Suffolk.............................. 225
Farahar & Dupre (Clive & Sophie), Wiltshire ... 251
Fifteenth Century Bookshop (The), East Sussex. 104
First Edition, The, Essex 109
Hay Cinema Bookshop Ltd., Powys............... 288
Heraldry Today, Wiltshire........................... 253
Heritage, West Midlands 238
Jade Mountain Bookshop, Hampshire 125
Kingfisher Book Service, Nottinghamshire 204
Lost Books, Northamptonshire...................... 200
New Strand, The, Herefordshire 127
Park Gallery & Bookshop (The), Northants 200
Piccadilly Rare Books, East Sussex 105
Quadrille at Delehar, London W................... 174
R. & A. Books, East Sussex 101
Saint Swithin's Illustrated & Children's Books,
   London W 174
Sax Books, Suffolk 228
Shacklock Books (David), Suffolk 226
Ventnor Rare Books, Isle of Wight................ 134
Wheen O'Books, Borders............................ 267
Yesterday's News, Conwy........................... 283

- EUROPEAN
Annie's Books, S Yorks 221
Dolphin Books, Suffolk.............................. 225
Kingfisher Book Service, Nottinghamshire 204
Orb's Bookshop, Grampian.......................... 273
Piccadilly Rare Books, East Sussex 105
Saintfield Antiques & Fine Books, Co. Down ... 261

ROYCROFT
Atholl Fine Books, Tayside 280

RUBAIYAT OF OMAR KHAYYAM
Baker - Books for the Collector (Colin), Devon. 89
Cornucopia Books, Lincolnshire 151
Fifteenth Century Bookshop (The), East Sussex. 104
Inner Bookshop (The), Oxfordshire............... 208
N1 Books, East Sussex 105
R. & A. Books, East Sussex 101

RUGS
Apocalypse, Surrey 232
Byrom Textile Bookroom (Richard), Lancashire 142
Cover to Cover, Merseyside......................... 185
Don Kelly Books, London W 172
Judith Mansfield, West Yorkshire.................. 249
Reading Lasses, Dumfries & Galloway 270
Sleepy Elephant Books & Artefacts, Cumbria ... 80

Smith Books (Keith), Herefordshire 128
Thornber (Peter M.), North Yorkshire............ 195
Trinders' Fine Tools, Suffolk 226
Whittle, Bookseller (Avril), Cumbria 80

RUPERT BEAR

Annie's Books, S Yorks 221
Beck (John), East Sussex 103
Bookmark (Children's Books), Wiltshire.......... 253
Charles Bossom, Cambridgeshire 65
Children's Bookshop (The), Herefordshire....... 127
Dales & Lakes Book Centre, Cumbria............ 79
Dennys Sanders & Greene Ltd, East Sussex 100
Draca Books, West Yorkshire...................... 248
Fifteenth Century Bookshop (The), East Sussex. 104
First Edition, The, Essex 109
Joel Segal Books, Devon 86
R. & A. Books, East Sussex 101
Simpson (Dave), Central 268
Stella Books, Monmouthshire 286

RURAL LIFE

2 Ravens, Cumbria.................................. 78
Anwoth Books Ltd, Dumfries & Galloway 269
Arden Books & Cosmographia, Warwickshire... 236
Arnold (Roy), Suffolk............................... 227
Backfold Books, Herefordshire..................... 127
Barn Books, Shropshire.............................. 214
Blest (Peter), Kent 138
Books for Content, Herefordshire.................. 127
Brad Books, Essex................................... 110
Campbell Hewson Books (R.), Fife................ 271
Carningli Centre, Pembrokeshire................... 286
Chalmers Hallam (E.), Hampshire................. 125
Chantrey Books, S Yorks 222
Church Green Books, Oxfordshire.................. 210
Clarke Books (David), Somerset 218
Cobbles Books, Somerset............................ 217
Coch-y-Bonddu Books, Powys...................... 290
Colonsay Bookshop, Isle of Colonsay............. 275
Cornucopia Books, Lincolnshire 151
Cottage Books, Leics................................ 145
Country Books, Derbyshire 82
Cover to Cover, Merseyside......................... 185
Cox (Geoff), Devon 90
Crabtree (Mrs. C.), Greater Manchester 120
Dales & Lakes Book Centre, Cumbria............ 79
Dolphin Books, Suffolk.............................. 225
Doorbar (P. & D.), Gwynedd 285
Dusty Books, Powys 290
Fifteenth Century Bookshop (The), East Sussex. 104
Fireside Bookshop, Cumbria........................ 81
Furneaux Books (Lee), Devon....................... 89
Greta Books, Durham 97
Grove Bookshop (The), North Yorkshire 195
Harvest Books, Lancashire.......................... 144
Home Farm Books, Warwickshire.................. 236
J & J Burgess Booksellers, Cambridgeshire....... 64
Joel Segal Books, Devon 86
Keeble Antiques, Somerset.......................... 218
Kelpie's Books, Fife................................. 271
Kilgour (Sporting Books) (Ian), Leics............. 147
Kingfisher Book Service, Nottinghamshire 204
Martin (Books and Pictures), (Brian P.), Surrey. 231
Martin (Brian), Surrey 231

McCrone (Audrey), Isle of Arran.................. 274
Mercat Books, Highland 274
Michael Bishop PBFA, Somerset 220
Missing Books, Essex 109
Moss End Bookshop, Berks 57
Mount's Bay Books, Cornwall 74
Murphy (C.J.), Norfolk............................. 189
Muttonchop Manuscripts, West Sussex 242
Orb's Bookshop, Grampian......................... 273
Park (Mike), London O 182
Petworth Antique Market (Bookroom),
    West Sussex.................................... 244
Phenotype Books, Cumbria......................... 79
Ramrod Antiques, North Yorkshire............... 195
Randall (Tom), Somerset............................ 218
Read - Gorleston Books, (C.&J.), Norfolk 187
River Reads Bookshop, Devon...................... 90
Roadmaster Books, Kent............................ 136
Rods Books, Devon 88
Rutland Bookshop (The), Rutland 211
Shacklock Books (David), Suffolk 226
Singleton (Anthony), S Yorks 221
Uncle Phil's Books, West Midlands 239
Wheen O'Books, Borders............................ 267
Woodbine Books, West Yorkshire.................. 245

SALES & MARKETING

Crabtree (Mrs. C.), Greater Manchester 120
PsychoBabel Books & Journals, Oxfordshire..... 205

SALVATION ARMY

Hollett and Son (R.F.G.), Cumbria 79
R. & A. Books, East Sussex 101
Roscrea Bookshop & Newsagents,
    Co. Tipperary 266
Samovar Books, Co. Dublin........................ 264

SATIRE

Adrem Books, Herts 130
Burmester (James), Bristol.......................... 58
Cornucopia Books, Lincolnshire 151
Fifteenth Century Bookshop (The), East Sussex. 104
Price (John), London N 158
Print Matters, London SE........................... 165
Yesterday's News, Conwy........................... 283

SCHOOL REGISTERS/
ROLLS OF HONOUR

Camilla's Bookshop, East Sussex 101
Coach House Books, Worcs 256
Delph Books, Greater Manchester.................. 120
Heraldry Today, Wiltshire........................... 253
Joel Segal Books, Devon 86
Military Bookworm, London SE..................... 164
Palladour Books, Hampshire 125
Tiffin (Tony and Gill), Durham 97
Townsend (John), Berks 57
Turton (John), Durham 98
Williams (Bookdealer), (Richard), N Lincs....... 153
Wise (Derek), East Sussex 104
World War Books, Kent 141

SCHOOLS - GENERAL

Barcombe Services, Essex............................ 108
Kirkpatrick (Robert J.), London W 173

Williams (Bookdealer), (Richard), N Lincs 153

SCIENCE
- GENERAL

Alba Books, Grampian 273
Andrew Hunter Rare Books, London SW 166
Aurora Books Ltd, Lothian........................ 275
Baldwin's Scientific Books, Essex 111
Barcombe Services, Essex........................... 108
Baron - Scientific Book Sales (P.J.), Somerset ... 216
Baron (Christopher), Cheshire.................... 68
Bernard Dixon and Kath Adams, London O.... 182
Beware of the Leopard, Bristol.................... 58
Bodders Books, Shropshire........................ 212
Book Annex (The), Essex 109
Bookcase, Cumbria................................. 76
Books & Collectables Ltd., Cambridgeshire 63
Bookshop (The), Co. Donegal..................... 263
Camden Books, Somerset 215
Carningli Centre, Pembrokeshire 286
Cheshire Book Centre, Cheshire................... 69
David (G.), Cambridgeshire........................ 63
Eagle Bookshop (The), Bedfordshire 53
Finch Rare Books Ltd. (Simon), London W.... 172
Gaskell Rare Books (Roger), Cambridgeshire ... 66
GfB: the Colchester Bookshop, Essex 108
Glenbower Books, Co. Dublin 264
Good for Books, Lincolnshire 149
Hay Cinema Bookshop Ltd., Powys.............. 288
Hollett and Son (R.F.G.), Cumbria 79
Hünersdorff Rare Books, London SW 168
Hurst (Jenny), Kent 137
Ice House Books, Wiltshire 254
Innes Books, Shropshire............................ 212
J.C. Books, Devon................................. 87
Jay Books, Lothian................................ 276
Jenny Hurst, Kent 138
Just Books, Cornwall 75
Lawson & Company (E.M.), Oxfordshire 206
Lenton (Alfred), Leics.............................. 145
Lewis (J.T. & P.), Cornwall 73
Little Stour Books, Kent 136
Lymelight Books & Prints, Dorset 93
Macfarlane (Mr. H.), Essex 111
McCrone (Audrey), Isle of Arran.................. 274
McGee (Terence J.), London O 180
Mogul Diamonds, West Midlands................. 240
Mollie's Loft, Swansea............................. 291
Moorside Books, Lancashire....................... 143
Much Binding, Norfolk............................ 186
O'Flynn Books, North Yorkshire.................. 197
Orangeberry Books, Oxfordshire.................. 207
Parkinsons Books, Merseyside..................... 185
Pauline Harries Books, Hampshire 123
Phillips (Nigel), Hampshire........................ 122
Pickering & Chatto, London W 174
Plurabelle Books, Cambridgeshire................. 65
Pollak (P.M.), Devon 88
Prospect House Books, Co. Down................. 261
PsychoBabel Books & Journals, Oxfordshire..... 205
Quaritch Ltd., (Bernard), London W.............. 174
Quinto of Charing Cross Road, London WC ... 178
R M Books, Herts................................. 132
Rebecca Hardie Rare Books, London W 171
Roberts Books, Strathclyde 279

Rogers Turner Books, London SE................. 165
Scrivener's Books & Bookbinding, Derbyshire... 82
Smith (David & Lynn), London O 181
Staniland (Booksellers), Lincolnshire 152
Stern Antiquarian Bookseller (Jeffrey), North
  Yorkshire...................................... 198
Stroh (M.A.), London E 154
The Sanctuary Bookshop, Dorset................. 94
Tony Hutchinson, Surrey.......................... 233
Transformer, Dumfries & Galloway............... 270
Turret House, Norfolk............................. 191
Wayside Books and Cards, Oxfordshire 206
Weiner (Graham), London N 158
Westons, Herts.................................... 132
Westwood Books Ltd, Cumbria................... 80
Wheen O'Books, Borders.......................... 267
Whistler's Books, London SW 169
Worcester Rare Books, Worcs..................... 256

- FOOD

baconboooks, London WC 176
Bernard Dixon and Kath Adams, London O.... 182
Parkinsons Books, Merseyside..................... 185
Pollak (P.M.), Devon 88
Westons, Herts.................................... 132

- FORENSIC

Bernard Dixon and Kath Adams, London O.... 182
Bolland Books, Bedfordshire....................... 53
Cheshire Book Centre, Cheshire................... 69
ForensicSearch, Herts.............................. 131
Pollak (P.M.), Devon 88
Wayside Books and Cards, Oxfordshire 206

- HISTORY OF

Axe Rare & Out of Print Books (Richard),
  North Yorkshire 193
Baldwin's Scientific Books, Essex 111
Barcombe Services, Essex........................... 108
Baron (Christopher), Cheshire.................... 68
Bernard Dixon and Kath Adams, London O.... 182
Booksets.com Ltd, Shropshire..................... 214
Camden Books, Somerset 215
Cheshire Book Centre, Cheshire................... 69
Chesters (G. & J.), Staffordshire 224
Clevedon Books, Somerset 217
David (G.), Cambridgeshire........................ 63
Dean Byass, Bristol............................... 60
Earth Science Books, Wiltshire 252
Erian Books, London N........................... 156
Esplin (David), Hampshire......................... 124
Fireside Bookshop, Cumbria....................... 81
Gladstone Books, Lincolnshire 150
Hamish Riley-Smith, Norfolk...................... 191
Hindsight Books, Herts............................ 131
Jay Books, Lothian................................ 276
Joel Segal Books, Devon 86
Judd Books, London WC.......................... 177
Kingswood Books, Dorset 94
Mair Wilkes Books, Fife 271
McGee (Terence J.), London O 180
Moorside Books, Lancashire....................... 143
N1 Books, East Sussex 105
Old Book Company, (The), West Yorkshire 248
Orb's Bookshop, Grampian........................ 273

Park (Mike), London O 182
Parkinsons Books, Merseyside...................... 185
Phelps (Michael), West Sussex...................... 242
Phillips (Nigel), Hampshire.......................... 122
Plurabelle Books, Cambridgeshire................. 65
Pollak (P.M.), Devon 88
Pordes Books Ltd., (Henry), London WC........ 177
Price (John), London N 158
PsychoBabel Books & Journals, Oxfordshire..... 205
Quaritch Ltd., (Bernard), London W.............. 174
R M Books, Herts..................................... 132
Rebecca Hardie Rare Books, London W......... 171
Roger Collicott Books, Cornwall 74
Rogers Turner Books, London SE................. 165
Rowan (P. & B.), Co. Antrim 260
Savona Books, Lincolnshire........................ 151
Smith (David & Lynn), London O 181
Stalagluft Books, Tyne and Wear.................. 235
Sue Lowell Natural History Books, London W . 175
Susanne Schulz-Falster Rare Books, London N. 158
Turret House, Norfolk............................... 191
Wayside Books and Cards, Oxfordshire 206
Weiner (Graham), London N 158
Westwood Books (Mark), Powys 289
Westwood Books Ltd, Cumbria.................... 80
Whitchurch Books Ltd., Cardiff.................... 281
Woburn Books, London N 159
Worcester Rare Books, Worcs...................... 256
Wyseby House Books, Berks 55

- PURE & APPLIED

Andrew Hunter Rare Books, London SW 166
Baldwin's Scientific Books, Essex 111
Barcombe Services, Essex........................... 108
Bernard Dixon and Kath Adams, London O.... 182
Book Annex (The), Essex 109
Glenbower Books, Co. Dublin 264
Old Book Company, (The), West Yorkshire..... 248
Parkinsons Books, Merseyside...................... 185
Pollak (P.M.), Devon 88
PsychoBabel Books & Journals, Oxfordshire..... 205
R M Books, Herts..................................... 132
Roberts Books, Strathclyde 279
The Sanctuary Bookshop, Dorset................. 94
Transformer, Dumfries & Galloway............... 270
Wayside Books and Cards, Oxfordshire 206
Weiner (Graham), London N 158
Westons, Herts.. 132

SCIENTIFIC INSTRUMENTS

Andrew Hunter Rare Books, London SW 166
Arnold (Roy), Suffolk................................ 227
Baron (Christopher), Cheshire...................... 68
Bernard Dixon and Kath Adams, London O.... 182
Formby Antiques (Jeffrey), Glos 115
Hadfield (G.K.), Cumbria 79
McGee (Terence J.), London O 180
Old Book Company, (The), West Yorkshire..... 248
Parkinsons Books, Merseyside...................... 185
Phelps (Michael), West Sussex...................... 242
Pollak (P.M.), Devon 88
Rogers Turner Books, London SE................. 165
Savona Books, Lincolnshire........................ 151
Smith (David & Lynn), London O 181

Tony Hutchinson, Surrey............................ 233
Trinders' Fine Tools, Suffolk 226
Turret House, Norfolk............................... 191
Wayside Books and Cards, Oxfordshire 206
Weiner (Graham), London N 158
Westons, Herts.. 132

SCIENTISTS

Baldwin's Scientific Books, Essex 111
Barcombe Services, Essex........................... 108
Bernard Dixon and Kath Adams, London O.... 182
Earth Science Books, Wiltshire 252
Gladstone Books, Lincolnshire 150
Joel Segal Books, Devon 86
K.S.C. Books, Cheshire.............................. 70
McGee (Terence J.), London O 180
Old Book Company, (The), West Yorkshire..... 248
Parkinsons Books, Merseyside...................... 185
Pollak (P.M.), Devon 88
R M Books, Herts..................................... 132
Wayside Books and Cards, Oxfordshire 206
Weiner (Graham), London N 158

SCOTTISH ENLIGHTENMENT

Atholl Fine Books, Tayside 280
Grampian Books, Grampian......................... 273
Hamish Riley-Smith, Norfolk....................... 191
Leakey's Bookshop, Highland 274
Loch Croispol Bookshop & Restaurant,
    Highland 273
Mercat Books, Highland 274
Orb's Bookshop, Grampian......................... 273
Pringle Booksellers (Andrew), Lothian............ 277
Quaritch Ltd., (Bernard), London W.............. 174
Susanne Schulz-Falster Rare Books, London N. 158

SCOTTISH INTEREST

Adrem Books, Herts 130
Alba Books, Grampian 273
Andrew Hunter Rare Books, London SW 166
Anwoth Books Ltd, Dumfries & Galloway 269
Armchair Books, Lothian 275
Atholl Fine Books, Tayside 280
Aurora Books Ltd, Lothian.......................... 275
Axe Rare & Out of Print Books (Richard),
    North Yorkshire 193
Backfold Books, Herefordshire..................... 127
Bell (Peter), Lothian................................. 275
Benny Gillies Books Ltd, Dumfries & Galloway 268
Big Bairn Books, Tayside 279
Blacket Books, Lothian.............................. 276
Books At The Barras, Lanarkshire 278
BookShop, The, Dumfries & Galloway........... 270
Bookworm (The), Lothian 276
Bouquiniste Bookshop, Fife......................... 271
Byre Books, Dumfries & Galloway................ 270
Caledonia Books, Strathclyde...................... 278
Cheshire Book Centre, Cheshire.................... 69
Chesters (G. & J.), Staffordshire 224
Coleman (Tom), Highland 273
Colonsay Bookshop, Isle of Colonsay............. 275
Cooper Hay Rare Books, Strathclyde 278
Cornucopia Books, Lincolnshire 151
Cottage Books, Leics 145
Craobh Rua Books, Co. Armagh 260

Creaking Shelves, Highland 274
Dalbeattie Books, Dumfries & Galloway 269
Darkwood Books, Co. Cork......................... 263
Duncan & Reid, Lothian 276
Farquharson, (Hilary), Tayside..................... 280
Ferguson (Elizabeth), Grampian 272
Fifteenth Century Bookshop (The), East Sussex. 104
Freader's Books, Tayside 279
G. C. Books Ltd., Dumfries & Galloway......... 270
Georgina Hobhouse, Argyll......................... 274
Glacier Books, Tayside 280
Grampian Books, Grampian......................... 273
Grayling (David A.H.), Cumbria 78
Greta Books, Durham 97
Jane Jones Books, Grampian 273
Kings Bookshop Callander, Central 268
Leakey's Bookshop, Highland 274
Linton Books, Borders............................... 267
Loch Croispol Bookshop & Restaurant,
   Highland 273
Logie Steading Bookshop, Grampian 273
M. and A.C. Thompson, Norfolk.................. 191
Mactaggart (Caroline), Dorset...................... 92
Main Point Books, Lothian.......................... 276
Mair Wilkes Books, Fife 271
McCrone (Audrey), Isle of Arran 274
McNaughtan's Bookshop, Lothian 276
Mercat Books, Highland 274
Midnight Oil Books, Fife 271
Ming Books, Dumfries & Galloway 270
Mr. Mac, Dumfries & Galloway 269
O'Flynn Books, North Yorkshire................... 197
Old Bookshelf (The), Strathclyde................... 278
Old Town Bookshop (The), Lothian 276
Oopalba Books, Cheshire............................ 71
Orb's Bookshop, Grampian.......................... 273
Penny Farthing, The, Lothian 277
Pinnacle Books, Lothian............................. 276
Poetry Bookshop (The), Powys..................... 289
Price (John), London N 158
Pringle Booksellers (Andrew), Lothian 277
Reading Lasses, Dumfries & Galloway 270
Rising Tide Books, Fife.............................. 270
Robert Temple, London N........................... 158
Roberts Books, Strathclyde 279
Second Nature at Knapton Bookbarn, N Yorks 197
Strathtay Antiquarian - Secondhand Books,
   Tayside 280
Stroma Books, Borders 267
Thistle Books, Strathclyde........................... 278
Updike Rare Books (John), Lothian 277
Wheen O'Books, Borders............................ 267

SCOUTS & GUIDES
Adrem Books, Herts 130
Annie's Books, S Yorks 221
Askew Books (Vernon), Wiltshire.................. 251
Books & Bygones (Pam Taylor), West Midlands 240
Collectables (W.H.), Suffolk 229
Fifteenth Century Bookshop (The), East Sussex. 104
Greta Books, Durham 97
Jean Hedger, Berks.................................. 55
Joel Segal Books, Devon 86
Knowles - Antiquary (Roger J.), Staffordshire... 223
Old Station Pottery & Bookshop (The), Norfolk 191

R. & A. Books, East Sussex 101
The Old Children's Bookshelf, Lothian 277
Wheen O'Books, Borders............................ 267
Yesterday's News, Conwy........................... 283

SCRIMSHAW
Don Kelly Books, London W 172

SCULPTURE
Birchden Books, London E 154
Bruce Holdsworth Books, East Sussex 105
Cornucopia Books, Lincolnshire 151
Cover to Cover, Merseyside......................... 185
Don Kelly Books, London W 172
Fifteenth Century Bookshop (The), East Sussex. 104
Heneage Art Books (Thomas), London SW 168
Joel Segal Books, Devon 86
Lighthouse Books (The), Dorset 92
Madalyn S. Jones, West Yorkshire 246
Martin - Bookseller (Colin), East Yorkshire 107
Trinders' Fine Tools, Suffolk 226

SEAFARING & SHIPPING
Barn Books, Buckinghamshire...................... 61
Browsers Bookshop, Cornwall...................... 72
Burroughs (Andrew), Lincolnshire 152
Carningli Centre, Pembrokeshire................... 286
Cavendish Rare Books, London N 156
Cofion Books, Pembrokeshire 286
Cox (Geoff), Devon 90
Curtle Mead Books, Isle of Wight................. 133
Debbage (John), Norfolk............................ 189
Fifteenth Century Bookshop (The), East Sussex. 104
Ford Books (David), Herts 130
Georgina Hobhouse, Argyll......................... 274
Greta Books, Durham 97
Jade Mountain Bookshop, Hampshire 125
Joel Segal Books, Devon 86
Loch Croispol Bookshop & Restaurant,
   Highland 273
Marine & Cannon Books, Cheshire 71
Marine and Cannon Books, Cheshire 69
Mercat Books, Highland 274
Milestone Books, Devon 89
Old Book Company, (The), West Yorkshire..... 248
Prior (Michael), Lincolnshire 152
Quaritch Ltd., (Bernard), London W............. 174
Robert Humm & Co, Lincolnshire 152
Sea Chest Nautical Bookshop (The), Devon 88
Sub Aqua Prints and Books, Hampshire 123
Wheen O'Books, Borders............................ 267
Wizard Books, Cambridgeshire..................... 67

SEAMANSHIP
Argent (Alan), Isle of Wight........................ 134
Cofion Books, Pembrokeshire 286
Cornucopia Books, Lincolnshire 151
Curtle Mead Books, Isle of Wight 133
Fifteenth Century Bookshop (The), East Sussex. 104
Footrope Knots, Suffolk............................. 227
Greta Books, Durham 97
Island Books, Devon................................. 85
Jade Mountain Bookshop, Hampshire 125
Joel Segal Books, Devon 86
Marine & Cannon Books, Cheshire 71

Marine and Cannon Books, Cheshire 69
McLaren Books Ltd, Strathclyde 279
Old Book Company, (The), West Yorkshire 248
Sub Aqua Prints and Books, Hampshire 123

SECRET SOCIETIES
Apocalypse, Surrey 232
Bookworms Paradise Ltd., West Sussex 242
Chapter Two, London SE.......................... 163
Green Man Books, East Sussex 101
Inner Bookshop (The), Oxfordshire................ 208
Joel Segal Books, Devon 86
Occultique, Northamptonshire..................... 199
SETI Books, West Midlands........................ 239

SEEDS
Park (Mike), London O 182

SELF-HELP
Annie's Books, S Yorks 221
Bookworms Paradise Ltd., West Sussex 242
Crabtree (Mrs. C.), Greater Manchester 120
Discovery Bookshop, Carmarthenshire............ 281
Fifteenth Century Bookshop (The), East Sussex. 104
Good for Books, Lincolnshire...................... 149
HCB Wholesale, Powys............................. 288
Inner Bookshop (The), Oxfordshire................ 208
Joel Segal Books, Devon 86
Just Books, Cornwall 75
Occultique, Northamptonshire..................... 199
Outcast Books, Herefordshire...................... 127
Reading Lasses, Dumfries & Galloway 270
SETI Books, West Midlands........................ 239

SELF-IMPROVEMENT
Annie's Books, S Yorks 221
Bookworms Paradise Ltd., West Sussex 242
Cornucopia Books, Lincolnshire 151
Esoteric Dreams Bookshop, Cumbria 77
Fifteenth Century Bookshop (The), East Sussex. 104
Inner Bookshop (The), Oxfordshire................ 208
Joel Segal Books, Devon 86
Occultique, Northamptonshire..................... 199
Outcast Books, Herefordshire...................... 127
Reading Lasses, Dumfries & Galloway 270

SELF-SUFFICIENCY
Books Only, Suffolk................................ 226
Coch-y-Bonddu Books, Powys 290
Colonsay Bookshop, Isle of Colonsay............. 275
Cornucopia Books, Lincolnshire 151
Country Books, Derbyshire 82
Fifteenth Century Bookshop (The), East Sussex. 104
Greta Books, Durham 97
Inner Bookshop (The), Oxfordshire................ 208
Joel Segal Books, Devon 86
Mount's Bay Books, Cornwall 74
Reading Lasses, Dumfries & Galloway 270

SERIES
Annie's Books, S Yorks 221

SETS OF BOOKS
Apocalypse, Surrey 232
Baxter (Steve), Surrey 233

Bernstein (Nicholas), London W 171
Bow Windows Book Shop, East Sussex 103
Browse Books, Lancashire 143
Cavern Books, Cheshire 70
Cheshire Book Centre, Cheshire................... 69
Crouch Rare Books, Surrey........................ 232
Dales & Lakes Book Centre, Cumbria............ 79
Ely Books, Cambridgeshire 65
Eton Antique Bookshop, Berks 57
Fisher & Sperr, London N 157
Foster (Stephen), London NW 160
Foster Bookshop (Paul), London SW 167
Fosters Bookshop, London W 172
Frew Limited (Robert), London SW 167
Golden Books Group, Devon 85
Grove Bookshop (The), North Yorkshire 195
Harrington (Adrian), London W................... 173
Harrington Antiquarian Bookseller (Peter),
    London SW.................................... 167
Hava Books, London SE........................... 164
High Street Books, Devon 86
Joel Segal Books, Devon 86
Kirkman Ltd., (Robert), Bedfordshire............. 54
Liddle (Steve), Bristol 58
Oak Tree Press, Oxfordshire 207
Old Town Bookshop (The), Lothian 276
Poetry Bookshop (The), Powys.................... 289
R. & A. Books, East Sussex 101
Sotheran Limited (Henry), London W 175
Staniland (Booksellers), Lincolnshire 152
Treasure Trove Books, Leics....................... 146
Williams (Bookdealer), (Richard), N Lincs....... 153

SETTE OF ODD VOLUMES
Cox Old & Rare Books (Claude), Suffolk 227
N1 Books, East Sussex 105

SEXOLOGY
Apocalypse, Surrey 232
Delectus Books, London WC....................... 176
Inner Bookshop (The), Oxfordshire................ 208
Paper Pleasures, Somerset 218
R M Books, Herts................................. 132
Reading Lasses, Dumfries & Galloway 270
Robert (Leslie), London W 174

SHEEP/SHEPHERDING
Byrom Textile Bookroom (Richard), Lancashire 142
Fifteenth Century Bookshop (The), East Sussex. 104
Greta Books, Durham 97
Hodgson (Books) (Richard J.), North Yorkshire 196
Joel Segal Books, Devon 86
Kelpie's Books, Fife 271
Phenotype Books, Cumbria 79
Thornber (Peter M.), North Yorkshire........... 195

SHERLOCKIANA
Askew Books (Vernon), Wiltshire.................. 251
Black Cat Bookshop, Leics 147
Ming Books, Dumfries & Galloway............... 270
Modern First Editions, West Yorkshire........... 247
Murder & Mayhem, Powys........................ 288
Post Mortem Books, West Sussex 242
Preston Book Company, Lancashire 144
Randall (Tom), Somerset........................... 218

Scrivener's Books & Bookbinding, Derbyshire... 82
Trinity Rare Books, Co. Leitrim 266
Vokes (Jeremiah), Durham........................... 97
Williams Rare Books (Nigel), London WC 179
Yesterday's News, Conwy.......................... 283

SHIP MODELLING
Aviabooks, Glos 114
Cover to Cover, Merseyside......................... 185
Curtle Mead Books, Isle of Wight 133
Fifteenth Century Bookshop (The), East Sussex. 104
Gerald Lee Maritime Books, East Sussex......... 105
Joel Segal Books, Devon 86
Marine & Cannon Books, Cheshire 71
Marine and Cannon Books, Cheshire 69
McLaren Books Ltd, Strathclyde 279
Milestone Books, Devon 89
Prior (Michael), Lincolnshire 152
Rods Books, Devon.................................. 88
Sub Aqua Prints and Books, Hampshire 123
Thomas Rare Books, Suffolk 226
Trinders' Fine Tools, Suffolk 226

SHIPBUILDING AND SHIPPING
Aardvark Books, Wiltshire.......................... 254
Anthony Vickers Books, North Yorkshire 195
Anvil Books, West Midlands 239
Bott, (Bookdealers) Ltd., (Martin),
   Greater Manchester 118
Burroughs (Andrew), Lincolnshire................. 152
Cheshire Book Centre, Cheshire................... 69
Cox (Geoff), Devon 90
Curtle Mead Books, Isle of Wight 133
Dales and Lakes Book Centre, Cumbria.......... 79
Fifteenth Century Bookshop (The), East Sussex. 104
G. C. Books Ltd., Dumfries & Galloway........ 270
Gerald Lee Maritime Books, East Sussex......... 105
Green Ltd. (G.L.), Herts 131
Joel Segal Books, Devon 86
Kerr (Norman), Cumbria 77
Marine & Cannon Books, Cheshire 71
Marine and Cannon Books, Cheshire 69
McLaren Books Ltd, Strathclyde 279
Milestone Books, Devon 89
Mulyan (Don), Merseyside.......................... 185
N1 Books, East Sussex 105
Nautical Antique Centre (The), Dorset 96
Phelps (Michael), West Sussex..................... 242
Prior (Michael), Lincolnshire 152
Railway Shop (The), Torfaen....................... 292
Roadmaster Books, Kent............................ 136
Rods Books, Devon.................................. 88
Roz Hulse, Conwy 284
Salway Books, Essex 112
Smith Maritime Aviation Books (Frank),
   Tyne and Wear.................................... 235
Stalagluft Books, Tyne and Wear.................. 235
Stroh (M.A.), London E 154
Sub Aqua Prints and Books, Hampshire 123
Thomas Rare Books, Suffolk 226
Trinders' Fine Tools, Suffolk 226
Yesteryear Railwayana, Kent....................... 139

SHIPWRECKS
Aardvark Books, Wiltshire.......................... 254

Cornucopia Books, Lincolnshire 151
Cox (Geoff), Devon 90
Curtle Mead Books, Isle of Wight 133
Dales and Lakes Book Centre, Cumbria.......... 79
Gerald Lee Maritime Books, East Sussex......... 105
Joel Segal Books, Devon 86
Marine & Cannon Books, Cheshire 69, 71
McLaren Books Ltd, Strathclyde 279
Prior (Michael), Lincolnshire 152
R. & A. Books, East Sussex 101
Rods Books, Devon.................................. 88
Sub Aqua Prints and Books, Hampshire 123

SHORTHAND
Ainslie Books, Strathclyde........................... 278

SHOW BUSINESS MEMORABILIA
Cofion Books, Pembrokeshire 286

SIGILLOGRAPHY
Knowles - Antiquary (Roger J.), Staffordshire... 223
Quaritch Ltd., (Bernard), London W.............. 174

SIGNED EDITIONS
Adrem Books, Herts 130
Ann & Mike Conry, Worcs......................... 257
Apocalypse, Surrey 232
Bibliophile Books, London E....................... 154
Black Cat Bookshop, Leics 147
books2books, Devon 88
BOOKS4U, Flintshire................................ 284
Bookstand, Dorset................................... 94
Corfe Books, Surrey................................. 230
Dales & Lakes Book Centre, Cumbria............ 79
Eastwood Books (David), Cornwall 72
Ellis, Bookseller (Peter), London WC 177
Ellwood Editions, Wiltshire 253
Ely Books, Cambridgeshire 65
Evans Books (Paul), West Sussex 243
Farahar & Dupre (Clive & Sophie), Wiltshire ... 251
Fifteenth Century Bookshop (The), East Sussex. 104
firstpagebooks, Norfolk 189
Firsts in Print, Somerset 219
Foster Bookshop (Paul), London SW 167
Fosters Bookshop, London W 172
Glacier Books, Tayside 280
Green Meadow Books, Cornwall 74
Greta Books, Durham 97
Harrington Antiquarian Bookseller (Peter),
   London SW....................................... 167
Heppa (Christopher), Essex 108
Hylton Booksearch, Merseyside 184
Ian Briddon, Derbyshire............................ 82
Ian McKelvie Bookseller, London N.............. 157
Jean Hedger, Berks.................................. 55
Karen Millward, Co. Cork.......................... 263
Kendall–Carpenter (Tim), Greater Manchester .. 119
Kevin S. Ogilvie Modern First Editions,
   Grampian 272
Kirkman Ltd., (Robert), Bedfordshire............. 54
L.M.S. Books, Herts 131
Little Stour Books, Kent 136
Loretta Lay Books, London NW 161
Marine and Cannon Books, Cheshire 69
Modern First Editions, West Yorkshire........... 247

Myra Dean Illustated Books, Powys 287
N V Books, Warwickshire..................... 236
Needham Books, (Russell), Somerset 219
Parker Books (Mike), Cambridgeshire 64
Poetry Bookshop (The), Powys.................... 289
Portobello Books, London W 174
Richard Thornton Books, London N 158
Riderless Horse Books, Norfolk................... 186
Robert (Leslie), London W 174
Robert Temple, London N......................... 158
SaBeRo Books, London SW....................... 169
Scrivener's Books & Bookbinding, Derbyshire... 82
Sensawunda Books, Cheshire....................... 68
Shacklock Books (David), Suffolk 226
Shakeshaft (Dr. B.), Cheshire 71
Simpson (Dave), Central 268
Slightly Foxed on Gloucester Road, London SW 167
Thorntons of Oxford Ltd., Oxfordshire........... 206
Till's Bookshop, Lothian 277
Trigon Books, Dorset............................... 95
Trinity Rare Books, Co. Leitrim 266
Updike Rare Books (John), Lothian 277
Williams Rare Books (Nigel), London WC 179
Woburn Books, London N 159
Woodbine Books, West Yorkshire................. 245
Words Etcetera Bookshop, Dorset................. 93

SILVERSMITHS

Don Kelly Books, London W 172
Nibris Books, London SW.......................... 169
R. & A. Books, East Sussex 101

SIXTIES, THE

Cornucopia Books, Lincolnshire 151
Joel Segal Books, Devon 86
McGee (Terence J.), London O 180
Riderless Horse Books, Norfolk................... 186
Sclanders (Beatbooks), (Andrew), London EC... 155

SLAVERY

Alec–Smith Books (Alex), East Yorkshire 107
Dolphin Books, Suffolk.............................. 225
Drury Rare Books (John), Essex................... 110
Empire Books, North Yorkshire 197
Michael Graves-Johnston, London SW 168
N1 Books, East Sussex 105
Old Book Company, (The), West Yorkshire 248
Pennymead Books, North Yorkshire 193
Quaritch Ltd., (Bernard), London W.............. 174
Reading Lasses, Dumfries & Galloway 270
Seydi Rare Books (Sevin), London NW 161
Star Lord Books, Greater Manchester 119

SMALL PRESS PUBLISHED BOOKS

Apocalypse, Surrey 232
Ballantyne–Way (Roger), Suffolk 228
Blackwell's Rare Books, Oxfordshire.............. 208
Booksets.com Ltd, Shropshire 214
Norton Books, North Yorkshire.................... 192
Riderless Horse Books, Norfolk................... 186
Robert Temple, London N........................... 158
Samovar Books, Co. Dublin........................ 264
Woburn Books, London N 159

SOCIAL ECONOMICS

Adrem Books, Herts 130
Delectus Books, London WC....................... 176
Drury Rare Books (John), Essex................... 110
Hamish Riley-Smith, Norfolk...................... 191
Hurst (Jenny), Kent 137
Johnson Rare Book Collections (C.R.),
London NW 161
Left on The Shelf, Cumbria......................... 78
Parkinsons Books, Merseyside..................... 185
PsychoBabel Books & Journals, Oxfordshire..... 205
Reading Lasses, Dumfries & Galloway 270
Woburn Books, London N 159

SOCIAL HISTORY

Adrem Books, Herts 130
Apocalypse, Surrey 232
Barcombe Services, Essex........................... 108
Bell (Peter), Lothian................................. 275
Bermondsey Basement Bookstore, London SE .. 163
Bibliophile Books, London E....................... 154
Black Cat Books, Norfolk.......................... 187
Blackpool Book Warehouse, Lancashire.......... 142
Bookworms Paradise Ltd., West Sussex 242
Brimstones, East Sussex 104
Byrom Textile Bookroom (Richard), Lancashire 142
Chesters (G. & J.), Staffordshire 224
Clifton Books, Essex 111
Cottage Books, Leics................................. 145
Country Books, Derbyshire 82
Cox (Geoff), Devon 90
Crabtree (Mrs. C.), Greater Manchester 120
Debbage (John), Norfolk............................ 189
Delectus Books, London WC....................... 176
Dolphin Books, Suffolk.............................. 225
Drury Rare Books (John), Essex................... 110
Duck (William), Hampshire......................... 124
Eggle (Mavis), Herts 130
Elaine Lonsdale Books, West Yorkshire.......... 247
Fifteenth Century Bookshop (The), East Sussex. 104
Fireside Bookshop, Cumbria........................ 81
Forest Books of Manchester, Cheshire............ 70
Gardener & Cook, London SW..................... 167
Gladstone Books, Lincolnshire 150
Graham (John), Dorset............................... 96
Harvest Books, Lancashire.......................... 144
Helion & Company, West Midlands 239
Hughes Rare Books (Spike), Borders.............. 267
Jarndyce Antiquarian Booksellers, London WC. 177
Joel Segal Books, Devon 86
Judd Books, London WC............................ 177
Kelsall (George), Greater Manchester 118
Left on The Shelf, Cumbria......................... 78
Maggy Browne, Lincolnshire 148
Maghreb Bookshop (The), London WC.......... 177
Marcan, Bookseller (Peter), London SE 164
Martin (Brian), Surrey 231
Meekins Books (Paul), Warwickshire............. 237
Murphy (C.J.), Norfolk............................. 189
N1 Books, East Sussex 105
Northern Herald Books, West Yorkshire......... 245
Outcast Books, Herefordshire....................... 127
Parkinsons Books, Merseyside..................... 185
Pollak (P.M.), Devon 88
PsychoBabel Books & Journals, Oxfordshire..... 205

R. & A. Books, East Sussex 101
Reading Lasses, Dumfries & Galloway 270
Rebecca Hardie Rare Books, London W 171
Red Star Books, Herts.............................. 129
Roadmaster Books, Kent............................ 136
Russell (Charles), London SW...................... 169
Scrivener's Books & Bookbinding, Derbyshire... 82
Sephton (A.F.), London W 174
South Downs Book Service, West Sussex......... 243
Stalagluft Books, Tyne and Wear.................. 235
Stern Antiquarian Bookseller (Jeffrey), N Yorks 198
Stevens (Joan), Cambridgeshire.................... 65
Symes Books (Naomi), Cheshire 71
Warnes (Felicity J.), London O 180
Weininger Antiquarian Books (Eva M.),
   London NW.. 161
Westwood Books Ltd, Cumbria.................... 80
Wetherell (Frances), Cambridgeshire 65
Whitchurch Books Ltd., Cardiff.................... 281
Whittle, Bookseller (Avril), Cumbria 80
Woburn Books, London N 159

SOCIAL SCIENCES
Adrem Books, Herts 130
Apocalypse, Surrey 232
Barcombe Services, Essex........................... 108
Bernard Dixon and Kath Adams, London O.... 182
Bracton Books, Cambridgeshire.................... 63
Brimstones, East Sussex 104
Cheshire Book Centre, Cheshire.................... 69
Chesters (G. & J.), Staffordshire 224
Dandy Lion Editions, Surrey 233
Delectus Books, London WC....................... 176
Drury Rare Books (John), Essex................... 110
Hamish Riley-Smith, Norfolk....................... 191
hullbooks.com, East Yorkshire 106
Ice House Books, Wiltshire 254
Judd Books, London WC 177
Left on The Shelf, Cumbria......................... 78
Northern Herald Books, West Yorkshire......... 245
O'Donoghue Books, Powys......................... 289
Orb's Bookshop, Grampian.......................... 273
Outcast Books, Herefordshire....................... 127
Parkinsons Books, Merseyside...................... 185
Price (John), London N 158
PsychoBabel Books & Journals, Oxfordshire..... 205
Quaritch Ltd., (Bernard), London W.............. 174
Reading Lasses, Dumfries & Galloway 270
Reid of Liverpool, Merseyside...................... 184
Scott (Peter), East Sussex........................... 104
Susanne Schulz-Falster Rare Books, London N. 158
Westwood Books Ltd, Cumbria.................... 80
Woburn Books, London N 159

SOCIALISM
Adrem Books, Herts 130
Berwick Books, Lincolnshire........................ 150
Delectus Books, London WC....................... 176
Dolphin Books, Suffolk............................. 225
Drury Rare Books (John), Essex................... 110
Gladstone Books, Lincolnshire 150
Hylton Booksearch, Merseyside 184
Left on The Shelf, Cumbria......................... 78
Northern Herald Books, West Yorkshire......... 245
Old Book Company, (The), West Yorkshire 248

Parkinsons Books, Merseyside...................... 185
PsychoBabel Books & Journals, Oxfordshire..... 205
Quaritch Ltd., (Bernard), London W.............. 174
Reading Lasses, Dumfries & Galloway 270
Red Star Books, Herts.............................. 129
Spurrier (Nick), Kent 137
Star Lord Books, G Manchester 119
Symes Books (Naomi), Cheshire 71
Trinity Rare Books, Co. Leitrim 266
Woburn Books, London N 159

SOCIOLOGY
Apocalypse, Surrey 232
Backfold Books, Herefordshire..................... 127
Barcombe Services, Essex........................... 108
Bracton Books, Cambridgeshire.................... 63
Brimstones, East Sussex 104
Chesters (G. & J.), Staffordshire 224
Delectus Books, London WC....................... 176
Gladstone Books, Lincolnshire 150
hullbooks.com, East Yorkshire 106
Hylton Booksearch, Merseyside 184
Left on The Shelf, Cumbria......................... 78
Northern Herald Books, West Yorkshire......... 245
O'Donoghue Books, Powys......................... 289
Old Book Company, (The), West Yorkshire 248
Outcast Books, Herefordshire....................... 127
Parkinsons Books, Merseyside...................... 185
Price (John), London N 158
PsychoBabel Books & Journals, Oxfordshire..... 205
Reading Lasses, Dumfries & Galloway 270
Red Star Books, Herts.............................. 129
Stalagluft Books, Tyne and Wear.................. 235
Tarka Books, Devon................................ 84
Trinity Rare Books, Co. Leitrim 266
Woburn Books, London N 159

SOUTH AUSTRALIANA
Empire Books, North Yorkshire 197

SOUTH SEAS
Adrem Books, Herts 130
Empire Books, North Yorkshire 197
Marine and Cannon Books, Cheshire 69
Michael Graves-Johnston, London SW 168

SOUTHERN AMERICANA
PsychoBabel Books & Journals, Oxfordshire..... 205

SPACE
Adrem Books, Herts 130
Bookworms Paradise Ltd., West Sussex 242
K Books, Cheshire................................. 70

SPANISH LITERATURE
Baldwin (Jack), Strathclyde 278
Hodgson (Judith), London W 173
Joel Segal Books, Devon 86
Orssich (Paul), London SW........................ 169
Quaritch Ltd., (Bernard), London W.............. 174
York (Graham), Devon............................. 86

SPECIAL COLLECTIONS
Kenny's Bookshop & Art Galleries Ltd.,
   Co. Galway 265

Kohler (C.C.), Surrey 230
Milestone Publications Goss & Crested China,
   Hampshire 123
Murphy (C.J.), Norfolk.............................. 189
Price (John), London N 158
Quaritch Ltd., (Bernard), London W.............. 174
Robert Temple, London N.......................... 158
Stalagluft Books, Tyne and Wear................. 235

SPIRITISM

Bookworms Paradise Ltd., West Sussex 242
Occultique, Northamptonshire...................... 199
Outcast Books, Herefordshire...................... 127

SPIRITUAL

Beckham Books Ltd., Suffolk 229
Bookbarrow, Cambridgeshire....................... 63
Bookworms Paradise Ltd., West Sussex 242
Canon Gate Books, West Sussex.................... 243
Chapter Two, London SE............................ 163
Inner Bookshop (The), Oxfordshire................ 208
Joel Segal Books, Devon 86
Just Books, Cornwall 75
Occultique, Northamptonshire...................... 199
Parkinsons Books, Merseyside...................... 185
S.P.C.K., Bristol 59
Star Lord Books, G Manchester 119
Susan Taylor Books, West Yorkshire 247

SPIRITUALISM

Atlantis Bookshop, London WC.................... 176
Bookworms Paradise Ltd., West Sussex 242
Cavern Books, Cheshire 70
Chthonios Books, East Sussex...................... 102
Craobh Rua Books, Co. Armagh.................... 260
Dawlish Books, Devon 86
Delectus Books, London WC....................... 176
Esoteric Dreams Bookshop, Cumbria 77
Facet Books, Dorset................................. 91
Forest Books of Manchester, Cheshire............ 70
Greensleeves, Oxfordshire 206
Holmes Books (Harry), East Yorkshire........... 107
Hurst (Jenny), Kent 137
Loretta Lay Books, London NW 161
Magis Books, Leics.................................. 146
Minster Gate Bookshop, North Yorkshire 197
Needham Books, (Russell), Somerset.............. 219
Occultique, Northamptonshire...................... 199
Old Book Company, (The), West Yorkshire 248
Orchid Book Distributors, Co. Clare.............. 262
Preston Book Company, Lancashire 144
PsychoBabel Books & Journals, Oxfordshire..... 205
R. & A. Books, East Sussex 101
Reading Lasses, Dumfries & Galloway 270
Saint Swithin's Illustrated & Children's Books,
   London W 174
SETI Books, West Midlands........................ 239
Tilleys Vintage Magazine Shop, S Yorks 222
Waxfactor, East Sussex 100
Wizard Books, Cambridgeshire..................... 67

SPORT
- GENERAL

Abacus Gallery, Staffordshire....................... 224
Adrem Books, Herts 130

Alexander's Books, Warwickshire.................. 237
Allinson (Frank & Stella), Warwickshire 236
Amos (Denis W.), Herts............................. 130
Ann & Mike Conry, Worcs.......................... 257
Annie's Books, S Yorks 221
Antique Map and Bookshop (The), Dorset 94
Antique Prints of the World, London N.......... 156
Archways Sports Books, Lothian 275
Armstrong's Books & Collectables, Leics......... 145
Aurora Books Ltd, Lothian......................... 275
Autumn Leaves, Lincolnshire...................... 150
Axe Rare & Out of Print Books (Richard),
   North Yorkshire 193
Baker (Gerald), Bristol.............................. 60
Bath Old Books, Somerset 215
Biff Books and Records, S Yorks.................. 221
Bob Mallory (Books), Derbyshire.................. 83
Bodyline Books, Surrey.............................. 232
Bookcase, Cumbria 76
Books Only, Suffolk 226
books2books, Devon................................. 88
Bookworms, Norfolk................................. 186
Bookzone, Berks 55
Border Bookshop, West Yorkshire 249
Capel Mawr Collectors Centre, Gwynedd 285
Carningli Centre, Pembrokeshire 286
Cavendish Books (Rupert), West Yorkshire...... 247
Chandos Books, Devon.............................. 85
Charlie Byrne's Bookshop, Co. Galway........... 265
Chaucer Bookshop, Kent............................ 136
Chris Phillips, Wiltshire............................ 252
Clements (R.W.), London O........................ 181
Clifford Milne Books, Grampian.................. 272
Cobweb Books, North Yorkshire 194
Cofion Books, Pembrokeshire...................... 286
Cotswold Internet Books, Glos..................... 113
Dandy Lion Editions, Surrey 233
Dublin Bookbrowsers, Co. Dublin................. 265
Eastcote Bookshop (The), London O 180
Edwards, Fiona, Nottinghamshire 203
Elmo Books, West Sussex 243
Esoteric Dreams Bookshop, Cumbria 77
Eton Antique Bookshop, Berks 57
Evans (Mark), Lincolnshire 151
Fifteenth Century Bookshop (The), East Sussex. 104
Ford Books (David), Herts 130
Fossgate Books, North Yorkshire 197
Freeman's Corner Shop, Norfolk 189
Garfi Books, Powys 291
Garwood & Voigt, Kent............................. 139
Gathern (D.), Conwy 283
George St. Books, Derbyshire 83
Good for Books, Lincolnshire 149
Grahame Thornton, Bookseller, Dorset........... 93
Gravity Books, Lincolnshire 149
Handsworth Books, Essex........................... 112
Hatchard & Daughters, West Yorkshire.......... 246
Hay Cinema Bookshop Ltd., Powys............... 288
HCB Wholesale, Powys............................. 288
High Street Books, Devon 86
Hollett and Son (R.F.G.), Cumbria 79
Hummingbird Books, Herefordshire.............. 128
Hurst (Jenny), Kent 137
Innes Books, Shropshire............................ 212
J & J Burgess Booksellers, Cambridgeshire....... 64

Jackson (M.W.), Wiltshire............................ 254
Jade Mountain Bookshop, Hampshire 125
JB Books & Collectables, West Sussex 243
Jenny Hurst, Kent 138
Joel Segal Books, Devon 86
Kingfisher Book Service, Nottinghamshire 204
Lyngheath Books, Norfolk 188
Malvern Bookshop (The), Worcs 255
Marble Hill Books, Outer London................. 182
McCrone (Audrey), Isle of Arran.................. 274
Mellon's Books, East Sussex........................ 101
Moore (C.R.), Shropshire 213
Morten (Booksellers) (E.J.), G Manchester....... 119
Mr. Pickwick of Towcester, Northamptonshire.. 199
Mundy (David), Herts 129
Murphy (C.J.), Norfolk.............................. 189
New Strand, The, Herefordshire 127
Old Book Company, (The), West Yorkshire 248
Old Station Pottery & Bookshop (The), Norfolk 191
Oopalba Books, Cheshire............................. 71
Parker Books (Mike), Cambridgeshire 64
Peter M Daly, Hampshire............................ 126
Portobello Books, London W 174
Price (R.W.), Nottinghamshire 203
Priestpopple Books, Northumberland 201
Quinto of Charing Cross Road, London WC ... 178
R. & A. Books, East Sussex 101
Richard Thornton Books, London N 158
Roberts Fine Books (Julian), Lincolnshire........ 151
Roland Books, Kent 138
Rutland Bookshop (The), Rutland 211
Saintfield Antiques & Fine Books, Co. Down ... 261
Scrivener's Books & Bookbinding, Derbyshire... 82
Stothert Old Books, Cheshire....................... 68
Stroma Books, Borders 267
Tarka Books, Devon.................................. 84
Tiffin (Tony and Gill), Durham 97
Treasure Trove Books, Leics........................ 146
Wadard Books, Kent 137
Wheen O'Books, Borders............................ 267
Wiend Books, Lancashire 143
Yewtree Books, Cumbria............................ 78

- AMERICAN FOOTBALL

Archways Sports Books, Lothian 275
Bodyline Books, Surrey.............................. 232
Saunders (Tom), Caerphilly 281

- ANGLING/FISHING

Acanthophyllum Books, Wirral 184
Annie's Books, S Yorks 221
Atholl Fine Books, Tayside 280
Barnacle Books, County Fermanagh 261
Baron (Christopher), Cheshire...................... 68
Big Bairn Books, Tayside 279
Blest (Peter), Kent 138
Bodyline Books, Surrey.............................. 232
Books Only, Suffolk 226
Chalmers Hallam (E.), Hampshire 125
Chevin Books, West Yorkshire...................... 249
Classics Bookshop (The), Oxfordshire............. 205
Coch-y-Bonddu Books, Powys 290
Cornucopia Books, Lincolnshire 151
Countrymans Gallery (The), Leics 145
Darkwood Books, Co. Cork......................... 263

Deeside Books, Grampian............................ 272
Dusty Books, Powys 290
Edmund Pollinger Rare Books, London SW..... 166
Eggle (Mavis), Herts 130
Fifteenth Century Bookshop (The), East Sussex. 104
Fylde Books, Lancashire 144
Garfi Books, Powys 291
Good Books, Shropshire 213
Grayling (David A.H.), Cumbria 78
Grove Bookshop (The), North Yorkshire 195
Hancock (Peter), West Sussex 241
Head (John & Judith), Wiltshire 253
Hereward Books, Cambridgeshire.................. 66
Home Farm Books, Warwickshire.................. 236
Intech Books, Northumberland 201
Internet Bookshop UK Ltd., Glos................. 113
Jackdaw Books, Norfolk 188
Joel Segal Books, Devon 86
Just Books, Cornwall 75
Keith Langford, London E 154
Keogh's Books, Glos.................................. 115
Kilgour (Sporting Books) (Ian), Leics............. 147
Lion Books, Worcs................................... 255
Lyonshill Books, Co. Dublin 265
Madoc Books, Conwy 284
Martin (Books and Pictures), (Brian P.), Surrey. 231
Martin (Brian), Surrey............................... 231
McEwan Fine Books, Grampian.................... 272
Murphy (C.J.), Norfolk.............................. 189
Not Just Books, Dorset.............................. 94
Pauline Harries Books, Hampshire 123
Peter M Daly, Hampshire............................ 126
Petersfield Bookshop (The), Hampshire........... 124
Petworth Antique Market (Bookroom),
    West Sussex...................................... 244
Philip Hopper, Essex................................. 110
Richard Thornton Books, London N 158
River Reads Bookshop, Devon...................... 90
Rothwell & Dunworth, Somerset 217
St Mary's Books & Prints, Lincolnshire 152
Sax Books, Suffolk 228
Stroh (M.A.), London E 154
Treasure Island (The), G Manchester 119
Vinovium Books, Durham 97
Worlds End Bookshop, London SW.............. 169
Yesterday Tackle & Books, Dorset 92

- ARCHERY

Bodyline Books, Surrey.............................. 232
Cader Idris Books, Powys........................... 290
Chalmers Hallam (E.), Hampshire................. 125
Coch-y-Bonddu Books, Powys 290
Head (John & Judith), Wiltshire 253
Joel Segal Books, Devon 86
Lake (Fred), Surrey 234
Meekins Books (Paul), Warwickshire.............. 237
Old Book Company, (The), West Yorkshire 248

- ATHLETICS

Archways Sports Books, Lothian 275
Bob Mallory (Books), Derbyshire.................. 83
Bodyline Books, Surrey.............................. 232
Bookworms Paradise Ltd., West Sussex 242
Bookzone, Berks...................................... 55
Gathern (D.), Conwy 283

Marathon Books, Lancashire 142
Rugby Relics, Glamorgan 285
Stroh (M.A.), London E 154

- BADMINTON
Archways Sports Books, Lothian 275
Bodyline Books, Surrey 232
Pennymead Books, North Yorkshire 193

- BALLOONING
Bodyline Books, Surrey 232
J.B. Books, Berks 57
Just Books, Cornwall 75
Old Book Company, (The), West Yorkshire 248
Postings, Surrey 233
Stroh (M.A.), London E 154

- BASEBALL
Archways Sports Books, Lothian 275
Bodyline Books, Surrey 232
Gathern (D.), Conwy 283

- BASKETBALL
Adrem Books, Herts 130
Archways Sports Books, Lothian 275
Bodyline Books, Surrey 232

- BIG GAME HUNTING
Allsworth Rare Books Ltd., London SW 166
Ayre (Peter J.), Somerset 219
Barnhill Books, Isle of Arran 274
Bates & Hindmarch, West Yorkshire 248
Bodyline Books, Surrey 232
Campbell Hewson Books (R.), Fife 271
Chalmers Hallam (E.), Hampshire 125
Coch-y-Bonddu Books, Powys 290
Deeside Books, Grampian 272
Edmund Pollinger Rare Books, London SW 166
Farahar & Dupre (Clive & Sophie), Wiltshire ... 251
Grayling (David A.H.), Cumbria 78
Head (John & Judith), Wiltshire 253
Home Farm Books, Warwickshire 236
Joel Segal Books, Devon 86
Kenya Books, East Sussex 100
Kilgour (Sporting Books) (Ian), Leics 147
Martin (Books and Pictures), (Brian P.), Surrey . 231
Martin (Brian), Surrey 231
McEwan Fine Books, Grampian 272
Peter M Daly, Hampshire 126
Popeley (Frank T.), Cambridgeshire 67
R.E. & G.B. Way, Suffolk 228
Vandeleur Antiquarian Books, Surrey 231

- BILLIARDS/SNOOKER/POOL
Archways Sports Books, Lothian 275
Ben–Nathan (Jack), London O 180
Bodyline Books, Surrey 232
Bookworms Paradise Ltd., West Sussex 242
Craobh Rua Books, Co. Armagh 260
R. S. & P. A. Scowen, London O 181
Richard Thornton Books, London N 158
Stroh (M.A.), London E 154

- BOWLS
Archways Sports Books, Lothian 275

Bodyline Books, Surrey 232
Cornucopia Books, Lincolnshire 151

- BOXING
Allinson (Frank & Stella), Warwickshire 236
Archways Sports Books, Lothian 275
Askew Books (Vernon), Wiltshire 251
Bodyline Books, Surrey 232
Bookzone, Berks 55
Burmester (James), Bristol 58
Cavendish Books (Rupert), West Yorkshire 247
Combat Arts Archive, Durham 97
Derek Stirling Bookseller, Kent 141
Dublin Bookbrowsers, Co. Dublin 265
Franks Booksellers, G Manchester 119
Gathern (D.), Conwy 283
Hedgerow Books, S Yorks 221
Joel Segal Books, Devon 86
McInnes (P.F. & J.R.), Dorset 91
Old Book Company, (The), West Yorkshire 248
Roland Books, Kent 138
Rugby Relics, Glamorgan 285

- CANOEING/KAYAKS
Baldwin (M. & M.), Worcs 255
Bodyline Books, Surrey 232
Craobh Rua Books, Co. Armagh 260
McLaren Books Ltd, Strathclyde 279

- CAVING (SPELAEOLOGY)
Bodyline Books, Surrey 232
Dales & Lakes Book Centre, Cumbria 79
Grove Bookshop (The), North Yorkshire 195
Jarvis Books, Derbyshire 83
Letterbox Books, Nottinghamshire 203
Merseyside Books, Merseyside 185
O'Reilly - Mountain Books (John), Derbyshire .. 83
Post–Horn Books, North Yorkshire 192

- CLIMBING & TREKKING
Allinson (Frank & Stella), Warwickshire 236
Bodyline Books, Surrey 232
Booth (Booksearch Service), (Geoff), Cheshire ... 68
Craobh Rua Books, Co. Armagh 260
Daisyroots Book Centre (Daisyroots Books Ltd),
    Cumbria 77
Dales & Lakes Book Centre, Cumbria 79
George St. Books, Derbyshire 83
Gildas Books, Cheshire 68
Glacier Books, Tayside 280
Hunter and Krageloh, Derbyshire 83
Jarvis Books, Derbyshire 83
Joel Segal Books, Devon 86
Little Bookshop (The), Cumbria 80
Madoc Books, Conwy 284
Main Point Books, Lothian 276
Old Book Company, (The), West Yorkshire 248
O'Reilly - Mountain Books (John), Derbyshire .. 83

- COURSING
Bodyline Books, Surrey 232
Chalmers Hallam (E.), Hampshire 125
Coch-y-Bonddu Books, Powys 290
Head (John & Judith), Wiltshire 253
Kilgour (Sporting Books) (Ian), Leics 147

Wychwood Books, Glos 116

- CRICKET
Aardvark Books, Lincolnshire 150
Acumen Books, Staffordshire 224
Annie's Books, S Yorks 221
Archways Sports Books, Lothian 275
Baker - Books for the Collector (Colin), Devon . 89
Barbican Bookshop, North Yorkshire 196
Bardsley's Books, Suffolk 225
Barmby (C. & A.J.), Kent 140
Beighton (Brian), Norfolk 186
Black Cat Bookshop, Leics 147
Black Five Books, Shropshire 214
Bob Mallory (Books), Derbyshire 83
Bodyline Books, Surrey 232
Bookworms Paradise Ltd., West Sussex 242
Bookzone, Berks 55
Booth (Booksearch Service), (Geoff), Cheshire... 68
Border Bookshop, West Yorkshire 249
Brad Books, Essex 110
Bright (P.G.), Cambridgeshire 65
Cavendish Books (Rupert), West Yorkshire 247
Chas J. Sawyer, Kent 140
Chevin Books, West Yorkshire 249
Christopher Saunders (Orchard Books), Glos.... 115
Classic Crime Collections, G Manchester 119
Coach House Books, Worcs 256
Cobbles Books, Somerset 217
Crabtree (Mrs. C.), G Manchester 120
Dales & Lakes Book Centre, Cumbria 79
David Summerfield Books, East Sussex 99
Derek Stirling Bookseller, Kent 141
Esoteric Dreams Bookshop, Cumbria 77
Fifteenth Century Bookshop (The), East Sussex. 104
First Edition, The, Essex 109
firstpagebooks, Norfolk 189
Gathern (D.), Conwy 283
GS Cricket Books / The Old Book Shop,
  West Midlands 240
Hambleton Books, North Yorkshire 196
Internet Bookshop UK Ltd., Glos 113
Jackson (M.W.), Wiltshire 254
Jade Mountain Bookshop, Hampshire 125
Joel Segal Books, Devon 86
Just Books, Cornwall 75
Keith Langford, London E 154
Kingfisher Book Service, Nottinghamshire 204
Lion Books, Worcs 255
Martin (Brian), Surrey 231
Maynard & Bradley, Leics 146
McCrone (Audrey), Isle of Arran 274
McEwan Fine Books, Grampian 272
McKenzie (J.W.), Surrey 232
Mellon's Books, East Sussex 101
My Back Pages, London SW 168
Old Book Company, (The), West Yorkshire 248
Old Bookshop (The), West Midlands 240
Park Gallery & Bookshop (The), Northants 200
Peter M Daly, Hampshire 126
Poor Richard's Books, Suffolk 226
Red Rose Books, G Manchester 118
Roberts Fine Books (Julian), Lincolnshire........ 151
Roland Books, Kent 138
Rugby Relics, Glamorgan 285

S Mary's Books & Prints, Lincolnshire 152
Sax Books, Suffolk 228
Tiffin (Tony and Gill), Durham 97
Treasure Island (The), G Manchester 119
Treasure Trove Books, Leics 146
William H. Roberts, West Yorkshire 247
Wood Cricket Books (Martin), Kent 139
Yesterday's News, Conwy 283

- CROQUET
Bodyline Books, Surrey 232
Edmund Pollinger Rare Books, London SW 166

- CYCLING
Ampersand Books, Norfolk 189
Annie's Books, S Yorks 221
Archways Sports Books, Lothian 275
Bodyline Books, Surrey 232
Dales & Lakes Book Centre, Cumbria 79
Engaging Gear Ltd., Essex 108
Kenya Books, East Sussex 100
Larkham Books (Patricia), Glos.................... 117
Old Book Company, (The), West Yorkshire 248
Rugby Relics, Glamorgan 285
Stroh (M.A.), London E 154
Weiner (Graham), London N 158

- DIVING/SUB-AQUA
Bodyline Books, Surrey 232
Bookworms Paradise Ltd., West Sussex 242
Cornucopia Books, Lincolnshire 151
Internet Bookshop UK Ltd., Glos 113
Stroh (M.A.), London E 154
Underwater Books, East Sussex 102

- DUELLING
Bodyline Books, Surrey 232
Combat Arts Archive, Durham 97

- FALCONRY
Barnhill Books, Isle of Arran 274
Blest (Peter), Kent 138
Bodyline Books, Surrey 232
Bookworms Paradise Ltd., West Sussex 242
Chalmers Hallam (E.), Hampshire 125
Coch-y-Bonddu Books, Powys 290
Countryside Books, Hampshire 121
Fifteenth Century Bookshop (The), East Sussex. 104
Grove Bookshop (The), North Yorkshire 195
Head (John & Judith), Wiltshire 253
Hereward Books, Cambridgeshire.................. 66
Home Farm Books, Warwickshire.................. 236
Kilgour (Sporting Books) (Ian), Leics 147
Martin (Books and Pictures), (Brian P.), Surrey. 231
Martin (Brian), Surrey 231
Peter M Daly, Hampshire 126
Winchester Bookshop (The), Hampshire.......... 126

- FENCING
Bodyline Books, Surrey 232
Chalmers Hallam (E.), Hampshire 125
Combat Arts Archive, Durham 97
Joel Segal Books, Devon 86

- FIELD SPORTS

Archways Sports Books, Lothian 275
Barnhill Books, Isle of Arran 274
Blest (Peter), Kent 138
Bodyline Books, Surrey............................. 232
Bookbox, Glos 115
Cader Idris Books, Powys.......................... 290
Cat Lit, Somerset 218
Cavendish Books (Rupert), West Yorkshire...... 247
Chalmers Hallam (E.), Hampshire................. 125
Coch-y-Bonddu Books, Powys 290
Cornucopia Books, Lincolnshire 151
Countrymans Gallery (The), Leics 145
Dales & Lakes Book Centre, Cumbria............ 79
Discovery Bookshop, Carmarthenshire............ 281
Edmund Pollinger Rare Books, London SW..... 166
Farquharson, (Hilary), Tayside.................... 280
Fifteenth Century Bookshop (The), East Sussex. 104
Fylde Books, Lancashire 144
Garfi Books, Powys 291
Good Books, Shropshire 213
Grahame (Major Iain), Suffolk.................... 225
Grayling (David A.H.), Cumbria 78
Grove Bookshop (The), North Yorkshire 195
Head (John & Judith), Wiltshire 253
Heartland Old Books, Devon....................... 89
Hereward Books, Cambridgeshire.................. 66
High Street Books, Devon 86
Hollett and Son (R.F.G.), Cumbria 79
Home Farm Books, Warwickshire.................. 236
Joel Segal Books, Devon 86
Karen Millward, Co. Cork.......................... 263
Kerr (Norman), Cumbria 77
Kilgour (Sporting Books) (Ian), Leics............. 147
Martin (Books and Pictures), (Brian P.), Surrey. 231
Martin (Brian), Surrey 231
Maynard & Bradley, Leics 146
McEwan Fine Books, Grampian.................... 272
Moss End Bookshop, Berks 57
Muttonchop Manuscripts, West Sussex 242
Neil Summersgill, Lancashire 142
Old Book Company, (The), West Yorkshire 248
Peter M Daly, Hampshire........................... 126
Petworth Antique Market (Bookroom),
  West Sussex....................................... 244
R.E. & G.B. Way, Suffolk 228
Ramrod Antiques, North Yorkshire............... 195
River Reads Bookshop, Devon...................... 90
Stacpoole (George), Co. Limerick.................. 266
Strathtay Antiquarian - Secondhand Books,
  Tayside 280
Vinovium Books, Durham 97
Winchester Bookshop (The), Hampshire.......... 126
Wychwood Books, Glos............................. 116

- FOOTBALL (AMERICAN)

Bodyline Books, Surrey............................. 232
Old Book Company, (The), West Yorkshire 248

- FOOTBALL (SOCCER)

Allinson (Frank & Stella), Warwickshire 236
Amos (Denis W.), Herts............................. 130
Ann & Mike Conry, Worcs.......................... 257
Annie's Books, S Yorks 221
Archways Sports Books, Lothian 275

Big Bairn Books, Tayside 279
Black Cat Bookshop, Leics 147
Bob Mallory (Books), Derbyshire.................. 83
Bodyline Books, Surrey............................. 232
books2books, Devon................................. 88
BOOKS4U, Flintshire............................... 284
Bookshop on the Heath, The, London SE 163
Bookworms Paradise Ltd., West Sussex 242
Bookzone, Berks.................................... 55
Booth (Booksearch Service), (Geoff), Cheshire... 68
Border Bookshop, West Yorkshire 249
Cavendish Books (Rupert), West Yorkshire...... 247
Chevin Books, West Yorkshire..................... 249
Crabtree (Mrs. C.), G Manchester................. 120
Delectus Books, London WC....................... 176
Elmo Books, West Sussex 243
Esoteric Dreams Bookshop, Cumbria 77
firstpagebooks, Norfolk............................. 189
Footballana, Berks 56
Franks Booksellers, G Manchester 119
Gathern (D.), Conwy 283
Green Meadow Books, Cornwall 74
Hambleton Books, North Yorkshire 196
Hedgerow Books, S Yorks 221
Jade Mountain Bookshop, Hampshire 125
Joel Segal Books, Devon 86
Karen Millward, Co. Cork.......................... 263
Kingfisher Book Service, Nottinghamshire 204
Lion Books, Worcs.................................. 255
Lyng Heath Books, Norfolk 190
McCrone (Audrey), Isle of Arran.................. 274
Moore (C.R.), Shropshire 213
Park Gallery & Bookshop (The), Northants 200
Peter White, Hampshire 121
Richard Thornton Books, London N 158
Roland Books, Kent 138
Rugby Relics, Glamorgan........................... 285
Soccor Books Limited, Lincolnshire 148
Stroh (M.A.), London E 154
Treasure Trove Books, Leics....................... 146
Wiend Books, Lancashire 143
Yesterday's News, Conwy........................... 283

- GOLF

Abrahams (Mike), Staffordshire.................... 223
Annie's Books, S Yorks 221
Archways Sports Books, Lothian 275
Big Bairn Books, Tayside 279
Bob Mallory (Books), Derbyshire.................. 83
Bodyline Books, Surrey............................. 232
Bookzone, Berks.................................... 55
Classic Crime Collections, G Manchester......... 119
Coupland (Terry W.), Staffordshire............... 223
Dublin Bookbrowsers, Co. Dublin.................. 265
Dunstan Books, Dorset.............................. 91
Esoteric Dreams Bookshop, Cumbria 77
Fifteenth Century Bookshop (The), East Sussex. 104
First Edition, The, Essex 109
Garfi Books, Powys 291
Gathern (D.), Conwy 283
Golfiana, London W................................ 172
Grant Books, Worcs 255
Gresham Books, Somerset 217
Hennessey Bookseller (Ray), East Sussex 100
Joel Segal Books, Devon 86

Keogh's Books, Glos 115
Little Stour Books, Kent 136
McEwan Golf Books (Rhod), Grampian 272
Morley Case, Hampshire 125
Murphy (C.J.), Norfolk 189
Old Book Company, (The), West Yorkshire 248
Penny Farthing, The, Lothian 277
Poor Richard's Books, Suffolk 226
Roland Books, Kent 138
Rugby Relics, Glamorgan 285
Schofield Golf Books (Steve), West Yorkshire ... 250
Seabreeze Books, Lancashire 144
Simpson (Dave), Central 268
Strathtay Antiquarian - Secondhand Books,
   Tayside 280
Stroh (M.A.), London E 154
Trinity Rare Books, Co. Leitrim 266

- GREYHOUND RACING
Bodyline Books, Surrey 232
Coch-y-Bonddu Books, Powys 290

- GYMNASTICS
Archways Sports Books, Lothian 275
Bodyline Books, Surrey 232
Rebecca Hardie Rare Books, London W 171

- HIGHLAND GAMES
Bodyline Books, Surrey 232
Webster (D.), Strathclyde 279

- HOCKEY
Archways Sports Books, Lothian 275
Bodyline Books, Surrey 232
Pennymead Books, North Yorkshire 193
Yesterday's Books, Dorset 92

- HORSE RACING (INC. RIDING/BREED-
ING/EQUESTRIAN)
Allinson (Frank & Stella), Warwickshire 236
Amos (Denis W.), Herts 130
Annie's Books, S Yorks 221
Archways Sports Books, Lothian 275
Askew Books (Vernon), Wiltshire 251
Bob Mallory (Books), Derbyshire 83
Bodyline Books, Surrey 232
books2books, Devon 88
Bookworms Paradise Ltd., West Sussex 242
Bookzone, Berks 55
Brown (Books) (Steve), Staffordshire 223
Browzers, G Manchester 118
Carters (Janet), Suffolk 225
Cobbles Books, Somerset 217
Cornucopia Books, Lincolnshire 151
Crabtree (Mrs. C.), G Manchester 120
Daisyroots Book Centre (Daisyroots Books Ltd),
   Cumbria 77
Dales & Lakes Book Centre, Cumbria 79
Edwards, Fiona, Nottinghamshire 203
Fifteenth Century Bookshop (The), East Sussex . 104
Garfi Books, Powys 291
Gathern (D.), Conwy 283
Gibbs Books, (Jonathan), Worcs 256
Grayling (David A.H.), Cumbria 78
Grove Bookshop (The), North Yorkshire 195

Hambleton Books, North Yorkshire 196
J.H. Day, Hampshire 124
Jane Badger Books, Northants 199
Joel Segal Books, Devon 86
Karen Millward, Co. Cork 263
Kelpie's Books, Fife 271
Kennedy & Farley, East Sussex 104
Kirkman Ltd., (Robert), Bedfordshire 54
Leeper (Romilly), London SW 168
MK Book Services, Cambridgeshire 66
Richard Thornton Books, London N 158
Roland Books, Kent 138
Treasure Island (The), G Manchester 119
Winchester Bookshop (The), Hampshire 126
Wychwood Books, Glos 116

- HUNTING
Baynton–Williams Gallery, West Sussex 241
Bodyline Books, Surrey 232
Bonham (J. & S.L.), London W 171
Booth (Booksearch Service), (Geoff), Cheshire ... 68
Cavendish Books (Rupert), West Yorkshire 247
Cobbles Books, Somerset 217
Coch-y-Bonddu Books, Powys 290
Cornucopia Books, Lincolnshire 151
Countrymans Gallery (The), Leics 145
Darkwood Books, Co. Cork 263
Deeside Books, Grampian 272
Edmund Pollinger Rare Books, London SW 166
Farquharson, (Hilary), Tayside 280
Fifteenth Century Bookshop (The), East Sussex . 104
Garfi Books, Powys 291
Grayling (David A.H.), Cumbria 78
Grove Bookshop (The), North Yorkshire 195
Hancock (Peter), West Sussex 241
Head (John & Judith), Wiltshire 253
Jane Badger Books, Northants 199
Joel Segal Books, Devon 86
Karen Millward, Co. Cork 263
Kennedy & Farley, East Sussex 104
Kilgour (Sporting Books) (Ian), Leics 147
Kirkman Ltd., (Robert), Bedfordshire 54
Martin (Books and Pictures), (Brian P.), Surrey . 231
Martin (Brian), Surrey 231
Muttonchop Manuscripts, West Sussex 242
Old Book Company, (The), West Yorkshire 248
Peter M Daly, Hampshire 126
Richard Thornton Books, London N 158
Rods Books, Devon 88
St Mary's Books & Prints, Lincolnshire 152
Saintfield Antiques & Fine Books, Co. Down ... 261
Vinovium Books, Durham 97
White (C.R.), London W 175
Wychwood Books, Glos 116

- ICE HOCKEY
Archways Sports Books, Lothian 275
Bodyline Books, Surrey 232

- ICE-SKATING
Archways Sports Books, Lothian 275
Bodyline Books, Surrey 232
Joel Segal Books, Devon 86

- MARTIAL ARTS
Archways Sports Books, Lothian 275
Bodyline Books, Surrey.............................. 232
Books Bought & Sold, Surrey 231
Bookworms Paradise Ltd., West Sussex 242
Combat Arts Archive, Durham 97
Joel Segal Books, Devon 86

- MOTOR RACING
Archways Sports Books, Lothian 275
Bob Mallory (Books), Derbyshire................. 83
Bodyline Books, Surrey.............................. 232
books2books, Devon.............................. 88
Bookworms Paradise Ltd., West Sussex 242
Booth (Booksearch Service) (Geoff), Cheshire... 68
Burroughs (Andrew), Lincolnshire................. 152
Collectors Carbooks, Northants................... 199
Cornucopia Books, Lincolnshire 151
Elmo Books, West Sussex 243
Falconwood Transport & Military Bookshop,
    London O.. 183
Gathern (D.), Conwy 283
Heritage, West Midlands 238
Joel Segal Books, Devon 86
Kerr (Norman), Cumbria 77
Knowles (John), Norfolk 187
Lion Books, Worcs.................................. 255
Morris Secondhand & Antiquarian Books
    (Chris), Oxfordshire 208
Richard Thornton Books, London N 158
Roadmaster Books, Kent............................ 136
St Paul's Street Bookshop, Lincolnshire 152
Simon Lewis Transport Books, Glos 114
Vintage Motorshop, West Yorkshire 245
Volumes of Motoring, Glos......................... 113

- OLYMPIC GAMES, THE
Archways Sports Books, Lothian 275
Bob Mallory (Books), Derbyshire................. 83
Bodyline Books, Surrey.............................. 232
Gathern (D.), Conwy 283
Rugby Relics, Glamorgan........................... 285

- PIG-STICKING
Bodyline Books, Surrey.............................. 232
Chalmers Hallam (E.), Hampshire................. 125
Coch-y-Bonddu Books, Powys 290
Edmund Pollinger Rare Books, London SW..... 166

- POLO
Askew Books (Vernon), Wiltshire................. 251
Blacklock's, Surrey 231
Bodyline Books, Surrey.............................. 232
Peter M Daly, Hampshire........................... 126

- POTHOLING
Bodyline Books, Surrey.............................. 232
Glacier Books, Tayside 280
Hunter and Krageloh, Derbyshire 83
Jarvis Books, Derbyshire 83
Letterbox Books, Nottinghamshire 203
Merseyside Books, Merseyside...................... 185

- PRIZEFIGHTING
McInnes (P.F. & J.R.), Dorset 91

- RACING
Bob Mallory (Books), Derbyshire................. 83
Bodyline Books, Surrey.............................. 232
Bookzone, Berks 55
Browzers, G Manchester 118
Cavendish Books (Rupert), West Yorkshire...... 247
Fifteenth Century Bookshop (The), East Sussex. 104
Grove Bookshop (The), North Yorkshire 195
Head (John & Judith), Wiltshire 253
Karen Millward, Co. Cork.......................... 263

- RACKET SPORTS
Bodyline Books, Surrey.............................. 232
Joel Segal Books, Devon 86
Stroh (M.A.), London E 154

- REAL TENNIS
Bodyline Books, Surrey.............................. 232
Edmund Pollinger Rare Books, London SW..... 166
Marlborough Rare Books Ltd., London W 173

- ROWING
Archways Sports Books, Lothian 275
Bodyline Books, Surrey.............................. 232
McLaren Books Ltd, Strathclyde 279
Vandeleur Antiquarian Books, Surrey............. 231

- RUGBY
Archways Sports Books, Lothian 275
Bodyline Books, Surrey.............................. 232
Bookworms Paradise Ltd., West Sussex 242
Bookzone, Berks 55
Cavendish Books (Rupert), West Yorkshire...... 247
Chas J. Sawyer, Kent 140
Dylans Bookstore, Swansea......................... 291
Franks Booksellers, G Manchester 119
Joel Segal Books, Devon 86
Just Books, Cornwall 75
Kingfisher Book Service, Nottinghamshire 204
Lion Books, Worcs.................................. 255
Old Book Company, (The), West Yorkshire..... 248
Poor Richard's Books, Suffolk 226
Roland Books, Kent 138
Rugby Relics, Glamorgan........................... 285
Saunders (Tom), Caerphilly 281
Treasure Island (The), G Manchester 119
Wiend Books, Lancashire 143

- RUNNING
Archways Sports Books, Lothian 275
Bodyline Books, Surrey.............................. 232
Bookzone, Berks 55
Rugby Relics, Glamorgan........................... 285

- SAILING
Argent (Alan), Isle of Wight 134
Bodyline Books, Surrey.............................. 232
Curtle Mead Books, Isle of Wight................. 133
Fifteenth Century Bookshop (The), East Sussex. 104
Greta Books, Durham 97
Joel Segal Books, Devon 86
Just Books, Cornwall 75
McLaren Books Ltd, Strathclyde 279
Portus Books, Hampshire 122
Rods Books, Devon.................................. 88

Sea Chest Nautical Bookshop (The), Devon 88
SETI Books, West Midlands........................ 239

- SHOOTING
Atholl Fine Books, Tayside 280
Blest (Peter), Kent 138
Bodyline Books, Surrey.............................. 232
Chalmers Hallam (E.), Hampshire................. 125
Coch-y-Bonddu Books, Powys 290
Countrymans Gallery (The), Leics 145
Darkwood Books, Co. Cork......................... 263
Edmund Pollinger Rare Books, London SW..... 166
Farquharson, (Hilary), Tayside..................... 280
Fifteenth Century Bookshop (The), East Sussex. 104
Fylde Books, Lancashire 144
Garfi Books, Powys 291
Grayling (David A.H.), Cumbria 78
Greta Books, Durham 97
Head (John & Judith), Wiltshire 253
Joel Segal Books, Devon 86
Karen Millward, Co. Cork........................... 263
Kilgour (Sporting Books) (Ian), Leics 147
Martin (Books and Pictures), (Brian P.), Surrey. 231
Martin (Brian), Surrey 231
Peter M Daly, Hampshire............................ 126
Roland Books, Kent 138
Vinovium Books, Durham 97
Winchester Bookshop (The), Hampshire.......... 126
Wychwood Books, Glos.............................. 116

- SKIING
Archways Sports Books, Lothian 275
Bodyline Books, Surrey.............................. 232
Frew Limited (Robert), London SW 167
Glacier Books, Tayside 280
Hunter and Krageloh, Derbyshire 83
Jarvis Books, Derbyshire 83
Joel Segal Books, Devon 86
Pinnacle Books, Lothian............................. 276

- SQUASH
Archways Sports Books, Lothian 275
Bodyline Books, Surrey.............................. 232
Joel Segal Books, Devon 86

- SUMO
Bodyline Books, Surrey.............................. 232
Combat Arts Archive, Durham 97

- SURFING
Bodyline Books, Surrey.............................. 232

- SWIMMING
Archways Sports Books, Lothian 275
Bodyline Books, Surrey.............................. 232
Joel Segal Books, Devon 86
Rugby Relics, Glamorgan............................ 285

- TENNIS
Amos (Denis W.), Herts.............................. 130
Archways Sports Books, Lothian 275
Bodyline Books, Surrey.............................. 232
Bookzone, Berks 55
Cavendish Books (Rupert), West Yorkshire...... 247
Dolphin Books, Suffolk.............................. 225

Gathern (D.), Conwy 283
Joel Segal Books, Devon 86
Old Book Company, (The), West Yorkshire 248
Stroh (M.A.), London E 154
Tennis Collectables, Cheshire 68

- WATERSPORTS
Archways Sports Books, Lothian 275
Bodyline Books, Surrey.............................. 232
Joel Segal Books, Devon 86

- WEIGHTLIFTING/BODYBUILDING
Archways Sports Books, Lothian 275
Bodyline Books, Surrey.............................. 232
Combat Arts Archive, Durham 97
Webster (D.), Strathclyde............................ 279

- WRESTLING
Bodyline Books, Surrey.............................. 232
Combat Arts Archive, Durham 97
Old Book Company, (The), West Yorkshire 248
Webster (D.), Strathclyde............................ 279

- YACHTING (& BOATING)
Baldwin (M. & M.), Worcs 255
Bodyline Books, Surrey.............................. 232
Bookends of Fowey, Cornwall 72
Books Afloat, Dorset................................. 96
Clapham (M. & B.), Hampshire..................... 124
Cornucopia Books, Lincolnshire 151
Crouch Rare Books, Surrey.......................... 232
Curtle Mead Books, Isle of Wight 133
Fifteenth Century Bookshop (The), East Sussex. 104
Footrope Knots, Suffolk............................. 227
G Collins Bookdealers, Herts....................... 130
Gerald Lee Maritime Books, East Sussex......... 105
Greta Books, Durham 97
Internet Bookshop UK Ltd., Glos.................. 113
Joel Segal Books, Devon 86
McLaren Books Ltd, Strathclyde 279
Milestone Books, Devon 89
Old Book Company, (The), West Yorkshire 248
Prior (Michael), Lincolnshire 152
Roland Books, Kent 138
Saintfield Antiques & Fine Books, Co. Down ... 261
Sea Chest Nautical Bookshop (The), Devon 88
Smith Maritime Aviation Books (Frank),
   Tyne and Wear.................................... 235

SPORT IN ART
Cavendish Books (Rupert), West Yorkshire...... 247

STAGE
Brock Books, North Yorkshire...................... 192
Dolphin Books, Suffolk.............................. 225
Fifteenth Century Bookshop (The), East Sussex. 104
Good for Books, Lincolnshire 149
Greenroom Books, West Yorkshire 247
Joel Segal Books, Devon 86
Morris Secondhand & Antiquarian Books
   (Chris), Oxfordshire 208
Old Book Company, (The), West Yorkshire 248
PsychoBabel Books & Journals, Oxfordshire..... 205
Richard Thornton Books, London N 158
Whittle, Bookseller (Avril), Cumbria 80

STAINED GLASS
Barmby (C. & A.J.), Kent............................ 140
Bennett & Kerr Books, Oxfordshire............... 205
Birchden Books, London E......................... 154
Don Kelly Books, London W....................... 172
Heneage Art Books (Thomas), London SW..... 168
Joel Segal Books, Devon............................ 86
Old Book Company, (The), West Yorkshire..... 248
Stained Glass Books, Kent.......................... 139
Staniland (Booksellers), Lincolnshire.............. 152
Trinders' Fine Tools, Suffolk....................... 226
Venables (Morris & Juliet), Bristol................. 59
Whittle, Bookseller (Avril), Cumbria.............. 80

STATES OF AMERICA
- ALASKA
Michael Graves-Johnston, London SW........... 168

- LOUISIANA
Apocalypse, Surrey................................... 232

STATES OF AUSTRALIA
- NEW SOUTH WALES
Roz Hulse, Conwy.................................... 284

- QUEENSLAND
Roz Hulse, Conwy.................................... 284

- TASMANIA
Roz Hulse, Conwy.................................... 284

STATISTICS
Adrem Books, Herts.................................. 130
Barcombe Services, Essex........................... 108
Old Book Company, (The), West Yorkshire..... 248
PsychoBabel Books & Journals, Oxfordshire..... 205
Roberts Books, Strathclyde......................... 279
Susanne Schulz-Falster Rare Books, London N. 158
Transformer, Dumfries & Galloway............... 270
Westons, Herts....................................... 132

STEAM ENGINES
Abrahams (Mike), Staffordshire.................... 223
All Books, Essex..................................... 111
Anthony Vickers Books, North Yorkshire....... 195
Boox-Box (The), Shropshire........................ 212
Bott, (Bookdealers) Ltd., (Martin), G Manchester 118
Brewin Books Ltd., Warwickshire................. 237
Browning Books, Torfaen........................... 292
Cassidy (Bookseller) (P.), Lincolnshire............ 151
Cornucopia Books, Lincolnshire.................... 151
Coulthurst (Richard), G Manchester............... 120
Cox (Geoff), Devon................................. 90
Dales and Lakes Book Centre, Cumbria.......... 79
Duck (William), Hampshire......................... 124
Empire Books, North Yorkshire.................... 197
J & J Burgess Booksellers, Cambridgeshire....... 64
Joel Segal Books, Devon............................ 86
Kenneth Ball, East Sussex.......................... 100
Kerr (Norman), Cumbria........................... 77
Liddle (Steve), Bristol.............................. 58
Marine & Cannon Books, Cheshire............... 71
Marine and Cannon Books, Cheshire............. 69
N1 Books, East Sussex............................. 105

Nautical Antique Centre (The), Dorset........... 96
Newband (D.M.), Powys............................ 290
Old Book Company, (The), West Yorkshire..... 248
Randall (Tom), Somerset........................... 218
Roadmaster Books, Kent............................ 136
Robert Humm & Co, Lincolnshire................. 152
Roberts Books, Strathclyde......................... 279
Roland Books, Kent................................. 138
Roz Hulse, Conwy................................... 284
Sedgeberrow Books, Worcs......................... 256
Uncle Phil's Books, West Midlands............... 239
Vintage Motorshop, West Yorkshire.............. 245
Wiend Books, Lancashire........................... 143
Yesteryear Railwayana, Kent....................... 139

STONE MASONRY
Courtney & Hoff, North Yorkshire................ 197

STUDENT ACTIVISM
Left on The Shelf, Cumbria......................... 78

SUFFOLK
Book For All Reasons (A.), Suffolk............... 228
Bookbarrow, Cambridgeshire....................... 63
Charles Bossom, Cambridgeshire................... 65
Debbage (John), Norfolk............................ 189

SUFFRAGETTES
Chapter Two, London SE........................... 163
Delectus Books, London WC....................... 176
Dolphin Books, Suffolk............................. 225
Elaine Lonsdale Books, West Yorkshire.......... 247
Joel Segal Books, Devon............................ 86
Old Book Company, (The), West Yorkshire..... 248
R. & A. Books, East Sussex........................ 101
Reading Lasses, Dumfries & Galloway........... 270

SUFISM
Bookbarrow, Cambridgeshire....................... 63
Fifteenth Century Bookshop (The), East Sussex. 104
Inner Bookshop (The), Oxfordshire............... 208
Joel Segal Books, Devon............................ 86
Needham Books, (Russell), Somerset.............. 219
Occultique, Northants............................... 199
Pittville Books, Glos................................ 113
Portobello Books, London W....................... 174
PsychoBabel Books & Journals, Oxfordshire..... 205
Riderless Horse Books, Norfolk.................... 186
The Sanctuary Bookshop, Dorset.................. 94

SUNDIALS
Country Books, Derbyshire......................... 82
Hadfield (G.K.), Cumbria........................... 79

SUPERNATURAL
Adrem Books, Herts................................. 130
Annie's Books, S Yorks............................. 221
Caduceus Books, Leics.............................. 145
Country Books, Derbyshire......................... 82
Cowley, Bookdealer (K.W.), Somerset............ 217
Crabtree (Mrs. C.), G Manchester................. 120
Delectus Books, London WC....................... 176
Enigma Books, Wiltshire............................ 252
Facet Books, Dorset................................. 91
Gildas Books, Cheshire.............................. 68

Green Man Books, East Sussex 101
Inner Bookshop (The), Oxfordshire.............. 208
Joel Segal Books, Devon 86
Loretta Lay Books, London NW 161
Occultique, Northants................................ 199
Old Book Company, (The), West Yorkshire 248
R. & A. Books, East Sussex 101
Robert Temple, London N........................... 158
SETI Books, West Midlands........................ 239
Star Lord Books, G Manchester 119
Zardoz Books, Wiltshire............................. 254

SURGERY
Bernard Dixon and Kath Adams, London O.... 182
Demetzy Books, Oxfordshire 206
G. C. Books Ltd., Dumfries & Galloway......... 270
Old Book Company, (The), West Yorkshire 248
Parkinsons Books, Merseyside...................... 185
Phelps (Michael), West Sussex...................... 242
PsychoBabel Books & Journals, Oxfordshire..... 205
R M Books, Herts..................................... 132
Rebecca Hardie Rare Books, London W 171
Weiner (Graham), London N 158
Westons, Herts 132

SURREALISM
Atlas, London N....................................... 156
Decorum Books, London N 156
Delectus Books, London WC........................ 176
Ellis, Bookseller (Peter), London WC 177
Joel Segal Books, Devon 86
Print Matters, London SE........................... 165
Riderless Horse Books, Norfolk.................... 186
Trinity Rare Books, Co. Leitrim 266

SURVEYING
Stroh (M.A.), London E 154
Whitchurch Books Ltd., Cardiff.................... 281

SURVIVAL
Coch-y-Bonddu Books, Powys 290
Greta Books, Durham 97

SYMBOLISM
Apocalypse, Surrey 232
Delectus Books, London WC........................ 176
Inner Bookshop (The), Oxfordshire.............. 208
Joel Segal Books, Devon 86
Occultique, Northants................................ 199
Pittville Books, Glos.................................. 113
Star Lord Books, G Manchester 119

TALKING BOOKS
Maggy Browne, Lincolnshire 148

TAPESTRY
Abington Books, Suffolk 227
Art Reference Books, Hampshire 124
Bennett & Kerr Books, Oxfordshire............... 205
Books, Oxfordshire................................... 205
Byrom Textile Bookroom (Richard), Lancashire 142
Cover to Cover, Merseyside......................... 185
Don Kelly Books, London W 172
Fifteenth Century Bookshop (The), East Sussex. 104
Heneage Art Books (Thomas), London SW 168

Hennessey Bookseller (Ray), East Sussex 100
Joel Segal Books, Devon 86
Judith Mansfield, West Yorkshire.................. 249
R. & A. Books, East Sussex 101
Sleepy Elephant Books & Artefacts, Cumbria ... 80
Trinders' Fine Tools, Suffolk 226
Whittle, Bookseller (Avril), Cumbria 80

TAXATION
Old Book Company, (The), West Yorkshire 248
Quaritch Ltd., (Bernard), London W.............. 174
Wayside Books and Cards, Oxfordshire 206

TAXIDERMY
Blest (Peter), Kent 138
Chalmers Hallam (E.), Hampshire................. 125
Coch-y-Bonddu Books, Powys 290
Home Farm Books, Warwickshire.................. 236
Martin (Books and Pictures), (Brian P.), Surrey. 231
Trade Priced Old Books, Powys.................... 289
White (C.R.), London W............................ 175

TEA
Gardener & Cook, London SW.................... 167
Joel Segal Books, Devon 86

TEACHING
Barcombe Services, Essex............................ 108
Cornucopia Books, Lincolnshire 151
Ice House Books, Wiltshire 254
Joel Segal Books, Devon 86
Old Book Company, (The), West Yorkshire 248
PsychoBabel Books & Journals, Oxfordshire..... 205
Reading Lasses, Dumfries & Galloway 270

TECHNICAL
Adrem Books, Herts 130
Barcombe Services, Essex............................ 108
Bernard Dixon and Kath Adams, London O.... 182
Brimstones, East Sussex 104
Cotswold Internet Books, Glos..................... 113
Duck (William), Hampshire......................... 124
Fine Books at Ilkley, West Yorkshire 247
Fylde Books, Lancashire 144
Kelly Books Ltd, Devon............................. 89
Moorhead Books, West Yorkshire.................. 245
Parkinsons Books, Merseyside...................... 185
PsychoBabel Books & Journals, Oxfordshire..... 205
Roberts Books, Strathclyde 279
Stroh (M.A.), London E 154
Weiner (Graham), London N 158
Westons, Herts 132
Yesteryear Railwayana, Kent....................... 139

TECHNOLOGY
Barcombe Services, Essex............................ 108
Baron (Christopher), Cheshire...................... 68
Batterham (David), London W...................... 171
Bernard Dixon and Kath Adams,
  London O... 182
Book House (The), Cumbria........................ 76
Bott, (Bookdealers) Ltd., (Martin),
  G Manchester 118
Chris Phillips, Wiltshire............................. 252
Clevedon Books, Somerset 217

Eagle Bookshop (The), Bedfordshire 53
Eggle (Mavis), Herts 130
Esplin (David), Hampshire 124
Gaskell Rare Books (Roger), Cambridgeshire ... 66
Gladstone Books, Lincolnshire 150
Hindsight Books, Herts 131
K.S.C. Books, Cheshire 70
Mollie's Loft, Swansea 291
Old Book Company, (The), West Yorkshire 248
Orangeberry Books, Oxfordshire 207
Parkinsons Books, Merseyside 185
Pauline Harries Books, Hampshire 123
Phelps (Michael), West Sussex 242
Phillips (Nigel), Hampshire 122
Pollak (P.M.), Devon 88
Roberts Books, Strathclyde 279
Rogers Turner Books, London SE 165
Stroh (M.A.), London E 154
Susanne Schulz-Falster Rare Books, London N. 158
Trinders' Fine Tools, Suffolk 226
Weiner (Graham), London N 158
Westons, Herts 132
Westwood Books (Mark), Powys 289
Whistler's Books, London SW 169

TEDDY BEARS

Bookmark (Children's Books), Wiltshire 253
DPE Books, Devon 87
Green Meadow Books, Cornwall 74
Jean Hedger, Berks 55
Joel Segal Books, Devon 86
R. & A. Books, East Sussex 101
Saint Swithin's Illustrated & Children's Books,
　London W 174

TELEGRAPH

Chris Phillips, Wiltshire 252
Elton Engineering Books, London W 172
Kelly Books Ltd, Devon 89
Roz Hulse, Conwy 284
Stroh (M.A.), London E 154
Weiner (Graham), London N 158
Yesteryear Railwayana, Kent 139

TELEVISION

Byre Books, Dumfries & Galloway 270
Cover to Cover, Merseyside 185
Decorum Books, London N 156
Evans (Mark), Lincolnshire 151
firstpagebooks, Norfolk 189
Fitzsimons (Anne), Cumbria 76
Greenroom Books, West Yorkshire 247
Hambleton Books, North Yorkshire 196
Joel Segal Books, Devon 86
Kelly Books Ltd, Devon 89
Maggy Browne, Lincolnshire 148
McGee (Terence J.), London O 180
Morris Secondhand & Antiquarian Books
　(Chris), Oxfordshire 208
Mr. Pickwick of Towcester, Northants 199
Old Book Company, (The), West Yorkshire 248
Paramor (C.D.), Suffolk 228
Pyecroft (Ruth), Glos 116
R. & A. Books, East Sussex 101
Stroh (M.A.), London E 154

Sugen & Co., North Yorkshire 193
Terence Kaye - Bookseller, London NW 161
Weiner (Graham), London N 158
Wiend Books, Lancashire 143
Williams (Bookdealer), (Richard), N Lincs 153
Wright (Norman), Dorset 95
Yesterday's News, Conwy 283
Zardoz Books, Wiltshire 254

TERRORISM/GUERRILLA WARFARE

Delectus Books, London WC 176
Left on The Shelf, Cumbria 78
Loretta Lay Books, London NW 161
MilitaryHistoryBooks.com, Kent 137
Red Star Books, Herts 129

TEUTONIC HISTORY & CULTURE

Joel Segal Books, Devon 86
MilitaryHistoryBooks.com, Kent 137
Thorntons of Oxford Ltd., Oxfordshire 206

TEXANA

Americanabooksuk, Cumbria 76

TEXTBOOKS

Barcombe Services, Essex 108
Cornucopia Books, Lincolnshire 151
Oopalba Books, Cheshire 71
Parkinsons Books, Merseyside 185
Roberts Books, Strathclyde 279
Stalagluft Books, Tyne and Wear 235
The Sanctuary Bookshop, Dorset 94
Yesteryear Railwayana, Kent 139

TEXTILES

Anthony Vickers Books, North Yorkshire 195
Art Reference Books, Hampshire 124
Batterham (David), London W 171
Black Cat Books, Norfolk 187
Brock Books, North Yorkshire 192
Byrom Textile Bookroom (Richard), Lancashire 142
Cover to Cover, Merseyside 185
Decorum Books, London N 156
Delph Books, G Manchester 120
Don Kelly Books, London W 172
Forest Books of Manchester, Cheshire 70
Gallimaufry Books, Herts 131
Hay Castle, Powys 288
Heneage Art Books (Thomas), London SW 168
Hennessey Bookseller (Ray), East Sussex 100
Joel Segal Books, Devon 86
Judith Mansfield, West Yorkshire 249
Meekins Books (Paul), Warwickshire 237
Old Book Company, (The), West Yorkshire 248
Potterton Books, North Yorkshire 196
R. & A. Books, East Sussex 101
Reading Lasses, Dumfries & Galloway 270
Sleepy Elephant Books & Artefacts, Cumbria ... 80
Stroh (M.A.), London E 154
Susan Taylor Books, West Yorkshire 247
Trinders' Fine Tools, Suffolk 226
Warnes (Felicity J.), London O 180
Whittle, Bookseller (Avril), Cumbria 80
Young (D. & J.), Powys 291

THEATRE

Addyman Books, Powys............................ 287
Annie's Books, S Yorks 221
Brock Books, North Yorkshire.................... 192
Byre Books, Dumfries & Galloway............... 270
Clark (Nigel A.), London SE 163
Cobbles Books, Somerset.......................... 217
Cofion Books, Pembrokeshire 286
Cover to Cover, Merseyside....................... 185
Cox Rare Books (Charles), Cornwall............. 73
DaSilva Puppet Books, Dorset 93
Debbage (John), Norfolk.......................... 189
Decorum Books, London N 156
Delectus Books, London WC..................... 176
Dolphin Books, Suffolk........................... 225
Draca Books, West Yorkshire..................... 248
Ely Books, Cambridgeshire 65
Evans (Mark), Lincolnshire 151
Fifteenth Century Bookshop (The), East Sussex. 104
Fitzsimons (Anne), Cumbria...................... 76
Forest Books of Manchester, Cheshire........... 70
Good for Books, Lincolnshire 149
Greenroom Books, West Yorkshire 247
Hancock & Monks Music Emporium, Powys ... 288
Ian McKelvie Bookseller, London N............. 157
Idler (The), Suffolk 227
J.C. Books, Norfolk 191
Jarndyce Antiquarian Booksellers, London WC. 177
Joel Segal Books, Devon 86
Junk & Spread Eagle, London SE 164
Just Books, Cornwall 75
McGee (Terence J.), London O 180
medievalbookshop, Herts.......................... 132
Morris Secondhand & Antiquarian Books
  (Chris), Oxfordshire 208
My Back Pages, London SW 168
Oopalba Books, Cheshire.......................... 71
Paramor (C.D.), Suffolk 228
Pastmasters, Derbyshire........................... 83
Pordes Books Ltd., (Henry), London WC........ 177
Portobello Books, London W 174
Price (John), London N 158
Primrose Hill Books, London NW 161
PsychoBabel Books & Journals, Oxfordshire..... 205
R. & A. Books, East Sussex 101
Readers World, West Midlands 238
Reading Lasses, Dumfries & Galloway 270
Reads, Dorset 95
Rhodes, Bookseller (Peter), Hampshire 125
Richard Thornton Books, London N 158
Robert Temple, London N......................... 158
SaBeRo Books, London SW....................... 169
Saint Swithin's Illustrated & Children's Books,
  London W 174
Scrivener's Books & Bookbinding, Derbyshire... 82
Sleepy Elephant Books & Artefacts, Cumbria ... 80
Terence Kaye - Bookseller, London NW 161
Theatreshire Books, North Yorkshire 192
Travis & Emery Music Bookshop, London WC 178
Whittle, Bookseller (Avril), Cumbria 80
Willmott Bookseller (Nicholas), Cardiff.......... 281
Wood (Peter), Cambridgeshire..................... 65
Yesterday's News, Conwy.......................... 283
Ystwyth Books, Ceredigion 282

THEOLOGY

Addyman Books, Powys............................ 287
Andrews Books & Collectables, Cheshire......... 69
Apocalypse, Surrey 232
Axe Rare & Out of Print Books (Richard),
  North Yorkshire 193
Barbican Bookshop, North Yorkshire............. 196
Barcombe Services, Essex.......................... 108
Bardsley's Books, Suffolk......................... 225
Beckham Books Ltd., Suffolk 229
Bell (Peter), Lothian.............................. 275
Berwick Books, Lincolnshire...................... 150
Bevan (John), Wiltshire 252
Beware of the Leopard, Bristol 58
Big Bairn Books, Tayside 279
Blythswood Bookshop, Highland 274
Book Aid, Durham................................ 97
Bookcase, Cumbria............................... 76
Bookshop (The), Co. Donegal..................... 263
Bookshop at the Plain, Lincolnshire.............. 149
Brimstones, East Sussex........................... 104
Broadwater Books, Hampshire 125
Butler Rare Books, Buckinghamshire 61
Capel Mawr Collectors Centre, Gwynedd 285
Carter, (Brian), Oxfordshire 210
Chapter Two, London SE.......................... 163
Chesters (G. & J.), Staffordshire 224
Cobnar Books, Kent 141
Colwyn Books, Conwy 283
Copnal Books, Cheshire........................... 69
Corder (Mark W.), Kent 139
Courtenay Bookroom, Oxfordshire................ 205
Delectus Books, London WC...................... 176
Edwards (Alan & Margaret), Kent 141
Edwards (London) Limited (Francis),
  London WC 176
Edwards in Hay-on-Wye (Francis), Powys 288
Evangelical Bookshop, Co. Antrim................ 260
Fotheringham (Alex), Northumberland 201
G. C. Books Ltd., Dumfries & Galloway......... 270
Gage Postal Books, Essex 111
Gilbert (R.A.), Somerset.......................... 219
Golden Age Books, Worcs 256
Gowan Books (John), Co. Fermanagh............ 261
Hab Books, London W............................ 172
Hellenic Bookservices, London NW 161
Heritage Books, Isle of Wight 133
Howes Bookshop, East Sussex 102
Humber Books, Lincolnshire 148
Island Books, Devon.............................. 85
J.E. Burns Booksellers, Merseyside 185
Kernaghans, Merseyside........................... 185
Kyrios Books, Nottinghamshire................... 203
Lewis (J.T. & P.), Cornwall 73
Magis Books, Leics 146
Main Point Books, Lothian 276
Martin's Books, Powys 290
Mercat Books, Highland 274
Modern Welsh Publications Ltd., Merseyside.... 184
New Strand, The, Herefordshire 127
Oasis Booksearch, Cambridgeshire................ 67
Old Aberdeen Bookshop, Grampian 272
Old Book Company, (The), West Yorkshire 248
Old Bookshop (The), West Midlands 240
Olynthiacs, Shropshire 213

Parkinsons Books, Merseyside 185
Pendleburys Bookshop, London N 158
Price (John), London N 158
PsychoBabel Books & Journals, Oxfordshire..... 205
Quaritch Ltd., (Bernard), London W.............. 174
Quinto of Charing Cross Road, London WC ... 178
Rose Books, G Manchester 119
Rosemary Pugh Books, Wiltshire 253
Rosley Books, Cumbria 81
Rutland Bookshop (The), Rutland 211
S.P.C.K., Bristol 59
S.P.C.K., Hampshire 126
St Philip's Books, Oxfordshire 208
Saintfield Antiques & Fine Books, Co. Down ... 261
Salsus Books, Worcs 256
Samovar Books, Co. Dublin 264
Scott (Peter), East Sussex 104
Singleton (Anthony), S Yorks 221
Spooner & Co, Somerset 219
Staffs Bookshop (The), Staffordshire 223
Stalagluft Books, Tyne and Wear 235
Staniland (Booksellers), Lincolnshire 152
Sterling Books, Somerset 220
Stokes Books, Co. Dublin 264
Thornber (Peter M.), North Yorkshire 195
Thorntons of Oxford Ltd., Oxfordshire 206
Trade Priced Old Books, Powys 289
Trotter Books (John), London N 158
Westwood Books (Mark), Powys 289
Winchester Bookshop (The), Hampshire 126

THEOSOPHY

Alpha Books, London N 156
Bookcase, Cumbria 76
Bookshop on the Heath, The, London SE 163
Inner Bookshop (The), Oxfordshire 208
Joel Segal Books, Devon 86
Needham Books, (Russell), Somerset 219
Occultique, Northants 199
Rosemary Pugh Books, Wiltshire 253
Star Lord Books, G Manchester 119
The Sanctuary Bookshop, Dorset 94
Woburn Books, London N 159

THERAPY - MARITAL & FAMILY

Joel Segal Books, Devon 86
Reading Lasses, Dumfries & Galloway 270

TILES

Buckland Books, West Sussex 243

TIMBER TECHNOLOGY

Joel Segal Books, Devon 86
Parkinsons Books, Merseyside 185
Reeves Technical Books, North Yorkshire 195

TOBACCO

Delectus Books, London WC 176
Game Advice, Oxfordshire 208
Joel Segal Books, Devon 86
Stroh (M.A.), London E 154
Susanne Schulz-Falster Rare Books, London N. 158

TOPOGRAPHY
- GENERAL

A. & H. Peasgood, Cambridgeshire 66
Abacus Gallery, Staffordshire 224
Addyman Books, Powys 287
Adrem Books, Herts 130
Alexander's Books, Warwickshire 237
Allhalland Books, Devon 84
Altea Antique Maps & Books, London W 171
Andrews Books & Collectables, Cheshire 69
Andron (G.W.), London N 156
Anthony Spranger, Wiltshire 252
Anthony Vickers Books, N Yorks 195
Antiquary Ltd., (Bar Bookstore), N Yorks 194
Antique Map and Bookshop (The), Dorset 94
Antiques on High, Oxfordshire 207
Anvil Books, West Midlands 239
Arden Books & Cosmographia, Warwickshire... 236
Arts & Antiques Centre (The), Cheshire 69
Atholl Fine Books, Tayside 280
Autolycus, Shropshire 212
Backfold Books, Herefordshire 127
Baker - Books for the Collector (Colin), Devon. 89
Baker (Gerald), Bristol 60
Bardsley's Books, Suffolk 225
Barnes (Peter), Wiltshire 253
Bath Old Books, Somerset 215
Beardsley (A.E.), Nottinghamshire 204
Bermondsey Basement Bookstore, London SE .. 163
Bolton Books, Hampshire 121
Bonham (J. & S.L.), London W 171
Bonython Bookshop, Cornwall 75
Bookbox, Glos 115
Books, Denbighshire 284
Books & Collectables Ltd., Cambridgeshire 63
Books Afloat, Dorset 96
books2books, Devon 88
BOOKS4U, Flintshire 284
Bookshop (The), Norfolk 191
Bookworms, Norfolk 186
Brinded (Scott), Kent 138
Broadhurst of Southport Ltd., Merseyside 185
Brock Books, North Yorkshire 192
Burden Ltd., (Clive A.), Herts 131
Carnforth Bookshop (The), Lancashire 142
Castle Bookshop, Essex 108
Castle Hill Books, Herefordshire 128
Cavern Books, Cheshire 70
Channel Islands Galleries Limited,
    Channel Islands 258
Chapter & Verse, Lincolnshire 150
Charles Bossom, Cambridgeshire 65
Chaucer Bookshop, Kent 136
Cheshire Book Centre, Cheshire 69
Chevin Books, West Yorkshire 249
Clarke Books (David), Somerset 218
Classic Bindings Ltd, London SW 166
Clent Books, Worcs 255
Clevedon Books, Somerset 217
Coach House Books, Worcs 256
Cobnar Books, Kent 141
Cobweb Books, North Yorkshire 194
Cofion Books, Pembrokeshire 286
Coombes (A.J.), Surrey 230
Cornucopia Books, Lincolnshire 151

Cotswold Internet Books, Glos..................... 113
Country Books, Derbyshire......................... 82
Crabtree (Mrs. C.), G Manchester 120
Craobh Rua Books, Co. Armagh.................. 260
Cumming Limited (A. & Y.), East Sussex........ 104
Daisyroots Book Centre (Daisyroots
   Books Ltd), Cumbria 77
Dales & Lakes Book Centre, Cumbria........... 79
Dandy Lion Editions, Surrey 233
D'Arcy Books, Wiltshire............................ 252
Dartmoor Book Gallery, Devon 87
Dartmoor Bookshop (The), Devon 84
David (G.), Cambridgeshire......................... 63
De Burca Rare Books, Co. Dublin 264
Debbage (John), Norfolk............................ 189
Delph Books, G Manchester....................... 120
Dunkheld Antiques, Tayside........................ 279
Edwards (Alan & Margaret), Kent 141
Elaine Lonsdale Books, West Yorkshire......... 247
Ellwood Editions, Wiltshire........................ 253
Elmfield Books, West Midlands.................... 238
Elstree Books, Herts................................. 130
Eton Antique Bookshop, Berks 57
Evergreen Livres, Glos.............................. 116
Farquharson, (Hilary), Tayside..................... 280
Fifteenth Century Bookshop (The), East Sussex. 104
Fisher & Sperr, London N.......................... 157
Ford Books (David), Herts 130
Freader's Books, Tayside........................... 279
Frost (Richard), Herts 129
G. C. Books Ltd., Dumfries & Galloway........ 270
Garfi Books, Powys 291
Gilbert and Son (H.M.), Hampshire.............. 126
Gillmark Gallery, Herts.............................. 130
Glenbower Books, Co. Dublin 264
Good for Books, Lincolnshire 149
Goodyer (Nicholas), London N.................... 157
Green (Mrs. D.M.), Surrey......................... 234
Grove Bookshop (The), North Yorkshire 195
Guildmaster Books, Cheshire...................... 70
Hab Books, London W.............................. 172
Hall's Bookshop, Kent 140
Handsworth Books, Essex.......................... 112
Harrington Antiquarian Bookseller (Peter),
   London SW...................................... 167
Hawes Books, Norfolk.............................. 190
Hay Cinema Bookshop Ltd., Powys............... 288
High Street Books, Devon 86
Hollett and Son (R.F.G.), Cumbria 79
Hummingbird Books, Herefordshire............... 128
Intech Books, Northumberland 201
InterCol London, London N 157
Jackson (M.W.), Wiltshire.......................... 254
Jade Mountain Bookshop, Hampshire 125
Janus Books, West Midlands 239
Joel Segal Books, Devon 86
John L Capes (Books Maps & Prints),
   North Yorkshire 196
Junk & Spread Eagle, London SE................. 164
Just Books, Cornwall 75
Kalligraphia (formerly Charmouth Bounty
   Books), Isle of Wight............................ 133
Kay Books, London W.............................. 173
Keegan's Bookshop, Berks.......................... 57
Kellow Books, Oxfordshire 206

Kemp Bookseller, Michael S, G Manchester..... 118
Kim's Bookshop, West Sussex................ 241, 242
Kingsmere Books, Bedfordshire.................... 53
Kingswood Books, Dorset 94
Letterbox Books, Nottinghamshire 203
Lewis (J.T. & P.), Cornwall........................ 73
Libris (Weston) Books, Somerset 216
Liddle (Steve), Bristol 58
Lowe (John), Norfolk............................... 188
M. and A.C. Thompson, Norfolk.................. 191
Madoc Books, Conwy 284
Malvern Bookshop (The), Worcs 255
Marcan, Bookseller (Peter), London SE 164
Marlborough Rare Books Ltd., London W...... 173
Martin (Books and Pictures), (Brian P.), Surrey. 231
Martin (Brian), Surrey 231
Martin Bookshop & Gallery (Richard), Hants... 123
Maynard & Bradley, Leics 146
McCrone (Audrey), Isle of Arran.................. 274
Merseyside Books, Merseyside..................... 185
Missing Books, Essex 109
Modlock (Lilian), Dorset............................ 93
Mundy (David), Herts 129
Murphy (C.J.), Norfolk............................. 189
Newlyn Books, Cornwall............................ 74
Nicolas - Antiquarian Bookseller, London N.... 157
Nineteenth Century Books, Oxfordshire 209
O'Flynn Books, North Yorkshire.................. 197
O'Flynn Books, North Yorkshire.................. 197
Old Book Company, (The), West Yorkshire..... 248
Old Station Pottery & Bookshop (The), Norfolk 191
Oopalba Books, Cheshire........................... 71
Ouse Valley Books, Bedfordshire 54
Over-Sands Books, Cumbria........................ 77
Oxley (Laurence), Hampshire...................... 121
Paper Moon Books, Glos 116
Park Gallery & Bookshop (The), Northants 200
Parlour Bookshop (The), Oxfordshire............. 206
Parrott Books, Oxfordshire 209
Past & Present Books, Glos........................ 114
Pauline Harries Books, Hampshire 123
Peter Lyons Books, Glos........................... 113
Peter M Daly, Hampshire 126
Peter White, Hampshire 121
Poor Richard's Books, Suffolk 226
Pordes Books Ltd., (Henry), London WC........ 177
Portus Books, Hampshire 122
Quentin Books Ltd, Essex.......................... 108
Quinto of Charing Cross Road, London WC ... 178
R. & A. Books, East Sussex 101
Read - Gorleston Books, (C.&J.), Norfolk 187
Reads, Dorset 95
Richard Thornton Books, London N 158
Robin Doughty - Fine Books, West Midlands... 238
Roger Collicott Books, Cornwall 74
Roland Books, Kent 138
Ross Old Books & Prints, Herefordshire 128
St Mary's Books & Prints, Lincolnshire 152
Samovar Books, Co. Dublin 264
Saunders (Tom), Caerphilly 281
Sax Books, Suffolk 228
Sedgeberrow Books, Worcs 256
Shacklock Books (David), Suffolk 226
Shakeshaft (Dr. B.), Cheshire...................... 71
Shakespeare Books (Colin), Staffordshire......... 223

Sharpe (Mary), Somerset 219
Singleton (Anthony), S Yorks 221
Smith (Clive), Essex 109
Sparrow Books, West Yorkshire 245
Stalagluft Books, Tyne and Wear 235
Stella Books, Monmouthshire 286
Sterling Books, Somerset 220
Stothert Old Books, Cheshire....................... 68
Suffolk Rare Books, Suffolk 229
Sykes (Graham), West Yorkshire 249
Temperley (David), West Midlands................ 238
Thornber (Peter M.), North Yorkshire........... 195
Thorntons of Oxford Ltd., Oxfordshire........... 206
Tilston (Stephen E.), London SE.................... 165
Tim Bryers Ltd, London WC 178
Titford (John), Derbyshire 82
Townsend (John), Berks 57
Treasure Trove Books, Leics....................... 146
Trinders' Fine Tools, Suffolk 226
Turton (John), Durham 98
Tyger Press, London N 158
ULoveBooks, Devon................................. 90
Unsworth's Booksellers, Suffolk.................... 225
Ventnor Rare Books, Isle of Wight................ 134
Vokes Books Ltd., North Yorkshire............... 194
Wadard Books, Kent 137
Wealden Books, Kent................................ 138
Westcountry Oldbooks, Devon..................... 90
Wheen O'Books, Borders............................ 267
Whitchurch Books Ltd., Cardiff.................... 281
Whitfield (Ken), Essex 110
Williams (Bookdealer), (Richard), Lincs 153
Winchester Bookshop (The), Hampshire.......... 126
Yewtree Books, Cumbria............................ 78

- LOCAL

2 Ravens, Cumbria................................... 78
Abacus Gallery, Staffordshire....................... 224
Abrahams (Mike), Staffordshire.................... 223
Aitchison (Lesley), Bristol 58
Alec–Smith Books (Alex), East Yorkshire........ 107
Altea Antique Maps & Books, London W....... 171
Ambra Books, Bristol................................ 58
Ampersand Books, Norfolk......................... 189
Andrews Books & Collectables, Cheshire......... 69
Anthony Spranger, Wiltshire....................... 252
Anthony Vickers Books, N Yorks 195
Anthony Whittaker, Kent 135
Antiquary Ltd., (Bar Bookstore), N Yorks....... 194
Antique & Book Shop, Powys...................... 291
Anvil Books, West Midlands 239
Arden Books & Cosmographia, Warwickshire... 236
Atholl Fine Books, Tayside......................... 280
Axe Rare & Out of Print Books (Richard),
    N Yorks... 193
Baker - Books for the Collector (Colin), Devon . 89
Baker (Gerald), Bristol.............................. 60
Barbican Bookshop, N Yorks 196
Barmby (C. & A.J.), Kent.......................... 140
Barn Books, Shropshire.............................. 214
Barnacle Books, County Fermanagh 261
Barnes (Peter), Wiltshire........................... 253
Bath Old Books, Somerset 215
Bear Island Books, Cardiff.......................... 281
Bell (Peter), Lothian................................ 275

Benny Gillies Books Ltd, Dumfries & Galloway 268
Bermondsey Basement Bookstore, London SE .. 163
Beware of the Leopard, Bristol..................... 58
Birchden Books, London E 154
Bird (Tony), Powys.................................. 291
Black Cat Bookshop, Leics 147
Blore's Bookshop (Geoffrey), Nottinghamshire .. 204
Bonython Bookshop, Cornwall..................... 75
Book Business (The), London W 171
Book For All Reasons (A.), Suffolk 228
Book Gallery (The), Cornwall 74
Book House (The), Cumbria........................ 76
Bookbarrow, Cambridgeshire 63
Bookbox, Glos 115
Bookcase, Cumbria.................................. 76
Bookends of Fowey, Cornwall 72
Books & Collectables Ltd., Cambridgeshire...... 63
Books Afloat, Dorset................................ 96
Books Bought & Sold, Surrey 231
Books Only, Suffolk 226
BOOKS4U, Flintshire............................... 284
Bookshop (The), Co. Donegal...................... 263
Bookshop on the Heath, The, London SE 163
BookShop, The, Dumfries & Galloway........... 270
Bookworms of Evesham, Worcs 257
Bookzone, Berks 55
Bott, (Bookdealers) Ltd., (Martin),
    G Manchester 118
Brewin Books Ltd., Warwickshire 237
Bridge Books, Cumbria............................. 81
Burden Ltd., (Clive A.), Herts..................... 131
Bury Bookshop, Suffolk 225
Carlton Books, Norfolk 189
Carnforth Bookshop (The), Lancashire 142
Cassidy (Bookseller) (P.), Lincolnshire 151
Castle Bookshop, Essex............................. 108
Castle Hill Books, Herefordshire 128
Cavern Books, Cheshire 70
Chandos Books, Devon.............................. 85
Channel Islands Galleries Limited, C Isles........ 258
Chapman (Neville), Lancashire..................... 144
Chapter & Verse, Lincolnshire...................... 150
Chaucer Bookshop, Kent............................ 136
Chaucer Head Bookshop, Warwickshire.......... 237
Cheshire Book Centre, Cheshire.................... 69
Chevin Books, West Yorkshire..................... 249
Chichester Bookshop (The), Herefordshire 241
Church Green Books, Oxfordshire.................. 210
Clarke Books (David), Somerset 218
Classic Bindings Ltd, London SW 166
Classic Crime Collections, G Manchester......... 119
Coach House Books, Worcs 256
Cobbles Books, Somerset 217
Cofion Books, Pembrokeshire 286
Collectors Corner, Wiltshire........................ 253
Colonsay Bookshop, Isle of Colonsay............. 275
Compass Books, Devon 85
Coombes (A.J.), Surrey 230
Copnal Books, Cheshire............................. 69
Copperplate Antique Maps and Prints, Herts.... 132
Corder (Mark W.), Kent 139
Cornucopia Books, Lincolnshire 151
Cotswold Internet Books, Glos..................... 113
Country Books, Derbyshire......................... 82
Courtwood Books, Co. Laois....................... 265

Cox Old & Rare Books (Claude), Suffolk 227
Cox, Andrew, Shropshire............................. 214
Creaking Shelves, Highland......................... 274
Daisyroots Book Centre (Daisyroots
  Books Ltd), Cumbria 77
Dales & Lakes Book Centre, Cumbria............ 79
Dandy Lion Editions, Surrey 233
D'Arcy Books, Wiltshire............................. 252
Dartmoor Book Gallery, Devon 87
Dartmoor Bookshop (The), Devon 84
Dave Jelfs, Devon 85
David (G.), Cambridgeshire......................... 63
Davidson Books, Co. Down 261
Debbage (John), Norfolk 189
Delph Books, G Manchester........................ 120
Dene Barn Books & Prints, Somerset 219
Dobson (Bob), Lancashire 142
Dolphin Books, Suffolk.............................. 225
Eastgate Bookshop, East Yorkshire 106
Elaine Lonsdale Books, West Yorkshire 247
Ellwood Editions, Wiltshire 253
Elmfield Books, West Midlands 238
Elstree Books, Herts................................. 130
Embleton (Paul), Essex 111
English (Toby), Oxfordshire........................ 209
Everett (Richard), Norfolk 187
Everett (Richard, at the Southwold Antiques
  Centre), Suffolk 229
Evergreen Livres, Glos.............................. 116
Exeter Rare Books, Devon.......................... 86
Farquharson, (Hilary), Tayside..................... 280
Ferdinando (Steven), Somerset 218
Fifteenth Century Bookshop (The), East Sussex. 104
Ford Books (David), Herts 130
Freader's Books, Tayside............................ 279
Furneaux Books (Lee), Devon...................... 89
Fylde Books, Lancashire 144
G Collins Bookdealers, Herts....................... 130
G. C. Books Ltd., Dumfries & Galloway......... 270
Garretts Antiquarian Books, Isle of Man........ 259
GfB: the Colchester Bookshop, Essex 108
Gibbard (A. & T.), East Sussex 101
Gilbert and Son (H.M.), Hampshire............... 126
Gildas Books, Cheshire 68
Gillmark Gallery, Herts.............................. 130
Gladstone Books, Lincolnshire 150
Good for Books, Lincolnshire 149
Greta Books, Durham 97
Grove Bookshop (The), North Yorkshire 195
Guisborough Bookshop (The), North Yorkshire 192
Hames (Peter), Devon............................... 84
Harlequin Books, Bristol............................ 59
Helmsley Antiquarian & Secondhand Books,
  North Yorkshire 193
Hennessey Bookseller (Ray), East Sussex 100
Heritage, West Midlands 238
High Street Books, Devon 86
Hill (Peter), Hampshire 122
Hill Books (Alan), S Yorks 222
Hollett and Son (R.F.G.), Cumbria 79
Holmes Books (Harry), East Yorkshire........... 107
Hornsey's, North Yorkshire......................... 194
Horsham Rare Books, West Sussex 242
Howes Bookshop, East Sussex 102
Hutchison (Books) (Larry), Fife.................... 271

Idle Booksellers (The), West Yorkshire 245
Idle Genius Books, London N 157
Intech Books, Northumberland 201
Invicta Bookshop, Berks............................. 56
Iona Bookshop (The), Isle of Iona................. 275
Island Books, Devon................................. 85
J.C. Books, Devon.................................... 87
Jade Mountain Bookshop, Hampshire............. 125
Janus Books, West Midlands 239
Jermy & Westerman, Nottinghamshire............ 204
Joel Segal Books, Devon 86
John Barton, Hampshire 126
John L Capes (Books Maps & Prints), North
  Yorkshire.. 196
Junk & Spread Eagle, London SE................. 164
Just Books, Cornwall 75
Keeble Antiques, Somerset 218
Keegan's Bookshop, Berks 57
Kellow Books, Oxfordshire 206
Kelsall (George), G Manchester.................... 118
Kemp Bookseller, Michael S,
  G Manchester 118
Kernaghans, Merseyside.............................. 185
Kerr (Norman), Cumbria 77
Key Books (Sarah), Cambridgeshire............... 64
Killeen (John), North Yorkshire 193
Kim's Bookshop, West Sussex...................... 242
Kim's Bookshop, West Sussex...................... 241
Kirkland Books, Cumbria 78
Lake (David), Norfolk............................... 190
Lawrence Books, Nottinghamshire 203
Leakey's Bookshop, Highland 274
Leigh Gallery Books, Essex 110
Letterbox Books, Nottinghamshire 203
Liddle (Steve), Bristol 58
Little Bookshop (The), Cumbria 80
Lymelight Books & Prints, Dorset................. 93
M. & D. Books, Worcs.............................. 255
Madoc Books, Conwy 284
Mair Wilkes Books, Fife 271
Malvern Bookshop (The), Worcs 255
Marcan, Bookseller (Peter), London SE 164
Martin (Books and Pictures), (Brian P.), Surrey. 231
Martin (Brian), Surrey 231
McCrone (Audrey), Isle of Arran.................. 274
Michael Bishop PBFA, Somerset 220
michaelsbookshop.com, Kent....................... 139
Missing Books, Essex 109
Modlock (Lilian), Dorset............................ 93
Mogul Diamonds, West Midlands 240
Moon's Bookshop (Michael), Cumbria 80
Moore (C.R.), Shropshire 213
Moorhead Books, West Yorkshire................. 245
Mount's Bay Books, Cornwall 74
Mulyan (Don), Merseyside.......................... 185
Mundy (David), Herts 129
Muttonchop Manuscripts, West Sussex 242
Newlyn Books, Cornwall 74
Niner (Marcus), Isle of Wight 133
Oakwood Books, Glos............................... 115
O'Flynn Books, North Yorkshire.................. 197
Old Book Company, (The), West Yorkshire 248
Old Bookshelf (The), Strathclyde................... 278
Old Bookshop (The), West Midlands 240
Old Hall Bookshop (The), Northants 199

Old Station Pottery & Bookshop (The), Norfolk 191
Old Town Bookshop (The), Lothian 276
Orb's Bookshop, Grampian.......................... 273
Ouse Valley Books, Bedfordshire 54
Over-Sands Books, Cumbria........................ 77
Oxley (Laurence), Hampshire...................... 121
P.H. Whetman, London N.......................... 159
Park Gallery & Bookshop (The), Northants 200
Past & Present Books, Glos........................ 114
Pendleside Books, Lancashire...................... 143
Periwinkle Press, Kent 136
Peter M Daly, Hampshire 126
Poor Richard's Books, Suffolk 226
Post–Horn Books, North Yorkshire.............. 192
Postings, Surrey..................................... 233
R. & A. Books, East Sussex 101
Randall (Tom), Somerset........................... 218
Rare & Racy, S Yorks.............................. 222
Reads, Dorset 95
Restormel Books, Worcs 257
Richard Thornton Books, London N 158
Richmond Books, North Yorkshire 194
Roadmaster Books, Kent........................... 136
Robin Doughty - Fine Books, West Midlands... 238
Rochdale Book Company, G Manchester 120
Roger Collicott Books, Cornwall 74
Ross Old Books & Prints, Herefordshire 128
Roundstone Books, Lancashire..................... 143
Rowan (H. & S.J.), Dorset 91
Rutland Bookshop (The), Rutland 211
St Paul's Street Bookshop, Lincolnshire 152
Salway Books, Essex 112
Scarthin Books, Derbyshire 82
Sedgeberrow Books, Worcs 256
Sillan Books, Co. Cavan............................ 262
Skyrack Books, West Yorkshire.................... 247
Sleepy Elephant Books & Artefacts, Cumbria ... 80
Smith (Clive), Essex 109
Smith Books (Keith), Herefordshire 128
Sparrow Books, West Yorkshire 245
Spooner & Co, Somerset 219
Staffs Bookshop (The), Staffordshire.............. 223
Staniland (Booksellers), Lincolnshire 152
Stella Books, Monmouthshire 286
Stinton (Judith), Dorset............................ 92
Stothert Old Books, Cheshire...................... 68
Sue Lowell Natural History Books, London W . 175
Suffolk Rare Books, Suffolk 229
Summerfield Books Ltd, Cumbria 79
Temperley (David), West Midlands................ 238
Thomas (E. Wyn), Conwy 284
Thornber (Peter M.), North Yorkshire............ 195
Tiffin (Tony and Gill), Durham 97
Tombland Bookshop, Norfolk 190
Townsend (John), Berks 57
Treasure Chest Books, Suffolk 226
Treasure Trove Books, Leics....................... 146
Tucker (Alan & Joan), Glos 116
Turton (John), Durham 98
Tyger Press, London N.............................. 158
Unsworth's Booksellers, Suffolk................... 225
Ventnor Rare Books, Isle of Wight................ 134
Victoria Bookshop (The), Devon................... 84
Wadard Books, Kent 137
Wealden Books, Kent............................... 138

Wembdon Books, Somerset........................ 216
Wheen O'Books, Borders........................... 267
Whitchurch Books Ltd., Cardiff.................... 281
White Eagle Books, London NW.................. 162
Williams (Bookdealer), (Richard), Lincs 153
Wilson (David), Buckinghamshire 61
Winchester Bookshop (The), Hampshire.......... 126
Wise (Derek), East Sussex.......................... 104
Words Etcetera Bookshop, Dorset................. 93
Wychwood Books, Glos............................. 116
Yates Antiquarian Books (Tony), Leics.......... 146
Yewtree Books, Cumbria........................... 78
Ystwyth Books, Ceredigion 282

TOPOLOGY

Debbage (John), Norfolk............................ 189
Eagle Bookshop (The), Bedfordshire 53
Madoc Books, Conwy 284
Trinity Rare Books, Co. Leitrim 266

TOWN PLANNING

Bookroom (The), Surrey............................ 233
Delectus Books, London WC....................... 176
Duck (William), Hampshire........................ 124
Haskell (R.H. & P.), Dorset 94
Inch's Books, Kent 137
Joel Segal Books, Devon 86
Reads, Dorset 95

TOWN PLANS

Burden Ltd., (Clive A.), Herts 131
Debbage (John), Norfolk............................ 189
Empire Books, North Yorkshire 197
Joel Segal Books, Devon 86
O'Flynn Books, North Yorkshire 197
Old Book Company, (The), West Yorkshire 248

TOYS

Addyman Books, Powys............................. 287
Adrem Books, Herts 130
Barmby (C. & A.J.), Kent........................... 140
Bianco Library, West Sussex....................... 241
Bookmark (Children's Books), Wiltshire.......... 253
Falconwood Transport & Military Bookshop,
    London O... 183
Game Advice, Oxfordshire 208
Green Meadow Books, Cornwall 74
Jean Hedger, Berks 55
Joel Segal Books, Devon 86
R. & A. Books, East Sussex 101
Saint Swithin's Illustrated & Children's Books,
    London W 174
Twigg (Keith), Staffordshire........................ 224
Whittle, Bookseller (Avril), Cumbria 80
Yesteryear Railwayana, Kent....................... 139

TRACTION ENGINES

Anvil Books, West Midlands 239
Bird Books (Nigel), Ceredigion.................... 283
Bott, (Bookdealers) Ltd., (Martin), G Manchester ...
    118
Cottage Books, Leics............................... 145
Country Books, Derbyshire 82
Cox (Geoff), Devon 90
Dales and Lakes Book Centre, Cumbria.......... 79

Debbage (John), Norfolk.............................. 189
Empire Books, North Yorkshire 197
Falconwood Transport & Military Bookshop,
   London O... 183
Fifteenth Century Bookshop (The), East Sussex. 104
Joel Segal Books, Devon 86
Jones (Barry), West Sussex.......................... 242
Kerr (Norman), Cumbria 77
N1 Books, East Sussex 105
Old Book Company, (The), West Yorkshire..... 248
Phenotype Books, Cumbria 79
Randall (Tom), Somerset............................ 218
Roadmaster Books, Kent............................. 136
Roberts (Booksellers), (Ray), Staffordshire 224
Salway Books, Essex 112
Simon Lewis Transport Books, Glos 114
Stroh (M.A.), London E 154
Vintage Motorshop, West Yorkshire 245
Winchester Bookshop (The), Hampshire.......... 126
Yesteryear Railwayana, Kent....................... 139

TRADE CATALOGUES
Black Cat Books, Norfolk............................ 187
Buckland Books, West Sussex 243
Debbage (John), Norfolk............................. 189
Don Kelly Books, London W 172
G. C. Books Ltd., Dumfries & Galloway......... 270
Hay Castle, Powys.................................... 288
Marlborough Rare Books Ltd., London W...... 173
Old Book Company, (The), West Yorkshire..... 248
Reeves Technical Books, North Yorkshire 195
Weiner (Graham), London N 158

TRADE UNIONS
Adrem Books, Herts 130
Berwick Books, Lincolnshire........................ 150
Byrom Textile Bookroom (Richard), Lancashire 142
Clifton Books, Essex 111
Debbage (John), Norfolk............................. 189
Delectus Books, London WC....................... 176
Dolphin Books, Suffolk.............................. 225
Empire Books, North Yorkshire 197
Joel Segal Books, Devon 86
Left on The Shelf, Cumbria......................... 78
Northern Herald Books, West Yorkshire......... 245
PsychoBabel Books & Journals, Oxfordshire..... 205
R. & A. Books, East Sussex 101
Reading Lasses, Dumfries & Galloway 270
Red Star Books, Herts............................... 129
Spurrier (Nick), Kent................................ 137
Symes Books (Naomi), Cheshire 71
Woburn Books, London N 159

TRADES & PROFESSIONS
Adrem Books, Herts 130
Garwood & Voigt, Kent............................. 139
Joel Segal Books, Devon 86
N1 Books, East Sussex 105
Susanne Schulz-Falster Rare Books, London N. 158

TRADITIONAL CHINESE MEDICINE
Inner Bookshop (The), Oxfordshire................ 208
Joel Segal Books, Devon 86
Orchid Book Distributors, Co. Clare 262

TRADITIONS
Country Books, Derbyshire......................... 82
Gildas Books, Cheshire 68
Joel Segal Books, Devon 86
Philip Hopper, Essex 110
Randall (Tom), Somerset............................ 218

TRANSPORT
Addyman Books, Powys.............................. 287
Adrem Books, Herts 130
Allinson (Frank & Stella), Warwickshire 236
Annie's Books, S Yorks 221
Anthony Vickers Books, North Yorkshire 195
Anvil Books, West Midlands 239
Archer (David), Powys............................... 290
Arden Books & Cosmographia, Warwickshire... 236
Armstrong's Books & Collectables, Leics......... 145
Aurora Books Ltd, Lothian.......................... 275
Autumn Leaves, Lincolnshire....................... 150
Backfold Books, Herefordshire...................... 127
Baker (Gerald), Bristol.............................. 60
Baldwin (M. & M.), Worcs 255
Barbican Bookshop, North Yorkshire............. 196
Bath Old Books, Somerset 215
Bianco Library, West Sussex........................ 241
Biff Books and Records, S Yorks................... 221
Bird Books (Nigel), Ceredigion..................... 283
Black Five Books, Shropshire 214
Book House (The), Cumbria......................... 76
Bookcase, Cumbria................................... 76
Books, Denbighshire 284
Books & Bygones (Pam Taylor), West Midlands 240
Books Afloat, Dorset................................. 96
Books at Star Dot Star, West Midlands 240
Bookworms, Norfolk................................. 186
Bookworms of Evesham, Worcs 257
Bosco Books, Cornwall 72
Bott, (Bookdealers) Ltd., (Martin),
   G Manchester 118
Brad Books, Essex.................................... 110
Brewin Books Ltd., Warwickshire 237
Browning Books, Torfaen............................ 292
Browse Books, Lancashire 143
Castle Bookshop, Essex.............................. 108
Cavern Books, Cheshire 70
Chaucer Bookshop, Kent............................ 136
Cheshire Book Centre, Cheshire................... 69
Chevin Books, West Yorkshire...................... 249
Chris Porter Books, Norfolk........................ 186
Classic Crime Collections, G Manchester......... 119
Clements (R.W.), London O......................... 181
Clevedon Books, Somerset 217
Clifton Books, Essex 111
Cobweb Books, North Yorkshire 194
Collectables (W.H.), Suffolk 229
Collectors Carbooks, Northants.................... 199
Collectors Corner, Wiltshire........................ 253
Cornucopia Books, Lincolnshire.................... 151
Coulthurst (Richard), G Manchester 120
Cover to Cover, Merseyside......................... 185
Crosby Nethercott Books, London O 180
Dales & Lakes Book Centre, Cumbria............. 79
Dales and Lakes Book Centre, Cumbria.......... 79
Dandy Lion Editions, Surrey 233
Deeside Books, Grampian........................... 272

Delectus Books, London WC 176
Dinnages Transport Publishing, East Sussex 103
Duck (William), Hampshire 124
Dunkheld Antiques, Tayside 279
Elton Engineering Books, London W 172
Falconwood Transport & Military Bookshop,
    London O 183
Fifteenth Century Bookshop (The), East Sussex . 104
Fireside Bookshop, Cumbria 81
George St. Books, Derbyshire 83
Green Ltd. (G.L.), Herts 131
Hall's Bookshop, Kent 140
Hatchard & Daughters, West Yorkshire 246
Hay Castle, Powys 288
J.B. Books, Berks 57
J.C. Books, Devon 87
Jade Mountain Bookshop, Hampshire 125
Joel Segal Books, Devon 86
Jones (Barry), West Sussex 242
Kelsall (George), G Manchester 118
Kerr (Norman), Cumbria 77
Kim's Bookshop, West Sussex 241
Kim's Bookshop, West Sussex 242
Kingfisher Book Service, Nottinghamshire 204
Kirkland Books, Cumbria 78
Knowles (John), Norfolk 187
M. and A.C. Thompson, Norfolk 191
Malvern Bookshop (The), Worcs 255
Marine & Cannon Books, Cheshire 71
Marine and Cannon Books, Cheshire 69
McGlynn (John), Lancashire 142
Milestone Books, Devon 89
Muttonchop Manuscripts, West Sussex 242
My Back Pages, London SW 168
New Strand, The, Herefordshire 127
Newband (D.M.), Powys 290
Old Book Company, (The), West Yorkshire 248
Over-Sands Books, Cumbria 77
Pauline Harries Books, Hampshire 123
Peter White, Hampshire 121
Pooks Motor Books, Leics 146
Postings, Surrey 233
Prior (Michael), Lincolnshire 152
PsychoBabel Books & Journals, Oxfordshire 205
Railway Shop (The), Torfaen 292
Randall (Tom), Somerset 218
Read - Gorleston Books, (C.&J.), Norfolk 187
Reid of Liverpool, Merseyside 184
Richard Thornton Books, London N 158
Roadmaster Books, Kent 136
Robert Humm & Co, Lincolnshire 152
Rochdale Book Company, G Manchester 120
Rods Books, Devon 88
Roland Books, Kent 138
Rolling Stock Books, G Manchester 120
Saintfield Antiques & Fine Books, Co. Down ... 261
Salway Books, Essex 112
Simon Lewis Transport Books, Glos 114
Stothert Old Books, Cheshire 68
Suffolk Rare Books, Suffolk 229
The Glass Key, West Yorkshire 246
Treasure Chest Books, Suffolk 226
Trinity Rare Books, Co. Leitrim 266
Vailima Books, Dumfries & Galloway 269
Ventnor Rare Books, Isle of Wight 134

Vintage Motorshop, West Yorkshire 245
Weiner (Graham), London N 158
Westwood Books Ltd, Cumbria 80
Whitfield (Ken), Essex 110
Yesteryear Railwayana, Kent 139

TRAVEL

- GENERAL

A. & H. Peasgood, Cambridgeshire 66
Abacus Gallery, Staffordshire 224
Addyman Books, Powys 287
Adrem Books, Herts 130
Allsworth Rare Books Ltd., London SW 166
Altea Antique Maps & Books, London W 171
Andron (G.W.), London N 156
Ann & Mike Conry, Worcs 257
Anne Harris Books & Bags Booksearch,
    Devon 88
Annie's Books, S Yorks 221
Antique Map and Bookshop (The), Dorset 94
Antiques on High, Oxfordshire 207
Arden Books & Cosmographia, Warwickshire ... 236
Armstrong's Books & Collectables, Leics 145
Arslan Books Etc., East Sussex 99
Askew Books (Vernon), Wiltshire 251
Aurora Books Ltd, Lothian 275
Autolycus, Shropshire 212
Autumn Leaves, Lincolnshire 150
Aviabooks, Glos 114
B D McManmon, Lancashire 144
Backfold Books, Herefordshire 127
Baedekers & Murray Guides, S Yorks 221
Barnhill Books, Isle of Arran 274
Bath Old Books, Somerset 215
Baynton–Williams Gallery, West Sussex 241
Beardsley (A.E.), Nottinghamshire 204
Beaumont Travel Books, London SE 163
Bianco Library, West Sussex 241
Bibliopola, London NW 160
Black Five Books, Shropshire 214
Blackwell's Rare Books, Oxfordshire 208
Bonham (J. & S.L.), London W 171
Book Business (The), London W 171
Bookcase, Cumbria 76
Bookpassage (The), Shropshire 212
Books & Collectables Ltd., Cambridgeshire 63
Books Afloat, Dorset 96
Books in Cardigan, Ceredigion 282
books2books, Devon 88
Bookshop (The), Co. Donegal 263
Bookshop at the Plain, Lincolnshire 149
Bookshop on the Heath, The, London SE 163
Bookworms, Norfolk 186
Bookworms of Evesham, Worcs 257
Bookworms Paradise Ltd., West Sussex 242
Booth (Booksearch Service), (Geoff), Cheshire... 68
Bosorne Books, Cornwall 75
Bracton Books, Cambridgeshire 63
Brad Books, Essex 110
Broadhurst of Southport Ltd., Merseyside 185
Broadwater Books, Hampshire 125
Brock Books, North Yorkshire 192
Burden Ltd., (Clive A.), Herts 131
Byre Books, Dumfries & Galloway 270
Campbell (Fiona), London SE 163

Carnforth Bookshop (The), Lancashire 142
Carningli Centre, Pembrokeshire 286
Catalyst Booksearch Services, Devon.............. 87
Chalmers Hallam (E.), Hampshire 125
Chandos Books, Devon.............................. 85
Charles Bossom, Cambridgeshire................... 65
Chaucer Bookshop, Kent............................ 136
Cheshire Book Centre, Cheshire................... 69
Chris Phillips, Wiltshire 252
Church Street Books, Norfolk 186
Clegg (David), Staffordshire........................ 223
Clements (R.W.), London O 181
Clent Books, Worcs 255
Clevedon Books, Somerset 217
Collectable Books, London SE 163
Collectables (W.H.), Suffolk 229
Cornucopia Books, Lincolnshire 151
Corvus Books, Buckinghamshire................... 61
Cotswold Internet Books, Glos.................... 113
Cox (Geoff), Devon 90
Cox Old & Rare Books (Claude), Suffolk 227
Craobh Rua Books, Co. Armagh................... 260
Cumming Limited (A. & Y.), East Sussex........ 104
D.C. Books, Lincolnshire........................... 149
Dales & Lakes Book Centre, Cumbria............ 79
Dandy Lion Editions, Surrey 233
D'Arcy Books, Wiltshire............................ 252
Darkwood Books, Co. Cork........................ 263
Dartmoor Book Gallery, Devon 87
Dartmoor Bookshop (The), Devon 84
Dave Jelfs, Devon 85
David (G.), Cambridgeshire........................ 63
David Warnes Books, Herefordshire 128
Deeside Books, Grampian.......................... 272
Demetzy Books, Oxfordshire 206
Dennys Sanders & Greene Ltd, East Sussex 100
Dolphin Books, Suffolk............................ 225
Driffield Bookshop (The), East Yorkshire 106
Eastern Traveller (The), Somerset................. 219
Edwards in Hay–on–Wye (Francis), Powys 288
Ellis, Bookseller (Peter), London WC 177
Ely Books, Cambridgeshire 65
Empire Books, North Yorkshire 197
Esoteric Dreams Bookshop, Cumbria 77
Evergreen Livres, Glos............................. 116
Farahar & Dupre (Clive & Sophie), Wiltshire ... 251
Ferdinando (Steven), Somerset 218
Fifteenth Century Bookshop (The), East Sussex. 104
Ford Books (David), Herts 130
Fosters Bookshop, London W 172
Freeman's Corner Shop, Norfolk 189
Frew Limited (Robert), London SW 167
Frost (Richard), Herts 129
Furneaux Books (Lee), Devon..................... 89
Garfi Books, Powys 291
Garwood & Voigt, Kent............................ 139
Gibbard (A. & T.), East Sussex 101
Glacier Books, Tayside 280
Glasheen-Books, Surrey 231
Glenbower Books, Co. Dublin 264
Golden Books Group, Devon 85
Goodyer (Nicholas), London N 157
Grahame Thornton, Bookseller, Dorset........... 93
Great Hall Bookshop, Buckinghamshire.......... 61
Hall's Bookshop, Kent............................. 140

Hancock (Peter), West Sussex 241
Handsworth Books, Essex........................... 112
Harrington (Adrian), London W.................... 173
Harrington Antiquarian Bookseller (Peter),
   London SW....................................... 167
Hay Cinema Bookshop Ltd., Powys............... 288
HCB Wholesale, Powys............................. 288
Heartland Old Books, Devon....................... 89
Hereward Books, Cambridgeshire.................. 66
High Street Books, Devon 86
Hill (Peter), Hampshire 122
Hodgson (Books) (Richard J.), North Yorkshire 196
Hogan (F. & J.), London N 157
Hollett and Son (R.F.G.), Cumbria 79
Howes Bookshop, East Sussex 102
Hurst (Jenny), Kent................................ 137
Hylton Booksearch, Merseyside 184
Innes Books, Shropshire............................ 212
Internet Bookshop UK Ltd., Glos................. 113
Island Books, Devon............................... 85
Jackson (M.W.), Wiltshire.......................... 254
Jade Mountain Bookshop, Hampshire 125
Jay Books, Lothian................................. 276
Joel Segal Books, Devon 86
Junk & Spread Eagle, London SE................. 164
Karen Millward, Co. Cork.......................... 263
Kay Books, London W............................. 173
Keeble Antiques, Somerset 218
Kenya Books, East Sussex 100
Kernaghans, Merseyside 185
Killeen (John), North Yorkshire 193
Kingfisher Book Service, Nottinghamshire 204
Kingswood Books, Dorset.......................... 94
Larkham Books (Patricia), Glos.................... 117
Leabeck Books, Oxfordshire 208
Lewis (J.T. & P.), Cornwall 73
Liddle (Steve), Bristol 58
Lighthouse Books (The), Dorset 92
Little Bookshop (The), G Manchester............. 119
Lloyd-Davies (Sue), Carmarthenshire 282
Lost Books, Northants.............................. 200
Lucas (Richard), London NW...................... 161
Lymelight Books & Prints, Dorset................. 93
Maggs Brothers Limited, London W............... 173
Malvern Bookshop (The), Worcs 255
Marble Hill Books, Outer London................. 182
Marcet Books, London SE.......................... 164
Marco Polo Travel & Adventure Books, Dorset 92
Marijana Dworski Books, Powys 288
Marlborough Rare Books Ltd., London W...... 173
Marshall Rare Books (Bruce), Glos 113
Martin Bookshop & Gallery (Richard), Hants... 123
McCarty, Bookseller (M.E.), Western Isles....... 275
McCarty, Bookseller (M.E.),
   Dumfries & Galloway.............................. 270
McNaughton's Bookshop, Lothian 276
Michael Bishop PBFA, Somerset 220
Michael Graves-Johnston, London SW........... 168
Miles Apart, Suffolk............................... 228
Modlock (Lilian), Dorset........................... 93
Morgan (H.J.), Bedfordshire....................... 54
Morten (Booksellers) (E.J.), G Manchester....... 119
Mulyan (Don), Merseyside 185
Murphy (C.J.), Norfolk............................. 189
Muse Bookshop (The), Gwynedd 285

My Back Pages, London SW 168
Nakota Curios, East Sussex......................... 102
Neil Summersgill, Lancashire 142
New Strand, The, Herefordshire 127
Nicolas - Antiquarian Bookseller, London N 157
Niner (Marcus), Isle of Wight 133
O'Flynn Books, North Yorkshire 197
Old Book Company, (The), West Yorkshire 248
Old Hall Bookshop (The), Northants 199
Old Station Pottery & Bookshop (The), Norfolk 191
Oopalba Books, Cheshire............................ 71
Orangeberry Books, Oxfordshire 207
Page (David), Lothian 276
Parker Books (Mike), Cambridgeshire 64
Parrott Books, Oxfordshire 209
Paul Hoare, Cornwall................................ 74
Pauline Harries Books, Hampshire 123
Peregrine Books (Leeds), West Yorkshire........ 248
Petersfield Bookshop (The), Hampshire........... 124
Pordes Books Ltd., (Henry), London WC........ 177
Portobello Books, London W 174
Portus Books, Hampshire 122
Preston Book Company, Lancashire 144
Price (John), London N 158
Price (R.W.), Nottinghamshire 203
Prospect House Books, Co. Down................. 261
Quaritch Ltd., (Bernard), London W............. 174
Quest Books, East Yorkshire 107
Quinto of Charing Cross Road, London WC ... 178
R. & A. Books, East Sussex 101
Reading Lasses, Dumfries & Galloway 270
Richard Thornton Books, London N 158
Richmond Books, North Yorkshire 194
Robert Temple, London N.......................... 158
Roberts (Booksellers), (Ray), Staffordshire 224
Roberts Fine Books (Julian), Lincolnshire........ 151
Rochdale Book Company, G Manchester 120
Roland Books, Kent 138
Roundstone Books, Lancashire..................... 143
Rowan (P. & B.), Co. Antrim 260
Roz Hulse, Conwy 284
Russell (Charles), London SW...................... 169
Saintfield Antiques & Fine Books, Co. Down ... 261
Samovar Books, Co. Dublin......................... 264
Sax Books, Suffolk 228
Shacklock Books (David), Suffolk 226
Shapero Rare Books (Bernard J.), London W... 175
Simply Read Books, East Sussex.................... 100
Singleton (Anthony), S Yorks 221
Slightly Foxed on Gloucester Road, London SW 167
Smith (Clive), Essex 109
Smith Books, (Sally), Suffolk 226
Sotheran Limited (Henry), London W 175
Spearman Books, East Sussex 104
Sterling Books, Somerset 220
Stothert Old Books, Cheshire....................... 68
Strathtay Antiquarian - Secondhand Books,
    Tayside 280
Stroma Books, Borders 267
Sturford Books, Wiltshire 254
Sue Lowell Natural History Books, London W . 175
Sykes (Graham), West Yorkshire 249
Temperley (David), West Midlands................ 238
The Glass Key, West Yorkshire..................... 246
Thorntons of Oxford Ltd., Oxfordshire........... 206

Till's Bookshop, Lothian 277
Tilston (Stephen E.), London SE.................... 165
Travel Bookshop (The), London W 175
Treadwell's Books, London WC 178
Treasure Island (The), G Manchester 119
Treasure Trove Books, Leics........................ 146
Trinity Rare Books, Co. Leitrim 266
Uncle Phil's Books, West Midlands 239
Vokes Books Ltd., North Yorkshire............... 194
Wembdon Books, Somerset......................... 216
Westwood Books Ltd, Cumbria..................... 80
Wheen O'Books, Borders............................ 267
Whitfield (Ken), Essex 110
Words Etcetera Bookshop, Dorset.................. 93
Worlds End Bookshop, London SW 169
Yesterday's Books, Dorset 92
Yesterday's News, Conwy........................... 283
Yewtree Books, Cumbria............................ 78

- AFRICA

Acanthophyllum Books, Wirral 184
Ayre (Peter J.), Somerset 219
Bonham (J. & S.L.), London W 171
Bow Windows Book Shop, East Sussex 103
Butcher (Pablo), Oxfordshire 206
Campbell Hewson Books (R.), Fife................. 271
Chalmers Hallam (E.), Hampshire.................. 125
Chandos Books, Devon.............................. 85
Coch-y-Bonddu Books, Powys 290
Ctesiphon Books, G Manchester 120
Deeside Books, Grampian........................... 272
Dolphin Books, Suffolk.............................. 225
Eastern Traveller (The), Somerset.................. 219
Edmund Pollinger Rare Books, London SW..... 166
Empire Books, North Yorkshire 197
Farahar & Dupre (Clive & Sophie), Wiltshire ... 251
Fine Books at Ilkley, West Yorkshire 247
Glacier Books, Tayside.............................. 280
Grayling (David A.H.), Cumbria 78
Hall, (Anthony C.) Antiquarian Bookseller,
    London O.. 183
Indoislamica, London SW........................... 168
J.C. Deyong Books (Previously of Snowden
    Smith Books), London SW..................... 168
Joel Segal Books, Devon 86
Keith Langford, London E 154
Kenya Books, East Sussex 100
Lloyd-Davies (Sue), Carmarthenshire 282
Maghreb Bookshop (The), London WC.......... 177
Michael Graves-Johnston, London SW............ 168
Old Book Company, (The), West Yorkshire 248
Page (David), Lothian 276
Peter M Daly, Hampshire........................... 126
Roz Hulse, Conwy 284
Samovar Books, Co. Dublin........................ 264
Shapero Rare Books (Bernard J.), London W... 175
Smith (Ray), Herts 129
Stokes Books, Co. Dublin........................... 264
Sutcliffe (Victor), Norfolk 187
Trinity Rare Books, Co. Leitrim 266
Vandeleur Antiquarian Books, Surrey............. 231
White (C.R.), London W............................ 175
Woolcott Books, Dorset............................. 92
Yesterday's Books, Dorset 92

- AMERICAS

Americanabooksuk, Cumbria........................ 76
Bonham (J. & S.L.), London W 171
Books on Spain, London O......................... 182
Burden Ltd., (Clive A.), Herts...................... 131
Butcher (Pablo), Oxfordshire 206
Chalmers Hallam (E.), Hampshire................. 125
Empire Books, North Yorkshire 197
Farahar & Dupre (Clive & Sophie), Wiltshire ... 251
Fine Books at Ilkley, West Yorkshire 247
Glacier Books, Tayside 280
Grayling (David A.H.), Cumbria 78
Joel Segal Books, Devon 86
Leapman Ltd. (G. & R.), Herts................... 130
Michael Graves-Johnston, London SW 168
Old Book Company, (The), West Yorkshire 248
Orssich (Paul), London SW........................ 169
Peter M Daly, Hampshire........................... 126
Pinnacle Books, Lothian............................ 276
Trinity Rare Books, Co. Leitrim 266
Vandeleur Antiquarian Books, Surrey............. 231

- ASIA

Acanthophyllum Books, Wirral 184
Alpha Books, London N............................ 156
Bates & Hindmarch, West Yorkshire.............. 248
Bonham (J. & S.L.), London W 171
Bow Windows Book Shop, East Sussex 103
Cavendish Rare Books, London N 156
Chalmers Hallam (E.), Hampshire................. 125
Coch-y-Bonddu Books, Powys 290
Craobh Rua Books, Co. Armagh................... 260
David Warnes Books, Herefordshire 128
Dolphin Books, Suffolk............................. 225
Eastern Traveller (The), Somerset................. 219
Eastgate Bookshop, East Yorkshire 106
Empire Books, North Yorkshire 197
Farahar & Dupre (Clive & Sophie), Wiltshire ... 251
Glacier Books, Tayside 280
Grayling (David A.H.), Cumbria 78
Hall, (Anthony C.) Antiquarian Bookseller,
    London O....................................... 183
Hunter and Krageloh, Derbyshire 83
J.C. Deyong Books (Previously of Snowden
    Smith Books), London SW 168
Jarvis Books, Derbyshire 83
Joel Segal Books, Devon 86
Lloyd-Davies (Sue), Carmarthenshire 282
Mannwaring (M.G.), Bristol 59
Moorside Books, Lancashire........................ 143
Old Book Company, (The), West Yorkshire 248
O'Reilly - Mountain Books (John), Derbyshire.. 83
Page (David), Lothian 276
Parrott (Jeremy), London E......................... 154
Peter M Daly, Hampshire........................... 126
Pinnacle Books, Lothian............................ 276
Rayner (Hugh Ashley), Somerset 215
Shapero Rare Books (Bernard J.), London W... 175
Smith (Clive), Essex 109
Traveller's Bookshelf (The), Somerset 218
Trinity Rare Books, Co. Leitrim 266
Vandeleur Antiquarian Books, Surrey............. 231
Verandah Books, Dorset 95
White Eagle Books, London NW.................. 162
Woolcott Books, Dorset............................ 92

- ASIA, SOUTH EAST

Antique Prints of the World, London N.......... 156
Butcher (Pablo), Oxfordshire 206
Chalmers Hallam (E.), Hampshire................. 125
Ctesiphon Books, G Manchester................... 120
David Warnes Books, Herefordshire 128
Dolphin Books, Suffolk............................. 225
Farahar & Dupre (Clive & Sophie), Wiltshire ... 251
Fine Books at Ilkley, West Yorkshire............. 247
J.C. Deyong Books (Previously of Snowden
    Smith Books), London SW 168
Jarvis Books, Derbyshire 83
Joel Segal Books, Devon 86
Keith Langford, London E 154
Leeper (Romilly), London SW 168
Mandalay Bookshop, London SW 168
Page (David), Lothian 276
Peter M Daly, Hampshire........................... 126
Shapero Rare Books (Bernard J.), London W... 175
Traveller's Bookshelf (The), Somerset 218
Trinity Rare Books, Co. Leitrim 266

- AUSTRALASIA/AUSTRALIA

Bonham (J. & S.L.), London W 171
Burden Ltd., (Clive A.), Herts...................... 131
Catalyst Booksearch Services, Devon............. 87
Cavendish Rare Books, London N 156
Chalmers Hallam (E.), Hampshire................. 125
Empire Books, North Yorkshire 197
Farahar & Dupre (Clive & Sophie), Wiltshire ... 251
Joel Segal Books, Devon 86
Michael Graves-Johnston, London SW 168
Moore (Peter), Cambridgeshire..................... 64
Old Book Company, (The), West Yorkshire 248
Peter M Daly, Hampshire........................... 126
Pinnacle Books, Lothian............................ 276
Trinity Rare Books, Co. Leitrim 266

- BALKANS

Craobh Rua Books, Co. Armagh.................. 260
Dolphin Books, Suffolk............................. 225
J.C. Deyong Books (Previously of Snowden Smith
    Books), London SW 168
Joppa Books Ltd., Surrey........................... 230
Marijana Dworski Books, Powys 288
Old Book Company, (The), West Yorkshire..... 248
Shapero Rare Books (Bernard J.), London W... 175
Traveller's Bookshelf (The), Somerset 218
Trinity Rare Books, Co. Leitrim 266
White Eagle Books, London NW.................. 162

- BURMA

Antique Prints of the World, London N.......... 156
Chalmers Hallam (E.), Hampshire................. 125
Dolphin Books, Suffolk............................. 225
Jackdaw Books, Norfolk 188
Mandalay Bookshop, London SW 168
Pinnacle Books, Lothian............................ 276
Rayner (Hugh Ashley), Somerset 215
Traveller's Bookshelf (The), Somerset 218
Trinity Rare Books, Co. Leitrim 266
Verandah Books, Dorset 95

- CARIBBEAN

Joel Segal Books, Devon 86

Michael Graves-Johnston, London SW 168
Pennymead Books, North Yorkshire 193
Peter M Daly, Hampshire 126

- CHINA

Cavendish Rare Books, London N 156
Craobh Rua Books, Co. Armagh 260
Fine Books at Ilkley, West Yorkshire 247
J.C. Deyong Books (Previously of Snowden
    Smith Books), London SW 168
Joel Segal Books, Devon 86
Lloyd-Davies (Sue), Carmarthenshire 282
Mandalay Bookshop, London SW 168
Old Book Company, (The), West Yorkshire 248
Page (David), Lothian 276
Shapero Rare Books (Bernard J.), London W ... 175
Traveller's Bookshelf (The), Somerset 218
Trinity Rare Books, Co. Leitrim 266

- EARLY

Altea Antique Maps & Books, London W 171
Coch-y-Bonddu Books, Powys 290
Joel Segal Books, Devon 86
Martin (Brian), Surrey 231
Old Book Company, (The), West Yorkshire 248
Shapero Rare Books (Bernard J.), London W ... 175
Trinity Rare Books, Co. Leitrim 266

- EUROPE

Acanthophyllum Books, Wirral 184
Bonham (J. & S.L.), London W 171
Books on Spain, London O 182
Broadwater Books, Hampshire 125
Campbell (Fiona), London SE 163
de Visser Books, Cambridgeshire 63
Dolphin Books, Suffolk 225
Doolin Dinghy Books, Co. Clare 262
Empire Books, North Yorkshire 197
Fifteenth Century Bookshop (The), East Sussex. 104
Fine Books at Ilkley, West Yorkshire 247
Glacier Books, Tayside 280
Hall, (Anthony C.) Antiquarian Bookseller,
    London O 183
Jarvis Books, Derbyshire 83
Keith Langford, London E 154
Martin (Books and Pictures), (Brian P.), Surrey. 231
Martin (Brian), Surrey 231
McGee (Terence J.), London O 180
Michael Graves-Johnston, London SW 168
Old Book Company, (The), West Yorkshire 248
Orssich (Paul), London SW 169
Page (David), Lothian 276
Peter M Daly, Hampshire 126
Samovar Books, Co. Dublin 264
Spelman (Ken), North Yorkshire 198
Sturford Books, Wiltshire 254
Trinity Rare Books, Co. Leitrim 266
Undercover Books, Lincolnshire 152
Vandeleur Antiquarian Books, Surrey 231
York (Graham), Devon 86

- FAR EAST

Cavendish Rare Books, London N 156
Fine Books at Ilkley, West Yorkshire 247
J.C. Deyong Books (Previously of Snowden

Smith Books), London SW 168
Joel Segal Books, Devon 86
Lloyd-Davies (Sue), Carmarthenshire 282
Old Book Company, (The), West Yorkshire 248
Page (David), Lothian 276
Shapero Rare Books (Bernard J.), London W ... 175
Transformer, Dumfries & Galloway 270
Traveller's Bookshelf (The), Somerset 218
Trinity Rare Books, Co. Leitrim 266
White Eagle Books, London NW 162

- GREECE

Frew Limited (Robert), London SW 167
Hellenic Bookservices, London NW 161
Joel Segal Books, Devon 86
Joppa Books Ltd., Surrey 230
Michael Graves-Johnston, London SW 168
Old Station Pottery & Bookshop (The), Norfolk 191
Quest Books, East Yorkshire 107
Seydi Rare Books (Sevin), London NW 161
Shapero Rare Books (Bernard J.), London W ... 175
Trinity Rare Books, Co. Leitrim 266
Trotter Books (John), London N 158
White Eagle Books, London NW 162

- INDIA

BookShop, The, Dumfries & Galloway 270
Butcher (Pablo), Oxfordshire 206
Catalyst Booksearch Services, Devon 87
Chalmers Hallam (E.), Hampshire 125
Fine Books at Ilkley, West Yorkshire 247
Glacier Books, Tayside 280
Joel Segal Books, Devon 86
Keith Langford, London E 154
Mandalay Bookshop, London SW 168
N1 Books, East Sussex 105
Old Book Company, (The), West Yorkshire 248
Page (David), Lothian 276
Peter M Daly, Hampshire 126
Rayner (Hugh Ashley), Somerset 215
Shapero Rare Books (Bernard J.), London W ... 175
Sutcliffe (Victor), Norfolk 187
Trinity Rare Books, Co. Leitrim 266
Verandah Books, Dorset 95

- ISLAMIC WORLD

Al Saqi Books, London W 171
Antique Prints of the World, London N 156
Arslan Books Etc., East Sussex 99
Butcher (Pablo), Oxfordshire 206
Clarke Books (David), Somerset 218
David Warnes Books, Herefordshire 128
J.C. Deyong Books (Previously of Snowden
    Smith Books), London SW 168
Joppa Books Ltd., Surrey 230
Kingswood Books, Dorset 94
Page (David), Lothian 276
Shapero Rare Books (Bernard J.), London W ... 175
Traveller's Bookshelf (The), Somerset 218
Trinity Rare Books, Co. Leitrim 266
Verandah Books, Dorset 95
White Eagle Books, London NW 162

- JAPAN

Fine Books at Ilkley, West Yorkshire 247

Joel Segal Books, Devon 86
Lloyd-Davies (Sue), Carmarthenshire 282
Murphy (C.J.), Norfolk............................. 189
Traveller's Bookshelf (The), Somerset 218
Trinity Rare Books, Co. Leitrim 266
White Eagle Books, London NW.................. 162

- MEXICO
Fine Books at Ilkley, West Yorkshire............. 247
Hodgson (Judith), London W 173
Michael Graves-Johnston, London SW 168
Orssich (Paul), London SW....................... 169
Sturford Books, Wiltshire 254
Trinity Rare Books, Co. Leitrim 266

- MIDDLE EAST
Al Saqi Books, London W.......................... 171
Arslan Books Etc., East Sussex..................... 99
Bonham (J. & S.L.), London W 171
Bookshop at the Plain, Lincolnshire.............. 149
Chalmers Hallam (E.), Hampshire................ 125
Clarke Books (David), Somerset 218
Craobh Rua Books, Co. Armagh................. 260
Ctesiphon Books, G Manchester................. 120
David Warnes Books, Herefordshire 128
Eastern Traveller (The), Somerset................ 219
Empire Books, North Yorkshire 197
Farahar & Dupre (Clive & Sophie), Wiltshire ... 251
Fine Books at Ilkley, West Yorkshire............. 247
Hall, (Anthony C.) Antiquarian Bookseller,
    London O.................................... 183
J.C. Deyong Books (Previously of Snowden
    Smith Books), London SW 168
Joel Segal Books, Devon 86
Joppa Books Ltd., Surrey 230
Kingswood Books, Dorset 94
Maghreb Bookshop (The), London WC.......... 177
Moorside Books, Lancashire....................... 143
Old Book Company, (The), West Yorkshire 248
P. and P. Books, Worcs 256
Page (David), Lothian 276
Peter M Daly, Hampshire.......................... 126
Prospect House Books, Co. Down................. 261
Quest Books, East Yorkshire 107
Shapero Rare Books (Bernard J.), London W... 175
Traveller's Bookshelf (The), Somerset 218
Trinity Rare Books, Co. Leitrim 266
Trotter Books (John), London N 158
Watkins (R.G.), Somerset 215
White Eagle Books, London NW.................. 162
Woolcott Books, Dorset............................ 92
Worlds End Bookshop, London SW 169

- MOUNTAIN
Hunter and Krageloh, Derbyshire 83

- POLAR
Bluntisham Books, Cambridgeshire................ 63
Bonham (J. & S.L.), London W 171
Cavendish Rare Books, London N 156
Chalmers Hallam (E.), Hampshire................ 125
David Warnes Books, Herefordshire 128
Deeside Books, Grampian.......................... 272
Empire Books, North Yorkshire 197
Farahar & Dupre (Clive & Sophie), Wiltshire ... 251

Fifteenth Century Bookshop (The), East Sussex. 104
Fine Books at Ilkley, West Yorkshire............. 247
Glacier Books, Tayside 280
Holmes Books (Harry), East Yorkshire........... 107
Hunter and Krageloh, Derbyshire 83
Internet Bookshop UK Ltd., Glos................. 113
Jarvis Books, Derbyshire 83
Joel Segal Books, Devon 86
Michael Graves-Johnston, London SW 168
Miles Apart, Suffolk............................... 228
Old Book Company, (The), West Yorkshire 248
O'Reilly - Mountain Books (John), Derbyshire.. 83
Page (David), Lothian 276
Peter M Daly, Hampshire.......................... 126
Pinnacle Books, Lothian........................... 276
Roz Hulse, Conwy 284
Shapero Rare Books (Bernard J.), London W... 175
Vandeleur Antiquarian Books, Surrey............ 231
White (C.R.), London W........................... 175

- REGIONAL
Bickford-Smith (G.) (formerly Snowden Smith
    Books), Surrey 232
Bookshop at the Plain, Lincolnshire.............. 149
Evergreen Livres, Glos............................. 116
Fifteenth Century Bookshop (The), East Sussex. 104
Joel Segal Books, Devon 86
Old Book Company, (The), West Yorkshire 248
Samovar Books, Co. Dublin....................... 264

- THAILAND
Apocalypse, Surrey 232
Mandalay Bookshop, London SW 168
Trinity Rare Books, Co. Leitrim 266

TRIALS
Bolland Books, Bedfordshire........................ 53
Clifford Elmer Books Ltd., Cheshire 68
Loretta Lay Books, London NW 161

TRIBAL
Bickford-Smith (G.) (formerly Snowden Smith
    Books), Surrey 232
Bracton Books, Cambridgeshire................... 63
David Warnes Books, Herefordshire 128
J.C. Deyong Books (Previously of Snowden
    Smith Books), London SW 168
Joel Segal Books, Devon 86
Kenya Books, East Sussex 100
Michael Graves-Johnston, London SW 168
Popeley (Frank T.), Cambridgeshire.............. 67
Traveller's Bookshelf (The), Somerset 218
Yesterday's Books, Dorset 92

TROPICAL FISH
Joel Segal Books, Devon 86
Steven Simpson Books, Norfolk 190

TROTSKYISM
Left on The Shelf, Cumbria......................... 78
Northern Herald Books, West Yorkshire......... 245
Reading Lasses, Dumfries & Galloway 270
Red Star Books, Herts............................. 129
Woburn Books, London N 159

TYPOGRAPHY

Ballantyne–Way (Roger), Suffolk 228
Batterham (David), London W...................... 171
Bettridge (Gordon), Fife......................... 271
Blackwell's Rare Books, Oxfordshire.............. 208
BOOKS4U, Flintshire.............................. 284
Brinded (Scott), Kent 138
Canterbury Bookshop (The), Kent 136
Collinge & Clark, London WC..................... 176
Cooper Hay Rare Books, Strathclyde.............. 278
Coupland (Terry W.), Staffordshire.............. 223
Cox Old & Rare Books (Claude), Suffolk 227
Debbage (John), Norfolk.......................... 189
English (Toby), Oxfordshire...................... 209
Forest Books, Nottinghamshire 204
Fox Books (J. & J.), Kent........................ 139
Hanborough Books, Oxfordshire................... 208
Joel Segal Books, Devon 86
Katnap Arts, Norfolk............................. 190
Keel Row Bookshop, Tyne and Wear 235
Macfarlane (Mr. H.), Essex 111
Mills Rare Books (Adam), Cambridgeshire 64
Myra Dean Illustated Books, Powys 287
Old Book Company, (The), West Yorkshire 248
Quentin Books Ltd, Essex......................... 108
Robin Doughty - Fine Books, West Midlands... 238
Taylor Rare Books (Michael), Norfolk 187
Thorntons of Oxford Ltd., Oxfordshire........... 206
Wakeman Books (Frances), Nottinghamshire.... 204

U.F.O.S

Alpha Books, London N........................... 156
Annie's Books, S Yorks 221
Apocalypse, Surrey 232
Bookbarrow, Cambridgeshire...................... 63
Bookworms Paradise Ltd., West Sussex 242
Cavern Books, Cheshire 70
Dawlish Books, Devon 86
Facet Books, Dorset............................... 91
Gildas Books, Cheshire 68
Greensleeves, Oxfordshire 206
Inner Bookshop (The), Oxfordshire............... 208
Joel Segal Books, Devon 86
Occultique, Northants............................ 199
Parker Books (Mike), Cambridgeshire 64
SETI Books, West Midlands....................... 239
Star Lord Books, G Manchester 119
Wizard Books, Cambridgeshire.................... 67

U.S. PRESIDENTS

Dolphin Books, Suffolk........................... 225
Hab Books, London W............................. 172
Shakeshaft (Dr. B.), Cheshire.................... 71

U-BOATS

Baldwin (M. & M.), Worcs 255
Bookworms Paradise Ltd., West Sussex 242
Burroughs (Andrew), Lincolnshire................ 152
Fifteenth Century Bookshop (The), East Sussex. 104
Green Ltd. (G.L.), Herts 131
Marine & Cannon Books, Cheshire 71
Marine and Cannon Books, Cheshire 69
Meekins Books (Paul), Warwickshire.............. 237
Rods Books, Devon 88

UMBRELLAS/PARASOLS

Adrem Books, Herts 130
Judith Mansfield, West Yorkshire................ 249

UNEXPLAINED, THE

Annie's Books, S Yorks 221
Bookworms Paradise Ltd., West Sussex 242
Dawlish Books, Devon 86
Esoteric Dreams Bookshop, Cumbria 77
Fantastic Literature, Essex 110
Fifteenth Century Bookshop (The), East Sussex. 104
Gildas Books, Cheshire 68
Inner Bookshop (The), Oxfordshire............... 208
Joel Segal Books, Devon 86
Loretta Lay Books, London NW 161
Occultique, Northants............................ 199
Old Celtic Bookshop (The), Devon 87
Parker Books (Mike), Cambridgeshire 64
SETI Books, West Midlands....................... 239
Till's Bookshop, Lothian 277

UNIVERSITY HISTORIES

Bernard Dixon and Kath Adams, London O.... 182
G. C. Books Ltd., Dumfries & Galloway......... 270
PsychoBabel Books & Journals, Oxfordshire..... 205
Stalagluft Books, Tyne and Wear................. 235

UNIVERSITY PRESS

Adrem Books, Herts 130
Barcombe Services, Essex......................... 108
Book Annex (The), Essex 109
Delectus Books, London WC...................... 176
G. C. Books Ltd., Dumfries & Galloway......... 270
Joel Segal Books, Devon 86
PsychoBabel Books & Journals, Oxfordshire..... 205
Stalagluft Books, Tyne and Wear................. 235
Woburn Books, London N 159

UNIVERSITY TEXTS

Barcombe Services, Essex......................... 108
Book Annex (The), Essex 109
Cornucopia Books, Lincolnshire 151
G. C. Books Ltd., Dumfries & Galloway......... 270
Hurst (Jenny), Kent.............................. 137
Murphy (C.J.), Norfolk........................... 189
Old Book Company, (The), West Yorkshire 248
Scrivener's Books & Bookbinding, Derbyshire... 82
Stalagluft Books, Tyne and Wear................. 235
Warrington Book Loft (The), Cheshire 71

URBAN HISTORY

Cornucopia Books, Lincolnshire 151
Inch's Books, Kent............................... 137
Joel Segal Books, Devon 86
Northern Herald Books, West Yorkshire......... 245
Reading Lasses, Dumfries & Galloway 270
Stern Antiquarian Bookseller (Jeffrey), North
  Yorkshire...................................... 198
Symes Books (Naomi), Cheshire 71

UTOPIAS

Delectus Books, London WC...................... 176
Quaritch Ltd., (Bernard), London W............. 174
Robert Temple, London N......................... 158
Seydi Rare Books (Sevin), London NW 161

Star Lord Books, G Manchester 119
Susanne Schulz-Falster Rare Books, London N. 158
Woburn Books, London N 159

VATICAN AND PAPAL HISTORY, THE
Adrem Books, Herts 130
Chapter Two, London SE.......................... 163
Dolphin Books, Suffolk............................ 225
R. & A. Books, East Sussex 101
Samovar Books, Co. Dublin....................... 264
Scrivener's Books & Bookbinding, Derbyshire... 82
Taylor & Son (Peter), Herts...................... 132
Tuft (Patrick), London O 181

VEGETARIANISM
Annie's Books, S Yorks 221
Books Only, Suffolk................................ 226
Edwards, Fiona, Nottinghamshire 203
Gardener & Cook, London SW................... 167
Inner Bookshop (The), Oxfordshire.............. 208
Occultique, Northants.............................. 199

VENTRILOQUISM
DaSilva Puppet Books, Dorset 93

VETERINARY
Alba Books, Grampian 273
Bookworms Paradise Ltd., West Sussex 242
Grahame Thornton, Bookseller, Dorset.......... 93
Kelpie's Books, Fife............................... 271
Parkinsons Books, Merseyside.................... 185
Phenotype Books, Cumbria 79
R. & A. Books, East Sussex 101
Westons, Herts..................................... 132

VICTORIAN MULTI-DECKERS
Beaton (Richard), East Sussex.................... 103
Burmester (James), Bristol......................... 58
Enigma Books, Wiltshire 252
Tiger Books, Kent.................................. 136
Valentine Rare Books, London W................ 175

VICTORIANA
Art Reference Books, Hampshire 124
Beaton (Richard), East Sussex.................... 103
Bell (Peter), Lothian............................... 275
Books at Star Dot Star, West Midlands 240
Bosco Books, Cornwall 72
Cornucopia Books, Lincolnshire 151
de Beaumont (Robin), London SW 166
Dolphin Books, Suffolk............................ 225
Don Kelly Books, London W 172
Embleton (Paul), Essex 111
Fifteenth Century Bookshop (The), East Sussex. 104
Goldman (Paul), Dorset 94
Joel Segal Books, Devon 86
N1 Books, East Sussex 105
R. & A. Books, East Sussex 101
Saint Swithin's Illustrated & Children's Books,
   London W 174
Shacklock Books (David), Suffolk 226
Symes Books (Naomi), Cheshire 71
Trinity Rare Books, Co. Leitrim 266
Yesterday's News, Conwy.......................... 283

VINTAGE CARS
Baldwin (M. & M.), Worcs 255
Bookworms Paradise Ltd., West Sussex 242
Camilla's Bookshop, East Sussex 101
Collectors Carbooks, Northants................... 199
Cornucopia Books, Lincolnshire 151
Cox (Geoff), Devon 90
Falconwood Transport & Military Bookshop,
   London O 183
Fifteenth Century Bookshop (The), East Sussex. 104
Joel Segal Books, Devon 86
Kenneth Ball, East Sussex......................... 100
Knowles (John), Norfolk........................... 187
Peake (Robin), Lincolnshire....................... 152
Pooks Motor Books, Leics 146
R. & A. Books, East Sussex 101
Roadmaster Books, Kent........................... 136
Roberts (Booksellers), (Ray), Staffordshire 224
Simon Lewis Transport Books, Glos 114
Stroh (M.A.), London E 154
Vintage Motorshop, West Yorkshire 245
Weiner (Graham), London N 158

VINTAGE PAPERBACKS
Black Cat Bookshop, Leics 147
Booth (Booksearch Service), (Geoff), Cheshire... 68
Cowley, Bookdealer (K.W.), Somerset 217
Dancing Goat Bookshop (The), Norfolk 187
Eggeling Books (John), West Yorkshire 249
Esoteric Dreams Bookshop, Cumbria 77
Fifteenth Century Bookshop (The), East Sussex. 104
Gildas Books, Cheshire 68
Good for Books, Lincolnshire 149
Heckmondwike Book Shop, West Yorkshire 249
Joel Segal Books, Devon 86
Katnap Arts, Norfolk 190
Morris Secondhand & Antiquarian Books
   (Chris), Oxfordshire 208
Much Binding, Norfolk............................ 186
Murphy (C.J.), Norfolk............................ 189
Old Station Pottery & Bookshop (The), Norfolk 191
Readers World, West Midlands 238
Roscrea Bookshop & Newsagents,
   Co. Tipperary 266
Ruebotham (Kirk), Cheshire....................... 71
Scrivener's Books & Bookbinding, Derbyshire... 82
Spike's Books, North Yorkshire.................... 192
Trevorrow (Edwin), Herts.......................... 129
Woburn Books, London N 159
Yorkshire Relics, West Yorkshire................. 246
Zardoz Books, Wiltshire........................... 254

VIROLOGY
Bernard Dixon and Kath Adams, London O.... 182
Parkinsons Books, Merseyside..................... 185
R M Books, Herts.................................. 132
Savona Books, Lincolnshire........................ 151
Westons, Herts..................................... 132

VISUAL
Joel Segal Books, Devon 86

VITICULTURE
Joel Segal Books, Devon 86
Keel Row Bookshop, Tyne and Wear 235

Lucas (Richard), London NW...................... 161
Price (John), London N 158
Roberts Wine Books (John), Bristol.............. 59
Thorne (John), Essex................................. 109

VOYAGES & DISCOVERY

Afar Books International, West Midlands....... 238
Allsworth Rare Books Ltd., London SW......... 166
Altea Antique Maps & Books, London W....... 171
Americanabooksuk, Cumbria........................ 76
Avedikian Rare Books, Somerset.................. 216
Barn Books, Buckinghamshire...................... 61
Books on Spain, London O......................... 182
BookShop, The, Dumfries & Galloway.......... 270
Campbell Hewson Books (R.), Fife............... 271
Cornucopia Books, Lincolnshire................... 151
Cox (Geoff), Devon 90
Dennys Sanders & Greene Ltd, East Sussex 100
Dolphin Books, Suffolk............................. 225
Eastern Traveller (The), Somerset................. 219
Edwards (London) Limited (Francis),
    London WC 176
Edwards in Hay–on–Wye (Francis), Powys 288
Ely Books, Cambridgeshire 65
Farahar & Dupre (Clive & Sophie), Wiltshire ... 251
Fifteenth Century Bookshop (The), East Sussex. 104
Gerald Lee Maritime Books, East Sussex........ 105
Glacier Books, Tayside 280
Harrington (Adrian), London W................... 173
Harrington Antiquarian Bookseller (Peter),
    London SW...................................... 167
Holmes Books (Harry), East Yorkshire........... 107
Indoislamica, London SW........................... 168
Joel Segal Books, Devon 86
Knowles - Antiquary (Roger J.), Staffordshire... 223
Lawson & Company (E.M.), Oxfordshire 206
Mandalay Bookshop, London SW 168
Marine & Cannon Books, Cheshire 71
Marine and Cannon Books, Cheshire 69
McEwan Fine Books, Grampian.................... 272
McLaren Books Ltd, Strathclyde 279
N1 Books, East Sussex 105
Nicholson of Chester (Richard), Cheshire 68
Old Book Company, (The), West Yorkshire..... 248
O'Reilly - Mountain Books (John), Derbyshire.. 83
Page (David), Lothian 276
Preston Book Company, Lancashire 144
Prior (Michael), Lincolnshire 152
Quaritch Ltd., (Bernard), London W.............. 174
Quinto of Charing Cross Road, London WC ... 178
R. & A. Books, East Sussex 101
Richard Thornton Books, London N 158
Rowan (P. & B.), Co. Antrim 260
Roz Hulse, Conwy 284
St Mary's Books & Prints, Lincolnshire 152
Saint Swithin's Illustrated & Children's Books,
    London W 174
Shapero Rare Books (Bernard J.), London W... 175
Smith (Clive), Essex 109
Vandeleur Antiquarian Books, Surrey............ 231
Wheen O'Books, Borders............................ 267

WALL STREET & STOCK EXCHANGE

Quaritch Ltd., (Bernard), London W.............. 174

WAR
- GENERAL

Adrem Books, Herts 130
Albion Books, West Midlands...................... 238
Annie's Books, S Yorks 221
Anthony Vickers Books, North Yorkshire 195
Antique Prints of the World, London N......... 156
Armstrong's Books & Collectables, Leics......... 145
Aurora Books Ltd, Lothian......................... 275
Backfold Books, Herefordshire..................... 127
Barbican Bookshop, North Yorkshire............. 196
Barn Books, Buckinghamshire...................... 61
Barnes (Peter), Wiltshire 253
Bath Old Books, Somerset 215
Beware of the Leopard, Bristol..................... 58
Book For All Reasons (A.), Suffolk 228
Bookcase, Cumbria.................................... 76
Books at Star Dot Star, West Midlands 240
books2books, Devon 88
BookShop, The, Dumfries & Galloway.......... 270
Bookworm (The), Lothian 276
Bookworms, Norfolk.................................. 186
Bookworms Paradise Ltd., West Sussex 242
Bowland Bookfinders, Lancashire 143
Brad Books, Essex 110
Broadhurst of Southport Ltd., Merseyside 185
Browsers Bookshop, Cornwall...................... 72
Bufo Books, Hampshire 125
Caliver Books, Essex 109
Cassidy (Bookseller) (P.), Lincolnshire 151
Catalyst Booksearch Services, Devon............... 87
Cavern Books, Cheshire 70
Charlie Byrne's Bookshop, Co. Galway.......... 265
Chelifer Books, Cumbria 80
Chris Phillips, Wiltshire............................. 252
Cofion Books, Pembrokeshire 286
Crabtree (Mrs. C.), G Manchester 120
Criterion Books, London O......................... 181
Dally (Andrew), Powys 289
Dandy Lion Editions, Surrey 233
Dartmoor Bookshop (The), Devon................ 84
Dolphin Books, Suffolk.............................. 225
Eastcote Bookshop (The), London O 180
Edwards, Fiona, Nottinghamshire 203
Embleton (Paul), Essex 111
Esoteric Dreams Bookshop, Cumbria.............. 77
Fifteenth Century Bookshop (The), East Sussex. 104
G. C. Books Ltd., Dumfries & Galloway......... 270
Gallimaufry Books, Herts 131
Golden Books Group, Devon 85
Good for Books, Lincolnshire 149
Grahame Thornton, Bookseller, Dorset........... 93
Hambleton Books, North Yorkshire 196
Handsworth Books, Essex........................... 112
Harlequin Books, Bristol 59
Harrington Antiquarian Bookseller (Peter),
    London SW...................................... 167
Harris (George J.), Co. Derry 260
Hay Cinema Bookshop Ltd., Powys.............. 288
HCB Wholesale, Powys.............................. 288
Hurst (Jenny), Kent 137
Island Books, Devon 85
Jackdaw Books, Norfolk............................. 188
Jackson (M.W.), Wiltshire.......................... 254
Jade Mountain Bookshop, Hampshire 125

Janus Books, West Midlands 239
Joel Segal Books, Devon 86
Just Books, Cornwall 75
Kingfisher Book Service, Nottinghamshire 204
Lewis (J.T. & P.), Cornwall 73
Lost Books, Northants.............................. 200
Marine & Cannon Books, Cheshire 71
Marine and Cannon Books, Cheshire 69
McCrone (Audrey), Isle of Arran 274
Meekins Books (Paul), Warwickshire.............. 237
MilitaryHistoryBooks.com, Kent................... 137
Much Binding, Norfolk............................. 186
Murphy (C.J.), Norfolk............................. 189
N1 Books, East Sussex 105
Nelson (Elizabeth), Suffolk........................ 226
New Strand, The, Herefordshire 127
Old Book Company, (The), West Yorkshire 248
Old Station Pottery & Bookshop (The), Norfolk 191
Palladour Books, Hampshire 125
Parker Books (Mike), Cambridgeshire 64
Pauline Harries Books, Hampshire 123
Peter M Daly, Hampshire........................... 126
Poetry Bookshop (The), Powys..................... 289
Priestpopple Books, Northumberland 201
Prior (Michael), Lincolnshire 152
Quaritch Ltd., (Bernard), London W.............. 174
Quinto of Charing Cross Road, London WC ... 178
R. & A. Books, East Sussex 101
Richard Thornton Books, London N 158
Richmond Books, North Yorkshire 194
Rods Books, Devon 88
Roland Books, Kent 138
Schull Books, Co. Cork 262
Scrivener's Books & Bookbinding, Derbyshire... 82
Smith Books, (Sally), Suffolk 226
Spurrier (Nick), Kent 137
Stevens (Joan), Cambridgeshire.................... 65
Stothert Old Books, Cheshire...................... 68
T V Coles Books, Cambridgeshire................. 67
The Sanctuary Bookshop, Dorset.................. 94
Thin Read Line, Merseyside 184
Tiffin (Tony and Gill), Durham 97
Treasure Trove Books, Leics....................... 146
Uncle Phil's Books, West Midlands 239
Wadard Books, Kent 137
War & Peace Books, Hampshire................... 122
Ward (R.F. & C.), Norfolk 187
Wheen O'Books, Borders........................... 267
Wiend Books, Lancashire 143
Williams (Bookdealer), (Richard), Lincs 153
World War Books, Kent 141
Yeoman Books, Lothian 277
Yesterday's News, Conwy 283
Zardoz Books, Wiltshire............................ 254

- AMERICAN CIVIL
Adrem Books, Herts 130
Americanabooksuk, Cumbria....................... 76
Booksets.com Ltd, Shropshire 214
Bookworm (The), Lothian 276
Bookworms Paradise Ltd., West Sussex 242
Broadhurst of Southport Ltd., Merseyside 185
Caliver Books, Essex 109
Chelifer Books, Cumbria 80
Farnborough Gallery, Hampshire................... 122

Helion & Company, West Midlands 239
Island Books, Devon 85
Joel Segal Books, Devon 86
Marble Hill Books, Outer London................. 182
Meekins Books (Paul), Warwickshire.............. 237
MilitaryHistoryBooks.com, Kent................... 137
Rods Books, Devon 88
Shakeshaft (Dr. B.), Cheshire...................... 71
Trinity Rare Books, Co. Leitrim 266
Wadard Books, Kent 137
Wiend Books, Lancashire 143

- AUSTRALIAN
Meekins Books (Paul), Warwickshire.............. 237
MilitaryHistoryBooks.com, Kent................... 137
Rods Books, Devon................................. 88
World War II Books, Surrey 234

- BOER, THE
Adrem Books, Herts 130
Antique Prints of the World, London N.......... 156
Boer War Books, North Yorkshire 197
Chalmers Hallam (E.), Hampshire 125
Chelifer Books, Cumbria 80
Dolphin Books, Suffolk 225
Embleton (Paul), Essex 111
Empire Books, North Yorkshire 197
Fifteenth Century Bookshop (The), East Sussex. 104
Helion & Company, West Midlands 239
Island Books, Devon 85
Kenya Books, East Sussex 100
Marine & Cannon Books, Cheshire 71
Marine and Cannon Books, Cheshire 69
Meekins Books (Paul), Warwickshire.............. 237
MilitaryHistoryBooks.com, Kent................... 137
N1 Books, East Sussex 105
Preston Book Company, Lancashire 144
Rods Books, Devon................................. 88
Sutcliffe (Victor), Norfolk 187
Thin Read Line, Merseyside 184
Wheen O'Books, Borders........................... 267

- BUSH WARS
Al Saqi Books, London W........................... 171
Bookworm (The), Lothian 276
Michael Graves-Johnston, London SW 168
MilitaryHistoryBooks.com, Kent................... 137
Rods Books, Devon................................. 88

- CIVIL & ENGLISH CIVIL WARS
Bookworm (The), Lothian 276
Caliver Books, Essex 109
Chelifer Books, Cumbria 80
Clifford Elmer Books Ltd., Cheshire 68
Dolphin Books, Suffolk............................. 225
Helion & Company, West Midlands 239
Island Books, Devon 85
Jackdaw Books, Norfolk 188
Joel Segal Books, Devon 86
John Underwood Antiquarian Books, Norfolk .. 189
Meekins Books (Paul), Warwickshire.............. 237
MilitaryHistoryBooks.com, Kent................... 137
N1 Books, East Sussex 105
Rods Books, Devon................................. 88
Roger Collicott Books, Cornwall 74

Shakeshaft (Dr. B.), Cheshire........................ 71
Spenceley Books (David), West Yorkshire........ 248
Trinity Rare Books, Co. Leitrim.................... 266
Wiend Books, Lancashire 143

- MEXICAN WAR
Americanabooksuk, Cumbria....................... 76
MilitaryHistoryBooks.com, Kent................... 137
Rods Books, Devon................................. 88

- NAPOLEONIC
Adrem Books, Herts 130
Armchair Books, Lothian 275
Barn Books, Buckinghamshire...................... 61
Books on Spain, London O.......................... 182
Bookworm (The), Lothian 276
Bookworms Paradise Ltd., West Sussex 242
Caliver Books, Essex................................ 109
Chelifer Books, Cumbria 80
Donovan Military Books (Tom), East Sussex.... 99
Falconwood Transport & Military Bookshop,
    London O.. 183
Green Ltd. (G.L.), Herts 131
Helion & Company, West Midlands 239
Island Books, Devon................................ 85
Joel Segal Books, Devon 86
Lost Books, Northants.............................. 200
Marine & Cannon Books, Cheshire 71
Marine and Cannon Books, Cheshire 69
Meekins Books (Paul), Warwickshire............. 237
Miles Apart, Suffolk 228
MilitaryHistoryBooks.com, Kent................... 137
N1 Books, East Sussex 105
Orssich (Paul), London SW 169
Prior (Michael), Lincolnshire 152
R. & A. Books, East Sussex 101
Rods Books, Devon................................. 88
Sutcliffe (Victor), Norfolk 187
Thin Read Line, Merseyside 184
Wadard Books, Kent 137

- REVOLUTIONARY
Americanabooksuk, Cumbria....................... 76
Apocalypse, Surrey 232
Bookworm (The), Lothian 276
Caliver Books, Essex................................ 109
Chelifer Books, Cumbria 80
Left on The Shelf, Cumbria......................... 78
MilitaryHistoryBooks.com, Kent................... 137
Rods Books, Devon................................. 88

- SPANISH CIVIL WAR
Bass (Ben), Wiltshire 251
Books on Spain, London O.......................... 182
Caliver Books, Essex................................ 109
Chelifer Books, Cumbria 80
Helion & Company, West Midlands 239
Left on The Shelf, Cumbria......................... 78
Little Stour Books, Kent 136
Meekins Books (Paul), Warwickshire............. 237
MilitaryHistoryBooks.com, Kent................... 137
Orssich (Paul), London SW 169
Red Star Books, Herts.............................. 129
Rods Books, Devon................................. 88
Woburn Books, London N 159

York (Graham), Devon.............................. 86

- VIETNAM
Anglo-American Rare Books, Surrey.............. 232
Bookworm (The), Lothian 276
Caliver Books, Essex................................ 109
Chelifer Books, Cumbria 80
Falconwood Transport & Military Bookshop,
    London O.. 183
Helion & Company, West Midlands 239
Meekins Books (Paul), Warwickshire............. 237
MilitaryHistoryBooks.com, Kent................... 137
Rods Books, Devon................................. 88
Woburn Books, London N 159

- WORLD WAR I
Aardvark Books, Wiltshire.......................... 254
Adrem Books, Herts 130
Albion Books, West Midlands...................... 238
Anglo-American Rare Books, Surrey.............. 232
Armchair Auctions, Hampshire 121
Arthur Hook, Bristol................................ 58
Avedikian Rare Books, Somerset 216
Aviabooks, Glos 114
Ballantyne–Way (Roger), Suffolk 228
Barbican Bookshop, North Yorkshire............. 196
Book For All Reasons (A.), Suffolk 228
Bookworm (The), Lothian 276
Bookworms Paradise Ltd., West Sussex 242
Browsers Bookshop, Cornwall...................... 72
Burroughs (Andrew), Lincolnshire 152
Caliver Books, Essex................................ 109
Chelifer Books, Cumbria 80
Cocks (Brian), Cambridgeshire 67
Cornucopia Books, Lincolnshire 151
Cox (Geoff), Devon 90
Dally (Andrew), Powys 289
Delectus Books, London WC........................ 176
Delph Books, G Manchester........................ 120
Dolphin Books, Suffolk............................. 225
Dormouse Bookshop (The), Norfolk 189
Ellis, Bookseller (Peter), London WC 177
Embleton (Paul), Essex 111
Falconwood Transport & Military Bookshop,
    London O.. 183
Farnborough Gallery, Hampshire.................. 122
Fifteenth Century Bookshop (The), East Sussex. 104
G&S Books, Kent 138
Gallimaufry Books, Herts 131
Garfi Books, Powys 291
Gerald Lee Maritime Books, East Sussex........ 105
Good for Books, Lincolnshire 149
Green Ltd. (G.L.), Herts 131
Hambleton Books, North Yorkshire............... 196
Helion & Company, West Midlands 239
Heppa (Christopher), Essex 108
Island Books, Devon................................ 85
Joel Segal Books, Devon 86
Kingfisher Book Service, Nottinghamshire 204
Lost Books, Northants.............................. 200
Maggy Browne, Lincolnshire 148
Marine & Cannon Books, Cheshire 71
Marine and Cannon Books, Cheshire 69
McCrone (Audrey), Isle of Arran 274
Meekins Books (Paul), Warwickshire............. 237

MilitaryHistoryBooks.com, Kent.................... 137
Ming Books, Dumfries & Galloway 270
My Back Pages, London SW........................ 168
N1 Books, East Sussex 105
Palladour Books, Hampshire 125
Peter M Daly, Hampshire........................... 126
Prior (Michael), Lincolnshire 152
R. & A. Books, East Sussex 101
Richard Thornton Books, London N 158
Richmond Books, North Yorkshire 194
Robert Humm & Co, Lincolnshire 152
Rods Books, Devon................................... 88
SaBeRo Books, London SW........................ 169
SETI Books, West Midlands........................ 239
Smith Books (Keith), Herefordshire 128
Stalagluft Books, Tyne and Wear.................. 235
Symes Books (Naomi), Cheshire 71
Thin Read Line, Merseyside 184
Tiffin (Tony and Gill), Durham 97
Tilston (Stephen E.), London SE.................... 165
Tony Hutchinson, Surrey............................. 233
Trinity Rare Books, Co. Leitrim 266
Tyger Press, London N............................... 158
Updike Rare Books (John), Lothian 277
Wadard Books, Kent 137
War & Peace Books, Hampshire.................... 122
Wheen O'Books, Borders............................ 267
White Eagle Books, London NW.................. 162
Wiend Books, Lancashire 143
Wizard Books, Cambridgeshire..................... 67

- WORLD WAR II

Aardvark Books, Wiltshire.......................... 254
Adrem Books, Herts 130
Annie's Books, S Yorks 221
Armchair Auctions, Hampshire 121
Arthur Hook, Bristol................................. 58
Aviabooks, Glos 114
Baldwin (M. & M.), Worcs 255
Barbican Bookshop, North Yorkshire............. 196
Barn Books, Buckinghamshire 61
Book For All Reasons (A.), Suffolk 228
Bookworm (The), Lothian 276
Bosorne Books, Cornwall 75
Browsers Bookshop, Cornwall...................... 72
Burroughs (Andrew), Lincolnshire 152
Caliver Books, Essex 109
Chaucer Bookshop, Kent............................ 136
Chelifer Books, Cumbria 80
Cocks (Brian), Cambridgeshire 67
Cornucopia Books, Lincolnshire 151
Dally (Andrew), Powys 289
Delectus Books, London WC....................... 176
Dolphin Books, Suffolk.............................. 225
Donovan Military Books (Tom), East Sussex.... 99
Dormouse Bookshop (The), Norfolk 189
Ellis, Bookseller (Peter), London WC 177
Embleton (Paul), Essex 111
English (Toby), Oxfordshire......................... 209
Falconwood Transport & Military Bookshop,
    London O.. 183
Farnborough Gallery, Hampshire................... 122
Fifteenth Century Bookshop (The), East Sussex. 104
Foster Bookshop (Paul), London SW.............. 167
G&S Books, Kent 138

Gallimaufry Books, Herts 131
Garfi Books, Powys 291
Gerald Lee Maritime Books, East Sussex......... 105
Good for Books, Lincolnshire 149
Green Ltd. (G.L.), Herts 131
Hab Books, London W............................... 172
Hambleton Books, North Yorkshire 196
Helion & Company, West Midlands 239
Island Books, Devon................................. 85
Joel Segal Books, Devon 86
Kingfisher Book Service, Nottinghamshire 204
Lost Books, Northants................................ 200
Maggy Browne, Lincolnshire 148
Mandalay Bookshop, London SW 168
Marine & Cannon Books, Cheshire 71
Marine and Cannon Books, Cheshire 69
McCrone (Audrey), Isle of Arran.................. 274
Meekins Books (Paul), Warwickshire.............. 237
MilitaryHistoryBooks.com, Kent.................... 137
Ming Books, Dumfries & Galloway................ 270
My Back Pages, London SW 168
Palladour Books, Hampshire 125
Prior (Michael), Lincolnshire 152
R. & A. Books, East Sussex 101
Richard Thornton Books, London N 158
Richmond Books, North Yorkshire 194
Robert Humm & Co, Lincolnshire 152
Rods Books, Devon................................... 88
Roland Books, Kent 138
SaBeRo Books, London SW........................ 169
Samovar Books, Co. Dublin........................ 264
SETI Books, West Midlands........................ 239
Stalagluft Books, Tyne and Wear.................. 235
Symes Books (Naomi), Cheshire 71
Thin Read Line, Merseyside 184
Tilston (Stephen E.), London SE.................... 165
Tony Hutchinson, Surrey............................. 233
Trinity Rare Books, Co. Leitrim 266
Tyger Press, London N............................... 158
Uncle Phil's Books, West Midlands 239
Updike Rare Books (John), Lothian 277
Vanstone - Aviation Books, (Derek), Suffolk 229
Wadard Books, Kent 137
War & Peace Books, Hampshire.................... 122
Wembdon Books, Somerset......................... 216
Wheen O'Books, Borders............................ 267
White Eagle Books, London NW.................. 162
Wiend Books, Lancashire 143
Wizard Books, Cambridgeshire..................... 67
World War II Books, Surrey 234

- WWII HOME FRONT UK (1939-45)

Annie's Books, S Yorks 221
Baldwin (M. & M.), Worcs 255
Book For All Reasons (A.), Suffolk 228
Browsers Bookshop, Cornwall...................... 72
Burroughs (Andrew), Lincolnshire 152
Chelifer Books, Cumbria 80
Cornucopia Books, Lincolnshire 151
Embleton (Paul), Essex 111
Falconwood Transport & Military Bookshop,
    London Outer..................................... 183
Farnborough Gallery, Hampshire................... 122
Fifteenth Century Bookshop (The), East Sussex. 104
Gerald Lee Maritime Books, East Sussex......... 105

Island Books, Devon 85
Joel Segal Books, Devon 86
Maggy Browne, Lincolnshire 148
Marchpane, London WC 177
Marine & Cannon Books, Cheshire 71
Marine and Cannon Books, Cheshire 69
MilitaryHistoryBooks.com, Kent 137
R. & A. Books, East Sussex 101
Read - Gorleston Books, (C.&J.), Norfolk 187
Richard Thornton Books, London N 158
Rods Books, Devon 88
SaBeRo Books, London SW 169
Stalagluft Books, Tyne and Wear 235
Symes Books (Naomi), Cheshire 71
Uncle Phil's Books, West Midlands 239
Wheen O'Books, Borders 267
Wiend Books, Lancashire 143

- ZULU
Aardvark Books, Wiltshire 254
Antique Prints of the World, London N 156
Bookworm (The), Lothian 276
Caliver Books, Essex 109
Chalmers Hallam (E.), Hampshire 125
Chelifer Books, Cumbria 80
Dolphin Books, Suffolk 225
Embleton (Paul), Essex 111
Island Books, Devon 85
Marine & Cannon Books, Cheshire 71
Marine and Cannon Books, Cheshire 69
Meekins Books (Paul), Warwickshire 237
MilitaryHistoryBooks.com, Kent 137
R. & A. Books, East Sussex 101
Rods Books, Devon 88
Sutcliffe (Victor), Norfolk 187
Thin Read Line, Merseyside 184
Wadard Books, Kent 137

WARGAMES
Bardsley's Books, Suffolk 225
Barnes (Peter), Wiltshire 253
Bookworm (The), Lothian 276
Caliver Books, Essex 109
Chelifer Books, Cumbria 80
Helion & Company, West Midlands 239
Meekins Books (Paul), Warwickshire 237
MilitaryHistoryBooks.com, Kent 137

WASHING
Judith Mansfield, West Yorkshire 249
Stroh (M.A.), London E 154

WATCHES
Hadfield (G.K.), Cumbria 79
www.AntiqueWatchStore.com, Herts 129

WATERCOLOURS
Abacus Books, G Manchester 118
Annie's Books, S Yorks 221
Booth (Booksearch Service), (Geoff), Cheshire ... 68
Bruce Holdsworth Books, East Sussex 105
Chalk (Old & Out of Print Books)
  (Christine M.), West Midlands 238
Clark (Nigel A.), London SE 163
Don Kelly Books, London W 172

Fifteenth Century Bookshop (The), East Sussex . 104
Joel Segal Books, Devon 86
McCrone (Audrey), Isle of Arran 274
R. & A. Books, East Sussex 101
Trinity Rare Books, Co. Leitrim 266

WAYSIDE AND WOODLAND
Annie's Books, S Yorks 221
Barn Books, Shropshire 214
Calluna Books, Dorset 95
Cornucopia Books, Lincolnshire 151
Dales & Lakes Book Centre, Cumbria 79
Island Books, Devon 85
J and J Books, Lincolnshire 149
Jackdaw Books, Norfolk 188
Lymelight Books & Prints, Dorset 93
Martin (Books and Pictures), (Brian P)., Surrey . 231
Prospect House Books, Co. Down 261

WEAPONS
Annie's Books, S Yorks 221
Barn Books, Buckinghamshire 61
Bookworm (The), Lothian 276
Coch-y-Bonddu Books, Powys 290
Gallimaufry Books, Herts 131
Old Book Company, (The), West Yorkshire 248
Prospect Books, Conwy 283

WEIRD & WONDERFUL
Adrem Books, Herts 130
Delectus Books, London WC 176
Gildas Books, Cheshire 68
Inner Bookshop (The), Oxfordshire 208
Joel Segal Books, Devon 86
Morris Secondhand & Antiquarian Books (Chris),
  Oxfordshire 208
N1 Books, East Sussex 105
Oak Tree Press, Oxfordshire 207
R. & A. Books, East Sussex 101
Stalagluft Books, Tyne and Wear 235
Star Lord Books, G Manchester 119
Trinity Rare Books, Co. Leitrim 266

WELSH INTEREST
Adrem Books, Herts 130
Bear Island Books, Cardiff 281
Books in Cardigan, Ceredigion 282
BOOKS4U, Flintshire 284
Brock Books, North Yorkshire 192
Browning Books, Torfaen 292
Cader Idris Books, Powys 290
Castle Bookshop, Powys 290
Chapter Two, London SE 163
Cheshire Book Centre, Cheshire 69
Coch-y-Bonddu Books, Powys 290
Cofion Books, Pembrokeshire 286
Colin Hancock, Ceredigion 282
Country Books, Derbyshire 82
Cymric Books, Berks 56
Dally (Andrew), Powys 289
Doorbar (P. & D.), Gwynedd 285
Dusty Books, Powys 290
Fifteenth Century Bookshop (The), East Sussex. 104
Gildas Books, Cheshire 68
Great Oak Bookshop (The), Powys 289

Joel Segal Books, Devon 86
Kingshead Books, Powys............................ 291
Lighthouse Books (The), Dorset 92
Lloyd-Davies (Sue), Carmarthenshire 282
Madoc Books, Conwy 284
Mollie's Loft, Swansea.............................. 291
Old Book Company, (The), West Yorkshire 248
Oopalba Books, Cheshire............................ 71
Poetry Bookshop (The), Powys..................... 289
Rhos Point Books, Conwy 283
Siop Lyfrau'r Hen Bost, Gwynedd 285
Siop y Morfa, Denbighshire 284
Stalagluft Books, Tyne and Wear 235
Stella Books, Monmouthshire 286
Stothert Old Books, Cheshire....................... 68
Willmott Bookseller (Nicholas), Cardiff........... 281

WEST YORKSHIRE LOCAL HISTORY
Hatchard & Daughters, West Yorkshire 246
Old Book Company, (The), West Yorkshire 248

WESTERN AMERICANA
Adrem Books, Herts 130
Americanabooksuk, Cumbria........................ 76
Clifford Elmer Books Ltd., Cheshire 68
Joel Segal Books, Devon 86

WESTERNS
Adrem Books, Herts 130
Americanabooksuk, Cumbria........................ 76
Esoteric Dreams Bookshop, Cumbria 77
firstpagebooks, Norfolk............................. 189
Ming Books, Dumfries & Galloway 270
Williams (Bookdealer), (Richard), Lincs 153

WHALING
Bluntisham Books, Cambridgeshire................ 63
Delectus Books, London WC 176
Georgina Hobhouse, Argyll......................... 274
Glacier Books, Tayside 280
Marine & Cannon Books, Cheshire 71
Marine and Cannon Books, Cheshire 69
McEwan Fine Books, Grampian.................... 272
Preston Book Company, Lancashire 144
Prior (Michael), Lincolnshire 152
Stroh (M.A.), London E 154

WHISKY
Annie's Books, S Yorks 221
Anthony Vickers Books, North Yorkshire 195
Edmund Pollinger Rare Books, London SW..... 166
Hava Books, London SE............................ 164
Joel Segal Books, Devon 86
Lucas (Richard), London NW...................... 161
McEwan Fine Books, Grampian.................... 272
R. & A. Books, East Sussex 101
Sleepy Elephant Books & Artefacts, Cumbria ... 80
Strathtay Antiquarian - Secondhand Books,
    Tayside 280
Thorne (John), Essex............................... 109

WINDMILLS & WATERMILLS
Abacus Books, G Manchester 118
Arnold (Roy), Suffolk............................... 227
Books Only, Suffolk................................. 226

Cornucopia Books, Lincolnshire 151
Cottage Books, Leics............................... 145
Country Books, Derbyshire 82
Cox (Geoff), Devon 90
Fifteenth Century Bookshop (The), East Sussex. 104
Island Books, Devon................................ 85
J and J Books, Lincolnshire......................... 149
Jackdaw Books, Norfolk 188
Joel Segal Books, Devon 86
R. & A. Books, East Sussex 101
Randall (Tom), Somerset............................ 218
Reads, Dorset 95
Robert Humm & Co, Lincolnshire 152
Salway Books, Essex 112
Stroh (M.A.), London E 154
Winchester Bookshop (The), Hampshire.......... 126

WINE
Annie's Books, S Yorks 221
Apocalypse, Surrey 232
Clarke (Janet), Somerset 215
Collectable Books, London SE 163
Cornucopia Books, Lincolnshire 151
Dusty Books, Powys 290
Fifteenth Century Bookshop (The), East Sussex. 104
Gresham Books, Somerset 217
Hava Books, London SE............................ 164
Joel Segal Books, Devon 86
Lucas (Richard), London NW...................... 161
Macbuiks, North Yorkshire......................... 193
Moorhead Books, West Yorkshire.................. 245
Mr. Mac, Dumfries & Galloway 269
Quaritch Ltd., (Bernard), London W............. 174
R. & A. Books, East Sussex 101
Roberts Wine Books (John), Bristol 59
Thorne (John), Essex............................... 109
Uncle Phil's Books, West Midlands 239

WINE - BURGUNDY
Annie's Books, S Yorks 221
Hava Books, London SE............................ 164
Thorne (John), Essex............................... 109

WITCHCRAFT
Adrem Books, Herts 130
Alpha Books, London N 156
Annie's Books, S Yorks 221
Atlantis Bookshop, London WC.................... 176
Bookbarrow, Cambridgeshire....................... 63
Bookworms Paradise Ltd., West Sussex 242
Caduceus Books, Leics.............................. 145
Chthonios Books, East Sussex...................... 102
Cornucopia Books, Lincolnshire 151
Country Books, Derbyshire 82
Edmund Pollinger Rare Books, London SW..... 166
Esoteric Dreams Bookshop, Cumbria 77
Gilbert (R.A.), Somerset............................ 219
Gildas Books, Cheshire............................. 68
Green Man Books, East Sussex 101
Inner Bookshop (The), Oxfordshire................ 208
Joel Segal Books, Devon 86
Occultique, Northants............................... 199
Old Book Company, (The), West Yorkshire 248
Old Celtic Bookshop (The), Devon................ 87
R. & A. Books, East Sussex 101

SETI Books, West Midlands......................... 239
Star Lord Books, G Manchester 119
Trinity Rare Books, Co. Leitrim 266
Walker Fine Books (Steve), Dorset 92
Waxfactor, East Sussex 100
Wizard Books, Cambridgeshire.................... 67

WOMEN

Adrem Books, Herts 130
Apocalypse, Surrey 232
Black Cat Books, Norfolk........................... 187
Book Annex (The), Essex 109
Books & Bygones (Pam Taylor), West Midlands 240
Burmester (James), Bristol........................... 58
Chesters (G. & J.), Staffordshire 224
Crawford (Elizabeth), London EC................ 155
Delectus Books, London WC....................... 176
Dolphin Books, Suffolk............................. 225
Drury Rare Books (John), Essex................... 110
Dylans Bookstore, Swansea........................ 291
Elaine Lonsdale Books, West Yorkshire 247
Fortune Green Books, London NW............... 160
Harvest Books, Lancashire.......................... 144
Hobgoblin Books, Hampshire 125
Jarndyce Antiquarian Booksellers, London WC. 177
Joel Segal Books, Devon 86
Lane Books (Shirley), Isle of Wight 134
Left on The Shelf, Cumbria......................... 78
Much Binding, Norfolk.............................. 186
Northern Herald Books, West Yorkshire......... 245
Old Book Company, (The), West Yorkshire 248
Orlando Booksellers, Lincolnshire 150
Pickering & Chatto, London W.................... 174
Polmorla Books, Cornwall 75
Price (John), London N 158
Quaritch Ltd., (Bernard), London W............. 174
Reading Lasses, Dumfries & Galloway 270
Rebecca Hardie Rare Books, London W 171
Scorpio Books, Suffolk 225
Spurrier (Nick), Kent 137
Stevens (Joan), Cambridgeshire.................... 65
Stone, (G.& R.), Borders 267
Susan Taylor Books, West Yorkshire 247
Susanne Schulz-Falster Rare Books, London N. 158
Symes Books (Naomi), Cheshire 71
Willmott Bookseller (Nicholas), Cardiff.......... 281
Woburn Books, London N 159

WOODCUT NOVELS

Elstree Books, Herts................................. 130
Hay Castle, Powys.................................. 288
Joel Segal Books, Devon 86
Myra Dean Illustated Books, Powys 287
Oak Tree Press, Oxfordshire 207
R. & A. Books, East Sussex 101
Roz Hulse, Conwy 284

WOODLAND CRAFTS

Abacus Books, G Manchester 118
Adrem Books, Herts 130
Cornucopia Books, Lincolnshire 151
Fifteenth Century Bookshop (The), East Sussex. 104
Island Books, Devon................................. 85
Joel Segal Books, Devon 86
Stobart Davies Limited, Carmarthenshire 282

WOODWORK

Abacus Books, G Manchester 118
Adrem Books, Herts 130
Arnold (Roy), Suffolk............................... 227
Backfold Books, Herefordshire 127
Birchden Books, London E 154
Brown-Studies, Strathclyde......................... 277
Camilla's Bookshop, East Sussex 101
Cavern Books, Cheshire............................. 70
Cheshire Book Centre, Cheshire.................... 69
Cornucopia Books, Lincolnshire 151
Cover to Cover, Merseyside......................... 185
Fifteenth Century Bookshop (The), East Sussex. 104
Joel Segal Books, Devon 86
N1 Books, East Sussex 105
Phillips of Hitchin (Antiques) Ltd., Herts......... 131
Stobart Davies Limited, Carmarthenshire 282
Trinders' Fine Tools, Suffolk 226
Trinity Rare Books, Co. Leitrim 266
Upper–Room Books, Somerset...................... 217
Whittle, Bookseller (Avril), Cumbria 80

WORLD FAIRS & EXHIBITIONS

Batterham (David), London W...................... 171
Don Kelly Books, London W 172
Inch's Books, Kent 137
Susanne Schulz-Falster Rare Books, London N. 158
Weiner (Graham), London N 158

WRISTWATCHES

Delph Books, G Manchester........................ 120
R. & A. Books, East Sussex 101

WRITING & WRITING EQUIPMENT

Adrem Books, Herts 130
Apocalypse, Surrey 232
Barcombe Services, Essex........................... 108
Byre Books, Dumfries & Galloway................ 270
Cornucopia Books, Lincolnshire 151
Joel Segal Books, Devon 86
R. & A. Books, East Sussex 101

X-RAY

Bernard Dixon and Kath Adams, London Outer 182
Phelps (Michael), West Sussex...................... 242

YACHTING AND BOATING

McCrone (Audrey), Isle of Arran.................. 274
Old Book Company, (The), West Yorkshire 248
SETI Books, West Midlands......................... 239

YEARBOOKS

Adrem Books, Herts 130
Books for Content, Herefordshire.................. 127
Collectors Carbooks, Northants.................... 199
McGee (Terence J.), London Outer 180
White (C.R.), London W............................ 175

YOGA

Annie's Books, S Yorks 221
Bookbarrow, Cambridgeshire....................... 63
Combat Arts Archive, Durham 97
Dales & Lakes Book Centre, Cumbria............ 79
Greensleeves, Oxfordshire 206
Inner Bookshop (The), Oxfordshire............... 208

Joel Segal Books, Devon 86
Magis Books, Leics.................................... 146
Occultique, Northants............................... 199
Orchid Book Distributors, Co. Clare............. 262
Portobello Books, London W 174
R. & A. Books, East Sussex 101
Roundstone Books, Lancashire.................... 143
Till's Bookshop, Lothian 277
Trinity Rare Books, Co. Leitrim 266

YORKSHIRE
Brock Books, North Yorkshire..................... 192
East Riding Books, East Yorkshire............... 107
Elaine Lonsdale Books, West Yorkshire.......... 247
Hornsey's, North Yorkshire......................... 194
Idle Booksellers (The), West Yorkshire 245
Kemp Bookseller, Michael S, G Manchester..... 118
Pennymead Books, North Yorkshire.............. 193

YOUTH MOVEMENTS
MilitaryHistoryBooks.com, Kent................... 137
R. & A. Books, East Sussex 101
Reading Lasses, Dumfries & Galloway 270

ZOOLOGY
Acanthophyllum Books, Wirral 184
Adrem Books, Herts 130
Alba Books, Grampian 273
Arden, Bookseller (C.), Powys..................... 287
Baldwin's Scientific Books, Essex 111
Baron - Scientific Book Sales (P.J.), Somerset ... 216
Blest (Peter), Kent 138
Demar Books (Grant), Kent........................ 140
Gladstone Books, Lincolnshire 150
Grayling (David A.H.), Cumbria 78
Harrington Antiquarian Bookseller (Peter),
   London SW... 167
Joel Segal Books, Devon 86
Lymelight Books & Prints, Dorset................. 93
Martin (Brian), Surrey 231
Old Book Company, (The), West Yorkshire 248
Orb's Bookshop, Grampian......................... 273
Parkinsons Books, Merseyside...................... 185
Pemberley Books, Buckinghamshire 62
Peter M Daly, Hampshire........................... 126
Phelps (Michael), West Sussex...................... 242
R M Books, Herts.................................... 132
R. & A. Books, East Sussex 101
Second Nature at Knapton Bookbarn, N Yorks 197
St Ann's Books, Worcs 255
Savona Books, Lincolnshire......................... 151
Steven Simpson Books, Norfolk 190
Sue Lowell Natural History Books, London W . 175
Westons, Herts 132
Wyseby House Books, Berks 55

ZOOS
Adrem Books, Herts 130
Glenbower Books, Co. Dublin 264
Joel Segal Books, Devon 86
Martin (Brian), Surrey 231
R. & A. Books, East Sussex 101

BOOKSEARCH SERVICE
Index of dealers who offer a booksearch service

A. & R. Booksearch, Cornwall 73
Adrem Books, Herts 130
Afar Books International, West Midlands 238
Ainslie Books, Strathclyde........................... 278
Albion Books, West Midlands...................... 238
Alexander's Books, Warwickshire.................. 237
Alton Secondhand Books, Hampshire............. 121
Americanabooksuk, Cumbria....................... 76
Ampersand Books, Norfolk......................... 189
Annie's Books, S Yorks 221
Antiquary Ltd., (Bar Bookstore), N Yorks....... 194
Anvil Books, West Midlands 239
Archer (Steve), London Outer 180
Armchair Auctions, Hampshire 121
Arnold (Roy), Suffolk............................... 227
Askew Books (Vernon), Wiltshire.................. 251
Autolycus, Shropshire............................... 212
Ayre (Peter J.), Somerset 219
Ballantyne–Way (Roger), Suffolk 228
Bardsley's Books, Suffolk........................... 225
Barn Books, Buckinghamshire...................... 61
Bass (Ben), Wiltshire 251
Bath Book Exchange, Somerset 215
Baxter - Books (Eddie), Somerset 220
Baxter (Steve), Surrey.............................. 233
Beardsley (A.E.), Nottinghamshire................. 204
Beaver Booksearch, Suffolk 225
Ben–Nathan (Jack), London Outer 180
Bertram Rota Ltd., London WC 176
Bilski (Gill), Buckinghamshire 61
Birmingham Books, West Midlands 238
Black Cat Bookshop, Leics 147
Black Voices, Merseyside 184
Blythswood Bookshop, Highland 274
Bonython Bookshop, Cornwall..................... 75
Book Depot (The), London NW.................... 160
Book House (The), Cumbria........................ 76
Bookcase, Cumbria.................................. 76
Bookends, Hampshire............................... 122
Bookmark (Children's Books), Wiltshire.......... 253
Books Bought & Sold, Surrey 231
Books for Content, Herefordshire.................. 127
books2books, Devon................................ 88
Bookseeker, Tayside................................ 280
Bookshelf – Aviation Books, West Sussex........ 241
Bookshop (The), G Manchester.................... 118
Bookshop (The), West Sussex 242
Bookshop (The), Co. Donegal....................... 263
Booktrace International, Devon.................... 86
Bookworld, Shropshire.............................. 213
Booth (Booksearch Service), (Geoff), Cheshire... 68
Bott, (Bookdealers) Ltd., (Martin),
  G Manchester 118
Bowland Bookfinders, Lancashire.................. 143
Broadhurst of Southport Ltd., Merseyside 185
Butts Books (Mary), Berks.......................... 56
Byblos Antiquarian & Rare Book, Hampshire .. 122
Caliver Books, Essex 109
Candle Lane Books, Shropshire.................... 213

Canon Gate Books, West Sussex................... 243
Capital Bookshop, Cardiff 281
Carningli Centre, Pembrokeshire................... 286
Catalyst Booksearch Services, Devon............. 87
Chandos Books, Devon............................. 85
Chapter House Books, Dorset...................... 94
Chapter Two, London SE............................ 163
Chapters Bookstore, Co. Dublin................... 264
Chaters Motoring Booksellers, London Outer ... 181
Cheshire Book Centre, Cheshire.................... 69
Children's Bookshop (The), Herefordshire........ 127
Chris Porter Books, Norfolk........................ 186
Christine's Book Cabin, Leics 147
Chthonios Books, East Sussex 102
Church Green Books, Oxfordshire................. 210
Church Street Books, Norfolk...................... 186
Clark (M.R.), West Yorkshire 245
Clark (Nigel A.), London SE 163
Clarke Books (David), Somerset 218
Classic Crime Collections, G Manchester......... 119
Coach House Books, Worcs 256
Coch-y-Bonddu Books, Powys 290
Cofion Books, Pembrokeshire 286
Collectors Carbooks, Northants.................... 199
Colwyn Books, Conwy 283
Corfe Books, Surrey................................ 230
Coulthurst (Richard), G Manchester 120
Cowley, Auto–in–Print (John), Essex.............. 108
Craobh Rua Books, Co. Armagh................... 260
D Robertson (Booksellers & Booksearch
  Services), Lothian 276
D. & M. Books, West Yorkshire.................... 249
D.C. Books, Lincolnshire............................ 149
Dales and Lakes Book Centre, Cumbria.......... 79
D'Arcy Books, Wiltshire............................ 252
Debbage (John), Norfolk............................ 189
Dolphin Books, Suffolk............................. 225
Dusty Books, Powys 290
Eastern Books of London, London SW 166
Eastgate Bookshop, East Yorkshire 106
Edwards, Fiona, Nottinghamshire 203
Elizabeth Ferguson, Grampian 272
Elstree Books, Herts................................ 130
Embleton (Paul), Essex 111
Emjay Books, Surrey................................ 231
English (Toby), Oxfordshire......................... 209
Erian Books, London N............................. 156
Eton Antique Bookshop, Berks 57
Evans (Mark), Lincolnshire 151
Facet Books, Dorset................................ 91
Fantastic Literature, Essex 110
Farquharson, (Hilary), Tayside..................... 280
Farringdon (J.M.), Swansea 291
Ferguson (Elizabeth), Grampian 272
Find That Book, West Yorkshire 248
First Edition, The, Essex 109
Fisher Nautical, East Sussex 99
ForensicSearch, Herts 131
Forest Books, Rutland.............................. 211

Foster (Stephen), London NW 160
Fosters Bookshop, London W 172
Framlingham Bookshop, Suffolk 227
Freeman's Corner Shop, Norfolk 189
Freya Books & Antiques, Norfolk 189
Fuchsia Books, Co. Wexford 266
Fullerton's Booksearch, Norfolk 188
G. C. Books Ltd., Dumfries & Galloway 270
Game Advice, Oxfordshire 208
Gardener & Cook, London SW 167
Gillmark Gallery, Herts.............................. 130
Glyn's Books, Shropshire........................... 212
Goldsworth Books, Surrey 234
Graham (John), Dorset 96
Grahame (Major Iain), Suffolk 225
Green (Paul), Cambridgeshire 67
Green Ltd. (G.L.), Herts 131
Greensleeves, Oxfordshire 206
Hadfield (G.K.), Cumbria 79
Halewood & Sons, Lancashire...................... 144
Harlequin Books, Bristol 59
Hava Books, London SE............................. 164
Hawley (C.L.), N Yorks............................. 195
Helion & Company, West Midlands 239
Hencotes Books & Prints, Northumberland 201
Heneage Art Books (Thomas), London SW 168
Heppa (Christopher), Essex 108
Heraldry Today, Wiltshire........................... 253
Heywood Hill Limited (G.), London W 173
Hicks (Ronald C.), Cornwall 73
Hill (John S.), Devon 86
Hollingshead (Chris), London Outer 182
Holmes Books (Harry), East Yorkshire........... 107
Home Farm Books, Warwickshire.................. 236
Hoovey's Books, East Sussex 102
HP Bookfinders, Central 268
Hughes (Ms. Sonia A.), Monmouthshire 286
Hutchison (Books) (Larry), Fife................... 271
Hylton Booksearch, Merseyside 184
Idler (The), Suffolk 227
Intech Books, Northumberland 201
Invicta Booksearch, Kent............................ 140
Jane Jones Books, Grampian 273
Jean Hedger, Berks 55
Jobson (N.W.), Oxfordshire......................... 206
Joel Segal Books, Devon 86
Just Books, Cornwall 75
Kalligraphia (formerly Charmouth Bounty
   Books), Isle of Wight.............................. 133
Katnap Arts, Norfolk................................. 190
Keeble Antiques, Somerset......................... 218
Kent (Books) (Mrs. A.), Suffolk 227
Kent T. G., Surrey 230
Kerr (Norman), Cumbria 77
Kingfisher Book Service, Nottinghamshire 204
Leapman Ltd. (G. & R.), Herts 130
Lee Rare Books (Rachel), Bristol 59
Letterbox Books, Nottinghamshire 203
Little Bookshop (The), G Manchester............. 119
Lloyd-Davies (Sue), Carmarthenshire 282
Lost Books, Northants................................ 200
Lymelight Books & Prints, Dorset 93
Madalyn S. Jones, West Yorkshire 246
Maggy Browne, Lincolnshire 148
Maghreb Bookshop (The), London WC.......... 177

Malvern Bookshop (The), Worcs 255
Marine & Cannon Books, Cheshire 71
Marine and Cannon Books, Cheshire 69
Martin (Books and Pictures), (Brian P.), Surrey. 231
Martin (Brian), Surrey............................... 231
Maynard & Bradley, Leics 146
Meekins Books (Paul), Warwickshire............. 237
Mellon's Books, East Sussex....................... 101
Melvin Tenner, London W........................... 173
Merlin Books, West Sussex 242
Minster Gate Bookshop, N Yorks................. 197
MK Book Services, Cambridgeshire.............. 66
Modlock (Lilian), Dorset............................ 93
Monmouth House Books, Monmouthshire 286
Moon's Bookshop (Michael), Cumbria 80
Moore (Sue), Cornwall 73
Morris Secondhand & Antiquarian
   Books (Chris), Oxfordshire...................... 208
Mr. Pickwick of Towcester, Northants........... 199
Murphy (C.J.), Norfolk.............................. 189
New Strand, The, Herefordshire 127
Newband (D.M.), Powys............................. 290
Nineteenth Century Books, Oxfordshire 209
Occultique, Northants................................ 199
Orbis Books (London) Ltd., London W 173
Over-Sands Books, Cumbria........................ 77
Palladour Books, Hampshire 125
Paramor (C.D.), Suffolk 228
Park (Mike), London Outer......................... 182
Park Gallery & Bookshop (The), Northants 200
Pedlar's Pack Books, Devon 84
Peel (Valerie), Berks 56
Petersfield Bookshop (The), Hampshire........... 124
Phelan Books, Co. Dublin 264
Phillip Robbins of Warwick, Warwickshire 237
Phillips of Hitchin (Antiques) Ltd., Herts........ 131
Pimpernel Booksearch, London SW.............. 169
Poetry Bookshop (The), Powys..................... 289
Potterton Books, N Yorks 196
Price (R.D.M. & I.M.) (Books), G Manchester.. 120
Quest Books, East Yorkshire 107
Quest Booksearch, Cambridgeshire............... 65
Raftery Books (Michael D.), Leics................ 147
Ramrod Antiques, N Yorks.......................... 195
Randall (Tom), Somerset............................ 218
Readers World, West Midlands 238
Rider Haggard Society (The), Tyne and Wear... 235
Roadmaster Books, Kent............................. 136
Rods Books, Devon 88
Rolling Stock Books, G Manchester 120
Roosterbooks, Northants............................. 199
Rosemary Pugh Books, Wiltshire 253
Roundstone Books, Lancashire..................... 143
Rowan (H. & S.J.), Dorset.......................... 91
Ruskin Books, Kent.................................. 135
S.P.C.K., Hampshire 126
St Mary's Books & Prints, Lincolnshire 152
Sansovino Books, West Sussex 244
Sax Books, Suffolk 228
Scarthin Books, Derbyshire 82
Schull Books, Co. Cork 262
Scrivener's Books & Bookbinding, Derbyshire... 82
Sea Chest Nautical Bookshop (The), Devon 88
Seeber (Liz), East Sussex 102
Sen Books, Hampshire............................... 126

Shacklock Books (David), Suffolk 226
Simmonds (Anthony J.), London SE.............. 165
Simply Read Books, East Sussex................... 100
Sims (Sue), Dorset.................................... 91
Skelton (Tony), Kent................................ 140
Skyrack Books, West Yorkshire.................... 247
Slightly Foxed on Gloucester Road, London SW 167
Solaris Books, East Yorkshire...................... 106
Sparrow Books, West Yorkshire 245
Spelman (Ken), N Yorks............................ 198
Spenceley Books (David), West Yorkshire........ 248
Spooner & Co, Somerset 219
Spurrier (Nick), Kent 137
Stacpoole (George), Co. Limerick................. 266
Sterling Books, Somerset 220
Sturford Books, Wiltshire 254
Symes Books (Naomi), Cheshire 71
Tarka Books, Devon................................. 84
Temperley (David), West Midlands............... 238
Terence Kaye - Bookseller, London NW 161
The Bookshop, Kirkstall, West Yorkshire........ 248
The Sanctuary Bookshop, Dorset.................. 94
Thornber (Peter M.), N Yorks 195
Thorntons of Oxford Ltd., Oxfordshire........... 206
Tiger Books, Kent................................... 136
Titford (John), Derbyshire 82
Tozer Railway Books (Nick), West Yorkshire ... 247
TP Children's Bookshop, West Yorkshire........ 245
Trevorrow (Edwin), Herts........................... 129
Trinity Rare Books, Co. Leitrim 266
Trotter Books (John), London N 158
Twiggers Booksearch, Bedfordshire............... 53
Undercover Books, Lincolnshire 152
Vokes (Jeremiah), Durham.......................... 97
Vokes Books Ltd., N Yorks 194
Warsash Nautical Bookshop, Hampshire......... 126
Webster (D.), Strathclyde........................... 279
Wells (Mary), London SW 169
Wembdon Books, Somerset......................... 216
Wetherell (Frances), Cambridgeshire 65
Whistler's Books, London SW 169
Whitchurch Books Ltd., Cardiff.................... 281
Woolcott Books, Dorset............................. 92
Worrallo (J. & M.A.), West Midlands 240
Wright Trace Books, West Midlands.............. 239
Yesterday's News, Conwy........................... 283

LARGE PRINT
Dealers who stock books in large print